IN TWO VOLUMES

RELATIVITY, ELECTROMAGNETISM AND QUANTUM PHYSICS

PHYSICS

IN TWO VOLUMES

♦ DONALD G. IVEY

♦♦ J. N. PATTERSON HUME

BOTH OF THE UNIVERSITY OF TORONTO

Donald G. Ivey, Ph.D., University of Notre Dame

is Professor of Physics and Principal of New College at the University of Toronto, and has maintained interests in high school physics education and his research field of polymer physics. Dr. Ivey has also held teaching appointments at the University of British Columbia as well as at Notre Dame.

J. N. Patterson Hume, Ph.D., University of Toronto

is Professor of Physics and also of Computer Science at the University of Toronto, with research interests in computer systems and applications as well as in physics education. Dr. Hume has taught at Rutgers University and has also been Associate Dean of the School of Graduate Studies at Toronto.

The authors, in a uniquely successful collaboration, have augmented classroom and laboratory activities with many films and television presentations that are widely acclaimed, winning awards from the Edison Foundation and The Ohio State University, and also from the Scientific Institute in Rome, and are extensively used in the United States and Canada for public and student education in physics.

Dr. Ivey / ǝɯnH ˙ɹꓷ

Are they in the same frame of reference? Which one is upside-down?

PHYSICS

IN TWO VOLUMES

♦

CLASSICAL MECHANICS
AND
INTRODUCTORY
STATISTICAL MECHANICS

♦

DONALD G. IVEY
UNIVERSITY OF TORONTO

THE RONALD PRESS COMPANY • NEW YORK

Frontispiece by Robert Lansdale

FOREWORD

The two volumes of Physics include the material necessary for a comprehensive two-year introductory physics course for students in the pure and applied sciences who are studying calculus concurrently. We present the subject as an integrated account of a challenging human activity; our aim is to produce a coherent understanding of the fundamentals of physics.

Each volume is independently complete, with its own index, appendixes, and problems. The division of material between the two volumes and the organization of each volume are based on our own experiences in teaching first and second year courses. At every stage we attempt to make clear where we have been and where we are headed, and therefore it should be possible to use the material in a different order, or to omit certain chapters, or to use the volumes independently of one another. The integrating factor, the thread that runs through these volumes, is based on a common attitude toward our subject; we share certain fundamental beliefs about what physics is—and is not.

We have used the pronoun *we* with the usual variety of meanings—*we* (mankind), *we* (scientists), *we* (readers and authors together), and the most common one, *we* (the authors). In a way this last *we* should be *I,* because of course each of us wrote what he wrote by himself, we did not do it as a duet. One reason *I* was not used is simply custom; textbooks are not commonly written in the first-person-singular, perhaps in the belief (mistaken, in our opinion) that the material in a textbook should be depersonalized. A more important reason is that what *I* wrote, *we* approved. Each of us wrote his own separate volume, but we accept some degree of mutual responsibility for both volumes because we critically examined each others work. Sometimes this criticism led to extensive revision. Occasionally the conflict factor was very high because we do not think alike, but we believe that this is what makes our interaction useful, adding an important dimension to the final result.

We hope that these volumes will reveal our own struggles to understand some of the basic ideas of physics, and in so doing help students to avoid the belief that "physics explains how it is" and instead recognize that physics is a way that we find useful to explain certain things to ourselves at present.

Donald G. Ivey
J. N. Patterson Hume

PREFACE

There are many books on basic physics and it may well be asked why another should be written. Like many teachers, I have sometimes wished that textbooks did certain things differently. What sort of things? It is difficult to write down precisely what it is that bothers me, and perhaps this is part of the point; once you give a feeling the status of print, it changes. It is not easy to present shades of gray in black and white and because textbooks often tend to present physics in rather absolute terms, it is difficult for students to recognize that in physics, as in every other human endeavor, there is room for opinion, for interpretation, for alternative approaches. Whether a student is heading toward a career as a professional scientist, or as an engineer, or is simply to become a scientifically literate member of society, I think the most important thing he carries away from his first college course in physics is a reasonable attitude toward the subject, one that encompasses its limitations as well as its strengths.

I wish I knew how to define or to produce an ideal attitude. I am sure that attitude, like character, is generated by example rather than by exhortation. Therefore in this volume I will cover (in the sense, I hope, of *travel over* rather than *conceal*) certain areas of physics, but the question of *how* it is covered is much more important to me than *how much* is covered. I have included whatever I felt was interesting or useful, but some of the material is not essential. I have assumed that it is easier for a user to omit part of what is included than to add what may not be, and some chapters, or sections of chapters, can be omitted without loss of continuity.

I have written this book for a first course in which students will be able to devote a full academic year to it. This may or may not be the first half of a two-year sequence, for which the other volume might be used in the second year. I know that students have learned a good deal about physics before coming to college, whether they formally called it the study of physics or not. Nowadays elementary school students are making models of atoms and of the solar system, and are discussing satellite orbits and moon shots. Therefore I assume that students have had some experience in dealing with physical situations, both qualitatively and quantitatively. Students know in general terms something about the structure of matter, about atoms and molecules and protons and electrons; they have met with the concepts of force, acceleration, momentum and energy. I consider it important to the student that this background be recognized and built upon, rather than ignored.

As a basis for operation, I have implicitly assumed that students approaching the text have some grasp of the concepts usually developed in a high school physics course. This does not mean that I expect recall of very much specific material, but simply indicates the level of preparation that may be required. Concerning mathematical background, some students will have been introduced to calculus in high school, while others will not. I have included a limited introduction to calculus in the second chapter and assume a concurrent course in mathematics including calculus. My intention is to help students to recognize the relationship between mathematics and physics, enabling them to distinguish between physical argument and mathematical technique.

The organization of subject matter in a textbook, the story line, is really a matter of taste—the author's taste, based on his experience. He has in mind the assumed background of a reader, the duration and level of a course for which the text might be used, and more important than anything else, his own basic goals. This Preface is followed by The Story Line for this volume, with some indication of the reasons for it. I would be surprised if some users did not find a different sequence of subjects more attractive.

Regarding the presentation of material in the text, a few comments are necessary. Sometimes in textbooks an effort is made to make the numbers in worked examples and problems appear to represent experimental data, by writing, for example, "A force of 2.00 pounds acts on a mass of 10.0 pounds for 3.00 seconds. Determine its change in velocity." I will not adopt this approach, but instead will say "A force of 2 pounds acts on a mass of 10 pounds for 3 seconds. Determine ———." The numbers used are invented, and I can invent them to any degree of accuracy I please. In general I shall use simple numbers, so that calculations will not be messy, and the numbers are to be assumed as exact, unless otherwise indicated. In general, calculations should be carried out with slide rule accuracy, and answers will be given to three figures. The treatment of real experimental data is discussed in Chapter 3. The text is illustrated throughout, with the diagrams placed close to the related text. To avoid reference to earlier pages, equations are repeated as required in a new context. I have chosen not to make references to original papers or other texts, in the belief that few students take advantage of such references at this stage, and that it is unrealistic to hope that many students, taking several other courses simultaneously, will have time to consult the literature.

Like all authors I owe a great deal to other authors, as well as to teachers, colleagues and students. The principal unique feature of this book is its organization; I have put the story of physics together in a way that appeals to me, but most of the physics is essentially the same as may be found in hundreds of other books. Some of these I have studied, some I have skimmed. My ideas have developed from reading, as well as from my teaching experience, but I will not attempt to acknowledge specifically the authors to whom I am most obligated because I do not really know who they are. Ideas simmer and develop in complex ways, and what I consider a fresh original thought may well have its origin in some apparently forgotten book or article, or conversation. I hope that my recognition of debt to all who have molded my thoughts, whoever and wherever they are, will suffice.

It was the initial enthusiasm of my colleague and co-author, Dr. Hume, that persuaded me to undertake what I knew would be a long and arduous task, and I believe our cooperation has been a fruitful one. He read my manuscript with critical care, and his insight added greatly to its development. Another colleague and friend, Dr. R. W. McKay, also read the entire manuscript critically, making a number of suggestions for revision and correction, and I was fortunate to be able to take advantage of his sound physical knowledge.

I am grateful to my secretary, Miss Ruth Reiffenstein, for her devotion to this project and for her patience and accuracy in interpreting and typing my often illegible material. The graphic artists, Mr. Robert Vandersluys and Mr. Gordon Long, have worked diligently to bring life and style to the illustrations, and have cooperated with the publisher to produce an attractive format.

By far my most important acknowledgment is to my family, and particularly to my wife, for their interest and forbearance during the time that I have been working on this volume. It is only because of the unflagging confidence and support of my wife that this work was ever completed, and it is with gratitude and affection that I dedicate it to her.

DONALD G. IVEY

THE STORY LINE

Part I—Introduction

Chapter 1 is an attempt to initiate an attitude toward physics which for many students may be different from what they will have developed out of their experience to date. Physics is emphasized to be an on-going intellectual and experimental activity of man.

Chapter 2 serves as an introduction to or review of basic calculus, and as a way of emphasizing the relationship between mathematics and physics.

Chapter 3 is on measurement. It can be argued that much of the material discussed here belongs in a physics laboratory manual. I take the view that the experimental and theoretical aspects of physics are inextricably interwoven, and should not be separated. However, rather than attempt to give an extensive description of appropriate experiments at each stage, complete with a discussion of technique and relative accuracy, I make here some general points about the accumulation and handling of experimental data. It is my experience that if much time is spent in discussing relevant experiments at each point, the story line can be lost. Furthermore, the gathering of good data, is an exacting and time-consuming task, and the difficulties are not usually adequately represented by textbook descriptions of experiments.

Part II—Kinematics

It is my belief that the concept of a frame of reference is of central importance in understanding mechanics, and therefore I have focused attention on this to a much greater extent than is usual. Transformations between reference frames are dealt with here, before dynamical concepts are developed, in order to emphasize the enormous influence of the choice of reference frame on the description of motion.

Chapter 4 introduces the concept of a frame of reference. In addition, some general points about operational definitions are made in connection with the fundamental quantities length and time. The vector quantity displacement is defined and the properties of vectors are summarized.

Chapter 5 deals with three simple forms of motion in a reference frame: motion with constant acceleration, circular motion and simple harmonic motion. Complete familiarity with these is necessary for much that comes later. A brief review of the three forms of force fields (gravitational, electrostatic and magnetostatic) is included here, and the basic law of dynamics is recalled, in order that a broad range of examples can be used.

Chapter 6 on the Galilean transformation (transformation between reference frames with constant relative velocity) also takes advantage of the assumption that this book is not a first exposure to physics. The most important Galilean transformation is one to the center-of-mass frame in "collision" situations, and in order to make effective use of this example some background in dynamics is necessary. The basic notions of conservation of momentum and kinetic energy reviewed here, and used in discussing collisions, will be given a more rigorous discussion later.

Chapter 7 deals with transformations between accelerated frames of reference, introducing the centripetal and coriolis accelerations. I believe that distinguishing between frames of reference in translation and in rotation before formally attacking dynamics is an important aid to understanding.

Part III—Dynamics of a Particle

In this section the basic dynamic relation $\mathbf{F} = m\mathbf{a}$ is applied to a single particle, or objects that can be treated as single particles.

Chapter 8 attempts to give some idea of the physical content of Newton's laws; it is a discussion that can be given only because some familiarity with these laws, and their application, is assumed. The concept of an inertial frame of reference is established here.

Chapter 9 then deals with a number of issues that must be considered in applying Newton's laws in an inertial frame. To some extent these are issues that may have been considered in high school physics, but it is hoped that additional insight is provided here.

Chapter 10 uses a number of specific examples to illustrate the use of Newton's laws in non-inertial reference frames, where there are inertial forces.

Chapter 11 discusses the observable effects that arise because the earth is not really an inertial frame.

Chapter 12 goes into the dynamics of simple harmonic motion, a form of motion that may not be familiar from high school physics.

Part IV—Dynamics of a System of Particles

While the motion of a single particle can be handled by the basic law $\mathbf{F} = m\mathbf{a}$, in dealing with systems of particles it is useful to have the law, or rather the physical content of the law, expressed in other ways.

Chapter 13 deals with impulse and linear momentum, concepts that should be familiar, at least in one-dimensional situations, from high school physics.

Chapter 14 introduces the angular quantities torque, angular impulse and angular momentum.

Chapter 15 then uses the arsenal of dynamical concepts to analyze the motion of the simplest possible system of particles, the two-particle system. The division of motion into translation, rotation and vibration is introduced here, and some of the features of rigid body dynamics are discussed.

The next four chapters of the section deal with rigid body dynamics; much of this material is not essential for later sections. Again the question of basic goals comes up. In some respects, the development of classical dynamics can be confined to the motion of single particles, because this is sufficient for going on to much of relativity, electromagnetic theory, nuclear physics, and so on. On the other hand, if students are to understand the motions of the real objects they can see around them, some rigid-body dynamics is necessary. It is my own view that students at this stage are ready to tackle this, and are interested in it, but certainly a dissenting user could omit some or all of these chapters.

Chapter 16 deals with pure rotation about a fixed axis.

Chapter 17 deals with oscillations about a fixed axis.

Chapter 18 goes on to translation plus rotation, for the particular case of motion of a rigid body in two dimensions, so that the vector character of angular quantities is not really apparent.

Chapter 19 gives some discussion of three-dimensional rigid body motion, the culmination of classical dynamics. Details are worked out only for the special cases, such as the gyroscope, where spin speed is very high as compared to precessional speed.

Part V—The Concept of Energy

The story line I have adopted is unusual in that the concept of energy is introduced formally somewhat later than usual; again this approach is possible because I assume some background in physics. The reason for doing this is to emphasize that energy is an alternative way of expressing the physical content of Newton's laws.

Chapter 20 develops the work–kinetic energy relation for a single particle, an integrated form of the equation of motion analogous to the impulse–linear momentum relation. It is pointed out that while the impulse–momentum relation also applies to a system of particles, the work–kinetic energy relation does not. This leads to the introduction of potential energy.

Chapter 21 defines potential energy for a particle.

Chapter 22 discusses the various ways of describing a force field.

Chapter 23 shows that a work–energy relation for a system of particles can be developed, for a conservative interaction between the particles.

Chapter 24 deals with motion in the earth's field.

Chapter 25 introduces the kinetic energy of rotation for systems of particles.

Chapter 26 describes various models for a system of gas molecules, in order to indicate what can be said on the basis of classical dynamics. This leads to an introduction of both statistical mechanics and quantum mechanics.

Part VI—Statistical Mechanics

While it is recognized that a satisfactory development of statistical mechanics is not really possible at this level, the aim here is to distinguish between the macroscopic theory of heat, *phenomenological thermodynamics,* and the microscopic theory of heat, *statistical mechanics.*

Chapter 27 deals in general terms with some of the differences between the two theories.

Chapters 28 and **29** develop the first and second laws of thermodynamics, in the belief that a discussion of statistical mechanics can not be meaningful for students having no experience in handling the concepts of thermodynamics.

Chapter 30, on random events, is essentially on mathematical statistics, but with a physics orientation.

Chapter 31 works out the distribution of molecular speeds as an example of the approach of statistical mechanics.

Chapter 32 develops the classical Maxwell–Boltzmann distribution, and a distinction is made between classical statistics and quantum statistics.

Chapter 33, on the distribution of electromagnetic radiation, concludes this discussion, and the volume, serving both to draw together some of the notions of statistical mechanics, and to introduce quantum mechanics and electromagnetic theory, subjects a student may study subsequently.

There are certain topics a user might expect to find in this volume that appear to be omitted—for example, the kinetic theory of gases. Most of the standard material of kinetic theory is included, but scattered throughout the text, sometimes appearing in problems. In discussing impulse and momentum, in Chapter 13, gas pressure and molecular flux are introduced. In Chapter 26 the idea of equipartition of energy and the concept of mean free path are introduced as a prelude to Part VI. Thermal properties of matter such as thermal expansion coefficient and specific heat capacity are introduced in problems.

Wave motion as a separate topic is not discussed, but simple harmonic motion is dealt with in some detail, so that an extension to include an understanding of wave propagation should not be difficult.

I hope that the student is left with the impression that he has had the opportunity to think about a good deal of physics—physics that is classical but not irrelevant. At the same time, I hope he is in a position to realize that there is a great deal of physics he has still to investigate. More than anything else, I hope that he is left with the feeling that physics is a stimulating and demanding activity of man.

D. G. I.

CONTENTS

Part I Introduction

Part II Kinematics

4 *Location of a Particle in a Frame of Reference*   **63**

Focusing on the frame as of central importance in understanding mechanics, discusses operational definition of fundamental quantities length and time; vector quantity displacement also defined; properties of vectors summarized.

Fundamental quantities, 63
Length, 64
Time, 65
Absolute length and time, 66
Frames of reference and
    co-ordinate systems, 67
Vectors, scalars, and invariance, 70
Displacement, 72

Adding displacements, 74
Vector components, 77
One vector ≡ three scalars, 80
Unit vectors, 80
Multiplication of vectors, 81
The scalar product, 81
Direction cosines, 83
The vector product, 84

5 *Motion of a Particle in a Frame of Reference*   **89**

Deals with three simple forms of motion: motion with constant acceleration, circular motion, and simple harmonic motion. Brief review of basic dynamics and force fields.

Displacement and time, 89
Velocity, 90
Acceleration, 92
Motion over an interval, 93
Numerical integration, 94
Constant acceleration, 98
Projectile motion, 101
Review of uniform fields, 104
An example of the motion of a
    charged particle in a uniform
    electric field, 106
Circular motion at
    constant speed, 109

An example of a charged particle
    moving at right angles to a
    uniform magnetic field, 116
Simple harmonic motion, 119
Non-Cartesian co-ordinate systems, 125
Non-uniform circular motion, 126
Translation in one dimension and
    rotation about a fixed axis of a
    rigid body, 130
Uniformly accelerated circular
    motion, 131
Motion in a curved path—
    center of curvature, 134

6 *Galilean Transformation of the Frame of Reference*   **145**

Transformations between frames of constant relative velocity; introduction of center-of-mass frame. Conservation of momentum and kinetic energy reviewed, and used in discussing collisions.

Frames of reference moving at
    constant relative velocity, 146
Transformation of constant
    velocities, 150
Relative velocity, 154
Center-of-mass frame of reference, 154

Collisions, 156
Head-on elastic collision, 160
Head-on non-elastic collision, 165
Elastic collision of equal masses, 171
Elastic collision of
    non-equal masses, 173

7 Transformations Between Accelerated Frames of Reference   198

*Distinguishes between frames in translation and in rotation, as prep-
aration for dynamics; introduces centripetal and coriolis accelerations.*

Part III   Dynamics of a Particle

8 The Foundations of Classical Mechanics   223

*Discusses the physical content of Newton's laws;
and establishes the concept of an inertial frame.*

9 Dynamics of a Particle in an Inertial Frame of Reference   249

*Some of the issues to be considered in ap-
plying Newton's laws in an inertial frame.*

Part IV   Dynamics of a System of Particles

Part V   The Concept of Energy

Part VI Statistical Mechanics

32 *Classical Statistical Mechanics*   **758**

Develops the classical Maxwell–Boltzmann distribution and gives examples of its application; distinguishes between classical statistics and quantum statistics.

33 *The Distribution of Electromagnetic Radiation*   **786**

Develops the Planck radiation law, in order to draw together some of the notions of statistical mechanics, and to introduce quantum mechanics and electromagnetic theory, which may be studied subsequently.

Introduction

PHYSICS—AN EXACT SCIENCE?

A BEGINNING

Beginning is the difficult part, whether beginning to write a book, or beginning the study of a science, or beginning a new science. Writing a book is not your problem, and you have already begun the study of physics; but have you thought about the beginning of physics itself? Suppose that man had never invented the system of ideas that is called physics. Where would *you* begin in an attempt to describe the physical universe to yourself? What preconceived ideas would you have about the way things behave—and would you realize that you had them?

Fortunately you do not have to invent physics for yourself—nor do we—but you will find it useful in studying physics to have in mind that man did invent it and that he had to begin somewhere. Physics does not tell you the way things really *are;* it tells you the way that man finds it convenient, or useful, or reasonable to describe things to himself. In inventing his descriptions he must make certain assumptions and he tries to be explicit about what these assumptions are, but sometimes there are implicit assumptions that he may not realize he is making.

In physics it is essential to define certain technical words, but we shall not begin by attempting to define physics because any definition would be inadequate or misleading. Perhaps the best definition is "physics is what physicists do," but this is not very helpful, and must be interpreted with the proviso "when they are functioning as physicists."

We begin by using a simple example of a physical situation to illustrate a few important ideas about physics.

THE ASSUMPTION OF ORDER

You have some notion of what a physicist does. You have learned that he looks for order in the world around him, that he performs experiments under carefully controlled conditions so that the effect of changes of one physical property on another can be observed, and that on the basis of the order he has observed he can make predictions about what will happen under different circumstances. You will have studied some physical situations for yourself so that, for example, you can probably predict that an object which falls 4 feet from rest will fall straight down and will take about $\frac{1}{2}$ second to fall.

Many objects released from rest to fall 4 feet will behave predictably, that is, fall straight down and take about $\frac{1}{2}$ second to fall. But suppose the object is a piece of paper. Without even performing the experiment you know that the result will not be predictable. You cannot even predict where the paper will land, let alone the time to fall.

One of the most basic assumptions of physics is that if you do exactly the same thing you will get exactly the same result, and yet in this very simple physical situation, even though you attempt to do exactly the same thing, there will be wide fluctuations in the observed result. In the search for order in the world, is this a poor example?

STATISTICAL PREDICTABILITY

The falling paper example may appear to be trivial, but it is useful to examine it more fully, in an experiment. You can do this mentally (perform a "thought experiment") but it is more satisfying if you really do it. We did and we shall describe our experiment—you can decide whether or not the results are convincing for you. We cut a circular paper disc of 2-in. diameter, set up a rigid support 4 ft off the floor, held the disc with its plane horizontal in a hole in the support, and attempted to release both sides simultaneously so that it did not receive any initial spin. The released disc fluttered to the floor and we marked where it landed. We did this 100 times and obtained 100 spots on the floor. These were our experimental results. What could we deduce from 100 more or less randomly distributed spots? We observed they were roughly symmetrically distributed with respect to the central point (directly below the point of release), the density of spots decreasing with distance away from the center. By drawing concentric circles around

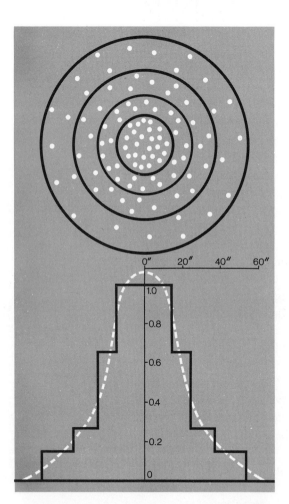

Distribution of spots observed for the falling paper disc, and a histogram showing spot density as a function of distance from the center.

the central point we found that a 30-in.-diameter circle encompassed 25 of the spots, a 48-in.-diameter circle 50 spots, and a 76-in.-diameter circle 75 spots, and that all 100 spots were within a 108-in.-diameter circle. We could interpret this as meaning that on a subsequent drop there would be a 25% chance of the disc landing in the inner circle, a 50% chance of it being in the next circle, and so on. Another way of interpreting the results was obtained by dividing the number of spots in each annular ring by the area of the ring, giving the number of spots per unit area (spot density) for each ring. The histogram in the diagram shows this spot density plotted against distance from the center. Presumably a larger number of spots and a more detailed analysis (more circles) would lead to a graph something like the one illustrated by the dotted line. This (or the histogram) can be interpreted as a graph of probability density versus position.

The analysis enabled us to make predictions as to what would happen on subsequent drops. These predictions can be expressed in various ways. For example, we can say that there is one chance in four that the disc will land in the inner circle—and one chance in four that it will land in the outer ring; or we can use the spot density and say that per unit area the disc is six times as likely to land in the inner circle as in the outer ring. The most probable position for the disc to land is at the center, even though in our experiment it never landed there! While we can make predictions, we can never say with certainty what will happen on a particular drop.

The predictions we made are **statistical predictions.** On the basis of systematically collected data (statistics) we make predictions about future measurements in the same situation.

We repeated the experiment 100 times. Is this enough? This is an unanswerable or meaningless question. Enough for what? If we dropped the disc 100 more times we would expect a result which is similar but not identical to the first 100 times. The diameters of the circles containing 25, 50, 75 or 100 spots would not be exactly the same. The physical situation is not described completely no matter how many observations are made, although we would expect that the distributions obtained from two 100-drop runs would be more closely similar to one another than those obtained from two 10-drop runs. We must decide at some point that further observations would not be fruitful. On the basis of the 100-drop run we made predictions as to what would happen on a subsequent drop. These predictions would have had more validity if based on a 1000-drop run, but still we would never be in a position to say exactly what will happen on a particular drop.

This is characteristic of all physical measurements. It is always necessary to make a decision, based on the particular circumstances, as to how many observations are necessary for a "good" measurement. Having done so there are certain accepted procedures for stating the result, including a measure of the degree of fluctuation.

FLUCTUATIONS

One reason for describing this simple falling disc experiment is to emphasize that in *every* experiment there are fluctuations in the results. The fluctuations with a paper disc are more obvious than when a steel ball is dropped, but the difference is only one of degree, not of kind. Although a steel ball might appear to land directly below the point of release each time, sensitive measurements would show fluctuations from this position.

The main reason for the fluctuations in the paper disc experiment is apparent —the effect of the air. If the paper is dropped in an evacuated enclosure it will behave more like the steel ball, but it is impossible to eliminate the effect of the air entirely because it is impossible to produce a perfect vacuum. Even in "free space" there are a few molecules of some kind moving around.

The more sensitive a measuring instrument, the more apparent the fluctuations in the measurements will be. Sometimes the variation can be reduced (in our experiment, by working in a vacuum).

There is a tendency to think of fluctuations as interfering with whatever it is that we are trying to measure—that is, that there is *a* measurement to be made. In some situations this might appear to be reasonable; without fluctuations caused by the random effect of the air, we might expect the paper disc always to fall straight down and land at the spot directly below the point of release, a single result. On the other hand, it is important to recognize that fluctuations are an intrinsic part of all measurements. Fluctuations arise because of real physical causes, and therefore in order to interpret the experimental results it is necessary to attempt to understand the origin of the fluctuations. Random fluctuations due to one cause may mask effects due to other causes. Conversely, what appears to be an effect due to one cause may actually be due to some other cause and inadequate statistics. To illustrate, think again about the falling disc.

In our experiment we observed that the spots seemed to be symmetrically distributed with respect to the central point. However, suppose that we measured the spot density in different radial directions and found that the distribution was not symmetric with respect to the center. We observe that there is a preferred direction. This systematic effect we could have explained to ourselves either by assuming that we had not released the discs completely freely (had given them a bias in a particular direction) or by assuming a steady air current in the room in the observed preferred direction. Probably further experimentation would have been necessary to distinguish between these hypotheses. However, suppose that we did not know what *should* happen—that is, that except for the effect of the air the disc should fall straight down, due to gravity. Then an analysis of the results might well have led us to conclude that the most probable landing position was other than directly below the point of release, and therefore that gravity did not act vertically. This seems ridiculous only because we do know (or think we know) what should happen.

If we dropped the disc only a few times, the result would almost certainly not be symmetric with respect to the center, and therefore would indicate a preferred direction. How could we distinguish between this effect and the effect produced by a steady air current in the room? Clearly, by taking enough measurements that the random effect of the air balances out when we calculate the average position for the disc to land. But how many measurements is this? As we stated before, the answer depends on the particular circumstances.

In physics we speak of *a* result of a set of measurements of a particular property. What this means is the average value determined from the measure-

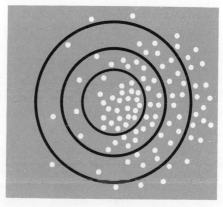

A non-symmetric distribution of observed spots. Is there a breeze, or does gravity not act straight down?

ments; it does not mean that there is a unique value of the property. The measurements show fluctuations from the calculated average value. These fluctuations arise both because of limitations in measuring instruments, and because there is not *a* value of the property. We will return to experimental measurements in Chapter 3.

AN EXACT SCIENCE

It is sometimes stated that physics is an exact science. What does this mean? It is meaningless to talk about an exact measurement of any real physical property, not only because no measuring device is infinitely precise, but also because of fluctuations in what is being measured. The term **experimental error** has been avoided so far, because of its implication that there really is an exact value to be measured and it is an error not to have done so. It will be given precise definition later.

Think about what at first might seem to be a definite fixed property, the distance between two parallel narrow scratches on a rigid metal bar. By means of some device for measuring length (a ruler or a traveling microscope) think about measuring this distance. As your measurement becomes more and more precise, at some point you will have to worry about the finite width of the "narrow" scratches, and about whether the scratches are really straight and really parallel. Furthermore, you will have to consider the possibility that the temperature of the bar is changing and affecting its length, or that as the metal grows older its crystal structure is changing, producing changes in its dimensions.

You will probably have realized that the bar described could be the **standard meter,** until recently the international standard of length on which all measurements of length were based. Even though the bar was maintained and used under carefully controlled conditions (of temperature, humidity, etc.) it is clear that it did not provide an infinitely precise standard of length. The new standard, based on the wavelength of a particular radiation from an isotope of krypton, has many advantages, though it too has limitations.

If physical **measurements** are not exact, what about the **calculations** used by physicists to make predictions about physical behavior?

The calculation of $\frac{1}{2}$ second for the time an object takes to fall 4 feet from rest is based on the assumptions that air resistance is zero, that the acceleration due to gravity is constant, and that its value is 32 ft/sec². Air resistance is never entirely absent—although sometimes its effect can be neglected as far as reasonable predictions are concerned. The acceleration due to gravity is not a constant but decreases as the distance from the earth increases; however, over a distance of 4 feet it would probably be impossible to measure this variation. The point is that while the calculation in some cases may be very accurate, it is made by assuming conditions that *never* really exist.

In physics we are always referring to idealizations of real physical situations—idealizations which are not completely achievable even under highly controlled experimental conditions, because there is always present the effect of some variables which we are not taking into account in our analysis. The physicist mentally strips away the effect of relatively unimportant (he hopes) variables and thus imagines the physical system to be isolated to a greater degree than is possible in reality. This idealization is called a **model,** and the physicist deals with models of reality in his attempts to see order in the universe.

It is important to recognize that physics is an experimental science—that is, it is based on observation of the real world—but it is equally important to understand that physics is an intellectual activity of man, and that in explaining his observations to himself the physicist invents idealizations of the real world. His explanations (his theories) ultimately turn out to be inadequate, either because his observations are not sufficiently detailed or because his model is too simple. As measuring techniques improve, the applicable data become more detailed and new theories, based on different or more sophisticated models, are invented. This does not necessarily mean that the old theories are wrong and the new ones right; the old ones often continue to explain quite adequately what they were invented to explain. The notions of right and wrong are not suitable here because of the implication they carry that there are "laws of nature" that man is discovering (like an explorer discovering a river), instead of recognizing that he is inventing the laws as he goes along. Some theories, of course, do turn out to be "wrong," in the sense that they provide inadequate explanations, but present day scientists do not believe that any theory is "right," if by that it is meant that the theory represents any kind of absolute truth. The laws of physics exist in the mind of man, not in the bosom of nature.

You know that classical (or Newtonian) mechanics provides a satisfactory systematic explanation of a wide range of phenomena within man's ordinary experience, but during this century it has been realized that this explanation is inadequate for certain phenomena. To explain the behavior of atomic or sub-atomic matter it has been necessary to invent a new system of mechanics called quantum mechanics, and in any situation where speeds close to the speed of light are involved it is necessary to use another system of mechanics called relativistic mechanics. These different systems (or theories, or explanations) have different "beginnings" (or postulates, or hypotheses) and each is a part of the complex of ideas that is physics.

If physics is not exact in the sense that exact measurements are made or that experiments are exactly repeatable, nor in the sense that it provides exact predictions of behavior in real physical situations, then in what sense is it exact? Perhaps only in the sense that the laws of physics are stated in an exact way. Any physical theory, to be accepted, must be made quantitative. Concepts must be defined precisely, and relationships between concepts must be expressed in mathematical terms. Only then can the theory be subjected to the ultimate test of experimental measurement.

It is commonly said that mathematics is the language of physics, in order to emphasize that the theories of physics must be precisely formulated in mathematical terms. But remember that a language is of no use without thoughts or ideas to be expressed in it. The statement is *not* that mathematics *is* physics.

PARTICLES

It is not always a simple matter to make physical concepts precise. For example, think about the concept of a particle. What does the word *particle* conjure up for you? A dot on a page? A grain of sand? A great deal of physics is formulated on the basis of the particle concept, and yet we cannot give a neat unambiguous definition of **particle** any more than we could do so for **physics.** Everything in the universe, from galaxies to electrons, can in some ways be considered to behave as particles. The key word is "behave." We will consider something a particle if, in the circumstances under which we are considering it, it behaves as a particle. Progress? Perhaps, but slight. What does "behave as a particle" mean? It means that in the particular situation the size, shape, and internal structure of the object (or system) can be ignored as unimportant. This sometimes means that the dimensions of the object are small on the scale of the physical situation; planets look small in the solar system, man looks small on the earth, baseballs look small in ball parks, atoms look small in bulk matter, electrons look small in atoms (or do they?). However, "looking small" is somewhat too limiting because we will sometimes apply particle consideration when the dimensions are not small. For example, since a spherically symmetric body acts, as far as its gravitational attraction for other objects is concerned, as though its mass is concentrated at its center, we may treat the earth as a particle even though its dimensions are large compared to our system. There will be circumstances in which an object moves in such a way that the motion of every particle in the object is the same; the overall object will be treated as a particle. We will be particularly interested in collisions between particles. Sometimes, as in the case of a collision between two protons, or between a meteor and the earth, "collision" means an electromagnetic or gravitational interaction and we do not have to think of physical "contact." However, we will also deal with collisions of solid objects such as billiard balls and while we will consider them as particles, it is clear that we cannot really think of them as having no size—or how can they meet?

The particle concept is used in order to simplify the description and explanation of motion; a particle is localizable—we can follow its motion in space and in time. However, even though we ignore some of the properties of an object (such as size, shape and internal structure) in labeling it a particle, we do retain certain other properties. Those we do not ignore are the inertial mass and also the properties that determine its interaction with other particles, because its motion depends on these interactions. You are familiar with the properties called **gravitational mass** and **electric charge** which are used in describing the gravitational and electromagnetic interactions, and there are others, such as spin and magnetic moment.

The particle is a model, but the idealizations that make it a model are different in different physical circumstances. You will see that we come back many times to the question "What is a particle?"

Perhaps we should have said "You know what we mean by a particle."

MACROSCOPIC VS. MICROSCOPIC PHYSICS

Until this century most of physics consisted of the search for interrelationships between variables which are more or less directly accessible to man's senses (macroscopic variables), whereas one of the principal aims of modern physics is to explain what is observed at the macroscopic level in microscopic terms, that is, in terms of the behavior of molecules or atoms or other microscopic constituents of matter. (**Microscopic** in this sense does not mean observable in a microscope.) Many macroscopic branches of physics continue to be fruitful and important and there are intimate connections between the macroscopic and the microscopic. Thermodynamics relates the macroscopic concepts of heat and work, while kinetic theory and statistical mechanics provide microscopic explanations for the laws of thermodynamics. Hydrodynamics (the mechanics of fluids) and elasticity and plasticity (the mechanics of deformable solids) are useful macroscopic descriptions of the way bulk matter behaves, but this behavior can be given microscopic explanations in terms of the interaction between atoms.

While some branches of physics can be labeled as either macroscopic (thermodynamics) or microscopic (nuclear physics) this is not so of mechanics. The concepts of mechanics such as mass, momentum and energy were first introduced and defined at the macroscopic level, in terms of experience, but it is assumed that they have significance at the microscopic level as well. We often think of the trajectories of planets or baseballs or atoms or nucleons as describable in the same terms. We treat the acceleration of an electron by an electric field in the same way as the acceleration of an apple by a gravitational field. We consider that a collision between two protons is similar to the collision between two billiard balls. We know, however, that in so doing we are assuming a system of mechanics and a model for microscopic matter that are sometimes not very satisfactory. It turns out, for example, that while the stream of electrons in a cathode ray tube can be thought of as having trajectories like a stream of bullets, it is not satisfactory to think of the electrons in an atom as having trajectories at all. The atom requires a quantum mechanical description, and the concept of a particle is quite different in quantum mechanics from what it is in classical mechanics.

PROPERTIES AND CONSTANTS

If you have consulted tables of physical constants you will know that there are two kinds of physical constants, those usually referred to as universal constants (such as the gravitational constant, G) and those describing a specific physical property (such as density) of a particular kind of matter, reasonably constant over a range of physical conditions. The values of both kinds of constant are determined by experiment.

You are familiar with such universal constants as G, the electronic charge e, the speed of light c, and the quantum constant h. While measurements of these have been made as accurately as possible, it is an act of faith to say that they are really constant; that is, their constancy is an explicit assumption of the theories of physics. If precise experiments show such assumptions are not valid, they demonstrate that the theories are inadequate, or at least limited in range of validity. The number of universal constants cannot be specified, because the basic assumptions are different in different systems of description; c is a universal constant in relativistic mechanics, but not in classical mechanics.

The physical constants that describe properties of matter are not really constants at all. However, the physical properties that it is useful to define are those that are reasonably constant over some range of physical conditions, and in this lies the origin of the term. These constants are used in the macroscopic description of the mechanical, thermal and electric properties of matter. The elastic constants (moduli) describe the deformations of matter by forces; thermal expansion coefficients describe deformations due to temperature changes. The coefficient of viscosity tells something about the flow properties of liquids. Specific heat capacity compares the differing abilities of different materials to absorb heat energy. Some physical constants which are useful are not characteristic of a single material, but of pairs of materials; the coefficient of restitution is a measure of the macroscopic interaction when two objects collide.

While such physical constants are useful in comparing the macroscopic behavior of different kinds of matter, they are also useful in seeking a microscopic theory of this behavior. The existence of physical behavior that is constant under some conditions is a fact which should be explicable on a microscopic basis, as should departures from this behavior. The theory of specific heats, for example, has been developed and refined to the extent that this particular aspect of thermal behavior can be reasonably well explained in terms of the behavior of atoms. While in some cases there are adequate (quantitative) microscopic explanations of the observed behavior of bulk matter, this is not generally the case. It is not possible to calculate numerical values for many of the physical properties of a particular substance using a knowledge of the atomic structure of the substance. Mostly it is the other way around—we make inferences about the structure from measurement of the properties.

PREVIEW AND REVIEW

We began by pointing out that beginning was difficult. So far we have not begun any systematic development of physics, but have simply made some general comments to try to give you some idea of our attitude towards physics. To really begin we will have to become quantitative. It is not enough to say that if you keep pushing on something it goes faster and faster. What does "faster and faster" mean? How do you measure a push? We cannot, of course, become quantitative about everything at once. Where shall we focus our attention first? If you think about it you will realize that **motion** is a basic characteristic of all physical phenomena. **Mechanics,** the study of motion, is central to all of physics and is the usual place for a study of physics to begin.

To restrict ourselves to beginning with the study of motion is not limitation enough: The motion of what? Of objects? Of atoms and molecules? Of electromagnetic waves? Of matter? Matter is complex. In fluids (gases and liquids) the various parts move with respect to one another in infinitely complex ways. If we confine our attention to solid objects, the motion is not so free but still may be complicated; solids stretch, compress, twist, vibrate. Even if we assume that solids are rigid (they never are, but this assumption is often useful in a model) their motion is not necessarily simple to describe—think of the flutter of our paper disc, or of a tennis racquet thrown through the air, spinning about its axis and turning end-over-end as well.

We will begin with the motion of a **particle.** As we have already pointed out, a particle is an idealization ("you know what a particle is"). We could proceed in easy stages, starting with motion in a straight line at constant speed, then constant acceleration, then variable acceleration, then motion in a plane (in two dimensions) and finally motion in three dimensions, but we are not going to do this. We will start with a general description of the motion of a particle in three dimensions. We can do this because we assume that you have studied physics before and therefore we do not need to start from scratch.

We assume you have some knowledge of physics, but what do we assume? If we state everything we assume, it is not necessary to assume it. The important thing is that because you have already been introduced to many of the concepts of physics it is not necessary for us to follow a completely systematic development. This does not mean that we intend to be unsystematic, but rather that we can use examples and make references as we proceed that take advantage of your background. We can refer to the concepts of force, or momentum, or energy before we have given them explicit definition. Many of you will have had a comprehensive course in basic physics, so that there will be some overlap with our development, but this background makes it possible for us to delve more deeply into fundamentals than would otherwise be possible.

Because we are assuming that you have had some previous experience with physics, we are not going to proceed immediately with the basic study of motion, but instead will continue, in the next two chapters, to develop some general ideas that have broad applicability in physics. To some extent we will be discussing mathematical techniques, but the emphasis is on the application of these techniques to physical situations. If mathematics is the language of physics, then you must develop some facility in the language; this can be done through the formal study of it, but the best way to learn any language is to have to use it in everyday life. If you have studied calculus and the theory of errors the next two chapters can be read rapidly, but we hope with some profit in terms of physical insight. If you have not studied these areas of mathematics, these chapters provide a very physics-oriented introduction.

It should be no surprise to you to learn that we are not going to deal with all of physics, or even most of physics, in this book. An intellectual edifice which has been under construction for at least three centuries, and is still being extended and altered at a furious pace, is not going to be explored completely in a term, in a year, or even in a lifetime. We shall inspect the foundation at a few places, visit some of the major apartments, and walk through some of the connecting passageways, in the hope that you will develop some feeling for the general architecture. Some of the rooms should be familiar and we shall pass through these quickly, pausing only long enough to point out features you may not have observed before. Other rooms will be as unfamiliar to your guides as to you and will be avoided—but feel free to do some exploring on your own. We hope that some of you will become involved in the exciting and never-completed tasks of demolition and reconstruction. Perhaps you may add a whole new wing.

Questions for discussion

It is suggested that the kinds of questions given here should be discussed both at the beginning and at the end of your study of this book.

1. What does the term **scientific method** convey to you?

2. Can you give a definition of **physics** that appeals to you? Can you do it without using any technical words?

3. Do you think the phrase **laws of nature** is a suitable one to use for the laws of physics?

4. It was once said that all science falls into two categories, physics and stamp collecting. What do you think was meant by this? Does it have any validity?

5. Do you think that in physics experimental measurements lead to theories; or do theories lead to experiments?

6. What does the term **model,** as used in physics, mean? Is it used in more than one way?

7. Do you think that **causality** (the doctrine that every effect has a cause) is basic to physics?

8. Is a **universal physical constant** a constant by definition, or by experiment, or both, or neither?

9. What is your mental picture of an **electron?**

10. What is **matter?**

11. Do you believe a falling object falls straight down? What do you mean by **straight?** What do you mean by **down?** What do you mean by **object?**

12. Do you think fluctuations in measurements are the same as experimental error?

13. Are there other kinds of predictions besides statistical predictions?

14. Why is **average value** often called **expected value?**

2

INSTANTANEOUS AND
INTEGRATED BEHAVIOR

In describing the motion of a particle we can think about its instantaneous behavior, that is what it is doing at some instant of time; but we are often interested in its behavior over a time interval, that is in the summation of its behavior over many instants of time. For example, at some instant a particle may be at rest 100 ft above the earth with a downward acceleration of 32 ft/sec². This is an instantaneous description, valid only at this instant. What happens to the particle in a time interval of 10 seconds after this instant? If we assume that the acceleration is due to gravity, and that it is independent of position, and that air resistance can be ignored, then we can calculate that the particle will fall to the earth, hitting it in 2.5 seconds. If it does not bounce it will remain at rest on the earth's surface for the rest of the 10-sec interval. If it bounces we would need to know how it bounced in order to describe its motion for the whole time interval.

Very often in physics an instantaneous description is used to predict what will happen over an interval, or conversely, instantaneous behavior is deduced from a knowledge of what happens over an interval. The branch of mathematics called calculus provides methods for handling both of these; differential calculus deals with instantaneous rates of change, and integral calculus with summation over an interval.

In this chapter we give a brief summary of the operations of differentiation and integration, emphasizing geometric and physical implications, but without much concern for mathematical rigor.

RATE OF CHANGE

Consider two quantities x and y having some sort of functional relationship $y = f(x)$, meaning that for every value of one there is a corresponding value for the other, as indicated by the curve on the graph. The notation $y = y(x)$

15

can as well be used. The **rate of change of y with respect to x,** denoted dy/dx (read "dee-y by dee-x"), is defined as the slope of the tangent to the curve at any point. If the tangent AB is drawn at a point (x,y) on the curve, its slope AC/BC can be obtained from the graph. Clearly the slope varies from point to point, and is therefore a function of x. It is usually denoted $f'(x)$. By drawing a series of tangents the second graph could be obtained from the first, but this is a cumbersome and inaccurate procedure because the tangents cannot be drawn accurately.

The differential calculus provides methods of determining dy/dx or $f'(x)$ from $y = f(x)$, if $f(x)$ is an analytic function. The notation dy/dx can be interpreted as an instruction to do something to y ("operate" on y) just as the notation $3 \times y$ is an instruction. Both "d/dx" and "$3 \times$" are **operators** (symbols denoting mathematical operations) but in neither case does the symbol tell *how* to do the operation. You know that if $y = 9x^2$, then $3 \times y$ is $27x^2$ because you have learned the operation called multiplication. Similarly if $y = 9x^2$, then you can calculate that $dy/dx = 18x$ if you know the operation of differentiation.

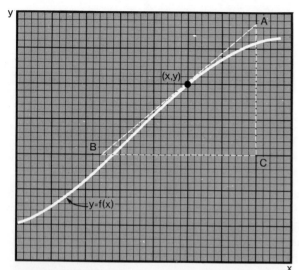

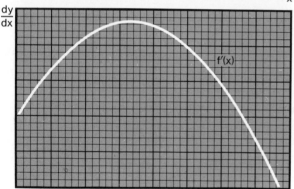

Graphs of a function $y = f(x)$ and its first derivative $dy/dx = f'(x)$.

DIFFERENTIATION

Consider the point (x,y) and another point $(x + \Delta x, y + \Delta y)$ on the curve $y = f(x)$. Since both points are on the curve they both satisfy the functional relationship $y = f(x)$.

$$y = f(x) \qquad y + \Delta y = f(x + \Delta x)$$

Therefore $\Delta y = f(x + \Delta x) - f(x)$. The slope of the straight line joining these two points (the chord) is $\Delta y/\Delta x = [f(x + \Delta x) - f(x)]/\Delta x$. As the second point is moved closer and closer to the first (i.e., as $\Delta x \to 0$) this slope becomes closer and closer to the slope of the tangent at (x, y); in the limit, as $\Delta x \to 0$, the slopes coincide. The rate of change of y with respect to x, or the **derivative** of y with respect to x, is then

$$\frac{dy}{dx} = \lim_{\Delta x \to 0} \frac{\Delta y}{\Delta x} = \lim_{\Delta x \to 0} \frac{f(x + \Delta x) - f(x)}{\Delta x}$$

This is the mathematical definition of the operation. The expression dy/dx means an infinitesimal change in y divided by an infinitesimal change in x. Writing dy instead of Δy is a notation to show that Δy has become infinitesimal; it is called the **differential** of y. Similarly dx is the differential of x. The result $dy/dx = f'(x)$ depends on what the function $f(x)$ is. To go further it is necessary to look at specific functional relations. It will be useful for us to do this for three examples: the derivative of a variable raised to a constant power, and the derivatives of the sinusoidal and exponential functions. The derivatives of other functions may be found by consulting calculus texts or tables.

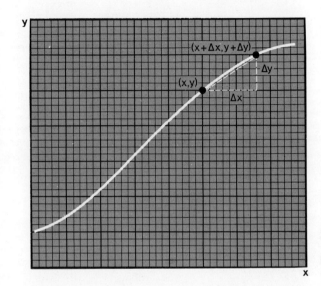

In the limit as $\Delta x \to 0$ the slope of the chord becomes the slope of the tangent at the point (x, y).

The Power Rule: Derivative of $y = x^n$, where n is constant ($n = 2$ or 3 or $\frac{1}{2}$ or -1.5, etc.).

Note that

$$f(x + \Delta x) = (x + \Delta x)^n = x^n (1 + \Delta x/x)^n$$

$$= x^n \left[1 + n\left(\frac{\Delta x}{x}\right) + \frac{n(n-1)}{2!}\left(\frac{\Delta x}{x}\right)^2 + \cdots + \left(\frac{\Delta x}{x}\right)^n \right]$$

:using the binomial expansion

$$\cong x^n \left[1 + n\left(\frac{\Delta x}{x}\right) \right]$$:for $\Delta x \lll x$

$$\therefore \frac{dy}{dx} = \lim_{\Delta x \to 0} \frac{(x^n + nx^{n-1}\Delta x + \cdots) - x^n}{\Delta x} = nx^{n-1}$$

You can verify for yourself that if $y = ax^n$, $dy/dx = nax^{n-1}$, and so can operate on $y = 9x^2$: $dy/dx = 9(2x) = 18x$.

The Sinusoidal Functions: If $y = \sin x$

$$f(x + \Delta x) = \sin(x + \Delta x)$$
$$= \sin x \cos \Delta x + \cos x \sin \Delta x \qquad \text{:recall } \sin(A + B)$$
$$\cong \sin x + \Delta x \cos x \qquad \text{as} \quad \Delta x \to 0$$
$$\text{:since as } \theta \to 0, \cos \theta \to 1 \text{ and } \sin \theta \to \theta$$

$$\therefore \frac{dy}{dx} = \lim_{\Delta x \to 0} \frac{(\sin x + \Delta x \cos x) - \sin x}{\Delta x} = \cos x$$

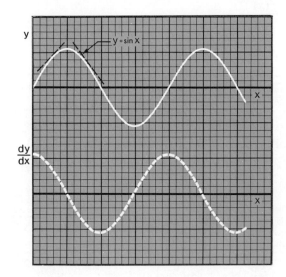

Graphs of $y = \sin x$ and its derivative $dy/dx = \cos x$.

By looking at the graph for $y = \sin x$, and visualizing the tangents to the curve, it will be seen that the result is reasonable. Similar procedures readily show that if $y = \sin ax$, $dy/dx = a \cos ax$, and that if $y = \cos ax$, $dy/dx = -a \sin ax$.

Exponential and Logarithmic Functions—$y = e^x$, $y = \ln x$: You are probably familiar with **common** logarithms, with the base 10, but may not be familiar with **natural** logarithms, where the base is the number e defined by

$$e = \lim_{x \to 0} (1 + x)^{1/x} = 2.71828\ldots$$

Natural logarithms are defined in the same way, and therefore have the same properties, as common logarithms. It is usual to use "log N" for "logarithm of N to the base 10" and "ln N" for "logarithm of N to the base e."

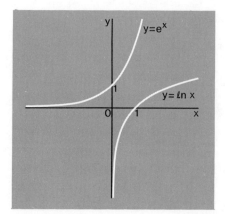

The exponential function $y = e^x$ and the logarithmic function $y = \ln x$ are related.

$$10^z = N \qquad z = \log_{10} N = \log N$$
$$e^x = N \qquad x = \log_e N = \ln N$$

Note by taking the logarithm that

$$\log e^x = x \log e = \log N$$

and therefore

$$x = \ln N = \frac{\log N}{\log e} = \frac{\log N}{0.4343} = 2.303 \log N$$

Tables of common logarithms can therefore be used to find natural logarithms, although most mathematical tables also provide a short table of natural logs.

The function $y = e^x$ is the **exponential function**; y is an exponential function of x. Taking the natural logarithm, $x = \ln y$. This is the **logarithmic function**; x is a logarithmic function of y. The exponential and logarithmic functions are said to be inverse functions. They are of interest in many physical situations, and therefore it will be useful to know how to find the derivative.

$$y = f(x) = \ln x$$

$$\frac{dy}{dx} = \lim_{\Delta x \to 0} \frac{\ln (x + \Delta x) - \ln x}{\Delta x}$$

$$= \lim_{\Delta x \to 0} \frac{1}{\Delta x} \ln \left(1 + \frac{\Delta x}{x}\right)$$

$$= \lim_{\Delta x \to 0} \frac{1}{x} \frac{x}{\Delta x} \ln \left(1 + \frac{\Delta x}{x}\right) = \lim_{\Delta x \to 0} \frac{1}{x} \ln \left(1 + \frac{\Delta x}{x}\right)^{x/\Delta x}$$

$$= \frac{1}{x} \ln e = \frac{1}{x}$$

Here we have used the properties of the logarithmic function, and the definition of the number e given earlier.

This result can be used to find the derivative of e^x.

$$y = f(x) = e^x \qquad \ln y = x \ln e = x$$

Differentiating *with respect to y*, $\frac{1}{y} = \frac{dx}{dy}$, showing that $\frac{dy}{dx} = y = e^x$. The exponential function is its own derivative.

You can verify that if $y = \ln ax$, $\frac{dy}{dx} = \frac{1}{x}$, and if $y = e^{ax}$, $\frac{dy}{dx} = ae^{ax}$.

The three functions for which we have worked out the derivatives will be sufficient to deal with most of the physical situations considered in this book. There are of course many situations in which the variation of y with x as measured in an experiment cannot be represented analytically by mathematical functions. In such cases the rate of change dy/dx may be found from the x–y graph, or by numerical procedures.

Higher derivatives: The function $dy/dx = f'(x)$ is called the first derivative of y with respect to x. Since it is a function of x, it can be differentiated again. This is called the second derivative of y with respect to x, and is denoted

$$\frac{d^2y}{dx^2} = \frac{d}{dx}\left(\frac{dy}{dx}\right) = f''(x)$$

The procedure can be repeated to find derivatives of higher order.

Examples: $y = 9x^2 \qquad \frac{dy}{dx} = 18x \qquad \frac{d^2y}{dx^2} = 18 \qquad \frac{d^3y}{dx^3} = 0$

$$y = Ax^{1/2} + Bx \qquad \frac{dy}{dx} = \tfrac{1}{2}Ax^{-1/2} + B \qquad \frac{d^2y}{dx^2} = -\tfrac{1}{4}Ax^{-3/2}$$

$$y = A \sin ax \qquad \frac{dy}{dx} = aA \cos ax \qquad \frac{d^2y}{dx^2} = -a^2A \sin ax = -a^2y$$

$$y = Ae^{-ax} \qquad \frac{dy}{dx} = -aAe^{-ax} = -ay \qquad \frac{d^2y}{dx^2} = a^2Ae^{-ax} = a^2y$$

CHANGES WITH TIME

In physics our interest in rates of change is often (but by no means always) in rates of change *with time*. You may have had some experience in plotting displacement–time (x–t) graphs and velocity–time (v–t) graphs for motion in one dimension, and observing that velocity v is the slope dx/dt on a x–t graph, and that acceleration a is the slope dv/dt on a v–t graph. Recall the equation for the displacement x at time t of a particle which at time zero had velocity v_0, and moves with constant acceleration a.

$$x = v_0 t + \tfrac{1}{2} a t^2$$

Differentiating this equation with respect to time, remembering that v_0 and a are constants, gives

$$\frac{dx}{dt} = v_0 + \tfrac{1}{2} a (2t) \qquad \text{or} \qquad v = v_0 + at$$

another relation for constant acceleration. Differentiating again gives

$$\frac{dv}{dt} = a$$

Thus we can go $x \rightarrow v \rightarrow a$ by differentiation. Can we go in the opposite or inverse direction $a \rightarrow v \rightarrow x$? Integration, the inverse operation to differentiation (just as division is the inverse of multiplication) enables us to do this.

First, one other point about differentiation. The equations just quoted describe uniformly accelerated motion in one dimension. The quantities x, v, a are vector quantities, but in a one-dimensional situation they can be treated as scalar quantities—that is, they can be handled algebraically, having regard to sign. In describing motion in general, this is not the case. A vector quantity $\mathbf{A}$ can vary with time in magnitude *and* in direction. What does $d\mathbf{A}/dt$ mean?

Think about a displacement vector $\mathbf{R}$, the displacement of a particle P from another particle O. Think of O as fixed in space, and of P moving (i.e., think of the motion of P with respect to O). The displacement $\mathbf{R}$ is a function of time $\mathbf{R}(t)$. It is sometimes convenient to **separate** the time dependence of its magnitude and of its direction by using the unit vector $\mathbf{r}$: then $\mathbf{R}(t) = R(t)\mathbf{r}(t)$. The magnitude R is a scalar, and varies in some way with time. The unit vector $\mathbf{r}$ may vary in quite a different way with time, but only in direction since its magnitude

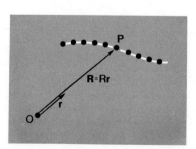

Displacement $\mathbf{R}$ is the product of the magnitude R and the unit vector $\mathbf{r}$.

is fixed. Thus **R** is expressed as the product of two quantities which may vary independently with time.

This is one reason the rule for differentiating a product will be of interest to us.

DERIVATIVE OF A PRODUCT

Consider two functions of x, say $y = y(x)$ and $z = z(x)$. We know how to find dy/dx and dz/dx now. How about $d(yz)/dx$?

By definition

$$\frac{d(yz)}{dx} = \lim_{\Delta x \to 0} \frac{y(x + \Delta x)z(x + \Delta x) - y(x)z(x)}{\Delta x}$$

Observe that $y(x + \Delta x)$ is the value of y at $x + \Delta x$, which may be obtained approximately by taking the value of y at x, and adding to it the rate of change of y with x, multiplied by the "distance" Δx; that is

$$y(x + \Delta x) = y(x) + \frac{dy}{dx} \Delta x$$

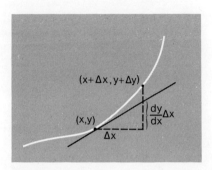

A finite change in y, Δy, is approximately equal to the product of the slope dy/dx and the finite change Δx.

The rate of change dy/dx is the rate *at* the point x, and not over the interval, but as $\Delta x \to 0$ the approximation becomes better and better. Using the same argument for $z(x + \Delta x)$ we may write

$$y(x + \Delta x)z(x + \Delta x) - y(x)z(x)$$

$$= \left[y(x) + \frac{dy}{dx} \Delta x \right]\left[z(x) + \frac{dz}{dx} \Delta x \right] - y(x)z(x)$$

$$= \left[y(x)z(x) + y(x)\frac{dz}{dx} \Delta x + z(x)\frac{dy}{dx} \Delta x + \frac{dy}{dx}\frac{dz}{dx} \Delta x^2 \right] - y(x)z(x)$$

$$= \left[y(x)\frac{dz}{dx} + z(x)\frac{dy}{dx} \right] \Delta x + \frac{dy}{dx}\frac{dz}{dx} \Delta x^2$$

As $\Delta x \to 0$, the term in Δx^2 can be neglected, and therefore

$$\frac{d(yz)}{dx} = y\frac{dz}{dx} + z\frac{dy}{dx}$$

Note: Such a procedure may not be necessary of course. Suppose $y = \sqrt{x}$ and $z = x^2$. Then

$$dy/dx = \tfrac{1}{2}x^{-1/2} \qquad dz/dx = 2x$$

$$\frac{d(yz)}{dx} = y\frac{dz}{dx} + z\frac{dy}{dx} = x^{1/2}(2x) + x^2(x^{-1/2}/2) = 2x^{3/2} + x^{3/2}/2 = 5x^{3/2}/2$$

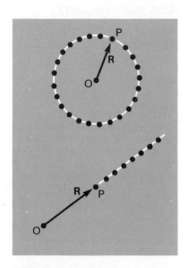

Displacement constant in magnitude or constant in direction.

but we could have said

$$yz = \sqrt{x}\, x^2 = x^{5/2} \quad \text{and} \quad \frac{d(yz)}{dx} = \frac{5}{2} x^{3/2}$$

at once. However, if, for example, $z = 4 \sin x$ and $y = x^2$, the procedure is very useful.

To return to the displacement vector $\mathbf{R}(t) = R(t)\mathbf{r}(t)$, we may write

$$\frac{d\mathbf{R}}{dt} = \frac{d}{dt}\left[R(t)\mathbf{r}(t) \right] = \mathbf{r}\frac{dR}{dt} + R\frac{d\mathbf{r}}{dt}$$

If the magnitude R of the displacement is constant (independent of time) the first term is zero; this would be circular motion of particle P about particle O. If the unit vector $\mathbf{r}$ is constant, the second term is zero; the point P moves in a straight line with respect to O. This is the case of one-dimensional motion, and as can be seen the time derivative of a vector quantity is not involved.

SUMMATION

The process of **differentiation** can be interpreted geometrically as finding the slope of a curve. The process of **integration** can be interpreted geometrically as finding the area "under" a curve, between certain limits. Integration always refers to an interval, say $x_1 \rightarrow x_2$. (If the limits of the interval are specified, it is called the definite integral; if they are not, it is called the indefinite integral, and involves an arbitrary constant.) The area under the curve means the area (shown shaded) bounded by the curve $z = F(x)$, the x-axis, and the limits of integration x_1 and x_2. As in the case of the slope, we could determine this area directly from the graph by making measurements—perhaps counting squares, or using a mechanical gadget called a planimeter. It should be noted that although this is an area on the graph, it may represent any physical quantity. For example, if the graph is a plot of velocity against time, then the area will have the units of velocity $\times$ time, or distance.

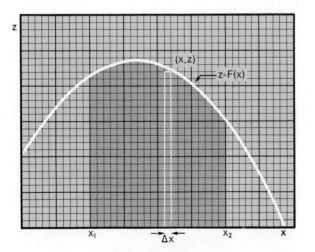

The shaded area is the area under the curve in the interval $x_1 \rightarrow x_2$.

INTEGRATION

In order to write an expression for the area in terms of the function, we can proceed as follows. Think of the area as divided into vertical strips, each of the same width Δx. (Again, the Δx means that it is finite, but is going to approach zero.) Look at the strip with its corner at the point (x,z). It has an area $z\,\Delta x$ (its height $\times$ width). This is not quite the area under the curve over this interval Δx, because of the bit of area at the top. However, if we let the strips get narrower and narrower (let $\Delta x \to 0$) then $z\,\Delta x$ will be closer and closer to the area under this piece of the curve. If we add up the areas of all such strips between x_1 and x_2, then in the limit as $\Delta x \to 0$ (and the number of strips approaches infinity) we will get the area required. We want

$$\lim_{\Delta x \to 0} \sum_{x=x_1}^{x_2} z\,\Delta x = \lim_{\Delta x \to 0} \sum_{x=x_1}^{x_2} F(x)\,\Delta x$$

where $\sum_{x=x_1}^{x_2}$ is notation for the "sum as x goes from x_1 to x_2." This summation and limit procedure is symbolized by the notation $\int_{x_1}^{x_2} z\,dx$ or $\int_{x_1}^{x_2} F(x)\,dx$, where as in the case of differentiation Δx has become dx to indicate that it has become infinitesimal. The integration symbol $\int$ was originally a form of the letter "S" for sum.

$$\int_{x_1}^{x_2} z\,dx = \lim_{\Delta x \to 0} \sum_{x=x_1}^{x_2} z\,\Delta x$$

This equation defines the operation of integration, but of course does not tell us how to integrate in the case of a particular function. Just as dy/dx symbolizes an operation on y, an instruction to do something to y, so $\int z\,dx$ symbolizes an operation on z, an instruction to do something to z. The result in a particular case depends on the function $z = F(x)$, and on the interval $x_1 \to x_2$. We are not going to have to work out what the operator does for any particular functions, because we are going to recognize that integration is the opposite to differentiation (sometimes it is called antidifferentiation).

To see this, we will introduce a quantity y which is a measure of the area under the curve. We will define **change** in y, rather than y, by denoting the area of the little strip as $\Delta y = z\,\Delta x$, or in the limit $dy = z\,dx$. This relates an infinitesimal change in y (the differential of y) to an infinitesimal change in x. Since the area of the strip, dy, depends where the strip is, or on x, it is clear that the function y will be a function of x: $y = f(x)$. Let its value be y_1 when x is x_1, and y_2 when x is x_2: $f(x_1) = y_1, f(x_2) = y_2$. As x goes from x_1 to x_2, y goes from y_1

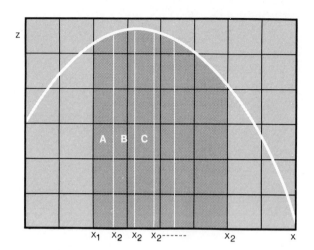

Finding the areas A, A + B, A + B + C, ⋯, determines $y = \int z\,dx$ as a function of x.

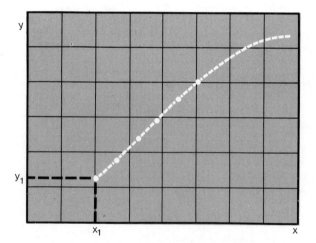

The function $y = f(x) = \int z\,dx$ for an arbitrary choice of (x_1, y_1).

to y_2, so we may write

$$\int_{x_1}^{x_2} z\,dx = \int_{y_1}^{y_2} dy = y_2 - y_1 = f(x_2) - f(x_1)$$

since $\int_{y_1}^{y_2} dy$ means the total change in y in going from y_1 to y_2.

To see what the function y looks like, we could fix the value of x_1 and y_1 and determine the y_2's corresponding to different x_2's; that is, determine the area A, and then the area $A + B$, then $A + B + C$, and so on. In this way we could plot y as a function of x—for this particular choice of x_1 and y_1. This is equivalent to defining the function as the indefinite integral.

$$y = f(x) = \int z\,dx + \text{a constant}$$

The value of the constant depends on the arbitrary choice of x_1, y_1. We still haven't said how to perform the operation $\int$, but from the definition of y, you will see we do not need to.

Since $dy = z\,dx$, then $z = dy/dx$; y is the function whose rate of change with x is z; or z is the function whose integral with respect to x is y. These are equivalent statements. The graphs shown here are the same graphs as used to illustrate differentiation, but reversed. In differentiating $y = f(x)$, we said that the resulting function dy/dx is usually called $f'(x)$, and as we have shown this is the function $z = F(x)$

$$\frac{dy}{dx} = f'(x) \qquad y = \int f'(x)\,dx$$

We can now write down the integrals for certain cases. Since if

$$y = x^n \qquad \frac{dy}{dx} = nx^{n-1}$$

then $\int x^n\,dx = \dfrac{x^{n+1}}{n+1} + \text{a constant}$. To see that this is so, differentiate, recognizing that a constant has zero rate of change.

$$\frac{d}{dx}\left(\frac{x^{n+1}}{n+1} + C\right) = \frac{(n+1)x^{n+1-1}}{n+1} = x^n$$

Note that this result is valid for all values of *n except n* $= -1$. We showed earlier that if $y = \ln x$, $dy/dx = 1/x$. Therefore

$$\int \left(\frac{1}{x}\right) dx = \ln x + \text{a constant}$$

You can verify by differentiating that

$$\int e^{ax}\, dx = (1/a)e^{ax} + \text{a constant}$$

$$\int \sin ax\, dx = (-1/a)\cos ax + \text{a constant}$$

DEFINITE AND INDEFINITE INTEGRATION

The indefinite integral of any function $y = F(x)$ is defined by

$$f(x) = \int y\, dx + C$$

where C is an arbitrary constant. The definite integral is defined by

$$f(x_2) - f(x_1) = \int_{x_1}^{x_2} y\, dx$$

To see the difference between these, we shall look at an example.

Example: The parabola $y = 4 + 2x^2$ is shown. We shall find the function $f(x)$ which is the integral of the function $y = 4 + 2x^2$.

$$f(x) = \int y\, dx + C$$

$$= \int (4 + 2x^2)\, dx + C$$

$$= \int 4\, dx + \int 2x^2\, dx + C$$

$$= 4\int dx + 2\int x^2\, dx + C$$

$$= 4x + 2(x^3/3) + C$$

Note that $df/dx = 4 + 2x^2$, as it must be. Let us evaluate the area under the parabola from $x = 2$ to $x = 4$

$$f(2) = 8 + 16/3 + C = 40/3 + C$$

$$f(4) = 16 + 128/3 + C = 176/3 + C$$

and the required area is

$$f(4) - f(2) = 176/3 - 40/3$$

$$= 136/3$$

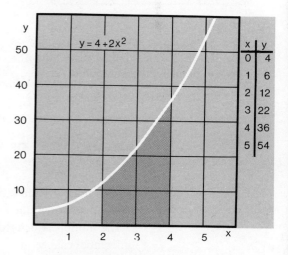

The area under the parabola $y = 4 + 2x^2$ in the interval $x = 2$ to $x = 4$.

The same operation expressed as a definite integral would be:

$$\text{Area} = \int_2^4 y\,dx = \int_2^4 (4 + 2x^2)\,dx = 4\int_2^4 dx + 2\int_2^4 x^2\,dx$$

$$= 4[x]_2^4 + 2[x^3/3]_2^4 = 4(4 - 2) + 2(4^3/3 - 2^3/3)$$

$$= 4(2) + 2(64/3 - 8/3) = 8 + 2(56/3) = 136/3$$

In this case the integrated function $f(x)$ is not introduced explicitly, since what is required is its value at certain points. Note that in achieving the result the value of the function at the "lower" limit (initial value) is subtracted from its value at the "upper" limit (final value), thus finding $f(x_2) - f(x_1)$. The terms upper and lower refer to the positions of the limits on the integral sign.

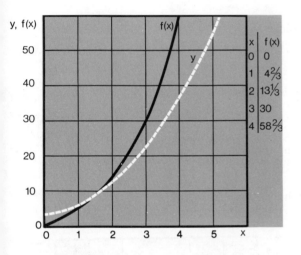

x	f(x)
0	0
1	$4\tfrac{2}{3}$
2	$13\tfrac{1}{3}$
3	30
4	$58\tfrac{2}{3}$

The function $y = 4 + 2x^2$ and its integral $\int y\,dx = f(x)$ plotted on the same axes. The vertical position of $f(x)$ is arbitrary.

The function $f(x)$ is determined only in form, not in absolute value, since it involves the arbitrary constant C. A value can be assigned arbitrarily to C. For example, in this case choose $f(x) = 0$ when $x = 0$. Then since $f(x) = 4x + 2x^3/3 + C, f(0) = 0 + C$, and $C = 0$. The function $f(x) = 4x + 2x^3/3$ is shown along with the initial function, but its vertical position is arbitrary.

The function $f(x)$ can also be produced from the definite integral by putting in a specific (arbitrary) initial value, and leaving the upper limit general; thus

$$f(x) = \int_0^x y\,dx = \int_0^x (4 + 2x^2)\,dx$$

$$= 4[x]_0^x + 2[x^3/3]_0^x = 4x + 2x^3/3$$

Substitution of $x = 0$ shows that $f(0) = 0$.

This could have been done for any value of x, say x_0. Then

$$f(x) = \int_{x_0}^x y\,dx = 4x + 2x^3/3 - (4x_0 + 2x_0^3/3)$$

giving a different origin on the f-axis: $f(0) \neq 0$.

DIFFERENT WAYS OF SAYING THE SAME THING

Let us now return to the example of one-dimensional motion with constant acceleration. We showed that we could go $x \to v \to a$ by differentiation; we now see that we can go the opposite direction by integration.

The motion is defined by $a = dv/dt$ being constant. This equation relates differential changes in v and in t, thus $dv = a\,dt$. To sum up the changes over an interval we write $\int dv = \int a\,dt = a\int dt$, where we can take a outside the $\int$ sign because it is constant. (If it was not constant, we would have to know how it depended on t in order to integrate $\int a\,dt$.) Let us choose $v = v_0$ when $t = 0$, that is, start measuring time t at some instant when the velocity is v_0.

$$\int_{v_0}^{v} dv = a \int_{0}^{t} dt$$
$$v - v_0 = at$$

or $v = v_0 + at$. We started with an **instantaneous** description of the motion, $a = $ constant. We now have a description of the motion over an **interval** $0 \rightarrow t$.

From the definition of velocity as rate of change of displacement

$$v = \frac{dx}{dt} = v_0 + at$$

or $dx = v_0\,dt + at\,dt$, relating the differentials dx and dt of displacement and time, and the constants v_0 and a. Over the interval $0 \rightarrow t$, the displacement will change from $x_0 \rightarrow x$.

$$\int_{x_0}^{x} dx = v_0 \int_{0}^{t} dt + a \int_{0}^{t} t\,dt$$
$$x - x_0 = v_0 t + at^2/2$$

We could have taken $x_0 = 0$, of course, which means starting to measure displacement at the same instant as t.

The first equation $a = dv/dt$ is an instantaneous or differential description of the motion—a **differential equation.** The second and third are integrated descriptions of the same motion—**integral equations.**

Many physical situations can be described in such terms. You may have already spent some time on the differential form of Newton's law of motion $F = dp/dt$ as well as on its integrated form $J = p_2 - p_1$, (where $J = \int_{t_1}^{t_2} F\,dt$). In the analysis of a particular system it is usually easier to deduce the differential equation than it is the integral equation, while the latter is usually more useful in applications. A good deal of physics seems to involve switching back and forth between these descriptions; but keep in mind that this is a mathematical operation, not physics. The physics is in the approximations and idealizations which make it possible to write down the differential or integral equation in the first place.

Sometimes even though it is possible to write down a differential equation it is not possible to integrate it analytically, that is to produce an integral equation in terms of known functions. Every function can be differentiated, but not every function can be integrated. In any case the integration (the evaluation of what happens over an interval) can be performed numerically. This turns out to be a tedious process, but can be performed readily nowadays using computers.

Problems

This is not a book on mathematics, so we will not provide a large number of problems on integration and differentiation to solve for this chapter. However, we will give a few examples that illustrate the use of calculus in analyzing physical situations. Throughout the text calculus will be used in working out examples, when necessary.

1. Sketch y vs. x and dy/dx vs. x for the following functions:

$$y = 4x + 3 \qquad y = 2x^2 + 4 \qquad y = 3 \sin 2x$$

2. The speed of a particle falling freely from rest is $v = 32t$ ft/sec, where t is in sec. Determine the acceleration and the displacement of the particle after 5 sec.

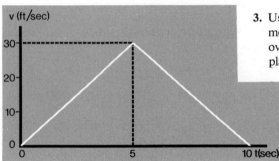

3. Using the velocity–time graph shown, plot a displacement–time graph and an acceleration–time graph over the same interval. What is the resultant displacement in the 10-sec interval?

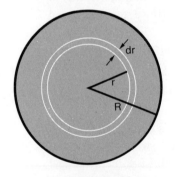

4. (a) Calculate the area of a circle of radius R by considering a ring of radius r, and of width dr, as shown. The area of the ring, if dr is infinitesimal, is its length times its width, $dA = (2\pi r)(dr)$. The area of the circle is $A = \int dA$. The variable is r, and it goes from 0 to R as the ring is moved over the whole area.

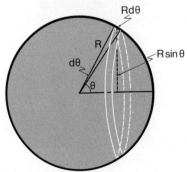

(b) Calculate the area of a sphere of radius R by considering a ring on the surface as shown. Use the angle θ as a variable: it goes from 0 to π as the ring is moved over the whole area. The width of the ring is $R\,d\theta$, and its radius is $R \sin \theta$, so $dA = 2\pi R^2 \sin \theta \, d\theta$.

(c) Calculate the volume of a sphere of radius R by considering a spherical shell of radius r, and thickness dr.

(d) Is it necessary to integrate to find the surface area and the volume of a circular cylinder of radius R, length L?

5. The motion of a hot rod leaving an intersection is described as to time t and speed v in the tabulation.

t, sec	v, ft/sec	t, sec	v, ft/sec
0	0	6	13.7
1	0.064	7	21.9
2	0.51	8	32.8
3	1.73	9	46.6
4	4.1	10	64.0
5	8.0		

Plot the v–t graph and use it to determine (a) the displacement in the 10-sec interval, by counting squares to find the area under the curve; (b) the acceleration at $t = 5$ sec, by drawing a tangent. (c) Plot $\log v$ vs. $\log t$. You will find that to a good approximation the points are on a straight line. Use this line to find the relation between v and t (the equation of the v–t graph), and from this check your results for (a) and (b) by integration and differentiation.

6. A particle moves on the x-axis of a co-ordinate system, its position as a function of time given by $x = At^2 + B \sin (Ct)$, where A, B and C are constants. If x is in cm, and t is in sec, what are the units of A, B and C? Determine expressions for the speed and for the acceleration of the particle, and check that the units are correct in each case.

7. The molar heat capacity c of a substance is defined by $c = \Delta Q / \Delta T$, where ΔQ is the amount of heat necessary to change the temperature of one mole of the substance by ΔT degrees. For many solids at very low temperatures the heat capacity varies with temperature according to the Debye T^3 law. For copper, for example, $c = 2.0 \times 10^{-5} T^3$ calories/mole-K°, where T is the temperature in degrees Kelvin (0 K° $\cong -273$ C°).

Determine the heat energy necessary (in calories) to change a 64-gm block of copper (one mole) from 10 K° to 15 K°, (a) by assuming that c can be taken as constant at its value at the mid-point of the interval, (b) by calculating c at the end points of the interval, and assuming a linear variation, (c) by integration. Note that since $c = \Delta Q / \Delta T$, the heat added in a finite temperature change is $Q = \int c \, dT$.

Use areas on a graph of c vs. T to show what you have calculated in each of the three cases.

8. (a) Exponential relations can often be used to represent physical behavior. These relations are usually in the form

$$y = A \, e^{bx} \quad \text{or} \quad y = A \, e^{-bx} \quad \text{or} \quad y = A(1 - e^{-bx})$$

where A and b are positive constants. Sketch graphs of each of these, marking the constants A and b on the graphs. Note that most mathematical tables give e^x and e^{-x} for a range of x.

(b) An object that is at a higher temperature than its surroundings loses heat because of radiation, conduction and convection. The rate of heat loss dQ/dt of an object at temperature T, when the surroundings are at a temperature T_0, depends on the temperature excess $T - T_0 = \theta$. If this temperature difference is not too large, it is found that the rate of loss is proportional to the excess.

$$\frac{dQ}{dt} \propto \theta \quad \text{or} \quad \frac{dQ}{dt} = -k\theta$$

This is known as Newton's law of cooling. The **cooling constant** k depends on cooling conditions such as the shape and surface condition of the object. The negative sign is put in so that k will be positive. This is necessary because θ is positive and dQ/dT is a negative quantity.

The temperature change ΔT of a body when a quantity of heat ΔQ is added to it depends on the heat capacity C of the body: $\Delta Q = C \Delta T$. The heat capacity can be considered constant for a limited range of temperature. Note that when ΔQ is positive (heat added), then ΔT is positive (temperature increase); when ΔQ is negative (heat loss), then ΔT is negative (temperature decrease). When heat is added at a rate dQ/dt, the temperature changes at a rate dT/dt, such that $dQ/dt = C\, dT/dt$.

Since $\theta = T - T_0$, where T_0 is the temperature of the surroundings (assumed to be constant), $d\theta/dt = dT/dt$; the rate of change of temperature excess is the same as the rate of change of temperature.

$$\left. \begin{aligned} \frac{dQ}{dt} &= -k\theta \\ &= C\frac{dT}{dt} = C\frac{d\theta}{dt} \end{aligned} \right\} \qquad \frac{d\theta}{dt} = -\frac{k}{C}\theta = -K\theta$$

where K is a constant (for the particular situation) combining the cooling constant and the heat capacity of the object.

We have formed a differential equation relating excess temperature θ and time t. Assume that at some instant $t = 0$ the excess temperature is θ_i, and integrate to find θ at any later time t. The result shows an exponential decay of temperature with time.

$$\theta = \theta_i\, e^{-Kt}$$

or in terms of actual temperatures

$$T - T_0 = (T_i - T_0)\, e^{-Kt}$$

You can see that in setting up the differential equation it is a simplification to use θ rather than T, but it is not essential.

This example has been used to emphasize the **physical** assumptions that are involved in setting up the differential equation. Can you enumerate three of them? The only mathematical step is the integration.

This situation, in which the rate of loss of something is proportional to the amount of "something" you have, is a common one, and not only in physics. It always leads to an exponential decay of the amount of the "something" with time. One example you may know is the decay of a radioactive material. Another is the decay of electric charge stored in a capacitor.

Exponential decay relations are often written in the form

$$\theta = \theta_i e^{-t/\lambda}$$

where λ is called either the time constant or the relaxation time. It is the time for θ to drop to a fraction $1/e$ of its initial value. Another time that is used is the **half-life** $t_{1/2}$, the time for θ to drop to $\frac{1}{2}$ its initial value. Work out the relation between λ and $t_{1/2}$.

9. Measurements of the excess temperature, θ, of an object, vs. time t, are as tabulated.

t, sec	θ, C°	t, sec	θ, C°
0	150	25	33
5	113	30	22
10	81	35	18
15	63	40	15
20	47		

Plot a graph of θ vs. t. Also plot $\log \theta$ vs. t and draw the best straight line you can to represent the data. Find the equation of this line, and in this way evaluate **(a)** θ_i and **(b)** K in $\theta = \theta_i e^{-Kt}$.

Draw tangents to the θ–t graph at 10, 20 and 30 sec and **(c)** compare your results to the slopes as calculated for these points from the equation for the θ–t graph.

Determine **(d)** the time constant and **(e)** the half-life for the decay. **(f)** How long would it be before the object is within 1 C° of its surroundings?

3

MEASUREMENT

THEORY VS. EXPERIMENT

At the beginning of this book we emphasized that physics is an **intellectual activity** of man, and that in order to explain the world to himself he thinks in terms of idealized physical situations (models) and develops explanations (theories) based on these models. Most of this book, like most physics textbooks, is devoted to describing these models. The theories that we discuss deal with **idealized situations**; friction is neglected or considered a constant force, or the gravitational field is considered constant, or matter is considered to be homogeneous and isotropic, or the earth is considered fixed in space, or . . . . The list is endless. Of course, in many cases the idealization may be a very good model of the real physical situation—so good that the theoretical result would agree with an experimental result as closely as could be measured.

Physics is also an **experimental activity** of man. Theories or models begin with observation—preferably quantitative observations, or measurements. The ultimate test of theory is measurement. It is sometimes stated that if something cannot be measured, and if it appears that it never will be possible to measure it, then it has no place as a concept in any theory in physics. This is a rather vague statement because it is sometimes difficult to decide whether something is really being measured or not. The **neutrino**, for example, a fundamental particle with zero mass, was first postulated as part of a theory (to explain certain experimental results) and was later "observed." This observation was certainly not direct, in the sense of bringing this elusive particle into the range of any of our senses, but was sufficient to convince physicists of the existence of the neutrino.

On the other hand, an all-pervasive fluid called the **aether** once held a prominent place in physics theory. All attempts to detect its existence were unsuccessful, and it has vanished as a concept—but it lasted for over 200 years.

The statement about measurability as a requisite for physical reality is made to emphasize the ultimate importance of measurement in physics. On the other hand, the criterion of measurability must not inhibit imagination and inventiveness. Whether or not a concept or a theory is subject to experimental verification is by no means obvious, as the examples of the neutrino and the aether show.

In this chapter we are going to discuss a few general aspects of measurement and the treatment of measurements. In a sense, this is a digression from our attempt to explore the intellectual edifice of physics, but in another sense it is central—an examination of the mortar holding the bricks together.

UNITS, DIMENSIONS, CONVERSIONS AND CONSISTENCY

We begin by looking at the manipulation of the numbers that are the result of the measurements of physical quantities.

If a length is measured as 3.5 cm and written as $l = 3.5$ cm, then this fixes the amount of the physical quantity length, but it can be expressed in various ways. In different units it will be a different number, but the same amount of length. The **conversion to different units** can be made by simple reasoning, thus: to convert l in cm to l in mm we must know the conversion factor 10 mm = 1 cm; this tells us that the mm is a smaller unit of length than the cm, and therefore in a given length there are more of them, so $l = 3.5$ cm = 3.5×10 mm = 35 mm. In this case, simple reasoning is likely to give the right answer, but it is easy to get such arguments backward unless the physical quantity is one that you can visualize, like length. Arguments equivalent to "since 1 mm is one-tenth of a cm, a length of 3.5 cm is one-tenth of 3.5, or 0.35 mm" are not uncommon. Therefore, a procedure which is more automatic is preferable, saving your logic for greater things.

All conversions can be made by multiplying the value of the quantity by something that does not change its value, unity. Stating that 10 mm = 1 cm, or 1 mm = 1/10 cm, means that $\dfrac{10 \text{ mm}}{1 \text{ cm}}$ and $\dfrac{1 \text{ cm}}{10 \text{ mm}}$ are both equal to 1:

$$l = 3.5 \text{ cm} \times \frac{10 \text{ mm}}{1 \text{ cm}} = 35 \text{ mm}$$

$$l = 3.5 \text{ cm} \times \frac{1 \text{ cm}}{10 \text{ mm}} = 0.35 \text{ cm}^2/\text{mm}$$

In both cases the value of l has been multiplied by unity, so its value is unchanged. Both results are correct, although the first may be more useful. By writing both down (or by observing mentally which way up will give you "cm" in both numerator and denominator) the desired result is obtained.

Since 1 m = 100 cm

$$l = 3.5 \text{ cm} \times \frac{1 \text{ m}}{100 \text{ cm}} = 3.5 \times 10^{-2} \text{ m}$$

Since 1 in. = 2.54 cm

$$l = 3.5 \text{ cm} \times \frac{1 \text{ in.}}{2.54 \text{ cm}} = 1.38 \text{ in.}$$

Why not 1.4 in.?

It may appear that it has been assumed that units can be multiplied, but this is really just symbolism; the numbers are combined arithmetically, and the units are written afterward as products, or whatever:

$$30 \text{ cm} \times 20 \text{ mm} = 600 \text{ cm-mm} \ (\text{cm} \times \text{mm})$$
$$30 \text{ cm} \times 2 \text{ cm} = 60 \text{ cm-cm} = 60 \text{ cm}^2$$
$$30 \text{ cm} \div 20 \text{ mm} = 1.5 \text{ cm/mm}$$
$$30 \text{ cm} \div 2 \text{ cm} = 15 \text{ cm/cm} = 15$$
$$30 \text{ cm} + 20 \text{ mm} = 50 \ (\text{cm} + \text{mm})$$
$$30 \text{ cm} + 2 \text{ cm} = 32 \text{ cm}$$

Some of these forms are more useful than others, but all are simply statements of arithmetic operations, the results of which may or may not be of interest. You can add 3 apples and 2 oranges to get 5 objects, if you are interested in counting fruit.

The result of dividing a length of 75 ft by a time of 3 sec is 25 ft/sec. In some circumstances this may be useful; if something moved the 75 ft in 3 sec it is said to have an average speed of 25 ft/sec. But the 75 ft could have been the diagonal of a square, and the 3 sec the time to walk around the perimeter. Then 25 ft/sec is a valid quantity, but it is not the average speed of anything. The physical quantities speed and velocity have units of length/time, whether ft/sec, miles/hr (mph), inches/century, or light-years/microsecond. A particular value of speed can be converted in units without thought. For example, since 30 miles/hr = 44 ft/sec

$$25 \text{ ft/sec} = 25 \text{ ft/sec} \times \frac{30 \text{ miles/hr}}{44 \text{ ft/sec}} = 17 \text{ miles/hr}$$

If the speed of an object changes from zero to 25 ft/sec in 10 sec, it is said to have an average acceleration of 2.5 (ft/sec)/sec, which is

$$2.5 \left(\frac{\text{ft}}{\text{sec}} \times \frac{1}{\text{sec}} \right) = 2.5 \text{ ft/sec}^2$$

It cannot be written 2.5 ft/sec/sec because this is ambiguous; it might be read as 2.5 ft/(sec/sec) = 2.5 ft.

A car which accelerates from rest to 25 miles/hr in 10 sec has an average acceleration of 2.5 (miles/hr)/sec = 2.5 miles/hr-sec. The hyphen in hr-sec indicates that "sec" is in the denominator as well as "hr," and saves writing brackets. This may be a useful way of expressing the acceleration, or it may be more convenient to convert it to miles/hr^2 or miles/sec^2 or ft/sec^2, e.g.,

$$2.5\, \frac{\text{miles}}{\text{hr-sec}} = 2.5\, \frac{\text{miles}}{\text{hr-sec}} \times \frac{3600\ \text{sec}}{1\ \text{hr}} = 9.0 \times 10^3\ \text{miles/hr}^2$$

Equations such as $x = v_0 t + \frac{1}{2}at^2$ written in symbolic form represent relations between measurable physical quantities in a generalized way, but are basically just relations between numbers, the specific values of x, v_0, a, and t. If a particle has an initial velocity of 10 ft/sec and an acceleration of -40 cm/sec^2, what is its displacement after $\frac{1}{2}$ minute? We could substitute these numbers and find

$$x = (10\ \text{ft/sec})(\tfrac{1}{2}\ \text{min}) + \tfrac{1}{2}(-40\ \text{cm/sec}^2)(\tfrac{1}{2}\ \text{min})^2$$
$$= 5\ \text{ft-min/sec} - 5\ \text{cm-min}^2/\text{sec}^2$$

which we would not say equaled zero (5 apples $-$ 5 oranges $\neq$ 0). If we convert the time $t = \frac{1}{2}$ min = 30 sec we find

$$x = 300\ \text{ft} - 18{,}000\ \text{cm}$$

which is still inconvenient. Using 1 ft $\cong$ 30 cm, we may write the result as

$$x = 9000\ \text{cm} - 18{,}000\ \text{cm} = -9 \times 10^3\ \text{cm} = -3 \times 10^2\ \text{ft}$$

showing that the particle is 300 ft away from its starting point in a direction opposite to the direction in which it started to move.

How long did it take altogether to get back to its starting point? The equation becomes

$$0 = (10\ \text{ft/sec})t + \tfrac{1}{2}(-40\ \text{cm/sec}^2)t^2$$
$$= (10\ \text{ft/sec} - 20\ \text{cm/sec}^2 \times t)t$$

with solution $t = 0$, or

$$t = \frac{10\ \text{ft/sec}}{20\ \text{cm/sec}^2} = \tfrac{1}{2}\ \text{ft-sec/cm}$$

Since this is an unusual time unit, we might use 1 ft $\cong$ 30 cm to obtain

$$t = \frac{1}{2}\ \frac{\text{ft-sec}}{\text{cm}} \times \frac{30\ \text{cm}}{1\ \text{ft}} = 15\ \text{sec}$$

We have handled this problem in this rather unusual way to emphasize that in working with numbers having units you don't have a choice about what you get; if you multiply 5 apples by 4 oranges you get 20 apple-oranges. We did nothing wrong in solving the problem, but it would be more usual to convert to a consistent system of units at the beginning (i.e., put all lengths in cm or ft, all times in sec or min). It is sometimes stated that equations must be consistent from the point of view of units; it is useful and usual, but not necessary. The equation $x = v_0 t + \frac{1}{2}at^2$ is a relation between 3 lengths: x, $v_0 t$ and $\frac{1}{2}at^2$. In any particular case the **amount** of length corresponding to each term is fixed, but they can be expressed in different units, as in $x = 300$ ft $- 18\,000$ cm.

While the 3 terms in the equation may be expressed in different units, they should each represent the same physical quantity if it is to be a useful relation. This is true of all the equations of physics (we don't add apples and oranges), and is expressed by saying that they are **dimensionally consistent.**

The term **dimension** specifies the physical quantity by label but without specifying its units. The fundamental quantities length and time are given arbitrary labels L and T. The dimensions of derived quantities can be expressed in terms of L and T; velocity has dimensions LT^{-1}, acceleration dimensions LT^{-2}. As the scope is broadened, other fundamental quantities have to be introduced. If **mass,** dimension M, is included, all of mechanics is encompassed. All the quantities defined in mechanics have dimensions expressible in terms of M, L and T. To include all electrical phenomena, another fundamental quantity, **charge,** dimension Q, is introduced. (Sometimes in electricity, **current** is chosen as the fundamental quantity.) To include thermal phenomena, **temperature,** dimension θ, is introduced.

The term dimension as applied to these labels presumably has its origin in dimension as a spatial concept. Area has dimensions L^2, volume has dimensions L^3. In relativity theory time is included as a fourth dimension. By using ct rather than t (where c is a constant, the speed of light), four dimensional space-time is given the dimension L^4.

Dimensional considerations can be useful in recalling the form of a physical relation, because equations must be dimensionally consistent. If one remembers that the period of a simple pendulum of length l, in a place where the acceleration due to gravity is g, is either $T = 2\pi\sqrt{l/g}$ or $T = 2\pi\sqrt{g/l}$, then the fact that $l/g = [L/LT^{-2}] = [T^2]$ (where the square brackets are notation for "has the dimensions") will help to decide the appropriate form. It will not, however, help in remembering dimensionless numerical constants such as 2π.

Dimensional analysis can be more generally useful, in that it may help to predict the form of a functional relationship. Suppose, for example, that we did not know the expression for the period of a pendulum, but were led from observation or cerebration to believe that it **could** depend on the length of the suspension l, on the mass of the bob m, on the acceleration due to gravity g, and **not** on other quantities. We could then predict how it would depend on these quantities; we postulate that period $T = l^x g^y m^z$, where x, y and z are powers to be determined.

Dimensionally, $[T] = [(L)^x (LT^{-2})^y (M)^z] = [L^{x+y}T^{-2y}M^z]$. For the equation to be dimensionally consistent, the powers of M, L, T on the left side must be the same as their respective powers on the right side.

Thus $0 = x + y$, $1 = -2y$, $0 = z$, with the solution $y = -\frac{1}{2}$, $x = \frac{1}{2}$, $z = 0$, so that $T \propto l^{1/2}g^{-1/2}$. Therefore $T = k\sqrt{l/g}$, where k is a dimensionless constant. This is the form of the equation if T depends only on l, g and m as assumed. If it depends also on the amplitude of swing (as it does, a little) the relation would not be correct (as it isn't, quite). The value of the numerical constant k is not predicted.

In the case of the pendulum a direct analysis in terms of the forces involved can be made, but there are physical situations so complex that this is not feasible. In considering fluid flow phenomena, for example, dimensional analysis provides useful information.

GRAPHICAL REPRESENTATION OF DATA

In some experiments the aim is to measure a single value y_1 of a physical quantity. In an elementary physics laboratory this might be the acceleration due to gravity, g, in the room, or the specific heat capacity, c, of copper; in a research laboratory it might be the lifetime of the K meson (in a high energy laboratory) or the specific heat capacity of copper at 0.1°K (in a low temperature laboratory). These examples emphasize that most physical quantities don't have "a" value; g depends on height, c depends on temperature, the lifetime of the K meson depends on—on what? We don't know. We do know that particles like mesons change into other particles in an unpredictable way, so there is a distribution of lifetimes, but it is possible to talk about an average lifetime for these random disintegrations.

Measurements of a single value y_1 are made with the physical situation, usually called the **environment,** kept as far as possible unchanged. The next step is to vary one component x of the environment, keeping everything else as far as possible unchanged, so that ideally all other factors that might affect y remain constant. The experimenter does his best to insure this, but it is never completely achieved.

The value of x is measured or set at certain values x_1, x_2, $\cdots$ and the corresponding values $y_1, y_2, \cdots$, of y are measured. The aim is to see how y depends on x, or vice versa, and perhaps to express this dependence in terms of analytic functions $y = f(x)$ and $x = F(y)$. Sometimes an experiment is performed simply to acquire information about the relationship between x and y, but more often it is designed to test a particular theory, which has predicted that there should be a certain relationship. Usually such theoretical predictions are expressed as analytic functions.

It is not easy by looking at a table of numbers of corresponding values of x and y to visualize how they are related, unless the relation is very simple,

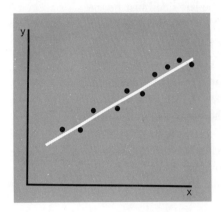

Is it reasonable to assume a linear relationship between the physical quantities x and y (as suggested by the straight line) for experimental results as shown by the points? Is it reasonable to assume that there is not a linear relationship?

for example that doubling x doubles y. You are familiar with the graphical representation of data. Plotting a graph helps to visualize the relationship, and in addition is often used to "smooth" the data. Since the numbers are measurements they are not exact, and drawing a smooth continuous line *may* be a reasonable way to represent the relationship.

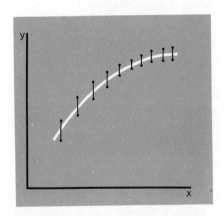

Error bars used to show uncertainty in the measured values of variable y. The corresponding values of variable x are assumed to be exact.

This is a risky procedure of course. For one thing it implies that x and y vary continuously, which may not be so. (If y is the number of times you get a certain number, x, in throwing a pair of dice, the x is certainly not continuous—it is an integer from 2 to 12. On the other hand, although y is also an integer if you throw a large enough number of times you can think of it as though it were a continuous variable.) Not all physical quantities vary continuously. The wavelength of standing waves on a string can have only certain values. The energy of an electron in an atom in a stationary state can only take on certain values. Quantity of electric charge can only occur in integral multiples of the fundamental electron charge e, although usually the number of electrons is so large that we think of charge (and current) as continuous variables.

For another thing, it is possible that something unusual happened between two of your discrete values of x. It helps a great deal to know how accurate your measurements are, that is, to know the **error**, Δx, in each value of x, and the error Δy in each value of y (we will come back to the determination of errors later). This is indicated on graphs by using **error bars** instead of points. If smoothing your data means drawing a line which misses your error bars, you may suspect that you have missed something and take some more data in this

At low temperatures the specific heat capacity of helium as a function of temperature is approximately as shown by the solid line. Experimental measurements at the points indicated might fail to reveal the anomalous peak. In drawing a smooth curve through a set of experimental points there is an implicit assumption that there is a functional relationship between the physical quantities that is continuous and well behaved. Interpolation is not always justified.

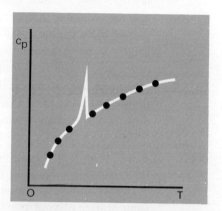

For many solids the specific heat capacity is observed to be approximately independent of temperature, for temperatures ranging upward from room temperature. However, extrapolating this result to lower temperatures is not justifiable.

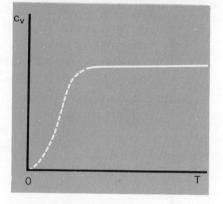

range. Usually the accuracy in one of your variables is much greater than in the other, and you only have to put error bars in one direction.

The process of **interpolation,** assuming what happens between two of your measurements, is risky but the process of **extrapolation,** assuming what happens *outside* your range of measurement, is even more so.

The search for an analytic functional relationship between x and y may be facilitated by the use of graphs. Usually you try to find some method of plotting x and y which gives a straight line. The x–y graph itself may be linear (or appear to be so, as far as you can tell from your data) so that the relation is of the form $y = ax + b$, or there may be a clue in the shape of the curve. It may look like a parabola, so you guess that the relation is of the form $y = ax^2 + b$. This can be verified by plotting y vs. x^2 to see if a straight line results; the plotting may be done using your original data, or numbers taken from your smoothed curve.

It is not easy to guess from the shape of a curve what function it might be, so you may try a number of different plots: y vs. x^2, y vs. x^3, y vs. $x^{3/2}$. However, a more generally successful procedure is to plot y vs. $\log x$, or $\log y$ vs. $\log x$

because these produce straight lines for a number of different relationships. If $y = ax^n$, where n and a are constants, then $\log y = \log a + n \log x$, so that a plot of $\log y$ vs. $\log x$ will be a straight line. **Exponential relationships** of the form $y = ae^{bx}$ are common in physics. Since $\log y = \log a + bx \log e$, a plot of $\log y$ vs. x will be a straight line. **Logarithmic plots** are so useful that graph paper with logarithmic scales in one direction (semi-log paper) or both directions (log-log paper) is made. By using it the values of x and y can be plotted directly, rather than looking up the logarithms of each number.

Sometimes you have to be quite devious to find a linear plot. For example, if a relation is of the form $y = ax^3 + bx$ you would have to plot y/x vs. x^2 (or $\log (y/x)$ vs. $\log x$) to get a straight line.

Having somehow established a linear plot, there will still be in most cases some scatter of your points. How do you decide which is the "best" straight line? You are familiar with the method of moving a transparent ruler around until you seem to have the points about evenly balanced on both sides of the straight edge. There are also systematic numerical procedures (the method of **least-squares,** for example) for doing the same thing. However, it is done, the straight line you determine is the best one only in the sense that you define best, not in any absolute sense.

The more accurate the measurements, the more confident you can be that these procedures will produce a valid relation between x and y. We can not tell you how to take accurate measurements, but we can give some methods for handling data systematically.

EXPERIMENTAL ERROR

You have made some measurements in physical situations. Some of you will have done this sort of thing: measured a quantity, say the time for an object to fall, six times and got 3.1, 3.3, 3.4, 3.0, 3.9 and 3.3 sec, using a stop watch reading to one-fifth of a second. You discarded the 3.9 value as being a mistake, and averaged the other five to get 3.22 sec as the time to fall. You felt that the extra figure was justified because you had taken several readings, but you weren't really convinced that the "correct" time to fall was between 3.215 and 3.225 sec. Perhaps you wrote 3.2(2) sec, or perhaps you had been instructed to estimate an experimental error so you wrote 3.22 ± 0.1 sec (because you read the stop clock to this accuracy) but then you felt this looked wrong so you wrote 3.2 ± 0.1 sec. Then perhaps you revised it to 3.22 ± 0.05 sec (because surely there must be some advantage to taking extra readings) or perhaps 3.22 ± 0.03 sec (because this seemed about right). Probably you were not very satisfied with the whole procedure, but you had done your best—your best being to some extent based on common sense, to some extent on intuition and taste.

We agree on both points—the procedure is not very satisfactory, and you did your best. Different people would write different results, and we would not like to say how it should be done, because there isn't enough information. There is a good deal of common sense and intuition involved in handling data, but there are also certain conventions. **Statistics means numerical facts systematically collected and handled.** If you follow normal statistical procedures in the collection of data and the specification of errors, then others will know what you have done. In this case you really didn't have enough measurements to apply these procedures, even if you are familiar with them. One difficulty with a physics laboratory (meaning places where students do experiments, not research laboratories) is that we try to do two things at once: to expose students to a wide variety of physical phenomena, and to give them some experience in making measurements and handling data. These aims are to some extent conflicting; systematic measurement is a painstaking, time-consuming process, and most laboratory experiments cannot allow time to acquire data which is suitable for detailed analysis. There is usually a painful compromise, of the sort given in the example. Realization that this is a compromise makes it less painful.

When the result of a number of measurements of a quantity x is written as $x \pm \Delta x$ (the use of "delta-x" implying that the error is small relative to the quantity) the **error** Δx may be due to error in measurement or due to fluctuations in the quantity itself; distinguishing between these is often difficult, and often important in interpreting the result. **Measuring errors,** sometimes called instrument errors, can arise due to calibration (Did you check your stopwatch against other clocks?) or use of an instrument (How did you start and stop your stopwatch? Should you have tried to estimate an extra figure beyond the smallest divisions on the dial?). They may be systematic, as in the case of calibration errors, or random, as is likely to be the case in estimating an extra figure.

We shall ignore considerations of the reasons for error for the moment, and give some elementary advice about handling data.

SIGNIFICANT FIGURES

You are probably already aware that a crude attempt to describe the accuracy of a measurement (or a number obtained by combining measurements) can be made by using only a certain number of figures in stating the result, but that there are no simple rules for doing this.

An example will illustrate the difficulty. Suppose that you measure the current through a resistor as $I = 0.31$ ampere and the potential difference across it as $V = 3.2$ volts, and wish to calculate the rate at which energy is dissipated $P = VI$. Putting in the numbers, $P = 3.2 \times 0.31 = 0.992$ watt. Probably you recognize that you are not justified in writing this, so you say that $P = 0.99$

watt: two significant figures since there were two significant figures in I and V. Now suppose that the current, instead of $I = 0.31$ ampere, had been 0.32 ampere. Now $P = 3.2 \times 0.32 = 1.024$ watts. How do you write this? 1 watt? 1.02 watts? 1.0 watt?

To decide, go back to I and V. What did $V = 3.2$ volts mean? In the absence of any other information, you *assume* it meant that V was between 3.15 and 3.25 volts. This is not necessarily so, of course. If V had been measured by a voltmeter reading to the nearest volt, then in the 3.2 the 2 is an estimate, and it might be better to say that $V = 3.2 \pm 0.1$ volts. However, **by convention, unless otherwise stated,** $V = 3.2$ volts means $V = 3.2 \pm 0.05$ volts. This means that you know V with an accuracy of about 1 part in 30. Similarly you assume that $I = 0.31$ ampere means $I = 0.31 \pm 0.005$ ampere, and you know I with an accuracy of about 1 part in 30. When you wrote $P = 0.99$ watt, by the same convention you imply that P is between 0.985 and 0.995 watt, and that you know P with an accuracy of about 1 part in 100. This is not so—you can't start with an accuracy of 1 part in 30 and end up with 1 part in 100. But what alternative have you? If you write $P = 1.0$ watt, you are implying an accuracy of 1 in 10, and you have thrown away some of your information. So you write $P = 0.99$ watt, because you don't want to lose any experimental information, recognizing that the second 9 is not as significant as the first 9.

In the second case the same considerations mean that you must write the result as 1.02 watts, implying that the result is between 1.015 and 1.025 watts, an accuracy of about 1 in 100 again. The fact that there are three figures instead of two does not matter. In both cases the last figure is *approximate*.

You can see that it is impossible to handle data in a very consistent way by this means. There is no definite rule that you must only get results having two significant figures if you multiply numbers having only two significant figures. You can make certain general statements, such as that a product should not be carried out to more than one more significant figure than the number of figures in the least accurate of its components, but such statements are just common sense. There are no simple rules which can be applied with blind faith.

Experimental error can only be reasonably specified by the $x \pm \Delta x$ notation, although this too has limitations.

COMBINATION OF ERRORS

In describing errors it is convenient to distinguish between **absolute error,** Δx, and **fractional** or **percentage** or **relative error,** $\Delta x/x$ or $(\Delta x/x) \times 100\%$. The absolute error has units, the units of x, while the fractional error is a pure number. (The term "absolute" should not be taken as implying that there is anything absolute about Δx, since in general it depends on a particular experiment.)

In the arithmetic operations of addition and subtraction, the resultant absolute error is the sum of the absolute errors; in the operations of multiplication and division, the resultant fractional error is the sum of the fractional errors (provided the errors are not too large). In the simple case of two experimental results, $x \pm \Delta x$ and $y \pm \Delta y$, this can be readily seen. Let us calculate $A = x \pm y$ (sum or difference), $P = xy$, and $Q = y/x$.

$$A \pm \Delta A = (x \pm \Delta x) \pm (y \pm \Delta y) = x \pm y \pm \Delta x \pm \Delta y = A \pm (\Delta x + \Delta y)$$

$$\therefore \Delta A = \Delta x + \Delta y \qquad \text{:the absolute errors add}$$

Note that if x and y are approximately the same, the error in $(x - y)$ may be as large as $(x - y)$ itself.

$$P \pm \Delta P = P \left(1 \pm \frac{\Delta P}{P}\right) = (x \pm \Delta x)(y \pm \Delta y) = xy \left(1 \pm \frac{\Delta x}{x}\right)\left(1 \pm \frac{\Delta y}{y}\right)$$

$$= P \left(1 \pm \frac{\Delta x}{x} \pm \frac{\Delta y}{y} \pm \frac{\Delta x}{x}\frac{\Delta y}{y}\right) \cong P \left[1 \pm \left(\frac{\Delta x}{x} + \frac{\Delta y}{y}\right)\right]$$

$$\text{:neglecting the product of two small terms}$$

$$\therefore \frac{\Delta P}{P} = \frac{\Delta x}{x} + \frac{\Delta y}{y} \qquad \text{:the fractional errors add}$$

$$Q \pm \Delta Q = Q \left(1 \pm \frac{\Delta Q}{Q}\right) = \frac{y \pm \Delta y}{x \pm \Delta x} = \frac{y}{x} \left(1 \pm \frac{\Delta y}{y}\right)\left(1 \pm \frac{\Delta x}{x}\right)^{-1}$$

$$\cong Q \left(1 \pm \frac{\Delta y}{y}\right)\left(1 \mp \frac{\Delta x}{x}\right) \qquad \text{:using } (1 + \epsilon)^{-1} = 1 - \epsilon \text{ for } \epsilon \ll 1.$$

$$\cong Q \left[1 \pm \left(\frac{\Delta x}{x} + \frac{\Delta y}{y}\right)\right] \qquad \text{:neglecting product of two small terms}$$

$$\therefore \frac{\Delta Q}{Q} = \frac{\Delta x}{x} + \frac{\Delta y}{y} \qquad \text{:the fractional errors add}$$

It is a straightforward matter to generalize these results to include more than two quantities.

Another common calculation involves errors in powers of x: what is the error in x^3, or $\sqrt{x}$, or $x^{-2/3}$? The binomial expansion is useful in such calculations:

$$(1 + \epsilon)^n = 1 + n\epsilon + n(n - 1)\epsilon^2/2! + \cdots \cong 1 + n\epsilon$$

if $\epsilon \ll 1$. Therefore $(x \pm \Delta x)^n = x^n \left(1 \pm \frac{\Delta x}{x}\right)^n \cong x^n \left(1 \pm n\frac{\Delta x}{x}\right)$. The fractional error in any number x raised to a power n ($n = \frac{1}{2}$, 2, $-3/2$, etc.) is the fractional error in x, times n.

The approximations made are usually reasonable for errors up to 10%. Consider two measurements of (3.3 ± 0.3) cm and (7.5 ± 0.5) cm and their product:

$$3.0 \times 7.0 = 21.00$$
$$3.3 \times 7.5 = 24.75 \quad \} \quad 3.75 \qquad 3.75/24.75 = 15.1\%$$
$$3.6 \times 8.0 = 28.80 \quad \} \quad 4.05 \qquad 4.05/24.75 = 16.4\%$$

The worst cases are 15.1% low and 16.4% high, the average error in the product being 15.7%. The errors initially were $0.3/3.3 = 9.1\%$ and $0.5/7.5 = 6.7\%$, with a sum of 15.8%. Since the errors are estimates it is usual to write (3.3 ± 0.3) cm = 3.3 cm $\pm 9\%$, and (7.5 ± 0.5) cm = 7.5 cm $\pm 7\%$, with the error in the product 16%. However, it makes no sense to write it as 24.75 cm^2 $\pm 16\%$, since the error is 4 cm^2. Perhaps (24.7 ± 4.0) cm^2 = 24.7 cm^2 $\pm 16\%$, might be written, but (25 ± 4) cm^2, or 25 cm^2 $\pm 20\%$, seems preferable for data as rough as these.

In every experiment there is usually one measurement that is more difficult (less precise) than others; the best possible value should be obtained for this measurement, and there is no point in obtaining results for other measurements which are much more accurate than this. It is worthwhile in every experiment to try to pick out the key measurement (or measurements) and concentrate on it, otherwise you may find you have measured some things to a much greater degree of accuracy than is useful.

SYSTEMATIC CALCULATION OF ERRORS

Suppose that you measure the diameter of a metal sphere with a vernier calipers, and obtain the results shown, which give an **average value** $\overline{D} = 7.54$ cm. How large an error should be attached to this? One possibility would be to take the

D, cm	δ, cm	D, cm	δ, cm
7.56	+0.02	7.52	−0.02
7.50	−0.04	7.58	+0.04
7.51	−0.03	7.57	+0.03
7.59	+0.05	7.55	+0.01
7.52	−0.02	7.50	−0.04

worst cases, and write $D = \left(7.54 \begin{smallmatrix} + 0.05 \\ - 0.04 \end{smallmatrix}\right)$ cm, but this isn't very sensible. What is required is some method of averaging the errors. This can be done in more than one way. Having calculated the mean $\overline{D}$, we can then write down δ, the **deviation** from the mean. If we take the signs of the deviations into account, then $\overline{\delta} = 0$. However, if we disregard the sign (take the absolute value), $|\overline{\delta}| \neq 0$. This is called the **average deviation.** Another way of getting rid of the sign is to square the deviations before averaging them. To give this the dimensions of the quantity we then take the square root. This root-mean-square deviation is called the **standard deviation.** This method of calculation gives greater emphasis (greater "weight") to large deviations than to small ones.

In the example $|\overline{\delta}| = 0.030$ cm and $\delta_{rms} = 0.032$ cm, so that the result would be written $D = (7.54 \pm 0.03)$ cm in either case. It turns out that in the theory of statistics the standard deviation is a more meaningful quantity than the average deviation, but as far as the representation of error is concerned the important thing is to state which deviation you have computed.

In general a set of N measurements $x_1, x_2, \cdots, x_N$ have a mean or average value

$$\overline{x} = \sum_{i=1}^{N} x_i/N$$

The deviation of the ith measurement is

$$\delta_i = x_i - \overline{x}$$

the average deviation

$$|\overline{\delta}| = \sum_{i=1}^{N} |\delta_i|/N = \sum_{i=1}^{N} |x_i - \overline{x}|/N$$

and the standard deviation

$$\delta_{rms} = \left[\sum_{i=1}^{N} \delta_i^2/N \right]^{1/2} = \left[\sum_{i=1}^{N} (x_i - \overline{x})^2/N \right]^{1/2}$$

The result may be stated as $\overline{x} \pm |\overline{\delta}|$ or as $\overline{x} \pm \delta_{rms}$.

In statistics the average of the sum of the squares of the deviation $\sum \delta_i^2/N$ is called either the **dispersion** or the **variance.** The standard deviation is the square root of the variance.

WEIGHTED AVERAGES

In a series of N measurements of a particular quantity (or in any series of numbers to be averaged, in general) it may be that some values are repeated a number of times. If there are n_1 values of x_1, n_2 values of x_2, $\cdots$, n_m values of x_m, the average can be expressed

$$\overline{x} = \frac{\sum_{i=1}^{m} n_i x_i}{\sum_{i=1}^{m} n_i} = \frac{1}{N} \sum_{i=1}^{m} n_i x_i \qquad \text{since} \qquad \sum_{i=1}^{m} n_i = N$$

The numbers n_i can be thought of as **probabilities.** If n_3 is twice as large as n_5, then x_3 is twice as probable as x_5 as a measurement. This is the **relative** probability of the two values. The number $n_i/N = P_i$ is the **absolute** probability of finding the result x_i. This simply means that of all the N values, n_i of them were x_i, and is the usual definition of probability, with

$$\sum_{i=1}^{m} P_i = \sum_{i=1}^{m} n_i/N = 1$$

The average $\bar{x}$ in this form is sometimes called a **weighted average,** with some values of x more heavily weighted (more probable) than others.

DISTRIBUTIONS

We have described how to determine the average value $\bar{x}$ of a series of measurements of a quantity x. Is $\bar{x}$ the "correct" value of x? This is a rather meaningless question. In the measurement of the diameter of a sphere, are the variations due to measurement error, or are they real variations in the diameter? Only a perfect sphere could have a single value of diameter, but there is no such thing as a perfect sphere, except as a geometric concept. Only by measurement is it possible to tell how closely a real sphere approximates this concept. If a number of measurements of an object's diameter are made, and the error observed in these measurements is less than the amount of variation in diameter you are prepared to tolerate, then the object is a sphere, by definition, and the average value of your measurements is its diameter, by definition. "Correct" value (like "best" straight line in graph fitting) is a matter of definition.

There are a few physical quantities, such as the **universal constants** G, e, c, h, which are *assumed* to have a correct value; but remember this constancy is a basic assumption of the theories in which these quantities appear. If precise measurement reveals that these are not constants, the theory would have to be revised.

All measurements show a variation about some average value and sometimes a knowledge of the average value is all that we are interested in. However, there are many circumstances in which we wish to know something of the way values are spread or distributed around the average value.

You are familiar with such social statistics as the average number of children per family, or the average lifetime of married men with more than four children, or the average income of professional physicists, or the average number of students per professor, or the average mark for a particular examination. In each case there is a **range** or **distribution** of values. The average value is a succinct way to give some information about the situation, but it gives no information as to how the values are distributed.

In these examples the details of the distribution are known, and used to calculate the average value. However, in physics it is often the case that we can measure the average value, but cannot measure the individual events which produce this average. For example, we cannot measure the speed of a single gas molecule, or watch how far it moves between collisions, or count how many molecules there are in a certain volume, but we can determine the average speed of gas molecules, the average distance a molecule moves without colliding with another, and the average number of molecules in a volume. We can do this because we can measure such macroscopic quantities as pressure, density and temperature which depend on the average behavior of microscopic quantities.

We can measure not only averages but sometimes fluctuations as well. Even the most sensitive pressure gauges indicate that the pressure of a gas under normal conditions is constant. However, if the pressure is made very low then fluctuations can be detected: we can measure both the average value and the deviation. This gives further information about the individual bombardment of molecules which produce the pressure. Similarly, sensitive measurements of very small electric currents show measurable fluctuations related to the individual behavior of electrons in a conductor.

Thus in physics we sometimes make inferences about individual behavior at the microscopic level from observed macroscopic average behavior. But how do we make these inferences? They are made on the basis of a **statistical theory**. In a statistical theory we *assume* something about individual behavior, and then calculate what to expect as overall or average behavior. Later on (Chapter 30) we will discuss in detail the kind of average behavior that results if the individual behavior is **random**. If in an experiment we observe this kind of average behavior, we can assume that it is based on randomness.

It will be useful to be familiar with descriptions of distributions in terms of histograms and distribution functions.

HISTOGRAMS

We have defined the weighted average

$$\bar{x} = \sum_{i=1}^{m} n_i x_i / N$$

of a set of numbers $x_1, x_2, \cdots, x_m$, which occur with frequency $n_1, n_2, \cdots, n_m$, respectively. There is a total of N numbers

$$N = \sum_{i=1}^{m} n_i$$

Suppose the number of children per family are counted for 100 families. The numbers that have $0, 1, 2, \cdots, 8$ children are 8, 20, 25, 21, 14, 7, 3, 1, 1, respectively. The results are shown by the heavy

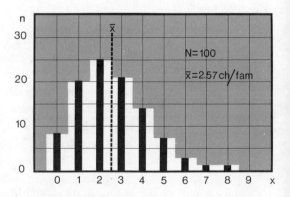

A combined bar graph and histogram showing the distribution of the number of children per family for a sample of 100 families.

vertical lines in the figure. This is a **bar graph.** They are also plotted as the white area, a **histogram,** even though the quantity x can only take on integral values (no family had a non-integral number of children). The advantage of the histogram is that the area under the graph is equal to the total number of children (note that the units of nx are: number of families $\times$ number of children per family = number of children). Here $\sum n_i x_i$ = area under graph = 257 children, and $\bar{x} = 2.57$ children/family. The graph shows the distribution of values in this example.

It is often more useful in statistics to consider the number of values which occur in certain **ranges** x_1 to x_2, x_2 to x_3, and so on, rather than the number with some precise value. This may be desirable either because the number of values of x is very large (or infinite, if it is a continuously variable quantity) or because the values of x are measurements, and are therefore inexact.

Look again at our sample of 100 families. The numbers that have annual incomes of $1, 2, 3, \cdots$, 7, 8, 9 thousands are 2, 3, 11, 19, 24, 20, 15, 4, 2, respectively. We assume that these are rounded off to the nearest thousand, and that therefore \$5,000 means in the range \$4,500–5,500. The histogram shows the distribution. The average family income $\bar{x} = \$5,120$. This graph may also be interpreted as a **probability graph** by changing the ordinate scale. If we define $P_i = n_i/N$, then P_i is the probability that n is in the range with x_i at its center. Thus the probability of a salary in the range \$4,500–5,500 is 0.24 or 24%. With this scale, the area under the histogram is equal to unity.

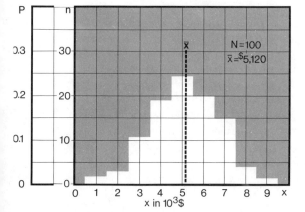

Histogram representing the distribution of annual family incomes for a sample of 100 families.

There are two other ways in which the ordinate scale may be expressed. When the x-intervals are equal in size, as they are in this example, we can define $N_i = n_i/\Delta x$ where Δx is the size of the interval. Then N_i is the number of values of n **per unit x-interval** in the range centering on x_i. The N_i are called number densities or frequencies. In the example there are 0.024 families per \$thousand interval in the range \$4,500–5,500. Expressing this in this form may seem somewhat pointless in this example, but its use will be apparent when we consider smaller and smaller values of Δx.

Similarly we can define $p_i = P_i/\Delta x = n_i/(N\Delta x) = N_i/N$ which is the **probability density,** or probability per unit x-interval that x will be in the range centering on x_i. Again this will be useful in the limit as $\Delta x \to 0$.

The histograms showing n_i, P_i, N_i and p_i as functions of x will all have the same shape, because they are related by the constant factors N and Δx.

In general, if there are n_1 values of x in the range x_1 to x_2, n_2 values in the range x_2 to x_3, $\cdots$

$$\bar{x} = \frac{\sum n_i x_i}{\sum n_i} = \sum n_i \bar{x}_i / N$$

where N is the total number of values of x, $\bar{x}_i$ is the value of x at the mid-point of the interval, and the summation is taken over all of the intervals.

Suppose that the size of the intervals Δx is made half as large. In our example we could use $500 intervals rather than $1,000 intervals. A somewhat different histogram would result, with perhaps a slightly different average value—a better average value, because the data are being analyzed more finely.

It would not be useful in this example, with a sample of only 100 families, to think of Δx becoming very small. However, there are many examples where the numbers involved are large, and where the quantity x either varies continuously or appears to do so on the scale of measurement used.

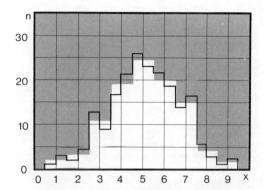

Using smaller income intervals for the distribution of family incomes produces a slightly different histogram.

DISTRIBUTION FUNCTIONS

As the Δx intervals of a histogram are made smaller and smaller, the histogram looks more and more like a continuous curve. In the limit as $\Delta x \to 0$ it becomes a continuous curve, representing a continuous function of the continuous variable x. But what does the function represent? In the histogram we plotted n as a function of x (a non-continuous function), where n was the number of x's in an interval Δx. But now there is no interval.

We get around this by using the quantity called **number density** defined previously, $N_i = n_i / \Delta x$. The number of x's in the range centering on $\bar{x}_i$ is $n_i = N_i \Delta x$, and the total of all the x's in this range is $n_i \bar{x}_i = N_i \bar{x}_i \Delta x$.

As $x \to 0$, $N_i \Delta x \to N(x)\,dx$ and $N_i \bar{x}_i \Delta x \to N(x)x\,dx$ where $N(x)$ is a continuous function of x. The average value in the limit is

$$\bar{x} = \lim_{\Delta x \to 0} \frac{\sum N_i \bar{x}_i \Delta x}{\sum N_i \Delta x} = \frac{\int N(x)x\,dx}{\int N(x)\,dx}$$

where the integration is over all values of x.

The quantity $N(x)$, the number of x's per unit x-interval, is sometimes called a **frequency,** and the distribution called a **frequency distribution.** It is usually easier to think of $N(x)\,\Delta x$, the number of x's in the range Δx.

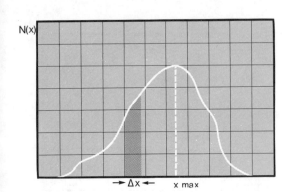

An arbitrary frequency distribution with a single maximum.

The number of x's in any finite range x_1 to x_2 is the area under the curve in this range:

$$N(x_1 \to x_2) = \int_{x_1}^{x_2} N(x)\, dx$$

If there are a finite number N of values of x, as there are in dealing with numbers of molecules, for example, then

$$N = \int_{\text{all } x} N(x)\, dx$$

but this is not always the case.

If the distribution curve has a single maximum, as shown, the value of x labeled $x_{\max}$ is called **the most probable value** of x. Note that it is *not* the maximum value of x, and in general is not $\bar{x}$. The values $x_{\max}$ and $\bar{x}$ do coincide in the special case where the distribution is symmetric with respect to its maximum.

For some purposes the **root-mean-square value** of x is a useful quantity.

$$\overline{x^2} = \frac{\int N(x)x^2\, dx}{\int N(x)\, dx} \qquad \text{and} \qquad x_{\mathrm{rms}} = (\overline{x^2})^{1/2}$$

where the integration is over all values of x. Note that this is **not** the standard (or root-mean-square) deviation, which is a measure of the spread of the distribution around its average value.

The standard deviation $\delta_{\mathrm{rms}} = \left[\overline{(x - \bar{x})^2}\right]^{1/2}$ but since $\overline{(x - \bar{x})^2} = \overline{x^2} - 2\bar{x}\bar{x} + \bar{x}^2 = \overline{x^2} - \bar{x}^2$, the standard deviation can be determined from $\overline{x^2}$ and $\bar{x}^2$.

In the special case of a quantity x which can take on both positive and negative values, and for which the distribution function is symmetric about the origin, then $\bar{x} = 0$ and $x_{\mathrm{rms}} = \delta_{\mathrm{rms}}$.

Instead of showing a distribution in terms of the number density $N(x)$, it is often plotted in terms of the probability density $p(x) = N(x)/N$. The distribution will have the same shape, but the total area under the curve will equal unity. Since an N can be introduced in both the numerator and denominator of the expressions for average value,

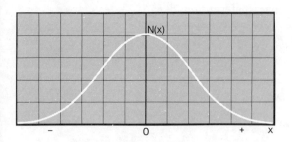

For a frequency distribution that is symmetric with respect to the origin, $\bar{x} = 0$ and $x_{\mathrm{rms}} = \delta_{\mathrm{rms}}$.

$$\bar{x} = \frac{\int p(x)x\, dx}{\int p(x)\, dx} = \int_{\text{all } x} p(x)x\, dx$$

Example: We will work out the mean value, the rms value, and the standard deviation for a distribution that is assumed to have a parabolic shape as indicated. All values of x lie in the range $0 \rightarrow x_0$. You can verify that the equation of the parabola in terms of x_0 is

$$N(x) = A(x - x^2/x_0)$$

where A is a constant. The average value of x is

$$\bar{x} = \frac{\int N(x)x\, dx}{\int N(x)\, dx}$$

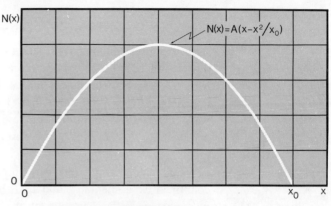

A frequency distribution of parabolic shape.

$$= \frac{\int_0^{x_0} A(x - x^2/x_0)x\, dx}{\int_0^{x_0} A(x - x^2/x_0)\, dx} = \frac{A\left[\dfrac{x^3}{3}\right]_0^{x_0} - \dfrac{A}{x_0}\left[\dfrac{x^4}{4}\right]_0^{x_0}}{A\left[\dfrac{x^2}{2}\right]_0^{x_0} - \dfrac{A}{x_0}\left[\dfrac{x^3}{3}\right]_0^{x_0}} = \frac{A\left(\frac{1}{3}x_0^3 - \frac{1}{4}x_0^3\right)}{A\left(\frac{1}{2}x_0^2 - \frac{1}{3}x_0^2\right)} = \frac{\frac{1}{12}Ax_0^3}{\frac{1}{6}Ax_0^2} = \frac{1}{2}x_0$$

As would be expected from symmetry, the mean value is at the mid-point. This is also the most probable value of x, x_{max}. To find x_{rms}, we find $\overline{x^2}$

$$\overline{x^2} = \frac{\int N(x)x^2\, dx}{\int N(x)\, dx} = \frac{\int_0^{x_0} A(x - x^2/x_0)x^2\, dx}{\frac{1}{6}Ax_0^2} = \frac{A\left[\dfrac{x^4}{4}\right]_0^{x_0} - \dfrac{A}{x_0}\left[\dfrac{x^5}{5}\right]_0^{x_0}}{\frac{1}{6}Ax_0^2}$$

$$= \frac{\frac{1}{20}Ax_0^4}{\frac{1}{6}Ax_0^2} = \frac{3}{10}x_0^2$$

$$x_{rms} = \sqrt{0.3}\, x_0 = 0.55x_0$$

For a distribution of parabolic shape the root-mean-square value is 5 % higher than the average value.

The standard deviation is found by determining $\overline{\delta^2}$, the variance.

$$\overline{\delta^2} = \overline{x^2} - \bar{x}^2$$

$$= \frac{3}{10}x_0^2 - \frac{1}{4}x_0^2$$

$$= \frac{1}{20}x_0^2$$

$$\delta_{rms} = \sqrt{0.05}\, x_0 = 0.22x_0$$

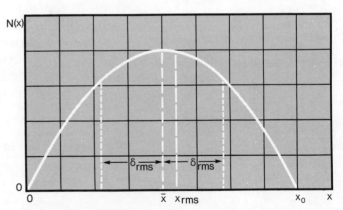

The average value, the rms value, and the standard deviation for the distribution of parabolic shape.

This is an indication of the distribution around the average. The calculated results are shown on the graph of the distribution.

EXAMPLES OF DISTRIBUTION FUNCTIONS

A distribution function $N(x)$ or $p(x)$ may be determined experimentally or theoretically. By taking a large number of measurements an experimental distribution may be determined, and used to make predictions about future measurements. Alternatively a distribution may be determined theoretically, on the basis of certain assumptions, and used to predict what might be observed experimentally. In Chapter 30 we develop some important distributions of this type.

We conclude this chapter with three examples of distributions that are well confirmed experimentally, and for which the theoretical derivations were important steps in the development of physics.

1. Distribution of molecular speeds. The 10^{20} or so molecules of gas in a system in equilibrium move around in random directions, colliding and changing speed. They would present a chaotic appearance if we could see them, but nevertheless produce very steady effects that we can observe. Disorderly or random behavior at the microscopic level produces orderly or predictable behavior at the macroscopic level, because the number of molecules is so large.

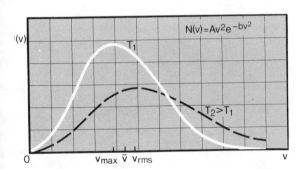

The distribution of molecular speeds at two temperatures.

Even though an individual molecule makes about 10^{10} collisions every second, and therefore keeps changing in speed, the overall picture of the speeds can be very accurately represented by a distribution function. This distribution is the **Maxwell** (or **Maxwell–Boltzmann**) **distribution** of molecular speeds. It may be derived by assuming randomness of molecular motions, or regarded as an experimental result (speeds can be measured in molecular beam experiments). $N(v)$ is the number of molecules per unit speed interval; the number of molecules with speeds in any range v to $(v + dv)$ is

$$N(v)\,dv = Av^2e^{-bv^2}\,dv$$

where A and b are constants involving the temperature of the gas (related to the average kinetic energy of the molecules), the molecular weight (related to the mass of individual molecules), and the total number of molecules N in the system.

The curves show the distribution for the same system at two different temperatures. The area under both curves is the same, since

$$\int_0^\infty N(v)\,dv = N$$

Since $N(v)$ is a known function, the most probable speed $v_{\max}$, the average speed $\bar{v}$ and the root-mean-square speed v_{rms} can be calculated. The averages are determined by using the definitions already given, and $v_{\max}$ by setting $dN(v)/dv$ equal to zero. The relation between these is

$$v_{\max} : \bar{v} : v_{\mathrm{rms}} = 1 : 2/\sqrt{\pi} : \sqrt{3/2} : = 1 : 1.128 : 1.224$$

We will develop this distribution, and the one in the next example, in Chapter 31.

2. Distribution of molecular velocities. Velocity is a vector quantity. It has both magnitude and direction and cannot be represented by a single distribution function. The previous distribution was for speed, or **magnitude** of velocity. This one shows the distribution of the **components** of velocity in a particular direction, the x-direction. There will be identical distributions in the y- and z-directions— or in any direction. By using components in a particular direction, we are dealing with vectors only in the sense that they can be $+$ or $-$.

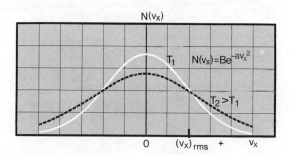

The distribution of one component of molecular velocities at two temperatures.

The number of molecules having x-components of velocity in the range v_x to $(v_x + dv_x)$ is

$$N(v_x)\,dv_x = Be^{-av_x^2}\,dv_x$$

As before, the total number of molecules, the area under the curves is

$$N = \int_{-\infty}^{\infty} N(v_x)\,dv_x$$

but this time the limits of integration are different. In this case both $(v_x)_{\max}$ and $\bar{v}_x$ are zero, but

$$(v_x)_{\mathrm{rms}} = \left[\frac{\int_{-\infty}^{\infty} N(v_x)v_x^2\,dv_x}{\int_{-\infty}^{\infty} N(v_x)\,dv_x}\right]^{1/2} = \frac{1}{\sqrt{2a}}$$

This is a measure of the spread of the distribution around the peak value. In terms of temperature T, the gas constant R and the molecular weight of the gas M, the constant a is

$$a = \frac{M}{2RT} \quad \text{so that} \quad (v_x)_{\mathrm{rms}} = \sqrt{\frac{RT}{M}}$$

The higher the temperature the greater the spread for a particular gas; at a particular temperature, gases of low molecular weight have a greater range of speeds than those of higher molecular weight.

This distribution is an example of what is called the **Gaussian** or **normal distribution,** with the distinctive bell-shaped curve. It always occurs when an overall result is produced by a large number of random events. We will develop the Gaussian distribution in Chapter 30.

3. Spectral distribution of radiation. This is an example of a distribution for which there is no fixed total number of "particles." Here $E(\lambda)\,d\lambda$ is the rate at which energy is emitted by unit area of a black body in the wavelength range λ to $\lambda + d\lambda$, at the temperature T. (A **black body** is one which absorbs all radiation falling on it, and is the best possible emitter of radiation.)

Then E, the total energy emitted per unit area in unit time, is given by

$$E = \int_0^\infty E(\lambda)\,d\lambda$$

This increases as the temperature increases ($E \propto T^4$) so that the area under successive distributions for increasing temperature will increase. If $T \sim 6000\ \text{K}^\circ$ the peak of the distribution is in the visible region of the spectrum. For $T < 1000\ \text{K}^\circ$ most of the energy is in the infrared and the eye cannot detect the radiation. The form of the distribution is

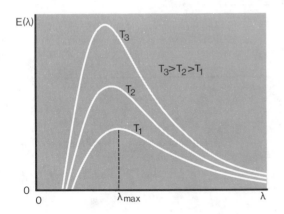

The spectral distribution of radiation from a black body at three temperatures.

$$E(\lambda) = \frac{c_1}{\lambda^5}\frac{1}{(e^{c_2/\lambda T} - 1)}$$

where c_1 and c_2 are constants. By setting $dE(\lambda)/d\lambda$ equal to zero it may be shown that the positions of the peaks of the curves, $\lambda_{\max}$, are related to the corresponding temperatures T by $\lambda_{\max}T = $ constant, the **Wien Displacement Law.**

This distribution is of interest historically. It was originally an experimentally observed result, and it was in his attempts to explain its shape that **Max Planck** put forward, in 1900, the **quantum hypothesis** that began the development of quantum mechanics. We will look at some of the details of the theoretical development of this distribution in Chapter 33.

Questions for discussion

1. Is the term **dimension** used in physics in the same way as in ordinary conversation? What about the terms **interpolation** and **extrapolation**? What about **environment**?

2. In performing experiments to measure the relationship between two variables x and y, it is usual to set one of them (say x) at certain values, and measure the corresponding values of the other one (y). When the data are plotted on a graph, the values of x are shown as exact, and errors shown on the measured values of y. Is it valid to assume that the x values are exact?

3. Can you sketch the histogram showing the distribution of results you would expect in throwing a pair of dice? What is the most probable result? What is the average result? What is the expected result?

4. When you use a transparent ruler to draw the "best" straight line through a set of points on a graph, balancing the points on each side of the line, what are you assuming about the measurements represented by the points?

5. The graphs show $y = x^2$ and $y = x^3$. Which is which? If you saw one of these alone, and did not know that the units on both axes were the same, would you be able to tell which it was?

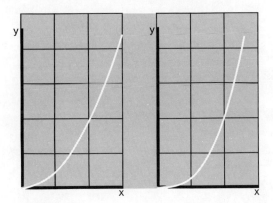

Problems

1. Rewrite the following in terms of percentage error:

   71 ± 2, 3.68 ± 0.005, 0.1178 ± 0.0010, 53.67 ± 0.03

2. Rewrite the following in terms of absolute error:

   $8.31 \pm 0.2\%$, $43 \pm 10\%$, $2500 \pm 3\%$, $2.5471 \times 10^{-3} \pm 0.05\%$

3. State the number of significant figures in each of the following:

   273, 13.596, 0.7, 95, 4.870, 2000, 0.0172, 800.0

4. Carry out the following computations assuming the numbers (except for $\frac{4}{3}\pi$) represent measurements:

   (a) 1.25×7.836 (c) $18.177 \times (3.5 \times 10^4)$
   (b) $\frac{4}{3}\pi(2.85 \times 10^{-8})^3 \times 7.63$ (d) $4.1 + 65.312 + 0.079$

5. Evaluate the following, assuming the numbers represent experimental data; use contracted methods (e.g. the binomial expansion) where possible:

   (a) $\sqrt[3]{27.0052}$ (e) $(1.0073)(6.0002)$
   (b) $\sqrt{224.00}$ (f) $(5.0016)(760.00)/(757.48)$
   (c) $(64.028)^{3/2}$ (g) $(39.142 \times 38.994)^{1/2}$
   (d) $(4.005)^2$ (h) $21.62 \times (273.15/281.56) \times (762.46/760.00)$

6. Angles can be measured with a certain instrument with an error of $\pm 0.5°$. Determine the corresponding percentage errors in $\sin 10°$, $\sin 80°$, $\cos 10°$, $\cos 80°$, $\tan 10°$, $\tan 80°$.

The results can be determined by looking up the values of sin 9.5°, sin 10°, sin 10.5°, etc., in tables, but try a more general method. For example, use the relation $\sin(A + B) = \sin A \cos B + \cos A \sin B$ to expand $\sin(x \pm \Delta x)$. From the series expansions

$$\sin \theta = \theta - \theta^3/3! + \theta^5/5! \cdots \qquad \cos \theta = 1 - \theta^2/2! + \theta^4/4! \cdots$$

(where angles are expressed in *radians*) you can see that $\sin \Delta x \cong \Delta x$ and $\cos \Delta x \cong 1$ when Δx is small, and use this to show that the percentage error in $\sin x$ is $(\Delta x)(\cot x)100\%$.

7. Data can be displayed graphically in a variety of ways. The table gives the vapor pressure p of mercury, in mm of mercury, as a function of temperature t, in °C.

t, °C	p, mm Hg	t, °C	p, mm Hg
−20°	2.3×10^{-5}	100°	2.8×10^{-1}
0°	2.0×10^{-4}	120°	7.5×10^{-1}
20°	1.3×10^{-3}	140°	1.85
40°	6.3×10^{-3}	160°	4.18
60°	2.6×10^{-2}	180°	8.77
80°	9.1×10^{-2}	200°	17.3

Plot graphs of (a) p vs. t, (b) $\log p$ vs. t, (c) $\log p$ vs. $1/T$, where T is the temperature in °K ($T = t + 273$). Graph (a) shows the disadvantage of presenting the data extending over this range on a linear graph, while graph (b) shows one way the data can be presented.

An empirical expression sometimes used to represent the variation of vapor pressure with temperature is $\log p = A - B/T$, where A and B are constants. Graph (c) shows that this representation is reasonable for mercury. Use this graph to evaluate A and B. Calculate p at 190°C and observe how well you have interpolated in drawing the p–t graph.

Determine, by drawing tangents on the p–t graph, the rate of change of vapor pressure with temperature at 100°C and at 200°C. Check your results by differentiating the vapor pressure equation.

8. The speed, v, of a sports car starting from rest increases with time, t, as follows:

t, sec	v, ft/sec	t, sec	v, ft/sec
0	0		
1	0.064	6	13.7
2	0.51	7	21.9
3	1.73	8	32.8
4	4.1	9	46.6
5	8.0	10	64.0

Do a numerical calculation to find the distance moved in the 10-sec interval. The distance moved Δx in each time interval Δt is $\Delta x = \bar{v}\,\Delta t$, where $\bar{v}$ is the average speed in the interval. Assume that the average speed in each 1-sec interval is $(v_1 + v_2)/2$, where v_1 is the speed at the beginning and v_2 the speed at the end of the interval.

Compare the result with that found in Problem 5 in Chapter 2. Why is it not identical?

9. The table gives the measured molar heat capacity, c, in millijoules/mole-K°, of a sample of gold at low temperatures, T.

T, °K	c, mj/mole-K°	T, °K	c, mj/mole-K°
1.30	1.9	3.40	19.8
1.60	3.0	3.80	27.1
1.90	4.4	4.10	33.6
2.20	6.3	4.40	40.0
2.50	8.8	4.60	46.8
2.90	13.0		

(a) Plot c against T and draw a smooth curve fitting the data. Extrapolate this curve in what seems a reasonable manner to 0 °K, and by counting squares determine the area under the curve in the range $T = 0$ to $T = 4.0$ °K.

(b) Plot c/T against T^2, and determine the equation of the straight line that best fits these points; express the result in a form giving c as a function of T. Integrate this to check the result found in (a) above.

10. (a) The resistance of a resistance thermometer can be represented by $R_t = R_0(1 + At + Bt^2)$ where R_t is the resistance at a temperature of $t°C$. Such a thermometer is calibrated at the ice, steam and sulphur points (0°C, 100°C, 444°C) and the corresponding resistances measured are 255, 355 and 675 ohms. Evaluate the constants R_0, A, B and determine the resistance at the melting point of tin (232°C).

(b) The variation of resistance with temperature is sometimes expressed by defining a **temperature coefficient of resistance,** the fractional change of resistance per unit temperature change. What is this coefficient at room temperature for this thermometer?

11. A piece of metal of length L expands in length an amount ΔL when its temperature is increased by ΔT. The **linear thermal expansion coefficient** α is defined as $\alpha = \dfrac{1}{L}\dfrac{\Delta L}{\Delta T}$. It is the fractional change in length per unit temperature change. It is given in tables in units (deg)$^{-1}$ and can be considered constant for reasonable temperature changes. For aluminum, $\alpha = 2.3 \times 10^{-5}$ (C°)$^{-1}$, for nickel $\alpha = 1.3 \times 10^{-5}$ (C°)$^{-1}$.

(a) A nickel measuring tape calibrated at 15°C is used at 45°C to measure the distance for a 100-m race. Is the distance established too large or too small? By how much?

(b) If the area A of a sheet of metal changes by ΔA when the temperature changes by ΔT, then $\Delta A = \beta A\,\Delta T$, where β is the **area thermal expansion coefficient.** Show by thinking of a square sheet of side L that it is a good approximation to use $\beta = 2\alpha$. Similarly think of a cube of side L, and show that the volume coefficient of thermal expansion is approximately 3α.

(c) If the temperature of an aluminum block is increasing at a rate of 0.1 C°/sec, at what rate is its density changing, expressed as percentage change in density/sec?

(d) There is a hole in a sheet of metal. If the temperature increases, does the area of the hole become larger or smaller?

(e) A perfectly circular hole is punched in an aluminum plate. Its diameter as determined at 30°C with a nickel micrometer calibrated at 15°C is 10.035 cm. Calculate the area of the hole at 100°C as accurately as is justifiable.

12. Determine the dimensions (in terms of M, L, and T) of all the physical quantities in mechanics with which you are familiar (e.g., density, velocity, acceleration, momentum, force, energy, work, impulse, . . . ?).

13. (a) When the parts of a fluid are moving with respect to one another, there is a force resisting the motion described by the physical property called **viscosity.** The **coefficient of viscosity** η is defined by $F = \eta A\,(dv/dx)$, where F is the shear force on area A of fluid, and dv/dx is the velocity gradient in the fluid. What are the dimensions of η? What is the cgs unit (it is called the poise)?

(b) One method of measuring η is to force a fluid to flow through a narrow (capillary) tube. The rate of flow of volume through a tube of radius r, length l, with a pressure difference $(p_1 - p_2)$ between the ends, is

$$\frac{dV}{dt} = \frac{\pi r^4}{8\eta l}(p_1 - p_2)$$

(Poiseuille's law)

What are the dimensions of η as determined by this relation?

(c) When a sphere falls through a fluid, there is a resistive force F that increases as the speed v increases. Assuming that F depends only on v, the radius of the sphere r, and the fluid viscosity η, how must it depend on these quantities?

(d) In describing fluid flow it is convenient to introduce a dimensionless parameter called Reynold's number R, defined by $R = \rho l v/\eta$, where ρ and η are the density and viscosity of the fluid, v is the flow velocity, and l is some important length of the system—for example, the radius of the pipe—in which the fluid is flowing. Verify that R is dimensionless.

For fluid flowing in a smooth pipe, experiments show that if $R < 1000$ the flow is streamline or steady flow, and if $R > 1000$ the flow is turbulent. At about what speed does the flow of water in a $\frac{1}{2}$-in. (diameter) pipe change from streamline to turbulent flow? How long would it take to fill a bathtub at this rate? (For water $\eta \sim 0.01$ poise.)

14. (a) This example will serve to show that interpolation is an approximation, and also to recall the barometer and Boyle's law.

One form of barometer is made by inverting a closed tube full of mercury into a reservoir of mercury. The varying pressure of the atmosphere on the surface of the mercury in the reservoir provides the force that holds the mercury column up to varying levels in the tube. The force of gravity acts down on the column, so the pressure exerted at the bottom of the column is $p = \rho g h$ where ρ is the density of mercury, g is the value of the acceleration due to gravity, and h is the height of the barometric column. This is equal to the atmospheric pressure, so $p_{\text{atmos}} \propto h$. Atmospheric pressure is often given in mm or cm of mercury.

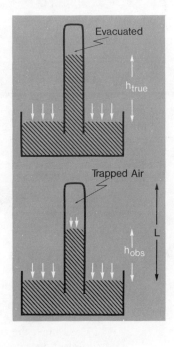

Normally the space above the mercury column is a vacuum, so that there is no pressure on the top of the column within the tube. However, if a barometer is set up carelessly there may be air left above the mercury, exerting a pressure on the top of the column. Then the column height observed, h_{obs}, will be less than the true height, h_{true}.

Suppose that the observed height is 756.0 mm when the true height is 781.0 mm, and is 720.0 mm when the true height is 736.0 mm. The problem is to determine the true height corresponding to an observed height of 740.0 mm. (Even if a barometer has been set up carelessly, it can be calibrated to give correct pressures.)

h_{obs}, mm	h_{true}, mm
756.0	781.0
740.0	?
720.0	736.0

The answer can be estimated by linear interpolation, that is by writing the corresponding heights in two columns and assuming that the differences in the two columns are proportional to one another. You can verify that this method gives a result of 761.0 mm for the unknown true pressure.

Such interpolation is justified only when there is a linear relationship between the quantities in the two columns, so that the differences are proportional. In order to show that this is not the case here, assume that Boyle's law can be applied to the air trapped above the column. Boyle's law is $pV = \text{constant}$, relating the pressure and volume of a quantity of an ideal gas at a constant temperature. Using the fact that the volume V of the trapped gas is proportional to the length $(L - h_{\text{obs}})$ of the "empty" part of the tube, you should be able to show that for this example $h_{\text{true}} = h_{\text{obs}} + 1600/(820 - h_{\text{obs}})$ and therefore there is not a linear relationship between h_{true} and h_{obs}. For $h_{\text{obs}} = 740.00$ mm, this gives $h_{\text{true}} = 760.0$ mm rather than 761.0 mm as found by interpolation.

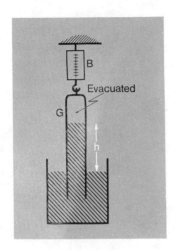

Evacuated

B

G

h

(b) This example will make you think about the barometer, and will recall the definition of work. The height of the barometer column is $h = 76$ cm. The thin-walled glass tube G has negligible weight and a diameter of 1 cm. What is the reading of the spring balance B? Is it holding up the mercury column? If B is raised 10 cm (the open end of the tube still below the surface of the mercury reservoir) how much work is done? What happens to it?

(c) The space above the mercury column in a barometer is not a complete vacuum, because it always contains some mercury vapor. Can the pressure of this gas be neglected? (Consult physical tables, or see Problem 7.)

15. In an examination written by 123 students, marks were distributed as follows: in the ranges 46–50, 51–55, 56–60, . . . , 91–95, 96–100 there were respectively 2, 18, 24, 30, 21, 7, 13, 4, 2, 0, 2 marks. Plot a histogram of the distribution and show on it the mean, median and root-mean-square marks as calculated from the data. The median is the mark such that there are equal numbers of marks above and below it: show that it divides the area of the histogram in half. (Note that the average mark in the range 51–55, say, should be taken as 53.)

Determine the standard deviation δ_{rms}, using $\overline{\delta^2} = \overline{x^2} - \overline{x}^2$. If an individual student does not know the details of the distribution, but is given $\overline{x} \pm \delta_{rms}$, where $\overline{x}$ is the mean value, is this information more useful to him than simply $\overline{x}$?

The average mark on the examination was actually 65.2. Why is the mean value you have calculated not exactly this?

16. For the three distributions shaped as shown calculate the mean value $\overline{x}$, the rms value x_{rms} and the standard deviation δ_{rms}, in each case in terms of x_0.

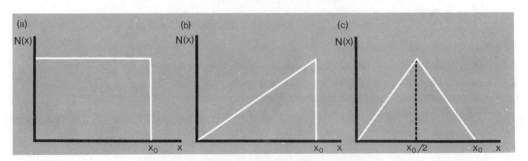

17. For the distribution function $N(x) = A \cos^2 (\pi x / x_0)$ for $-x_0/2 \leq x \leq x_0/2$
$$= 0 \qquad \text{for } |x| > x_0/2$$

determine **(a)** the value of A, in terms of x_0, such that $\int_{-\infty}^{\infty} N(x)\, dx = 1$, **(b)** the values of $\overline{x}$, x_{rms}, and δ_{rms} in terms of x_0. Consult tables for integrals of the form $\int x^n \cos^m x\, dx$.

Kinematics II

We mentioned that mechanics, the study of motion, is central to all of physics; we now begin the development of the system of ideas called **classical mechanics.** Initially, we restrict ourselves to **kinematics,** the description of motion, without worrying about the agencies that affect the motion, and we consider primarily the motion of particles. We may seem to have limited ourselves to a trivial situation, the description of the motion of a particle, but as you will see in the next four chapters there is a good deal to be said about this simple situation.

Chapter 4, on specifying the location of a particle in space and in time, begins with the fundamental quantities, length and time, that are necessary for this specification. The concept of a **frame of reference,** extremely important in understanding mechanics and describing motion, is then introduced. The vector quantity, displacement, the change of position of a particle in a frame of reference, is defined; the rest of the chapter is a summary of the properties of vectors.

Chapter 5 describes three simple forms of motion of a particle in a frame of reference, motion with constant acceleration, circular motion, and simple harmonic motion. Complete familiarity with these is helpful for much that follows.

The final two chapters introduce transformations between frames of reference, Chapter 6 dealing with transformations between reference frames with constant relative velocity and Chapter 7, which covers transformations between accelerated frames, introducing centripetal and coriolis accelerations. The same motion is different as described in different frames of reference, and an understanding of these differences while distinguishing between frames in translation and in rotation is a necessary background for the development of dynamics in Part III.

Although we do not undertake the development of dynamics until Part III, here in these chapters on kinematics we do use some basic dynamic concepts, such as force and momentum, in our examples. We can do this because we assume that you have some familiarity with these concepts, and in Chapter 5 under the heading "Review of Uniform Fields," review some of them briefly. It should be emphasized, however, that the primary goal in Part II is to show how *the description of motion depends on the choice of frame of reference.*

4

LOCATION OF A PARTICLE
IN A FRAME OF REFERENCE

FUNDAMENTAL QUANTITIES

We begin kinematics by choosing two **fundamental quantities,** length and time. Later we will use these to define certain useful **derived quantities**: displacement, velocity, acceleration. Derived physical quantities are those that are defined explicitly in terms of other physical quantities, and fundamental quantities are those that are not. Does this mean that fundamental quantities are undefined? In a way, yes—it comes back to the fact that we have to begin our description somewhere.

Although we do not specify what length and time *are*, in terms of anything else, we do specify how to *measure* them. Length is what is measured by counting measuring rods; time is what is measured by counting the ticks of a clock. Such specifications are called **operational definitions.** The operation of measuring is defined, but the quantity itself is not. What is a measuring rod? It is a straight rigid rod. What does straight mean? What does rigid mean? We could define a straight line in some physical way, for example as the path of a particle un-influenced by anything else, or as the path of a beam of light in a vacuum, but it would then be unsatisfactory to state, as laws of physics, that uninfluenced particles and light beams in a vacuum travel in straight lines. Essentially we assume we know what a straight line is, which means we assume that Euclidean geometry is valid. Similarly, although we will later be able to define a rigid body as one whose component particles are at rest with respect to one another, we can hardly do this before we have defined motion so that we know what "at rest" means. Because we cannot define exactly what we mean by a measuring rod or a clock, operational definitions are not very satisfying, but they are essential in beginning to describe the physical world.

The choice of length and time as fundamental is arbitrary; we could choose velocity and acceleration as fundamental and then length and time would be derived quantities. We choose length and time because we think we know what we mean by these quantities. We cannot avoid having some sort of intuitive notion of an absolute three-dimensional Euclidean space, extending to infinity, which exists whether or not there are any objects in it. Similarly we have an idea of absolute time, flowing on quite apart from our attempts to measure it, and completely independent of space.

While such intuitive assumptions help us to accept length and time as fundamental quantities, it is important to realize that the operational definitions do *not* depend on these assumptions. The procedures for measuring are specified, and by definition length and time are what are measured by these procedures.

Operational definitions require the choice of a **standard** (a particular measuring rod, and a particular clock) as well as the specification of procedures for making comparisons with the standard, and thereby establishing a scale. Sometimes the standard provides the basic unit (as with the standard meter) but this is not necessary.

Specification of procedure of measurement is a field which specialists have developed to a high art, and we shall not attempt to describe the various techniques used to measure large and small distances, or long and short times. However, the evolution of existing standards has involved a great deal of physics as well as a great deal of technology, and some comments are pertinent.

LENGTH

The most important feature of a standard is its **invariance.** In attempting to achieve invariance, there may be a single standard, or the standard may be reproducible—that is, the standard may consist of the specifications for reproducing what is thought to be an invariant amount of the quantity. A reproducible standard has the advantage of accessibility.

Until 1960 there was a single standard of length, the distance between two scratches on a platinum–iridium bar called the standard meter. Not so very long ago, when we were students, there was another bar as well, the standard yard, but now the yard is defined in terms of the meter. The standard meter had the appearance of invariance, with the limitations mentioned in the first chapter, but was not easily accessible. Secondary standard bars for distribution throughout the world were made by comparison with the primary standard.

The present standard of length specifies the meter as a distance equal to 1,650,763.73 wavelengths of the orange light emitted by krypton-86 under certain well-defined conditions. The number was chosen to make the new standard agree as closely as possible with the old, and illustrates the degree of precision to which modern standards are stated. This standard of length does not have to be maintained anywhere; any laboratory can produce its own standard. The wavelength of the radiation depends on the structure of krypton-86 atoms, and reproducibility depends on the assumption that all such atoms are the same and that this structure does not change as time goes on. There is at present no evidence that such changes do occur, but it is important to realize that invariance always, when you come right down to it, is an assumption.

TIME

The concept of time is more difficult than that of length, because it is not as concrete. We can think of fixing our attention on the length of a particular piece of matter, and calling it a standard, more easily than we can think of fixing our attention on a particular chunk of time and maintaining it as a standard of time. Nevertheless, this is exactly what was done until recently. Until 1967 the standard of time was the solar year 1900. The unit of time, the second, was defined so that there were 31,556,925.9747 seconds in the year 1900. It could equivalently be said that the standard of time was the second, defined as 1/31,556,925.9747 of the solar year 1900. Just how the year 1900 was remembered with this degree of precision is something we will not go into because we do not understand it.

Our measurements of time are all based on the fact that certain motions appear to be periodic—that is, repetitive in equal time intervals. But how do we know the time intervals are equal? By comparing other periodic motions. The essential thing that a clock does is tick (some sort of periodic motion) although some clocks also keep track of the number of ticks (a simple counting operation). A good clock is one which ticks regularly; the only way to check this is to compare it with other clocks. Good clocks agree with one another. Our operational definition of time is that time is what clocks measure.

We choose as our standard of time the tick of some particular good clock. This is not so simple, however, because clocks wear, and their tick changes. Since motion is necessary, clocks have moving parts (for ordinary clocks, pendulums or balance wheels or tuning forks or vibrating crystals) and friction produces wear. Changes in the period may be very gradual, but we are looking for an invariant standard.

Originally the standard of time, the second, was defined in terms of the rotation of the earth because this seemed to be a steady motion—the earth spins freely in space; one revolution is one tick of the earth clock. There were some problems in deciding how to measure one revolution because it depends on the frame of reference chosen: one revolution relative to the sun is not the same as one revolution relative to the stars, and the period is variable because of the variable speed of the earth in its orbit around the sun. The second was defined as 1/86,400 of a mean solar day, the mean solar day being the average solar day (one revolution relative to the sun) over one year. Thus a standard was established, but it turned out not to be invariant. There are other astronomical clocks (the other planets and their satellites) and comparison showed that the earth clock is slowing down; the length of the day is increasing by about 10^{-3}

seconds per century (assuming that the second is not defined in terms of the day!). Not much, but enough to make clocks wrong by several hours if they have been running for centuries. The earth clock, like our earth-bound clocks, is running down due to friction—tidal friction. It is for this reason that a particular tick (or rather series of ticks—the year 1900) of the earth clock was taken as the standard of time.

Just as there is now an atomic standard of length, there is now an atomic standard of time. For some years there have been experiments to develop atomic clocks, that is clocks whose rate is determined by the vibrations in atoms or molecules. It is assumed that atoms and molecules do not change as time goes on, and therefore that the period of such vibrations is invariant. For about twenty years it has been possible to build atomic clocks with an accuracy hundreds of times that of other types of clock, but an atomic standard of time was not adopted until 1967. One reason an atomic standard was not adopted sooner is that there is such an enormous variety of atomic vibrations to choose from; which one provides the best standard? The introduction of a new standard is a cumbersome legal process requiring international cooperation, and standards are not changed whimsically. Another technical problem that had to be investigated was to make sure that the microscopic atomic vibration was used to control a macroscopic (observable) system in such a way that the period of vibration was not affected; the atomic clock must drive a large scale clock, and not vice versa.

Such problems as these and many others were sorted out, and in 1967 the Thirteenth General Conference on Weights and Measures adopted an atomic standard of time based on vibrations in an isotope of cesium. The second is defined as the duration of 9,192,631,770 periods of the radiation corresponding to the transition between two hyperfine levels of the fundamental state of an atom of cesium-133. Note that an atom can be used as a clock only if it changes its state. There is no way that we can observe the vibrations of an atom when it is in a steady state. Only when it changes from one steady state to another by emitting or absorbing radiation does it provide any information about itself. It is the transition between two different steady states of the cesium atom that provides a standard of time.

ABSOLUTE LENGTH AND TIME

You can see from the operational definitions of length and time that it is impossible to introduce one without reference to the other. Measurement of length involves comparison with a measuring rod, but one cannot look simultaneously at both ends of a measuring rod, so time is involved—and what does simultaneous mean? The definition of time depends on periodic motion, a motion in space, and we are defining length and time in order to describe motion!

Nonetheless, the procedures for measurement are specified, and following them enables us to assign numbers to values of length and time. We have not specified the procedures, but detailed specification is important because, as you will see if you study relativity theory, following these procedures under conditions where high speeds (close to the speed of light) are involved gives rise to numbers for length and time which depend on the speed. The length of a rod changes when it is moving (and therefore depends on time). The time between two events is different as measured by two observers who are moving relative to one another. These results, the relativity of length and time intervals, contradict our intuitive notions of space and time as independent absolutes. Does this mean that our intuitive notions are wrong? This may be a valid question in philosophy but with no meaning in physics, because physics is based on measurement. Length and time are what are measured in precisely defined ways.

There are many subtle and important questions involved in the concepts of fundamental quantities; subtle because, as we have said, beginning is the difficult part, and important because all of physics is based on these concepts.

FRAMES OF REFERENCE AND CO-ORDINATE SYSTEMS

Having assumed that it is possible to measure length and time, it becomes possible to describe the motion of a particle by measuring its position as a function of time. In order to do this we must choose a reference time and a reference position. If we call the reference time $t = 0$, then one number t specifies any later time, but position cannot be specified by a single number. We assume that space is three-dimensional and Euclidean and therefore that three numbers are necessary and sufficient to specify position. These three numbers will specify position in a particular co-ordinate system. In a Cartesian co-ordinate system, for example, three lines at right angles to one another, passing through point O, define three planes, and the three numbers are the three lengths which are the distances to these planes. These are the co-ordinates (x,y,z) of the particle P, keeping in mind that they are numbers with units; they are lengths. We have a reference position, the origin of co-ordinates O, but the single length OP does not specify the position of the particle uniquely—there are an infinite number of positions a distance OP from O, lying on the sphere of radius OP. The position of P with respect to O can be specified in different ways; for

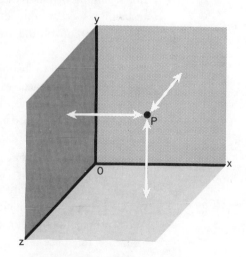

Specification of position of a particle with respect to a particular Cartesian co-ordinate system.

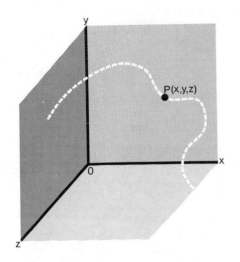

Path or trajectory of a particle described with respect to a particular co-ordinate system.

example, in a spherical co-ordinate system the position is stated in terms of a length (*OP*) and two angles, but it always requires three numbers.

By measuring the lengths x, y, z at various times t, we obtain $x(t)$, $y(t)$, $z(t)$, and can plot the path of the particle. This picture of the motion may be useful, but it does not contain all the information because it does not show when the particle was at successive positions. For many purposes position–time graphs (e.g., x vs. t) turn out to be more useful.

So far we have assumed that the co-ordinate system is at rest. Sometimes it is convenient in describing the motion to think of a moving co-ordinate system; if, for example, we think of a co-ordinate system that moves in the x-direction along with the particle, then in this co-ordinate system the motion is two-dimensional, confined to the y–z plane. But "at rest" and "in motion" are relative terms. We could choose a co-ordinate system moving with the particle, and in this system the particle is at rest.

What did it mean to say "we assumed that the co-ordinate system is at rest" at the beginning of this paragraph? It meant that the co-ordinate system was at rest with respect to some other co-ordinate system, that the position of the point O and all points on the axes did not change in the other co-ordinate system as time went on.

It will be useful to distinguish between a co-ordinate system and what we will call a **frame of reference.** Measurements are not made with respect to co-ordinate systems—they are made with respect to real objects. A co-ordinate system is a convenient way to record and describe measurements, but it is not a real physical entity. A frame of reference does have physical reality; it may be a room, or the earth, or a ship, or a star, or an atom. To be specific, think of three straight rigid rods at right angles to one another, meeting at a point. This is similar to the Cartesian co-ordinate system described before, and if we wish we can think of co-ordinate axes coincident with the rods, but it is not the same—it is **real.** We can make measurements of the motion of a particle P with respect to this frame of reference. We can describe these measurements with respect to co-ordinate axes coincident with the rods, or we can choose axes which are in a different position or have a different orientation. However, to describe the motion of P with respect to this particular frame of reference we stipulate that **any co-ordinate system used must be at rest with respect to the frame of reference.** The co-ordinate axes may be rotated to different angles, or the origin may be translated to different positions, so that in each co-ordinate system the three numbers specifying the position of P in this frame of reference are different, but the co-ordinate systems are all at rest. A particle which is at rest in one system is at rest in all systems. A particle whose path or trajectory is a straight line in one system will have a straight line trajectory in all systems. In general, we can say that all co-ordinate systems which are at rest with respect to one another are **equivalent** for describing the motion of particles; all such equivalent co-ordinate systems constitute the frame of reference.

To describe a particular motion in this frame of reference an appropriate co-ordinate system can be chosen: for motion in a straight line, a system with one of the axes along the path of the motion will be chosen; for motion in a plane, a system will be chosen such that the path lies in one of the co-ordinate planes; for motion confined to the surface of a sphere, a system will be chosen with its origin at the center of the sphere.

Thus the description of a particular motion can be simplified by the choice of co-ordinate system, but remember that the motion is **measured** with respect to the frame of reference.

We will label a particular frame of reference S. The symbol can be thought of as representing the system of all co-ordinate systems that are at rest with respect to one another.

The motion of a particle can be measured in different frames of reference. An observer standing still can make measurements on a falling object with respect to the earth as a frame of reference, and an observer on a moving train can make measurements on the same falling object with respect to the train as a frame of reference. The path of the object will be different in the different frames of reference.

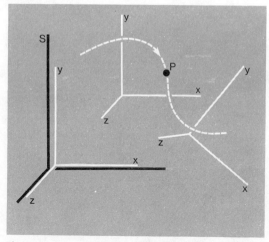

The trajectory of a particle is described differently in different co-ordinate systems in a particular frame of reference.

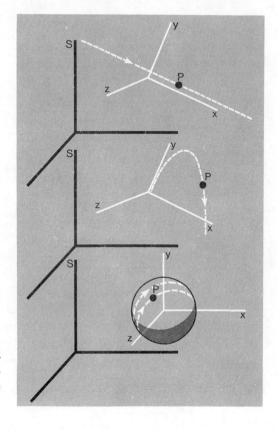

The specification of the trajectory of a particle in a frame of reference can be simplified by an appropriate choice of co-ordinate system.

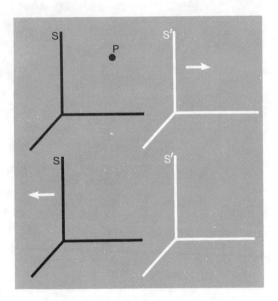

Two frames of reference S and S' in relative motion with respect to one another.

If we label two frames of reference S and S', a particle P which is at rest in S is moving in S'. This means that the particle is at rest in all S co-ordinate systems, and moving in all S' co-ordinate systems. How its motion is described in S' depends on which co-ordinate system is chosen.

The distinction between frames of reference and co-ordinate systems has been established here because we are going to introduce a method of describing motion in a given frame of reference that is **independent** of the co-ordinate system chosen. Instead of describing motion by quantities such as $x(t)$, $y(t)$, $z(t)$ which depend on a particular co-ordinate system, we are going to be able to describe motion by such quantities as $r(t)$, $v(t)$, $a(t)$ which depend only on the frame of reference. We will then be in a better position to compare motions in different frames of reference. We will discover that the choice of a frame of reference is a fundamental part of the explanation of motion and, furthermore, that frame-of-reference considerations are embedded deeply in mechanics.

VECTORS, SCALARS AND INVARIANCE

We are ready to introduce our first derived physical quantity, **displacement.** It is defined as **change in position,** but as with most definitions, some further explanation is required.

Displacement is defined to be a vector quantity; this means that displacements have magnitude and direction and are to be combined with one another in a certain way. Displacement is the model or prototype for all vector quantities. There are a number of physical quantities (velocity, acceleration, force, momentum, electric field, to recall a few) which it is convenient to define, and to identify as vector quantities. This means that they follow the rules for combination of vectors which are introduced for displacements: forces combine in the same way as displacements, therefore force is a vector quantity.

There are two kinds of physical quantities with which we will be concerned, scalars and vectors. There are others which we will not introduce but which are used in physics because they simplify the description of behavior. A quantity called a tensor, for example, is useful in describing stresses in matter.

A scalar quantity is completely specified by its magnitude, in appropriate units; examples are length, time, mass, density, charge, temperature, heat capacity. Scalars are combined by the ordinary rules of arithmetic, used in a sensible way. If two objects are at 20 °C and 30 °C, the sum 50 °C has no meaning. What is meant by calling temperature a scalar quantity is that if an object is heated through 20 C° and then through 30 C° its total temperature rise is 50 C°. However, if an object is displaced through 20 cm and then displaced through 30 cm its total displacement is not necessarily 50 cm. Vectors do not combine by the ordinary rules of arithmetic because direction is involved.

Whether a quantity is vector or scalar is sometimes a matter of definition, but may be something that must be established by experiment. We choose mass, length and time as fundamental quantities, which means that we do not define what they are, we give them operational definitions that specify how to measure them. They are scalar quantities by experiment; experiments show that they can be combined arithmetically. On the other hand, velocity and acceleration are vector quantities by definition; they are defined in terms of the vector displacement. Whether force is a vector quantity by definition or by experiment is a question we shall consider later—and we will find that we cannot give an unambiguous answer.

When we say that a vector has a direction, a natural question is "a direction relative to what?" Direction depends on the choice of co-ordinate system; "up" in one co-ordinate system is "down" in another. Specification of a vector can only be accomplished with respect to a particular co-ordinate system. However, the feature which makes vectors useful is that neither their values (i.e., the value of the physical quantity) nor the relation between them (the way they are combined) depend on the choice of co-ordinate system.

This does *not* mean that vectors remain the same in different frames of reference, that is, in co-ordinate systems moving with respect to one another. It means they remain the same if the co-ordinate system is rotated to a different angle, or translated to a different position.

Vectors were invented because by using them the laws of physics can be stated in simple forms. Intuitively we would expect that physical behavior should not depend on the arbitrary location and orientation of the co-ordinate system we choose for describing the behavior. This intuitive feeling (unlike some of our intuitive ideas) is borne out by experiment. **The laws of physics are observed by experiment to be invariant under translation or rotation of the co-ordinate system.** Vectors were invented to take advantage of this experimental fact.

The rest of this chapter is devoted to reviewing the properties of vectors, as illustrated by the prototype vector, displacement.

DISPLACEMENT

Think about a point P_1 somewhere in a frame of reference, and another point P_2 somewhere else in the same frame of reference. The displacement from P_1 to P_2 is the straight line going from P_1 to P_2.

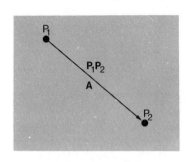

The displacement has a length P_1P_2, the distance between the points, and a direction which depends on the position of both points. (There are an infinite number of points which are a distance P_1P_2

The displacement of point P_2 with respect to point P_1.

$$\overrightarrow{P_1P_2} \equiv \vec{A}$$
$$P_1P_2 = A$$
$$|\overrightarrow{P_1P_2}| = A$$
$$|\mathbf{A}| = A$$

from P_1.) We call the displacement $\overrightarrow{P_1P_2}$ to indicate there is more to it than just length P_1P_2. To shorten the notation we can call the displacement **A**, with length A. (In writing it is easy to label vectors with an arrow on top $[\vec{A}]$, but this is not so simple to accomplish in print so boldfaced type is used [**A**]). The labeling, of course, does not tell us what the displacement is; in a particular case we must say "the displacement is 5 miles due south," or "the displacement is 10 cm in the $+x$-direction."

It may be useful to think of a particle as moving from P_1 to P_2 (by any path whatsoever), but this is not necessary. A displacement is sometimes called a "step in space" but nothing has to make the step.

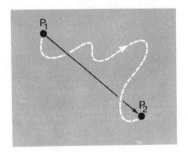

The displacement of a particle that moves from point P_1 to point P_2 does not depend on the path of the particle.

Now think about a number of differently placed and differently oriented coordinate systems in the space around **A**. While it would be described differently with respect to each of these, "it" (i.e., its magnitude and direction) is independent of them. Displacement (or any other vector quantity) has physical reality, and its value does not depend on our description of it.

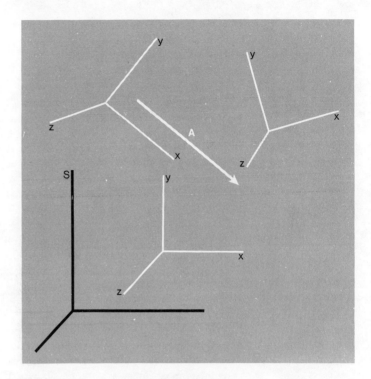

The vector **A** in the frame of reference S is described differently in different co-ordinate systems in S.

Now think about two other points in the same frame of reference, P_1' and P_2', so located that the displacement between them, **A′**, has the same length and the same direction as **A**. Then **A′** is the *same* displacement as **A**; we can say that **A′** and **A** are equal, or identical. This is necessary because when you thought of the two points P_1 and P_2 you could only do so with respect to a particular co-ordinate system—there's no other way. Since we wish to define displacement as independent of any co-ordinate system, we must state that **A′** is the same as **A**.

This may look a little silly at first; a displacement of 10 miles south from Toronto is the same as one 10 miles south from Chicago? Ignoring the fact that south is a slightly different direction in Toronto than in Chicago, they are the same **by definition.**

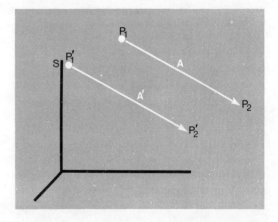

The vectors **A** and **A′** are the same vector.

The fact that the two displacements do not end up at the same point is irrelevant; displacement is **change** in position. Of course, in combining displacements we will have to be sensible; adding displacements of objects at Toronto and Chicago would be like adding the temperatures of two different objects.

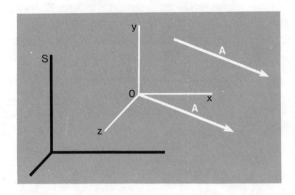

The vector **A** can be thought of as located anywhere with respect to a particular co-ordinate system in the frame of reference.

The fact that vectors are independent of a co-ordinate system means that they can be moved around in a given system to any point that is convenient—to the origin, or to the end of another vector.

ADDING DISPLACEMENTS: $2 + 2 = 3$

The operation of adding vectors is called addition because the meaning is the same as in ordinary arithmetic. If you are given 2 apples and then 3 apples the result is the same as if you have been given 5 apples at once. Similarly a vector **C** is the sum of the vectors **A** and **B** if the result **C** is the same as the result of **A** and **B**. This is denoted by $C = A + B$ but the operation indicated by $+$ is not simple addition; the meaning is the same but the method is different. Operations such as addition or multiplication have to be redefined for vectors.

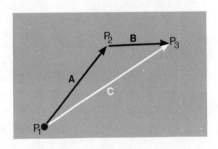

The addition of two vectors **A** and **B**; $A + B = C$ means that the displacement **C** is the same as the combined displacements **A** and **B**.

If the displacement of a particle is **A**, from P_1 to P_2, and **B** from P_2 to P_3, the result is the same as if it had been displaced from P_1 to P_3, the displacement **C**. It does not matter whether the displacements **A** and **B** are thought of as sequential or simultaneous; we are only concerned with change in position, not time. The vector **C** is called the **sum,** or the **net** or **resultant** displacement. The magnitude C can range from $A + B$ to $A - B$, depending on the positions of the points P_1, P_2, P_3.

The figures summarize vector addition. Thinking of the vectors as displacements, the results are obvious. Any other vector quantity behaves the same way by definition; vectors are quantities which combine like displacements.

A + B = C $A + B = C$

A + B = C $A - B = C$

A + B = C $A^2 + B^2 = C^2$
$$\tan (A,C) = B/A$$

A + B = C
$$A^2 + B^2 - 2AB \cos (A,B) = C^2$$
$$B/\sin (A,C) = C/\sin (A,B)$$

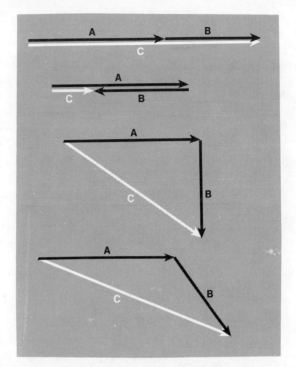

Addition of two vectors in the same direction, in opposite directions, at right angles, and at an arbitrary angle.

A + B = B + A

= C

Commutative law for addition; the order in which vectors are added does not matter.

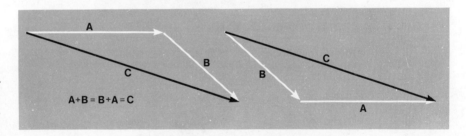

A+B = B+A = C

Vectors originating at a common point can be added by completing the parallelogram.

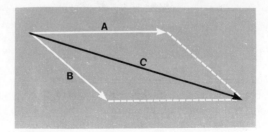

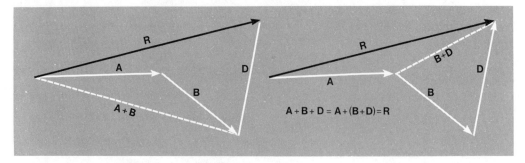

Distributive law for addition; the way that vectors are grouped for addition does not matter. (Note that the vectors do not necessarily lie in the same plane; the diagrams can be thought of as three-dimensional.)

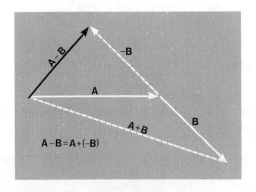

The vector difference **A** − **B** is the vector sum **A** + (−**B**).

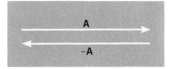

$$\mathbf{A} + (-\mathbf{A}) = 0$$

The vector −**A** has the same magnitude but the opposite direction to vector **A**.

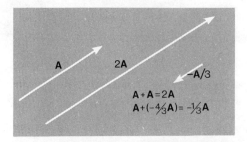

Multiplying a vector by a positive scalar changes its magnitude but not its direction; multiplying by a negative scalar changes its magnitude and reverses its direction.

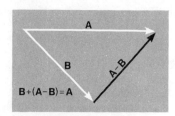

The vector difference may be found most readily by thinking of the two vectors as originating at the same point.

The sum **C** can be found by geometric construction, drawing figures to scale, or by using trigonometry. The order of combination does not matter—the commutative and distributive laws of addition hold.

The magnitude of a vector can be changed by multiplying it by a number (positive or negative). More generally, a vector can be multiplied by any scalar quantity. Since scalar quantities have magnitude only, by definition, the direction of the vector will not change; however, since scalar quantities in general have units (they are physical quantities) the new vector may be a different physical quantity. Multiplying a displacement of 10 cm down by a time of 2 sec gives a vector of 20 cm-sec down. Multiplying it by a reciprocal time of $\frac{1}{2}$ sec^{-1} (dividing it by 2 sec) gives a vector of 5 cm/sec down. The second happens to be more useful, but both operations are valid.

VECTOR COMPONENTS

In adding a number of vectors having different directions, a graphical solution may be inaccurate and a direct trigonometric solution messy, so it is sometimes convenient to introduce a particular co-ordinate system (note that one has *not* been necessary so far) and use it to arrange to add only vectors in the same line. This is done by **resolving** each vector into **components.**

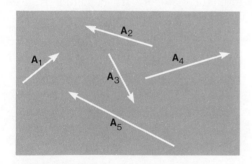

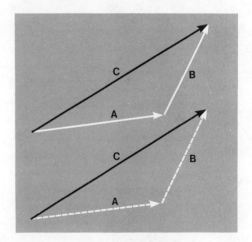

What is the best way to find the sum of a number of vectors?

A vector can be replaced by any number of component vectors.

Just as the vector **C** has the same result as **A** and **B** combined, so that we can replace **A** + **B** by **C**, so the opposite can be done. We can replace **C** by two vectors **A** and **B** or by any number of vectors. We can resolve **C** into a number of component vectors in an infinite number of ways. We will restrict the term component to mean **rectangular** components, meaning that we will choose three

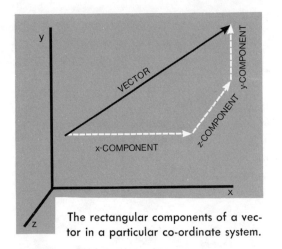

The rectangular components of a vector in a particular co-ordinate system.

components which are mutually at right angles. (Since space is three-dimensional, we can choose at most three such components). We choose these components in the three directions determined by the x-, y-, and z-axes of a particular co-ordinate system. Since the orientation of the co-ordinate system is arbitrary, we still have an infinite choice of components.

Suppose there are n vectors to be added. Label them $\mathbf{A}_1$, $\mathbf{A}_2$, $\mathbf{A}_3$, $\cdots$ $\mathbf{A}_n$. Let $\mathbf{A}_i$ represent any one of them. Resolve each vector into components $(\mathbf{A}_i)_x$, $(\mathbf{A}_i)_y$, $(\mathbf{A}_i)_z$. By adding all of the parallel x-components we get the x-component of the resultant vector $\mathbf{R}$:

$$\mathbf{R}_x = (\mathbf{A}_1)_x + (\mathbf{A}_2)_x + \cdots (\mathbf{A}_n)_x$$

$$= \sum_{i=1}^{n} (\mathbf{A}_i)_x$$

This is shown as a vector sum, but since all the vectors are in the same direction it is simply an arithmetic sum of positive and negative quantities.

Similarly $\mathbf{R}_y = \sum (\mathbf{A}_i)_y$, and $\mathbf{R}_z = \sum (\mathbf{A}_i)_z$. We now use the components $\mathbf{R}_x$, $\mathbf{R}_y$, $\mathbf{R}_z$, to determine the resultant vector $\mathbf{R}$. Its magnitude is given by $R^2 = R_x^2 + R_y^2 + R_z^2$ since the components are perpendicular, and its direction with respect to the co-ordinate system can be specified.

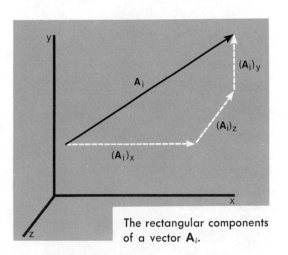

The rectangular components of a vector $\mathbf{A}_i$.

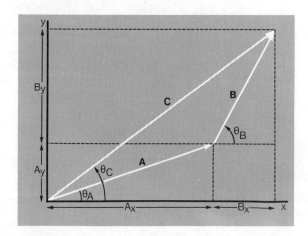

The use of components to add two vectors in the xy plane.

$$\mathbf{A} + \mathbf{B} = \mathbf{C}$$
$$A_x = A \cos \theta_A, \ A_y = A \sin \theta_A$$
$$B_x = B \cos \theta_B, \ B_y = B \sin \theta_B$$
$$C_x = A_x + B_x$$
$$C_y = A_y + B_y$$
$$C^2 = C_x^2 + C_y^2$$
$$\tan \theta_C = C_y/C_x$$

It is difficult to picture things in three dimensions, either mentally or on a two-dimensional page. The figure shows the additions of two vectors only, so that they define a plane. This plane is chosen to be the xy plane of the co-ordinate system, so that the z-component of both vectors is zero. The steps involved in determining the magnitude and direction of the resultant are shown. Note that it makes no difference where on the diagram the vectors are placed; **B** could have been placed at the origin. It was placed at the end of **A** so that geometrically it is clear that $C_x = A_x + B_x$, but the analytic solution does not depend on this.

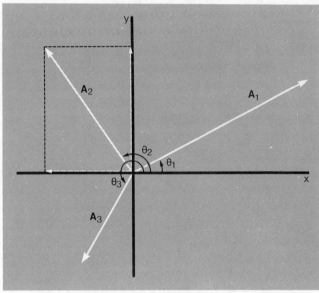

$$\mathbf{R} = \sum \mathbf{A}_i$$
$$(A_i)_x = A_i \cos \theta_i$$
$$(A_i)_y = A_i \sin \theta_i$$
$$R_x = \sum (A_i)_x = \sum A_i \cos \theta_i$$
$$R_y = \sum (A_i)_y = \sum A_i \sin \theta_i$$
$$R^2 = R_x^2 + R_y^2$$
$$\tan \theta_R = R_y / R_x$$

The addition of a set of vectors in the xy plane.

The above figure summarizes the analytic solution for a set of vectors all lying in the xy plane. Each vector is specified by its magnitude A_i and the angle θ_i measured counterclockwise from the positive x-axis. By measuring the angles in this way the signs of the components are automatically included. The vector A_2, for example, has a positive y-component and a negative x-component; θ_2 is between $\pi/2$ and π and has a positive sine and negative cosine.

In resolving a vector into its components it is important to remember that it has been **replaced** by its components. The vector and its components are equivalent; we have *either* the vector *or* its components, not both. This is the reason that we have shown in all vector diagrams the resultant as a dotted line if the components are solid lines, or vice versa. In using force diagrams it seems to be particularly easy to forget that if a force is replaced by its components it is no longer there.

In this section we stopped referring specifically to the displacement vector and just used the term vector. Remember that all vectors combine like displacements.

ONE VECTOR ≡ THREE SCALARS

We said that vectors were invented because they simplified the way in which the laws of physics could be expressed, providing a sort of shorthand. One way in which this is so can now be seen: a vector is equivalent to three scalars.

Think about a displacement vector **A** in a particular co-ordinate system (x, y, z) in which it has components A_x, A_y, A_z. These are vectors in the sense that they have direction, but as we have seen, the x-components of a number of vectors can be added as scalars. Certainly we can say, in any case, that the vector **A** uniquely specifies three lengths A_x, A_y, A_z in this co-ordinate system.

Now think about a different co-ordinate system (x', y', z') with a different origin and orientation than the first. In this system the same vector **A** uniquely specifies a different set of three lengths $A_{x'}$, $A_{y'}$, $A_{z'}$.

Thus a vector quantity always represents three scalar quantities, but while the particular scalar quantities depend on the choice of co-ordinate system, the vector quantity does not. The magnitude and orientation of the vector are independent of the co-ordinate system chosen; the vector is said to be **invariant** for the co-ordinate systems in the frame of reference.

Some of the equations of physics look very simple in vector notation, but contain a great deal of information. Consider three vectors **A**, **B**, **C**, with a resultant **R**. The vector equation $\mathbf{R} = \mathbf{A} + \mathbf{B} + \mathbf{C}$ is equivalent to three scalar equations

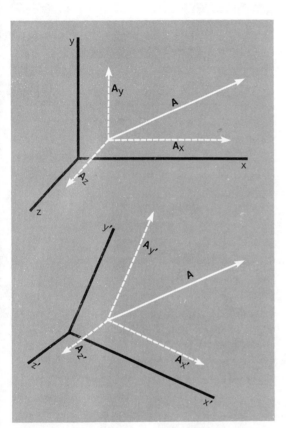

The same vector has different components in different co-ordinate systems.

$$R_x = A_x + B_x + C_x \quad R_y = A_y + B_y + C_y \quad R_z = A_z + B_z + C_z$$

and these can only be written down by choosing a particular co-ordinate system.

UNIT VECTORS

A notation which will be convenient is that of the **unit vector.** Any vector **A** has a magnitude A and a direction. One way of specifying the direction is to introduce a vector **a** of unit magnitude (a unit vector) in the same direction as **A**.

Then $\mathbf{A} = A\mathbf{a}$. This separates the vector $\mathbf{A}$ into a magnitude part A and a direction part $\mathbf{a}$. One way of specifying a particular co-ordinate system is by three unit vectors $\mathbf{i}, \mathbf{j}, \mathbf{k}$ in the x-, y-, z-directions, respectively. Then any vector $\mathbf{A}$ can be written as

$$\mathbf{A} = \mathbf{A}_x + \mathbf{A}_y + \mathbf{A}_z$$
$$= A_x\mathbf{i} + A_y\mathbf{j} + A_z\mathbf{k}$$

The term "x-component" is used both for $\mathbf{A}_x$ and for A_x. Which is meant has to be determined from the context.

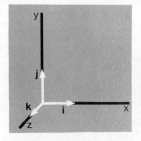

Unit vectors used to specify three co-ordinate directions.

MULTIPLICATION OF VECTORS

So far the only vector operations introduced have been addition and subtraction, where the definition in terms of the behavior of displacements is intuitively reasonable. We now go on to vector multiplication, where the definitions will not be immediately obvious, but will turn out to be equally useful.

The multiplication of a vector by a scalar is ordinary multiplication, the scalar quantity multiplying the magnitude of the vector to give a vector in the same direction but with different magnitude, and perhaps representing a different physical quantity. But what is the product of two vectors? Is it a vector or a scalar? It is useful to define two kinds of products, one of which is a scalar, the other a vector. Both operations are called multiplication, because in some cases the result is the same as that of ordinary multiplication of the component vectors, though in general it is not. The result of an operation producing a scalar is called the **scalar product,** and of that producing a vector the **vector product.**

THE SCALAR PRODUCT

One choice of product that would be a scalar would simply be what is obtained by multiplying the magnitudes of the two vectors together. However, this would not at all take account of the fact that the vectors have direction; the result would not depend on the angle between the vectors. This is taken into account by defining the scalar product as the magnitude of one vector multiplied by the magnitude of the **component** of the second vector which is in the same direction as the first. If the angle between vectors $\mathbf{A}$ and $\mathbf{B}$ is θ, the scalar product (or "dot" product, in honor of the symbol used to denote the operation) is defined as

$$\mathbf{A}\cdot\mathbf{B} \equiv AB \cos \theta$$

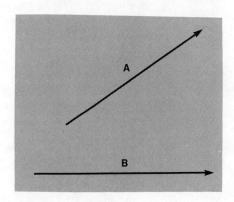

What is meant by the product of these two vectors?

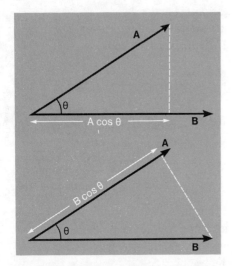

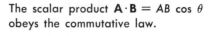

The scalar product $\mathbf{A} \cdot \mathbf{B} = AB \cos \theta$ obeys the commutative law.

Since $B(A \cos \theta) = A(B \cos \theta)$ the commutative law is true for the scalar product:

$$\mathbf{A} \cdot \mathbf{B} = \mathbf{B} \cdot \mathbf{A}$$

The distributive law also holds as can be seen geometrically

$$\mathbf{C} = \mathbf{A} + \mathbf{B}$$

$$\mathbf{C} \cdot \mathbf{D} = (\mathbf{A} + \mathbf{B}) \cdot \mathbf{D} = \mathbf{A} \cdot \mathbf{D} + \mathbf{B} \cdot \mathbf{D}$$

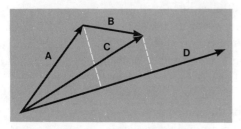

The scalar product obeys the distributive law.

The sum of the components of $\mathbf{A}$ and $\mathbf{B}$ along $\mathbf{D}$ is the component of $\mathbf{C}$ along $\mathbf{D}$. Note that if we had defined the scalar product as simply the product of the magnitudes, this would not be true; $CD \neq AD + BD$ in general.

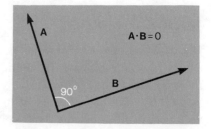

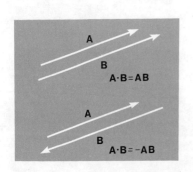

The scalar product of parallel and anti-parallel vectors.

The scalar product of perpendicular vectors is zero.

For parallel vectors (with the same direction) $\theta = 0$ and $\mathbf{A} \cdot \mathbf{B} = AB$. For identical vectors $\mathbf{A} \cdot \mathbf{A} = A^2$. For perpendicular vectors $\mathbf{A} \cdot \mathbf{B} = 0$. If $0 \leq \theta < 90°$, the scalar product is positive; for $90° < \theta \leq 180°$ it is negative. Forming the dot product of two vectors gives a quick test for orthogonality: if the result is zero, the vectors are orthogonal.

The scalar product is defined without reference to a co-ordinate system. What is the quantity produced, in terms of a particular co-ordinate system? A vector **A** may be considered to represent three scalars A_x, A_y, A_z. What does **A·B** represent?

The calculation will be simplified by using the unit vectors **i**, **j**, **k** and noting that because they are orthogonal (mutually perpendicular)

$$\mathbf{i} \cdot \mathbf{j} = \mathbf{j} \cdot \mathbf{j} = \mathbf{k} \cdot \mathbf{k} = 1 \qquad \mathbf{i} \cdot \mathbf{j} = \mathbf{j} \cdot \mathbf{k} = \mathbf{k} \cdot \mathbf{i} = 0$$

Then

$$\begin{aligned}
\mathbf{A} \cdot \mathbf{B} &= (A_x \mathbf{i} + A_y \mathbf{j} + A_z \mathbf{k}) \cdot (B_x \mathbf{i} + B_y \mathbf{j} + B_z \mathbf{k}) \\
&= A_x B_x \mathbf{i} \cdot \mathbf{i} + A_x B_y \mathbf{i} \cdot \mathbf{j} + A_x B_z \mathbf{i} \cdot \mathbf{k} \\
&\quad + A_y B_x \mathbf{j} \cdot \mathbf{i} + A_y B_y \mathbf{j} \cdot \mathbf{j} + A_y B_z \mathbf{j} \cdot \mathbf{k} \\
&\quad + A_z B_x \mathbf{k} \cdot \mathbf{i} + A_z B_y \mathbf{k} \cdot \mathbf{j} + A_z B_z \mathbf{k} \cdot \mathbf{k}
\end{aligned}$$

(since the dot product is distributive)

$$= A_x B_x + A_y B_y + A_z B_z$$

(using the above relations for unit vectors)

The scalar product in terms of components: $\mathbf{A} \cdot \mathbf{B} = A_x B_x + A_y B_y + A_z B_z$.

In a particular co-ordinate system the scalar product of two vectors is shorthand for the sum of the products of the parallel components of the vectors.

In a different co-ordinate system (x', y', z') the components will be different, so that

$$\mathbf{A} \cdot \mathbf{B} = A_{x'} B_{x'} + A_{y'} B_{y'} + A_{z'} B_{z'}$$

but the form remains the same and so does the value of the product formed.

Remember that physical events, and the laws of physics that describe them, are independent of the co-ordinate system used. Vectors and quantities formed by combining vectors are invariant for different co-ordinate systems, and therefore are useful in representing physical situations. For example, you are familiar with the definition of the physical quantity work as force times distance, taking only the component of the force in the direction of motion. This can be expressed more conveniently and therefore more usefully as the scalar product of the vector quantities force and displacement as we will see.

DIRECTION COSINES

A vector can be specified in a particular co-ordinate system in a variety of ways. We have seen that $\mathbf{A} = A_x \mathbf{i} + A_y \mathbf{j} + A_z \mathbf{k}$ specifies it in terms of the unit vectors of the system, and its components in the system. Another possibility is to use the angles α, β, γ which it makes with the x, y, z-directions, respectively, of the system. Then $A_x = \mathbf{A} \cdot \mathbf{i} = A \cos \alpha$, $A_y = \mathbf{A} \cdot \mathbf{j} = A \cos \beta$, $A_z = \mathbf{A} \cdot \mathbf{k} = A \cos \gamma$, and $\mathbf{A} = A(\mathbf{i} \cos \alpha + \mathbf{j} \cos \beta + \mathbf{k} \cos \gamma)$ so $\mathbf{a} = \mathbf{i} \cos \alpha + \mathbf{j} \cos \beta + \mathbf{k} \cos \gamma$, the

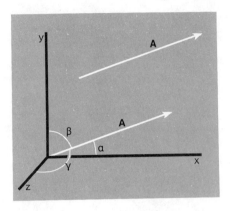

unit vector in the **A** direction. Forming **a·a** gives $1 = \cos^2 \alpha + \cos^2 \beta + \cos^2 \gamma$. The quantities $\cos \alpha$, $\cos \beta$ and $\cos \gamma$ are called the direction cosines of **A**, and the sum of their squares is one.

Specification of the direction of a vector in a particular co-ordinate system using the direction cosines.

THE VECTOR PRODUCT

Having defined the scalar product of two vectors in terms of the component of one vector in the direction of the other, what other possibilities remain? Clearly one is to multiply the magnitude of one vector by the magnitude of the component of the second vector which is perpendicular to the direction of the first. This turns out to be useful, if interpreted as a vector.

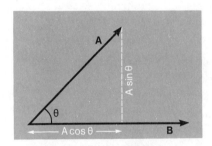

If the angle between two vectors A and B is θ, the vector product **A × B** (or "cross" product, because of the notation) is another vector **C**, defined by

$$\mathbf{C} = \mathbf{A} \times \mathbf{B} = \mathbf{c}AB \sin \theta$$

$(A \cos \theta)B$ is interpreted as a scalar; $(A \sin \theta)B$ is interpreted as a vector.

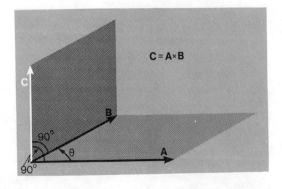

The vector product **A × B** has magnitude $AB \sin \theta$ and a direction at right angles to both **A** and **B**.

The magnitude of **C** is $C = AB \sin \theta$, and its direction is given by the unit vector **c**. What direction is this? This too is a matter of definition, made so that the result will be useful. The direction is perpendicular to both **A** and **B**; that is, perpendicular to the plane defined by **A** and **B**.

But this is still not enough—which perpendicular, "up" or "down"? The definition includes the **right hand rule**; think of the angle θ as measured *from* **A** *to* **B** (the smaller angle), and using the right hand, curl the fingers in this direction, with thumb extended— the thumb gives the **c** direction. Equivalently, think of rotating **A** into **B**; the direction of **C** is that which an ordinary (right-hand) screw would move on such a rotation.

Since **B** × **A** gives a vector in the opposite direction, **B** × **A** = − **A** × **B** and the commutative law is *not* obeyed by the vector product.

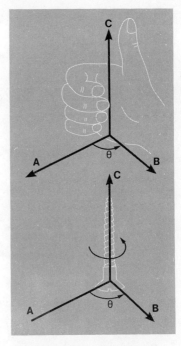

Two methods of determining the direction of **A** × **B**.

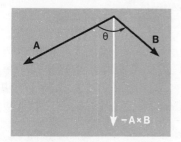

The vector product does not obey the commutative law.

The distributive law is obeyed

$$(\mathbf{A} + \mathbf{B}) \times \mathbf{D} = \mathbf{A} \times \mathbf{D} + \mathbf{B} \times \mathbf{D}$$

as you can verify by expressing the vectors in terms of components.

The cross product of parallel or anti-parallel vectors is zero, and this fact gives a quick method of testing whether two vectors are parallel. The magnitude of the cross product of perpendicular vectors is the product of their magnitudes; $|\mathbf{A} \times \mathbf{B}| = AB$ in this case.

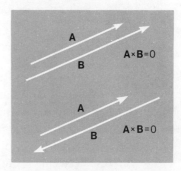

The cross product of parallel or anti-parallel vectors is zero.

The cross product of perpendicular vectors.

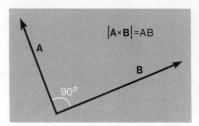

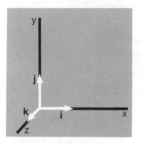

Right-handed Cartesian
co-ordinate system.

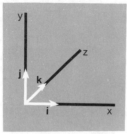

Left-handed Cartesian
co-ordinate system.

The definition of the cross product did not depend on any co-ordinate system, so the vector produced is independent of a co-ordinate system. However, in a particular system, what does it represent?

Again we use the properties of the Cartesian unit vectors $\mathbf{i}, \mathbf{j}, \mathbf{k}$, noting that $\mathbf{i} \times \mathbf{i} = \mathbf{j} \times \mathbf{j} = \mathbf{k} \times \mathbf{k} = 0$, but that it now becomes necessary to distinguish between right-handed and left-handed co-ordinate systems. By convention, Cartesian systems are usually right-handed, defined by $\mathbf{i} \times \mathbf{j} = \mathbf{k}$, so that following the right-hand rule, $\mathbf{j} \times \mathbf{k} = \mathbf{i}$ and $\mathbf{k} \times \mathbf{i} = \mathbf{j}$, but $\mathbf{j} \times \mathbf{i} = -\mathbf{k}$, $\mathbf{k} \times \mathbf{j} = -\mathbf{i}$ and $\mathbf{i} \times \mathbf{k} = -\mathbf{j}$. (For any cyclic order ijk, jki, kij the sign is positive.)

For any two vectors $\mathbf{A}$ and $\mathbf{B}$, then,

$$
\begin{aligned}
\mathbf{A} \times \mathbf{B} &= (A_x\mathbf{i} + A_y\mathbf{j} + A_z\mathbf{k}) \times (B_x\mathbf{i} + B_y\mathbf{j} + B_z\mathbf{k}) \\
&= A_xB_x\mathbf{i} \times \mathbf{i} + A_xB_y\mathbf{i} \times \mathbf{j} + A_xB_z\mathbf{i} \times \mathbf{k} + A_yB_x\mathbf{j} \times \mathbf{i} + A_yB_y\mathbf{j} \times \mathbf{j} \\
&\quad + A_yB_z\mathbf{j} \times \mathbf{k} + A_zB_x\mathbf{k} \times \mathbf{i} + A_zB_y\mathbf{k} \times \mathbf{j} + A_zB_z\mathbf{k} \times \mathbf{k} \\
&= (A_yB_z - A_zB_y)\mathbf{i} + (A_zB_x - A_xB_z)\mathbf{j} + (A_xB_y - A_yB_x)\mathbf{k}
\end{aligned}
$$

The vector product of $\mathbf{A}$ and $\mathbf{B}$ gives a vector with components $C_x = A_yB_z - A_zB_y$, etc. The vector notation is clearly an effective shorthand in this case. The result may also be expressed in determinant notation:

$$
\mathbf{A} \times \mathbf{B} = \begin{vmatrix} \mathbf{i} & \mathbf{j} & \mathbf{k} \\ A_x & A_y & A_z \\ B_x & B_y & B_z \end{vmatrix}
$$

In a different co-ordinate system (x',y',z') the product vector $\mathbf{C}$ would have different components, such as $C_{x'} = A_{y'}B_{z'} - A_{z'}B_{y'}$ but its form is invariant.

One physical quantity that appears as the vector product is torque or moment, the turning effect of a force about an axis, defined as the vector product of force and displacement. Note that

Force · Displacement = Work   and   **Force × Displacement** = **Torque**

The same two vector quantities, force and displacement, combine to produce two quite different physical quantities, one a scalar and one a vector. This emphasizes that the vector operations themselves have physical significance.

There are other mechanical properties, for example, angular velocity and angular momentum, which are vector products. Although our use of it in mechanics will not be extensive, some practice in using it is desirable because it is essential in dealing with electromagnetic theory.

Questions for discussion

1. Does a unit vector have units, or must it be dimensionless?

2. Can two vectors differing in magnitude have a zero resultant? Can three vectors that are not all in the same plane have a zero resultant?

3. Is a **physical standard** invariable by definition, by experiment, or both, or neither?

4. Is a **frequency standard** equivalent to a **time standard?**

5. What does **simultaneous** mean? Can two events at two different places occur simultaneously? How could you tell? Can two events, one on a moving train and one beside the track, occur simultaneously? How could you tell?

6. Does a **single standard** (such as the old standard meter) have any advantage over a **reproducible standard** (such as the krypton radiation)?

7. Do you think quantities such as length and time that are called **fundamental physical quantities** are really more fundamental than **derived quantities** such as acceleration and momentum?

8. We once prepared a film called *Frames of Reference* as part of the Physical Science Study Committee course in Physics. This film begins with one of us inverted, the other right side up. We have a conversation about who is really upside down, and settle it by tossing a coin (see the frontispiece). Then one says to the other, "Why don't you come into my frame of reference?" Was it correct to imply that we were in two different frames of reference?

Problems

1. Assume that the length of the day is increasing uniformly at a rate of 10^{-3} sec/century. By how much would a clock whose calibration is based on the "earth clock" be wrong after 20 centuries?

2. A salesman leaves his home town A; visits town B, 50 mi due NE; then travels to town C, 20 mi E of B; then on to town D, 75 mi from C in a direction 60° S of E. Find his displacement from home **(a)** by drawing a scale diagram, **(b)** by using trigonometry to solve successive triangles, **(c)** by using components in an appropriate co-ordinate system.

3. If $|A + B| = |A - B|$ for two vectors **A** and **B**, what is the angle between the vectors?

4. Show that for two vectors with equal magnitudes A and with an angle θ between them, the magnitude of their sum is $2A \cos(\theta/2)$ and of their difference is $2A \sin(\theta/2)$.

5. How is the area of the triangle contained between the vectors **A** and **B** related to the vector product $A \times B$?

6. Consider the triangle formed by the vectors **A**, **B**, **C**, where $C = A + B$. Show that forming the scalar product $C \cdot C$ leads to the trigonometric law of cosines, and forming the vector product $C \times C = C \times (A + B)$ leads to the trigonometric law of sines.

7. Find the angle θ between the following pairs of vectors **A** and **B** by calculating both $\cos\theta = \mathbf{A}\cdot\mathbf{B}/AB$ and $\sin\theta = |\mathbf{A}\times\mathbf{B}|/AB$.

(a) $\mathbf{A} = 3\mathbf{i} + 2\mathbf{j}$ $\mathbf{B} = \mathbf{i} + 4\mathbf{j}$ (d) $\mathbf{A} = 3\mathbf{i} + 2\mathbf{j}$ $\mathbf{B} = -\mathbf{i} - 4\mathbf{j}$

(b) $\mathbf{A} = 3\mathbf{i} + 2\mathbf{j}$ $\mathbf{B} = -\mathbf{i} + 4\mathbf{j}$ (e) $\mathbf{A} = 3\mathbf{i} + 2\mathbf{j}$ $\mathbf{B} = \mathbf{i} - 4\mathbf{j}$

(c) $\mathbf{A} = 3\mathbf{i} + 2\mathbf{j}$ $\mathbf{B} = -4\mathbf{i} + \mathbf{j}$

Is it necessary to find both $\sin\theta$ and $\cos\theta$ to determine the angle?

8. Consider the parallelogram formed with two vectors **A** and **B** as sides. How is the area of this parallelogram related to the magnitude of the vector product $|\mathbf{A}\times\mathbf{B}|$?

9. A vector can be specified in a particular co-ordinate system by visualizing its tail at the origin, and giving the co-ordinates of its head; e.g., the point (2,3,4) corresponds to the vector $2\mathbf{i} + 3\mathbf{j} + 4\mathbf{k}$.

Which of the following pairs represent vectors perpendicular to each other?

    (2,3,4)   and $(-1,2,-1)$

    (2,3,4)   and $(-1,2,1)$

    (3,3,3)   and $(2,-5,3)$

    (3,3,3)   and $(2,-5,-3)$

What is the angle between the vectors where it is not a right angle?

10. Using components and unit vectors, show that the distributive law is obeyed for the vector product: $(\mathbf{A} + \mathbf{B})\times\mathbf{D} = \mathbf{A}\times\mathbf{D} + \mathbf{B}\times\mathbf{D}$.

11. A plane area can be represented by a single vector whose magnitude is equal to the surface area and whose direction is perpendicular to the surface. Show that in a particular co-ordinate system the components of the vector in the three co-ordinate directions represent the projections of the area in the three co-ordinate planes.

12. Show that the magnitude of the volume of the parallelopiped defined by any three vectors **A**, **B**, **C** is $\mathbf{A}\cdot(\mathbf{B}\times\mathbf{C})$, and therefore that $\mathbf{A}\cdot(\mathbf{B}\times\mathbf{C}) = \mathbf{B}\cdot(\mathbf{C}\times\mathbf{A}) = \mathbf{C}\cdot(\mathbf{A}\times\mathbf{B})$. Verify this using components.

13. (a) The displacements of two particles A and B with respect to a fixed point O in a frame of reference are given by the vectors $\mathbf{A} = 4\mathbf{i} + 2\mathbf{j} + 3\mathbf{k}$, $\mathbf{B} = -5\mathbf{i} - \mathbf{j} + 2\mathbf{k}$, where **i**, **j**, **k** are unit vectors in three mutually perpendicular directions, and all lengths are in meters. Determine $|\mathbf{A}|$, $|\mathbf{B}|$, $\mathbf{A}\cdot\mathbf{B}$, $\mathbf{A}\times\mathbf{B}$, $\mathbf{A} + \mathbf{B}$, and $\mathbf{A} - \mathbf{B}$. Find the angle between the vectors **A** and **B**. State the vector that gives the displacement of particle B with respect to particle A. Determine the distance between A and B. Find a unit vector perpendicular to both **A** and **B**.

(b) Think of the unit vectors in (a) above as defining a co-ordinate system (x,y,z) with origin at O. Keeping the z-axis fixed, rotate the x- and y-axes through an angle of 37° (counter-clockwise as viewed from the $+z$-direction), and determine **A** and **B** in terms of new unit vectors $\mathbf{i}'$, $\mathbf{j}'$, $\mathbf{k}'$ in the directions of the axes of the new system. (Take $\sin 37° = 0.6$, $\cos 37° = 0.8$.) Repeat the calculations of (a) above, and note from your results that although the components of the vectors are different, the vectors themselves are the same.

5

MOTION OF A PARTICLE
IN A FRAME OF REFERENCE

In this chapter we will develop general methods for describing motion in a particular frame of reference, and consider three examples of motion that are simple to describe. Then in the next chapter we will consider transformations between frames of reference; motions which appear complex in one frame of reference can sometimes be handled simply by choosing a more appropriate frame of reference. This is *not* the same as choosing a different co-ordinate system for the description.

DISPLACEMENT AND TIME

We started our description of the motion of a particle by pointing out that the path (often called the **trajectory**) of the particle as measured in a particular frame of reference can be specified if its co-ordinates (x,y,z) in some co-ordinate system in this frame of reference are given as functions of time t. For every value of t there are values of x, y, and z giving the position of the particle with respect to the co-ordinate system. Successive positions define the path. Measurements of position cannot be made at every instant of time, but even when we make observations of position that are discontinuous we assume that the path is continuous.

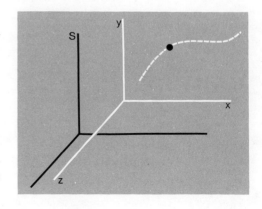

Trajectory of a particle in frame of reference S referred to a co-ordinate system by means of co-ordinates (x, y, z).

By using the concept of displacement we can describe the motion of a particle in a particular frame of reference without introducing a particular co-ordinate system. We specify the trajectory of the particle with respect to some arbitrary fixed point O in our frame of reference by the single vector function of time $\mathbf{r}(t)$ where $\mathbf{r}$ is the **displacement from O**, or **position vector** with respect to O. Knowing $\mathbf{r}(t)$ is equivalent to knowing the three scalar quantities $x(t)$, $y(t)$, $z(t)$ in a particular co-ordinate system. The point O may or may not be on the particle trajectory, so that $\mathbf{r}(t) = 0$ at some instant, or not.

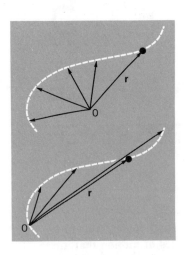

Trajectory of a particle in frame of reference S referred to a fixed point O by means of the displacement vector $\mathbf{r}$.

If we know $\mathbf{r}(t)$ we know **all about the motion.** No further physical information can be generated by mathematical manipulation. However, by introducing the time derivatives of $\mathbf{r}$ we find that the description of certain special cases of motion is simplified. In addition, the time derivatives turn out to have a significant role in dynamics.

VELOCITY

Think about the positions P_1, P_2, P_3, $\cdots$, of a particle at successive intervals of time spaced Δt apart. These positions are defined with respect to a point O by the displacements $\mathbf{r}_1$, $\mathbf{r}_2$, $\mathbf{r}_3$, $\cdots$ at times 0, Δt, $2\Delta t$, $\cdots$. Each displacement may be obtained from the preceding one by adding the displacements $\Delta \mathbf{r}_1$, $\Delta \mathbf{r}_2$, $\Delta \mathbf{r}_3$, $\cdots$.

$$\mathbf{r}_2 = \mathbf{r}_1 + \Delta \mathbf{r}_1, \; \mathbf{r}_3 = \mathbf{r}_2 + \Delta \mathbf{r}_2, \; \cdots$$

The **average velocity** $\bar{\mathbf{v}}$ over any time interval is defined as the displacement in the time interval divided by the time interval.

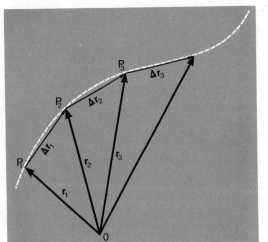

Finite displacements $\Delta \mathbf{r}$ along a trajectory.

In the interval P_1 to P_2, $\bar{\mathbf{v}}(P_1 \to P_2) = \Delta\mathbf{r}_1/\Delta t$. Similarly $\bar{\mathbf{v}}(P_2 \to P_3) = \Delta\mathbf{r}_2/\Delta t$, or in general, for any displacement $\Delta\mathbf{r}$ in time Δt, the average velocity is $\bar{\mathbf{v}} = \Delta\mathbf{r}/\Delta t$. Average velocity is a vector because it is obtained by multiplying the vector quantity displacement $\Delta\mathbf{r}$ by the scalar quantity $1/\Delta t$. The direction of $\bar{\mathbf{v}}$ is the same as the direction of $\Delta\mathbf{r}$.

The **instantaneous velocity v** (usually just referred to as **the velocity**) is defined by

$$\mathbf{v} = \lim_{\Delta t \to 0} \frac{\Delta\mathbf{r}}{\Delta t} = \frac{d\mathbf{r}}{dt}$$

The velocity varies from point to point along the trajectory, both in magnitude and direction. Its direction is the direction of $\Delta\mathbf{r}$ in the limit. For example, as $\Delta t \to 0$, P_2 approaches P_1 and the direction of $\Delta\mathbf{r}_1$, which is the direction of the chord joining P_1 to P_2, becomes the direction of the particle trajectory at P_1. (Note that the direction of $\bar{\mathbf{v}}_1$ is *not* the direction of the particle's motion, in general: in any **finite** time interval, the direction of the particle motion may change, and the only unique direction that can be specified for the interval is the direction of the displacement $\Delta\mathbf{r}_1$.) The velocity vector is tangent to the path, pointing in the direction of motion. The magnitude of the velocity, v, is called the **speed.**

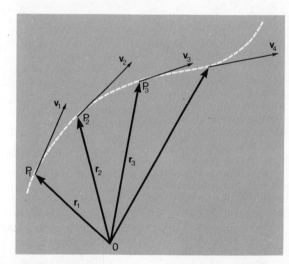

Velocity vectors $\mathbf{v}_1$, $\mathbf{v}_2$, $\mathbf{v}_3$, $\cdots$ can be shown on the same diagram used previously for successive points P_1, P_2, P_3, $\cdots$ spaced Δt apart. The **r** vectors and the **v** vectors are two different kinds of vector, representing different physical quantities, and we cannot add them together any more meaningfully than we could add distance and time.

Instantaneous velocity is sometimes called **velocity at a point,** meaning the average velocity over an infinitesimal interval that includes the point.

The path or trajectory we have shown is a path in space—or, to be precise, in the space defined by our particular frame of reference. Showing some of the velocity vectors on this path helps to visualize the motion, but of course the particle has a velocity $\mathbf{v}(t)$ at every instant of time, just as it has a displacement $\mathbf{r}(t)$ at every instant.

Velocity vectors are tangential to the trajectory.

Rather than thinking of the velocity vectors on a path in space, think of them all as originating at the same point. Since the position of the particle is different at different times, this is not a point in real space. Such a diagram defines **velocity space;** the ends of the vectors are said to indicate the "trajectory" of the particle in velocity space. The diagram shows the velocity vectors $\mathbf{v}_1$, $\mathbf{v}_2$, $\mathbf{v}_3$ $\cdots$ corresponding to times 0, Δt, $2\Delta t$, $\cdots$. It is similar to the original dia-

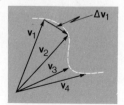

The trajectory of a particle in velocity space.

gram, with velocity vectors instead of displacement vectors. We have defined the rate of change of displacement dr/dt as velocity $\mathbf{v}$, and we can now follow a similar procedure to define the rate of change of velocity $d\mathbf{v}/dt$.

ACCELERATION

If the velocity changes from $\mathbf{v}$ to $\mathbf{v} + \Delta\mathbf{v}$ in a time interval Δt, the **average acceleration** over the interval is defined to be $\bar{\mathbf{a}} = \Delta\mathbf{v}/\Delta t$. It is a vector with the same direction as $\Delta\mathbf{v}$.

The **instantaneous acceleration a** (usually just **the acceleration**) is defined as

$$\mathbf{a} = \lim_{\Delta t \to 0} \frac{\Delta\mathbf{v}}{\Delta t} = \frac{d\mathbf{v}}{dt}$$

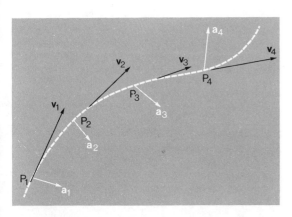

The acceleration vectors $\mathbf{a}_1$, $\mathbf{a}_2$, $\mathbf{a}_3$, $\cdots$ for successive points P_1, P_2, P_3, $\cdots$ can be shown on the **original** diagram that showed the path of the particle in space. Since the direction depends on the vector difference $\Delta\mathbf{v}$ (in the limit), the direction of $\mathbf{a}$ at a point is in general *not* the same as that of $\mathbf{v}$ at the point.

The acceleration vectors are only shown on the diagram at certain points, but the particle has an acceleration $\mathbf{a}(t)$ at every instant, and in general the magnitude and direction vary from instant to instant, or point to point along the path.

Acceleration vectors are not tangential to the trajectory.

The acceleration can be defined in terms of the displacement vector $\mathbf{r}$

$$\mathbf{a} = \frac{d\mathbf{v}}{dt} = \frac{d}{dt}\left(\frac{d\mathbf{r}}{dt}\right) = \frac{d^2\mathbf{r}}{dt^2}$$

Velocity is the first derivative of displacement with respect to time; acceleration is the second derivative of displacement with respect to time.

We could continue this process of successive differentiation by forming da/dt, $d^2\mathbf{a}/dt^2$, $\cdots$ but we will not do so because we have gone as far as it is useful to go. The reason we have gone this far is that acceleration has an important property. Like all vector quantities, displacement, velocity and acceleration are invariant under translation or rotation of the co-ordinate system in a particular frame of reference. In addition, as we will show in the next chapter, acceleration is invariant with respect to co-ordinate systems that are moving at a constant velocity with respect to one another; that is, it is an invariant for frames of reference moving at constant relative velocities. This important result is sometimes regarded as a fundamental attribute of nature; we would prefer to regard it as a useful fact that emerges in man's description of nature.

MOTION OVER AN INTERVAL

We have introduced the quantities **r**, **v** and **a** which are useful in describing motion in three dimensions. Note that the diagrams used so far in this chapter can be thought of as three-dimensional; the vectors r_1, r_2, r_3, $\cdots$ did not necessarily lie in a plane. The three quantities are each functions of time $r(t)$, $v(t)$, $a(t)$ but not independent functions. They are related by their definitions, so that given the time dependence of one, the time dependence of the others can be calculated. The motion of any particle, no matter how complex, is known if $r(t)$ or $v(t)$ or $a(t)$ is measured.

We have gone as far as we can go in a **general** description of motion in a particular frame of reference. Displacement, velocity and acceleration are instantaneous quantities—the motion may change from instant to instant. In order to go farther with our description of motion we will consider some limitations on the motion so that we can describe the motion not only instantaneously but also over a time interval. For example, if $r(t)$ is a constant (i.e., independent of time) then we know that the particle is at rest in the frame of reference. If $v(t)$ is a constant then we know that the path of the particle is a straight line in the frame of reference, and it moves at constant speed so that the displacement in any time interval is proportional to the size of the interval. If $r(t)$ is constant in direction but not in magnitude then we know that the motion is in a straight line, but cannot go further unless we know how the magnitude $r(t)$ varies with time. If $r(t)$ is constant in magnitude but not in direction we know that the motion is confined to the surface of a sphere. If $v(t)$ is constant in magnitude but not in direction we call it motion at constant speed.

At present we are concerned with kinematics, not dynamics—that is, we are simply describing motion without considering the reasons for the particular motion. However, you know that one way of explaining motion is in terms of the concept called force. The basis of classical dynamics is Newton's law $\mathbf{F} = m\mathbf{a}$, relating the resultant force **F** on a particle of mass m to its acceleration **a**. Depending on what the origin of the force is, particular restrictions on the motion may be most conveniently expressed in terms of **a**, or **v**, or **r**.

Think of a few examples. (1) A resultant force $\mathbf{F} = 0$ on a particle means that $\mathbf{a} = 0$ and **v** is a constant. (2) A constant force **F** produces a constant acceleration **a**. (3) If a particle moves under a central force, this means that the force on it is always directed toward a fixed point in the frame of reference; one important kind of central force is an inverse-square force, where the magnitude of the force F is inversely proportional to the square of the distance of the particle from the fixed point: $F \propto 1/r^2$. (4) There are other situations in which the central force depends directly on the displacement from the fixed point: $\mathbf{F} \propto -\mathbf{r}$. (5) In a uniform magnetic field, the magnitude of the magnetic force on a charged particle is proportional to the speed v of the particle.

These examples illustrate some of the variety of ways that restrictions on motion over a time interval can be specified. If the restrictions are known (whether expressed in terms of force or not) a complete description of the motion over the interval can be worked out. Note that this does *not* necessarily mean that analytic expressions can be written down to describe the motion over the interval. This is possible in some situations, but in general a numerical calculation (numerical integration) must be done.

NUMERICAL INTEGRATION

We will do two examples to illustrate the procedure. First, suppose that the motion of a particle is restricted to the x-axis, that it moves in such a way that its speed and displacement are related by $v = 8\sqrt{x}$, where v is in feet/sec and x is in ft, and that at the instant $t = 0$ the particle is at the origin. We wish to calculate the displacement of the particle 1 sec later. It might appear that, since at $t = 0$ both $x = 0$ and $v = 0$, the particle will not move, but this is not so. The particle has an acceleration; we could determine this by finding dv/dt but we shall avoid the methods of calculus for the moment in this example.

At some instant $v = 8\sqrt{x}$. A short time Δt later the speed will have changed to $(v + \Delta v)$ and the displacement to $(x + \Delta x)$ but the same relation exists between them

$$v + \Delta v = 8\sqrt{x + \Delta x} = 8\sqrt{x}(1 + \Delta x/x)^{1/2} \cong 8\sqrt{x}\left(1 + \frac{1}{2}\frac{\Delta x}{x}\right)$$

$$= 8\sqrt{x} + 4\frac{\Delta x}{\sqrt{x}} \qquad \text{:assuming } \Delta x \text{ is small}$$

$$\therefore \Delta v = 4\frac{\Delta x}{\sqrt{x}} = 32\frac{\Delta x}{v}$$

The acceleration over the interval is $a = \dfrac{\Delta v}{\Delta t} = \dfrac{32}{v}\dfrac{\Delta x}{\Delta t} = 32$ ft/sec², since $v = \Delta x/\Delta t$. The velocity and acceleration are actually average values over the interval Δt.

We could equally as well have specified the limitation of the motion by stating that the motion was one-dimensional with a constant acceleration of 32 ft/sec². We did not do so in order to recall to your mind the relation between Δx, Δv and Δt, because we are going to calculate the displacement after 1 sec, $x(1)$ numerically.

We will first use a time interval $\Delta t = 0.2$ sec. In every Δt interval, the speed increases by an amount $\Delta v = a\,\Delta t = 32 \times 0.2 = 6.4$ ft/sec. At $t = 0$, and $v(0) = 0$, then $v(0.2) = 6.4$, $v(0.4) = 6.4 + 6.4 = 12.8$, $v(0.6) = 12.8 + 6.4 = 19.2$, $v(0.8) = 19.2 + 6.4 = 25.6$, $v(1.0) = 25.6 + 6.4 = 32$; all speeds are in ft/sec.

In every Δt interval, the displacement changes by an amount $\Delta x = v\,\Delta t$, but v is not constant; as an approximation we use $v(0.2)$ as the speed over the interval $0 \rightarrow 0.2$ sec, and so on. Then

$$x(0) = 0$$
$$x(.2) = x(0) + v\,\Delta t = 0 + 6.4 \times 0.2 = 1.28$$
$$x(.4) = 1.28 + 12.8 \times 0.2 = 1.28 + 2.56 = 3.84$$
$$x(.6) = 3.84 + 19.2 \times 0.2 = 3.84 + 3.84 = 7.68$$
$$x(.8) = 7.68 + 25.6 \times 0.2 = 7.68 + 5.12 = 12.80$$
$$x(1.0) = 12.80 + 32 \times 0.2 = 12.80 + 6.40 = 19.20 \text{ ft}$$

To see what difference the size of the time interval makes, we repeat the calculation for $\Delta t = 0.1$ sec.

$v(0) = 0$	$x(0) = 0$
$v(.1) = 3.2$	$x(.1) = 3.2 \times 0.1 = 0.32$
$v(.2) = 6.4$	$x(.2) = 0.32 + 6.4 \times 0.1 = 0.96$
$v(.3) = 9.6$	$x(.3) = 0.96 + 0.96 = 1.92$
$v(.4) = 12.8$	$x(.4) = 1.92 + 1.28 = 3.20$
$v(.5) = 16.0$	$x(.5) = 3.20 + 1.60 = 4.80$
$v(.6) = 19.2$	$x(.6) = 4.80 + 1.92 = 6.72$
$v(.7) = 22.4$	$x(.7) = 6.72 + 2.24 = 8.96$
$v(.8) = 25.6$	$x(.8) = 8.96 + 2.56 = 11.52$
$v(.9) = 28.8$	$x(.9) = 11.52 + 2.88 = 14.40$
$v(1.0) = 32.0$	$x(1.0) = 14.40 + 3.20 = 17.60 \text{ ft}$

You may feel that this is wasted arithmetic, because you know what the displacement after 1 sec should be, 16 ft, but how do you know this? Because you learned in studying elementary physics that for uniformly accelerated motion with acceleration a, starting from rest, the displacement $x(t) = \frac{1}{2}at^2$ so that for $a = 32$ ft/sec^2 and $t = 1$ sec, $x = 16$ ft. The equation $x = \frac{1}{2}at^2$ is the result of integrating the instantaneous relation $a = dv/dt$ with the restriction that the acceleration a is constant. It gives the result of the numerical procedure in the limit as $\Delta t \rightarrow 0$. The value of $x(1)$ for $\Delta t = 0.2$ sec was 19.2 ft, the value for $\Delta t = 0.1$ sec was 17.6 ft, and the exact result for $\Delta t \rightarrow 0$ is 16 ft. The smaller the value of Δt used in the numerical calculations, the closer the result will be to 16 ft.

You may have observed that we could have improved the numerical method by recognizing that in calculating $\Delta x = v\,\Delta t$ for an interval it would be better to use an average value of v over the interval rather than the value of v at the end of the interval. In the interval $0 \rightarrow 0.2$ sec we could use the average of $v(0)$ and $v(0.2)$ to get a more accurate value of Δx for the interval. In this particular example this method will give the exact result because v varies linearly with time, but this is not generally so.

The point of the numerical example is to emphasize that a similar procedure can *always* be followed, whether or not the instantaneous description of the motion can be integrated in terms of analytic functions. If $v = dx/dt$ is known to be some function $f(x)$, whether from empirical observations or some force law, then $x(t)$ can be calculated whether $f(x)$ is an integrable function or not. Similarly, if acceleration $a = d^2x/dt^2$ is known to be some function of x, then $x(t)$ can be calculated.

As a second example, think of the motion of a particle which is moving on the x-axis in such a way that its acceleration $a = -4x$, where x is in cm and a in cm/sec². At some instant the particle is at the origin moving with a speed $v = 10$ cm/sec. Where is it one second later? Perhaps you know the solution of the differential equation $d^2x/dt^2 = -4x$, but you can calculate the result to any accuracy you wish even if you do not.

At $t = 0$, $x(0) = 0$, $a(0) = 0$, $v(0) = 10$ cm/sec. We will use $\Delta t = 0.1$ sec, and this time be careful to use the average value over an interval; that is, to get x at 0.1 sec, $x(0.1)$, we will use $v(0.05)$ in finding $v \Delta t$. We will build up our results using

$$x(t + \Delta t) = x(t) + \Delta t \times v(t + \Delta t/2)$$
$$v(t + \Delta t/2) = v(t - \Delta t/2) + \Delta t \times a(t)$$
$$a(t) = -4x(t)$$

We will not write units: all x are in cm, all v in cm/sec, and all a in cm/sec². To start with, we need $v(0.05)$. Since $v(0) = 10$, $x(0.05)$ is about 0.50 and $a(0.05)$ is about $(-4)(0.50) = -2.0$, so the average acceleration in the range $0 \to 0.05$ is about -1.0, giving

$$v(0.05) = 10 + (-1.0)(0.05) = 10 - 0.05 = 9.95$$

$x(0.1) = x(0) + \Delta t \, v(0.05) = 0 + 0.1 \times 9.95 = 0.995$
    $a(0.1) = -(4)(0.995) = -3.98$
    $v(0.15) = v(0.05) + \Delta t \, a(0.1) = 9.95 - 0.40 = 9.45$

$x(0.2) = x(0.1) + \Delta t \, v(0.15) = 0.995 + 0.945 = 1.94$
    $a(0.2) = -7.76$ $v(0.25) = 9.45 - 0.78 = 8.67$

$x(0.3) = 1.94 + 0.87 = 2.81$ $a(0.3) = -11.24$ $v(0.35) = 8.67 - 1.12 = 7.55$

$x(0.4) = 2.81 + 0.76 = 3.57$ $a(0.4) = -14.28$ $v(0.45) = 7.55 - 1.43 = 6.12$

$x(0.5) = 3.57 + 0.61 = 4.18$ $a(0.5) = -16.72$ $v(0.55) = 6.12 - 1.67 = 4.45$

$x(0.6) = 4.18 + 0.45 = 4.63$ $a(0.6) = -18.52$ $v(0.65) = 4.45 - 1.85 = 2.60$

$x(0.7) = 4.63 + 0.26 = 4.89$ $a(0.7) = -19.56$ $v(0.75) = 2.60 - 1.96 = 0.64$

$x(0.8) = 4.89 + 0.06 = 4.95$ $a(0.8) = -19.80$ $v(0.85) = 0.64 - 1.98 = -1.34$

$x(0.9) = 4.95 - 0.13 = 4.82$
    $a(0.9) = -19.28$ $v(0.95) = -1.34 - 1.93 = -3.27$

$x(1.0) = 4.82 - 0.33 = 4.49$

A displacement–time graph shows the calculated values of $x(t)$. The smooth curve passing through the points is the function

$$x = 5 \sin 2t$$

which is a solution of the differential equation $d^2x/dt^2 = -4x$, subject to the conditions that at $t = 0$, $x = 0$ and $v = 10$ cm/sec (the **boundary conditions**). This may be verified by differentiating twice

$$v = \frac{dx}{dt} = 10 \cos 2t$$

$$a = \frac{dv}{dt} = \frac{d^2x}{dt^2} = -20 \sin 2t = -4x$$

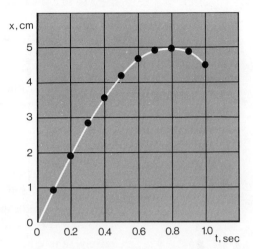

The function $x = 5 \sin 2t$ and the points calculated numerically.

Both displacement x and acceleration a have maximum values at a time given by $2t = 90° = \pi/2$ radians, or $t = \pi/4 = 0.785$ sec. The maxima are $x_{max} = 5$ cm, $a_{max} = -20$ cm/sec², and these are consistent with the numerical calculations. The maximum value of speed, $v_{max} = 10$ cm/sec, occurs at $t = 0$, as specified by the initial conditions.

At $t = 1$

$$x = 5 \sin 2 \text{ (where 2 is an angle in radians)}$$
$$= 5 \sin 114.6° = 5 \sin 65.4° = 5 \times 0.909 = 4.55 \text{ cm}$$

The result produced by the numerical procedure is 4.49 cm, within 2% of the accurate value. If we had used smaller time intervals Δt, for example 0.01 sec, the result would have been even closer. Such a calculation by hand would be tedious, but is trivial with modern computers.

There was an exact solution in this example, so that we could state our result was within 2% of a correct value. If such a solution does not exist, how do you know how accurate the result is? How do you know the time intervals used are small enough? The only way is by trial; you keep on doing the calculation for successively smaller Δt's until a change in Δt does not change your result to beyond the tolerance of the accuracy you require. In the computer program you can put in the successive values of Δt, and look at the results, or you can write the program in such a way that the computer does this itself.

Later in this chapter we will be discussing the kind of motion illustrated by this example more fully; we have used it here simply to demonstrate the numerical procedure.

While the numerical procedure can always be followed, it is of course convenient to find an analytic solution when this is possible, and most of this book is devoted to analyzing situations where this can be done. This always involves some idealization of the real physical situation. For example, a good approximation for the motion of a satellite around the earth can be made by assuming that the only force acting on the satellite is the gravitational attraction of the earth, and treating this as a central inverse-square force. With this model the orbit of the satellite can be calculated analytically—it is an ellipse. One of the assumptions made is that the gravitational attraction of the other planets and the sun is negligible. These forces can be put in, using the law of gravitation, but then an analytic solution is not possible. A numerical solution involves an enormous amount of computation, and would once have been impossible in practice, even though possible in principle. The development of high-speed computers has made such calculations possible, even routine.

The point is that even though we devote ourselves primarily in this book to relatively simple idealized situations, the techniques developed are applicable to more complex situations.

There are three special motions that have applicability to a wide variety of physical situations, and we will in this chapter explore them in detail. They are: motion with constant acceleration, motion in a circle, and simple harmonic motion.

CONSTANT ACCELERATION

Motion with **a** constant, that is motion with an acceleration that is constant both in magnitude and direction, is of interest because it includes the motion of a particle in a uniform gravitational field, or of a charged particle in a uniform electric field. Whenever the resultant force on a particle is constant, **a** is constant.

We shall measure displacement of the particle with respect to its position O at some time $t = 0$, and think about the motion over a time interval $0 \rightarrow t$. At

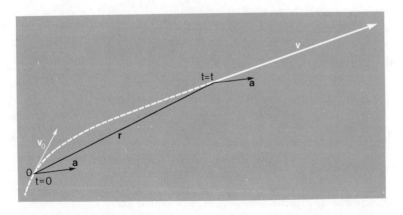

Displacement **r** and change in velocity $\mathbf{v} - \mathbf{v}_0$ in a time interval t for a particle with constant acceleration **a**.

time $t = 0$ the particle has displacement $\mathbf{r}(0) = 0$ and some velocity, say $\mathbf{v}_0$. We will calculate its velocity $\mathbf{v}$ and displacement $\mathbf{r}$ at any later time t, assuming it has a constant acceleration $\mathbf{a}$ that is not necessarily in the same direction as $\mathbf{v}_0$.

Since the acceleration $\mathbf{a}$ is constant, the average acceleration $\bar{\mathbf{a}}$ over the interval is the same as the acceleration $\mathbf{a}$ at any point.

$$\bar{\mathbf{a}} = \frac{\mathbf{v} - \mathbf{v}_0}{t} = \mathbf{a} \qquad \text{or} \qquad \mathbf{v} = \mathbf{v}_0 + \mathbf{a}t$$

This result may also be obtained by integration. Since $\mathbf{a} = d\mathbf{v}/dt$, $d\mathbf{v} = \mathbf{a}\, dt$ and over the interval

$$\int_{\mathbf{v}_0}^{\mathbf{v}} d\mathbf{v} = \int_0^t \mathbf{a}\, dt$$

We must be careful to note that we are dealing with vector quantities. The $\int_0^t \mathbf{a}\, dt$ involves the vector $\mathbf{a}$ which in general varies with time in both magnitude and direction, so we cannot in general find $\int_0^t \mathbf{a}(t)\, dt$. The integration can be performed here because $\mathbf{a}$ is constant. The right side of the relation $\mathbf{a}\, dt$ involves a change only in the scalar quantity time, and can be integrated.

$$\int_0^t \mathbf{a}\, dt = \mathbf{a} \int_0^t dt = \mathbf{a}t$$

The integral on the left side $\int_{\mathbf{v}_0}^{v} d\mathbf{v}$ means the total change in velocity in the interval, and we see that this is in the $\mathbf{a}$ direction. The resultant velocity $\mathbf{v}$ is the vector sum of $\mathbf{v}_0$ and $\mathbf{a}t$.

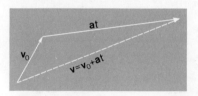

Resultant velocity after an interval.

$$\mathbf{v} = \mathbf{v}_0 + \mathbf{a}t$$

This shows that the left side of the integral $\int_{\mathbf{v}_0}^{v} d\mathbf{v}$ can be correctly interpreted as the vector difference $\mathbf{v} - \mathbf{v}_0$.

Since $\mathbf{v} = d\mathbf{r}/dt$, $d\mathbf{r} = \mathbf{v}\, dt = \mathbf{v}_0\, dt + \mathbf{a}t\, dt$. To integrate this we observe that the right side of the equation has two terms, each of which has a fixed direction

$$\int_0^t \mathbf{v}_0\, dt = \mathbf{v}_0 \int_0^t dt = \mathbf{v}_0 t$$

$$\int_0^t \mathbf{a}t\, dt = \mathbf{a} \int_0^t t\, dt = \mathbf{a}t^2/2$$

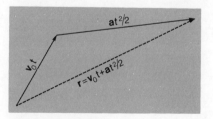

Resultant displacement after an interval.

The first term is the displacement in the original $\mathbf{v}_0$ direction during the time t, the second is the displacement in the $\mathbf{a}$ direction during the time t. The resultant displacement is the vector sum

$$\mathbf{r} = \mathbf{v}_0 t + \mathbf{a}t^2/2$$

In the diagrams the vectors $\mathbf{v}_0$ and $\mathbf{v}_0 t$ are in the same direction, and the vectors $\mathbf{a}t$ and $\mathbf{a}t^2/2$ are in the same direction, but the vector triangles are *not* similar because the lengths of the vectors are not proportional: $\mathbf{v}_0$ is multiplied by t, while $\mathbf{a}t$ is multiplied by $t/2$. Therefore $\mathbf{v}$ and $\mathbf{r}$ are not in the same direction.

The two equations describing motion in the interval $0 \to t$

$$\mathbf{v} = \mathbf{v}_0 + \mathbf{a}t \qquad \text{and} \qquad \mathbf{r} = \mathbf{v}_0 t + \mathbf{a}t^2/2$$

appear to be similar to the equations for uniformly accelerated motion in one dimension, but are much more general because like all vector equations they each represent three scalar equations. We can write these down in a particular co-ordinate system, but first note that this is not really three-dimensional motion. The two independent directions fixed by $\mathbf{v}_0$ and $\mathbf{a}$ can be thought of as defining a plane, and the motion takes place in this plane. We will choose a co-ordinate system such that its xy plane coincides with this plane, and such that the fixed point O from which the displacement $\mathbf{r}$ is measured is at the origin of the system.

In this system the scalar equations equivalent to the two vector equations are

$$x = v_{0x}t + \tfrac{1}{2}a_x t^2 \qquad y = v_{0y}t + \tfrac{1}{2}a_y t^2$$
$$v_x = v_{0x} + a_x t \qquad v_y = v_{0y} + a_y t$$

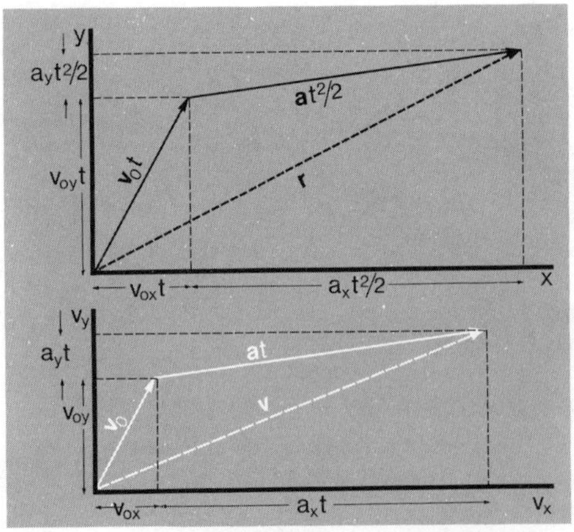

The vectors are shown in real space and in velocity space. The motion is now described as two simultaneous one-dimensional motions in the x- and y-directions, with constant accelerations a_x and a_y. It is sensible, of course, to choose axes in such a way that either $\mathbf{v}_0$ or $\mathbf{a}$ is in the direction of one of the axes. Suppose, for example, that we choose the y-axis in the direction of the acceleration $\mathbf{a}$. Then $a_x = 0$, and the equations become

$$x = v_{0x}t \qquad y = v_{0y}t + \tfrac{1}{2}at^2$$
$$v_x = v_{0x} \qquad v_y = v_{0y} + at$$

The equation of the path may be obtained by eliminating t from the x and y equations, since this gives simultaneous values of x and y for a particular t. Substituting

Displacement and velocity vectors and components with respect to particular co-ordinate directions.

$$t = x/v_{0x} \quad \text{gives} \quad y = \left(\frac{v_{0y}}{v_{0x}}\right)x + \left(\frac{a}{2v_{0x}^2}\right)x^2$$

which is of the form $y = Ax + Bx^2$, a parabola. The trajectory of any particle moving with a constant acceleration is a parabola. The axis of symmetry of the parabola is parallel to the acceleration; the component of velocity that is perpendicular to the acceleration does not change with time, and the component of velocity that is parallel to the acceleration increases (or decreases) uniformly with time. In the special case where **a** and v_0 are in the same direction, the parabola degenerates into a straight line.

PROJECTILE MOTION

For a particle moving near the earth's surface after being given an initial velocity v_0, a projectile, it is reasonable to assume that the acceleration due to gravity is a constant. It is not so reasonable to assume that the effect of air resistance can be neglected, but if we do, the equations just derived describe the motion. The acceleration **g** is downward, and this is the direction we have chosen for the y-axis in our co-ordinate system. It is more usual, though not necessary, to think of axes with the y-axis upward, which means that the acceleration a_y is $-g$. The equations become

$$x = v_{0x}t \qquad y = v_{0y}t - gt^2/2$$
$$v_x = v_{0x} \qquad v_y = v_{0y} - gt$$

and the equation of the trajectory is

$$y = \left(\frac{v_{0y}}{v_{0x}}\right)x - \left(\frac{g}{2v_{0x}^2}\right)x^2$$

The path and the velocity components are shown for a projectile shot at an angle θ above the horizontal, so that $v_{0x} = v_0 \cos \theta$ and $v_{0y} = v_0 \sin \theta$.

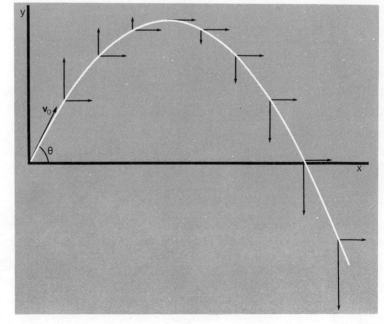

Parabolic trajectory for a particle shot upward at an angle in a uniform downward gravitational field.

The path can be considered to apply to the motion of any projectile with this particular value of $v_x = v_{0x}$; all that is necessary is to move the origin of the co-ordinate axes to the point corresponding to the initial projection of the particle. The shape or width of the parabola depends on v_x. If $v_x = 0$, the path becomes a straight line; the particle is shot vertically upward or downward.

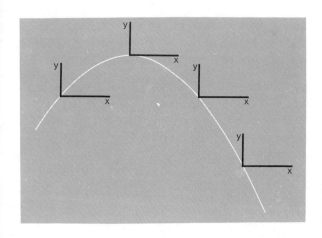

In a particular gravitational field, the shape of the trajectory is determined by the component of velocity perpendicular to the field direction.

The paths of particles with the same vertical component of initial velocity v_{0y}, but different values of v_{0x}, are parabolas of different shapes. In each case the

Trajectories of particles with the same initial vertical component of velocity, but different horizontal components of velocity.

maximum height reached by the particle is the same, but the horizontal distance covered, or range, is not.

Example: Determine the range R and the maximum height H in terms of the initial velocity components v_{0x} and v_{0y}, and determine the projection angle θ for maximum range for a particular initial speed v_0.

Since $y = \left(\dfrac{v_{0y}}{v_{0x}} - \dfrac{g}{2v_{0x}^2}\,x\right)x$ then $y = 0$ at $x = 0$, and at $x = \dfrac{2v_{0x}v_{0y}}{g}$. These correspond to the point of projection and of maximum horizontal range, so that $R = 2v_{0x}v_{0y}/g$.

The range R and maximum height H of a projectile.

By symmetry the value of x at the peak of the path is half that at maximum range, or $v_{0x}v_{0y}/g$, but this can also be obtained as follows. The slope of the path at any point is obtained by finding the derivative $\dfrac{dy}{dx} = \dfrac{v_{0y}}{v_{0x}} - \dfrac{g}{v_{0x}^2}\,x$. At the top of the path, the slope is zero, and setting $dy/dx = 0$ gives the value $x = v_{0x}v_{0y}/g$. This value of x substituted into the equation of the path gives

$$y = H = \left(\frac{v_{0y}}{v_{0x}}\right)\left(\frac{v_{0y}v_{0x}}{g}\right) - \left(\frac{g}{2v_{0x}^2}\right)\left(\frac{v_{0x}^2 v_{0y}^2}{g^2}\right) = \frac{1}{2}\frac{v_{0y}^2}{g}$$

Note that the maximum height does not depend on the horizontal component of velocity.

For a projection angle θ above the horizontal, $v_{0x} = v_0 \cos\theta$ and $v_{0y} = v_0 \sin\theta$ so that

$$R = 2v_0^2 \sin\theta \cos\theta/g$$
$$= v_0^2 \sin 2\theta/g$$

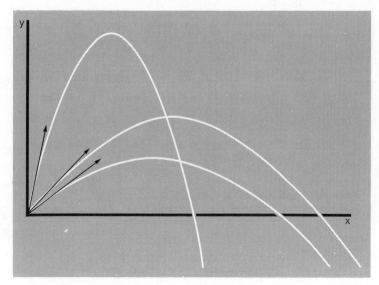

The dependence of the trajectory on the angle of projection, for the same initial speed of projection.

using the trigonometric identity $\sin 2x = 2 \sin x \cos x$. The maximum value of $\sin 2\theta$ is unity, corresponding to $2\theta = 90°$, or $\theta = 45°$. The maximum range is achieved for a projection angle of $45°$ (in the absence of air resistance).

As an exercise in differentiation, this result may be obtained by forming $dR/d\theta$ and setting it equal to zero. If you think of an R–θ graph, it will have zero slope at its maximum. Using the rule for differentiating a product

$$\frac{dR}{d\theta} = \frac{2v_0^2}{g} \left[\sin \theta(- \sin \theta) + \cos \theta(\cos \theta) \right] = 0$$

$$\sin^2 \theta = \cos^2 \theta \qquad \tan^2 \theta = 1 \qquad \tan \theta = 1 \qquad \theta = 45°$$

REVIEW OF UNIFORM FIELDS

Even though at present we are restricting our systematic development of physics to kinematics, we assume that you have some background in basic physics. We will later be giving careful attention to the concepts of force, field and energy but for the moment will take advantage of your previous experience. We will briefly review a few useful ideas.

The acceleration $\mathbf{a}$ of a particle is determined by the resultant force $\mathbf{F}$ acting on it and its inertial mass m_i, related by Newton's law $\mathbf{F} = m_i\mathbf{a}$. If the force is a gravitational interaction, it is proportional to the gravitational mass of the particle m_g. It is an experimental fact that the gravitational and inertial mass are proportional to one another, and therefore if units are properly chosen $m_i = m_g$ and we speak of *the* mass m of the particle. Since $\mathbf{a} = \mathbf{F}/m$, and $\mathbf{F}$ is proportional to m if the only force acting is gravitational, the acceleration is **independent** of mass for a particle in a gravitational field. Thus we can speak of the acceleration due to gravity $\mathbf{g}$ for all particles in the uniform gravitational field near the earth's surface. The results of the last section apply to the trajectory of any particle near the earth's surface, independent of its mass.

The electrical interaction depends on a property of the particle called its charge q, rather than on its mass, and therefore we do not have the simplification that the acceleration is the same for all particles in a uniform electric field, independent of their masses.

Think of two parallel plates made of a material which is electrically conducting, with equal and opposite amounts of electric charge on the plates ($+Q$ on one, $-Q$ on the other). If the area of the plates is large compared to the spacing between them d, then there is an electric field between the plates which is uniform, except near the edges. (The term **uniform** is usually used to mean constant

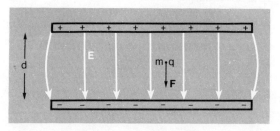

There is a uniform electric field between two parallel conducting plates carrying equal and opposite electric charges, except near the edges of the plates.

in space, the term **constant** to mean constant in time). This means that there is a constant force $\mathbf{F} = \mathbf{E}q$ on a particle of charge q in the region between the plates, where $\mathbf{E}$ is the **electric field.** It is a quantitative way of describing the effect of the charged plates. The field $\mathbf{E}$ is said to exist at any point, whether there is a charge at the point or not. It has the units of force/charge; if force is in newtons, and charge in coulombs, then $\mathbf{E}$ is in newtons/coulomb. The field $\mathbf{E}$ is a vector quantity, and the field is called a vector field. The direction of $\mathbf{E}$ at any point is the direction of the force $\mathbf{F}$ on a **positive** charge $+q$ at the point. The arrows in the figure show the field direction for a positive charge on the upper plate and a negative charge on the lower.

In addition to describing the electric field in terms of the vector quantity $\mathbf{E}$, it can be described in terms of a scalar quantity, potential. Because there is an electric force on a charged particle in the field, work is done in moving it from one point in the field to another point. This work is the difference in electric potential energy between the two points. By calling the potential energy zero at some arbitrary point, we can speak of the potential energy at any other point. Even if there is no charged particle at a point, we can speak of the potential V at the point, where V is the potential energy per unit charge. The potential energy of a charge q at the point is Vq. All potential energies are potential energy differences, and all potentials are potential differences.

Potential energy is measured in any energy unit, for example in joules, and potential in units of energy/charge, for example in joules/coulomb. The joule/coulomb is given a name, the volt.

If there is a potential difference V between the two charged plates, this means that work Vq is necessary to move a charge $+q$ from the negative to the positive plate. Since there is a force $\mathbf{E}q$ on the charge, and a distance d between the plates, the work can also be expressed as Eqd. Therefore, $Vq = Eqd$, or $E = V/d$. The electric field strength can be expressed in units of potential/length, e.g. 1 volt/meter $\equiv$ 1 joule/coulomb-meter $\equiv$ 1 newton-meter/coulomb-meter $\equiv$ 1 newton/coulomb.

Later in this chapter we will use as an example the motion of a charged particle in a uniform magnetic field. A magnetic field is produced by charges in motion. For example, around any wire carrying an electric current there is a magnetic field, although not a uniform one. It is not easy to produce a uniform magnetic field in the laboratory, but the field between the poles of a large electromagnet may be made quite uniform by shaping the pole pieces.

The effect of a magnetic field on a charged particle is more complicated than that of an electric field, because the force depends on the **velocity** (both in magnitude and direction) of the particle. The force on a charge q in an electric field $\mathbf{E}$ is $\mathbf{F} = q\mathbf{E}$, so that a uniform field produces a constant force and constant acceleration $\mathbf{a}$, the particular case of motion we are dealing with. In a magnetic field $\mathbf{B}$ the force is $\mathbf{F} = q\mathbf{v} \times \mathbf{B}$ where $\mathbf{v}$ is the velocity of the particle and $\mathbf{v} \times \mathbf{B}$ is the vector product, which means that the force produced is at right angles to both $\mathbf{v}$ and $\mathbf{B}$. Therefore the acceleration $\mathbf{a}$ produced by the magnetic force $\mathbf{F}$ cannot be constant; the acceleration perpendicular to $\mathbf{v}$ will produce a change in $\mathbf{v}$ which will produce a change in $\mathbf{a}$, and so on. However, we will see that the motion produced by a uniform magnetic field can be described in a fairly simple way.

We can visualize the vector field $\mathbf{E}$ in terms of lines of force giving the direction of the force on a positive charge in the electric field. The vector field $\mathbf{B}$ can also be visualized in terms of lines called lines of magnetic induction or lines of magnetic flux; they do not give the direction of the force—the force is at right angles to them. The quantity $\mathbf{B}$ we will call the magnetic flux density to emphasize that it is a different kind of quantity than the electric field $\mathbf{E}$. As we have introduced it, it does not even have the same dimensions as $\mathbf{E}$, which was force/charge. Sometimes the magnetic force is written $\mathbf{F} = (q/c)\mathbf{v} \times \mathbf{B}$, where c is speed of light (a constant) and then $\mathbf{E}$ and $\mathbf{B}$ have the same dimensions. However, we will not worry about different systems of units at present.

Think about a magnetic field directed straight into the page: the little x's represent the back ends of arrows. They are spread uniformly to indicate that this is a uniform magnetic field of flux density B. A particle of charge q is moving with a speed v perpendicular to the field. The magnetic force is $F = qvB$, perpendicular to the field direction and to $\mathbf{v}$; it is upward if q is a positive charge, downward if q is negative. Suppose that F is 1 newton, v is 1 meter/sec and q is 1 coulomb. Then B is 1 newton-sec/coulomb-meter, and is called 1 weber/m². This is the unit of magnetic flux density in what are called rationalized mks units. A common magnetic field unit is the gauss: 1 weber/m² $= 10^4$ gauss.

You will later be considering electric and magnetic fields in detail in electromagnetic theory, and will see that in general they always exist together. We have been talking about two special cases called the electrostatic and magnetostatic fields, but they will be sufficient for use in some examples in mechanics.

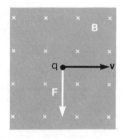

If a charged particle is moving at right angles to a magnetic field there is a force on it at right angles to direction of motion and to field lines.

AN EXAMPLE OF THE MOTION OF A CHARGED PARTICLE IN A UNIFORM ELECTRIC FIELD

An electron is accelerated from rest by an electron gun through a potential difference of 1000 volts. When it leaves the gun it is moving horizontally. It then enters the space midway between two parallel horizontal metal plates 10 cm across, spaced 1 cm apart, and with a potential difference of 16 volts between them. Will the electron emerge from between the plates? If so, what is its velocity? Use the electron charge $e = -1.6 \times 10^{-19}$ coulombs, electron mass $m = 9.1 \times 10^{-31}$ kg.

The electron gun does an amount of work eV_1 on an electron, producing kinetic energy $\frac{1}{2}mv_1^2$, where v_1 is the speed of the electron when it leaves the gun.

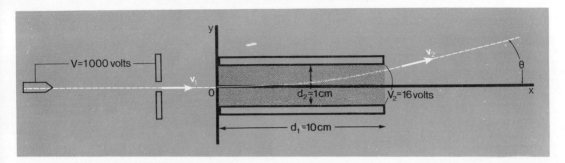

An electron accelerated by an electron gun
and deflected by an electric field.

$$eV_1 = \tfrac{1}{2}mv_1^2$$

$$v_1 = \sqrt{\frac{2eV_1}{m}} = \sqrt{\frac{2 \times 1.6 \times 10^{-19} \times 10^3}{9.1 \times 10^{-31}}}$$

$$= 1.9 \times 10^7 \text{ m/sec}$$

(This speed is low enough compared to the speed of light, 3×10^8 m/sec, that a classical or non-relativistic calculation is valid.)

In most physical situations it is better to work out the desired result in terms of symbols rather than numbers, because it is less cumbersome, there is less possibility of error, and sometimes simplifications occur.

The electron enters the uniform electric field between the charged plates with a velocity v_1 which is at right angles to the electric field E. The field has a magnitude $E = V_2/d_2$, exerts a constant force $F = Ee$ on the electron, producing an acceleration $a = \dfrac{F}{m} = \dfrac{Ee}{m} = \dfrac{V_2 e}{d_2 m}$. By thinking of a co-ordinate system with its origin at the point where the electron enters the uniform field, oriented with its x-axis in the direction of motion of the electron and its y-axis vertical, we have $v_{0x} = v_1$, $v_{0y} = 0$, $a_x = 0$, $a_y = a$. As the electron moves through the field it acquires a velocity component v_y in the vertical direction, but its horizontal component of velocity is constant.

Moving the horizontal distance d_1, the extent of the electric field, will take a time $t = d_1/v_{0x} = d_1/v_1$. In this time the vertical displacement will be

$$y = v_{0y}t + \tfrac{1}{2}a_yt^2 = 0 + \tfrac{1}{2}a\left(\frac{d_1}{v_1}\right)^2 = \tfrac{1}{2}\left(\frac{V_2 e}{d_2 m}\right)\left(\frac{d_1^2 m}{2eV_1}\right) = \frac{V_2 d_1^2}{4V_1 d_2}$$

This is the displacement as the electron leaves the field, provided it does not hit one of the plates: this means that y must be less than 0.5 cm, since the electron entered midway between the plates. Using the numerical values $V_1 = 10^3$ volts, $V_2 = 16$ volts, $d_1 = 10$ cm $= 10^{-1}$ m, $d_2 = 1$ cm $= 10^{-2}$ m

$$y = \frac{16 \times 10^{-2}}{4 \times 10^3 \times 10^{-2}} = 4 \times 10^{-3} \text{ m} = 0.4 \text{ cm}$$

therefore the electron will miss the plates and emerge.

We could, of course, have used the equation of the parabolic path previously determined to find the value of y when $x = d_1$

$$y = \left(\frac{v_{0x}}{v_{0y}}\right)x + \left(\frac{a}{2v_{0x}^2}\right)x^2 = \tfrac{1}{2}\frac{a}{v_1^2}d_1^2$$

as before.

Note that it did not matter that the particle was an electron; the quantities e and m have disappeared—the result is the same for any charged particle that started from the electron gun. Whether the particle is deflected up or down depends on the kind of charge and the field direction. The diagram shows the upward deflection that would occur if the particle is an electron and the upper plate is positive. A proton or a positron would be deflected downward the same amount by the same field.

Note also that we have not attempted any indication of the numerical accuracy of the result. The calculation applies to an idealized situation, and the calculated value 0.4 cm is an exact result for the idealization. In the actual physical situation the values V_1, V_2, d_1, d_2 would be measured, and the error in y would depend on their accuracy. The value of d_1, the extent of the field, would be the most doubtful because the field is not uniform up to a sharp cut-off at the edge of the plates—there is *no* precise value of d_1. The idealized calculation assumes conditions that never exist, and therefore error arises not only because of errors in measurement but also because the model does not exactly represent the real physical situation. In every such calculation there are a number of implicit assumptions made; for example, we ignored the effect of gravity. For charged particles like electrons or protons this is a very good assumption, but is it a good assumption if the particle is a lead pellet with a small static charge? How many excess electrons would a 0.1-gm lead pellet have to carry in order that the electric force on it between the plates is equal to the gravitational force?

The electron does emerge from the field, and we must now determine its velocity v_2. The components of velocity on emergence will be

$$v_{2x} = v_{0x} = v_1 = \sqrt{\frac{2eV_1}{m}}$$

$$v_{2y} = v_{0y} + a_y t = 0 + \left(\frac{V_2 e}{d_2 m}\right)\left(\frac{d_1}{v_1}\right) = \frac{V_2 d_1}{d_2}\sqrt{\frac{e}{2V_1 m}}$$

It appears that we will have to do the calculations, putting in the values of e and

m, to find v_2. However, let us first find the angle θ which the path makes with the horizontal on emergence

$$\tan\theta = \frac{v_{2y}}{v_{2x}} = \frac{V_2 d_1}{d_2}\sqrt{\frac{e}{2V_1 m}}\sqrt{\frac{m}{2eV_1}} = \frac{V_2 d_1}{2V_1 d_2}$$

$$= \frac{16\times 10^{-1}}{2\times 10^{-2}\times 10^3} = 0.08, \qquad \theta = 4.5°$$

Again the result is independent of the values of e and m. The fact that the angle is so small tells us that the component v_{2y} is small compared to v_{2x}, and therefore that the emergent speed v_2 is approximately equal to the speed $v_{2x} = v_1$. To verify this, note that

$$v_2^2 = v_{2x}^2 + v_{2y}^2 = \frac{2eV_1}{m} + \frac{V_2^2 d_1^2}{d_2^2}\frac{e}{2V_1 m}$$

$$= \frac{2eV_1}{m}\left(1 + \frac{V_2^2 d_1^2}{4V_1^2 d_2^2}\right) = v_1^2(1+\epsilon)$$

The value of ϵ is

$$\epsilon = \frac{V_2^2 d_1^2}{4V_1^2 d_2^2} = \frac{16^2\times 10^{-2}}{4\times 10^6\times 10^{-4}} = 0.64\times 10^{-2}$$

Since $\epsilon \ll 1$, it is a good approximation to say that $v_2^2 = v_1^2$, or $v_2 = v_1 = 1.9\times 10^7$ m/sec. The error in v_2^2 is 0.6%, or the error in v_2 is 0.3%. The emergent velocity of the electron is $\mathbf{v}_2 = 1.9\times 10^7$ m/sec at an angle of 4.5° with the horizontal. The **shape** of the path does *not* depend on the particular values of charge or mass of the particle, but the velocities, and the time to traverse the path, *do* depend on the particular particle.

The charge and mass appear in the calculation only as the charge to mass ratio e/m, so that different particles with the same v_1 and with the same charge-to-mass ratio would cover the path in equal times and emerge with the same velocities. For example a deuteron (the nucleus of a heavy hydrogen atom $_1H^2$) has a charge $+e$ and mass of 2.014 amu (atomic mass units, based on the carbon-12 atom having a mass of exactly 12 amu). An α-particle (the nucleus of a normal helium atom $_2He^4$) has charge $+2e$ and mass 4.002 amu. These two particles would emerge with nearly identical velocities.

Although this section has been based on a particular situation, it has enabled us to make a number of general comments. The most useful message may be one you have already learned—don't put in the numbers too soon.

CIRCULAR MOTION AT CONSTANT SPEED

In the first particular example of motion, that of a particle moving with constant acceleration $\mathbf{a}$, we first introduced the limitation that $\mathbf{a}$ was constant, independent of time, worked out general expressions for $\mathbf{v}$ and $\mathbf{r}$ as functions

of time, and then showed that the trajectory of the particle was always a parabola. We are now going to consider another particular example of motion of a
particle, but this time we begin by stating that the trajectory is a circle. We
impose the additional limitation at present that the speed v of the particle is
constant; the velocity $\mathbf{v}$ of course cannot be constant because the velocity
vector is always tangent to the path, and the path is a circle.

What does it mean to say that the path is a circle? Does the tip of an aircraft
propeller move in a circle? Does a stone caught in the tread of a tire move in
a circle? You know that the answers depend on the frame of reference. If the
aircraft is moving along the ground, the propeller tip is moving in a circle in
the frame of reference of the aircraft, but is moving in a corkscrew path (a helix)
in a frame of reference attached to the earth. If the tire is on a moving bicycle,
the stone is moving in a circle in a frame of reference fixed to the bicycle, but
has a sort of hopping path (a cycloid) in the frame of reference of the earth.

Sometimes frames of reference are described in terms of observers. To an
observer on the bicycle, the path of the stone is a circle; to an observer standing
watching the bicycle go by, it is not. This is a satisfactory procedure provided
it is emphasized that an observer means a measurer; an observer at rest on the
earth's surface makes measurements relative to a frame of reference attached
to the earth's surface. There is a risk that **observer** may be taken to mean
watcher; if you watch a bicycle going by you probably see the wheels moving in
a circle by moving your eyes along and mentally putting yourself in the frame
of reference of the bicycle. It is difficult to avoid doing this. For this reason we
have usually avoided the term observer, and emphasized that measurements
are always made in a particular frame of reference.

When we say that the path of a particle is a circle, then, we mean that its path
is a circle in a particular frame of reference. If the particle moving in a circle is
the earth, then the frame of reference is the sun (i.e., a frame of reference in
which the sun is fixed). If the particle is a man at rest on the earth, the frame of
reference is one in which the earth is fixed in position but is rotating. If the
particle is a child on a merry-go-round, the frame of reference is the earth. This
is the most common frame of reference, but as we have seen by no means the
only useful one; many motions are more simply described from some other
frame of reference. In the next chapter we will be dealing with transformations
between frames of reference.

We will in describing circular motion use the geometric idealization of a
perfect circle, but the degree to which this idealization is approached in any
physical situation depends on the situation—and on how closely it is examined.
We idealize physical situations in order to be able to describe them. The validity
of the idealizations or models is better in some cases than in others—and sometimes there are better models. For some purposes it is adequate to consider
that the orbit of the earth is a circle, for others it is necessary to recognize that

it is an ellipse. This is still a model—the orbit is not a perfect geometric ellipse—but it is a better model than the circle.

All points on a circle lie in a plane and are equidistant from a fixed point in the plane. We choose this fixed point as the point O in the frame of reference from which displacement **r** is measured. Then the displacement of a particle P moving in the circular path is constant in magnitude but not in direction. This choice of displacement vector is called the **radius vector.** Not all directions are possible for the radius vector; it moves in a plane. With the additional restriction that the speed of the particle is constant, the radius vector rotates uniformly in the plane. At some instant $t = 0$ it points in a particular direction in the frame of reference. At any later time t it will have rotated through an angle θ such that $\theta = \omega t$ where ω (Greek omega) is a constant.

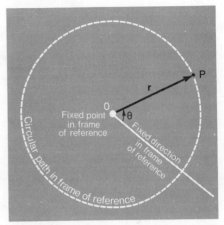

Specification of a circular path in a frame of reference.

With these restrictions on the motion, there is little advantage in continuing with a general vector discussion—that is, a discussion independent of a choice of co-ordinate system in the frame of reference. Initially we will choose a Cartesian co-ordinate system, even though it is probably apparent to you that polar co-ordinates would be more appropriate, because some useful information will be more evident.

We choose a co-ordinate system whose xy plane coincides with the plane of the circular path, whose origin coincides with the fixed point O from which the radius vector **r** is measured, and whose x-axis coincides with the fixed direction in the frame of reference determined by the direction of **r** at $t = 0$. We will call the magnitude of the radius vector R; this is the constant radius of the circular path.

In this co-ordinate system the co-ordinates of the particle P at any time t are

$$x = R \cos \theta = R \cos \omega t$$
$$y = R \sin \theta = R \sin \omega t$$

These are the x and y components of displacement **r**. The components of the velocity **v** are

$$v_x = dx/dt = -\omega R \sin \omega t$$
$$v_y = dy/dt = \omega R \cos \omega t$$

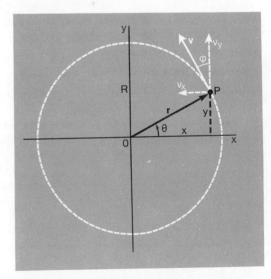

Specification of a circular path in a particular co-ordinate system.

The magnitude of the velocity **v** is given by

$$v^2 = v_x^2 + v_y^2 = \omega^2 R^2 (\sin^2 \omega t + \cos^2 \omega t) = \omega^2 R^2, \qquad v = R\omega$$

This is the speed, which is a constant; we assured this by our definition of the constant ω.

The direction of **v** is always tangent to the path; in this case since the path is a circle with **r** as radius, **v** is perpendicular to **r**. This is verified with the components: if φ is the angle between **v** and the y-direction, then in magnitude

$$\tan \varphi = v_x/v_y = \sin \omega t / \cos \omega t = \tan \omega t = \tan \theta$$

The angles θ and φ are the same, and as can be seen from the figure **v** is perpendicular to **r**.

The components of the acceleration **a** are

$$a_x = dv_x/dt = -\omega^2 R \cos \omega t \qquad a_y = dv_y/dt = -\omega^2 R \sin \omega t$$
$$= -\omega^2 x \qquad\qquad\qquad = -\omega^2 y$$

The magnitude of **a** is given by

$$a^2 = a_x^2 + a_y^2 = \omega^4 (x^2 + y^2) = \omega^4 R^2 \qquad a = R\omega^2$$

The acceleration, like the velocity, is constant in magnitude but continuously changing in direction. If ψ is the angle between **a** and the x-direction, then

$$\tan \psi = a_y/a_x = y/x = \tan \theta$$

Therefore **r** and **a** are in the same line, but are oppositely directed.

The acceleration of a particle moving at constant speed in a circle is directed toward the center of the circle. It is called the **central** or **radial** or **centripetal** acceleration, and has a constant magnitude

$$a = R\omega^2 = v^2/R$$

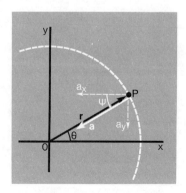

A particle moving in a circle at constant speed has an acceleration that is constant in magnitude and is directed towards the center of the circle.

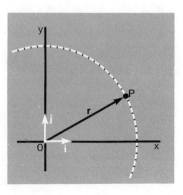

The use of unit vectors to specify two coordinate directions.

The results we have deduced may be written in vector notation by using the concept of **unit vectors** introduced in Chapter 4. Think of two vectors **i** and **j** that are fixed in direction in the frame of reference, at right angles to one another, and that each have unit magnitude. For the moment, think of them as being in the x- and y-directions of our Cartesian co-ordinate system. Then $\mathbf{r} = \mathbf{i}x + \mathbf{j}y = \mathbf{i}R \cos \omega t + \mathbf{j}R \sin \omega t$.

In this way we have $\mathbf{r}(t)$ expressed in terms of the constant quantities R, ω, **i** and **j**, and the variable t. The co-ordinates of a particular co-ordinate system do not appear: **i** and **j** define two perpendicular directions in the frame of reference.

$$\mathbf{v} = \frac{d\mathbf{r}}{dt} = -\mathbf{i}\omega R \sin \omega t + \mathbf{j}\omega R \cos \omega t$$

$$\mathbf{a} = \frac{d\mathbf{v}}{dt} = -\mathbf{i}\omega^2 R \cos \omega t - \mathbf{j}\omega^2 R \sin \omega t = -\omega^2 \mathbf{r}$$

We have immediately that **a** is a vector in the opposite direction to that of **r**, of magnitude $a = R\omega^2$. To determine the magnitude and direction of **v**, we form the scalar products $\mathbf{v} \cdot \mathbf{v}$ and $\mathbf{r} \cdot \mathbf{v}$, using the fact that $\mathbf{i} \cdot \mathbf{i} = \mathbf{j} \cdot \mathbf{j} = 1, \mathbf{i} \cdot \mathbf{j} = 0$.

$$\mathbf{v} \cdot \mathbf{v} = v^2 = (-\mathbf{i}\omega R \sin \omega t + \mathbf{j}\omega R \cos \omega t) \cdot (-\mathbf{i}\omega R \sin \omega t + \mathbf{j}\omega R \cos \omega t)$$
$$= \omega^2 R^2 \sin^2 \omega t + \omega^2 R^2 \cos^2 \omega t = \omega^2 R^2$$
$$\mathbf{r} \cdot \mathbf{v} = (\mathbf{i}R \cos \omega t + \mathbf{j}R \sin \omega t) \cdot (-\mathbf{i}\omega R \sin \omega t + \mathbf{j}\omega R \cos \omega t)$$
$$= -\omega R^2 \cos \omega t \sin \omega t + \omega R^2 \sin \omega t \cos \omega t = 0$$

These show that **v** is a vector perpendicular to **r** and of constant magnitude $v = R\omega$.

Uniform circular motion, the motion of a particle moving in a circle at constant speed, is an example of **periodic motion.** Any motion which is repeated at regular intervals of time is periodic motion; the time to complete one complete cycle of the motion, whatever it is, is called the **period,** T. The number of cycles of the motion that are repeated in unit time is called the **frequency,** f. Since each cycle requires time T, there are $1/T$ cycles per unit time, so that $f = 1/T$.

The period has dimensions of time, and the frequency has the dimensions of (time)$^{-1}$. If the period is $1/60$ sec, the frequency is 60 sec^{-1}. However, it is usual to say "60 cycles per second," rather than "60 per second" or "60 seconds to the minus one" or "60 reciprocal seconds." Often the abbreviation 60 cps is used for 60 cycles/sec. However, remember that a frequency is the **number** of cycles per unit time, and has the dimensions of (time)$^{-1}$ only. The term hertz is often used: 1 hertz $\equiv$ 1 cycle/sec.

To determine the period or frequency for uniform circular motion, think about the quantity ω that we introduced as a proportionality constant between the angle θ and the time t. If the angle increased uniformly with time, the particle P moved uniformly (at constant speed) around the circle, so we set $\theta = \omega t$. The dimensions of ω are (angle/time), so we can use such units as degrees/sec or revolutions/min. Later it will be useful to express angles in **radians.**

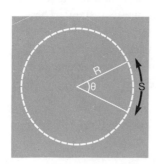

One radian is the angle at the center of a circle subtended by an arc of length equal to the radius. In general

$$\theta \text{ (in radians)} = S/R$$

Definition of the radian as a measure of angle: $\theta = S/R$.

For a complete revolution (360°) $S = 2\pi R$, and $\theta = 2\pi$: 1 revolution = 360° = 2π radians

$$1 \text{ radian} = (360/2\pi)° = 57.3°$$

The radian is defined as the ratio of two lengths, and therefore is a pure number; it has no dimensions.

If the angle θ is measured in radians then the quantity ω has dimensions (time)$^{-1}$, but the units are usually expressed as radians/sec, or rad/min, etc.

It is clear that ω is an **angular speed**, since it is the angle rotated in unit time. However, it is also called the **angular frequency.** It has the same dimensions as frequency f, but it is *not* the same quantity. The time for one complete cycle of the periodic motion of the particle P is the time for it to return to its initial position. In this time T the angle θ will have increased by 2π radians. From the definition $\theta = \omega t$, therefore $2\pi = \omega T$

$$T = 2\pi/\omega \quad \text{and} \quad f = 1/T = \omega/2\pi \quad \text{or} \quad \omega = 2\pi f$$

The angular frequency ω is a factor 2π greater than the frequency f. Using the terms radians/sec and cycles/sec helps to keep the distinction clear. However, when combined with other quantities the non-dimensional "radians" and "cycles" are omitted. A particle moving in a circular orbit of 2-m radius with angular frequency (or angular speed) of 3 radians/sec has an orbital speed

$$v = R\omega = 6 \text{ m/sec} \quad \text{(not 6 m-rad/sec)}$$

and a centripetal acceleration

$$a = R\omega^2 = 18 \text{ m/sec}^2 \quad \text{(not 18 m-rad}^2\text{/sec}^2\text{)}$$

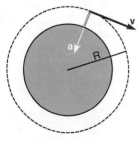

Satellite in a circular orbit around the earth.

Example 1: An earth satellite in a circular orbit 400 miles above the surface of the earth makes one revolution around the earth in 98 minutes. Determine its speed and acceleration.

The measurements on the earth satellite are made with respect to the earth—the earth is the frame of reference. The mean radius of the earth is 3960 miles, so the radius of the circular orbit is $R = 4360$ miles. The period of rotation is $T = 98$ minutes.

The angular speed

$$\omega = 2\pi/T = 2\pi/98 \text{ rad/min}$$

The speed in orbit

$$\begin{aligned} v = R\omega &= 4360 \times 2\pi/98 = 280 \text{ miles/min} \\ &= 16{,}800 \text{ miles/hr} \\ &= 16{,}800 \times 88/60 \text{ ft/sec} = 24{,}600 \text{ ft/sec} \\ &= 24{,}600 \times 0.305 \text{ m/sec} = 7500 \text{ m/sec} \end{aligned}$$

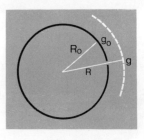

The acceleration

$$a = R\omega^2 = v\omega = 280 \times 2\pi/98 = 17.9 \text{ miles/min}^2$$

$$= 17.9 \frac{\text{mile}}{\text{min}^2} \times 5280 \frac{\text{ft}}{\text{mile}} \times \frac{1}{60^2} \frac{\text{min}^2}{\text{sec}^2} = 26.3 \text{ ft/sec}^2$$

The acceleration due to gravity depends on the distance from the center of the earth.

This is the centripetal acceleration of the satellite. The force providing this acceleration is the gravitational attraction of the earth so this is the acceleration due to gravity at this height. You know that the force of gravity (and therefore the acceleration due to gravity) is inversely proportional to the square of the distance from the center of the earth, so that g at radius R compared to the value g_0 at the earth's surface (radius R_0) is

$$g = (R_0/R)^2 g_0$$

In this example, $g = (3960/4360)^2 \times 32 = 26.3 \text{ ft/sec}^2$.

Example 2: Determine T, f, ω, v and a for the uniform circular motion of a man standing on the surface of the earth at the equator.

Clearly the frame of reference is not the earth. As we pointed out earlier, the frame of reference in which the man is in uniform circular motion is one in which the earth is fixed in position but rotating on its axis. You may have a model on your desk.

It is a good approximation to treat the man as a particle since the radius of his circular path is the equatorial radius $R = 3964$ miles $= 6.38 \times 10^6$ m. We will use different units this time for variety. The earth rotates once a day so the period $T = 1$ day $= 8.64 \times 10^4$ sec. (We mentioned in our discussion of the choice of a standard of time that there was a difficulty here; the earth rotates once a day relative to what? We ignore the difficulty here, but will return to it later in dynamics.)

$$\begin{aligned} T &= 8.64 \times 10^4 \text{ sec} \\ f &= 1/T = 1.16 \times 10^{-5} \text{ cycle/sec} \\ \omega &= 2\pi f = 7.28 \times 10^{-5} \text{ rad/sec} \\ v &= R\omega = 4.64 \times 10^2 \text{ m/sec} \\ a &= R\omega^2 = v\omega = 3.38 \times 10^{-2} \text{ m/sec}^2 = 3.38 \text{ cm/sec}^2 \end{aligned}$$

What difference would it make if the man were standing in Toronto (latitude 43° 40′) rather than at the equator?

The values of $T, f,$ and ω are the same, but the radius of the circular path R is less.

$$\begin{aligned} R &= R_0 \cos 43° \, 40′ = 6.38 \times 10^6 \times 0.955 \\ &= 6.09 \times 10^6 \text{ m} \\ v &= R\omega = 4.43 \times 10^2 \text{ m/sec} \\ a &= v\omega = 3.22 \times 10^{-2} \text{ m/sec}^2 \end{aligned}$$

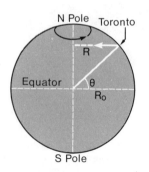

In the axis frame of reference the angular speed of points on the earth surface is independent of latitude, but the linear speed is not.

As the location of the man approaches either pole, the values of v and a approach zero.

The acceleration calculated in this example is not the acceleration due to gravity. It exists because of the earth's rotation, not because of the earth's gravity. However, in measuring the value of g_0 at the earth's surface you measure what it is, not what causes it. The measured value of g_0 varies from 983.22 cm/sec² at the north pole to 978.03 cm/sec² at the equator. Part of this large scale variation is caused by the earth's rotation, and part is due to its ellipsoidal shape.

At the equator the acceleration due to gravity is **downward** and the centripetal acceleration is **downward.** Why is it then that the effect of the earth's rotation is to make the measured value of g_0 at the equator **low** rather than **high?** We will answer this question fully later on in dynamics, but note we must always be careful to identify the frame of reference in which measurements are made. The values of g_0 are measured in a frame of reference fixed on the earth, but the acceleration we have just calculated would be measured in a *different* frame of reference—in which the earth is rotating. It is possible to compare measurements made in two different frames, but only if we make a transformation from one to the other—we will see how to do this in the next chapters.

You can see that similar care must be taken in considering the motion of the satellite in the previous example. We described its motion in the frame of reference of the earth. It had a speed relative to the surface of the earth of 7500 m/sec. A man on the earth at the equator has a significant speed, 460 m/sec, relative to a *different* frame of reference, one in which the earth is rotating. How would the motion of the satellite be described in this frame of reference? Would it be a circular motion, or some more complex path? As you can guess, this would depend on the orientation of the satellite orbit with respect to the earth; only if the orbit is above the equator will it be a circle in the frame of reference in which the earth is rotating.

AN EXAMPLE OF A CHARGED PARTICLE MOVING AT RIGHT ANGLES TO A UNIFORM MAGNETIC FIELD

An electron is accelerated from rest by an electron gun through a potential difference of 1000 volts. It then enters a uniform magnetic field of magnetic flux density $B = 2 \times 10^{-3}$ weber/m², entering the field perpendicular to the lines of magnetic flux density, and our concern is to describe its subsequent motion while it is in the magnetic field. In our earlier summary of the forces produced by uniform fields we pointed out that the magnetic force on a charged particle depended on the velocity **v** of the particle and therefore produced a continuously changing velocity and acceleration. In the special case that the velocity is perpendicular to the field direction, the motion is circular; the velocity and acceleration are changing in direction, but are constant in magnitude. In uniform circular motion the acceleration is constant in magnitude but always perpendicular to the velocity; this condition is fulfilled here. In general the magnetic force **F** on a charge q is $\mathbf{F} = q\mathbf{v} \times \mathbf{B}$, a vector perpendicular to both **v** and **B**. With **v** and **B** perpendicular to one another, the magnitude of F is $F = qvB$.

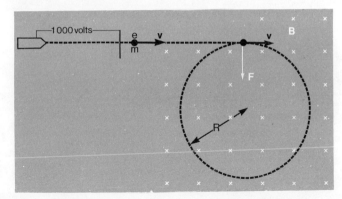

An electron accelerated by an electron gun and projected at right angles to a uniform magnetic field.

This is constant in a uniform field **B** if the speed v is unchanged and **v** and **B** remain perpendicular.

In the diagram the x's represent a uniform magnetic field of strength B directed into the page. The electron, charge $-e$ and mass m, leaves the electron gun after acquiring a speed v and enters the field at right angles. The force $F = evB$ will be down. It produces an acceleration $a = F/m = evB/m$ in the same direction. This acceleration will produce a change in direction of **v** downward but it remains perpendicular to the field, and therefore **a** is unchanged in magnitude and **v** is unchanged in magnitude. The path of the electron is a circle of radius R and the acceleration is a centripetal acceleration. Since $a = R\omega^2 = v^2/R$, the radius of the circle

$$R = \frac{v^2}{a} = \frac{v^2 m}{evB} = \frac{mv}{eB}$$

The angular frequency of the motion $\omega = v/R = eB/m$. The value of ω does not depend on the speed v; it is the same for all particles of the same charge to mass ratio e/m in the uniform field B. It is called the cyclotron frequency because it is involved in the acceleration of particles in a cyclotron.

Magnetic fields are used to hold charged particles in orbit in different types of particle accelerators, and in mass spectrographs. In one type of mass spectrograph, for example, positive ions formed by heating are first passed through a velocity filter consisting of crossed electric and magnetic fields. In the diagram the electric field E between the charged plates exerts a force Ee to the left on a positive charge q, while the magnetic field B into the page exerts a force qvB to the right. Only particles of a speed v such that these forces are equal will get through the plates—particles with speed $v = E/B$. Thus all ions enter the region where there is only a magnetic field with the same speed. If they all have the same charge to mass ratio, they all bend in the same circular path. However, ions of the same charge but different masses have different radii.

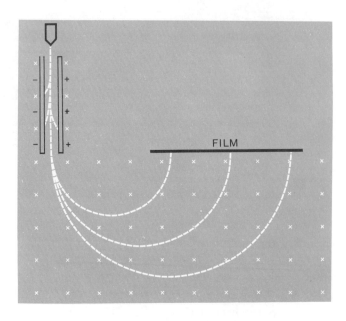

Charged particles passing through a velocity selector and entering a uniform magnetic field.

After turning through a semicircle they strike a sheet of photographic film. The amount of darkening of the film gives the amount of each ion present. The whole apparatus must be in a vacuum to minimize collisions with gas molecules.

The fact that the radius of the circular path depends on the speed (or momentum $p = mv$) means that if the orbit can be observed the momentum and energy can be readily calculated. Photographs taken in cloud chambers or bubble chambers placed in magnetic fields reveal the circular paths of charged particles such as electrons or protons.

To return to the example, the angular frequency of the electron is

$$\omega = \frac{eB}{m} = \frac{1.6 \times 10^{-19} \times 2 \times 10^{-3}}{9.1 \times 10^{-31}} = 3.5 \times 10^8 \text{ rad/sec}$$

or $\qquad f = \omega/2\pi = 5.6 \times 10^7 \text{ cycle/sec} \qquad T = 1.8 \times 10^{-8} \text{ sec}$

These are independent of the speed of the electron as it enters the field. The radius of path R does depend on the speed. We calculated in a previous example that an electron accelerated by a potential difference of 1000 volts acquires a speed of 1.9×10^7 m/sec.

$$R = v/\omega = 1.9 \times 10^7/3.5 \times 10^8 = 5.4 \times 10^{-2} \text{ m} = 5.4 \text{ cm}$$

The centripetal acceleration

$$a = R\omega^2 = v\omega = 6.6 \times 10^{15} \text{ m/sec}^2$$

The high-speed particle is bent into a very tight circle by the magnetic field and therefore has an enormous acceleration. As long as the electron is in the uniform magnetic field it will continue in a circle of radius 5.4 cm, making 56 million revolutions every second. We shall not worry about the technical question of getting it into the field in such a way that it does not emerge during its first orbit.

The strength of the magnetic field used in this example is about one hundred times that of the earth's magnetic field, and a factor of about a thousand less than that of fields used in some particle accelerators.

Remember that in this example we have dealt only with charged particles moving **perpendicular** to a magnetic field. What would you expect the path to be if a charged particle entered a uniform magnetic field at a different angle? We shall return to this in the next chapter.

SIMPLE HARMONIC MOTION

We pointed out that circular motion is an example of a motion repeated at regular intervals of time, or **periodic motion.** Such motions are also called **harmonic motion,** because any periodic motion can be described in terms of the sine or cosine functions, and expressions containing these functions are sometimes called harmonic functions.

Because a periodic motion is repeated, the path must be a closed path; if we describe the motion over one complete cycle, that is, over the time interval T, then we have described the motion completely. If the motion is back and forth over the same path, it is **oscillatory motion** or **vibratory motion.** Circular motion is periodic but not oscillatory.

Vibration is a characteristic motion of a great variety of physical systems. There is an intimate connection between vibrations and waves; the production of waves is related to vibrations of the source and the transmission of a wave is related to vibrations in the medium carrying the wave.

All periodic motions, no matter how complex, can be described in terms of the particular periodic motion called **simple harmonic motion** (SHM). This motion may be defined in a number of ways: geometrically, or dynamically (in terms of the kind of force producing it), or kinematically by giving the differential equation describing SHM or by stating the solution of the differential equation. It is a motion in which the acceleration **a** is proportional to the displacement **r** but in the opposite direction: $\mathbf{a} \propto -\mathbf{r}$, or $\mathbf{a} = -K\mathbf{r}$ where K is a constant. But recall that for circular motion $\mathbf{a} = -\omega^2\mathbf{r} = -K\mathbf{r}$, and circular motion is not SHM, so that stating $\mathbf{a} \propto -\mathbf{r}$ is not sufficient to define SHM. We need the additional restriction that the motion is confined to a straight line, or is one-dimensional.

Simple harmonic motion is motion in one-dimension for which the acceleration is proportional to the displacement, and in the opposite direction. We could equally well state that in SHM $\mathbf{a} \propto -\mathbf{r}$ and the velocity $\mathbf{v}$ is in the same line.

One advantage of the vector description of motion is that in general one vector equation is equivalent to three scalar equations. However, for motion in one-dimension we can choose a co-ordinate system so that there is only one scalar equation. By lining up the x-axis in the direction of the motion, $\mathbf{a} = -K\mathbf{r}$

A particle whose acceleration $\mathbf{a}$ is in the opposite direction to its displacement $\mathbf{r}$; if $|\mathbf{a}| \propto |\mathbf{r}|$, the motion is simple harmonic.

gives the single scalar equation $a_x = -Kr_x$. If the origin of the co-ordinate system is placed at the point O in the frame of reference from which displacement is measured, then $r_x = x$, and $a_x = d^2r_x/dt^2 = d^2x/dt^2$. Then SHM is defined by the single equation

$$\frac{d^2x}{dt^2} = -Kx$$

This is the **differential equation of SHM.** It describes the motion at some instant of time t. To describe the motion over an interval of time we must integrate the equation to find $x(t)$.

The solution of a differential equation is often a matter of trial and error, of guessing at a solution and trying it to see if it works. Sometimes the equation is familiar in another context, and this is so here. In discussing uniform circular motion we saw that in the x-direction the components of acceleration and displacement are related by $a_x = -\omega^2x$; similarly in the y-direction $a_y = -\omega^2y$. These equations both have the form of the equation for SHM. We know the relation between the displacement components and time for uniform circular motion: $x = R \cos \omega t$, $y = R \sin \omega t$. Therefore, either of these is a solution of the differential equation for SHM. Remember that in uniform circular motion R and ω are constants, the radius of the circle and the angular frequency.

By analogy then we try a solution of the SHM equation

$$x = x_0 \cos \sqrt{K}\, t$$

where x_0 and K are constants.

$$\frac{dx}{dt} = -\sqrt{K}\, x_0 \sin \sqrt{K}\, t$$

$$\frac{d^2x}{dt^2} = -(\sqrt{K})^2 x_0 \cos \sqrt{K}\, t = -Kx$$

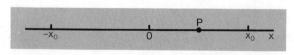

The particle P oscillates between the limits $+x_0$ and $-x_0$, where x_0 is the amplitude of the motion.

This verifies that we have a solution of the equation. It is not the only solution; clearly $x = x_0 \sin \sqrt{K}\, t$ is also a solution, for example.

What are the physical meanings of the constants x_0 and K in the solution? The maximum value of the cosine function is unity, and thus the maximum displacement of the particle P from the origin is x_0. It is called the **amplitude** of the SHM. The particle is confined to the range $-x_0$ to $+x_0$. What about its period T, the time for one complete cycle?

At time t, $x = x_0 \cos \sqrt{K} t$. At time $(t + T)$, there must be the same value of x, $x = x_0 \cos \sqrt{K}(t + T)$. Therefore

$$\cos \sqrt{K} t = \cos \sqrt{K}(t + T) = \cos \sqrt{K} t \cos \sqrt{K} T - \sin \sqrt{K} t \sin \sqrt{K} T$$
$$= \cos \sqrt{K} t \qquad provided \ \sqrt{K} T = 2\pi$$

The constant K of the motion is related to the period $T = 2\pi/\sqrt{K}$, so that for a particle in SHM

$$x = x_0 \cos 2\pi t/T$$

where x_0 is the amplitude and T is the period. As a convenience **in notation** this is often written in terms of the angular frequency ω, defined by $\omega = \sqrt{K} = 2\pi/T$, but note that there is no motion involved at a constant angular speed ω.

The general solution of the differential equation is

$$x = x_0 \cos (\omega t + \delta)$$

where there is introduced a third constant δ called the **phase** or **phase angle** of the motion. This simply allows for the measurement of time to begin at a different instant. The displacement–time graph is shown for $\delta = 0$. If $\delta = -\pi/2$,

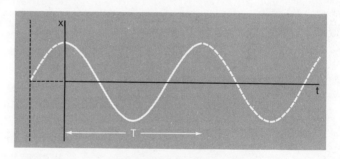

A change in phase shifts the origin of the x–t graph.

$\cos (\omega t - \pi/2) = \sin \omega t$; the effect is to shift the origin of time an amount $t = \delta/\omega = (\pi/2)\omega = T/4$ to the left. In describing a single SHM it does not matter what value of δ is used, but in comparing or combining SHM's the origin of time must be taken into account.

The displacement–time, velocity–time and acceleration–time graphs are plotted for $\delta = 0$. When the particle P is at its maximum displacement x_0 or $-x_0$ it is instantaneously at rest $(v = 0)$ and has its maximum acceleration $\omega^2 x_0$ towards O. At the instant its displacement is zero its acceleration is zero, and it has its maximum velocity $v = \pm\omega x_0$. The relationship between the three quantities is sometimes described by saying that the displacement lags behind

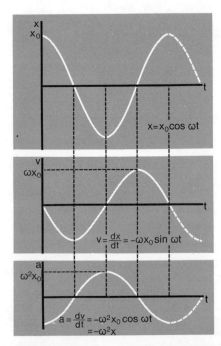

$$x = x_0 \cos \omega t$$

$$v = \frac{dx}{dt} = -\omega x_0 \sin \omega t$$

$$a = \frac{dv}{dt} = -\omega^2 x_0 \cos \omega t = -\omega^2 x$$

For a particle in simple harmonic motion, the displacement, velocity and acceleration are each sinusoidal functions of time.

the velocity by 90° or $\pi/2$ (in phase angle) or by one quarter cycle $T/4$ (in time); similarly velocity lags behind acceleration by 90° or $\pi/2$ or $T/4$. As the graphs show, the peak shifts left one quarter cycle as we move from $x \to v \to a$. Clearly **lagging** by 90° or $T/4$ is the same as **leading** by 270° or $3T/4$.

The geometric definition of SHM is that it is the projected motion on a diameter of a particle moving in a circle at constant speed. It is clear from our description of uniform circular motion that this is so. The x-position of a particle P is given by $x = R \cos \omega t$. A particle P' moving back and forth on the x-axis as the projection of P is moving in SHM with amplitude $x_0 = R$. The x-component of velocity of P is, in magnitude, $v_x = v \sin \theta = R\omega \sin \omega t$. This is the magnitude of the velocity of P'. The x-component of acceleration of P is, in magnitude, $a_x = a \cos \theta = R\omega^2 \cos \omega t$, the magnitude of the acceleration of P'. Period, frequency and angular frequency are the same for both periodic motions.

Sometimes in describing SHM the term reference circle is used to indicate that if a particle is in SHM with angular frequency ω, it is the same as the projection on a diameter of a particle moving in a circle with constant angular speed ω. But, it is probably better to emphasize there is no circular motion in SHM; it is oscillatory motion on a straight line.

We stated earlier that all periodic motions can be described in terms of simple harmonic motion. By combining SHM's of different amplitudes, period, and phase any periodic motion can be produced. The process of doing this is called **harmonic synthesis;** breaking a particular periodic motion up into its various SHM's is called **harmonic analysis** or **Fourier analysis.**

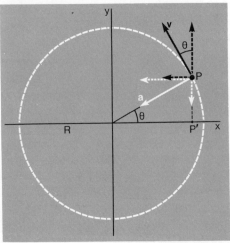

If the particle P moves at constant speed in a circle, its projection P' on a diameter moves in simple harmonic motion.

Uniform circular motion is a periodic motion and it is evident that it is the result of combining two SHM's at right angles at a common origin; the SHM's have the same amplitude and frequency but differ in phase by $\pi/2$ (or $T/4$).

The two SHM's, $x = R \cos \omega t$, and $y = R \sin \omega t = R \cos (\omega t - \pi/2)$, produce uniform circular motion.

What if we combine two identical SHM's at right angles at a common origin? If $x = R \sin \omega t$ and $y = R \sin \omega t$ are combined, then at $t = 0$ both x and y are

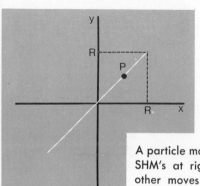

A particle moving with two identical SHM's at right angles, but differing in phase, in general moves in an elliptic path.

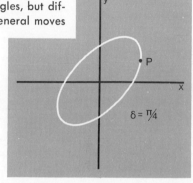

A particle moving with two identical SHM's at right angles to one another moves in SHM of increased amplitude.

zero, and as t increases x and y increase at the same rate, reaching a maximum value of R at the same instant, then decreasing together. At any instant $\tan \theta = y/x = \sin \omega t/\sin \omega t = 1, \theta = 45°$. Motion is in a straight line at an angle of $45°$ with the axes. The displacement r from the origin at any instant is given by

$$r^2 = x^2 + y^2 = R^2 \sin^2 \omega t + R^2 \sin^2 \omega t = 2R^2 \sin^2 \omega t$$
$$r = \sqrt{2}\, R \sin \omega t$$

The result is a new SHM of the same frequency but with amplitude $\sqrt{2}\, R$.

If two SHM's with the same amplitude and frequency but differing in phase by δ, where $0 < \delta < \pi/2$, are combined at right angles the path that results is between a circle and a straight line. It turns out to be an ellipse, with eccentricity depending on the value of δ.

If two SHM's at right angles with different frequencies are combined, the result in general will not be periodic, but will if the frequency ratio is the ratio of two integers. For the path shown, $y = R \sin \omega t$, $x = R \sin 2\omega t$. Figures of this kind are **Lissajous patterns.** The simplest way to observe them is to use two audio oscillators to apply sinusoidal signals to the x and y deflecting plates of an oscilloscope.

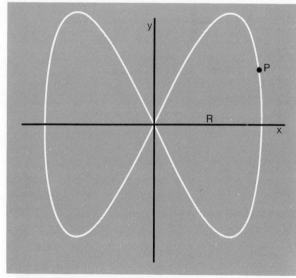

Lissajous pattern produced by combing two SHM's at right angles, for the case in which the amplitudes are equal and the frequencies are in the ratio two-to-one.

Combinations of simple harmonic motions at right angles are useful in dealing with certain physical situations, for example, polarized light or alternating current circuits. However, combinations of SHM's in the same line are of more general interest, because they are important in the study of interference and diffraction effects for all kinds of wave motion. Different waves passing a point produce a number of different SHM's of a particle at the point; the resultant particle motion is the sum or **superposition** of the individual SHM's.

The figure below shows a displacement–time graph for the superposition of the two SHM's $x_1 = R \sin \omega t$ and $x_2 = R \sin 2\omega t$. The resultant motion is periodic but not simple harmonic.

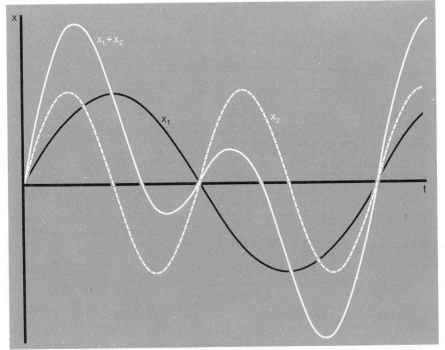

Combining simple harmonic motions in the same line produces motions that are periodic but not SHM's.

Periodic motions with abrupt discontinuities such as the square wave or saw-tooth wave shown cannot be reproduced exactly by the superposition of harmonic motions, but can be reproduced to any desired degree of accuracy. Conversely, the harmonic components of such motions can be found to any desired accuracy by the techniques of Fourier analysis.

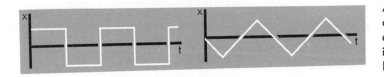

A periodic motion of any kind can be produced, to any desired degree of accuracy, by combining a sufficient number of simple harmonic motions.

As we have seen, simple harmonic motion can be defined geometrically, as the projection on a diameter of uniform circular motion, or by the differential equation $d^2x/dt^2 = -\omega^2 x$, or by stating $x(t)$: $x = x_0 \cos(\omega t + \delta)$. We will later in dynamics give still another possible definition, that SHM results whenever there is a restoring force proportional to displacement.

Example: The tip of a 256-cps tuning fork vibrates through a total distance of 0.4 mm. Determine its maximum speed and maximum acceleration.

The motion of the tip is not exactly in a straight line, but it is a good approximation to consider that it is and to treat the vibrations as simple harmonic motion. It is a characteristic of most oscillating systems that if the amplitude of vibration is small, the motion can be considered simple harmonic.

If the displacement of the tip from equilibrium is y, then $y = y_0 \sin \omega t$, where $y_0 = 0.2$ mm (the amplitude is one-half the total distance moved), and $\omega = 2\pi f = 2\pi \times 256 = 1.6 \times 10^3$ rad/sec. The speed $dy/dt = \omega y_0 \cos \omega t$, so the maximum speed is $\omega y_0 = 1.6 \times 10^3 \times 0.2 = 3.2 \times 10^2$ mm/sec. The acceleration $d^2y/dt^2 = -\omega^2 y_0 \sin \omega t$, so the maximum acceleration is $\omega^2 y_0 = 1.6 \times 10^3 \times 3.2 \times 10^2 = 5.1 \times 10^5$ mm/sec $= 5.1 \times 10^4$ cm/sec $= 52\,g$, where g is the acceleration due to gravity of 980 cm/sec².

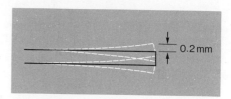

The motion of the tip of a tuning fork can be considered simple harmonic.

NON-CARTESIAN CO-ORDINATE SYSTEMS

The motion of a particle P is completely specified with respect to a particular frame of reference by the single vector quantity $\mathbf{r}(t)$, the displacement of P from a fixed point O in the frame of reference. The displacement $\mathbf{r}$ represents three scalar quantities, and these depend on the choice of co-ordinate system in the frame of reference. In a particular Cartesian system $\mathbf{r}$ represents r_x, r_y, r_z, its three components in the three directions determined by the axes of the system. If the origin of the co-ordinate system is at O, then $r_x = x$, $r_y = y$ and $r_z = z$, where x, y, z are the co-ordinates of P. With this choice of co-ordinate system the vector $\mathbf{r}$ is called the **radius vector** or **position vector** as well as the displacement from O. The motion of the particle is described by $\mathbf{r}(t)$ or by the three scalar functions $x(t)$, $y(t)$, $z(t)$.

Our assumption that space is Euclidean means three independent numbers are required to specify the position of a particle P in a frame of reference,

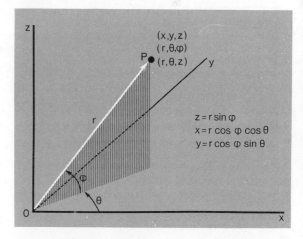

The position of a particle can be specified in spherical or cylindrical co-ordinates as well as in Cartesian co-ordinates.

but it is not necessary to choose a Cartesian co-ordinate system. The position of the particle P is uniquely specified with respect to the fixed point O in the frame of reference by its Cartesian co-ordinates (x,y,z), or by its **spherical co-ordinates** (r,θ,φ) or by its **cylindrical co-ordinates** (r,θ,z). The vector **r** represents any set of these.

In spherical co-ordinates (r,θ,φ) r is the magnitude of **r**, φ is the angle between **r** and its projection in the xy plane (the azimuth angle) and θ is the angle between the projection and the x-axis (the polar angle). For motion confined to the xy plane the **polar co-ordinates** (r,θ) are sufficient.

In place of the vector function **r**(t) we can consider three scalar functions of time $r(t)$, $\theta(t)$, $\varphi(t)$ and introduce their rates of change dr/dt, d^2r/dt^2, $d\theta/dt$, $d\varphi/dt$, etc. For two-dimensional motion the quantity dr/dt is called the radial speed, $d\theta/dt$ the angular speed.

In describing circular motion it is simplest to choose a co-ordinate system so that the circle is in the xy plane, with the origin at the center of the circle, and use polar co-ordinates (r,θ). Then since $dr/dt = 0$ there is a single scalar function of time, $\theta(t)$.

NON-UNIFORM CIRCULAR MOTION

We described uniform circular motion using Cartesian co-ordinates (x,y,z) because this made clear the relationship between this motion and simple harmonic motion. However, to describe circular motion in which the speed is not constant we will use the more appropriate polar co-ordinates, and introduce the concepts of angular displacement, angular speed, and angular acceleration.

The motion of the particle P is circular in the frame of reference in which the motion is being measured. We choose a polar co-ordinate system with its plane in the plane of the circular path, its origin at the origin of the radius vector **r**, and measure the angle θ with respect to a fixed direction in the frame of reference, the direction determined by **r** at time $t = 0$. The constant magnitude of **r** we call R, and we describe the motion of P not in terms of displacement **r** but in terms of **angular displacement** θ. If P moves a distance s along the circular path, it has an angular displacement θ, where $s = R\theta$, assuming that

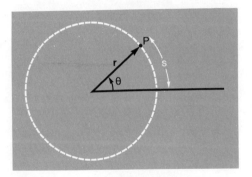

Circular motion of a particle is described most simply by appropriately choosing polar co-ordinates.

θ **is measured in radians.** The angular displacement θ is of course the polar co-ordinate θ, but we use the term angular displacement to emphasize that θ is a measured physical quantity in the frame of reference. As the particle moves from a position P_1 to a position P_2 in time Δt, its angular displacement changes by $\Delta\theta$ and it has moved a distance $\Delta s = R\,\Delta\theta$ along the path.

The average angular speed over the interval Δt is defined as $\bar{\omega} = \Delta\theta/\Delta t$. The instantaneous angular speed (usually just **the angular speed**) is defined as

$$\omega = \lim_{\Delta t \to 0} \frac{\Delta\theta}{\Delta t} = \frac{d\theta}{dt}$$

This is the angular speed of the particle at the position P_1.

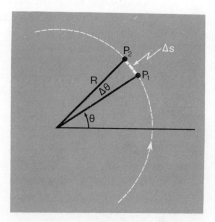

Path length Δs and angular displacement $\Delta\theta$ are related by $\Delta s = R\,\Delta\theta$.

The displacement in time Δt is the vector $\mathbf{P_1P_2}$ and the average velocity is $\mathbf{P_1P_2}/\Delta t$. The distance Δs is not the same as the chord length P_1P_2 and therefore $\Delta s/\Delta t$, the average speed over the interval, is *not* the magnitude of the average velocity over the interval. Remember that the speed is the magnitude of the

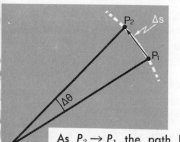

As $P_2 \to P_1$ the path length Δs becomes the magnitude of the displacement $\mathbf{P_1P_2}$ in the interval.

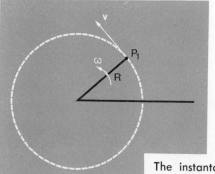

The instantaneous velocity $\mathbf{v}$ is tangent to the circular path.

velocity only for instantaneous values. However, as $\Delta t \to 0$ (and therefore $\Delta s \to 0$ and $P_2 \to P_1$) the arc length approaches the chord length and the magnitude of the velocity at P_1 is $v = \lim_{\Delta t \to 0} \Delta s/\Delta t$. The direction of $\mathbf{v}$ is that of the chord in the limit, which is that of the tangent at P_1; as always the velocity vector is tangent to the path, pointing in the direction of motion.

$$v = \lim_{\Delta t \to 0} \frac{\Delta s}{\Delta t} = \lim_{\Delta t \to 0} R\frac{\Delta\theta}{\Delta t} = R\lim_{\Delta t \to 0} \frac{\Delta\theta}{\Delta t} = R\omega$$

The relation $v = R\omega$ between the instantaneous speed and the instantaneous angular speed is the same as that developed before for uniform circular motion. It can be obtained directly by differentiating the scalar equation $s = R\theta$ with respect to time.

$$\frac{ds}{dt} = R\frac{d\theta}{dt} \qquad \text{or} \qquad v = R\omega$$

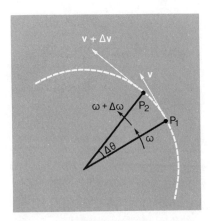

The angular speed ω and the linear speed v are related by $v = R\omega$.

In general the angular speed ω at P_1 will not be the same as at P_2, a time Δt later. If the change is $\Delta\omega$, the average angular acceleration over the time interval Δt is defined as $\bar{\alpha} = \Delta\omega/\Delta t$ and the instantaneous angular acceleration (usually the **angular acceleration**) is defined as

$$\alpha = \lim_{\Delta t \to 0} \frac{\Delta\omega}{\Delta t} = \frac{d\omega}{dt} = \frac{d^2\theta}{dt^2}$$

Differentiating $v = R\omega$ with respect to time gives

$$\frac{dv}{dt} = R\frac{d\omega}{dt} = R\alpha$$

This dv/dt is an acceleration, but we know that it is not the total acceleration of the particle; if it is moving at constant speed in the circular path then v and ω are constants and dv/dt and α are zero, but it does have a changing velocity $\mathbf{v}$ (in direction) and therefore dv/dt is not zero. We saw in describing uniform circular motion that there is an acceleration of magnitude $R\omega^2$ directed toward the center. We call this **central** or **centripetal** or **radial** acceleration $\mathbf{a}_R$ now to distinguish it from the part of the acceleration that arises from the change in speed, $dv/dt = R\alpha$. This latter we call the **tangential** acceleration, because its direction is along the tangent at P_1, in the same direction as $\mathbf{v}$ if the speed is increasing or in the opposite direction if the speed is decreasing. This can be seen from the vector diagrams. In the first diagram, the velocity $\mathbf{v}_2$ after the interval Δt is the same in magnitude as $\mathbf{v}_1$ before the interval. The vector difference $\Delta v = \mathbf{v}_2 - \mathbf{v}_1 = \mathbf{v}_2 + (-\mathbf{v}_1)$ points inward. As $\Delta\theta$ gets smaller, Δv becomes closer to being perpendicular to $\mathbf{v}_1$ and $\mathbf{v}_2$. In the limit it becomes perpendicular, and since $\mathbf{v}$ at P_1 is directed along the tangent, $\mathbf{a}_R$ at P_1 is directed inward along the radius. The magnitude of $\mathbf{a}_R$ can also be determined from

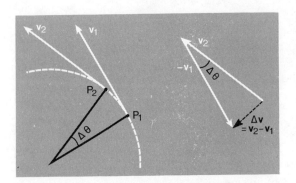

Vector diagram for velocity changing in direction but not in magnitude, so that there is a radial acceleration only.

the vector triangle. Approximately $\Delta v = v \Delta \theta$ where v is the magnitude of $\mathbf{v}_1$ and $\mathbf{v}_2$; this is approximate because the chord length Δv is not equal to the arc length. However, in the limit it becomes so. Dividing by Δt,

$$\lim_{\Delta t \to 0} \frac{\Delta v}{\Delta t} = \lim_{\Delta t \to 0} \frac{v \Delta \theta}{\Delta t} = v \lim_{\Delta t \to 0} \frac{\Delta \theta}{\Delta t}$$

since v is constant. The right side is $v\omega$, the left side is defined as a_R: $a_R = v\omega$. Since $v = R\omega$, $a_R = v\omega = R\omega^2 = v^2/R$. The result agrees with the previous analysis.

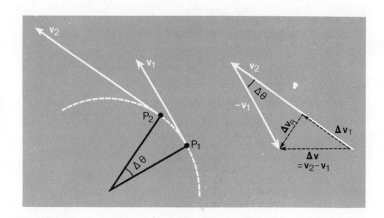

Vector diagram for velocity changing in both direction and magnitude, so that there is both a radial and a tangential acceleration.

The second diagram shows $\mathbf{v}_2$ greater than $\mathbf{v}_1$, an increase in speed in the interval Δt. The velocity difference $\Delta \mathbf{v}$ as before is $\mathbf{v}_2 - \mathbf{v}_1$. This time it has been shown as the sum of two components, $\Delta \mathbf{v}_T$ in the $\mathbf{v}_2$ direction and $\Delta \mathbf{v}_R$ corresponding to the previous diagram. In the limit $a_R = \lim_{\Delta t \to 0} \Delta v_R/\Delta t$, and $a_T = \lim_{\Delta t \to 0} \Delta v_T/\Delta t$. The direction of $\mathbf{a}_T$ at point P_1 is the same as the direction of $\mathbf{v}$ in this case. If the speed is decreasing, $v_2 < v_1$, it would be in the opposite direction. Note that since $\alpha = d\omega/dt$, α will be negative for decreasing speed, and $a_T = R\alpha$ will be negative.

The resultant acceleration $\mathbf{a} = \mathbf{a}_R + \mathbf{a}_T$. Its magnitude is $a = \sqrt{a_R^2 + a_T^2} = \sqrt{(R\omega^2)^2 + (R\alpha)^2} = R\sqrt{\omega^4 + \alpha^2}$ and its direction can be given in terms of the components: $\tan \varphi = a_T/a_R$. It is continuously changing in magnitude and direction. Usually only when rotation is just beginning does the tangential acceleration $\mathbf{a}_T$ make a significant

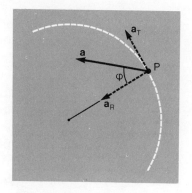

The resultant acceleration.

contribution to **a**. Very shortly a_R becomes dominant and the resultant acceleration is effectively inward toward the center of rotation, as it is for rotation at constant speed, although its magnitude keeps increasing as the angular speed increases.

TRANSLATION IN ONE DIMENSION AND
ROTATION ABOUT A FIXED AXIS OF A RIGID BODY

The motion of a particle in a circle of radius R in a particular frame of reference can be described by the quantities **r**, **v** and **a** independent of a co-ordinate system, or by the angular quantities θ, ω and α in a particular co-ordinate system in the frame of reference. The magnitudes of the vector quantities are related to the angular quantities by: $r = R$, $v = R\omega$, $a = R\sqrt{\omega^4 + \alpha^2}$. In considering the motion of a single particle, either description may be convenient. However, the angular quantities have a great advantage in describing the rotation of a **system** of particles, all of which are at rest with respect to one another, because for such a system the description in terms of the angular quantities θ, ω and α is the *same* for every particle.

We have so far used a **particle model** for all objects; that is we have considered only the motion of particles, and have used as examples situations where the dimensions of real objects are small on the scale of observation (e.g., a man rotating on the earth) or have fixed our attention on a particle in the object (e.g., a particle at the tip of an aircraft propeller or at the tip of a tuning fork). Later on we will use as a model of a real object a **rigid body**, in which it is assumed that a body is a collection of particles and that every particle is at rest relative to all other particles. Neither internal stresses (due to heating it, or spinning it) nor external stresses (due to pulling it, or squeezing it) change the relative positions of the particles in a rigid body. There is really no such object, but most solid objects under many conditions are good approximations of a rigid body.

The motion of a rigid body can be complicated to describe, as we shall see in a later chapter, but there are two special cases that are relatively simple. If a rigid body is moving in a frame of reference in a straight line without rotating, then the motion of every particle in the body is described in exactly the same way. The displacement x, the velocity v and the acceleration a are the same for all particles; since this is one-dimensional or rectilinear motion, the vector character of these quantities means only that they can take on positive or negative values. This motion is called **pure translation in one dimension.**

If a rigid body is moving in a frame of reference in such a way that every particle in the body is moving in a circle about a fixed axis, this is called **pure rotation about a fixed axis.** The axis is a fixed line in the frame of reference; it need not pass through the body. Note that an axis is not an axle; the axis may coincide with an axle (e.g., a propeller shaft) or there may be no axle (e.g., the earth's axis). The important feature is that the axis is a **fixed** line in the frame of reference, and therefore the motion of each particle is confined to a plane, the plane of its circular path. If the motion of the particles in the body is described in terms of the angular displacement θ,

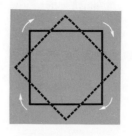

Pure rotation of a body about an axis through its center.

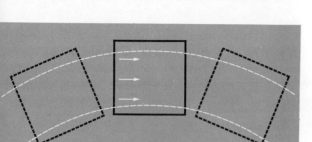

Pure rotation of a body about an axis that does not pass through the body.

the angular velocity ω, and the angular acceleration α, the situation is completely analogous to that of pure translation in one dimension, because these quantities have the same value (at a particular instant) for every particle in the body. We can speak of the angular velocity of a particular particle in the body, or that of the body itself—they are the same.

The angular quantities have been defined as scalar quantities that can take on positive or negative values; in describing rotations in three-dimensions in a later chapter, we will see that they can be defined as vectors.

UNIFORMLY ACCELERATED
CIRCULAR MOTION

So far in describing non-uniform circular motion we have defined the instantaneous angular quantities θ, ω and α and related them to the instantaneous linear quantities $\mathbf{r}$, $\mathbf{v}$ and $\mathbf{a}$. To go further and describe non-uniform circular motion over a time interval we will look at the special case in which α is constant.

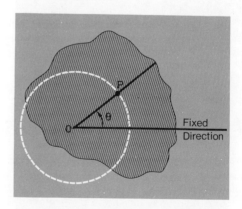

The angular displacement, velocity and acceleration are the same for all points in a rigid body rotating around a fixed axis.

It does not matter if we think of the rotation of a rigid body about the axis through O (perpendicular to the page in the diagram) or the circular motion of any particle P in the body. At time $t = 0$ an arbitrary line OP in the body, perpendicular to the axis, is in a particular direction in the frame of reference.

We measure angular displacement θ between OP and this fixed direction. Then $\theta = 0$ at $t = 0$. We assume at this instant there is an angular speed ω_0. The angular acceleration α is constant. We wish to find $\theta(t)$ and $\omega(t)$.

$$\alpha = \frac{d\omega}{dt} \qquad d\omega = \alpha\, dt \qquad \int_{\omega_0}^{\omega} d\omega = \int_0^t \alpha\, dt = \alpha \int_0^t dt$$

$$\omega - \omega_0 = \alpha t \qquad \text{or} \qquad \omega = \omega_0 + \alpha t$$

$$\omega = \frac{d\theta}{dt} \qquad d\theta = \omega\, dt \qquad \int_0^{\theta} d\theta = \int_0^t \omega\, dt = \int_0^t (\omega_0 + \alpha t)\, dt = \omega_0 \int_0^t dt + \alpha \int_0^t t\, dt$$

$$\theta = \omega_0 t + \tfrac{1}{2}\alpha t^2$$

These give $\theta(t)$ and $\omega(t)$. We could eliminate t from these relations to find an expression involving only the angular quantities θ, ω_0, ω and α or we can derive the expression directly.

$$\omega = \frac{d\theta}{dt} = \frac{d\theta}{d\omega}\frac{d\omega}{dt} = \frac{d\theta}{d\omega}\alpha \qquad \text{or} \qquad \omega\, d\omega = \alpha\, d\theta$$

$$\int_{\omega_0}^{\omega} \omega\, d\omega = \int_0^{\theta} \alpha\, d\theta = \alpha \int_0^{\theta} d\theta$$

$$\tfrac{1}{2}(\omega^2 - \omega_0^2) = \alpha\theta \qquad \text{or} \qquad \omega^2 = \omega_0^2 + 2\alpha\theta$$

These derivations and the resulting relations are exactly the same as those for uniform acceleration of a particle in one dimension (or a rigid body in pure translation in one dimension) with x, v and a replaced by the corresponding angular quantities θ, ω and α.

In using relations such as $\omega = \omega_0 + \alpha t$ it does not matter what units are used for angular quantities. For example, if a flywheel speeds up uniformly from rest to 60 rpm in 10 sec, its angular acceleration is

$$\alpha = \frac{\omega - \omega_0}{t}$$

$$= \frac{60 - 0}{10}\left(\frac{\text{rev}}{\text{min}}\right)\left(\frac{1}{\text{sec}}\right)$$

$$= 6\ (\text{rev/min})/\text{sec}$$

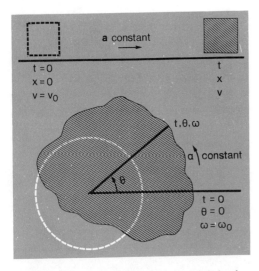

Analogy between motion of a rigid body moving in pure translation in one dimension with constant linear acceleration, and motion of a rigid body moving in pure rotation about a fixed axis with constant angular acceleration.

This may be converted to other units.

$$\alpha = 6\,\frac{\text{rev}}{\text{min-sec}} \times \frac{1\ \text{min}}{60\ \text{sec}} = 0.1\ \text{rev/sec}^2$$

$$= 0.1\,\frac{\text{rev}}{\text{sec}^2} \times \frac{2\pi\ \text{rad}}{1\ \text{rev}} = 0.63\ \text{rad/sec}^2$$

These are equivalent values of the angular acceleration. If the acceleration had not been uniform, this would be the average angular acceleration.

In converting angular quantities to linear quantities we must be a little careful, because the relations $v = R\omega$ and $a = R\sqrt{\omega^4 + \alpha^2}$ were derived on the assumption that angles are measured in radians. This does not really matter of course because the units always take care of themselves. Suppose for example that we calculate the speed of a point on the flywheel 2 ft from the axis of rotation, at the end of the 10-sec interval.

$$v = R\omega = 2 \times 60 \text{ ft-rev/min}$$

$$= 120 \frac{\text{ft-rev}}{\text{min}} \times \frac{2\pi \text{ rad}}{1 \text{ rev}} = 240\pi \text{ ft-rad/min}$$

The radian was defined as a dimensionless ratio of two lengths, and we can write this as 240π ft/min or 4π ft/sec. However, we cannot ignore the "revolutions" in ft-rev/min. The revolution as a unit is a pure number (that is, it has no physical dimensions), but it is not defined in such a way that it can be ignored in writing the units for physical quantities. It is not wrong to write the speed as 120 ft-rev/min, but it is a rather unusual unit for speed. Ordinarily in dealing with rotation angles are expressed in radians at the outset.

If we compare the radial and tangential accelerations of the point on the flywheel after 10 sec we have

$$a_T = R\alpha = 2 \times 0.63 \text{ ft-rad/sec}^2 = 1.26 \text{ ft/sec}^2$$

$$a_R = R\omega^2 = 2 \times (2\pi)^2 \text{ ft-rad}^2/\text{sec}^2 = 79 \text{ ft/sec}^2$$

We see that at this instant, even at the relatively low speed of 60 rpm = 1 rev/sec = 2π rad/sec, the centripetal acceleration a_R completely overshadows the tangential acceleration a_T. The magnitude of the resultant acceleration a is nearly that of a_R.

$$a = \sqrt{a_R^2 + a_T^2} = a_R\sqrt{1 + a_T^2/a_R^2} = a_R\sqrt{1 + (R\alpha)^2/(R\omega^2)^2}$$

$$= a_R\sqrt{1 + \alpha^2/\omega^4} \cong a_R(1 + \alpha^2/2\omega^4)$$

$$= a_R\left[1 + (0.2\pi)^2/2(2\pi)^4\right] = a_R\left[1 + 10^{-2}/8\pi^2\right]$$

$$= a_R(1 + 1.3 \times 10^{-4})$$

Therefore $a = a_R$ to within about one one-hundredth of 1%. The direction of **a** will essentially be inward toward the axis.

You can verify for yourself that $a_R = a_T$ at a time $t = 1/\sqrt{\alpha} = 1.3$ sec after the rotation begins.

MOTION IN A CURVED PATH—CENTER OF CURVATURE

We have seen that a particle moving in a circle can be considered to have two components of acceleration, a_R related to changes in **direction** of velocity and a_T related to changes in **magnitude** of velocity (changes of speed). The accelera-

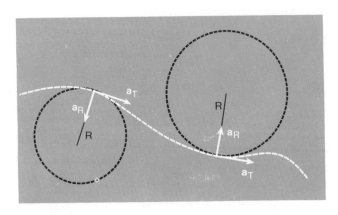

It is possible to define a radius of curvature for every point in a curved path.

tion of a particle moving in *any* path can be resolved in components a_T parallel to the path and a_R perpendicular to the path. This acceleration, perpendicular to the path, at any instant is the same as if the particle were moving in a circular path of radius R determined by $a_R = v^2/R$. This R is called the instantaneous **radius of curvature** of the path. The vector a_R points toward the instantaneous **center of curvature**, a distance R away.

A projectile at the top of its parabolic path, for example, has an acceleration g which at this instant is perpendicular to its velocity v and therefore is a_R. Its radius of curvature is

$$R = v^2/g$$

If $v = 0$, the projectile was shot straight up, and $R = 0$. As the trajectory becomes flatter the speed v at the top increases, and R increases. If v is large enough, R becomes the radius of the earth R_e. Giving a projectile a horizontal velocity $v = \sqrt{gR_e}$ will put it into orbit at the earth's surface. Neglect air resistance and keep your head down.

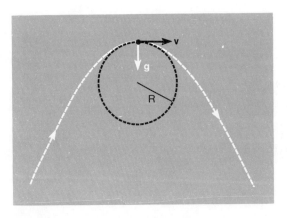

A projectile has a downward acceleration **g** at every point, and at the top of its trajectory this is its radial acceleration.

Example: A projectile has a speed of 16 ft/sec at the top of its trajectory. Determine the radius of curvature of its path at this instant, and one second later. Use $g = 32$ ft/sec².

Let $v_0 = 16$ ft/sec; this is v_x, the constant horizontal velocity of the projectile. Initially

$$R = \frac{v_0^2}{g} = \frac{16^2}{32} = 8 \text{ ft}$$

After $t = 1$ sec, the projectile also has a vertical component of velocity

$$v_y = v_{0y} - gt$$
$$= 0 - 32 \times 1 = -32 \text{ ft/sec}$$

We will use the same orientation of axes used previously, with y upward, so that downward directions are negative.

After 1 sec the speed is $v = \sqrt{16^2 + 32^2} = 16\sqrt{5}$ ft/sec. The velocity **v** makes an angle θ with the vertical direction, where

$$\tan \theta = v_x/v_y = 0.5$$

This is the direction of the path at this point. The acceleration **g** is vertically downward, and therefore the components parallel to and perpendicular to the path are $a_T = g \cos \theta$, $a_R = g \sin \theta$. Since $\tan \theta = 1/2$, $\sin \theta = 1/\sqrt{5}$,

$$a_R = \frac{v^2}{R} = g \sin \theta$$

$$R = \frac{v^2}{g \sin \theta} = \frac{16^2 \times 5}{32 \times 1/\sqrt{5}} = 40\sqrt{5} \cong 90 \text{ ft}$$

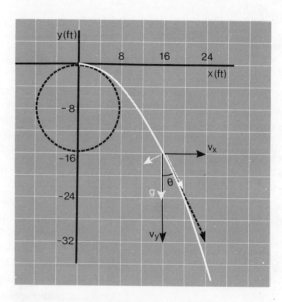

The radial acceleration is $a_R = g \sin \theta$. The angle θ is determined from the velocity components.

The instantaneous radius of curvature has increased from 8 to 90 ft in the 1-sec interval.

The example may also be solved using the equation of the path and the methods of calculus to find the **curvature.** The curvature of any line is the inverse of the radius of curvature; the smaller the radius, the sharper the curve and the greater the curvature. It can be shown that the curvature at any point is

$$\frac{1}{R} = \frac{d^2y}{dx^2} \bigg/ \left[1 + \left(\frac{dy}{dx}\right)^2\right]^{3/2}$$

In this example the equation of the path is

$$y = \left(\frac{v_{0y}}{v_{0x}}\right) x - \left(\frac{g}{2v_{0x}^2}\right) x^2 = -\frac{32}{2 \times 16^2} x^2 = -\tfrac{1}{16} x^2$$

$$\frac{dy}{dx} = -\tfrac{1}{8} x \qquad \frac{d^2y}{dx^2} = -\tfrac{1}{8}$$

At $t = 0$, $x = 0$, $\dfrac{dy}{dx} = 0$, $\dfrac{1}{R} = \dfrac{d^2y}{dx^2} = -\dfrac{1}{8}$, or $R = 8$ ft (with curvature downward).

At $t = 1$ sec, $x = v_{0x}t = 16$ ft, $\dfrac{dy}{dx} = -\tfrac{1}{8}x = -2$, $\dfrac{1}{R} = \dfrac{(-1/8)}{[1 + (-2)^2]^{3/2}}$,

$$R = -8 \times 5\sqrt{5} = -40\sqrt{5} \text{ ft.}$$

Questions for discussion

1. The motion of a particle can be described in a particular frame of reference by its displacement $\mathbf{r}(t)$ with respect to a fixed point in the frame, without introducing a co-ordinate system. However, when we want to visualize the motion, or plot it on a graph, we must always do so with respect to a particular co-ordinate system. If this is so, what use is the description in terms of displacement?

2. Are there physical assumptions made in defining **velocity** by $\mathbf{v} = d\mathbf{r}/dt$ or is this a purely mathematical operation?

3. Think of the molecules of a gas moving around, colliding with one another and with the walls of a container. At any instant each molecule will have a certain velocity. Think of all these velocity vectors as originating at the same point; the ends of the vectors define points in velocity space. As the molecules move and make collisions with one another in real space, the points move in velocity space. Is the motion of the points similar to the motion of the molecules?

4. Which of **instantaneous velocity** and **velocity at a point** do you find a more satisfactory term?

5. Is a numerical solution of a problem less useful, less accurate, or less satisfying than an analytical one?

6. Does the fact that an object may have zero velocity and a non-zero acceleration seem reasonable to you?

7. Think of a ball thrown straight up and then returning to its starting point. If air resistance is not neglected, would you expect the time for the ball to rise to be greater than, the same as, or less than the time it takes to fall? Sketch a displacement–time graph for the motion. Is it a parabola? Is it symmetric?

8. A particle at a point near the earth has a **gravitational potential energy** that depends on the mass of the particle. Even if there is no mass at the point, we say that at the point there is a gravitational potential. Is gravitational potential energy a property of the particle, or a combined property of the particle and its environment? If it is the second, can we talk about conservation of energy for the particle alone? (We will be discussing this important point in Part V.)

9. A battery-operated record player is used in a house trailer moving along a highway. What is the path of a particle at the edge of a record, in the frame of reference of the trailer, and of the earth? Can you think of other examples of motion that are circular in an appropriate frame of reference, and are confined to a horizontal plane but are not circular in the earth frame?

10. The description of the motion of a rigid body moving in a frame of reference with pure translation at constant velocity, using the variables x, v, t, is identical to a

description of the motion of a rigid body moving in pure rotation about a fixed axis in a frame of reference, using the variables θ, ω, t. However, as we will discuss in dynamics, there is an important difference between these motions, related to the acceleration of the particles of the body. What is this difference?

Problems

Use $g = 32 \text{ ft/sec}^2 = 9.8 \text{ m/sec}^2$.

1. The velocity of a uniformly accelerating car on a straight road doubles in a distance of 90 ft, and the distance is covered in 3 sec. What was the speed at the start of the interval?

2. A window is 8 ft high. It is observed that a falling object takes $\frac{1}{4}$ sec to pass the window. From how high above the top of the window was the object dropped?

3. Assume that a particle has a constant acceleration g, where $g = 9.8 \text{ m/sec}^2$. Starting from rest, how long would it take to reach a velocity of magnitude $c = 3 \times 10^8$ m/sec, and what would its displacement be?

4. The velocity of a particle moving in a straight line with a constant acceleration changes from v_1 to v_2 in a time interval $t_2 - t_1$, and over a displacement interval $x_2 - x_1$. Determine, in terms of v_1 and v_2, its velocity at mid-time, its velocity at mid-displacement, and its average velocity.

5. (a) The speed of a particle moving in a straight line changes from 10 to 30 m/sec in 10 sec. During this time the particle moves 150 m. What is its average speed? Is its acceleration constant? Sketch possible v–t and x–t graphs.

   (b) Suppose that the particle in (a) above moves at constant speed for part of the interval, and then with constant acceleration. Determine the time at which the motion changes, and sketch the v–t and x–t graphs.

6. A projectile is shot vertically upward with an initial velocity of 128 ft/sec; 2 sec later another projectile is shot vertically upward with an initial velocity of 192 ft/sec, from a point (a) at the same height as the first, (b) at a height 64 ft below the first. For each case calculate when and where the projectiles are at the same height, and also the time when their velocities are equal in magnitude but opposite in direction. To help visualize the motions, sketch displacement–time and velocity–time graphs using the same set of axes for both projectiles.

7. Car A starts from rest with a constant acceleration that will give it a velocity of 30 mph in 11 sec. At the instant it starts, car B is 44 ft behind it, moving toward it at a constant speed of 15 mph. Will the cars pass, and if so when? Sketch displacement–time graphs for both cars on the same diagram, and also sketch a graph showing the displacement of car A relative to car B.

8. A particle moves on the x-axis with acceleration $a = -k/x^2 \text{ m/sec}^2$, where k is a constant and x is in meters. At $t = 0, x = 2 \text{ m}, a = -1 \text{ m/sec}^2$ and $v = 0$; that is, the particle is released at this point, and moves toward the origin with an acceleration that increases as the displacement decreases. How long would it take to reach a displacement of 1 m if the acceleration were constant? Perform a numerical calculation, using time intervals of 0.1 sec, to find the time it takes to reach this displacement. Also find its velocity at this point.

Start with $v(0.05) = -0.05$ m/sec: then $x(0.1) = 2 - 0.005 = 1.995$ m, $a(0.1) = -4/(1.995)^2 = -1.005$ m/sec^2, etc. As a check, plot graphs of v vs. t, and x vs. t. Errors in computation will show up as discontinuities in these graphs.

Integration of the differential equation $\dfrac{d^2x}{dt^2} = -\dfrac{4}{x^2}$ to find the velocity and the time is possible, but is not simple. For the boundary conditions given, the results are

$$v^2 = 4(2 - x)/x \qquad t = \tfrac{1}{2}\sqrt{2x - x^2} + \text{arc sin } \sqrt{1 - x/2}$$

This is an important example, because **inverse-square forces** (and therefore **inverse-square accelerations**) occur frequently in physical situations.

9. At one instant the velocity and acceleration of a particle are $\mathbf{v}_0 = 3\mathbf{i} - \mathbf{j} + 2\mathbf{k}$ m/sec, $\mathbf{a} = 4\mathbf{i} + 2\mathbf{j}$ m/sec^2. Assuming the acceleration is constant, determine the displacement in a 3-sec interval, and the velocity at the end of the interval. What is the magnitude of the displacement, and the change in speed?

10. A particle has a constant acceleration 0.5 m/sec^2 in magnitude. The speed of the particle at one instant is $v_0 = 10$ m/sec, and 30 sec later the speed has doubled. Determine the angle between the initial velocity $\mathbf{v}_0$ and the constant acceleration $\mathbf{a}$.

11. At $t = 0$ the velocity and acceleration of a particle are $\mathbf{v}_0 = 5\mathbf{j}$ m/sec, $\mathbf{a} = 6\mathbf{i} - 8\mathbf{j}$ m/sec^2. (a) Assuming the acceleration is constant, state the displacement (from the $t = 0$ position) and the velocity of the particle at any time t. (b) Calculate the magnitude of the displacement and the speed at $t = 2$ sec. (c) Determine the equation of the trajectory in a co-ordinate system with origin at the $t = 0$ position and x and y axes in the $\mathbf{i}$ and $\mathbf{j}$ directions. (d) Express the initial velocity and the acceleration in terms of unit vectors $\mathbf{i}'$ and $\mathbf{j}'$, such that $\mathbf{a}$ is in the $-\mathbf{j}'$ direction. (e) State the displacement and velocity at time t in terms of $\mathbf{i}'$ and $\mathbf{j}'$. (f) Again determine the magnitudes r and v at $t = 2$ sec. (g) Determine the equation of the trajectory in a co-ordinate system with axes in the $\mathbf{i}'$, $\mathbf{j}'$ directions. (h) Sketch the path of the particle, showing both sets of axes on the graph.

12. By flying on a parabolic trajectory at the speed that a freely falling projectile would have on the same path, **zero-gravity conditions** can be established in an aircraft for a limited period. A pilot starts such a trajectory with an initial velocity of 500 mph at 70° above the horizontal, and pulls out when he has returned to his initial altitude. For how long has the zero-gravity condition been maintained? What is the aircraft speed and the radius of curvature of the path at the highest point?

13. A projectile is fired with a velocity of 200 m/sec at 53° above the horizontal. Determine its vertical, horizontal, radial and tangential components of acceleration (a) at the instant it leaves the gun and (b) at the top of its path. (c) Determine the radius of curvature of the path at these points. (d) Determine the range and maximum height of the projectile, and sketch its path. Show on the diagram the circle it follows at the top of its path.

14. A projectile has a maximum horizontal range for a projection angle $\theta = 45°$. Show that for any two projection angles, $45° \pm \theta_0$ (greater than and less than 45° by the same amount) the two ranges are equal.

15. A baseball in traveling 60 ft from the pitcher's hand to the plate seems to have a very flat trajectory. What would you guess the maximum elevation above a straight

line path to be? Check your guess, assuming that the speed of the ball is 60 mph (88 ft/sec), that the ball arrives at the plate at the same height that it leaves the pitcher's hand, and neglecting the influence of the air. The speed of the ball is not constant in its path. For the situation assumed, by what percentage does it change? Would you expect the effect of the air to make the maximum elevation greater or less?

16. In a demonstration a "gun" shooting a pellet A is aimed precisely at a suspended pellet B. At the instant pellet A leaves the gun, pellet B is released to fall freely. Prove that the pellets will always collide, no matter what initial velocity A is given.

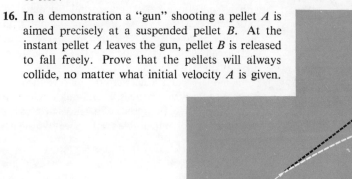

17. A boy can throw a ball a maximum horizontal distance of 100 ft. He stands 40 ft from an upright pole, the top of which is 20 ft above him. At what angle must he throw the ball, using his maximum speed, in order to hit the top of the pole?

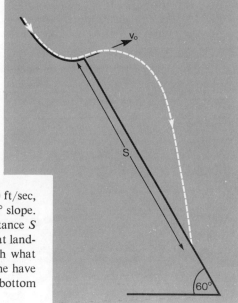

18. A skier leaves a ski jump at a velocity of 40 ft/sec, 20° above the horizontal, at the top of a 60° slope. If there were no air resistance, at what distance S down the slope would he land, and with what landing speed? If the slope is 500 ft long, with what speed (at 20° above the horizontal) would he have to leave the ski run in order to land at the bottom of the slope?

19. An evacuated tube of length $L = 1$ mile is constructed on the earth's surface, following the curvature of the earth ($R = 4000$ miles). Determine the depression

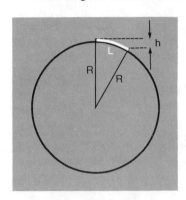

h (in feet) of one end compared to the "horizontal" at the other end. Suppose a particle is projected straight into the tube at one end, and is acted on only by the force of gravity. Treat it as a projectile with a constant acceleration **g**, and calculate its initial speed v_0 so that it drops an amount h in moving a distance L. Is its path really parabolic or is it circular? Compare the speed of a satellite in orbit at the earth's surface.

Some modern particle accelerators involve the construction of evacuated tubes several miles in length. Would you expect the speeds of particles in such accelerators to be comparable to the speed you have calculated?

20. For particles with speeds v approaching the speed of light c, a classical description of motion is inadequate; for example, the classical expression for kinetic energy $K = \frac{1}{2}mv^2$ must be replaced by a relativistic expression. However, up to speeds of about 10% of c a classical description is quite satisfactory.

There are two charged metal plates with a difference in electric potential V volts between them; a charged particle released at one plate is accelerated toward the other. Determine the maximum value of V, such that a classical description of the particle's motion can be used, if the particle is **(a)** an electron, **(b)** a proton, **(c)** a singly ionized uranium atom (atomic weight 238).

21. An electron moving with a constant horizontal velocity of 1.8×10^7 m/sec enters the space between two horizontal parallel plates 3 cm long. While it is between the plates it experiences a constant downward electrical force of 4×10^{-15} n. Determine the vertical deflection of the electron from its original path as it emerges from the space between the plates, and the velocity with which it emerges.

22. In a cathode ray tube electrons are accelerated through a potential difference of 800 volts, travel 2 cm through deflecting plates, and then 30 cm farther to hit the

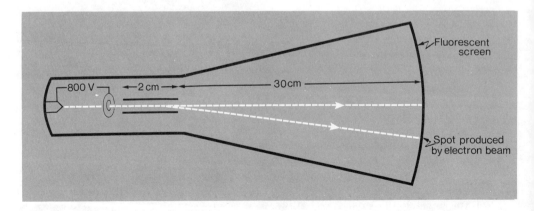

fluorescent end of the tube. The deflecting plates are 4 mm apart. Calculate the deflection of the spot on the tube if a potential difference of 30 volts is applied to the deflecting plates.

23. The deflection of an electron beam (for example in cathode ray tubes) can be produced by an electric field or a magnetic field. The shaded area, radius $r = 1.2$

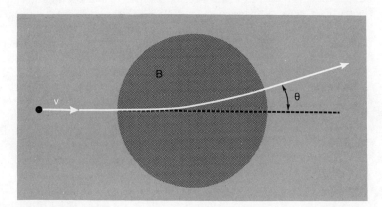

cm, represents the region between the pole pieces of an electromagnet, producing a uniform magnetic field of flux density $B = 2 \times 10^{-4}$ weber/m² perpendicular to the page. Electrons with a speed of 10^7 m/sec enter the field as shown. Calculate the angle θ through which the electron beam is deflected. (Note that the field diameter is small compared to the radius of curvature of the electron path, so that the angle of deflection is small and the distance traveled in the field is approximately $2r$.)

24. A physics student knows that the train he is on is moving on the horizontal at a steady speed of 30 mph. At one instant his handy pocket accelerometer shows him that there is a sideways acceleration of $0.1g$. What does he deduce?

25. Determine the speed and the centripetal acceleration (in units of g), in a frame of reference in which the motion is assumed to be circular, for each of the following (in each case think about what frame of reference you are using):

(a) A boy 10 ft from the center of a merry-go-round making 1 revolution every 20 sec.

(b) A particle 5 mm from the axis of an ultracentrifuge making 3500 rev/sec.

(c) A point on the crankshaft, 4 in. from the axis, in an automobile engine turning over at 3000 rpm.

(d) A man in a car rounding a curve of $\frac{1}{4}$-mile radius at 60 mph.

(e) A stomach in a man in a car moving at 20 mph through a road depression of radius of curvature 20 ft.

(f) A pebble caught in the tread of the tire of a car with 30-in. wheels, moving at 60 mph.

(g) The moon in orbit around the earth: distance 240 thousand miles, period 27.3 days.

(h) The earth in orbit around the sun: distance 93 million miles, period 1 year.

(i) An electron moving in a **betatron** (a form of particle accelerator) in an orbit of radius 1 m, at approximately the speed of light.

26. A **cyclotron** is a device for accelerating charged particles to high energies, while keeping them confined to a small region of space using a strong magnetic field. The particles move in an evacuated chamber, at right angles to the magnetic field,

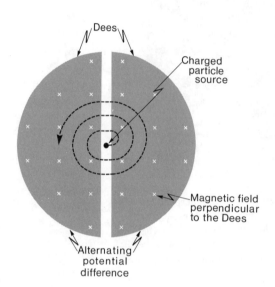

and inside a flat metal box which is in two halves (the **dees** of the cyclotron). There is an electric potential difference between the two dees, which alternates at a frequency such that the potential difference is reversed in the time that it takes for a particle to make a half-revolution in the magnetic field. Thus a particle is accelerated from one dee to the other, makes a half-circle and is accelerated back to the first dee. Each time it passes the gap between the dees, it is accelerated, receiving energy from the electric field. As its speed increases, the radius of its orbit increases. A cyclotron to accelerate protons ($e = 1.6 \times 10^{-19}$ coul, $m = 1.67 \times 10^{-27}$ kg) uses a magnetic field of flux density $B = 1$ weber/m² , extending over an area of radius 14 cm. (These are roughly the characteristics of the first cyclotron, designed by E. O. Lawrence in 1930 at Berkeley.) Calculate the frequency of the alternating field applied to the dees, and the energy of a proton in orbit at the outer edge of the cyclotron. Note that the speed of the proton is not close to c, the speed of light, and therefore a classical (non-relativistic) calculation is satisfactory.

27. Determine the maximum speed and the maximum acceleration (in units of g) for each of the following, assuming that the motion is simple harmonic (think about what frame of reference you are using in each case):

(a) The end of a diving board makes 3 vibrations/sec, moving through a total distance of 4 in.

(b) The piston of a car moves through a total distance of 4 in.; the motor is turning over at 3000 rpm.

(c) A car bounces up and down on its springs through a total distance of 3 in., with a period of 1 sec.

(d) A boy on a swing pulled sideways 4 ft and released returns to his initial position in 5 sec.

(e) A saucer is 14 cm in diameter; a marble released at one edge reaches the center in 0.2 sec.

(f) An electrically driven quartz crystal produces an ultrasonic signal of frequency 1 Mc/sec; the crystal is 1 mm thick, and when vibrating its thickness changes by ±1 × 10⁻⁴%.

(g) As surface waves on water pass a floating cork it bobs up and down 3 times every second, with an amplitude of 1 cm.

(h) A loud sound of frequency 1000 cps transmitted through the air involves an amplitude of vibration of the air of about 10^{-5} m.

(i) A faint sound of frequency 1000 cps transmitted through the air involves an amplitude of vibration of the air of about 10^{-11} m.

(j) A tunnel is drilled through the earth, along a diameter; a stone dropped at one end reaches the other in 42.2 min.

(k) An atom in a solid vibrates about its mean position with a frequency of 10^{13} cps and an amplitude of 0.1 angstrom unit.

28. Show that if the motion of a particle is described by $x = x_0 \sin (\omega t + \delta)$, then $\tan \delta = \omega x_1/v_1$, where x_1 and v_1 are the displacement and velocity at $t = 0$. What difference does it make in this expression if the cosine instead of the sine function is used for the SHM?

29. The motion of a particle on the x-axis is described by $x = 20 \cos (5\pi t + 0.4\pi)$ cm, where t is in sec. (a) State the amplitude, angular frequency, frequency, and period of the motion. (b) State the phase angle in radians and degrees, and the phase in seconds and as a fraction of the period. (c) Determine the displacement, velocity, and acceleration of the particle at $t = 0$.

30. A particle oscillates in SHM on the x-axis between $x = 10$ cm and $x = 40$ cm. At $x = 15$ cm its speed is 20 cm/sec. Determine its period.

31. An object sits on a shelf which moves up and down in SHM with an amplitude of 10 cm. What is the shortest period of vibration possible if the object is to remain in contact with the shelf at all times?

32. A particle oscillates in simple harmonic motion with amplitude x_0. At what displacement is its acceleration one-half its maximum acceleration? At what displacement is its speed one-half its maximum speed?

33. Two particles are moving with SHM along the same line and about the same origin. They have the same amplitude and frequency, and pass one another each time that their displacement is (a) half their amplitude, (b) one-quarter their amplitude. Determine their phase difference in each case.

34. A particle undergoes two simultaneous simple harmonic motions, represented by $x_1 = 5 \sin (2\pi t/5)$, $x_2 = 10 \sin (2\pi t/10)$, where x_1 and x_2 are in cm, and t is in sec.

(a) If the SHM's are in the same line about the same origin, sketch x_1, x_2, and $(x_1 + x_2)$ as a function of time, from 0 to 10 sec.

(b) If the SHM's are at right angles to one another, about the same origin, sketch the path of the particle in the x_1-x_2 plane.

35. A wheel, initially at rest, rotates about a fixed axle and reaches a speed of 750 rpm after 35 complete revolutions. Assuming that its angular acceleration is uniform, how long did the acceleration take?

36. At time $t = 0$ a wheel is rotating at a speed of 2 rad/sec, and is given an angular acceleration α of $\alpha = 3t$ rad/sec^2, where t is in seconds. At what value of t will the wheel have made 1 rev?

37. Two flywheels, A of radius 1 ft and B of radius 6 in., on separate shafts, are rotating at 300 rpm and 100 rpm, respectively. The power to both is removed at the same instant and A comes to rest in 1 min, B in 2 min, both with uniform deceleration. (a) How many revolutions does each make in stopping? (b) At what instant is the angular speed the same for each? What is this speed? (c) At what instant is the (linear) speed of a point on the rim of A the same as that of a point on the rim of B? What is this speed?

38. Show that if any rotating system is started from rest at time $t = 0$, and has a constant angular acceleration α, then the radial and tangential components of acceleration of any point in the system are equal in magnitude after a time $t = 1/\sqrt{\alpha}$, and show that there is an error of less than 1% in assuming that the resultant acceleration of any point is equal to the radial acceleration after a time $t = \sqrt[4]{50/\alpha^2}$. Determine these times, and the corresponding angular speeds, for a gyroscope wheel accelerated uniformly from rest to 6000 rpm in a period of 1 hr.

6

GALILEAN TRANSFORMATION
OF THE FRAME OF REFERENCE

The last chapter was devoted to the general description of motion of a particle in a frame of reference, and to certain special motions that are simple to describe in an appropriate frame of reference. The quantities **r**, **v** and **a** were defined; they are independent of any particular co-ordinate system in the frame of reference, and may be used to specify limitations on the motion.

The frame of reference used to describe a motion is a matter of choice. Although measurements are made with respect to one frame of reference, it may be convenient to describe the motion with respect to a different frame of reference. The transformation of the frame of reference in which a motion is described is one of the most useful intellectual devices in physics.

We wish to develop the transformation relations that make it possible to transform the quantities **r**, **v** and **a** describing the motion of a particle in one frame of reference S to the quantities **r**′, **v**′ and **a**′ describing the motion in a different frame S'.

The frame of reference S includes all co-ordinate systems that are at rest in S, independent of their position or orientation, therefore what is meant by a different frame S' is one that is **moving** with respect to S. All co-ordinate systems in S' are at rest in S'.

We shall consider in this chapter only transformations in which S and S' are moving with respect to one another **at constant velocity.** In the next chapter we will look at transformations in which S and S' are accelerated with respect to one another.

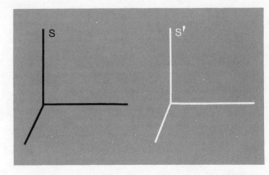

If S and S' represent different frames of reference, these must be moving with respect to one another.

We are still primarily concerned with the description of motion, but we will in this chapter, as we did in the last chapter, assume in some of the examples a knowledge of such basic dynamical concepts as momentum and energy, and in this way provide a review of such concepts.

FRAMES OF REFERENCE MOVING AT CONSTANT RELATIVE VELOCITY

Think about two frames of reference that are moving at a constant velocity **V** with respect to one another. This means that a particle at rest in S' is moving with a velocity **V** if measured with respect to S; a particle at rest in S is moving with a velocity $-$**V** with respect to S'.

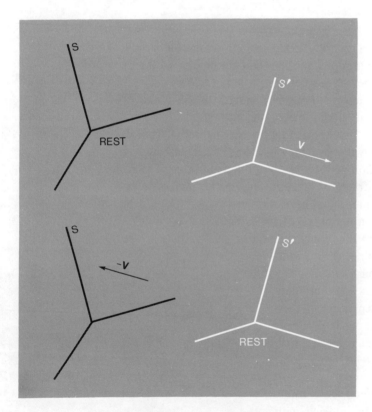

If frame S' is moving at velocity **V** with respect to S, then frame S is moving at velocity $-$**V** with respect to S'.

The quantities **r**, **v** and **a** do not depend on the orientation or position of co-ordinate systems in either frame of reference, so that it is convenient, in order to visualize the situation, to consider two Cartesian co-ordinate systems (x,y,z) in S and (x',y',z') in S', oriented so that **V** is a vector in both the $+x$ and $+x'$

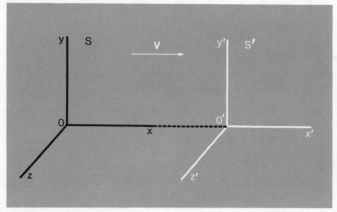

It is convenient to choose co-ordinate systems (x, y, z) in S and (x', y', z') in S' oriented so that the respective axes are parallel, and such that the x and x' axes are in the **V** direction and coincide.

directions and all the respective axes are parallel, and positioned so that the x and x' axes coincide.

In order to be able to describe motion over a time interval $0 \rightarrow t$, we think of the axes positioned so that the origins O and O' coincide at time $t = 0$. Then at any later time t, the origin O' is at $x = Vt$, and the origin O is at $x' = -Vt$, where $V = |\mathbf{V}|$.

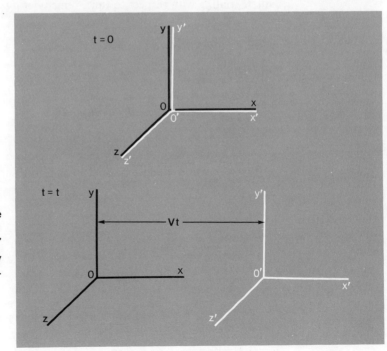

Co-ordinate systems are chosen such that at $t = 0$ the origins O and O' coincide; at time t they are separated by a distance Vt.

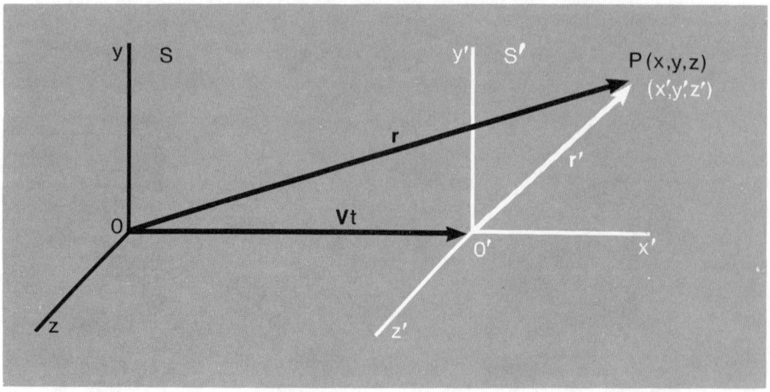

Displacement of a particle P referred to the fixed point O in S, and to the fixed point O' in S'.

The displacement of a particle P in the frame of reference S can be referred to any point in S. Choosing $\mathbf{r}$ as the displacement from the point O, it is the radius vector in this particular co-ordinate system. Choosing $\mathbf{r}'$ as the displacement from the point O' in the frame S' means that at $t = 0$, when O and O' coincide, displacement in both systems is measured from the same point. The relation between displacements at any other time t can be seen from the diagram

$$\mathbf{r} = \mathbf{r}' + \mathbf{V}t$$

Differentiating with respect to time, remembering that $\mathbf{V}$ is a constant

$$\frac{d\mathbf{r}}{dt} = \frac{d\mathbf{r}'}{dt} + \mathbf{V} \qquad \text{or} \qquad \mathbf{v} = \mathbf{v}' + \mathbf{V}$$

Differentiating once again

$$\frac{d\mathbf{v}}{dt} = \frac{d\mathbf{v}'}{dt} \qquad \text{or} \qquad \mathbf{a} = \mathbf{a}'$$

These are the transformation equations for displacement, velocity and acceleration between the two frames of reference. Knowing $\mathbf{r}'$, $\mathbf{v}'$ and $\mathbf{a}'$ in S', we can calculate $\mathbf{r}$, $\mathbf{v}$ and $\mathbf{a}$ in S. The inverse transformations

$$\mathbf{r}' = \mathbf{r} - \mathbf{V}t$$
$$\mathbf{v}' = \mathbf{v} - \mathbf{V}$$
$$\mathbf{a}' = \mathbf{a}$$

may be written as

$$\mathbf{r}' = \mathbf{r} + (-\mathbf{V})t$$
$$\mathbf{v}' = \mathbf{v} + (-\mathbf{V})$$
$$\mathbf{a}' = \mathbf{a}$$

which is exactly the same form as the initial transformations, with the S and S' variables interchanged, and with $\mathbf{V}$ replaced by $-\mathbf{V}$. If $\mathbf{V}$ is the velocity of frame S' with respect to S, then $-\mathbf{V}$ is the velocity of frame S with respect to S', and it can be seen that the general transformation relations for two frames of reference moving at constant relative velocity are

$$\begin{pmatrix} \text{Displacement} \\ \text{in one frame} \end{pmatrix} = \begin{pmatrix} \text{Displacement} \\ \text{in 2nd frame} \end{pmatrix} + \begin{pmatrix} \text{Velocity of 2nd} \\ \text{frame re 1st} \end{pmatrix} \begin{pmatrix} \text{Time} \\ \text{interval} \end{pmatrix}$$

$$\begin{pmatrix} \text{Velocity} \\ \text{in one frame} \end{pmatrix} = \begin{pmatrix} \text{Velocity} \\ \text{in 2nd frame} \end{pmatrix} + \begin{pmatrix} \text{Velocity of 2nd} \\ \text{frame re 1st} \end{pmatrix}$$

$$\begin{pmatrix} \text{Acceleration} \\ \text{in one frame} \end{pmatrix} = \begin{pmatrix} \text{Acceleration} \\ \text{in 2nd frame} \end{pmatrix}$$

These are vector relations, and do not depend on the position or orientation of co-ordinate systems in the two frames of reference. In the particular co-ordinate systems that we used to help visualize the two frames of reference, the scalar transformations are

$$
\begin{aligned}
x &= x' + Vt & x' &= x - Vt \\
y &= y' & y' &= y \\
z &= z' & z' &= z \\
v_x &= v_{x'} + V & v_{x'} &= v_x - V \\
v_y &= v_{y'} & v_{y'} &= v_y \\
v_z &= v_{z'} & v_{z'} &= v_z \\
a_x &= a_{x'} & a_{x'} &= a_x \\
a_y &= a_{y'} & a_{y'} &= a_y \\
a_z &= a_{z'} & a_{z'} &= a_z
\end{aligned}
$$

The term **Galilean transformation** is used for these, whether in vector or in scalar form. They appear to be rather simple and straightforward, following directly from the definitions of displacement, velocity and acceleration in a single frame of reference. It is therefore rather surprising that in certain physical situations these transformations turn out to be wrong. It is an experimental fact that if any of the velocities involved are close to the speed of light in magnitude, these transformations are incorrect. This means that in developing them there must have been some assumptions made that are invalid. The implicit assumptions that would have to be examined are that length as measured in S and in S' is the same, and that time as measured in S and S' is the same; the transformation $t = t'$ was not stated, but was assumed. We have considered that if a particle is in a position P_1 at time t_1, and a position P_2 at time t_2 then in the time interval $(t_2 - t_1)$ the particle will have moved a certain distance, independent of

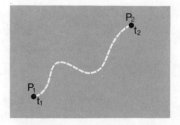

In classical mechanics it is implicitly assumed that the change in position of a particle measured in a certain time interval is independent of the frame of reference in which the measurements are made.

the frame of reference in which measurements of position and time are made; in other words, we have considered that length (necessary to specify position) and time are independent absolute quantities. This is a basic assumption of classical or Newtonian mechanics, but an assumption that is relinquished in relativistic or Einsteinian mechanics.

In spite of the fact that classical mechanics turns out to be inadequate in dealing with motions where speeds close to the speed of light are involved, it is a system of mechanics that is completely satisfactory for handling an enormous variety of physical situations where this limitation does not apply. Since one basic aim of physics is to develop methods of unifying the description of a range of physical phenomena, classical mechanics remains an important part of the structure of physics. The fact that it is not "true" in some absolute sense does not lessen its importance as a useful physical theory. In addition to its usefulness in analyzing physical situations, to the student of physics an understanding of classical mechanics is a necessary background for the understanding of other systems of mechanics, relativistic mechanics and quantum mechanics.

The Galilean transformations show that for two frames of reference S and S' moving at constant velocity with respect to one another the accelerations $\mathbf{a}$ and $\mathbf{a}'$, measured for a particle, are the same in both frames. This means that the acceleration is the same in *all* frames of reference moving at constant relative velocities; this is expressed by stating that acceleration is an invariant under a Galilean transformation, and leads to the statement that all such frames of reference are **dynamically equivalent.** It is for this reason that the Galilean transformation is particularly useful and important. We shall see in discussing dynamics that there are certain frames of reference called **inertial frames** in which Newton's laws of dynamics are valid. If one inertial frame of reference can be found, all frames of reference moving at constant velocity with respect to it are also inertial frames. The Galilean transformation applies to all transformations between inertial frames.

At present we are concerned primarily with the description of motion, and we go on to look at the application of the Galilean transformations to a number of examples. The simplest example is the transformation for an object at rest in S'; then $\mathbf{v}' = 0$, and $\mathbf{v} = \mathbf{V}$ is constant. The next step is to consider motion in S' at constant velocity $\mathbf{v}'$; then $\mathbf{v} = \mathbf{v}' + \mathbf{V}$ is also constant. There are many situations where this transformation is useful, and we shall look at some of these.

TRANSFORMATION OF CONSTANT VELOCITIES

Example 1: A river one-half mile wide flows due south at a steady rate of 3 mph. A boat that travels at an average speed of 5 mph in still water makes three different 1-mile trips on the river: trip I, from point A to a point B $\frac{1}{2}$ mile downstream and back to A;

II, from point A to a point C directly across the river and back; and III, from point A to a point D 1 mile away on the opposite bank. Calculate the time for each trip.

The three paths are specified in a frame of reference fixed on the earth, but the boat moves at a steady speed of 5 mph in the frame of reference of the river. The transformation relation is

$$\mathbf{v}_E = \mathbf{v}_R + \mathbf{V}$$

where $\mathbf{v}_E$ is the velocity of the boat relative to the earth (i.e., relative to a frame of reference fixed on the earth), $\mathbf{v}_R$ is the velocity of the boat relative to the river, and $\mathbf{V}$ is the velocity of the river relative to the earth. The vector $\mathbf{V}$ is fixed in magnitude and direction: it is 3 mph due south. The vector $\mathbf{v}_R$ is fixed in magnitude as 5 mph, but its direction depends on the direction the boat is headed.

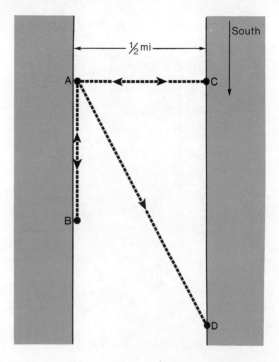

Three boat trips
of equal length.

For trip I, as the boat heads downstream from A to B, $\mathbf{v}_R$ and $\mathbf{V}$ are in the same direction and $\mathbf{v}_E = 8$ mph due south. On the return journey $\mathbf{v}_R$ and $\mathbf{V}$ are in opposite directions, and $\mathbf{v}_E = 2$ mph due north. The boat travels $\frac{1}{2}$ mile at 8 mph and $\frac{1}{2}$ mile at 2 mph (both distances and speeds relative to the earth) and the total time for the trip is

$$\frac{1/2}{8} + \frac{1/2}{2} = \frac{5}{16} \text{ hr}$$

For trip II, it is apparent that if the boat heads straight out from the bank at A, toward the point C directly across the river, it will be carried downstream by the current. The path straight across is specified relative to the earth, and this means that the velocity $\mathbf{v}_E$ (not $\mathbf{v}_R$) must be along this path. Therefore to travel due east the boat must head upstream at an angle φ as shown. (Note that the angle φ gives the direction that the boat heads in the frame of reference of the river.) The resultant vector diagram is a right-angled triangle;

$$v_E^2 = v_R^2 - V^2 = 25 - 9 = 16 \qquad v_E = 4 \text{ mph} \qquad \sin \varphi = 3/5 \qquad \varphi = 37°$$

Similarly on the return journey from C to A, the boat must head 37° north of west, and on both parts of the trip the speed relative to the earth is 4 mph. The total time for trip II is $\frac{1}{4}$ hr.

Velocity diagrams
for trip I.

The boat will not go straight across the river if it heads straight out from the bank.

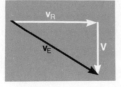

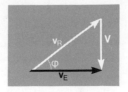

Velocity diagram
for trip II.

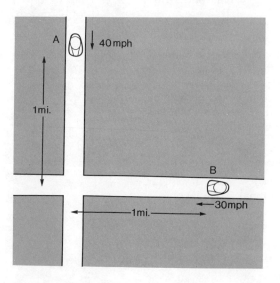

For trip III, the boat must head along the path AD, which is 60° south of east since ACD is a right-angled triangle with $AC = \frac{1}{2}$ mi, $AD = 1$ mi. From the vector triangle, using the law of cosines

$$v_R^2 = v_E^2 + V^2 - 2v_E V \cos 30°$$
$$25 = v_E^2 + 9 - 3\sqrt{3}\, v_E$$

Solution of the quadratic gives $v_E = 7.37$ mph. The angle θ can be determined (although it is not required)

$$v_E \cos 60° = v_R \cos \theta$$
$$\cos \theta = 7.37 \times 0.5/5 = 0.737$$
$$\theta = 42.5°$$

Alternatively, the angle θ can first be determined and used to find v_E. From the law of sines

$$5/\sin 30° = 3/\sin (60° - \theta)$$

$$\sin (60° - \theta) = 0.3 \qquad 60° - \theta = 17.5°$$

The time for trip III is $1/7.37 = 0.136$ hr.

Velocity diagram
for trip III.

While this example has been expressed in terms of a specific familiar situation, the approach has a broad applicability.

Example 2: Two automobiles are approaching an intersection. Car A is moving south at 40 mph, car B west at 30 mph. At one instant each car is one mile from the intersection. Determine the distance of closest approach of the cars.

The faster car A will reach the intersection first: after $\frac{1}{40}$ hr, it will be at the intersection and B will have moved $\frac{3}{4}$ mi and be $\frac{1}{4}$ mi away. After $\frac{1}{30}$ hr, B will be at the intersection and A will have moved a total of $\frac{4}{3}$ mi and be $\frac{1}{3}$ mi past the intersection. Is $\frac{1}{4}$ mi the distance of closest approach?

In the previous example the paths were specified with respect to the frame of reference of the earth, and therefore the calculations were made in that frame of reference. In this example the question posed does not relate to the earth, but to the two cars, and therefore is answered most easily by analyzing the motion in a frame of reference fixed to one of the cars. Velocities are given with respect to the earth: $\mathbf{v}_{A\,re\,E} = 40$ mph south, $\mathbf{v}_{B\,re\,E} = 30$ mph west. We wish to describe the motion in a frame of reference fixed to one of the cars,

Two cars approaching
an intersection.

say car A. Then $v_{A\,re\,A} = 0$, and we need $v_{B\,re\,A}$. The general transformation relation is

$$v_{B\,re\,A} = v_{B\,re\,E} + v_{E\,re\,A}$$

but since $$v_{E\,re\,A} = -v_{A\,re\,E}$$

$$v_{B\,re\,A} = v_{B\,re\,E} + (-v_{A\,re\,E})$$
$$= v_{B\,re\,E} - v_{A\,re\,E}$$

The resultant of the velocity $v_{B\,re\,E}$ of 30 mph west and the velocity $-v_{A\,re\,E}$ of 40 mph north is the velocity $v_{B\,re\,A}$ of magnitude 50 mph and direction $\theta = 53°$ north of west.

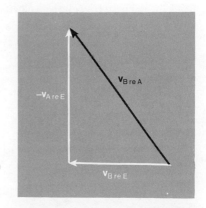

Velocity of car B with respect to car A.

This result does not depend on the relative positions of A and B. At one instant (say $t = 0$) the cars are $\sqrt{2}$ miles apart, as shown. The motion of B with respect to A (i.e., in the frame of reference of A) is shown by the dotted path in the direction of $v_{B\,re\,A}$, 53° north of west, or 8° away from the line joining A and B at $t = 0$. The distance of closest approach D is the perpendicular distance from A to the path:

$$D = \sqrt{2} \sin 8° = 0.20 \text{ mi}$$

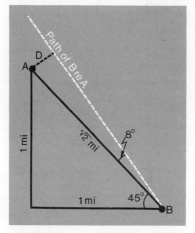

Path of car B in the frame of reference of car A.

As a check on this result, we can determine the position of the cars in the frame of reference of the earth at the instant of closest approach. Relative to car A, car B moves a distance $\sqrt{2} \cos 8° = 1.4$ mi, at a speed $v_{B\,re\,A} = 50$ mph, so the time required is $1.4/50 = 0.028$ hr. In this time, relative to the earth, car A moves $40 \times 0.028 = 1.12$ mi, and car B moves $30 \times 0.028 = 0.84$ mi; car A is 0.12 mi past the intersection, car B has 0.16 mi farther to go to reach it. Their distance apart at this instant is

$$\sqrt{0.12^2 + 0.16^2} = 0.20 \text{ mi}$$

the distance of closest approach.

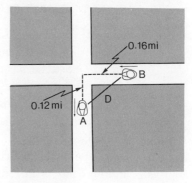

Positions of cars in the earth frame at the instant of closest approach.

RELATIVE VELOCITY

The term **relative velocity** is sometimes defined in physics as velocity **difference,** as follows. If a particle A has velocity $\mathbf{v}_A$, and particle B has velocity $\mathbf{v}_B$, then the velocity of B with respect to A is

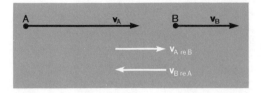

$$\mathbf{v}_{B \text{ re } A} = \mathbf{v}_B - \mathbf{v}_A$$

and similarly the velocity of A with respect to B is

$$\mathbf{v}_{A \text{ re } B} = \mathbf{v}_A - \mathbf{v}_B$$

Relative velocity for parallel velocity vectors.

From the previous example it is clear that this definition is consistent with the Galilean velocity transformation that we have developed. We do not emphasize this definition of relative velocity because **all velocities are relative velocities.** That is, all velocities are measured in a particular frame of reference, and are velocities relative to that frame. The velocities $\mathbf{v}_A$ and $\mathbf{v}_B$ referred to are velocities in some arbitrary "rest" frame of reference. Forming the relative velocity as defined is simply a transformation to a different frame of reference.

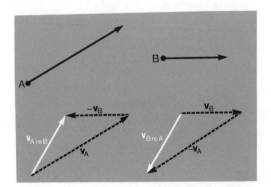

Relative velocity for non-parallel velocity vectors.

We feel that it is important to have in mind that "at rest" and "in motion" are always relative terms, and therefore we focus our attention on the reference frame in which motions are described.

CENTER-OF-MASS FRAME OF REFERENCE

Almost all of the information about the behavior of fundamental particles comes from experiments involving **collisions** between particles—or, to be more precise, **interactions** between particles. It is not possible to examine a proton or a neutron or an electron or an atomic nucleus by looking at it with the naked eye, or under a microscope. Our information about particles is not obtained directly through our senses, but indirectly through various devices that extend the range of observability. The path of a charged particle can be observed in a number of ways (in a cloud chamber or a bubble chamber, or with photographic film) because of its ionization effect. Also the arrival of a charged particle at a certain place can be detected in various ways—with a fluorescent screen, or an ionization chamber, or a scintillation counter.

Knowing the path of a particle *before* it interacts with another particle, and observing its path *after* the interaction, it is sometimes possible to determine something about the nature of the interaction. Such an experiment is usually called a **scattering** experiment because the particle is scattered from its original path by interactions (or "collisions") with other particles. If the particle interacts with more than one other particle, it is usually not possible to deduce what happened, but it is often possible to establish experimental conditions where it is reasonable to assume that scattering occurs because of two-particle interactions. A great deal of physics involves the analysis of two-body interactions, because much of our information about the fundamental constituents of matter is derived from scattering experiments.

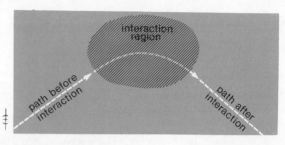

Scattering of a particle.

At present we are focusing our attention on the description of the motion of a single particle, and we have established that the description depends on the frame of reference chosen. The analysis of a two-particle interaction is often simplified by considering the motion in a special frame of reference called the center-of-mass frame, and we shall introduce it here even though it makes it necessary for us to use concepts such as force, mass and momentum which we have not yet discussed in detail. However, these concepts should be familiar.

The path of a particle is observed in an experiment in a frame of reference fixed in the laboratory in which the experiment is performed; this is the **laboratory frame of reference.** The path of the particle is affected by its interaction with another particle; transformation from the lab frame to the center-of-mass frame of reference (c-of-m frame) is often useful.

Two particles, of masses m_1 and m_2, have displacements $\mathbf{r}_1$ and $\mathbf{r}_2$ with respect to a fixed point O in the lab frame, and velocities $\mathbf{v}_1$ and $\mathbf{v}_2$ in this frame. The **center of mass** of the system of two particles is defined as the position specified by the displacement

$$\mathbf{r}_c = \frac{m_1 \mathbf{r}_1 + m_2 \mathbf{r}_2}{m_1 + m_2}$$

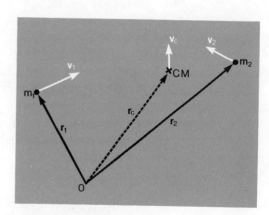

Center of mass of a two-particle system.

Differentiation with respect to time, noting that the masses m_1 and m_2 are assumed to be constant, and that $d\mathbf{r}_1/dt$ and $d\mathbf{r}_2/dt$ are the velocities $\mathbf{v}_1$ and $\mathbf{v}_2$, shows that the velocity of the c-of-m is

$$\mathbf{v}_c = \frac{d\mathbf{r}_c}{dt} = \frac{m_1 \mathbf{v}_1 + m_2 \mathbf{v}_2}{m_1 + m_2}$$

This can equally well be taken as the definition of the center of mass.

The position of the c-of-m is always on the line joining the positions of m_1 and m_2 as may be seen as follows. At any instant the displacement can be referred to the position of m_1: then $\mathbf{r}_1 = 0$, and $\mathbf{r}_c = m_2\mathbf{r}_2/(m_1 + m_2)$, so $\mathbf{r}_c$ is in the same direction as $\mathbf{r}_2$, but is of a different magnitude. If $m_1 = m_2$, $\mathbf{r}_c = \mathbf{r}_2/2$, and the c-of-m is midway between the particles; for any other ratio of masses $d_1/d_2 = m_2/m_1$: if $m_1 > m_2$, then $d_2 > d_1$ and the c-of-m is closer to m_1. The c-of-m is a weighted average position, weighted on the basis of mass. Similarly the velocity $\mathbf{v}_c$ is a weighted average velocity for the system of particles. The diagrams are drawn for $m_2 = 2m_1$, so that $\mathbf{v}_c = \frac{1}{3}\mathbf{v}_1 + \frac{2}{3}\mathbf{v}_2$.

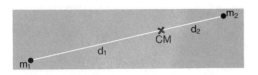

The center of mass lies on the line joining the two particles.

If $\mathbf{v}_1$ and $\mathbf{v}_2$ are constant velocities, as would be the case if the two particles were each moving freely (i.e., without being acted on by any unbalanced forces), then $\mathbf{v}_c$ is also constant. Then we can use the Galilean velocity transformation to determine the velocities $\mathbf{v}_{1c}$ and $\mathbf{v}_{2c}$ of the two particles in **the c-of-m frame of reference.**

The velocity of the c-of-m in the lab frame is $\mathbf{v}_c$, therefore the velocity of the lab frame in the c-of-m frame is $-\mathbf{v}_c$. From the transformation relation

$$\mathbf{v}_{1c} = \mathbf{v}_1 + (-\mathbf{v}_c) = \mathbf{v}_1 - \frac{m_1\mathbf{v}_1 + m_2\mathbf{v}_2}{m_1 + m_2} = \frac{m_2}{m_1 + m_2}(\mathbf{v}_1 - \mathbf{v}_2)$$

$$\mathbf{v}_{2c} = \mathbf{v}_2 + (-\mathbf{v}_c) = \mathbf{v}_2 - \frac{m_1\mathbf{v}_1 + m_2\mathbf{v}_2}{m_1 + m_2} = \frac{m_1}{m_1 + m_2}(\mathbf{v}_2 - \mathbf{v}_1) = -\frac{m_1}{m_2}\mathbf{v}_{1c}$$

This shows that in the c-of-m frame the particles are moving in opposite directions along the same line, as would be expected since the c-of-m is always on the line joining them. In the special case where $m_1 = m_2$, the particles have equal and opposite velocities in the c-of-m frame.

The relation $m_1\mathbf{v}_{1c} + m_2\mathbf{v}_{2c} = 0$ may be written $\mathbf{p}_{1c} + \mathbf{p}_{2c} = 0$

where $\mathbf{p} = m\mathbf{v}$ is the **momentum** of a particle of mass m moving with a velocity $\mathbf{v}$. Momentum is a vector quantity, and its value depends on the frame of reference. In the c-of-m frame the momenta of the two particles are equal and opposite, and the **total momentum is zero.** This is another way in which the c-of-m frame may be defined.

COLLISIONS

We have defined the c-of-m frame of reference for a system of two freely moving particles, and have stated that it is useful in considering a collision or interaction of the two particles. In order to see how it is useful, it will be necessary to recall certain basic considerations of dynamics. A discussion of collisions therefore is an opportunity to review some of the fundamentals of dynamics, as well as an important application of transformation of the frame of reference.

If two particles interact only with one another, then there is no external unbalanced force on the system of two particles, and this means, from Newton's laws of dynamics, that the total momentum of the system is unchanged by the interaction; momentum is conserved in the collision. The principle of the conservation of momentum is a corollary of Newton's laws that you will have met before, at least for one-dimensional situations.

There is conservation of momentum whether the motion of the particles is described in the lab frame of reference, or in the c-of-m frame. However, in the c-of-m frame the total momentum is zero, both before and after the collision, and this sometimes makes the collision simpler to analyze.

Think about the collision of two particles of masses m_1 and m_2, moving before the collision with constant velocities $\mathbf{v}_1$ and $\mathbf{v}_2$ in the lab frame. After the collision they have velocities $\mathbf{v}_1'$ and $\mathbf{v}_2'$, again considered to be constant. If the collision is thought of as the impact between two perfectly rigid solid objects that exert a force on one another only during the instant of contact, then the path of each particle consists of two straight line segments. However, this is not a very realistic model. For collisions between steel pellets or billiard balls, solid objects that come into physical contact, it may give an adequate picture, but for collisions between fundamental particles the term "contact" is meaningless. For such particles it is more sensible to think about an **interaction region.** In general

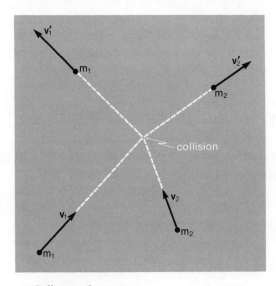

Collision of two
particles at a point.

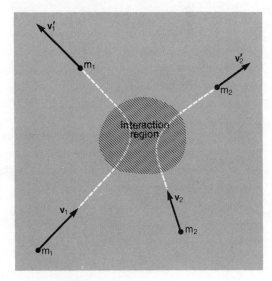

"Collision" of two
interacting particles.

there will be a force between the two particles that is larger the closer they are together (there will always be the inverse-square gravitational force of attraction, for example, and there will be as well electromagnetic or nuclear interactions) so that if they are far enough apart the force may be considered negligible, and the particles considered to be moving freely with velocities $\mathbf{v}_1$ and $\mathbf{v}_2$. If the particles are approaching one another, at some point their influence on one another will become sufficient to affect their motion, and over some time interval they will interact; they may combine to form a single particle, so that $\mathbf{v}_1' = \mathbf{v}_2'$, or they may move apart so that they can again be considered to be moving freely with constant velocities $\mathbf{v}_1'$ and $\mathbf{v}_2'$. The essential factor in considering that momentum is conserved in the interaction is that external forces on the system produce a negligible effect during the time interval of the interaction.

The term **collision** is used for convenience even for interactions where it is unreasonable to think of physical contact. If it can be assumed that momentum is conserved in a collision, then in the lab frame of reference

$$m_1\mathbf{v}_1 + m_2\mathbf{v}_2 = m_1\mathbf{v}_1' + m_2\mathbf{v}_2'$$

or

$$\mathbf{p}_1 + \mathbf{p}_2 = \mathbf{p}_1' + \mathbf{p}_2'$$

In the c-of-m frame of reference

$$m_1\mathbf{v}_{1c} + m_2\mathbf{v}_{2c} = m_1\mathbf{v}_{1c}' + m_2\mathbf{v}_{2c}' = 0$$

or

$$\mathbf{p}_{1c} + \mathbf{p}_{2c} = \mathbf{p}_{1c}' + \mathbf{p}_{2c}' = 0$$

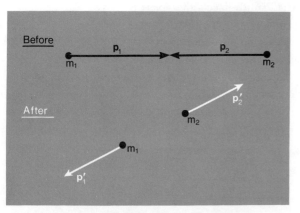

Momenta of two particles in the c-of-m frame of reference before and after a collision.

Before the collision the momenta are equal and opposite, and after the collision the momenta are equal and opposite.

Note that this does *not* mean that the momenta are in the same direction before and after the collision, and does *not* mean that the magnitude of the momenta are the same before and after the collision. Conservation of momentum places some limitation on what can happen in a collision, but does not uniquely determine the result.

Another factor that is convenient in describing collisions is energy. If the total kinetic energy is conserved in the collision it is called an **elastic collision.**

Then

$$\tfrac{1}{2}m_1v_1^2 + \tfrac{1}{2}m_2v_2^2 = \tfrac{1}{2}m_1v_1'^2 + \tfrac{1}{2}m_2v_2'^2 = K_1$$

or

$$\tfrac{1}{2}m_1v_{1c}^2 + \tfrac{1}{2}m_2v_{2c}^2 = \tfrac{1}{2}m_1v_{1c}'^2 + \tfrac{1}{2}m_2v_{2c}'^2 = K_2$$

The constant total energy is different in the two different frames of reference; you will recall that there is an arbitrary zero associated with any definition of energy. The collisions of any two macroscopic objects is never elastic because there is always some mechanical energy converted into heat energy in the collision, although collisions between rigid solids such as steel or glass spheres can be treated as elastic to a good approximation. The only collisions that can really be considered elastic occur at the microscopic or atomic level. At normal temperatures the collisions between molecules of a gas are usually elastic: only if the collision produces excitation or dissociation of a molecule is it not elastic, and the thermal energy of gas molecules at normal temperatures is not high enough for this to be a likely event. Collisions between fundamental particles such as protons, electrons or neutrons that are not considered to have an internal structure are elastic unless the particles become bound together in the interaction; then some of the initial kinetic energy becomes stored as potential energy.

Collisions that are not elastic have a final kinetic energy that may be less than the initial kinetic energy (due to transformation to some other form of energy) or greater than the initial kinetic energy (due to the release of some form of energy); collisions of the latter kind are sometimes called explosive. Collisions in which the two objects stick together after the collision are usually called **inelastic,** although sometimes this term is used for any non-elastic collision, and ones in which the particles stick together are then called completely inelastic. For such a collision in the c-of-m frame of reference $\mathbf{p}'_{1c} = \mathbf{p}'_{2c} = 0$; both particles are at rest at the c-of-m.

Another factor that influences what happens in a collision is the relative orientation of the particle paths. A particularly simple kind of collision occurs if the orientation is such that the momenta before and after collision are in the

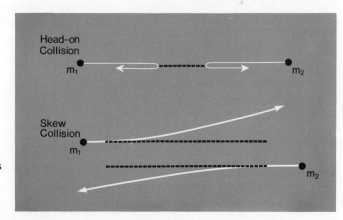

Head-on and skew collisions of interacting particles.

same direction. Such a collision is called **head-on** or **direct** and can be described readily because the motion is confined to one dimension. Any other collision is called a **skew** collision and involves motion in two or three dimensions.

In macroscopic situations it is possible to arrange one-dimensional collision experiments by using cars confined to tracks, or suspended pendula, but microscopic head-on collisions are relatively rare events. Nonetheless it will be useful to analyze one-dimensional collisions, considering the motion both from the lab frame of reference and the c-of-m frame.

HEAD-ON ELASTIC COLLISION

Rather than use the prime notation $\mathbf{v}'$ for velocities after collision, it will be more convenient to use the symbol $\mathbf{u}$ for velocities before collision and the symbol $\mathbf{v}$ for velocities after collision. Assuming conservation of momentum in the collision

$$m_1\mathbf{u}_1 + m_2\mathbf{u}_2 = m_1\mathbf{v}_1 + m_2\mathbf{v}_2$$

This vector equation in general is equivalent to three scalar equations. However, the collision is specified to be head-on, so the velocity vectors all lie in the same line. By choosing a co-ordinate system with one of its axes along this line one of the scalar equations is $m_1u_1 + m_2u_2 = m_1v_1 + m_2v_2$ where u_1, u_2, v_1, v_2, the velocity components along the line, can be treated as algebraic quantities. The velocity components in the other two co-ordinate directions are all zero.

In the first diagram, above, all velocity vectors are shown in the same direction, to the right, normally taken as the positive direction; u_1, u_2, v_1, v_2 are all positive. However, the scalar equation describes any one-dimensional collision, for example that represented by the second diagram, where u_1 is positive and u_2 is negative.

The collision is specified to be elastic, which means that kinetic energy is conserved.

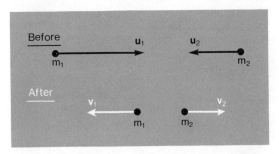

Velocities of two particles in the lab frame of reference before and after a head-on collision.

Another example of a head-on collision described in the lab frame of reference.

$$\tfrac{1}{2}m_1u_1^2 + \tfrac{1}{2}m_2u_2^2 = \tfrac{1}{2}m_1v_1^2 + \tfrac{1}{2}m_2v_2^2$$

Rewriting this as

$$m_1(u_1^2 - v_1^2) = m_2(v_2^2 - u_2^2)$$

and the momentum equation as

$$m_1(u_1 - v_1) = m_2(v_2 - u_2)$$

and dividing the first by the second gives

$$u_1 + v_1 = v_2 + u_2 \qquad \text{or} \qquad u_1 - u_2 = -(v_1 - v_2)$$

This shows that the relative velocity of the particles is reversed in the collision: $(u_1 - u_2)$ is the velocity of m_1 relative to m_2 before the collision, and $(v_1 - v_2)$ is the velocity of m_1 relative to m_2 after the collision.

Substituting $v_2 = u_1 + v_1 - u_2$ into the momentum equation and solving for v_1 gives

$$v_1 = \left(\frac{m_1 - m_2}{m_1 + m_2}\right) u_1 + \left(\frac{2m_2}{m_1 + m_2}\right) u_2$$

and similarly solving for v_2 gives

$$v_2 = \left(\frac{2m_1}{m_1 + m_2}\right) u_1 + \left(\frac{m_1 - m_2}{m_1 + m_2}\right) u_2$$

Note that if $m_1 = m_2$, $v_1 = u_2$ and $v_2 = u_1$; in a head-on elastic collision of two particles of equal mass, they exchange velocities.

One possible transformation of the reference frame would be to that of one of the particles before (or after) the collision. For example, we could examine the collision in the frame moving with velocity $\mathbf{u}_2$. However, since we have not assigned specific values to the velocities in the laboratory frame of reference, an equivalent procedure is to set $u_2 = 0$ in the results already obtained. Then

$$v_1 = \left(\frac{m_1 - m_2}{m_1 + m_2}\right) u_1, \qquad v_2 = \left(\frac{2m_1}{m_1 + m_2}\right) u_1$$

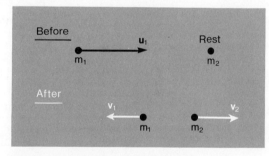

Head-on collision, with one particle initially at rest in lab frame.

where u_1, v_1 and v_2 are velocities in the frame of reference in which m_2 is initially at rest. This is of course the laboratory frame in the particular case where $u_2 = 0$.

If $m_1 = m_2$, $v_1 = 0$ and $v_2 = u_1$. The object initially moving stops and the second one moves off with the same velocity that the initial one had. Billiard players will recognize this result. Collisions between billiard balls are not perfectly elastic, and the spin of the ball is a complication, but the situation is approximated surprisingly well by the idealized calculation.

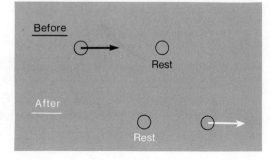

In a head-on elastic collision of identical particles, they exchange velocities.

If $m_1 \ll m_2$, $v_1 \cong -u_1$ and $v_2 \cong 0$. If a light object makes an elastic collision with a massive one at rest, it rebounds with almost its initial speed, and the massive object is almost unaffected. There are many examples where the conditions here are at least approximately fulfilled: the bounce of a ball on the earth, or the reflection of a gas molecule at the wall of a container.

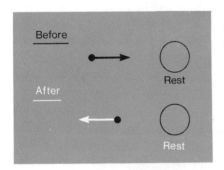

Elastic head-on collision of a light particle with a massive particle at rest.

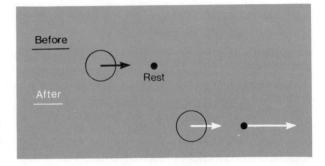

Elastic head-on collision of a massive particle with a light particle at rest.

If $m_1 \gg m_2$, $v_1 \cong u_1$ and $v_2 \cong 2u_1$. If a massive object makes an elastic collision with a light one at rest, the massive object continues its motion at almost the same speed, and the light object takes off at twice this speed. In a collision between a golf club and ball, the ball does not just acquire the speed of the club head, but a larger speed; while it is an oversimplification to treat such a collision in this way (momentum and energy conserved) it does give a rough indication of the motion.

These results illustrate the general principle that only in collisions between objects of about the same mass is there a large transfer of energy, and this has implications in the design of experiments. An example is the choice of moderator in a nuclear reactor. In the fission of uranium neutrons are produced, and these neutrons produce more fissions in a chain reaction. The neutrons released in the fission reaction are moving at a very high speed, and to be effective in producing other fissions they must be slowed down, or moderated in speed. This is accomplished by allowing the neutrons to make collisions with a material that will slow them down. The neutrons interact with the nuclei of the moderator, and if the nuclei are massive (material of high atomic weight) the neutrons will bounce off with speed essentially unaffected. From this point of view hydrogen would be the best moderator because the mass of the nucleus of the hydrogen atom, a proton, is almost the same as the mass of a neutron. It turns out that hydrogen is not the best choice because protons tend to capture neutrons, making them unavailable for producing fission, but the argument shows that a material of low atomic weight should be chosen as a moderator.

So far we have described the head-on elastic collision of two particles in the lab frame of reference, including the special case where one of the particles is initially at rest. It is not always instructive to consider the motion in the c-of-m frame of reference, but sometimes it is. Using the subscript c to denote velocities in the c-of-m frame, and u's and v's to denote velocities before and after collision, the transformation of the last section gives for the one-dimensional motion

$$u_{1c} = \frac{m_2}{m_1 + m_2}(u_1 - u_2) \qquad u_{2c} = \frac{m_1}{m_1 + m_2}(u_2 - u_1) = -\frac{m_1}{m_2}u_{1c}$$

The kinetic energy in the c-of-m frame is

$$\begin{aligned} K_c &= \tfrac{1}{2}m_1 u_{1c}^2 + \tfrac{1}{2}m_2 u_{2c}^2 \\ &= \tfrac{1}{2}\frac{m_1 m_2^2}{(m_1 + m_2)^2}(u_1 - u_2)^2 + \tfrac{1}{2}\frac{m_2 m_1^2}{(m_1 + m_2)^2}(u_2 - u_1)^2 \\ &= \tfrac{1}{2}\frac{m_1 m_2}{(m_1 + m_2)}(u_1 - u_2)^2 \\ &= \tfrac{1}{2}\mu U^2 \end{aligned}$$

where $U = u_1 - u_2$ is the relative velocity of the particles, which is **independent** of the frame of reference in which the motion is described, and μ is the **reduced mass** of the two-particle system.

$$\frac{1}{\mu} = \frac{1}{m_1} + \frac{1}{m_2} \qquad \text{or} \qquad \mu = \frac{m_1 m_2}{m_1 + m_2}$$

Note that if, for example, $m_1 \gg m_2$ then $\mu \cong m_2$ and $K_c \cong \tfrac{1}{2}m_2 U^2$. If one of the masses is much larger than the other, the motion of the c-of-m is very close to the motion of the massive particle, and the kinetic energy in the c-of-m frame of reference is essentially the kinetic energy of the other (lighter) particle. The concept of reduced mass is often useful in describing the interaction of two particles, as we shall see.

There is an arbitrary zero in the value of kinetic energy; that is, its value depends on the frame of reference chosen. For the two-particle system its value K_c in the c-of-m frame is less than it is in any other frame. To see this, we write the energy K in the lab frame

$$\begin{aligned} K &= \tfrac{1}{2}m_1 u_1^2 + \tfrac{1}{2}m_2 u_2^2 = \tfrac{1}{2}m_1(u_{1c} + u_c)^2 + \tfrac{1}{2}m_2(u_{2c} + u_c)^2 \\ &= (\tfrac{1}{2}m_1 u_{1c}^2 + \tfrac{1}{2}m_2 u_{2c}^2) + \tfrac{1}{2}(m_1 + m_2)u_c^2 + (m_1 u_{1c} + m_2 u_{2c})u_c \end{aligned}$$

The first term is the kinetic energy K_c in the c-of-m frame. The second term is $\tfrac{1}{2}$(total mass)u_c^2, the kinetic energy of the total mass moving with the speed of the c-of-m in the lab frame. The third term is zero because the total momentum is zero in the c-of-m frame.

$$K = K_c + \tfrac{1}{2}(m_1 + m_2)u_c^2$$

If the frame of reference is the c-of-m frame, $u_c = 0$ and the value of K is a minimum, K_c.

After collision the velocities in the lab frame are v_1 and v_2, or in the c-of-m frame

$$v_{1c} = \frac{m_2}{m_1 + m_2}(v_1 - v_2) \qquad v_{2c} = \frac{m_1}{m_1 + m_2}(v_2 - v_1)$$

but we have already seen that in the head-on elastic collision the relative velocity is reversed, or

$$u_1 - u_2 = -(v_1 - v_2)$$

therefore $v_{1c} = -u_{1c}$ and $v_{2c} = -u_{2c}$

In the c-of-m frame the collision is symmetric; the velocity of each particle is reversed in the collision. The kinetic energy of course is unchanged because the collision is specified as elastic.

Example: In order to help to see the difference between collisions described in the lab frame and the c-of-m frame we shall look at the particular example where one particle has twice the mass of the other, and the massive particle is initially at rest in the lab frame. Then $m_2 = 2m_1$ and $u_2 = 0$. We can express all velocities in terms of $u_1 = u$.

$$v_1 = \left(\frac{m_1 - m_2}{m_1 + m_2}\right)u_1 + \left(\frac{2m_2}{m_1 + m_2}\right)u_2 = -\tfrac{1}{3}u$$

$$v_2 = \left(\frac{2m_1}{m_1 + m_2}\right)u_1 + \left(\frac{m_1 - m_2}{m_1 + m_2}\right)u_2 = \tfrac{2}{3}u$$

$$u_c = \frac{m_1 u_1 + m_2 u_2}{m_1 + m_2} = \tfrac{1}{3}u$$

$$u_{1c} = \frac{m_2}{m_1 + m_2}(u_1 - u_2) = \tfrac{2}{3}u$$

$$u_{2c} = \frac{m_1}{m_1 + m_2}(u_2 - u_1) = -\tfrac{1}{3}u$$

$$v_{1c} = -u_{1c} = -\tfrac{2}{3}u$$

$$v_{2c} = -u_{2c} = \tfrac{1}{3}u$$

The diagrams show successive positions of the particles at equal time intervals, both in the lab frame and the c-of-m frame. All velocities are constant so that equal distances are moved in equal times, and on the equally spaced diagrams used the successive positions lie on diagonal straight lines.

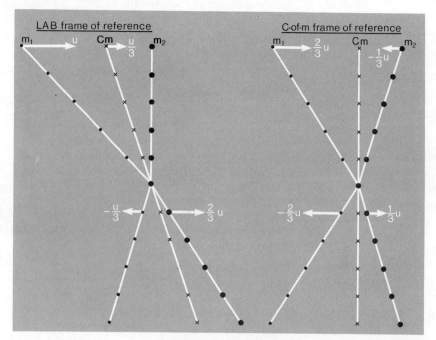

Elastic head-on collision of a particle of mass m_1 = $m_2/2$ with particle m_2 initially at rest, showing successive positions of the particles at equal time intervals in both the lab and the c-of-m frames of reference.

HEAD-ON NON-ELASTIC COLLISION

For an elastic collision in one dimension in which no external forces act, the motion is described completely by the two scalar equations

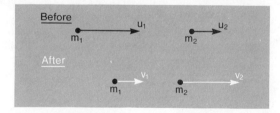

Head-on collision in lab frame of reference.

$$m_1u_1 + m_2u_2 = m_1v_1 + m_2v_2$$

$$\tfrac{1}{2}m_1u_1^2 + \tfrac{1}{2}m_2u_2^2 = \tfrac{1}{2}m_1v_1^2 + \tfrac{1}{2}m_2v_2^2$$

representing conservation of momentum and of kinetic energy. However, there are many collisions in which it is reasonable to assume that momentum is conserved, but not that kinetic energy is conserved. Then the energy equation is not valid, and the momentum condition alone does not determine a unique result. Particular initial values of velocity u_1 and u_2 do not determine specific final values v_1 and v_2. The collision is only described completely if there is some other specification besides conservation of momentum. For example, it may be specified that the particles stick together in the collision, then $v_1 = v_2$ and there is a unique final velocity

$$v = \frac{m_1u_1 + m_2u_2}{m_1 + m_2}$$

This is of course the velocity of the center of mass of the system; if the particles stick together they are at rest in the c-of-m frame of reference. Such a collision is called an **inelastic** collision, and in the c-of-m frame all the initial kinetic energy is "lost" (transferred to other forms) in the collision. Note, however, that while in the c-of-m frame there is zero kinetic energy after collision, in general there is kinetic energy remaining in the lab frame of reference after an inelastic collision.

We have pointed out that in non-elastic collisions the final kinetic energy may be greater or less than the initial kinetic energy, depending on whether some form of potential energy is released or stored in the collision. For the moment we shall consider head-on collisions between macroscopic "particles," meaning solid objects that are confined to move in one dimension. Then there is always some energy dissipated in the form of heat, and the final kinetic energy is less than the initial kinetic energy. For such collisions it is sometimes convenient to define a quantity called **coefficient of restitution** e

$$e = -\frac{\text{Relative velocity after impact}}{\text{Relative velocity before impact}} = -\frac{v_1 - v_2}{u_1 - u_2}$$

In any collision the relative velocity of the two particles is reversed, so that e is defined in such a way as to be positive. In an elastic collision the relative velocity is unchanged in magnitude, $v_1 - v_2 = -(u_1 - u_2)$ so that $e = 1$; in an inelastic collision $v_1 = v_2$ so that $e = 0$. Therefore e, ranging from 0 to 1, is a measure of the elasticity of the collision. It is a measurable physical quantity but is a rather odd sort of property (like coefficient of friction) in that it depends on two materials that may be different; it can be used to describe collisions between steel and steel, or steel and glass, or steel and wood, and so on. It is invalid to

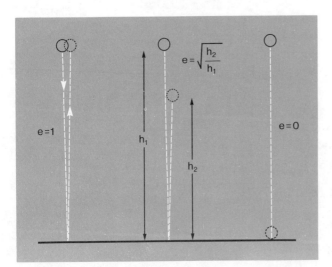

$$e = \sqrt{\frac{h_2}{h_1}}$$

$e = 1$

$e = 0$

h_1

h_2

The coefficient of restitution e can be determined by measuring the height of successive bounces; it ranges from $e = 0$ for an inelastic collision to $e = 1$ for an elastic collision.

assume that all steel–steel collisions have the same value of e, just as it is invalid to assume that all pieces of steel have the same density, or the same elastic modulus, or the same thermal expansion coefficient. Nonetheless some information about collisions between steel and glass in general is obtained by measuring e for a particular steel–glass collision. This can be done by using steel and glass pendula, or more simply by dropping a glass ball on to a massive steel plate from a height h_1, and observing the height of its bounce h_2. Then $u_1 = \sqrt{2gh_1}$, $v_1 = -\sqrt{2gh_2}$, and $u_2 = v_2 \cong 0$, so that $e = \sqrt{h_2/h_1}$.

The coefficient of restitution e can be related to the dissipation of kinetic energy in a collision. The difference in kinetic energy

$$(\tfrac{1}{2}m_1u_1^2 + \tfrac{1}{2}m_2u_2^2) - (\tfrac{1}{2}m_1v_1^2 + \tfrac{1}{2}m_2v_2^2)$$

can be shown, using the two relations

$$m_1u_1 + m_2u_2 = m_1v_1 + m_2v_2 \quad \text{and} \quad e = -\frac{v_1 - v_2}{u_1 - u_2}$$

to be equal to

$$\tfrac{1}{2}\left(\frac{m_1m_2}{m_1 + m_2}\right)(u_1 - u_2)^2(1 - e^2) = \tfrac{1}{2}\mu U^2(1 - e^2)$$

To show this directly in the lab frame of reference is a rather cumbersome algebraic task, but the calculation in the c-of-m frame is relatively simple. We showed previously that in the c-of-m frame the kinetic energy is

$$K_c = \tfrac{1}{2}\mu U^2$$

a result that depends only on the relative velocity $U = u_1 - u_2$ of the particles. After collision the relative velocity is $v_1 - v_2 = -e(u_1 - u_2) = -eU$ and the kinetic energy is

$$K_c = \tfrac{1}{2}\mu e^2 U^2$$

Therefore the loss in kinetic energy is $\tfrac{1}{2}\mu U^2(1 - e^2)$. The loss ranges from zero for $e = 1$, an elastic collision, to $\tfrac{1}{2}\mu U^2$ for $e = 0$, an inelastic collision. This result, an energy **difference** rather than an absolute value of energy, does not depend on the frame of reference used to describe the motion.

Example 1: A 10-lb mass moving at 4 ft/sec makes a head-on collision with a 5-lb mass moving at 6 ft/sec in the opposite direction. Calculate the velocities after collision if 50% of the mechanical energy is lost.

We choose a co-ordinate axis along the line of the one-dimensional motion, with the positive direction that in which the 10-lb mass is moving before impact. The velocities after impact are v_1 (for 10-lb mass) and v_2 (for 5-lb mass).

A head-on
collision.

Assuming conservation of momentum

$$10(4) + 5(-6) = 10v_1 + 5v_2$$
$$8 - 6 = 2v_1 + v_2, \qquad v_2 = 2 - 2v_1$$

If half the mechanical energy is lost in impact

$$\tfrac{1}{2}[\tfrac{1}{2}(10)\,4^2 + \tfrac{1}{2}(5)\,6^2] = \tfrac{1}{2}(10)v_1^2 + \tfrac{1}{2}(5)v_2^2$$
$$34 = 2v_1^2 + v_2^2$$
$$= 2v_1^2 + (2 - 2v_1)^2$$
$$= 2v_1^2 + 4 + 4v_1^2 - 8v_1$$
$$3v_1^2 - 4v_1 - 15 = 0$$

$$v_1 = \frac{4 \pm \sqrt{16 + 180}}{6} = \frac{4 \pm 14}{6} = 3 \quad \text{or} \quad -5/3$$

and
$$v_2 = 2 - 2v_1 = -4 \quad \text{or} \quad 16/3$$

For the solution $v_1 = 3$ ft/sec, $v_2 = -4$ ft/sec, the two masses would have to pass through one another. This is possible if, for example, the 5-lb mass is a lead projectile and the 10-lb mass is a blob of butter, but in general the second solution is more probable. Then $v_1 = -5/3$ ft/sec, and $v_2 = 16/3$ ft/sec, and the masses bounce off one another.

Note that the coefficient of restitution in the two cases is

$$e = -\frac{v_2 - v_1}{u_2 - u_1} = -\frac{-4 - 3}{-6 - 4} = -0.7$$

and
$$e = -\frac{16/3 - (-5/3)}{-6 - 4} = 0.7$$

There is the same numerical value in each case, corresponding to the same energy loss, but a negative value when the objects pass through one another, because e is defined in such a way as to be positive in the more usual situation where the objects bounce off one another, and the relative velocity is reversed.

The calculation may also be performed in the c-of-m frame of reference although there is no particular advantage to doing so in this example. The velocity of the c-of-m in the lab frame is

$$u_c = \frac{10(4) + 5(-6)}{10 + 5} = \frac{2}{3} \text{ ft/sec}$$

and the initial velocities in the c-of-m frame are

$$u_{1c} = u_1 - u_c = 4 - 2/3 = 10/3 \text{ ft/sec}$$
$$u_{2c} = u_2 - u_c = -6 - 2/3 = -20/3 \text{ ft/sec}$$

The total momentum $10u_{1c} + 5u_{2c} = 0$ as it must be in the c-of-m frame. Before impact $u_{2c} = -2u_{1c}$ and after impact $v_{2c} = -2v_{1c}$.

The condition that 50% of the mechanical energy is lost can *not* be written in terms of energies in the c-of-m frame, because this would represent a different energy loss: the value of the kinetic energy depends on the frame chosen.

In the lab frame the original kinetic energy is

$$K = \tfrac{1}{2}(10)\,4^2 + \tfrac{1}{2}(5)\,6^2 = 170 \text{ ft-pndl}$$

and the loss in energy is 85 ft-pndl. Therefore in the c-of-m frame

$$[\tfrac{1}{2}(10)u_{1c}^2 + \tfrac{1}{2}(5)u_{2c}^2] - [\tfrac{1}{2}(10)v_{1c}^2 + \tfrac{1}{2}(5)v_{2c}^2] = 85$$

Using
$$u_{2c} = -2u_{1c} \quad \text{and} \quad v_{2c} = -2v_{1c}$$
$$(2u_{1c}^2 + 4u_{1c}^2) - (2v_{1c}^2 + 4v_{1c}^2) = 170/5 = 34$$
$$u_{1c}^2 - v_{1c}^2 = 34/6 = 17/3$$
$$v_{1c}^2 = u_{1c}^2 - 17/3 = (10/3)^2 - 17/3 = 49/9 \qquad v_{1c} = \pm 7/3$$

In lab frame, $v_1 = v_{1c} + u_c = \pm 7/3 + 2/3 = 3$ or $-5/3$. The two values of v_1, 3 ft/sec and $-5/3$ ft/sec, are the same as calculated directly in the lab frame.

Example 2: Two pendula, metal spheres *A* of 8-lb mass and *B* of 10-lb mass, hang side by side so that they are in contact. If *A* is drawn back through an angle of 40° and released, it stops when it hits *B*. Through what angle will *A* be displaced when *B* returns and hits it?

The important step in analyzing any real physical situation is that of deciding what principles of physics may reasonably be applied. In hypothetical "real" situations, such as those posed as problems in textbooks, you are not in a position to examine the situation for yourself and decide what measurements you should make. You have to decide what may reasonably be assumed on the basis of the information provided, and your experience with similar situations.

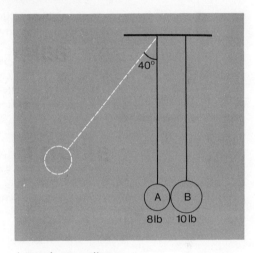

An inelastic collision of two pendula.

Velocities before and after the first collision, and after the second collision.

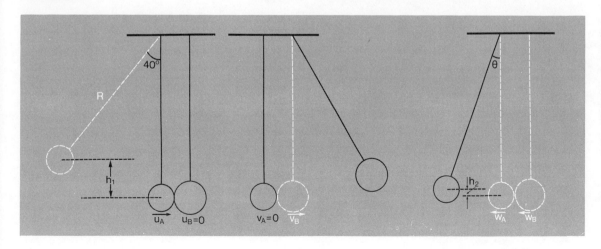

In this example the two collisions take place when the pendulum strings are vertical. The diagram shows the spheres touching in such a way that the surfaces in contact are vertical. At the instant before collision the moving sphere has a horizontal velocity, and at the instant after collision velocities will be horizontal. It must be assumed that pendulum A is pulled back in the plane defined by the two pendula, otherwise it could not be brought to rest in the collision. With this description of the situation, it is reasonable to assume that momentum is conserved in the collisions because the resultant external force (due to gravity and the supporting strings) is zero at the instant of collision, and also it is reasonable to treat the collision as one-dimensional.

Having assumed conservation of momentum, we know that kinetic energy is not conserved in the collision because we have seen that when a mass makes a head-on elastic collision with an equal mass at rest the first mass is brought to rest. Here the first mass is brought to rest, but the masses are not equal, therefore the collision is not elastic. We will assume, however, that the coefficient of restitution is the same for the successive collisions, that is that the ratio of relative velocities is the same for the two collisions. This assumption can only be validated on the basis of experiment or experience.

While we cannot assume conservation of mechanical energy in impact, we will assume conservation of mechanical energy in the swings of the pendula, that is, that the gravitational potential energy of mass A when it is released from a height h_1 (corresponding to a 40° deflection) becomes completely kinetic energy at impact.

$$m_A g h_1 = \tfrac{1}{2} m_A u_A^2$$

Similarly we assume that pendulum B which takes off with a velocity v_B after the first collision returns with an equal and opposite velocity $-v_B$ just before the second collision. While we know that this is not a completely valid assumption, because there is always some energy loss due to friction with the air in a pendulum swing, we also know that the energy loss in a single swing is relatively small for such large masses as these, and therefore it is a sensible assumption.

Using u's for velocities just before the first impact, v's for velocities just after the first impact, and w's for velocities just after the second impact, as shown on the diagrams, and choosing the initial direction of u_A as the positive direction, conservation of momentum gives

$$8u_A + 10u_B = 8v_A + 10v_B \qquad u_B = 0,\, v_A = 0$$

or
$$v_B = 0.8u_A \qquad e = -\frac{v_B - v_A}{u_B - u_A} = -\frac{0.8u_A - 0}{0 - u_A} = 0.8$$

Assuming conservation of energy in the swing of B, its velocity just before the second impact is $-v_B$.

$$8(0) + 10(-v_B) = 8w_A + 10w_B$$

Assuming the same coefficient of restitution

$$e = 0.8 = -\frac{w_B - w_A}{-v_B - 0} \qquad 0.8v_B = w_B - w_A$$

Eliminating w_B
$$-10v_B = 8w_A + 10(w_A + 0.8v_B)$$
$$w_A = -v_B = -0.8u_A$$

After the two collisions, mass A starts off with 80% of its initial speed, and mass B is now also moving, with an initial velocity

$$w_B = w_A + 0.8v_B = -0.2v_B = -0.16u_A$$

Assuming conservation of mechanical energy in the swings of pendulum A,

$$\tfrac{1}{2}m_A u_A^2 = m_A g h_1 \qquad u_A = \sqrt{2gh_1}$$

and similarly $0.8u_A = \sqrt{2gh_2}$ so that $h_2 = 0.8^2 h_1 = 0.64h_1$

The height h is related to the deflection angle θ by

$$h = R - R \cos \theta = R(1 - \cos \theta)$$

where R is the length of the pendulum.

Therefore $h_1 = R(1 - \cos 40°)$ $h_2 = R(1 - \cos \theta)$

$$\frac{h_2}{h_1} = 0.64 = \frac{1 - \cos \theta}{1 - \cos 40°}$$

$$\cos \theta = 0.36 + 0.64 \cos 40° = 0.36 + 0.64(0.766) = 0.85$$
$$\theta = 32°$$

The energy loss in each collision is $\tfrac{1}{2}\mu U^2 (1 - e^2)$. As a check on the calculations you might verify that the total loss is equal to the difference between the initial and final energies

$$\tfrac{1}{2}m_A u_A^2 - (\tfrac{1}{2}m_A w_A^2 + \tfrac{1}{2}m_B w_B^2)$$

The calculations may also be made in the c-of-m frame of reference, but there is no advantage to doing so in this example because the equations are simple to handle in the lab frame. Note that the c-of-m frame is *not* the same for the two collisions; for the first collision the c-of-m moves with a velocity $4u_A/9$, for the second it moves with a velocity $-4u_A/9$. This is because there is a horizontal force acting (by the pendulum support) during this interval.

This example has been used in order to emphasize the kind of idealizations and assumptions that are made in trying to analyze any real physical situation.

ELASTIC COLLISION OF EQUAL MASSES

We have spent some time on head-on collisions because of the simplicity of working in one dimension, but we pointed out that at the microscopic level, where the paths of particles cannot be controlled, a head-on collision is an unlikely event. For fundamental particles it is often reasonable to assume conservation of kinetic energy. We shall first look at an elastic collision between

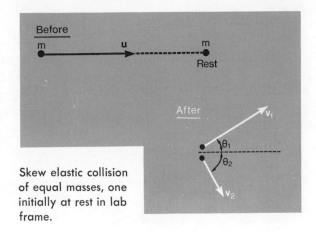

Skew elastic collision of equal masses, one initially at rest in lab frame.

particles of equal mass, such as two protons. For convenience we shall assume also that one of the two particles is initially at rest in the lab frame of reference; before the collision the incident particle has velocity $\mathbf{u}$, after the collision the particles have velocities $\mathbf{v}_1$ and $\mathbf{v}_2$, directed at angles θ_1 and θ_2 with respect to the direction of the incident particle.

Assuming conservation of momentum and kinetic energy,

$$m\mathbf{u} = m\mathbf{v}_1 + m\mathbf{v}_2$$
$$\tfrac{1}{2}mu^2 = \tfrac{1}{2}mv_1^2 + \tfrac{1}{2}mv_2^2$$

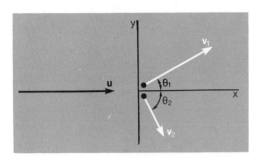

Choosing an appropriate co-ordinate system.

The vector momentum relation is equivalent to three scalar relations, but by choosing a co-ordinate system with one axis in the direction $\mathbf{u}$, and another perpendicular to this and in the plane defined by the vectors $\mathbf{v}_1$ and $\mathbf{v}_2$, the components of velocity in the third co-ordinate direction are all zero, and the two non-zero equations are

$$mu = mv_1 \cos \theta_1 + mv_2 \cos \theta_2$$
$$0 = mv_1 \sin \theta_1 + mv_2 \sin \theta_2$$

There are four undetermined quantities v_1, v_2, θ_1 and θ_2, for a particular incident velocity u, and therefore the result is not uniquely determined by the three equations. However, if one of the particles is observed to be scattered through a particular angle θ_1, or to have a particular energy (so that v_1 is known), the other quantities may be calculated.

There is one general observation that can be made: the angle between the paths of the two particles after collision is always a right angle. This may be shown by manipulation of the three scalar equations to show that $\sin (\theta_1 + \theta_2) = 1$, or $\cos (\theta_1 + \theta_2) = 0$, so that $\theta_1 + \theta_2 = 90°$, but it can be seen immediately from the two relations

$$\mathbf{u} = \mathbf{v}_1 + \mathbf{v}_2$$
$$u^2 = v_1^2 + v_2^2$$

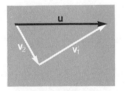

Vector triangle representing $\mathbf{u} = \mathbf{v}_1 + \mathbf{v}_2$.

In the vector triangle the magnitudes are given by the Pythagorean relation, and therefore the angle between $\mathbf{v}_1$ and $\mathbf{v}_2$ is a right angle.

This result may also be deduced by considering the collision in the c-of-m frame of reference. The velocity of the center of mass in the lab frame is

$$\mathbf{u}_c = \frac{m\mathbf{u} + m(0)}{m + m} = \frac{\mathbf{u}}{2}$$

and in the c-of-m frame the velocities before collision are $\mathbf{u}_{1c} = \mathbf{u} - \mathbf{u}_c = \mathbf{u}/2$, $\mathbf{u}_{2c} = 0 - \mathbf{u}_c = -\mathbf{u}/2$. After collision the total momentum remains zero $m\mathbf{v}_{1c} + m\mathbf{v}_{2c} = 0$, or $\mathbf{v}_{1c} = -\mathbf{v}_{2c}$. In addition the kinetic energy is unchanged and therefore the magnitudes of the equal and opposite velocities are the same after as before impact; $|\mathbf{v}_{1c}| = |\mathbf{v}_{2c}| = u/2$. The velocities after impact make some angle φ with respect to the original $\mathbf{u}$ direction. The angle φ is not determined —it depends on the particular collision.

To transform from the symmetric collision, as described in the c-of-m frame, back to the lab frame requires the addition of the velocity $\mathbf{u}_c = \mathbf{u}/2$. The vector triangles are both isosceles, so that

$$\varphi = 2\theta_1 \qquad \text{and} \qquad \pi - \varphi = 2\theta_2$$

Adding, $\theta_1 + \theta_2 = \pi/2 = 90°$.

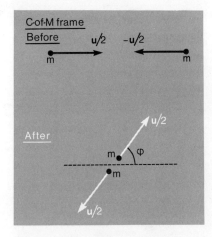

Skew elastic collision of equal masses in c-of-m frame.

Transformation from c-of-m frame to lab frame.

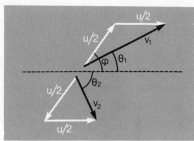

Diagram representing particle tracks in a cloud chamber.

Particle tracks as recorded by photographs of cloud chambers sometimes show the kind of event assumed here—a single track that becomes two tracks at right angles. This may be taken as evidence that a single particle has made an elastic collision with another particle of the same mass initially at rest; a proton might be scattered by the nucleus of a hydrogen atom (another proton) for example. It must be remembered that a photograph shows an event in two dimensions, and if the plane of the collision is not in the plane of the photograph the angle between the tracks after collision will not appear to be a right angle.

ELASTIC COLLISION OF NON-EQUAL MASSES

Again it will be convenient to assume that one of the two particles is at rest in the lab frame initially. We shall develop an expression for the angle θ_1 that a mass m_1 is scattered through by a collision with a mass m_2 initially at rest.

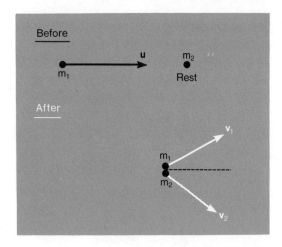

Skew elastic collision of non-equal masses, one at rest in lab frame.

Conservation of momentum and kinetic energy does not give a unique result, but we should be able to demonstrate, for example, that a heavy particle cannot be bounced backward by a light one.

Choosing co-ordinate axes as in the previous example, in the lab frame of reference the two conservation laws give

$$m_1 u = m_1 v_1 \cos \theta_1 + m_2 v_2 \cos \theta_2$$
$$0 = m_1 v_1 \sin \theta_1 + m_2 v_2 \sin \theta_2$$
$$\tfrac{1}{2} m_1 u_1^2 = \tfrac{1}{2} m_1 v_1^2 + \tfrac{1}{2} m_2 v_2^2$$

These equations are sufficient to analyze a particular situation: for example, for a given pair of particles (m_1 and m_2) and initial energy ($\tfrac{1}{2} m_1 u^2$) and given that m_1 loses half of its energy in the collision, it is possible to solve the equations to determine v_1, v_2, θ_1 and θ_2.

It will be more useful for us to describe the collision in the c-of-m frame of reference, in which the particles have oppositely directed velocities $\mathbf{u}_{1c}$ and $\mathbf{u}_{2c}$ before collision and oppositely directed velocities $\mathbf{v}_{1c}$ and $\mathbf{v}_{2c}$ after collision.

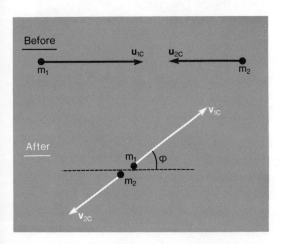

Skew elastic collision of non-equal masses in c-of-m frame.

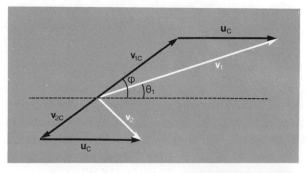

Transformation from c-of-m frame to lab frame.

These velocities make some angle φ with respect to the original velocities. This angle is undetermined—it lies between 0 and π, depending on the particular collision.

To transform back to the lab frame, the velocity of the c-of-m $\mathbf{u}_c$ in the lab frame must be added. From the vector diagram

$$\tan \theta_1 = \frac{\sin \theta_1}{\cos \theta_1} = \frac{v_1 \sin \theta_1}{v_1 \cos \theta_1} = \frac{v_{1c} \sin \varphi}{v_{1c} \cos \varphi + u_c}$$

In order to simplify this expression we shall express both v_{1c} and u_c in terms of u_{1c}.

In the c-of-m frame $m_1 \mathbf{u}_{1c} = -m_2 \mathbf{u}_{2c}$ and $m_1 \mathbf{v}_{1c} = -m_2 \mathbf{v}_{2c}$, or in **magnitude** $u_{1c}/v_{1c} = u_{2c}/v_{2c}$, or $u_{1c}/u_{2c} = v_{1c}/v_{2c}$. The **ratios** of the magnitudes of velocities are the same before and after impact, in the c-of-m frame. This is a result of conservation of momentum; if there is also conservation of kinetic energy, as we have assumed, then the velocity of *each* particle is unchanged in magnitude. It is clear that $|\mathbf{u}_{1c}| = |\mathbf{v}_{1c}|$ and $|\mathbf{u}_{2c}| = |\mathbf{v}_{2c}|$ is a sufficient condition to conserve energy, but it is also a necessary condition. In the c-of-m frame

$$\tfrac{1}{2}m_1 u_{1c}^2 + \tfrac{1}{2}m_2 u_{2c}^2 = \tfrac{1}{2}m_1 v_{1c}^2 + \tfrac{1}{2}m_2 v_{2c}^2$$

or

$$u_{1c}^2 \left(1 + \frac{m_2}{m_1} \frac{u_{2c}^2}{u_{1c}^2} \right) = v_{1c}^2 \left(1 + \frac{m_2}{m_1} \frac{v_{2c}^2}{u_{1c}^2} \right)$$

Since $u_{2c}/u_{1c} = v_{2c}/v_{1c}$, the bracketed terms cancel and $u_{1c}^2 = v_{1c}^2$ or $|u_{1c}| = |v_{1c}|$. In the c-of-m frame the speed of a particle is conserved in a two-particle elastic collision, whether or not the collision is head-on.

The velocity of the c-of-m in the lab frame is

$$\mathbf{u}_c = \frac{m_1 \mathbf{u} + m_2(0)}{m_1 + m_2} = \frac{m_1}{m_1 + m_2} \mathbf{u}$$

$$= \frac{m_1}{m_1 + m_2} (\mathbf{u}_{1c} + \mathbf{u}_c) \qquad \text{using} \quad \mathbf{u}_{1c} = \mathbf{u} - \mathbf{u}_c$$

or therefore $\qquad \mathbf{u}_c = \dfrac{m_1}{m_2} \mathbf{u}_{1c}$

Using the scalar results $v_{1c} = u_{1c}$ and $u_c = \dfrac{m_1}{m_2} u_{1c}$ in the expression for $\tan \theta_1$, the result is

$$\tan \theta_1 = \frac{u_{1c} \sin \varphi}{u_{1c} (\cos \varphi + m_1/m_2)}$$

$$= \frac{\sin \varphi}{\cos \varphi + m_1/m_2}$$

In general the scattering angle φ in the c-of-m frame can take any value $0 \le \varphi \le \pi$ and therefore $-1 \le \cos \varphi \le 1$. If $m_1 = m_2$, the denominator $(\cos \varphi + 1)$ goes to infinity for $\varphi = \pi$, and then $\theta_1 = \pi/2$; for equal masses $0 \le \theta_1 \le \pi/2$. If $m_1 > m_2$, $m_1/m_2 > 1$, and the denominator $(\cos \varphi + m_1/m_2)$ can never go to infinity, and therefore θ_1 is always less than $\pi/2$; a heavy mass is never scattered backward by a lighter one. If $m_1 < m_2$, any value $0 \le \theta_1 \le \pi$ is possible.

AN EXAMPLE OF A COLLISION
BETWEEN A NEUTRON AND A NUCLEUS

A thermal neutron collides with a helium atom at rest. If the collision is head-on, what fraction of its energy does the neutron lose? If it loses half of its energy, through what angle is it scattered?

We shall solve this problem first by using the lab frame of reference, and then the c-of-m frame of reference.

A thermal neutron is one with an energy corresponding to that of an atomic particle in a system in equilibrium at normal temperatures. This means that its kinetic energy is of the order of kT, where k is Boltzmann's constant (1.38×10^{-16} erg/K°) and $T \sim 300$ K°.

$$\therefore \quad K = \tfrac{1}{2}mv^2 \sim kT \sim 4 \times 10^{-14} \text{ erg} \sim 0.02 \text{ electron volts}$$

The mass of the neutron is about 1.7×10^{-24} gm, so that its speed is $v = \sqrt{2K/m} \sim 2 \times 10^5$ cm/sec.

A neutron in colliding with an atom does not interact with the electrons, but only with the nucleus. Thermal neutrons do not in general have sufficient energy to excite the nucleus, or produce a nuclear reaction, and therefore the collisions can be assumed to be elastic. (Thermal neutrons do produce fission of certain massive nuclei, however.) A classical calculation is valid because the speeds involved do not approach the speed of light.

We shall take the masses of the neutron and the helium atom as about 1 amu (atomic mass unit) and 4 amu, so that essentially the collision we are considering is an elastic one between particles of masses m and $4m$. If the collision is head-on, the three velocity vectors are in the same line and conservation of momentum and energy gives two scalar equations

$$mu = mv_1 + 4mv_2$$
$$\tfrac{1}{2}mu^2 = \tfrac{1}{2}mv_1^2 + \tfrac{1}{2}(4m)v_2^2$$

In order to calculate the fraction ϵ of its kinetic energy lost by the neutron, we require

$$\epsilon = \frac{\text{energy loss}}{\text{initial energy}} = \frac{\tfrac{1}{2}mu^2 - \tfrac{1}{2}mv_1^2}{\tfrac{1}{2}mu^2} = 1 - \left(\frac{v_1}{u}\right)^2$$

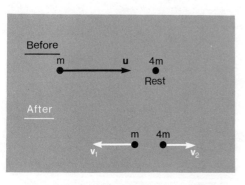

Idealized head-on elastic collision of neutron with helium nucleus at rest.

From the momentum condition $v_2 = (u - v_1)/4$. Using this in the energy relation

$$u^2 = v_1^2 + 4v_2^2 = v_1^2 + (u - v_1)^2/4$$
$$4u^2 = 4v_1^2 + u^2 + v_1^2 - 2uv_1$$

$$5 \left(\frac{v_1}{u} \right)^2 - 2 \left(\frac{v_1}{u} \right) - 3 = 0$$

$$\frac{v_1}{u} = \frac{2 \pm \sqrt{4 + 60}}{10} = \frac{2 \pm 8}{10} = 1.0 \quad \text{or} \quad -0.6$$

The solution $v_1 = u$ (giving $v_2 = 0$) corresponds to the neutron passing through the helium atom without energy loss. For the solution $v_1 = -0.6u$, the neutron bounces back and the atom acquires a speed $v_2 = (u + 0.6u)/4 = 0.4u$.

$$\epsilon = 1 - \left(\frac{v_1}{u} \right)^2 = 1 - 0.36 = 0.64 = 64\%$$

This shows that if the neutron is scattered through an angle π, it loses 64% of its energy. For smaller scattering angle, it loses less energy. We wish to calculate the angle for an energy loss of 50%, so that the total energy is shared

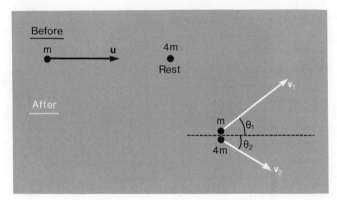

Skew elastic collision of neutron with helium nucleus at rest.

equally by the two particles after the collision. The conservation of energy condition is the same as before, but the momentum condition is now

$$m\mathbf{u} = m\mathbf{v}_1 + 4m\mathbf{v}_2$$

or in a suitable co-ordinate system

$$mu = mv_1 \cos \theta_1 + 4mv_2 \cos \theta_2$$
$$0 = mv_1 \sin \theta_1 + 4mv_2 \sin \theta_2$$

If the neutron loses half its energy

$$\tfrac{1}{2}mv_1^2 = \tfrac{1}{2}(\tfrac{1}{2}mu^2)$$
$$v_1^2 = \tfrac{1}{2}u^2 \qquad v_1 = u/\sqrt{2}$$

(Note that $v_1^2 = u^2/2$ gives $v_1 = \pm u/\sqrt{2}$ but it is not necessary to take the negative root. The components of the vector $\mathbf{v}_1$ are $v_1 \sin \theta_1$ and $v_1 \cos \theta_1$ where

$v_1 = |\mathbf{v}_1|$; the components will be positive or negative depending on the value of θ_1.)

From the energy relation

$$4v_2^2 = u^2 - v_1^2 = u^2 - u^2/2 = u^2/2 \qquad v_2^2 = u^2/8$$

The second momentum relation gives

$$v_1^2 \sin^2 \theta_1 = 16 v_2^2 \sin^2 \theta_2$$

$$\tfrac{1}{2} u^2 \sin^2 \theta_1 = 16 \left(\frac{u^2}{8}\right) \sin^2 \theta_2$$

$$\sin^2 \theta_1 = 4 \sin^2 \theta_2$$

The first momentum relation gives

$$u - v_1 \cos \theta_1 = 4 v_2 \cos \theta_2 \qquad 1 - \frac{v_1}{u} \cos \theta_1 = 4 \frac{v_2}{u} \cos \theta_2$$

Squaring $\quad 1 - 2 \dfrac{v_1}{u} \cos^2 \theta_1 + \left(\dfrac{v_1}{u}\right)^2 \cos^2 \theta_1 = 16 \left(\dfrac{v_2}{u}\right)^2 \cos^2 \theta_2$

$$1 - 2 \left(\frac{1}{\sqrt{2}}\right) \cos \theta_1 + \tfrac{1}{2} \cos^2 \theta_1 = 16(\tfrac{1}{8}) \cos^2 \theta_2 = 2(1 - \sin^2 \theta_2)$$

$$= 2(1 - \tfrac{1}{4} \sin^2 \theta_1)$$
$$= 2[1 - \tfrac{1}{4}(1 - \cos^2 \theta_1)]$$
$$= \tfrac{3}{2} + \tfrac{1}{2} \cos^2 \theta_1$$

$$1 - \sqrt{2} \cos \theta_1 = 3/2 \qquad \cos \theta_1 = -1/2\sqrt{2} = -0.353$$

$$\cos^{-1} 0.353 = 69° \qquad \therefore \quad \theta_1 = 180° - 69° = 111°$$

The neutron is scattered through an angle of 111° in the collision that halves its energy. This is the specific result we set out to find, but the other values after collision may be readily found.

$$\sin \theta_1 = \sin 111° = \sin 69° = 0.934$$

$$\therefore \quad \sin \theta_2 = \pm 0.5 \sin \theta_1 = \pm 0.467 \qquad \theta_2 = \pm 28°$$
$$v_1 = u/\sqrt{2} = 0.71u \qquad v_2 = u/2\sqrt{2} = 0.35u$$

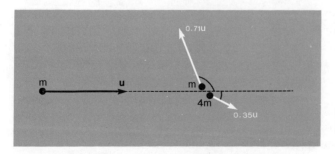

Scattering of neutron and helium nucleus in lab frame.

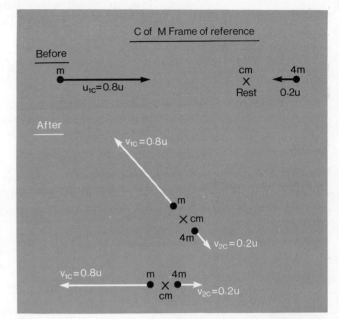

For the elastic collision of neutron and helium nucleus as described in the c-of-m frame of reference, the speeds after collision are the same whether the collision is head-on or not.

This analysis in the lab frame of reference is straightforward but leads to some rather tedious algebra. Transformation to the c-of-m frame of reference makes calculations much simpler. The velocity of the c-of-m in the lab frame is

$$\mathbf{u}_c = \frac{m\mathbf{u} + 4m(0)}{m + 4m} = \tfrac{1}{5}\mathbf{u}$$

$$\mathbf{u}_{1c} = \mathbf{u} - \mathbf{u}_c = \tfrac{4}{5}\mathbf{u} \qquad \mathbf{u}_{2c} = -\tfrac{1}{4}\mathbf{u}_{1c} = -\tfrac{1}{5}\mathbf{u}$$

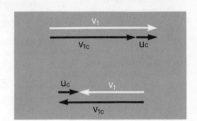

Transformation to the lab frame for head-on collision.

We know that the velocities $\mathbf{v}_{1c}$ and $\mathbf{v}_{2c}$ after collision are oppositely directed and that, since the collision is elastic, of the same magnitude as before collision

$$v_{1c} = u_{1c} = 0.8u \qquad v_{2c} = u_{2c} = 0.2u$$

This is so no matter what the orientation of the final velocities is. Transformation back to the lab frame is given by

$$\mathbf{v}_1 = \mathbf{v}_{1c} + \mathbf{u}_c$$

For the **head-on collision** we know that the velocities all lie in the same line. Taking the initial **u** direction as positive,

$$u_c = 0.2u \qquad \text{and} \qquad v_{1c} = \pm 0.8u$$

$$\therefore \quad v_1 = v_{1c} + u_c = \pm 0.8u + 0.2u = u \qquad \text{or} \qquad -0.6u$$

The result $v_1 = u$ corresponds to the neutron passing through the atom without energy loss, the result $v_1 = -0.6u$ to the neutron bouncing backward and transferring some of its energy to the atom. As before, the fraction lost or transferred is

$$\epsilon = 1 - \left(\frac{v_1}{u}\right)^2 = 0.64 = 64\%$$

If the neutron is to lose 50% of its energy, the collision cannot be head-on. Note that this statement about energy loss refers specifically to the lab frame of reference; in the c-of-m frame of reference the energy of the neutron is unchanged in the elastic collision.

We require, as before, $\frac{1}{2}mv_1^2 = \frac{1}{2}(\frac{1}{2}mu^2)$, or $v_1 = u/\sqrt{2}$. In the vector triangle $\mathbf{v}_1 = \mathbf{v}_{1c} + \mathbf{u}_c$ we know the magnitudes $v_1 = u/\sqrt{2}$, $v_{1c} = 0.8u$, $u_c = 0.2u$. Recognizing that the angle between $\mathbf{u}_c$ and $\mathbf{v}_1$ is the angle θ_1 we can use the law of cosines

$$v_{1c}^2 = u_c^2 + v_1^2 - 2uv_1 \cos \theta_1$$
$$0.8^2 = 0.2^2 + (1/\sqrt{2})^2 - 2(0.2)(1/\sqrt{2}) \cos \theta_1$$
$$0.64 = 0.04 + 0.5 - 0.2\sqrt{2} \cos \theta_1$$
$$0.10 = -0.2\sqrt{2} \cos \theta_1, \quad \cos \theta_1 = -1/2\sqrt{2}$$

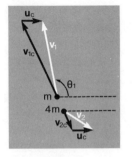

Transformation to the lab frame for skew collision.

This result is the same as that obtained by working completely in the lab frame of reference. Shifting back and forth between the lab frame and the c-of-m frame requires more practice, but it is a very useful intellectual device.

TRANSFORMATION OF UNIFORMLY ACCELERATED MOTION

The Galilean transformation between two frames of reference S and S' moving at a constant relative velocity $\mathbf{V}$ is

$$\mathbf{r} = \mathbf{r}' + \mathbf{V}t$$
$$\mathbf{v} = \mathbf{v}' + \mathbf{V}$$
$$\mathbf{a} = \mathbf{a}'$$

We have been using the transformation for situations where the velocities $\mathbf{v}$ and $\mathbf{v}'$ are constant, and $\mathbf{a} = \mathbf{a}' = 0$. We now look at the situation where $\mathbf{a} = \mathbf{a}'$ is constant.

In the S frame of reference the displacement and velocity of a particle at time t, developed in the previous chapter, are

$$\mathbf{r} = \mathbf{v}_0 t + \tfrac{1}{2}\mathbf{a}t^2$$
$$\mathbf{v} = \mathbf{v}_0 + \mathbf{a}t$$

where $\mathbf{v}_0$ is the velocity at $t = 0$, and $\mathbf{r} = 0$ at $t = 0$; i.e., the displacement $\mathbf{r}$ is measured with respect to the position at $t = 0$. We saw that in general the path

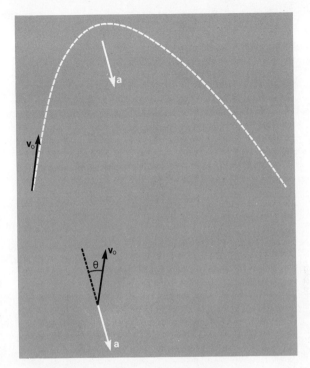

Parabolic path of any particle moving with constant acceleration **a**.

of the particle is a parabola whose axis of symmetry is parallel to the **a** direction; there is motion at constant velocity in the direction perpendicular to **a**. In the special case where $\mathbf{v}_0$ is parallel to **a**, the parabola becomes a straight line; the motion is in one-dimension. If the angle between the **a** direction and the $\mathbf{v}_0$ direction is θ, the particle moves at a constant velocity $v_0 \sin \theta$ in a direction at right angles to the **a** direction.

By making a transformation to a frame S' moving with a velocity $\mathbf{V} = v_0 \sin \theta$, the parabolic path in S is transformed into a straight-line path in S'.

Another possible transformation is to a frame S' that is moving with a velocity $\mathbf{V} = \mathbf{v}_0$ with respect to S, so that the particle is initially at rest in S'. However, in many situations the results can be deduced without a formal transformation of the reference frame.

Example: A flat car moves on a straight horizontal track at a constant speed of 40 ft/sec. A cannon (designed for use in physics problems) mounted on the flat car shoots a ball with a muzzle speed of 50 ft/sec. What is the resultant horizontal displacement (relative to the earth) of the ball if the cannon is shot (a) straight up, (b) at 53° above the horizontal, in the direction of motion of the car, (c) at 53° above the horizontal at right angles to the direction of motion. (d) What direction should it be pointed for maximum displacement? Assume that air resistance can be neglected.

The acceleration due to gravity $g = 32$ ft/sec² is vertically downward in the frame of reference of the earth—or in any frame moving at constant velocity on its surface.

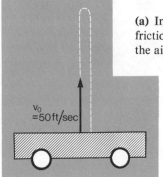

Cannon mounted
on a moving car,
fired straight up.

(a) In the frame of the car, the ball shot vertically upward will return to the car. If air friction is neglected it will arrive back with its initial velocity reversed. The time in the air is

$$t = \frac{v - v_0}{a} = \frac{50 - (-50)}{32}$$

$$= \frac{100}{32} \text{ sec}$$

In the frame of the earth it has a horizontal velocity of 40 ft/sec and therefore has a displacement

$$40 \times \frac{100}{32} = 125 \text{ ft}$$

in the direction of motion, in this time. The velocity of the ball in the earth frame at any instant is the vector sum of the velocity in the car frame and the constant velocity of the car frame

$$\mathbf{v}_{earth} = \mathbf{v}_{car} + \mathbf{v}_{car \ re \ earth}$$

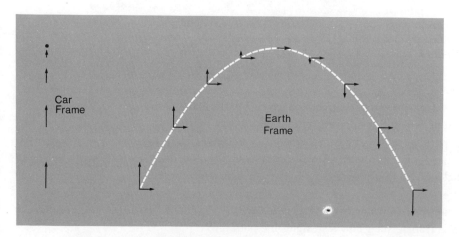

Motion of the
ball in the car
frame and the
earth frame.

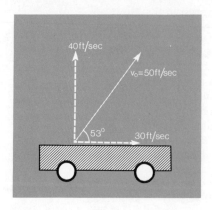

Cannon fired at 53° above
the horizontal.

(b In the frame of the car, the ball shot at an angle of 53° above the horizontal has components of velocity $v_0 \sin 53° = 40$ ft/sec in the vertical direction, and $v_0 \cos 53° = 30$ ft/sec in the horizontal direction. The time in the air is $t = [40 - (-40)]/32 = 5/2$ sec. In this time the ball has a displacement $30 \times 5/2 = 75$ ft horizontally relative to the car, and the car a displacement $40 \times 5/2 = 100$ ft relative to the ground.

If the ball is shot in the direction of motion of the car, the resultant displacement is 75 + 100 = 175 ft, in the direction of motion.

Horizontal component of ball velocity in the direction of motion of the car.

(c) If the ball is shot at right angles to the direction of motion, the resultant displacement is $\sqrt{75^2 + 100^2} = 125$ ft, at 37° away from the direction of motion.

These calculations could equally well have been made by transforming the velocity into the earth frame. Then in case (b) for example, the horizontal velocity is 30 + 40 = 70 ft/sec and the displacement is

$$\frac{5}{2} \times 70 = 175 \text{ ft}$$

(d) The maximum range in the earth frame occurs when the angle of projection in this frame = 45°, as we saw in the previous chapter; this means that the horizontal and vertical components of initial velocity are equal. The maximum contribution to the horizontal components occurs when the ball is shot forward. The cannon is tilted at an angle θ such that

$$50 \sin \theta = 50 \cos \theta + 40 \qquad \sin \theta = \cos \theta + 0.8$$

with solution $\theta = 79.4°$

For maximum displacement the cannon is pointed in the forward direction, at an angle 79.4° above the horizontal.

Horizontal component of ball velocity at right angles to the direction of motion of the car.

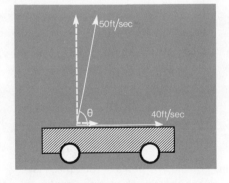

Cannon tilted for maximum range in the earth frame of reference.

TRANSFORMATION OF UNIFORM CIRCULAR MOTION

In the last chapter we pointed out that the path of a stone in the tread of a moving bicycle wheel is a circle, and the path of the tip of the propeller of a moving aircraft is a circle, provided the motion is described in a frame of reference fixed to the bicycle, or to the aircraft. In neither case is the motion circular in a frame of reference fixed to the earth. We now consider transformations of circular motion from one frame of reference into another in the two particular cases of a frame moving parallel to the plane of the circular

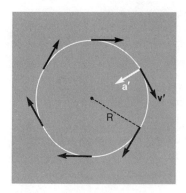

Path of a particle moving at constant speed v' in a frame of reference in which the path is circular.

motion, as for the bicycle wheel, and one moving at right angles to this, as for the propeller. We deal only with uniform circular motion, that is, the motion of a particle moving in a circle at constant speed.

Think about a particle in uniform motion in a circle of radius R in a frame of reference S'. Its velocity $\mathbf{v}'$ is constant in magnitude but uniformly changing direction (in the same plane) giving an acceleration $\mathbf{a}'$ of constant magnitude $(v')^2/R$, always directed toward the center of the circular path. Transformation to any other frame of reference S moving at a constant relative velocity $\mathbf{V}$ does not change the values of $\mathbf{a}'$, since $\mathbf{a} = \mathbf{a}'$, but does change the values of velocity: $\mathbf{v} = \mathbf{v}' + \mathbf{V}$.

If $\mathbf{V}$ is at right angles to the plane of the circle the speed of the particle in the S frame will be constant, of magnitude $v = [(v')^2 + V^2]^{1/2}$. The path of the particle in this plane is a helix or spiral. It can be visualized as a line drawn on the surface of a cylinder of radius R, the line having a constant pitch θ where $\tan \theta = V/v'$. The acceleration $\mathbf{a}$ is always directed toward the center of the cylinder, and has a magnitude $(v')^2/R$, *not* v^2/R. We shall later give an example where this motion occurs.

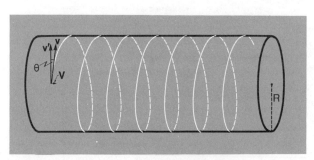

Path of the particle in a frame of reference moving at constant velocity $\mathbf{V}$ at right angles to the plane of the circular path.

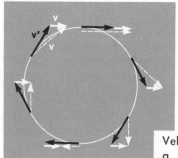

Velocity vectors in a frame of reference moving at constant velocity $\mathbf{V}$ in the plane of the circular path.

If $\mathbf{V}$ is in the same plane as $\mathbf{v}'$ the velocity $\mathbf{v}$ in the S frame is not constant in magnitude or direction. The diagram shows the velocity $\mathbf{v}'$ of the particle in S' at successive intervals of time, and the velocity $\mathbf{V}$ added to each to give successive values of $\mathbf{v} = \mathbf{v}' + \mathbf{V}$. However, this diagram does not represent the path in S, because in successive time intervals the particle will move off the circular path, since $\mathbf{v}$ is not tangential.

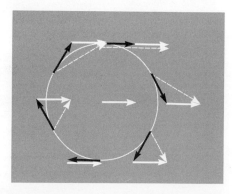

Velocity vectors in the special case where the magnitude of the frame velocity V is equal to the speed v' in the circular path.

In order to work out the path in S, we will first look at the particular transformation where $V = v'$; the transformation is made into a frame moving at a velocity whose magnitude is the speed of the particle in the S' frame. The particle then comes to rest in S periodically, the period being that of the circular motion in **S'**.

One example of this motion is that of a particle on the circumference of a wheel that rolls without slipping along a straight line. The point of contact between wheel and line is always at rest, in the frame of reference of the line. Once each revolution a particle on the circumference of the wheel will come to rest. The diagram can be interpreted as a velocity diagram **for the wheel** at any instant, showing the velocity of six different points on its circumference. Fix your attention on a particle that is at the lowest point on the wheel at some instant. It is in contact with the line, and is instantaneously at rest. As the wheel rolls the particle takes successive positions as shown in the diagrams; the positions are shown for times one-sixth of a period apart. The velocity vector shows the direction of motion (the tangent to the path) at any instant. The acceleration vectors are not shown on the diagrams; they are constant in length and always directed toward the center of the circle. The magnitude of the acceleration is $a = (v')^2/R = V^2R$ where V is the speed of the wheel along the straight line.

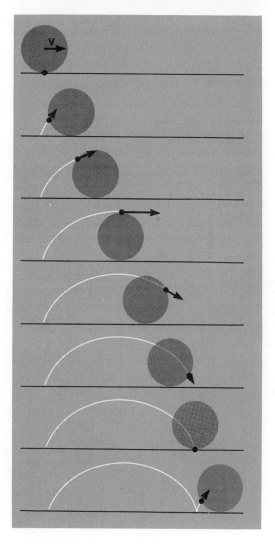

Path of the particle in the S frame for the special case $|\mathbf{V}| = v'$.

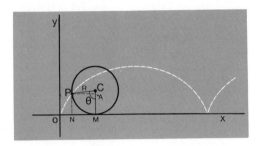

Choosing an appropriate co-ordinate system in the S frame.

We will determine the equations of the path in the frame of reference of the fixed line (the lab frame) both using a purely geometric argument and using transformation of the reference frame. We choose axes so that the circle (of radius R) rolls along the x-axis. The point P on the circle touches at the origin O, so that the arc length PM equals OM. The angle PCM, or θ is the angle through which the radius PC has turned. The co-ordinates of the point P are

$$x = ON = OM - NM = PM - NM = R\theta - R\sin\theta = R(\theta - \sin\theta)$$
$$y = NP = MC - AC = R - R\cos\theta = R(1 - \cos\theta)$$

These are the equations of the path in parametric form, expressed in terms of the parameter θ. It is possible to eliminate θ and obtain the single equation in Cartesian co-ordinates

$$x = \arccos\left(\frac{R-y}{R}\right) - \sqrt{2Ry - y^2}$$

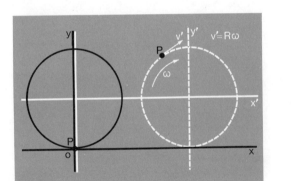

Relation between co-ordinate systems (x',y') in S' and (x,y) in S.

however, this is rather awkward and the parametric form is more useful. The path is called a **common cycloid**.

We showed in the last chapter that uniform circular motion of a particle in a frame of reference S' can be described in a Cartesian co-ordinate system by

$$x' = -R\sin\omega t$$
$$y' = -R\cos\omega t$$

where ω is the angular velocity or angular frequency: $\omega = 2\pi f = 2\pi/T$, where T is the period. The co-ordinate system in S' is chosen so that at $t = 0$ the particle P is at $(0, -R)$. As t increases x' becomes negative initially, so that the rotation is clockwise.

We will transform this circular motion in S' into a frame S. We choose co-ordinate axes in S such that at $t = 0$, y and y' coincide, $(x = x')$ and $y = y' + R$, and such that the axes (x',y') move in the $+x$-direction with velocity $\mathbf{V}$. The transformation equation $\mathbf{r} = \mathbf{r}' + \mathbf{V}t$ becomes for these axes

$$x = x' + Vt \qquad y = y' + R$$

and the circular motion in S' is described in S by

$$x = Vt - R \sin \omega t \qquad y = R - R \cos \omega t$$

To correspond to rolling without slipping, the velocity **V** must have the same magnitude as the speed $v' = R\omega$ of the particle in the S' frame. Then

$$x = R(\omega t - \sin \omega t) \qquad y = R(1 - \cos \omega t)$$

These are the parametric equations for a common cycloid, as deduced in the geometric argument. However, here the parameter is the quantity ωt, rather than θ. For rotation at a constant angular speed ω, the angle turned through by a radius in time t is $\theta = \omega t$. The geometric development shows the path for rolling without slipping is a common cycloid whether or not the speed is constant.

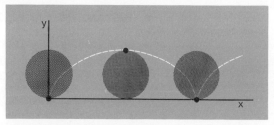

The common cycloid in S, path for a particle with $V = v'$.

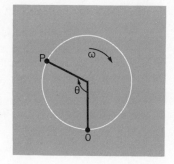

Angular displacement θ related to angular speed ω: $\theta = \omega t$.

We have established that if a particle is moving in a circle of radius R with speed v' in a reference frame S', its path in a frame of reference S moving with velocity **V** in the plane of the circle is a common cycloid, provided $V = v'$. What is its path in S if $V \neq v'$?

The path will be a cycloid, but of a different kind. As we have already stated, a common cycloid is the curve traced by a point on the circumference of a circle rolling on a straight line. A **prolate cycloid** is traced by a point on the extension of a radius beyond the circumference. A **curtate cycloid** is traced by a point on a radius but within the circumference. Therefore if the transformation of circular motion of speed v' is made to a frame moving with speed $V < v'$, the path will be a prolate cycloid; if $V > v'$, the path will be a curtate cycloid.

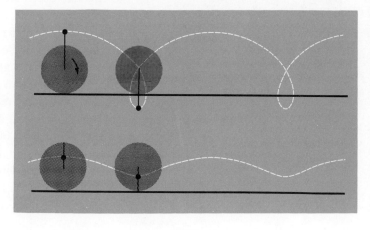

For a particle moving in S' in a circular path at constant speed v', the path in a frame S moving at velocity **V** with respect to S' is a prolate cycloid if $V < v'$, or a curtate cycloid if $V > v'$.

INSTANTANEOUS AXIS

In describing the particular case of motion of a rigid object such as a wheel that is rolling without slipping along a line in a frame of reference, it is sometimes useful to think of the instantaneous motion as one of pure rotation. The diagram showing velocities at various points on a rolling wheel is reproduced here, with only the resultant velocity $\mathbf{v} = \mathbf{v}' + \mathbf{V}$ for each point. Since the wheel is rolling without slipping $V = v'$ where v' is the speed of points on the circumference (in frame moving with the wheel). The point of contact I is instantaneously at rest. It is called the **instantaneous axis** because the motion can be thought of at this instant as pure rotation about an axis through I, perpendicular to the plane.

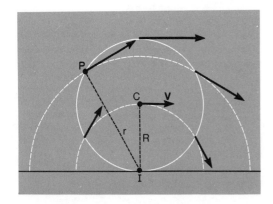

Rolling without slipping can be considered pure rotation about an instantaneous axis.

In the moving frame of reference S' the point I has a speed $v' = R\omega$ with respect to the center point C, where ω is the angular speed. In the lab frame of reference S the point C has a speed V with respect to the point I. But $V = v' = R\omega$, and therefore C has an angular speed ω with respect to I. We saw in the last chapter that the angular speed of all points in a rigid body is the same, with respect to a particular axis. Therefore, the angular speed with respect to I is ω for *any* point P in the body, and the speed of P is $v = r\omega$ where r is the length PI. The direction of $\mathbf{v}$ is at right angles to the line PI. The point P is anywhere in the body, not necessarily on the circumference. At the top of the wheel the speed is $v = (2R)\omega = 2V$.

It is important to emphasize that this description is only valid at a particular instant. We cannot consider that there is rotation at **constant** angular speed ω about the point I, because if so we could determine the acceleration $a = v^2/r = r\omega^2$ at any point. The point I would have zero acceleration, the point C an acceleration V^2/R, directed toward I, and so on. This is not correct for the reference frames S or S': in both of these the acceleration of the center C is zero, and the acceleration of any point on the circumference has magnitude V^2/R and is directed toward C.

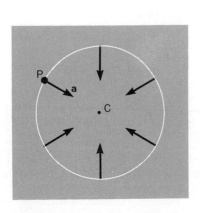

Acceleration vectors in S and in S'.

It might appear that describing the motion as pure rotation with respect to the point I is a description in the reference frame S', since I is a fixed point in S'.

However, this is not so, because C is a fixed point in S', and it is moving with respect to I if we take I as an instantaneous axis. The description in terms of the instantaneous axis means that we have made a transformation into a frame of reference that is **rotating** with respect to S'. In the next chapter we shall look at transformations between frames rotating at constant angular velocity with respect to one another, and will see that the acceleration in such frames depends on the frame used. Such reference frames are *not* dynamically equivalent.

AN EXAMPLE OF A CHARGED PARTICLE
IN A UNIFORM MAGNETIC FIELD

In the last chapter we saw that a charged particle moving at right angles to a uniform magnetic field **B** had a circular path of radius $R = mv/eB$ where m, v and e were the particle's mass, speed and electric charge (an electron, charge e, was used in the example). We will now deal with the general motion of a particle of mass m, charge q, moving in a uniform magnetic field **B** that is uniform and constant.

We stated previously that the force on a moving charged particle in a magnetic field is $\mathbf{F} = q\mathbf{v} \times \mathbf{B}$ and this produces an acceleration

$$\mathbf{a} = \frac{\mathbf{F}}{m} = \frac{q}{m}\mathbf{v} \times \mathbf{B}$$

We choose a co-ordinate system in the frame of reference being used such that the uniform field **B** is in the z direction. Then $B_x = B_y = 0$, $B_z = B$. Recalling the definition of vector product

$$(\mathbf{v} \times \mathbf{B})_x = v_y B_z - v_z B_y = v_y B$$
$$(\mathbf{v} \times \mathbf{B})_y = v_z B_x - v_x B_z = -v_x B$$
$$(\mathbf{v} \times \mathbf{B})_z = v_x B_y - v_y B_x = 0$$

The components of acceleration are

$$a_x = \frac{q}{m}v_y B \qquad a_y = -\frac{q}{m}v_x B \qquad a_z = 0$$

or
$$a_x = \frac{dv_x}{dt} = \omega v_y \qquad a_y = \frac{dv_y}{dt} = -\omega v_x \qquad a_z = 0$$

where $\omega = qB/m$ is a constant.

These equations give an instantaneous description of the motion. To describe the motion over a time interval they must be integrated or solved. Recalling the discussion of circular motion in the last chapter, we recognize that if we set

$$v_x = v_0 \sin \omega t \qquad \text{and} \qquad v_y = v_0 \cos \omega t$$

where v_0 is a constant, then

$$\frac{dv_x}{dt} = \omega v_0 \cos \omega t \quad \text{and} \quad \frac{dv_y}{dt} = -\omega v_0 \sin \omega t$$

$$= \omega v_y \qquad\qquad\qquad = -\omega v_x$$

and the a_x and a_y equations are satisfied. The equation $a_z = 0$ gives $v_z = $ constant: the component of velocity in the z-direction, parallel to the magnetic field direction, is constant.

The velocity component equations can be integrated, or a solution found by trial. Introducing constants x_0, y_0, z_0 and r_0, a solution is

$$x = x_0 - r_0 \cos \omega t \qquad v_x = \frac{dx}{dt} = \omega r_0 \sin \omega t$$

$$y = y_0 + r_0 \sin \omega t \qquad v_y = \frac{dy}{dt} = \omega r_0 \cos \omega t \qquad \left. \right\} \quad \therefore \; \omega r_0 = v_0$$

$$z = z_0 + v_z t \qquad\quad v_z = \frac{dz}{dt} = v_z = \text{constant}$$

The components of displacement $\mathbf{r}$, velocity $\mathbf{v}$, and acceleration $\mathbf{a}$ of the charged particle in the uniform magnetic field are

$$
\begin{array}{lll}
x = x_0 - r_0 \cos \omega t & v_x = v_0 \sin \omega t & a_x = \omega v_y \\
y = y_0 + r_0 \sin \omega t & v_y = v_0 \cos \omega t & a_y = -\omega v_x \\
z = z_0 + v_z t & v_z = v_z = \text{constant} & a_z = 0
\end{array}
$$

Each set of these describes the motion completely. What does the path of the particle look like? The x-displacement is simple harmonic motion, with amplitude r_0, about the point x_0. The y-displacement is simple harmonic motion, with amplitude r_0, about the point y_0, but $\pi/2$ out of phase with the SHM in the x-direction. We saw in the last chapter that combining two SHM's of the same amplitude and frequency, at right angles and differing in phase by $\pi/2$, produced uniform circular motion. The **projection** of the motion in the xy plane is a circle of radius r_0 and speed v_0. The angular frequency is $\omega = qB/m$. It depends on the charge-to-mass ratio of the particle q/m and on the strength of the field B, and *not* on how fast the particle is moving. It is the same quantity that occurred in the example of the last chapter, called the cyclotron frequency. However, note that here there is *not* periodic motion of the particle: the projection in the xy plane is circular, but the path of the particle is a helix. The particle has a constant velocity v_z at right angles to the circular motion, and this produces a helical path of constant pitch as described earlier. By choosing axes so that x_0 and y_0 are zero, the z-axis becomes the axis of the helix. The radius of the helix is

$$r_0 = \frac{v_0}{\omega} = \frac{mv_0}{qB}$$

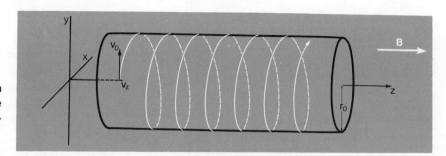

Helical path of a charged particle in a uniform magnetic field.

sometimes called the gyroradius or cyclotron radius. The speed of the particle in its helical path is constant: v_0 is *not* its speed, but the speed of its projection in the xy plane.

Any charged particle entering a uniform magnetic field with a velocity $\mathbf{v}$, with components v_0 perpendicular to the field and v_z parallel to the field, moves at a constant speed v on a spiral path of radius mv_0/qB, making one turn of the spiral in a time $T = 2\pi/\omega = 2\pi m/qB$. The direction of motion (clockwise or counterclockwise) depends on the sign of the charge q.

A transformation to a frame of reference moving at a velocity v_z simplifies the description of the motion, because in this frame the path of the particle is a circle of radius r_0, and the particle speed is v_0. It is important to realize that this transformation does not affect the dynamic situation; the acceleration of the particle has a magnitude v_0^2/r_0 in both frames, and is directed toward the center in both frames. The force producing the acceleration is the same in both frames. (This assumes that the magnetic field $\mathbf{B}$ is the same in both frames, and this is not valid for values of v approaching the speed of light.)

AN EXAMPLE OF A CHARGED PARTICLE
IN CROSSED ELECTRIC AND MAGNETIC FIELDS

In the last example we described the motion of a charged particle acted upon by the magnetic force $q\mathbf{v} \times \mathbf{B}$ produced by a uniform magnetic field. In the last chapter we described the motion produced by the electric force $q\mathbf{E}$ in a uniform electric field; the constant force produces constant acceleration. We now tackle a description of the motion of a charged particle acted upon by both an electric and a magnetic field, in the particular case where the fields are **crossed,** meaning at right angles to one another. Again we consider that both fields are uniform (the same at each point in space, in the region they exist) and constant (independent of time); they are better described as uniform crossed electrostatic and magnetostatic fields.

In general the resultant force is

$$\mathbf{F} = q\mathbf{E} + q\mathbf{v} \times \mathbf{B}$$

(called the Lorentz force) producing an acceleration $\mathbf{a} = \mathbf{F}/m$. If we choose co-ordinate axes so that $\mathbf{B}$ is in the z-direction and $\mathbf{E}$ is in the x-direction, then $B_x = B_y = E_y = E_z = 0$ and $B_z = B$, $E_x = E$. Reference to the previous example shows that the components of the acceleration $\mathbf{a}$ are

$$a_x = \frac{q}{m}E + \omega v_y \qquad a_y = -\omega v_x \qquad a_z = 0$$

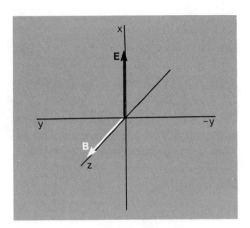

Choosing a co-ordinate system for **E** and **B** fields at right angles.

where the constant $\omega = qB/m$ has again been introduced.

These equations are satisfied by a solution

$$v_x = v_0 \sin \omega t \qquad v_y = v_0 \cos \omega t - E/B \qquad v_z = \text{constant}$$

where v_0 is a constant. This can be verified by differentiating

$$a_x = \frac{dv_x}{dt} = \omega v_0 \cos \omega t = \omega(v_y + E/B) = qE/m + \omega v_y$$

$$a_y = \frac{dv_y}{dt} = -\omega v_0 \sin \omega t = -\omega v_x$$

$$a_z = \frac{dv_z}{dt} = 0$$

Integrating again, the components of displacement are

$$x = x_0 - \frac{v_0}{\omega} \cos \omega t = x_0 - r_0 \cos \omega t$$

$$y = y_0 + \frac{v_0}{\omega} \sin \omega t - \frac{E}{B} t = y_0 + r_0 \sin \omega t - \frac{E}{B} t$$

$$z = z_0 + v_z t$$

where we have set $r_0 = v_0/\omega$ as in the previous example.

What is the shape of the path represented by these equations? We will first rewrite the displacement equations for a special relationship between the constants: we assume that $v_0 = E/B$. Then, if we choose $x_0 = r_0$

$$x = x_0 - r_0 \cos \omega t = r_0(1 - \cos \omega t)$$
$$y = y_0 + r_0 \sin \omega t - v_0 t = y_0 + r_0(\sin \omega t - \omega t) = y_0 - r_0(\omega t - \sin \omega t)$$
$$z = z_0 + v_z t$$

Now look back at the parametric equations we developed for the common cycloid

$$x = R(\omega t - \sin \omega t) \qquad y = R(1 - \cos \omega t)$$

which are similar to the x and y displacement equations for the charged particles, except that x and y are interchanged, and one sign is reversed. The **projection** of the path of the particle in the xy plane is a common cycloid, the path produced by rolling a circle of radius r_0 without slipping along the y-axis (in the negative direction) with a speed $v_0 = r_0\omega = E/B$. The actual path of the particle does not lie in the xy plane because of the constant component of velocity v_z in the z-direction (perpendicular to the page in the diagram).

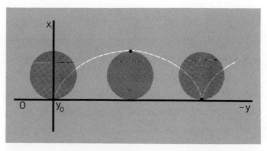

Projection in the xy plane of the path of a charged particle moving in crossed **E** and **B** fields.

This was for the particular relationship $v_0 = E/B$. In general this will not be so. If $v_0 > E/B$ the projection of the path in the xy plane will be a prolate cycloid, and if $v_0 < E/B$ the projection will be a curtate cycloid.

The path of the particle in the laboratory frame of reference is rather complex—it is cycloidal with a uniform drift in the z-direction. However, a transformation of the frame of reference simplifies the description. If a transformation is made to a reference frame S' moving with velocity $\mathbf{V}$ with respect to S, where $V_x = V_z = 0$ and $V_y = -E/B$, the velocity components become

$$v'_x = v_x - V_x = v_0 \sin \omega t$$
$$v'_y = v_y - V_y = v_0 \cos \omega t$$
$$v'_z = v_z - V_z = v_z$$

identical to those in the previous example for a particle in a uniform magnetic field. In this frame the projection of the path in the $x'y'$ plane is a circle, and the path in S' is a helix. In this frame the particle moves as though only the magnetic field were present.

A transformation simplifying the description still more is to a frame S'' moving with respect to S with velocity components $V_x = 0$, $V_y = -E/B$, $V_z = v_z$. In this frame the particle moves in a circle of radius r_0 with a constant speed v_0. It has a constant angular speed $\omega = v_0/r_0 = qB/m$. In describing the motion in the lab frame we introduced the quantities r_0, v_0 and ω as useful constants, but in the lab frame the motion is not periodic—that is, the path is not retraced with a period $T = 2\pi/\omega$—although an identically shaped path is repeated with a time interval T. The path of the particle is not a circle of radius r_0, but the motion is confined to a region parallel to the yz plane of thickness r_0.

The path in a particular experiment will depend on the way the charged particle is introduced into the field region—that is, on the magnitude and

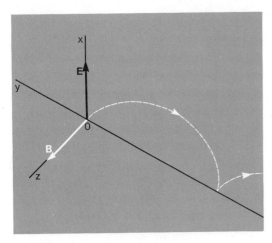

Path of a charged particle released from rest in crossed **E** and **B** fields.

direction of its initial velocity. Its direction of curvature will depend on the sign of charge q and the field directions.

A positive charge **released from rest** at the origin will initially have an acceleration $a = qE/m$ upward. Once it acquires any velocity there will be a force to the right due to the magnetic field; this force $q\mathbf{v} \times \mathbf{B}$ will always be at right angles to its path, so it will curve around achieving a maximum speed $2v_0 = 2E/B$ to the right, and then curve back to the y-axis, coming instantaneously to rest, and then starting over on a similar path. The motion is confined to the xy plane—if there is initially no z-component of velocity, there never will be one since $v_z = $ constant.

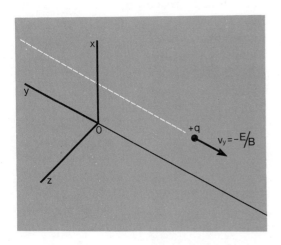

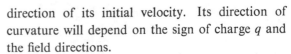

The path of a charged particle in crossed **E** and **B** fields will be a straight line for a particular value of the velocity.

A positive charge with an initial y-component of velocity $v_y = -E/B$, and moving parallel to the yz plane ($v_x = 0$) will move in a straight line through the crossed fields; the forces due to the two fields are equal and opposite in this case. In this way the fields act as a velocity selector, as described in the example of the last chapter. The v_z component does not matter; if $v_z = 0$, the straight line is parallel to the y-axis, as shown in the diagram. Otherwise it makes an angle θ with the y-direction, where $\tan \theta = v_z/v_y = -Bv_z/E$. In the S'' frame of reference the particle is at rest.

Questions for discussion

1. Think about the statement that all frames of reference moving at constant velocities with respect to one another are **dynamically equivalent.** What do you think this means? We will be discussing this at length in Chapter 8, but it is worth thinking about in advance.

2. Why is it more precise to speak of particles as **interacting** than as **colliding**?

3. A ball, tied to a support by a long elastic band, is dropped. It stretches the elastic as it falls, and then bounces upward. What does it make a collision with? What provided the interaction? Is it an elastic collision?

4. Can you think of examples of explosive, elastic, non-elastic and inelastic collisions for which it is reasonable to assume conservation of momentum?

5. Can a head-on collision between two particles always be described completely in one dimension? Can a skew collision always be described completely in two dimensions? Can an inelastic skew collision always be described completely in two dimensions?

6. In any two-particle elastic collision the speed of each particle is conserved in the c-of-m frame of reference. Do you think it strange that this conservation law is not true in the lab frame of reference? Is either the lab frame or the c-of-m frame a unique frame?

7. If you saw a motion picture of a two-particle elastic collision, would you be able to tell if the film was being run forward or backward?

(We will return to this question of **reversibility of processes** in Part VI.)

Problems

We used conservation of momentum for two-particle collisions in this chapter in order to emphasize the importance of the center-of-mass frame of reference, but our primary interest here is transformation of the reference frame. Therefore we include here only a few problems involving momentum conservation; we will return to this topic in Chapter 13.

1. Aircraft A is flying east at 300 mph. Aircraft B is flying at 400 mph. Calculate the velocity of B relative to A if B is flying (a) west, (b) east, (c) north, (d) northwest.

2. A caravan 7.5 miles long is moving at constant speed across a desert. A rider at the rear is asked to take a message to the leader. He sets off, delivers the message, and immediately returns to the rear, traveling at a steady rate. He notes that the caravan has advanced 12 miles while he has been away from his position. How far did he travel? (Note that the result does not depend on knowing the speeds of the caravan or the rider.)

3. A river 2 miles wide has a current of 5 mph. A ferry moves at 10 mph relative to the water. (a) What is the minimum time in which it can cross the river? (b) What is the time to cross if it moves straight across?

   A passenger walks on the deck at 3 mph while the ferry is moving as in (b). What is his speed relative to the river bank if he is walking (c) from bow to stern? (d) from port to starboard?

4. Solve Problem 7 of Chapter 5 by making the calculation in a frame of reference fixed to car B.

5. Two cars A and B approach an intersection. Car A is on an E–W road moving W at 30 mph, car B is on a NW–SE road moving SE at 40 mph. When car A is 4 miles from the intersection of the roads, car B is 5 miles from the intersection.

Determine the distance of closest approach of the cars, and the time elapsed in reaching this position.

6. A plane flies at a constant speed of 200 mph with respect to the air. It is to travel due west to a certain point, and then return to its starting point. If there is no wind, the time for the round trip is 8 hr. Calculate the difference in time for the round trip if there is a steady wind of 50 mph (a) from the east, (b) from the north.

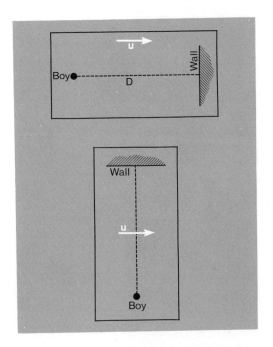

7. The speed of sound in air is V; this does not depend on the speed of the source of the sound, or of the receiver. A boy sets off a firecracker at a distance D from a wall. If he stays at the same spot, he hears the sound reflected from the wall after a time $t_0 = 2D/V$. Calculate the time before he hears the reflection (in terms of t_0) if he walks with a constant speed u (a) toward the wall, (b) away from the wall, (c) parallel to the wall.

Suppose that the boy stays at rest with respect to the wall, but boy and wall are on an open flat car which moves with a constant velocity **u** through still air. Calculate the time before the boy hears the reflected sound (in terms of t_0) if the line between boy and wall is (d) parallel to **u**, (e) at right angles to **u**.

Calculations similar to this are made in connection with the famous Michelson experiment on the propagation of light.

8. A block of wood is slid along the horizontal floor of a train moving on a horizontal straight track at a constant speed of 3 mph. Given an initial speed of 10 ft/sec, the block comes to rest after sliding 10 ft along the floor. What is its acceleration? What frame of reference did you use in your calculation? Can you make the calculation in a different frame?

   Calculate the magnitude of the displacement of the block from its original position, relative to the earth, if it is slid in the same direction as the train is moving, and if it is slid at right angles to this. Would your calculations necessarily be correct if the acceleration of the block is not uniform?

9. Two particles of masses $m_1 = 1$ kg, $m_2 = 2$ kg, move in the same plane with velocities given by $\mathbf{u}_1 = 3\mathbf{i} + 2\mathbf{j}$ m/sec, $\mathbf{u}_2 = \mathbf{i} + 4\mathbf{j}$ m/sec. Determine (a) the angle between the paths of the particles, (b) the velocity of the center of mass, (c) the velocity of m_1 with respect to m_2, (d) the velocity of m_1 with respect to the c-of-m.

   Suppose that the particles collide and stick together. Find (e) their velocity, (f) the fraction of the initial kinetic energy lost in the collision.

10. Consider an elastic collision between two particles of masses m and $2m$, for example a neutron and a deuteron. Make calculations both in the lab frame and the center-of-mass frame of reference.

(a) If mass $2m$ is initially at rest, and mass m makes a head-on elastic collision with it, calculate the fraction of the energy transferred.

(b) If mass m is initially at rest, and mass $2m$ makes a head-on elastic collision with it, calculate the fraction of the energy transferred.

(c) If mass $2m$ is initially at rest, calculate the angle through which mass m is scattered if it loses 50% of its energy in the elastic collision. What is the scattering angle φ in the center-of-mass frame?

11. A ball dropped from the top of an elevator shaft bounces on the top of the elevator. When the elevator is stopped with the top 16 ft below the top of the shaft the ball rebounds to a point 7 ft below the top of the shaft. How high would it have bounced if it had hit the elevator at the same point, but the elevator was moving at 8 ft/sec **(a)** downward, **(b)** upward? **(c)** If the elevator leaves the top of the shaft at a constant speed of 8 ft/sec, and the ball is dropped 2 sec later, how high will it bounce?

It is suggested that you perform your calculations in one frame of reference, for example, the earth frame, and then verify them by working in the elevator frame. Assume that the coefficient of restitution for the collision is a constant, and that the time of contact is negligible.

12. A vibrator driven electrically at 60 hertz carries a pen that executes SHM with an amplitude of 0.5 cm. A paper strip is moving under the pen, at right angles to its direction of vibration, at a speed of 0.2 m/sec. Choosing appropriate x and y axes, determine the equation of the line drawn on the paper strip by the pen.

13. A cement truck moving at 3 mph carries cement in a 6-ft-diameter drum which rotates at 10 rpm about an axis along the direction of motion of the truck. Find the acceleration of a point on the circumference of the drum, and compare the distance such a point moves to the distance the truck moves.

14. A teenager carries his battery-operated record player while walking at a steady pace. In his frame of reference, calculate the speed of a point on the edge of a 12-inch 33-rpm record. Think of the motion of this point in the earth frame of reference. At what walking speed is the path a common cycloid? Roughly sketch the path for a walking speed half as great and twice as great.

15. Suppose that a proton (charge-to-mass ratio $e/m = 9.6 \times 10^7$ coul/kg) after being accelerated through a potential difference of 10^6 volts (a 1-Mev proton) enters a uniform magnetic field of flux density $B = 1$ weber/m² at an angle of 60° to the lines of magnetic flux. Determine the radius of the helical path, time to make one turn of the helix, and distance advanced in the field direction while making one turn.

16. A boy on a bicycle travels a distance of 1 mile in 15 minutes at constant speed. Calculate the speed (with respect to the ground) of a pebble caught in the tread of a tire when it is **(a)** at the top of the wheel, **(b)** at the foremost point of the wheel. **(c)** Determine the total distance the pebble moves as the boy moves 1 mile.

Note re (c): Using the parametric equations of the cycloid $x = R(\theta - \sin \theta)$, $y = R(1 - \cos \theta)$, show that the differential length ds along the path is given by

$$ds = (dx^2 + dy^2)^{1/2} = \sqrt{2}\, R(1 - \cos \theta)^{1/2}\, d\theta = 2R \sin (\theta/2)\, d\theta$$

and that the length of one arch of the cycloid (as θ varies from 0 to 2π) is $s = 8R$.

7

TRANSFORMATIONS BETWEEN ACCELERATED FRAMES OF REFERENCE

FRAMES OF REFERENCE IN PURE TRANSLATION

The Galilean transformation developed in the last chapter describes transformation between frames of reference S and S' moving at **constant velocity** V with respect to one another. This means that all particles at rest in S' have a velocity $v = v' + V = V$ in S. For example, think of three rods at right angles in S'; every particle in these rods has a constant velocity V in S, and the trajectory of each particle in S is a straight line. This means that the motion of S' with respect to S is **pure translation.** The Galilean transformation deals with frames of reference moving in pure translation relative to one another, at a constant velocity V.

It is possible to have the frames of reference moving relative to one another in pure translation, but with a relative velocity that is not constant. If all particles at rest in S' have at every instant the same velocity V with respect to S, then the

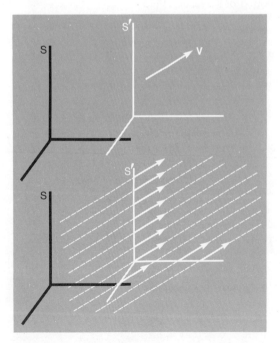

Frame S' moving at constant velocity V relative to frame S.

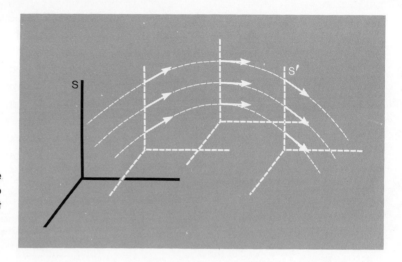

Frame S' moving in pure translation with respect to frame S, but not at constant velocity.

path of every particle is the same in S, and S' is moving in pure translation with respect to S. This means that the displacement of every particle is the same as that of every other particle in the same time interval. Fixing your attention on particles at rest in three mutually perpendicular rods in S', you can see that this means that the relative **orientation** of the two frames of reference does not change.

In general, then, for pure translation the relative velocity $\mathbf{V}$ of the two frames may change with time, $\mathbf{V}(t)$. The velocity transformation

$$\mathbf{v} = \mathbf{v}' + \mathbf{V}$$

relating the instantaneous velocities $\mathbf{v}$ and $\mathbf{v}'$ of a particle, as measured in S and S', is still valid, however, as can be seen as follows.

Vectors $\mathbf{r}$ and $\mathbf{r}'$ are displacements of a particle P as measured with respect to fixed points O and O' in S and S'. The displacement of O' with respect to O at any instant is $\mathbf{R}$. From the diagram $\mathbf{r} = \mathbf{r}' + \mathbf{R}$, and differentiating

$$\frac{d\mathbf{r}}{dt} = \frac{d\mathbf{r}'}{dt} + \frac{d\mathbf{R}}{dt}$$

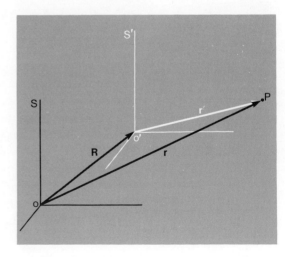

Displacements of a particle referred to fixed points O' in S' and O in S.

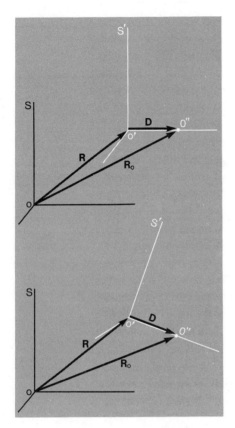

If S' is moving in pure translation with respect to S, the vector $\mathbf{D}$ between the fixed points O' and O'' must be constant in magnitude and direction.

The instantaneous velocities of P in S and S' are $\mathbf{v} = d\mathbf{r}/dt$ and $\mathbf{v}' = d\mathbf{r}'/dt$. The quantity $d\mathbf{R}/dt$ is the velocity $\mathbf{V}$ of S' with respect to S at this instant. It is the same for any two fixed points in S and S' *provided* their relative motion is pure translation; note that this is *not* so if they are rotating with respect to one another. Think about a second fixed point O'' in S'. At some instant the three displacements $\mathbf{R}$, $\mathbf{R}_0$ and $\mathbf{D}$ are as shown

$$\mathbf{R}_0 = \mathbf{R} + \mathbf{D}$$

and $d\mathbf{R}_0/dt = d\mathbf{R}/dt = \mathbf{V}$ provided $d\mathbf{D}/dt = 0$, that is, provided $\mathbf{D}$ is a vector that is fixed in magnitude and direction.

Thus for pure translation

$$\mathbf{v} = \mathbf{v}' + \mathbf{V}$$

the same as the Galilean transformation, but the Galilean transformation for acceleration $\mathbf{a} = \mathbf{a}'$ is *not* valid.

$$\frac{d\mathbf{v}}{dt} = \frac{d\mathbf{v}'}{dt} + \frac{d\mathbf{V}}{dt}$$

or

$$\mathbf{a} = \mathbf{a}' + \mathbf{A}$$

where $\mathbf{A}$ is the acceleration of frame S' relative to S. This acceleration may be a function of time $\mathbf{A}(t)$, but at any instant every fixed point in S' has the same acceleration re S.

We pointed out in the last chapter that frames of reference moving at **constant** relative velocity $\mathbf{V}$ are said to be dynamically equivalent, but if $\mathbf{V}$ is not constant they are not. Measurements made in frame S on a particle of mass m give an acceleration $\mathbf{a}$, which according to Newton's law is produced by an unbalanced force $\mathbf{F} = m\mathbf{a}$. Measurements made in frame S' give an acceleration $\mathbf{a}'$, produced by a force $\mathbf{F}' = m\mathbf{a}' = m\mathbf{a} - m\mathbf{A} = \mathbf{F} - m\mathbf{A}$. Which is the correct force? They both are, as we will see, but we shall return to this question later in discussing dynamics. For the moment we simply want to emphasize that the forces measured depend on the frame of reference in which the measurements are made. For example, in a frame of reference fixed to a freely falling body, the body is at rest, and therefore there is no unbalanced force on it in this frame of reference.

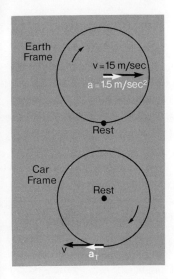

Velocities in the earth frame and in the car frame.

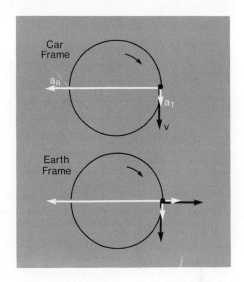

Acceleration in the car frame and in the earth frame.

Example: A European sports car with wheels 0.6 m in diameter accelerates uniformly from rest to 54 km/hr in 10 seconds. Calculate the velocity and acceleration of a particle at the foremost point of one of the wheels, 1 sec and 10 sec after starting.

The car reaches a velocity

$$v = 54 \text{ km/hr} = 54 \times \frac{1000}{3600} \text{ m/sec} = 15 \text{ m/sec}$$

in 10 sec with a constant acceleration

$$a = \frac{v - v_0}{t} = 1.5 \text{ m/sec}^2$$

The center of a wheel has this acceleration and this velocity at this instant, and a point on the bottom of the wheel, in contact with the road, is at rest. This is in the earth frame of reference. We assume that the values of velocity and acceleration to be calculated are in the earth frame, but it will be convenient to make some calculations in the car frame, where the motion of the wheel is pure rotation. In this frame, the center of the wheel is at rest, and a point at the bottom (or any other point on the circumference) has a speed of 15 m/sec and a tangential acceleration a_T of 1.5 m/sec². Therefore the wheel has an angular speed $\omega = v/R = 15/0.3 = 50$ rad/sec at this instant and a constant angular acceleration $\alpha = a_T/R = 1.5/0.3 = 5$ rad/sec².

After accelerating for 1 sec, the wheel acquires an angular speed $\omega = \alpha t = 5$ rad/sec, a tangential speed

$$v = R\omega = 0.3 \times 5 = 1.5 \text{ m/sec}$$

and accelerations

$$a_R = R\omega^2 = 0.3 \times 5^2 = 7.5 \text{ m/sec}^2$$
$$a_T = 1.5 \text{ m/sec}^2$$

These are in the car frame. At this instant the car has a velocity of 1.5 m/sec and an acceleration 1.5 m/sec² relative to the earth frame, and these must be added to give velocities and accelerations in the earth frame. The resultant velocity of a point at the

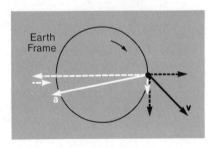

front of a wheel is $1.5\sqrt{2} = 2.1$ m/sec directed at an angle $45°$ below the horizontal in the forward direction. The resultant acceleration is $\sqrt{1.5^2 + 6.0^2} = 6.2$ m/sec² directed at an angle arc tan $(1.5/6.0)$ below the horizontal in the backward direction.

Resultant velocity and acceleration of a point at the front of a wheel, in the earth frame.

After 10 sec, the radial acceleration has become

$$a_R = R\omega^2 = 0.3 \times 50^2 = 750 \text{ m/sec}^2$$

This means that it does not matter whether we assume that the car is still accelerating or not. This acceleration is so large compared to the other component $a_T = 1.5$ m/sec², and to the car acceleration $a = 1.5$ m/sec², that essentially the acceleration is 750 m/sec² toward the center of the wheel for *any* point on the circumference, in *either* frame. The velocity of the foremost point on a wheel at this instant is $15\sqrt{2} = 21$ m/sec directed at an angle $45°$ below the horizontal in the forward direction.

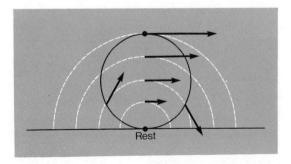

Pure rotation around an instantaneous axis.

In describing rolling without slipping in the previous chapter we have pointed out that it is sometimes convenient to consider the motion as one of pure rotation about the point of contact as an instantaneous axis. We emphasize again that this represents a transformation to a frame of reference that is **rotating** with respect to the earth frame. This introduces accelerations that are not present in the other two frames of reference.

FRAMES OF REFERENCE ROTATING RELATIVE TO ONE ANOTHER AT CONSTANT ANGULAR VELOCITY

We have examined transformations between frames of reference moving in pure translation, in particular (in the previous chapter) with constant relative velocity. We now look at transformations for **pure rotation**. This means, for two reference frames S and S', that any particle at rest in S' has a circular trajectory in S (and vice versa). There will be a fixed axis, common to the two frames of reference. Any particle at rest in S will move in a circle in S', with this axis as center, and vice versa. Recalling the definitions of angular displacement and velocity, this means that we can refer to *the* angular displacement θ or angular velocity ω of S' with respect to S; the values of θ and ω are the same for all points in S'.

A general vector development of the transformation for pure rotation will not be given, because while the vector treatment is succinct, it requires some sophistication in vector algebra to be meaningful. Instead we will work out the transformation for a particular choice of co-ordinate axes in S and S' and state the general result later.

We choose co-ordinate systems (x,y,z) in S and (x',y',z') in S' such that both z-axes lie along the common axis of rotation and the x–y, x'–y' axes lie in the same plane. For the motion of a particle P, the z-co-ordinate will always be the

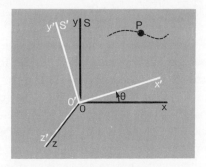

Choosing co-ordinate systems in S and S' for pure rotation.

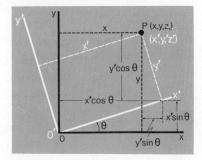

The relation between co-ordinates (x,y) and (x',y') for rotation around a common z–z'-axis.

same in both frames and the z-transformation is $z = z'$. At some instant $t = 0$ the x- and x'-axes will coincide. At any time t the axes make an angle θ with respect to one another—that is, the angular displacement of S' re S is θ. The relation between the co-ordinates in the two frames may be seen from the diagram to be

$$x = x' \cos \theta - y' \sin \theta$$
$$y = x' \sin \theta + y' \cos \theta$$
$$z = z'$$

We will restrict ourselves to the transformation for **uniform** rotation, that is for rotation at a constant angular velocity ω. Then $\theta = \omega t$, and the transformation equations for the components of displacement are

$$x = x' \cos \omega t - y' \sin \omega t$$
$$y = x' \sin \omega t + y' \cos \omega t$$
$$z = z'$$

The transformations for the velocity and acceleration components are obtained by differentiation. Before doing this we look at two simple examples, the transformation for a particle at rest in S', and the transformation for a particle moving uniformly in S'.

Think first of a particle at rest in S', on the x'-axis at a position $x' = R$. Then $y' = z' = 0$ and $x = R \cos \omega t$, $y = R \sin \omega t$, $z = 0$. The velocity and acceleration components are obtained by differentiating with respect to time

$$v_x = dx/dt = -\omega R \sin \omega t = -\omega y \qquad a_x = dv_x/dt = -\omega^2 R \cos \omega t = -\omega^2 x$$
$$v_y = dy/dt = \omega R \cos \omega t = \omega x \qquad a_y = dv_y/dt = -\omega^2 R \sin \omega t = -\omega^2 y$$
$$v_z = 0 \qquad a_z = 0$$

and the magnitudes of the velocity $\mathbf{v}$ and acceleration $\mathbf{a}$ are given by

$$v^2 = v_x^2 + v_y^2 = \omega^2 R^2 \qquad v = R\omega$$
$$a^2 = a_x^2 + a_y^2 = \omega^4 R^2 \qquad a = R\omega^2$$

These of course are the equations representing circular motion—the path of the particle in S is a circle. The particle has a speed $v = R\omega$ tangent to its path and an acceleration $a = R\omega^2$ directed toward the origin O. Thus a particle with $\mathbf{v}' = 0$ and $\mathbf{a}' = 0$ has a velocity $\mathbf{v}$ and $\mathbf{a}$ in S that are continuously changing. This emphasizes the fact that transformations between frames of reference that are rotating with respect to one another introduces accelerations that are different in the two frames, and the frames are not dynamically equivalent. The particle has **zero** acceleration as measured in S', but an acceleration of magnitude $R\omega^2$ as measured in S. This is called the **centripetal acceleration**.

Now think of a particle that starts at the origin of S' at $t = 0$ and moves along the x-axis with a constant speed v_0, so that $x' = v_0 t$, $y' = z' = 0$. We consider the motion for a time $T = 2\pi/\omega$, in which time S' will have made one revolution with respect to S. In this time the particle moves a distance $x' = v_0 T = 2\pi v_0/\omega$ in S'; we will call this distance R.

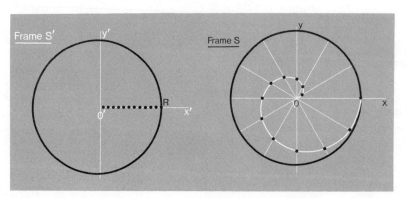

A particle moving at constant velocity away from the origin in S' has a spiral path in S.

The diagrams show the paths of the particle in S' and in S for the time interval $0 \to T$. Positions are plotted for time intervals $T/12$ apart. The path in S' is a straight line; the velocity $\mathbf{v}'$ is constant and the acceleration $\mathbf{a}'$ is zero. The path in S is not simple; clearly the velocity $\mathbf{v}$ and acceleration $\mathbf{a}$ are continuously changing in magnitude and direction. The path is an **Archimedes spiral** and its equation in polar co-ordinates is $r = b\theta$, where b is a constant.

The co-ordinates of displacement in S are

$$x = x' \cos \omega t - y' \sin \omega t = v_0 t \cos \omega t$$
$$y = x' \sin \omega t + y' \cos \omega t = v_0 t \sin \omega t$$
$$z = z' = 0$$

Therefore the distance r from the origin O is given by

$$r^2 = x^2 + y^2 = v_0^2 t^2 \cos^2 \omega t + v_0^2 t^2 \sin^2 \omega t = v_0^2 t^2$$
$$r = v_0 t = (v_0/\omega)\theta = b\theta$$

showing that the path is an Archimedes spiral, with the constant b determined by the values of v_0 (the constant velocity in S') and ω (the constant angular velocity of S' relative to S).

The components of velocity in S are obtained by differentiating, recalling the rule for differentiating a product:

$$\frac{d(AB)}{dx} = A\frac{dB}{dx} + B\frac{dA}{dx}$$

Therefore

$$v_x = \frac{dx}{dt} = v_0 \cos \omega t - \omega v_0 t \sin \omega t$$

$$v_y = \frac{dy}{dt} = v_0 \sin \omega t + \omega v_0 t \cos \omega t$$

The magnitude of the velocity $\mathbf{v}$ in S is v given by

$$
\begin{aligned}
v^2 &= v_x^2 + v_y^2 \\
&= v_0^2 \cos^2 \omega t + \omega^2 v_0^2 t^2 \sin^2 \omega t \\
&\quad - 2\omega v_0^2 t \sin \omega t \cos \omega t + v_0^2 \sin^2 \omega t \\
&\quad + \omega^2 v_0^2 t^2 \cos^2 \omega t \\
&\quad + 2\omega v_0^2 t \sin \omega t \cos \omega t \\
&= v_0^2 + \omega^2 v_0^2 t^2 = v_0^2 + \omega^2 r^2
\end{aligned}
$$

The velocity $\mathbf{v}$ as measured in S has an outward radial component v_0, constant in magnitude, and a component $r\omega$ at right angles to this. This component steadily increases in magnitude as r increases. The resultant speed is

$$v = v_0(1 + \omega^2 t^2)^{1/2} = (v_0^2 + \omega^2 r^2)^{1/2}$$

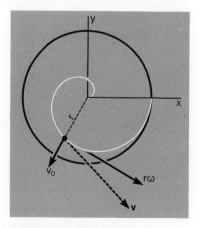

Velocity vectors at time $t = 2T/3$.

You can verify that at a time $t = \frac{2}{3}T$ the component $r\omega$ has a magnitude $(\frac{4}{3}\pi)v_0$, and therefore the velocities are as shown in the figure at this instant.

The length of the path in S travelled in the time interval $0 \rightarrow T$ may be obtained by integration. Since in general $v = ds/dt$ the path length in the interval $0 \rightarrow T$ is

$$S_{0 \rightarrow T} = \int_0^T v \, dt = v_0 \int_0^T (1 + \omega^2 t^2)^{1/2} \, dt$$

Consulting a table of integrals, and substituting $T = 2\pi/\omega$

$$S_{0 \rightarrow T} = \frac{v_0}{\omega} \left\{ \pi(1 + 4\pi^2)^{1/2} + \frac{1}{2} \ln\left[2\pi + (1 + 4\pi^2)^{1/2}\right] \right\}$$

or in terms of the distance $R = 2\pi v_0/\omega$ travelled in S'

$$S_{0 \rightarrow T} = \frac{R}{2}(1 + 4\pi^2)^{1/2} + \frac{R}{4\pi} \ln\left[2\pi + (1 + 4\pi^2)^{1/2}\right] = 3.38R$$

In the time required for one revolution of the frame of reference S', the particle travels 3.38 times as far in S as in S'.

The components of acceleration in S are obtained by differentiating again. Combining terms

$$a_x = -2\omega v_0 \sin \omega t - \omega^2 v_0 t \cos \omega t = -2\omega y/t - \omega^2 x$$
$$a_y = 2\omega v_0 \cos \omega t - \omega^2 v_0 t \sin \omega t = 2\omega x/t - \omega^2 y$$
$$a_z = 0$$

The magnitude of the acceleration $\mathbf{a}$ in S is a given by

$$a^2 = 4\omega^2(x^2 + y^2)/t^2 + \omega^4(x^2 + y^2)$$
$$= 4\omega^2 r^2/t^2 + \omega^4 r^2$$
$$= 4\omega^2 v_0^2 + \omega^4 r^2$$

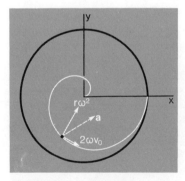

Acceleration vectors at time $t = 2T/3$.

There are two components of the acceleration $\mathbf{a}$, one of magnitude $r\omega^2$ directed inward toward the origin O, and the other, of magnitude $2\omega v_0$, at right angles to this. The first is centripetal acceleration, similar to that of a particle at rest in S' and moving in a circle in S; its magnitude increases as r increases. The second component is called the **coriolis acceleration.** You can verify that at time $t = \frac{2}{3}T$ the magnitude of the coriolis acceleration $2\omega v_0$ is $3/(2\pi)$ times that of the centripetal acceleration $r\omega^2$, and therefore that the accelerations are as shown in the figure at this instant.

The coriolis acceleration is sometimes called a sideways acceleration, because its direction is at right angles to the direction of motion *in S'*, that is, it is perpendicular to $\mathbf{v}'$. This does *not* mean that it is at right angles to the path in S. In our example the particle is moving radially outward in S', and the coriolis acceleration is therefore at right angles to the centripetal acceleration. In general this will not be the case.

The two simple examples (a particle at rest in S', and moving uniformly in S') have served to introduce the essential features of the transformation for rotation of two frames of reference at constant angular velocity ω. *Any* particle moving with an acceleration $\mathbf{a}'$ as measured in S' will have, if measurements are made in S, an additional acceleration which it is convenient to think of as being made up of two parts, a centripetal or central acceleration and a coriolis or sideways acceleration. The magnitude of the central acceleration depends on the distance $r = r'$ of the particle from the common axis of the two frames of reference and it is directed toward this axis. The magnitude of the coriolis acceleration depends on the velocity $\mathbf{v}'$ of the particle in the S' frame; it is in a direction at right angles to this velocity and at right angles to the common axis of the two frames.

The general velocity and acceleration transformations are obtained by differentiating the displacement transformations given earlier. Note that

$$d(x' \cos \omega t)/dt = (dx'/dt) \cos \omega t + x' d(\cos \omega t)/dt$$
$$= v_{x'} \cos \omega t - \omega x' \sin \omega$$

The results are
$$v_x = v_{x'} \cos \omega t - \omega x' \sin \omega t - v_{y'} \sin \omega t - \omega y' \cos \omega t$$
$$v_y = v_{x'} \sin \omega t + \omega x' \cos \omega t + v_{y'} \cos \omega t - \omega y' \sin \omega t$$
$$v_z = v_{z'}$$
$$a_x = a_{x'} \cos \omega t - 2\omega v_{x'} \sin \omega t - \omega^2 x' \cos \omega t$$
$$\quad - a_{y'} \sin \omega t - 2\omega v_{y'} \cos \omega t + \omega^2 y' \sin \omega t$$
$$a_y = a_{x'} \sin \omega t - 2\omega v_{x'} \cos \omega t - \omega^2 x' \sin \omega t$$
$$\quad + a_{y'} \cos \omega t - 2\omega v_{y'} \sin \omega t - \omega^2 y' \cos \omega t$$
$$a_z = a_{z'}$$

It is not obvious from these rather messy component equations that the acceleration in S may be thought of as having three parts, as we have suggested. This is more readily seen from the vector relations which the component equations represent for the particular set of co-ordinate axes in S and S' that we have used. These are

$$\mathbf{v} = \mathbf{v}' + \boldsymbol{\omega} \times \mathbf{r}'$$
$$\mathbf{a} = \mathbf{a}' + 2\boldsymbol{\omega} \times \mathbf{v}' + \boldsymbol{\omega} \times (\boldsymbol{\omega} \times \mathbf{r}')$$

These involve the vector or cross product, and consideration of the angular velocity ω as a vector quantity $\boldsymbol{\omega}$. We shall discuss the treatment of angular quantities as vectors later in this chapter. For the moment we state that $\boldsymbol{\omega}$ is to be considered a vector whose magnitude is the relative angular speed of S and S', and whose direction is along the axis of rotation.

The vector transformations giving **v** and **a** do not depend on the choice of co-ordinate systems in S and S'. They can be shown to give the component equations we developed for the particular co-ordinate systems where z and z' lie along the common axis of rotation of S and S'. The vector **ω** then has only a z-component in both frames of reference: $\omega_z = \omega_{z'} = \omega$, and $\omega_x = \omega_y = \omega_{x'} = \omega_{y'} = 0$. This can be used to show that the vector equations give the component equations already derived.

To show this for the component a_x, we need the projection in the x-direction of the three terms $\mathbf{a}'$, $2\boldsymbol{\omega} \times \mathbf{v}'$ and $\boldsymbol{\omega} \times (\boldsymbol{\omega} \times \mathbf{r})$.

Think about the displacement vector $\mathbf{r}'$ in the S' frame. It has components x', y' and z' in the S' frame, and in the S frame an x-component

$$(\mathbf{r}')_x = x = x' \cos \omega t - y' \sin \omega t$$

This same transformation will apply to *any* vector in S'. Thus the vector $\mathbf{a}'$ has components $a_{x'}$, $a_{y'}$ and $a_{z'}$ in the S' frame, and in the S frame an x-component

$$(\mathbf{a}')_x = a_{x'} \cos \omega t - a_{y'} \sin \omega t$$

The cross product $(\boldsymbol{\omega} \times \mathbf{v}')$ has components in S'

$$\left.\begin{array}{l}
(\boldsymbol{\omega} \times \mathbf{v}')_{x'} = \omega_{y'} v_{z'} - \omega_{z'} v_{y'} = -\omega v_{y'} \\
(\boldsymbol{\omega} \times \mathbf{v}')_{y'} = \omega_{z'} v_{x'} - \omega_{x'} v_{z'} = \omega v_{x'} \\
(\boldsymbol{\omega} \times \mathbf{v}')_{z'} = \omega_{x'} v_{y'} - \omega_{y'} v_{x'} = 0
\end{array}\right\} \begin{array}{l} \boldsymbol{\omega} \text{ is a vector in the} \\ z\text{- and } z'\text{-directions} \end{array}$$

and therefore the x-component of $2(\boldsymbol{\omega} \times \mathbf{v}')$ in the S frame is

$$2(\boldsymbol{\omega} \times \mathbf{v}')_x = -2\omega v_{y'} \cos \omega t - 2\omega v_{x'} \sin \omega t$$

The cross product $(\boldsymbol{\omega} \times \mathbf{r}')$ has components $-\omega y'$, $\omega x'$, 0 in S'. The cross product $\boldsymbol{\omega} \times (\boldsymbol{\omega} \times \mathbf{r}')$ has components in S'

$$[\boldsymbol{\omega} \times (\boldsymbol{\omega} \times \mathbf{r}')]_{x'} = -\omega^2 x' \qquad [\boldsymbol{\omega} \times (\boldsymbol{\omega} \times \mathbf{r}')]_{y'} = -\omega^2 y' \qquad [\boldsymbol{\omega} \times (\boldsymbol{\omega} \times \mathbf{r}')]_{z'} = 0$$

and therefore in S $\qquad [\boldsymbol{\omega} \times (\boldsymbol{\omega} \times \mathbf{r}')]_x = -\omega^2 x' \cos \omega t + \omega^2 y' \sin \omega t$

Adding the three contributions together

$$\begin{aligned}
a_x &= (\mathbf{a}')_x + (\boldsymbol{\omega} \times \mathbf{v}')_x + [\boldsymbol{\omega} \times (\boldsymbol{\omega} \times \mathbf{r}')]_x \\
&= a_{x'} \cos \omega t - a_{y'} \sin \omega t + 2\omega(-v_{y'} \cos \omega t - v_{x'} \sin \omega t) \\
&\qquad\qquad + \omega^2(-x' \cos \omega t + y' \sin \omega t)
\end{aligned}$$

This is the same result for a_x as derived previously for this choice of co-ordinate axes.

The general vector transformation

$$\mathbf{a} = \mathbf{a}' + 2\boldsymbol{\omega} \times \mathbf{v}' + \boldsymbol{\omega} \times (\boldsymbol{\omega} \times \mathbf{r}')$$

shows that the acceleration **a** in the S frame may be thought of as having three terms, the acceleration $\mathbf{a}'$ in the S' frame, the coriolis acceleration $2\boldsymbol{\omega} \times \mathbf{v}'$ perpendicular to the velocity $\mathbf{v}'$ in the S' frame, and the centripetal acceleration $\boldsymbol{\omega} \times (\boldsymbol{\omega} \times \mathbf{r}')$. This assumes that the value of $\boldsymbol{\omega}$ is constant; if the angular velocity is changing with time, there will be an additional acceleration $d\boldsymbol{\omega}/dt \times \mathbf{r}'$.

We emphasize again that while we are discussing kinematics, the description of motion, that there are obvious implications for dynamics. We see that accelerations of a particle of mass m are different as measured in different frames of reference S and S'. If we attribute the acceleration $\mathbf{a}$ to a resultant force $\mathbf{F} = m\mathbf{a}$, and the acceleration $\mathbf{a}'$ to a resultant force $\mathbf{F}' = m\mathbf{a}'$, this means that the forces are different as measured in the two frames of reference. Which force is the real force? They both are, as we have already stated. In dynamics we will distinguish between forces that have their origins in matter (gravitational, electromagnetic, and nuclear forces) and forces that arise because of the frame of reference in which measurements are made (inertial forces, sometimes called fictitious forces). There is a particular set of frames of reference, called **inertial frames,** in which the only forces measured are those having their origins in matter. In any other frame of reference there will be measured, in addition, inertial forces; sometimes these are given special names. Suppose, for example, that S is an inertial frame of reference, and S' is a non-inertial frame rotating with respect to S with an angular velocity $\boldsymbol{\omega}$. The acceleration $\mathbf{a}$ measured in S would be attributed to a force $\mathbf{F} = m\mathbf{a}$, sometimes called a true force or a fundamental force because it has its origin in matter. The acceleration $\mathbf{a}'$ measured in S' would be attributed to a force

$$\mathbf{F}' = m\mathbf{a}' = m\mathbf{a} - 2m\boldsymbol{\omega} \times \mathbf{v}' - m\boldsymbol{\omega} \times (\boldsymbol{\omega} \times \mathbf{r}')$$
$$= \mathbf{F} + \mathbf{F}_1 + \mathbf{F}_2$$

where the forces $\mathbf{F}_1$ and $\mathbf{F}_2$ are inertial forces called the **coriolis force** and **centrifugal force.** These are real forces in the sense that they exist in the frame S'. It is because frames of reference have physical reality, that is, introduce physically measurable quantities, that we are focusing attention on this concept.

Some of you may have seen a film *Frames of Reference* that we made as part of the Physical Science Study Committee course in physics. In one part of this film we were sitting at opposite sides of a glass-topped table, pushing a low friction dry ice puck back and forth across the table. The table and our chairs were mounted on a large turntable that rotated at a constant angular speed. (The speed was not really quite constant, because the turntable was kept rotating by an assistant who trotted around in a circle, pushing it. He tended to tire as the day wore on! For a film we made later on universal gravitation the turntable was provided with an electric motor. This was smoother, but less fun.) The motion of the puck on the table was filmed with two cameras, one fixed on the rotating table and therefore recording the motion in the S' frame, and one fixed on the earth, recording the motion in the S frame of reference.

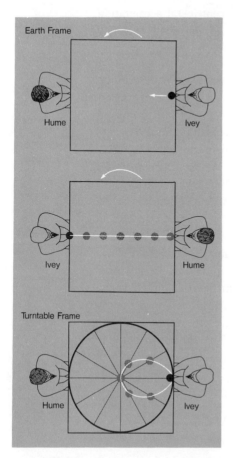

A puck sliding at constant velocity in the earth frame of reference does not move in a straight line in the frame of reference of the rotating table.

One of us pushed the puck toward the other, giving it an initial velocity such that it reached the opposite side of the table in the time required for one-half revolution, so that the one who pushed the puck also caught it. In the earth frame of reference there were practically no horizontal forces acting on the low friction puck, and its path was a straight line—remember Newton's first law, sometimes called the law of inertia? Six positions of the puck at equal time intervals are shown in the diagram. How does the motion look as recorded by the camera in the rotating frame—or to us in the rotating frame? The six positions of the puck are as shown, and the path is indicated. There is an acceleration of the puck, and this is attributed to the centripetal and coriolis forces in the rotating frame. These are real measurable forces in this frame, but they do not exist in the earth frame of reference, assumed to be an inertial frame.

You know that the earth frame, in which most experimental measurements are made, is only approximately an inertial frame. We live in a rotating frame, and this is one reason that the example of a rotating frame is a particularly important one for us. The earth is spinning on its axis, as well as rotating around the sun, and this has implications for the measurements we make on earth. We shall return to this example later and see, for example, that the rotation of cyclones can be related to the coriolis force due to the earth's rotation.

ROTATION IN THREE DIMENSIONS

We have distinguished between frames of reference that are moving with respect to one another in pure **translation** (either in one dimension or three dimensions) and in pure **rotation**. The criterion for pure rotation is that the two frames of reference share a common axis, so that every particle at rest in one frame is moving in a circle in the other frame. We have developed the transformation equations for two frames moving at **constant** relative angular velocity. This means that the axis common to the two frames remains fixed as time goes on. This is analogous to pure translation in one dimension, where the two frames of reference share a common axis.

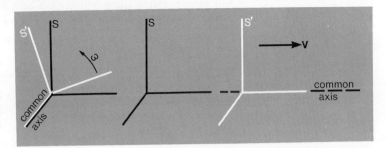

Pure rotation of two frames about a common axis is analogous to pure translation in one dimension.

Now think about a frame of reference S' that is rotating with respect to another S. We could think of three rods in S', but it may be easier to think of a wheel that is spinning on an axle. Frame S' is fixed on the wheel; the common axis is along the axle. For convenience think of co-ordinate axes (x,y,z) and (x',y',z') as shown. A particle P on the circumference of the wheel, at rest in S', is moving in a circle in the xy plane in S.

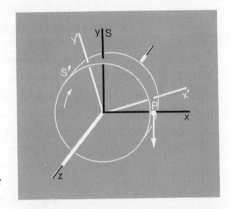

Rotation of frame S' about a fixed z–z'-axis.

Now think about what happens if the axle of the wheel is rotating in the xz plane as shown, so that the frame S' is rotating about the y-axis as well as the z-axis of S. The particle P will move out of the xy plane. Its path in S will not be a circle, but will be on the surface of a sphere.

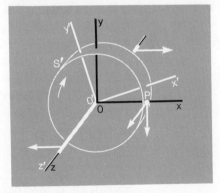

Simultaneous rotations of frame S' about the z-axis and about the y-axis of S.

Now we can think about a third rotation of the S' frame, this time about the x-axis of O. The motion of S' with respect to S is now complex. Can it be considered to be pure rotation? It can because *at any instant* every particle at rest in S' is moving in a circle in S, and we can speak of *the* angular velocity of S' re S, the same for every point in S'. However, the angular velocity is not constant, but varies with time. In general it will vary in both magnitude and direction.

For pure rotation there will always be a fixed point that is common to both S and S'—in the above figure the point O, or O'. If particle displacements $\mathbf{r}$ and $\mathbf{r}'$ are referred to this point, then the displacement is the same in both frames: $\mathbf{r} = \mathbf{r}'$.

We have already stated the general transformation relations

$$\mathbf{r} = \mathbf{r}'$$
$$\mathbf{v} = \mathbf{v}' + \boldsymbol{\omega} \times \mathbf{r}$$
$$\mathbf{a} = \mathbf{a}' + 2\boldsymbol{\omega} \times \mathbf{v}' + \boldsymbol{\omega} \times (\boldsymbol{\omega} \times \mathbf{r}) + \frac{d\boldsymbol{\omega}}{dt} \times \mathbf{r}$$

that are applicable for pure rotation at any instant. We shall not develop these relations, but will spend a little time on the vector nature of angular variables.

You will recall that in the earlier chapter on special motions we pointed out that in describing circular motion of a particle in a particular frame of reference it could be conveniently done in terms of angular displacement θ, angular velocity ω, and angular acceleration α rather than in terms of displacement $\mathbf{r}$, velocity $\mathbf{v}$ and acceleration $\mathbf{a}$. For motion in a circle of radius R, the magnitudes of these quantities were related by $r = R$, $v = R\omega$ and $a = R\sqrt{\alpha^2 + \omega^4}$. One advantage of using the angular quantities is that for circular motion of a **rigid body,** the values of the angular quantities for every particle in the body are the same.

A frame of reference is a sort of rigid body, or perhaps it would be better described as rigid space: all particles at rest in a frame of reference remain a fixed distance apart. Describing the rotation of a frame of reference S' with respect to a frame S is the same as describing the rotation of a rigid body in frame S—we used a rigid wheel in the earlier discussion of this section to help visualize frame S'.

In the previous discussion of circular motion of a rigid body we were dealing with rotation **about a fixed axis** in the frame of reference, and the quantities θ, ω, and α were treated as scalar quantities, taking on positive and negative values. To deal with rotation in general, it is necessary to consider whether or not these quantities may be treated as vectors.

ANGULAR QUANTITIES AS VECTORS

In developing the general vector transformation relations for **translation** of two frames of reference S and S', we observed how displacements $\mathbf{r}$ and $\mathbf{r}'$ in the two frames were related, and then differentiated to obtain the transformations for velocity and acceleration.

The difficulty in providing a vector development for **rotation** arises because while angular velocity ω and angular acceleration α behave as vector quantities, angular displacement θ does not. This may seem rather odd, since ω and α are

defined in terms of θ by $\omega = d\theta/dt$, $\alpha = d^2\theta/dt^2$, but observe that ω and α involve
infinitesimal angular displacements, which do behave as vectors.

Remember that a vector quantity is one that has magnitude and direction and,
in addition, obeys the combination laws as described for displacement. A finite
angular displacement θ has a magnitude (the amount of rotation in radians or

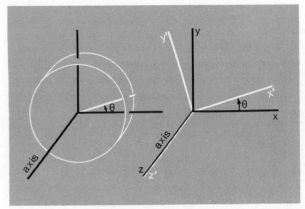

Finite angular displace-
ments θ of a rigid body
and of a frame of reference.

degrees or revolutions) and we can associate a unique direction with it, the
direction of the axis. However, two such rotations do not obey the commutative
law of addition, as can be seen from the figure.

Think about two 90° rotations in the frame of reference defined by the page
and the perpendicular to it. One rotation, θ_1, is about the vertical direction as
axis, counterclockwise looking down. The other, θ_2, is about the horizontal direction in the plane of the page, counterclockwise looking to the left. The first

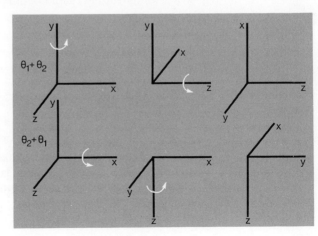

Successive rotations of co-ordinate
axes to show that finite angular displacements do not obey the commutative law of addition.

diagram shows $\theta_1 + \theta_2$, and the second $\theta_2 + \theta_1$, and the result is different $\theta_1 + \theta_2 \neq \theta_2 + \theta_1$. Recalling that a vector quantity in a given frame of reference must be independent of the co-ordinate system used, you can see that this would not be true for finite angular displacements.

It is perhaps not difficult to accept that the order in which **infinitesimal** angular displacements are combined does not matter, since they are infinitesimal. The

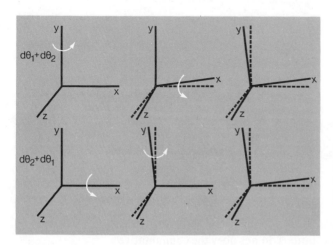

Successive rotations of co-ordinate axes to suggest that infinitesimal angular displacements do obey the commutative law of addition.

figure makes this plausible, but of course does not prove it. We simply state that treating $d\theta$ as a vector quantity $d\boldsymbol{\theta}$ leads to experimentally verifiable results.

If infinitesimal displacement $d\boldsymbol{\theta}$ is a vector, then angular velocity $\boldsymbol{\omega} = d\boldsymbol{\theta}/dt$ is a vector since it is obtained by multiplying a vector by a scalar, $1/dt$. Similarly $\boldsymbol{\alpha} = d\boldsymbol{\omega}/dt$ is a vector.

We have stated that there is a unique direction, the direction of the axis, that can be considered for the vector quantities $d\boldsymbol{\theta}$, $\boldsymbol{\omega}$ and $\boldsymbol{\alpha}$. The axis has two directions (left and right, $+$ and $-$, east and west, $\cdots$) and the rotation has two directions (clockwise and counterclockwise, $+$ or $-$, $\cdots$). In order to relate these uniquely a right-hand rule is used; we introduced a similar rule in defining the vector product. If the fingers of the right hand are curled in the direction of rotation, the thumb points in the direction of the vector.

The figures are shown for a rigid wheel, but can equally well be thought of as representing a rotating frame of reference—for example, one fixed to the wheel.

For an infinitesimal change in angular displacement $d\boldsymbol{\theta}$ the direction of $d\boldsymbol{\theta}$ is as shown. The corresponding angular velocity $\boldsymbol{\omega} = d\boldsymbol{\theta}/dt$ will always be in the same direction as $d\boldsymbol{\theta}$, just as the velocity $\mathbf{v}$ is always in the direction of motion.

If in a time interval dt the angular speed of the wheel increases by an amount $d\boldsymbol{\omega}$ in the same direction as $\boldsymbol{\omega}$ then the direction of $\boldsymbol{\alpha} = d\boldsymbol{\omega}/dt$ will be the same as that of ω. However, if in the time interval the angular speed **decreases** by an amount $d\omega$, then $d\omega$ will be in the opposite direction to ω, and α will be in the opposite direction.

All of these diagrams describe the case of rotation we have already considered, rotation about a fixed axis. The vector character of ω and α for such examples means only that they can take on positive or negative values. This is analogous to one dimensional translation.

However, in general α can make any angle with respect to ω, just as in general **a** can make any angle with respect to **v**. The motion is not about a fixed axis unless α and ω are in the same (or opposite) directions.

We shall look at one particular example, that where α is constant in magnitude and always at right angles to ω. This is analogous to the particular case of uniform circular motion of a particle, where **a** is constant in magnitude and always at right angles to **v**.

In a time interval Δt the angular velocity changes from ω_0 to $\omega_0 + \Delta\omega = \omega_0 + \alpha\Delta t$, where $\Delta\omega$ has the direction of α. If α is always perpendicular to ω, the change $\Delta\omega$ will not change the **magnitude** of ω_0 (the speed of spin), only the direction. The wheel (or a frame of reference in the wheel) will rotate about an axis that is perpendicular to both the ω_0 and α directions. This motion is called **precession**. If in a time Δt the wheel rotates through an angle $\Delta\varphi$, the angular speed of precession Ω (capital omega) is defined by

$$\Omega = \lim_{\Delta t \to 0} \frac{\Delta\varphi}{\Delta t}$$

From the figure, since ω and ω_0 have the same magnitude, $\Delta\omega \cong \omega_0 \Delta\varphi$.

$$\lim_{\Delta t \to 0} \frac{\Delta\omega}{\Delta t} = \lim_{\Delta t \to 0} \omega_0 \frac{\Delta\varphi}{\Delta t} = \omega_0 \lim_{\Delta t \to 0} \frac{\Delta\varphi}{\Delta t}$$

or

$$\alpha = \omega_0 \Omega$$

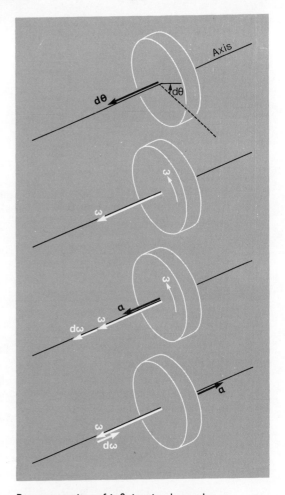

Representation of infinitestimal angular displacement $d\theta$, angular velocity ω and angular acceleration α as vectors.

Combining two rotations about axes at right angles to one another.

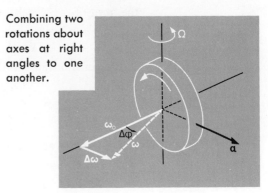

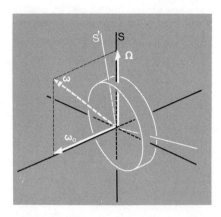

Thus in this special case the angular speed of precession $\Omega = \alpha/\omega_0$. We shall see later in rotational dynamics that this sort of analysis is involved in describing the motion of a gyroscope.

We used a rigid wheel in this example because it is easy to visualize a gyroscope wheel spinning about a horizontal axis with a constant angular speed ω_0,

Two rotations at angular velocities ω_0 and Ω are equivalent to a single rotation at angular velocity ω, where $\omega = \omega_0 + \Omega$.

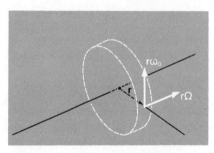

Instantaneous velocity of a point at the front of a wheel.

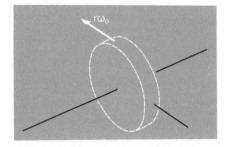

Instantaneous velocity of a point at the top of a wheel.

and at the same time rotating about a vertical axis at a constant angular speed Ω. Now think about a frame of reference S fixed in the page and a frame S' fixed to the gyroscope. The frame S' may be thought of as having two rotations at angular velocities ω_0 and Ω with respect to S, or it may be thought of as having a **single** rotation at an angular velocity $\omega = \omega_0 + \Omega$ with respect to S. The motion of any particle fixed in S' can be described in S using either approach. For example, the instantaneous velocity of a particle at a displacement $\mathbf{r}$ when it is at the front of the wheel as shown has two components $r\omega_0$ and $r\Omega$ *at* right angles. The magnitude of the resultant velocity ($\omega \times \mathbf{r}$) is $\omega r = r\sqrt{\omega_0^2 + \Omega^2}$. When it is at the top of the wheel, ω and $\mathbf{r}$ are not at right angles, and its speed is $r\omega_0$.

The general transformation relations for pure rotation have been stated.

$$\mathbf{r} = \mathbf{r}' \qquad \mathbf{v} = \mathbf{v}' + \omega \times \mathbf{r}$$

$$\mathbf{a} = \mathbf{a}' + 2\omega \times \mathbf{v}' + \omega \times (\omega \times \mathbf{r}) + \frac{d\omega}{dt} \times \mathbf{r}$$

For a particle at rest in S', $\mathbf{v}' = \mathbf{a}' = 0$ and the velocity and acceleration as measured in S are

$$\mathbf{v} = \omega \times \mathbf{r} \qquad \text{and} \qquad \mathbf{a}_T = \alpha \times \mathbf{r} \qquad \mathbf{a}_R = \omega \times (\omega \times \mathbf{r})$$

where we have used $\alpha = d\omega/dt$, and have expressed the acceleration in terms of two components, a tangential and a radial component.

Recalling that the magnitude of the vector product of two **perpendicular** vectors is simply the product of their magnitudes, we see that the relations derived previously for rotation about a fixed axis, $v = r\omega$, $a_T = r\alpha$, $a_R = r\omega^2$, are valid.

MOTION OF A SYSTEM OF PARTICLES

We have discussed the description of the motion of a single particle in a particular frame of reference, and have seen how to transform this description into other frames of reference. One essential feature of the particle model is that the particle has negligible dimensions in the frame of reference used; it is completely described if its trajectory is known, because its orientation does not matter. In describing the motion of objects of finite size, this model may be inadequate.

In Chapter 5 we introduced the concept of a rigid body; solid objects can often be approximated by this model. A rigid body is a system of particles all of which remain at rest relative to one another. As we have seen, the description of the motion of a rigid body with respect to a frame of reference S is the same as the description of a frame of reference S' with respect to S. A frame of reference is in a sense a rigid body, in that all points in a frame of reference remain at rest relative to one another. Perhaps it would be better to call a frame of reference rigid space; but again, a frame of reference has physical reality—measurements are made with respect to real objects fixed in the frame of reference.

We have made a distinction between two frames of reference S and S' moving in pure translation or moving in pure rotation. For pure translation, at any instant every particle at rest in S' is moving with the same velocity $\mathbf{V}$ in S, so that the displacement of every particle is the same as that of every other particle in the same time interval. For pure rotation, at any instant every particle at rest in S' is moving with the same angular velocity ω in S. In either case the velocity

Comparison of pure translation and pure rotation of two frames of reference.

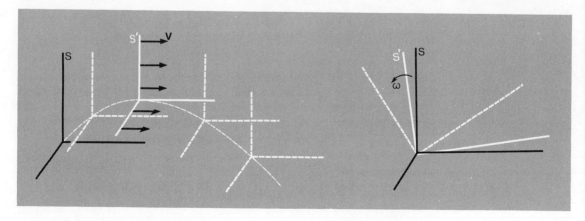

(**V** or **ω**) may be a function of time **V**(t) or **ω**(t), but at any instant every particle at rest in S' will have the same acceleration **a** in S, for pure translation, or the same acceleration **α** in S, for pure rotation.

Now instead of a frame of reference S' think about a rigid body moving with respect to S, that is, moving in the S frame of reference. Its motion may be pure translation, or pure rotation, but in general it will be some combination of the two. It is always possible to make a transformation to a frame of reference in which the motion is pure translation, or pure rotation—or of course, in which there is no motion (a frame fixed to the rigid body). In attempting to analyze the motion it is often convenient to make such transformations. As we shall see in dynamics a resultant force acting at the center of mass of a body produces pure translational acceleration; otherwise rotational acceleration is produced as well.

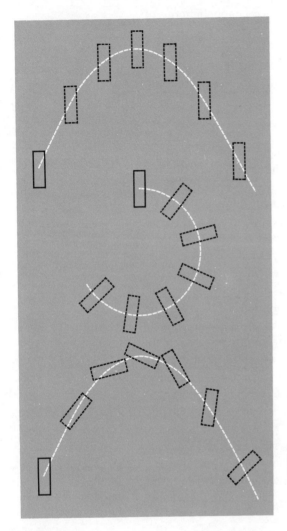

A rigid body in pure translation, in pure rotation, and with both translation and rotation.

Questions for discussion

1. The displacements of the particles in a frame of reference can all be referred to a single fixed point in the frame. Does this mean that a single point is sufficient to determine a frame of reference?

2. Can you think of three different ways of describing the fact that two frames of reference are moving in pure translation with respect to one another?

3. Visualize a solid cubic chunk of wood in front of you. Can you think of it moving, with respect to your frame of reference, in **(a)** pure translation at constant velocity,

(b) pure translation in one dimension with variable velocity, (c) pure translation at constant speed but variable velocity, (d) pure rotation at constant angular velocity about a fixed axis through its center parallel to an edge, (e) pure rotation at constant angular velocity about a fixed axis through its center but not parallel to any edge, (f) pure rotation at constant angular velocity about a fixed axis that does not pass through the body at all, (g) pure rotation at constant angular speed but variable velocity, for example two simultaneous rotations at constant speeds about two perpendicular axes both passing through the center? If you threw the block through the air, would it be likely to have any of these motions?

4. In describing the motion of a wheel that is rolling without slipping it is sometimes useful to think of the motion as pure rotation around an instantaneous axis. A description of motion is always made with respect to a particular frame of reference. Is the instantaneous axis frame of reference moving with respect to the earth frame in pure translation, pure rotation, or both?

Problems

1. Two cars are approaching one another on a single-lane road, car A moving at 20 m/sec, car B at 30 m/sec in the opposite direction. When the cars are 300 m apart, the driver of car A sees car B and applies his brakes, decelerating at a constant 2 m/sec^2. One second later, the driver of car B sees car A and applies his brakes, decelerating at a constant 1 m/sec^2. (Note that the driver with the slow reactions and bad brakes is driving faster.) Calculate when and where the cars meet, and the relative speed of impact. Why are there two solutions? Try the calculation both in the earth frame of reference (it may be useful to plot the motions of both cars on the same displacement-time graph) and in a frame of reference fixed to one of the cars.

2. Solve Problem 7 of Chapter 5 by making the calculation in a reference frame fixed to car A.

3. A ball dropped to the floor of an elevator from a height of 5 ft bounces to a height of 2 ft when the elevator is at rest. Released from the same height, how high does it bounce if the elevator is (a) moving upward with a constant velocity of 8 ft/sec, (b) moving with a constant acceleration of 4 ft/sec^2 upward. Do you find the result for (b) surprising? Note how much easier it is to work in the elevator frame of reference, a non-inertial frame, in case (b), than in any inertial frame.

4. An elevator is at rest. The cable breaks, and the elevator falls freely. A pellet is projected horizontally (with respect to the elevator) at a speed of 16 ft/sec from one side of the elevator. The elevator is 8 ft wide and the pellet is projected from a point 6 ft off the floor. Determine how far above the floor it hits the opposite wall if it is projected (a) at the instant the cable breaks, (b) 1 sec later. (c) Calculate how far the pellet moves vertically with respect to the elevator shaft in each case.

5. A truck with wheels 2.5 ft in diameter starting from rest reaches a speed of 30 mph in 15 sec. Assuming that its acceleration is uniform, calculate (a) the angular acceleration of the wheels, (b) the number of revolutions each turns in the first 8 sec of motion, (c) the instantaneous acceleration of a point at the top of a wheel at 1 sec and 15 sec after the motion starts.

6. (a) A car with wheels of radius R accelerates from rest with a constant acceleration a, without skidding. Determine the magnitude of the acceleration (with respect to the ground) of a particle at the top of the wheel after a time t. Note its value as $t \rightarrow 0$, and as t becomes large.

(b) A stone is caught in the tread of a tire of a car that accelerates uniformly from rest to 30 mph in 10 sec. The wheel radius is 1 ft. The stone flies out of the tread when it is at the top of the wheel, and at the instant its acceleration (relative to the ground) has a magnitude of $2g$. Calculate the time the car has been moving, and the initial velocity of the free stone (relative to the ground).

7. Relative to a frame of reference in which the earth's axis is at rest, and the earth is rotating once per day, calculate **(a)** the centripetal acceleration of a particle at rest at the equator, **(b)** the coriolis acceleration of a particle moving with a velocity of 9.8 m/sec straight down at the equator.

8. A ferris wheel of 32-ft diameter rotates at a constant 4 rpm. A blob of grease falls from the axle of the wheel. Calculate the magnitudes of its velocity and acceleration (relative to the passenger) just before it hits a passenger at the bottom of the wheel.

9. A merry-go-round of 20-ft diameter rotates at a constant angular speed, making one revolution in 20 sec. A man starts at the center and walks at a constant speed of 0.4 ft/sec out along a radius. **(a)** What is the length of his path relative to the ground, from the time he starts to the time the merry-go-round has made one revolution? **(b)** Is his path length relative to the ground equal to a constant times the distance he moves relative to the merry-go-round? **(c)** Calculate the magnitudes of his velocity and acceleration, relative to the ground, at the instant he reaches the edge of the merry-go-round.

10. A gyroscope wheel of 6-cm diameter spins about a horizontal axle with an angular speed ω. The axle is rotating in a horizontal plane about a vertical axis through the wheel, making one revolution in 4 sec. Calculate the resultant speed of a point A that is instantaneously at the front of the wheel, and of a point B that is instantaneously at the top of the wheel, for a spin speed of **(a)** 6 rpm, **(b)** 60 rpm, **(c)** 6000 rpm. Approximations that can be made when the spin speed is large compared to the precessional speed will be used when we discuss the dynamics of the gyroscope.

Dynamics of a particle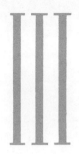

In Part II we were primarily interested in the description of motion, both of a single particle and of systems of particles. Although we assumed that you have some familiarity with the basic ideas of dynamics, and therefore we could use the concepts of force, momentum, and energy in some of our examples, we have not yet developed the basis of dynamics or discussed its origin, and that is the purpose here in Part III.

In Chapter 8 we attempt to take a close look at precisely what information about the physical world is summarized by Newton's laws of motion; that is, we discuss the **physical content** of these laws. Trying to really understand the fundamentals is not easy (remember we began this book with "Beginning is the difficult part") but it is important. It is because we know that you have had some exposure to the laws of dynamics, not just in science courses but in your everyday experience, that we can try to tackle the foundations of classical mechanics in this chapter. The all-important concept of an inertial frame of reference is introduced here.

In Chapter 9 we discuss a number of specific concerns that arise in applying Newton's laws in an inertial frame of reference, for example systems of units, the notion of isolation of a particle, and recognition of certain types of forces. In Chapter 10 it is demonstrated how Newton's laws can be used in non-inertial frames of reference, provided inertial forces are introduced. The effects that arise because the earth itself is not an inertial frame are discussed in Chapter 11. To conclude Part III, Chapter 12 deals with the dynamics of simple harmonic motion, a particularly important kind of motion because it is involved in understanding all vibrational or wave phenomena.

In all of Part III the emphasis is on the application of Newton's basic law $\mathbf{F} = m\mathbf{a}$ to the motion of a single particle, or to systems in which all the particles move in the same way. In dealing with the motions of systems of particles in general, it is useful to express Newton's laws in other ways, and this is developed in Parts IV and V.

8

THE FOUNDATIONS OF
CLASSICAL MECHANICS

You may have been wondering when we were going to get around to dealing with the laws of physics. The last four chapters have been devoted to the **description** of motion, kinematics, and we are not yet in a position to make predictions, based on the laws of physics, about what motions will occur in a specific physical situation. Although we have used your previous knowledge of concepts such as force and mass in some of the examples, we have given explicit definition only to the fundamental quantities length and time, and quantities that can be derived from these.

We have taken this approach because we think it is important to emphasize that the first step in understanding any physical phenomenon is to give a precise description of it, based on measurement. It might appear that this is a trivial step in principle, involving only experimental technique, but this is not the case. The establishment of procedures for description involves making certain assumptions. These assumptions may be made explicitly, or may be implicit, arising from our preconceived ideas about the physical universe.

For example, in establishing the procedures by which the motion of a particle can be described, we have made many assumptions. To state only three of these: (1) we have assumed that we know what a straight line is; (2) we have assumed that if two clocks tick at the same rate when they are together they will tick at the same rate if moving with respect to one another; (3) we have assumed that the methods of calculus can be used to manipulate variables representing physical quantities, which means we have assumed that these quantities vary continuously, not in discrete steps. Such assumptions are only justifiable if they work—that is, their validity depends on experiment. Each of the three assumptions mentioned has been found to be a very good one for a wide range of experience, and they are accepted as valid assumptions in classical mechanics. On the other hand, each has been found to be invalid under certain conditions and that is why there are other systems of mechanics, quantum mechanics and relativistic mechanics, based on different assumptions.

DEFINITIONS AND THE LAWS OF PHYSICS

Sometimes in physics an attempt is made to distinguish between definitions and physical laws, but such a distinction seems to us to be difficult to justify.

A physical law is a relationship between physical quantities which is a summary of experience, for example, Newton's law of universal gravitation. Based on observation and measurement of the way the physical quantities are related under some conditions, the law is a statement that the relation will be valid in general. This is an hypothesis, which is another way of saying that it is an assumption. It makes no sense to speak of proving the laws of physics—unlike the laws of mathematics. However, experiment may disprove a law of physics, by showing that it is not valid under certain conditions. It may nevertheless remain as a useful summary of experience, valid under certain conditions—or it may be superseded by a new law of more general validity.

A definition in physics is also a relationship between physical quantities; for example, we defined acceleration as the rate of change of velocity $\mathbf{a} = d\mathbf{v}/dt$. It is sometimes said that, since we can define anything we please, a definition may have no physical content, meaning that it does not contain any information about the physical world in it. This is certainly so; we can, for example, define a quantity we might call duacceleration $\mathbf{A}$ by $\mathbf{A} = 2\mathbf{a}$. However, deciding whether or not there is physical content may not be simple, because if assumptions about the physical world are involved in making the definition, assumptions that can only be validated by experiment, then there is physical content. As we have seen, it is not always clear what assumptions are being made, or indeed that assumptions are being made at all.

In defining the vector quantity displacement $\mathbf{r}$ we made assumptions about the properties of space. In defining velocity $\mathbf{v}$ and acceleration $\mathbf{a}$ we assumed that time is a continuously variable quantity. If such assumptions are invalid, then our definitions are invalid, or at least limited in range of validity.

Thus in a sense the definitions of physics are themselves physical laws. If someone says (as someone often does) "but such-and-such is just a matter of definition, and you can define anything you please" he is correct, but remember that the definitions of physics must be related to observations that can be made on the real world if they are to be useful.

Look back at the development of the Galilean transformation $\mathbf{r} = \mathbf{r}' + \mathbf{V}t$ at the beginning of Chapter 7. It might appear that the transformation is a direct consequence of our definitions as applied in two frames of reference S and S', and therefore that there is no additional physical content in it. However, its validity depends on the assumption that identical clocks and identical measuring rods are used to make measurements of length and time in the two frames of reference, an assumption that becomes invalid if the relative velocity $\mathbf{V}$ of the two frames is too large. The Galilean transformation must be considered to be a law of classical physics. The transformation is different in relativistic mechanics.

THE BASIS OF CLASSICAL DYNAMICS

We have discussed the terms assumption, hypothesis, definition, and law at this point because we are going to consider the basic law of classical dynamics, Newton's law of motion $\mathbf{F} = m\mathbf{a}$. This simple expression provides an extraordinarily powerful tool for describing and analyzing an enormous number of different physical situations. You have probably had experience in applying this law.

The amazing thing is that even though this law looks simple, and has been used successfully for nearly 300 years, there is still confusion as to what it really *is*. It is an assumption about how the physical world behaves, but exactly what is being assumed? What is its physical content? Does it define force or mass or both or neither? It works, but why does it work?

The difficulty is that the law brings together a number of assumptions about the physical world all at once, and it does not seem to be possible to develop it through a sequence of logical steps, introducing assumptions one at a time. It is a synthesis of many aspects of experience, which means that there are interlocking pieces; examining one piece at a time does not really tell the story. Suddenly "splat" it's all there.

It has been argued that because there are logical difficulties in understanding Newton's law it is not really fundamental. It is possible to adopt different bases for classical dynamics. As we shall see, introducing the concept of energy makes the basis look quite different. A more sophisticated approach can be taken which shows that the law is a logical consequence of assuming certain symmetries in nature. However, such alternative formulations occurred long after Newton proposed his formulation, and $\mathbf{F} = m\mathbf{a}$ remains a powerful and widely used tool in physics and other sciences.

Perhaps the sensible thing to do would be to apply this law to a number of idealized physical situations, and let these examples speak for themselves. Instead, in this chapter, we are going to discuss the nature of the law. We do this not so much because the law is the basis of classical physics, but because it was the first example in physics of a major synthesis.

Generally we are not taking an historical approach to physics, because we are more interested in trying to explain what the structure of physics is than in how it got that way. Often the historical approach is not the most pedagogically useful one. However, in this chapter we will begin with the law as originally formulated by Newton in the 17th century, before commenting on the modifications we make in using it today, and on what the limitations on its use are.

NEWTON'S LAWS OF MOTION

We have for convenience spoken of Newton's law of motion $\mathbf{F} = m\mathbf{a}$ as though there were only one, and this is a possible point of view if the equation is interpreted in a certain way. It will be more useful to us to write down three separate laws as Newton did, although we will find we cannot discuss them separately and therefore in a sense there is only one law; in more or less original form:

Law I: Every body perseveres in its state of rest or uniform motion in a straight line unless change in that state is compelled by impressed forces.

Law II: Change of motion is proportional to the force impressed and takes place in the direction of the straight line in which such force is impressed.

Law III: Reaction is always equal and opposite to action; that is, the mutual actions of two bodies upon each other are always equal and directly opposite.

Several words appear which require definition, and that is the crux of the problem. What are *impressed force*, *change of motion*, *action*, and *reaction*? It turns out that by *change of motion* Newton means "rate of change of quantity of motion with time," where "quantity of motion" means "mass times velocity," which we call **momentum**. In symbols, if a body has mass m and velocity $\mathbf{v}$ its momentum $\mathbf{p}$ is $\mathbf{p} = m\mathbf{v}$ and *change of motion* is $d\mathbf{p}/dt = d(m\mathbf{v})/dt = m(d\mathbf{v}/dt) = m\mathbf{a}$ if m is a constant. In writing this we have assumed that m is a **constant scalar quantity,** and that is a fundamental part of the story we shall return to. **Mass** will have to be defined.

Newton identifies *action* and *reaction* as forces, thus "an impressed force is any action upon a body which changes, or tends to change, its state of rest or uniform motion in a straight line." This sounds rather like Law I, so perhaps Law I is just a definition of force. However, it is not a quantitative definition.

We are now down to two quantities requiring definition, mass m and *impressed force* which we shall call $\mathbf{F}$. Writing $\mathbf{F}$ assumes that force is a vector quantity, and that is a fundamental part of the story. We know too, that we must interpret *impressed force* as meaning resultant force, and that's part of the same story.

In our symbols the first two laws are:

Law I: If $\mathbf{F} = 0$, $\mathbf{a} = 0$
Law II: $\mathbf{F} = m\mathbf{a}$

which appears to make Law I a special case of Law II, and therefore unnecessary, but we shall see there is more to it than that.

Law II relates two undefined quantities, force and mass. Newton tried to give a definition of mass as "quantity of matter" in a body, which in turn is defined as "the product of its density and volume." Unfortunately the definition of density is "mass of a unit of volume" so that the circle is complete and no information about mass emerges. Mass is also sometimes called the quantitative measure of inertia where inertia is the quantity which determines how hard it is to accelerate something, which brings us back to Law II.

We recognize that the fundamental quantities length and time, and the quantities displacement, velocity and acceleration which we have derived from them, are not sufficient to encompass the quantities of dynamics. It is time to introduce another fundamental quantity. You recall that a fundamental quantity is one that is not defined in terms of other physical quantities, but instead is given an operational definition. We could choose any dynamical quantity (force, mass, momentum, or others we shall define later) as fundamental. Both force and mass are used, but we shall choose mass for now.

MASS DEFINED

To give an operational definition for mass, we must choose a standard mass and specify procedures by which other masses are compared to the standard. The quantity measured by these procedures is by definition mass.

Law III and Law II together provide one method of doing this. Law III states that if a body 1 exerts a force $\mathbf{F}_{21}$ on another body 2, then body 2 exerts a force $\mathbf{F}_{12} = -\mathbf{F}_{21}$ on body 1; the forces are equal in magnitude and opposite in direction.

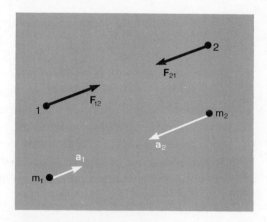

Equal and opposite forces along the same line.

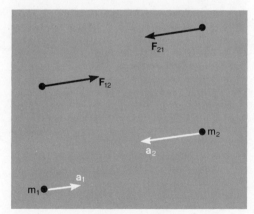

Equal and opposite forces that are not along the same line.

Using Law II, $m_1\mathbf{a}_1 = -m_2\mathbf{a}_2$, or $m_1/m_2 = -\mathbf{a}_2/\mathbf{a}_1$. The forces $\mathbf{F}_{12}$ and $\mathbf{F}_{21}$ may be in the same line or not—they may simply be parallel. In any case the ratio $-\mathbf{a}_1/\mathbf{a}_2$ is a unique positive number, the mass ratio m_2/m_1. Thus the masses of the two bodies can be compared by allowing them to interact and measuring their accelerations. Since acceleration has been defined, this gives an operational definition of mass. All masses can be compared with a standard mass.

Just as we could not give an operational definition of time without some intuitive ideas about space, so we cannot give an operational definition of mass without intuitive ideas about force. We don't have to have a quantitative definition of force, but we have to believe that it exists as a physical quantity and has certain characteristics.

There are other ways of giving an operational definition of mass than as above, but they all depend on some assumptions about force. Our definition of time was based on periodic motion which meant we had to assume we knew what we meant by "the same point" in space. Similarly a definition of mass can be given which assumes that we know what we mean by "the same force": if a force gives a mass m_1 a measured acceleration $\mathbf{a}_1$, and the same force gives a mass m_2 a measured acceleration $\mathbf{a}_2$, then Law II gives $m_1\mathbf{a}_1 = m_2\mathbf{a}_2$ and $m_1/m_2 = \mathbf{a}_2/\mathbf{a}_1$ gives a method of comparing masses, and therefore an operational definition.

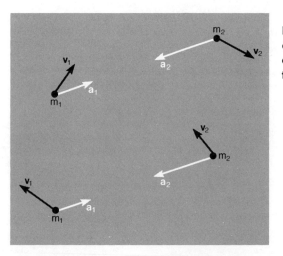

It is assumed that mass is a property of a particle that is independent of the position and velocity of the particle, and is a scalar.

What assumptions have we made about mass in making our operational definition? We have not specified how far apart the bodies 1 and 2 are, or what their relative velocity is. Therefore we are assuming that mass is a property of a body which is independent of its position and independent of its velocity. The equations we wrote assumed mass was a scalar quantity, and therefore that masses can be added like numbers. These assumptions are all based on experiment, and are some of the assumptions made in writing Newton's laws. They are part of the physical content of these laws.

THE SUPERPOSITION ASSUMPTION

We now know how to measure mass, and therefore Law II can be said to **define** force in terms of known quantities: the mass m, a scalar; and the acceleration $\mathbf{a}$, a vector. Since the product of a scalar and a vector is a vector, force is a vector by definition

$$\mathbf{F} = m\mathbf{a}$$

This says that a force F_{12} on m_1 due to a body 2 and the force F_{13} on m_1 due to a body 3 combine to give a resultant force F determined by the rule for adding vectors.

How do we know that the force F_{12} due to body 2 is the same whether body 3 is there or not? We assume it is, and this is another part of the physical content of Newton's laws. We assume that the interactions are independent of one another, so that the resultant force on a body 1 due to any number of other bodies 2, 3, 4, $\cdots$, is the sum of the forces that they would exert individually. Without this assumption it would be difficult to make much sense out of Newton's laws.

The superposition assumption is that the force F_{12} on m_1 due to m_2 is the same whether or not there are other forces on m_1.

The general statement, that the resultant effect of a number of individual effects is the sum of the effects considered independently, is a basic assumption of physics called the **Principle of Superposition.** This principle has application to a wide variety of physical situations. Whether or not it is a valid principle must always be subject to the test of experiment.

We have said that force is a vector by definition. It is sometimes stated as an experimental fact that force is a vector. This is a perfectly valid point of view because Newton's laws synthesize a variety of experimental facts, and the facts can be introduced in various ways. By introducing force as a vector by experiment, it is possible to avoid stating Law III, which is an advantage as we will see.

THE CONCEPT OF FORCE

We have an intuitive feeling of what we mean by force. We think of pushes and pulls by objects in contact, and of forces between objects at a distance—the earth on the moon, the sun on the earth, and forces deflecting electrons in our television set, and so on. We also have a definition of force in $F = ma$. Well, then, what is this concept force?

Newton's laws assume that the force on a body has its origin in other bodies; that is one important step, the recognition that bodies have an influence on one another which we attribute to an entity called force. The second step is Newton's recognition that this influence is mutual; one body cannot influence another without itself being affected.

Apparently Newton thought principally of forces occurring during contact between bodies. Following Law III he says, "If you press a stone with your finger, the finger is also pressed by the stone." Although he used this law in deducing his law of gravitation, the fact that the gravitational attraction acted over a distance bothered Newton considerably as evidenced in a letter to a friend. "It is inconceivable that inanimate brute matter should without mediation of something else which is not material operate upon and affect other matter without mutual contact." Although he said he made no hypotheses about gravity, his writings indicate that he thought of a medium, the aether, to pass the force along from one body to another. He even hints of a finite time for the action to take place, although in his gravitational calculations he assumes, as a necessary approximation, that the action is instantaneous.

We have come to accept the notion of **action at a distance,** which Newton found hard to imagine. We know that the moon is accelerating toward the earth, and we attribute this to a force exerted on the moon by the earth. We accept the fact that the earth exerts a force on us, which accelerates us toward it if we are not in contact with it.

Having stated that the force on a body has its origin in other bodies raises a question. If you are seated in a car at rest you "feel" a downward force because the seat is pushing up on you. You attribute this to the earth, which is pulling down on you. Now what happens as the car starts up? As the car accelerates you "feel" a backward force as well, because the back of the seat is now pushing forward on you. What body is pulling back on you?

You know the answer to this question. There *is* a backward force on you, but *no* body is pulling back on you. We reconcile this with the statement that forces originate in bodies by deciding there are other kinds of forces than those appearing in Newton's laws.

Remember that force is a concept invented by man, a word he uses to describe something he can measure. For example, using a spring balance you can measure the downward force on an object in the car at rest, or the resultant downward and backward force in the accelerating car. You can tell from the reading of the spring balance what the magnitude and direction of the force is, but not what its origin is.

Newton's laws state that forces exist due to interactions between material bodies; we call forces that have their origins in matter **fundamental** forces, in order to distinguish them from forces like the backward force in the car that do not originate in matter.

It turns out that the concept of force is not always an appropriate way to describe the interactions between material bodies, and therefore in general we speak of the fundamental interactions.

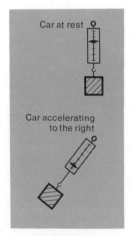

Car at rest

Car accelerating to the right

A mass suspended by a spring balance will hang straight down in a car at rest or moving with constant velocity, but at an angle in an accelerating car.

FUNDAMENTAL INTERACTIONS

Physics is sometimes defined as the attempt to understand the fundamental interactions of matter. This emphasizes the central importance of these interactions.

For the moment, it will be sufficient to recall briefly what these interactions are, and the circumstances in which they are important. There are only three, or perhaps four, that are recognized at present: the gravitational interaction, the electromagnetic interaction and the nuclear interactions. The nuclear interactions are sub-classified as strong and weak interactions. The gravitational and electromagnetic interactions are well understood, in the sense that we can describe how they behave, though *not* why they exist. The description of nuclear interactions is much less adequate and is the subject of a great deal of present day physics research.

The gravitational interaction is an attraction between all bodies in the universe that depends on a property of a body called mass, which turns out by experiment to be the same as the mass in Newton's laws of motion. The force between any two bodies is described by Newton's law of gravitation, and does not depend on the velocities of the bodies (except for velocities approaching c, the speed of light). It is a very weak interaction and is only important if one of the bodies involved is of astronomical size.

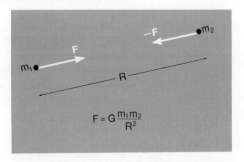

The gravitational interaction between two particles.

Electromagnetic interactions have their origins in electric charges. Charges are of two kinds, called plus $(+)$ and minus $(-)$ because their effects cancel out (to some extent). A charged particle means one that has an excess of one kind of charge; this is a property of the particle, and the electrical force between two charged particles that are at rest depends on the property **charge** just as the gravitational force between particles depends on the property **mass.** The Coulomb law describes this interaction which can be either attractive or repulsive. In the case of **moving** charged particles there is an additional force, the magnetic force, that depends on the velocity of the charges. For each particle the magnetic force is in a direction at right angles to the motion of the particle.

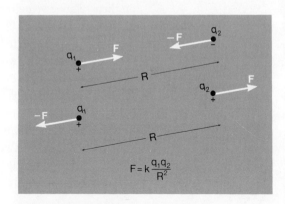

The electrical interaction between two charged particles.

The electromagnetic interaction is many orders of magnitude larger than the gravitational interaction, and is the basis for almost all the phenomena we experience in any direct way. It is the force that holds atoms together to make up a molecule, or holds molecules together to make up a liquid or a solid. It is the basis of chemical and biological processes. Newton's pushes and pulls, or contact forces, exist because of the electromagnetic interaction.

The nuclear interactions are believed to be responsible for binding the nucleons together in the nucleus. The effect of the nuclear interaction decreases with distance much more rapidly than the inverse-square behavior of the gravitational or electromagnetic interaction, and this interaction is only important for nuclear distances of the order of 10^{-15} meters. It appears to be a complex interaction with characteristics that are not yet understood in terms of any single theory. We will later see that certain calculations with respect to nuclear processes can be made using the concept of energy, rather than the concept of force.

NEWTONIAN FORCES

From our brief summary of the fundamental interactions you can see that Newton's laws do *not* adequately describe all forces that have their origin in matter.

These laws were developed initially to describe contact forces and the gravitational force, the only forces Newton knew about, and appeared to be completely successful in doing so. They were later applied in situations where the interaction was electromagnetic, to two bodies that are not in contact. However, it was recognized that the magnetic force was not a force as described or defined by Newton's laws, because the magnetic force between two particles depends on their relative velocities. The forces are not equal and opposite and Newton's Law III is not valid. Nevertheless, Newton's Law II is still useful because the motion of a **single** particle can be described by $F = ma$, where F is the resultant force on the particle, without reference to the origin of the force.

Forces of the kind correctly described by Newton's laws are called Newtonian forces or sometimes classical forces. The magnetic force is a non-Newtonian force. It should be noted, however, that there are many practical circumstances in which the magnetic force can be treated as Newtonian. Newton's Law III is valid for the forces between permanent magnets, or the forces between complete circuits carrying steady currents, and therefore these magnetic forces can be considered Newtonian.

INERTIAL FRAMES OF REFERENCE

We have still not explained the backward force on you in the accelerating car, a force that does not have its origin in matter at all; it is not a Newtonian force, and it is not a fundamental force.

How do you know the car is accelerating? By referring to your surroundings, either by looking out the window or by watching the speedometer needle go up.

Newton's laws deal with motion, and we have seen that motion can only be described with respect to a frame of reference. We showed in kinematics how the description of motion changed as measured in different frames of reference.

A particle can be at rest in one frame of reference, and accelerating in another. You are at rest in the car frame of reference, but accelerating in the earth frame of reference.

Think about your motion as described in the earth frame of reference. There is a downward force F_1 on you due to the gravitational attraction of the earth, and an equal and opposite upward force F_2 on you due to the car seat because there is no acceleration in the vertical direction. Note these are *not* an action–reaction pair, because they are both forces on you. Law III says that if body A exerts a force on body B, then body B exerts an equal and opposite force **on body** A; an action–reaction pair are forces **on two different bodies.** The reaction to the force F_1 is the upward gravitational force you exert **on the earth,** and the reaction to the force F_2 is the downward force that you exert **on the seat.**

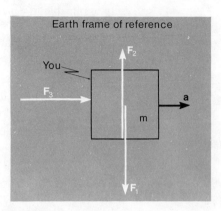

Forces on you in an accelerating car, in the earth frame of reference.

The back of the car seat exerts a forward force F_3 on you, producing your acceleration $a = F_3/m$, where m is your mass. The reaction to F_3 is the backward force that you exert **on the seat.**

Now think about your motion as described in the car frame. The three forces F_1, F_2, F_3 on you exist as before, and their reactions exist as before; the force diagram shows only the forces **on you.** In this frame of reference there is a backward force F_4 on you. It is equal in magnitude to F_3, but it is *not* the reaction to F_3, because both F_3 and F_4 are forces **on you.** What is the reaction force to F_4? **There is no reaction force.** Does F_4 really exist? Certainly it does—you can measure the backward force on you using any force measuring device **in the car.** It exists in the car frame of reference, but does not exist as far as measurements made in the earth frame of reference are concerned. If the force F_3 should vanish (the back of the seat collapses) then the force F_4 would produce a backward acceleration, as measured in the car frame of reference. In the earth frame there would be no forces in the horizontal direction on you, and no acceleration.

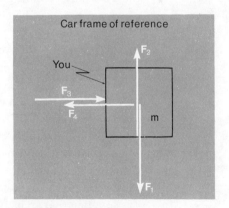

Forces on you in an accelerating car, in the car frame of reference.

What about the validity of Newton's laws of motion? Law I seems to be all right, because in this frame of reference we have zero resultant force on you $F = 0$ and zero acceleration $a = 0$. However, we are in trouble with Law III because there is no reaction force for F_4, and Law III says there is *always* an equal and opposite reaction.

This difficulty is resolved by recognizing that Newton's laws of motion are only applicable in a particular kind of frame of reference, a kind that the laws themselves define.

Look at Law I again. It says that the motion of a body is uniform unless it is acted upon by a force, or more precisely unless there is a resultant or unbalanced force acting on it. If $F = 0, a = 0$. This seems to say very little; a body's motion is uniform or it is not. You must go on in the laws to appreciate that anything is being said at all. Then you recognize that an acceleration of one body is to be associated with the presence of one or more other bodies mutually interacting with it. Then Law I says that if a body is observed to move uniformly, either there are no other bodies mutually interacting with it, or the other bodies are so positioned that they produce at all times a resultant acceleration of zero.

Law I says the natural (uninfluenced) state of a body is one of uniform motion. The law is often called Galileo's law of inertia because Galileo first stated it, and it represented a great step forward from the idea that had been held from the days of the Greek philosophers, that uniform motion had to be maintained by constant effort.

Now examine what "uniform motion" of a body means. Motion can only be described with respect to a frame of reference, which means that motion can only be described **with respect to other bodies.** Therefore uniform motion of a body is only possible if the reference bodies produce no net acceleration of the body. A system of bodies providing such a frame of reference is called an **inertial frame of reference,** because in it the law of inertia holds. Holds for what? For a single body, or for every body? Now we come to the key point about Law I, its real physical content. The law does not say "a body's motion is uniform unless . . . ," it says "**every** body's motion is uniform unless . . . ." If you have a single body then you can always fix up a frame of reference so that its motion can be **described** as uniform. But Law I says that if you fix up such a frame for a body, and if the body is in the natural state (i.e., uninfluenced) then **every** uninfluenced body will move uniformly in the same frame of reference. This is another fundamental assumption embodied in Newton's laws. Law I can be regarded as a definition of an inertial frame of reference, and it is based on the assumption that an inertial frame of reference exists. An inertial frame of reference is sometimes called a Galilean frame of reference.

Law I mentions **every** body, Law II applies to **one** body, and Law III deals with **two** bodies. The three laws taken together define a system of mechanics, a system for relating the motions of different bodies. In applying the law $F = ma$ to a single body we seem to be using only Law II, but it is all the laws that have defined the concept F for us.

INERTIAL FORCES–FICTITIOUS?

Back to you and the accelerated car again. Newton's laws define an inertial frame of reference, and are to be used therein. From the frame of reference of the earth, assumed, for now, to be an inertial frame, there is no backward force on you. The force forward on you exerted by the back of the seat is an unbalanced force, producing your acceleration. The backward force which you observe is there because you are in the accelerated frame of reference, where Newton's laws are not intended to apply.

Forces such as the backward force on you that arise in accelerated frames of reference are described or labeled in various ways. They are not fundamental forces, originating in the interactions of matter, and they are not Newtonian forces, those defined by Newton's laws. They are often called **fictitious forces**, or sometimes pseudo forces, because they do not exist in any inertial frame of reference, but this is confusing because they are real measurable forces in the accelerated frame of reference. Probably the best choice is to call them **inertial forces** because they arise due to the inertia of matter, its resistance to being accelerated. If you had no mass, there would be no backward force on you in the accelerated car.

Newton's laws taken as a whole define an inertial frame of reference and are applicable in such a frame. However, the relation $F = ma$, applying to a single body, can be used even in a non-inertial frame provided the resultant force F includes *all* the forces that are acting on the body, no matter what their origin. In the last chapter we mentioned the particular inertial forces called centrifugal and coriolis forces, and we shall return to these in Chapter 10.

THE SEARCH FOR
AN INERTIAL FRAME OF REFERENCE

We have glibly suggested that all that is necessary to find an inertial frame of reference is to find an object that moves uniformly with respect to some frame, and that has no resultant force on it; then the frame is an inertial frame. But how do you decide that an object has no resultant force on it? Our criterion for no force is no acceleration, and there is no independent way of deciding that the object has no force on it. Newton's laws postulate that an inertial frame exists, but do not explain how to find it.

An inertial frame can only be established by experiment. If Newton's laws work for *all* bodies in a frame of reference, then it is an inertial frame.

The laws were developed to describe motion in a frame of reference fixed on the earth. However, we know that this is not really an inertial frame, but only approximately one. The earth is rotating on its axis and therefore there is an acceleration toward the axis of about 3 cm/sec^2 at the equator, decreasing to zero at the poles. Because of the motion of the earth in orbit around the sun there is an acceleration of about 0.6 cm/sec² toward the sun. The sun is moving in our galaxy with an acceleration toward the center of the galaxy that is not known but is estimated to be of the order of 10^{-8} cm/sec². Remember that each of these accelerations is referred to a different frame of reference.

You know that there is an acceleration due to gravity of about 980 cm/sec² toward the center of the earth for all objects on the earth's surface. The three accelerations described are small compared to this, and are masked by it, but the first two are certainly not negligible. For most experiments in laboratories on earth it is satisfactory to assume that we are in an inertial frame of reference, but if we really want an inertial frame we must make a transformation of the frame. A transformation to what frame? We have been observing the positions of the stars for quite a long time, and know that they seem to give a fixed background against which the motions of the solar system can be described. We *assume* that the stars provide an inertial frame of reference. This assumption is strengthened by the fact that the stars are on the average about 10 light-years or 10^{17} meters apart. All the fundamental forces we know fall off quite rapidly with distance, at least as fast as an inverse-square law, and therefore it seems reasonable to think of the stars as being in their natural state, uninfluenced by their mutual interactions.

The transformation to the frame of reference of the stars makes allowance for the three motions of the earth already described, and is the best we know how to do in establishing an inertial frame of reference.

The point we wish to stress is not the specific way that an inertial frame is established, but rather the fact that it can only be established by experiment. Therefore we can never really *know* we have an inertial frame, we must *assume* it.

THE EQUIVALENCE OF INERTIAL FRAMES

In Chapter 7 we developed the Galilean transformations for the physical quantities **r**, **v** and **a** as measured in two frames of reference S and S' moving at a constant relative velocity. The acceleration transformation is $\mathbf{a} = \mathbf{a}'$. The accelerations measured in *all* frames of reference moving at constant velocities with respect to one another are the same. We stated that this meant that such frames are dynamically equivalent, and we now see the significance of this.

Think about a particle of mass m in an inertial frame of reference S. A resultant force **F** on the particle will produce an acceleration **a**, where $\mathbf{F} = m\mathbf{a}$. Now think about the motion of the particle as described in a second frame of reference S' moving at constant velocity with respect to the first. The accelerations measured in both frames are the same $\mathbf{a} = \mathbf{a}'$, from the Galilean transformation. The position and velocity of the particle will be different as measured in the two frames, but since we have assumed in formulating classical dynamics that mass is a property that does *not* depend on position or velocity, the mass of the particle is the same in both frames $m = m'$. Therefore $F' = m'a' = ma = F$; the forces are the same in both frames. The relation $F = ma$ is the same in both frames; it is an **invariant** for a Galilean transformation of the frame of reference. If you can find one inertial frame of reference, then *any* frame moving at constant velocity with respect to it will also be an inertial frame.

When we introduced vectors we pointed out that they were useful because the laws of physics were invariant for different co-ordinate systems in the same frame of reference. The laws of physics are descriptions of physical events, and what happens in a physical event does not depend on the orientation or position of the co-ordinate system used to describe it. By expressing the laws of physics in vector form they can be written, for a particular frame of reference, without reference to a particular co-ordinate system. The law $F = ma$ stands for three equations $F_x = ma_x$, $F_y = ma_y$, $F_z = ma_z$ in a particular co-ordinate system. Now we see that this law is also invariant for all frames of reference moving at constant velocities with respect to one another. What is the significance of this? It is worth looking at what Newton said about it.

THE PRINCIPLE OF RELATIVITY

Newton's laws were originally published in his famous *Principia*. Along with the laws he gave a number of corollaries that were either deductions from the laws, or statements of assumptions made in formulating them. One of these dealt with the superposition of forces which we have already discussed. Another had to do with the invariance of the laws of motion in different inertial reference frames. He expressed it this way. "The motions of bodies included in a given space are the same among themselves whether that space is at rest or moves uniformly forward in a straight line." This says that it is not possible to tell from measurements of the motions of a group of interacting bodies ("the motions of the bodies among themselves") in a particular inertial frame of reference ("a given space") whether the frame of reference is at rest or moving uniformly.

The idea that there is some sort of absolute space, or space at rest, is an intuitively satisfying one. We must accept the idea that we are not really at rest because we are spinning about the earth's axis, and whirling in orbit around the sun, but we have the deeply ingrained feeling that there is some absolute frame of reference—perhaps the frame of reference of the stars—that is really at rest. In Newton's time, and for about two hundred years afterward, this idea led to the concept of the aether. Absolute space was a frame of reference in which the aether was at rest.

The invariance of Newton's laws in different inertial frames of reference meant that it was not possible to determine how a frame of reference was moving with respect to absolute space, that is to establish an "absolute speed," by observing the motion of bodies. Since Newton's laws form the basis of mechanics, this meant that it was not possible to tell by any experiment in mechanics how a frame of reference was moving in absolute space. This did not rule out the possibility of identifying absolute space by some other non-mechanical means, for example, by experiments with light beams. The notion of absolute space persisted until about the end of the last century, but experimental attempts to detect it always gave negative results. The notion was really given up only with the development of the system of mechanics called special relativity.

The fact that the laws of mechanics are invariant from one inertial frame to another is implicit in Newton's formulation of the laws. However, this particular aspect of his formulation has a validity beyond that of the laws themselves. Even though the laws of classical mechanics have been found to be inadequate under certain conditions, there remains a general principle called the **Principle of Relativity**: The laws of **physics** are invariant from one inertial frame to another. The consequences of this principle are discussed in the theory of special relativity.

Let us digress for a moment to look again at the terminology of physics. At the beginning of this chapter we discussed the use of words like **definition, law, assumption,** and **hypothesis.** Where does **principle** fit in? Is there a difference between a law of physics and a principle of physics?

As far as we can see there does not seem to be any fundamental difference between these terms as used in physics. In general it seems that the term **law** is used when a statement can be made in precise quantitative form, while the term **principle** is applied to general statements that do not lend themselves to a precise formulation in mathematical terms. Nevertheless a principle of physics must be interpreted with precision. There does not seem to be complete uniformity in the way a particular statement is labeled. For example, you may be familiar with a relation that describes the flow of a fluid under certain conditions, the statement variously called the Bernoulli principle, the Bernoulli law, the Bernoulli hypothesis, or the Bernoulli equation.

The important thing is that *all* the statements of physics, whether called hypotheses, assumptions, definitions, laws, or principles, are subject to the test of experiment.

THE AIM OF MECHANICS

Before continuing our discussion of Newton's laws, think for a moment of what the aim of mechanics is—or, more generally, what the aim of physics is. It is to comprehend the physical world, that is to understand what has happened, what is happening, what will happen. This means that the laws of physics should enable us to make predictions. We observe what is happening now, and the laws of physics are rules for making calculations about what will happen next.

The aim of mechanics is to enable us to make these calculations for motion: knowing the motion of a body now, the laws of mechanics enable us to predict its motion in the future. In principle if we know the positions and velocities of all bodies at some instant and the interactions between them, then the laws of mechanics would enable us to calculate their positions and velocities at any time in the future—or, for that matter, in the past.

Newton focused attention on the interaction between bodies as producing changes in motion, and he described these interactions by introducing the concept of **force**. In principle, if we know the positions and velocities of all particles at some instant, and the **forces** between them, then Newton's laws of motion would enable us to calculate their positions and velocities at any future time.

What does this mean for a single particle? If at some instant we know its position and velocity and the net force F on it, from $F = ma$ we can calculate its acceleration and therefore predict where it will be at the next instant. However, at the next instant the force on the particle may be different, both because it has moved and because whatever is producing the force may have moved. Therefore we must do the calculation again. The point is that $F = ma$ is an instantaneous law, a law in differential form, as you recognize if it is written as $F = m(dv/dt)$. To calculate what happens to a particle over any finite time interval would require in principle an infinite number of calculations, although by dividing the time interval up into small intervals, and doing the calculation for smaller and smaller intervals, we can come as close to the exact description as we wish; recall the examples of numerical integration given in Chapter 6.

Sometimes the calculation of motion over an interval is simple. For example, if the force is constant, independent of time, the acceleration is constant. We used some examples of motion in a uniform force field in Chapter 5. An even simpler example occurs when the force is zero. Then the acceleration is zero, and the velocity and momentum of the particle are constant.

When the force is not constant the calculation of what happens over a time interval may be difficult. Even the calculation of what happens during the interaction of only two particles does not appear to be simple. From instant to instant the positions of both particles change, and therefore the force that each exerts on the other changes. If there are more than two interacting particles, the calculations become more formidable.

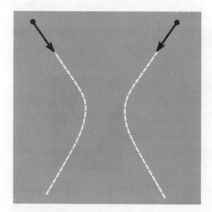

The paths of two interacting particles.

You know that there are methods of dealing with interactions in which the force does not enter the calculations. We described these methods in Chapter 6, and saw that they depend on the concepts of momentum and energy. The concept of energy was not introduced until about two centuries after Newton, but that of momentum was introduced by Newton as "quantity of motion."

Two of Newton's corollaries provide one basis for describing interactions without using force explicitly. Having described interactions by introducing this concept, Newton then showed that in certain situations the forces need not enter the calculations. His third corollary dealt with the quantity of motion (momentum) generated in the mutual interaction of two bodies, and led to the principle of conservation of momentum. His fourth corollary introduced the idea of center of mass of a system of particles. He called it center of gravity, and the fourth corollary stated that the motion of the center of gravity of a system of bodies is not changed by their mutual interactions.

In Chapter 6 we defined center of mass and discussed conservation of momentum for two interacting particles. We now develop these ideas for a system of interacting particles. This development does not involve any additional assumptions about the physical world, it is simply expressing the information in Newton's laws in a different form.

MOTION OF A SYSTEM OF PARTICLES

Think about a system of N particles, of masses $m_1, m_2, \cdots, m_N$. The system may be a rigid body in which the particles are all in fixed positions relative to one another, or it may be a system in which the particles are all moving with respect to one another. This motion we call internal motion of the system. We are interested in what can be said about the motion of the system as a whole, based on Newton's laws. It is perhaps surprising that no matter how complex the internal motion, it is always possible to talk about motion of the **system,** and define a system velocity.

Motion can only be described with respect to a frame of reference. At any instant the N particles have displacements $\mathbf{r}_1, \mathbf{r}_2, \cdots, \mathbf{r}_N$ with respect to some fixed point O in the frame of reference, and have velocities $\mathbf{v}_1, \mathbf{v}_2, \cdots, \mathbf{v}_N$, momenta $\mathbf{p}_1, \mathbf{p}_2, \cdots, \mathbf{p}_N$, and accelerations $\mathbf{a}_1, \mathbf{a}_2, \cdots, \mathbf{a}_N$.

Center of mass of a
system of particles.

The **center of mass** of the system of particles is defined as the point with a displacement

$$\mathbf{R}_c = \frac{m_1\mathbf{r}_1 + m_2\mathbf{r}_2 + \cdots + m_N\mathbf{r}_N}{m_1 + m_2 + \cdots + m_N} = \frac{\sum\limits_{i=1}^{N} m_i\mathbf{r}_i}{\sum\limits_{i=1}^{N} m_i}$$

The center of mass is a property of the system. We will use capital letters to represent properties of the system, and small letters to represent properties of the individual particles. The limits $i = 1$ to N on the summation notation will not be written hereafter, because in each case $\sum$ means the sum over all of the N particles. The sum of all the particle masses $\sum m_i$ is the total mass of the system M. We assume that the masses of the individual particles, and the total mass, do not change as time goes on. That is, we assume **conservation of mass.** This is a fundamental assumption of classical physics, and of course is subject to experimental verification.

The displacement $\mathbf{R}_c$ of the center of mass (c-of-m) depends on the particular reference point O in the frame of reference, but the location of the c-of-m does *not* depend on this; it depends only on the masses of the particles and their positions relative to one another. It can be described as a mass-weighted average position of the particles.

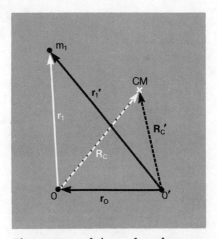

To see that the position of the c-of-m does not depend on the choice of O, consider the displacements of the particles $\mathbf{r}'_i$ from some other fixed point O'. The displacement $\mathbf{R}'_c$ of the c-of-m is defined as

$$\mathbf{R}'_i = \frac{\sum m_i\mathbf{r}'_i}{\sum m_i}$$

If the displacement of the fixed point O from the fixed point O' is $\mathbf{r}_0$, then for every particle

$$\mathbf{r}'_i = \mathbf{r}_i + \mathbf{r}_0$$

so that

$$\mathbf{R}'_c = \frac{\sum m_i\mathbf{r}_i}{\sum m_i} + \frac{\sum m_i\mathbf{r}_0}{\sum m_i} = \mathbf{R}_c + \mathbf{r}_0$$

showing that the position of the c-of-m is the same as if displacements were referred to the point O.

The position of the c-of-m of a system of particles is independent of the choice of fixed point O to which displacements are referred.

The position of the c-of-m of the system is defined by the displacement $\mathbf{R}_c$ at any instant, but of course as time goes on the displacements of the particles will change and the displacement of the c-of-m will change. We use the relation $M = \sum m_i$ to write

$$MR_c = \sum m_i r_i$$

and then differentiate with respect to time, remembering that M and the m_i are constants.

$$M\left(\frac{dR_c}{dt}\right) = \sum m_i \left(\frac{dr_i}{dt}\right) \quad = \sum m_i v_i \quad = \sum p_i$$

The quantity dR_c/dt is the velocity V_c of the c-of-m of the system. The right side of the equation is the sum of the momenta of the individual particles, and therefore this relation shows that we can think of the total momentum of the system $P = MV_c = \sum p_i$. The total momentum is the product of the total mass and the velocity of the c-of-m.

Now differentiate again with respect to time

$$\frac{dP}{dt} = \sum \frac{dp_i}{dt}$$

$$= \sum F_i$$

We have introduced F_i, the resultant force on the ith particle, which according to Newton's laws of motion is given by $F_i = m_i a_i = m_i(dv_i/dt) = dp_i/dt$.

The resultant force on any particle is made up of **external** forces, forces produced by agencies outside the system of particles, and **internal** forces, forces exerted on the particle by the other particles of the system. However, Newton's third law tells us that the internal forces will contribute nothing to the vector sum $\sum F_i$ because they occur in equal and opposite pairs. For any force F_{ij} exerted on particle i by particle j, there will be a force F_{ji} exerted on particle j by particle i, and the third law says that $F_{ji} = -F_{ij}$ so that when the sum is taken over all the particles these internal force pairs make no contribution. This means that $\sum F_i$ can be interpreted as the sum of the **external** forces acting on the system, which we will label F_{ext}.

We can now write

$$F_{ext} = \frac{dP}{dt} = M\frac{dV_c}{dt} = MA_c = M\frac{d^2R_c}{dt^2}$$

involving the displacement R_c, velocity V_c and acceleration A_c of the c-of-m of the system, the total momentum P of the system, and the resultant external force. **The center of mass of a system of particles moves as though all the mass of the system is at this point, and all the external forces act at this point.**

Now think about the situation where there is no resultant external force on the system, $F_{ext} = 0$. Then

$$\frac{dP}{dt} = 0 \quad \text{and} \quad P = \sum p_i = \text{constant}$$

The total momentum of the system is constant, or **conserved.** This result is called the principle of the conservation of momentum, or the law of conservation of momentum, or the conservation of momentum theorem.

The significance of Newton's fourth corollary can now be seen; it stated that the motion of the center of mass of a system of bodies is not changed by their mutual interaction. As time goes on the particles in the system may move around in complex ways, but the point called the center of mass stays at rest or moves uniformly if there is no resultant external force on the system, or moves as though the external force acted at the c-of-m if there is an external force.

If there is no external force the seething internal motions of the system can be ignored, and we can think of the system moving along sedately in uniform motion. Furthermore we can make a transformation to the frame of reference in which the center of mass is at rest—the center of mass frame of reference.

The notion of a system velocity is a useful one, and in relativistic mechanics it is possible to redefine mass in such a way as to maintain this useful property of a system of particles, even though the idea of center of mass does not survive.

CONSERVATION OF LINEAR MOMENTUM

When the resultant external force acting on a system is zero, the total momentum of the system is constant.

We have already seen in Chapter 6 applications of this important result to a system of two particles. Certain predictions about the behavior of the particles could be made without worrying about how the force between the particles changed from moment to moment.

Note that the result P = constant is a vector equation, equivalent to three scalar equations in a particular co-ordinate system. Note also that although we use the term momentum for the quantity $p = mv$, it should more properly be called **linear momentum,** because we will later introduce a quantity called angular momentum.

We have shown that conservation of linear momentum is a direct theoretical result of Newton's laws. Remember that the laws are summaries of experience, synthesizing a variety of experimental facts. It is possible to put in the experimental information, or pull out theoretical predictions, in a variety of ways. In many modern treatments of classical mechanics conservation of momentum is introduced as an **experimental** fact, rather than a theoretical result. Then it is not necessary to give Newton's Law III the same emphasis as the other two.

We used all of Newton's laws to deduce conservation of momentum. Instead we could have taken conservation of momentum as an experimental fact, and used it to deduce Newton's Law III under certain conditions. It is likely that Newton himself decided to propose Law III because of observations of what happened when material objects collided.

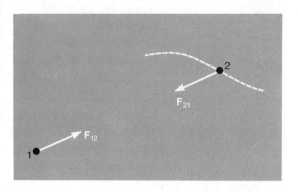

Is there an instantaneous signal
from particle 2 to particle 1?

You can see that there is a difficulty with Law III. It says that $F_{12} = -F_{21}$ *always*, that the forces are equal and opposite at every instant. If particle 2 is moving relative to particle 1 the force between the particles is changing in magnitude and direction, but Law III says that particle 1 knows **instantly** what particle 2 is doing, and vice versa. Some sort of signal would have to pass between the bodies instantaneously, with zero transit time. While we have come to accept the idea of "action at a distance" we do not accept the idea of "action at a distance instantaneously." This is the difficulty with Law III. The only forces that Newton knew about were contact forces, the forces between macroscopic objects in contact, and gravitational forces. Law III works for contact forces between objects because they are in contact and no transit time is necessary for signals. Law III appears to work for the gravitational interaction between objects because it is a very weak force, and therefore objects for which the gravitational force is significant are so massive that they are only accelerated to velocities that are relatively low. This means that as far as describing their motions is concerned the transit time for signals between them is effectively zero. Newton worried about the transit time for gravitational signals, but assumed, in order to see what the consequences would be, that it could be taken as zero. The success of his theory of gravitation and theory of motion showed that this was a very good assumption.

We have already pointed out in describing the fundamental interactions that the electromagnetic interaction is not adequately described by Newton's laws. Law III is not valid for the interaction between charged particles because the transit time is not zero. However, in spite of this it has been possible to maintain conservation of momentum for the electromagnetic interactions by the clever device of assigning momentum to the space in between the interacting particles, as well as to the particles themselves. We introduce the concept of an electromagnetic field in the space between the particles, and assign momentum to the field. When the particles are far apart the field is approximately zero, and all the momentum is associated with the particles. During the interaction the momentum of particles and field together is conserved, and after the interaction the momentum of the particles is the same as before. Moment by moment during the interaction the momentum of the particles alone is *not* conserved.

Conservation laws are perhaps the most useful tools of physics, as you may have found already. Therefore although theories of physics may change, every effort is made to maintain conservation laws wherever possible. Conservation of momentum had its origins in Newton's laws, but it was kept for the electro-

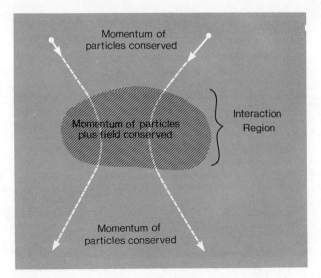

To maintain conservation of momentum for the electromagnetic interaction, it is necessary to assign momentum to the electromagnetic field.

magnetic interaction, even though electromagnetic forces were not Newtonian forces, by the device of assigning momentum to the electromagnetic field.

It is sometimes said that the conservation of momentum principle is more fundamental than Newton's laws, because it applies in circumstances where Newtonian mechanics breaks down. We worry that this sort of statement makes it sound as though the laws of physics are laws of nature, rather than laws of man; that is, laws that man concocts to describe nature. We prefer to think that conservation of momentum has a broader applicability than Newton's laws of classical mechanics because man has arranged that in new systems of mechanics conservation of momentum is maintained as a principle, not because nature has decreed that it be so. Physicists take different points of view with respect to such questions, and it is important for you to realize that such differences exist.

We will see that similar considerations apply to the concept of energy. We will introduce conservation of energy by defining certain kinds of energy in a way consistent with Newton's laws, but the principle of conservation of energy will be carried into all of physics by appropriately redefining the different kinds of energy.

NEWTON AS THE FOUNDATION—A SUMMARY

In this chapter we have discussed the essentials of classical mechanics as drawn together by Newton's laws of motion. Newton's attempt to relate the motion of one body in the universe to the motions of all the other bodies set the pattern for all subsequent work in mechanics. He framed his mechanics in terms of the concepts of force and mass, concepts closely related to our experience. Mass is related to the act of counting objects or measuring volumes, reflected in Newton's "quantity of matter." Force is related to our feelings of pushing or pulling, and as defined by Newton led to the satisfying simplicity of the third law. Newton said in his *Rules of Reasoning* "We are certainly not to relinquish the evidence of experiments for the sake of dreams and vain fictions of our own devising; nor are we to recede from the analogy of Nature, which is wont to be simple and always consonant to itself."

Experiments with two bodies give opposite accelerations; Newton gave us the simplicity of opposite and **equal** forces. This part of Newton's mechanics we have gradually lost because this simplicity is not present in electromagnetic and nuclear interactions. We feature instead another part of Newton's foundation, the idea of conservation of momentum. We maintain this principle even though it requires a new definition of mass and an association of momentum with the space between bodies, because statements of unchanging entities in the presence of change are as appealing to us as to Newton. We prefer to regard this as a matter of our taste, rather than the nature of Nature.

There have been many regroupings of the information summarized in Newton's laws and corollaries, but it was Newton who gathered these together and set the pattern for future thought. This is the reason we have presented the laws more or less as originally stated, along with an appraisal of what we thought they were saying.

In discussing the laws we emphasized the assumptions made and also the circumstances in which the assumptions are not valid. We conclude the chapter by summarizing the essential limitations.

The laws are limited to the interaction between bodies that are not moving at speeds near the speed of light. This is because Newton's formulation neglects the fact that interactions at a distance are not instantaneous. Although the introduction of the non-Newtonian magnetic force allows the laws to be used at low speeds, the proper mechanics for electromagnetic interactions is Einstein's relativistic mechanics. It was investigation of the magnetic and electric interactions that led to the development of this system of mechanics by Einstein in 1905. He called it the special theory of relativity because it arose in trying to relate observations of an electromagnetic interaction in one inertial frame of reference to those in a frame moving uniformly relative to the first. In order to maintain the laws of physics the same in both frames (the principle of relativity) it was necessary to revise the Galilean transformations—but all this will come later.

Another limitation on classical mechanics that we have not mentioned is that the bodies involved must be reasonably massive, in order that the uncertainties in their behavior as described by quantum mechanics can be neglected. We cannot specify what "reasonably massive" means because it depends on a variety of factors. In some experiments the essential features of the motions of electrons can be described by the methods of classical mechanics; others require quantum mechanics; still others require relativistic quantum electrodynamics.

The point is that there are an enormous variety of physical situations for which classical mechanics provides a completely adequate description. In the next chapters we investigate some typical situations.

Questions for discussion

1. We have taken the position that there is no fundamental difference between the **laws** of physics and the **definitions** of physics because both must have physical content in order to be useful. Some physicists would not agree with this view. How about you?

2. The phrase **physical content** has a nice ring to it. What does it mean? Is it a simple matter to identify the physical content of a physical law?

3. We have said that hypotheses are assumptions, and the laws of physics are based on hypotheses, so **the laws of nature are really the assumptions of man.** Do you find this view of physics disappointing, or stimulating—or neither?

4. On what basis is mass chosen to be a scalar property of matter?

5. We said in Chapter 4 that we would later consider the question of whether force is a vector by definition or by experiment, but that we would be unable to answer the question unambiguously. Can you see now why we made this remark?

6. The **Principle of Superposition** will appear often in your study of physics—sometimes you may not realize you are using it. Can you think of examples in ordinary experience where it is applicable, and where it is inapplicable? Is it valid for the income of a lawyer in private practice; for the income of a welfare recipient? Is it valid for the coins put in a parking meter?

7. Do you believe that action at a distance can be instantaneous, or do you think that there must be a finite transit time for all force **signals?** Does classical mechanics allow for the second possibility?

8. Can you think of any observable effects that show the earth frame of reference is not an inertial frame?

9. The **Principle of Relativity** is a statement that the laws of physics are invariant from one inertial frame to another. Do you think you understand what this means? Is it a law of physics to say that a dropped object falls straight down? Will an object dropped from a moving train fall straight down? Will an object dropped in a moving train fall straight down?

10. We proved, using vectors, the very general and important result relating the resultant external force on a system of interacting particles to the motion of the center of mass of the system. Can you visualize trying to prove this without using the vector concept?

11. What is the basic condition that must be fulfilled if the momentum of a system of particles is to be conserved? Is it likely that it is ever completely fulfilled?

12. When a book rests on a table the force of gravity acts down on the book and the table exerts an equal and opposite upward force on it. Is this an action and reaction pair of forces?

13. In case your reaction to the last question was to answer in the affirmative, what happens if the table is removed?

14. For each of the objects mentioned below, can you identify the forces acting that are likely to be affecting the motion (or the absence of motion)? Are they fundamental forces? Newtonian forces? Inertial forces? What frame of reference did you use in deciding what the forces were? Can you identify what the reactions to the forces are, remembering that the reaction always acts on some other body? We will be focusing our attention in coming chapters on some of the questions that your analysis here should raise.

A book rests on a table.

A ship floats in the ocean.

A balloon floats in the air.

A magnet "floats" in the air above another magnet.

A table tennis ball "sits" on an upward jet of air.

A toy balloon, rubbed on a sleeve, sticks to the ceiling.

A bubble, formed at the bottom of a soft drink bottle, rises with constant velocity.

The water in a pail upside down while being swung in a vertical circle does not fall out.

An astronaut sits in his spacecraft at the top of a rocket as it is fired.

An astronaut rests in his spacecraft orbiting the earth.

An astronaut "walks in space" beside his spacecraft, half-way between the earth and the moon.

A motorcyclist rides around the inside vertical wall of a circular drum.

A meteor passing the earth leaves a visible trail.

An electron beam striking the fluorescent face of a cathode ray tube leaves a visible line.

A spinning top tilted at an angle does not fall over.

9

DYNAMICS OF A PARTICLE
IN AN INERTIAL
FRAME OF REFERENCE

In the last chapter we examined the foundations of classical mechanics, and now we go on to look at the application of these ideas in a variety of physica situations.

Newton's laws make it possible to calculate the motion of a body if the forces acting on it are known. Conversely, if the motion of a body is measured, Newton's laws make it possible to calculate what resultant force must be acting on it. The latter use of the laws, in what is called an inductive process, is the important one as far as the development of physics is concerned, because it is the study of motion that provides information about the fundamental interactions of matter. Such understanding as we have of the gravitational, electromagnetic and nuclear interactions has come about from observing the motions of bodies subject to these interactions. You probably know how Newton's law of gravitation arose from a knowledge of the motions of the bodies in the solar system.

Using Newton's laws to deduce what the motion of a body is from a knowledge of the forces acting on it is called a deductive process, and this process is important in making predictions about the behavior of physical systems. We will be concentrating on this aspect of Newton's laws.

Here in Part III we will be using only the basic relation $\mathbf{F} = m\mathbf{a}$, an instantaneous equation relating the resultant force on a particle and the acceleration of the particle. In some cases, for example, if the force is constant, we will be able to predict what happens over an interval. Later, in Parts IV and V, we will see that in describing the cumulative or integrated effects of forces acting over an interval it is sometimes convenient to express Newton's laws in terms of other concepts, and we will introduce the ideas of impulse, work and energy.

SYSTEMS OF UNITS

In order to use the physical quantities force, mass and momentum in physical situations we must have units in which these quantities can be measured and expressed. The question of what to do about systems of units is always a perplexing one for authors of physics textbooks. One possibility is to describe one particular system of units, and work only in that system. This means that attention can be focused on physics principles without getting bogged down in technical details, but such an approach ignores the fact that there are several systems of units in common use. We think that it is worth while at this stage to outline these systems, because you will have had some experience in working with particular systems in mechanics.

We have already introduced units for the fundamental quantities length and time, and for the kinematic quantities displacement, velocity and acceleration defined from them. The dynamic relation $\mathbf{F} = m\mathbf{a}$ makes it necessary to introduce another fundamental quantity, which means a quantity given an operational definition as opposed to a definition in terms of other physical quantities. We could choose any dynamical quantity for this; if mass is chosen, this leads to systems of units that are called **absolute**; if force is chosen, this leads to systems of units that are called **gravitational.** We will consider absolute systems first.

ABSOLUTE SYSTEMS OF UNITS

The operational definition of mass requires the choice of a standard mass, and specification of procedures for comparing other masses to the standard. The standard is the **standard kilogram,** a cylinder of platinum maintained at the International Bureau of Weights and Measures in France. We saw in the last chapter how masses could be compared. In principle, two masses are allowed to interact and their accelerations are measured: $m_1/m_2 = -\mathbf{a}_2/\mathbf{a}_1$. In practice masses are compared on an equal-arm balance. It is assumed that the effect of gravity is uniform over the region of the balance, and therefore that identical masses on the two sides will be acted upon by identical forces. There is a further assumption here that we will not go into in detail; this is that the **inertial mass** of a body (the mass that appears in Newton's law of motion $\mathbf{F} = m\mathbf{a}$) is proportional to the **gravitational mass** of the body (the mass that determines the gravitational interaction between the body and other bodies). It is not obvious that these two quite different physical properties should be proportional, but it is an experimental fact. Very precise measurements have been made to try and detect any difference, measurements that could detect a difference of 1 part in 10^8—but none has been found. We return to this point in Chapter 12.

For convenience there are copies of the standard kilogram distributed in standards laboratories throughout the world, but all must be referred to the original standard. At one time there was a standard pound as well, but now the pound is defined in terms of the kilogram. We pointed out in Chapter 4 that there are now atomic standards of length and of time. It might be thought that an atomic standard of mass would be possible by specifying the standard as a certain number of atoms of a particular kind. However, it turns out that the precision with which masses can be compared on a balance exceeds the precision with which the number of atoms in a chunk of matter can be determined, and therefore an atomic standard of mass is not a possibility at our present stage of knowledge and technology. Note that although there is not an atomic *standard* of mass there is an atomic *unit* of mass that is useful in describing atomic and nuclear reactions. The **atomic mass unit** (amu) is defined by stating that a neutral carbon-12 atom has a mass of exactly 12 amu. This unit is related to other mass units by experiment (see Problem 4).

There are three absolute systems of units in common use, based on different units of the fundamental quantities mass, length and time. These are the mks (meter-kilogram-second) system, the cgs (centimeter-gram-second) system, and the fps (foot-pound-second) system, sometimes called the British absolute system. The standards for the fundamental quantities are the same for each system, the meter, the kilogram and the second. Other units are defined in terms of these: the gram is defined as exactly 0.001 kg, the pound as exactly 0.45359237 kg. This formidable number arises because the defined pound is made to be the same as the old standard pound as precisely as possible; the number gives an indication of the accuracy to which masses can be compared.

Units for all defined quantities in these three systems follow from the definitions. For example in mks units displacement $\mathbf{r}$ is in meters (abbreviation m), velocity $\mathbf{v} = d\mathbf{r}/dt$ is in m/sec, acceleration $\mathbf{a} = d\mathbf{v}/dt$ is in m/sec², momentum $\mathbf{p} = m\mathbf{v}$ is in kg-m/sec, force $\mathbf{F} = m\mathbf{a}$ is in kg-m/sec². Such combinations of units are sometimes cumbersome to write or to say, so special names are invented for some of them, in particular for the units of force. The term **newton** is used instead of kg-m/sec²: a force of 5 kg-m/sec² is called a force of 5 newtons, abbreviated 5 n. Another way of saying the same thing is to define a force of 1 newton as that force that produces an acceleration of 1 m/sec² when applied to a mass of 1 kg, but this makes it look as though we are defining something new instead of just giving a new name to a physical quantity we already have. Again, a matter of taste.

In cgs units the unit of force is the gm-cm/sec², called the **dyne.** Perhaps we should point out that the accepted abbreviation for gram is g, but we use gm because the abbreviation g sometimes becomes confused with the magnitude of the acceleration due to gravity g. We apologize to all international committees on nomenclature for this breach.

In British absolute units the unit of force is the lb-ft/sec², called the **poundal**.

Our discussion so far has not required any mention of the force of gravity; the force units to which we have given special names have nothing to do with gravity, and are uniquely defined. However, the gravitational attraction of the earth is a roughly constant force that is always acting on an object on the surface of the earth, where almost all of us are, and this has led to the definition of certain **gravitational units of force**. We use the term weight for the gravitational force exerted by the earth. A 1-kg mass is said to have a weight of one kilogram. This means that any force the same size as the force of gravity on a 1-kg mass is called a force of one kilogram. Similarly the weight of a 1-gm mass is one gram and the weight of a 1-lb mass is one pound. Note that these do *not* give unambiguous units of force, because the force due to gravity is not quite constant over the earth's surface.

Think of a 1-kg mass released near the earth's surface. It will fall with an acceleration g downward, where g is approximately 9.8 m/sec². From Newton's law the force on it is

$$F = ma = 1 \times g \text{ kg-m/sec}^2 = g \text{ newtons}$$

The gravitational force on a 1-kg mass.

The force varies slightly (by about 3%) depending on where on earth the mass is. However, no matter where it is, the force on it in gravitational force units is said to be one kilogram. Thus a force of 1 kilogram is equivalent to a force of g newtons $\cong$ 9.8 newtons; the kilogram as a unit of force is not uniquely determined.

Similar arguments show that a force of 1 gram is equivalent to a force of approximately 980 dynes, and a force of 1 pound is equivalent to a force of approximately 32 poundals.

It is unfortunate that the same name is used for units of mass and of force, but it is a fact that cannot be ignored. If reference is made to a "5-kg object" does this mean an object of mass 5 kg or of weight 5 kg? To the extent that the variation in g can be neglected, it does not matter. However, in precise terms the reference is ambiguous, and it would have to be stated whether mass or weight was being specified.

GRAVITATIONAL SYSTEMS OF UNITS

The situation is not helped by the fact that in addition to absolute systems of units, in which **mass** is chosen as a fundamental quantity, there are also gravitational systems of units, in which **force** is chosen as the fundamental quantity. Since the only gravitational system in common use is a system using British units, we will describe only this system.

The British gravitational system of units is sometimes called the British engineering system because it is used by engineers—though not only engineers—in

Britain. Like the British absolute system it is an fps system, but here the pound is defined operationally as a unit of force, not of mass. If force is to be taken as fundamental, then some standard force must be chosen. The standard of force, called a force of one pound, is defined to be the force that gives a mass of 0.45359237 kg an acceleration of 32.1740 ft/sec². This odd definition has of course an historical origin. The standard force was defined to be the gravitational force on the particular chunk of matter called the standard pound (now defined in terms of the standard kilogram) but since this force was different at different points on the earth's surface, it was defined as the gravitational force at sea level and latitude 45°N. This might lead you to believe that the acceleration due to gravity at sea level and latitude 45°N is 32.1740 ft/sec², but this is not the case. At the time the pound as a standard of force was defined, this was thought to be the value of g under these conditions, but subsequent measurements showed that this was not quite correct.

This messy story was mentioned simply to show the sort of problem that can arise. The important point is that in the British gravitational system force is the fundamental quantity, defined operationally. Although it might appear at first that the definition depends on gravity, you can see that this is really not so: the pound is defined as the force that gives a particular chunk of matter a particular acceleration.

As we have said it is an unfortunate fact that the same names, kilogram, gram and pound, are used for units of both force and mass. Sometimes an attempt is made to avoid confusion by using terms like pound-mass and pound-force. Another convention is to use the abbreviation pd for the pound as a unit of force and lb for the pound as a unit of mass.

Since force is fundamental in the British gravitational system, mass is a derived quantity. From $m = F/a$, the unit of mass is the pd-sec²/ft, a unit that is given the rather homely name of the **slug**. A force of 1 pound produces an acceleration of 1 ft/sec² when acting on a mass of 1 slug. Again note that gravity does not enter this statement. The term "gravitational system of units" arises because of the origin of the system, not because gravity affects the definitions.

Now think about an object released near the earth's surface, of mass such that the gravitational force on it is exactly 1 pound. This force will give it an acceleration of g ft/sec², where g is approximately 32 ft/sec², its value depending on where on the earth the object is. From Newton's law the mass of the object is

$$m = F/a = 1/g \text{ pd-sec}^2/\text{ft} = 1/g \text{ slug}$$

The mass varies slightly over the earth's surface; that is, different masses would have to be at different places in order that the force be exactly 1 pound in all cases. In all cases, however, we would describe this as an object of mass 1 pound, using the pound as a unit of mass. Therefore a mass of 1 pound is approximately

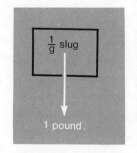

The mass of an object acted on by a gravitational force of 1 pound.

equivalent to a mass of $1/g$ slug $\cong 1/32$ slug. In this system of units the pound as a unit of mass is not uniquely determined.

USING UNITS

By now you may be somewhat confused, and in order to see whether or not there are real problems in dealing with units we will look carefully at a numerical example. In this example we state the numbers with three-figure accuracy in order to emphasize the small differences that arise.

Example: Think first about a 16.0-lb mass acted upon by an unbalanced force of 64.0 poundals, and calculate its acceleration. Both force and mass are given in units in the British absolute system, and the acceleration is

$$a = \frac{F}{m} = \frac{64.0}{16.0}\frac{\text{pndl}}{\text{lb}} = 4.00 \frac{\text{lb-ft/sec}^2}{\text{lb}} = 4.00 \text{ ft/sec}^2$$

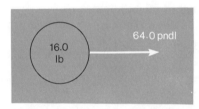

Absolute units.

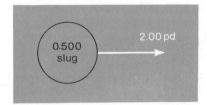

Gravitational units.

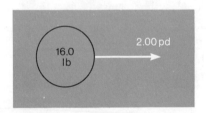

Absolute or gravitational units?

There is no ambiguity in the situation. Now think about a 0.500-slug mass acted upon by an unbalanced force of 2.00 pounds. Again there is no ambiguity, because both force and mass are given in units in the British gravitational system, and the acceleration is

$$a = \frac{F}{m} = \frac{2.00}{0.500}\frac{\text{pd}}{\text{slug}} = 4.00 \frac{\text{pd}}{\text{pd-sec}^2/\text{ft}}$$

$$= 4.00 \text{ ft/sec}^2$$

Now think about a 16.0-lb mass acted upon by an unbalanced force of 2.00 pounds. It is not clear whether to use absolute or gravitational units. Suppose that we think first in the absolute system. The mass is given in pounds, and we must convert the force to poundals. A force of 2.00 pounds is the gravitational force on a 2.00-lb mass, giving it the acceleration g. If $g = 32.0$ ft/sec², then

$$F = 2.00 \times 32.0 \text{ lb-ft/sec}^2 = 64.0 \text{ pndl}$$

and

$$a = \frac{F}{m} = \frac{64.0}{16.0} = 4.00 \text{ ft/sec}^2$$

On the other hand, if $g = 32.2$ ft/sec^2, then

$$F = 2.00 \times 32.2 \text{ lb-ft/sec}^2 = 64.4 \text{ pndl}$$

and

$$a = \frac{F}{m} = \frac{64.4}{16.0} = 4.25 \text{ ft/sec}^2$$

The acceleration is not uniquely determined, but depends on the value of g used. We could write the result in general by stating

$$F = 2.00g \text{ pndl} \quad \text{and} \quad a = \frac{F}{m} = \frac{2.00g}{16.0} = 0.125g$$

Now instead of thinking in absolute units we use the gravitational system. The force is given in pounds, and we must convert the mass to slugs. A mass of 16.0 lb is one that a gravitational force of 16.0 pd will give an acceleration g. If $g = 32.0$ ft/sec^2, then

$$m = \frac{16.0}{32.0} \frac{\text{pd}}{\text{ft/sec}^2} = 0.500 \text{ slug} \quad \text{and} \quad a = \frac{F}{m} = \frac{2.00}{0.500} = 4.00 \text{ ft/sec}^2$$

Similarly if $g = 32.2$ ft/sec^2, $a = 4.25$ ft/sec^2.

These results are exactly the same as obtained using the gravitational system. There is not a unique numerical result for the problem because of the mixture of units used, but the **system** of units used to make the calculation does not matter. Either system gives the result $a = 0.125g$.

Suppose that we had applied Newton's law $F = ma$ directly without worrying about systems of units at all, and calculated

$$a = \frac{F}{m} = \frac{2.00}{16.0} \frac{\text{pd}}{\text{lb}} = 0.125 \text{ pd/lb}$$

If we read both "pd" and "lb" as "pounds" we appear to have acceleration expressed as a pure number, with no units, but we know that acceleration is defined as a physical quantity whose numerical value depends on the units used. Mixing the pound as a unit of both force and mass in the same problem has automatically introduced the value of g, the ratio between absolute and gravitational force units (in the absolute system) or between absolute and gravitational mass units (in the gravitational system). The abbreviations pd and lb help to remind us that force and mass are not the same physical quantity, even though we use the same name for units of both.

We can summarize the three approaches taken in the numerical example by writing Newton's law for a body of mass m pounds acted upon by an unbalanced force of F pounds in three ways.

$$Fg = ma \qquad \text{:absolute}$$

$$F = \left(\frac{m}{g}\right)a \qquad \text{:gravitational}$$

$$F = m\left(\frac{a}{g}\right) \qquad \text{:aeronautical}$$

The first symbolizes the absolute system; force in pounds is converted to poundals by the factor g. The second represents the gravitational system; mass in pounds is converted to slugs by the factor g. The third represents an approach often adopted in aeronautical engineering; acceleration is treated as a dimensionless quantity by expressing accelerations in terms of g. The three approaches are different ways of saying the same thing.

It is sometimes argued that it is essential in making calculations in physics to work in a consistent system of units. We pointed out in Chapter 3 that it may be desirable or convenient, but it is not essential. The important thing is that in making calculations **you have no choice about the units.** If you multiply 5 kg by 2 m/sec², the result is 10 kg-m/sec²; whether or not this result has physical significance is a separate question. Suppose you know that an unbalanced force of 5 kg acting on an object produces an acceleration of 2 m/sec². You can multiply these two numbers and find the quantity 10 kg-m/sec² $\equiv$ 10 newtons, but this has no significance in this situation. This is the force that would give a 5-kg mass an acceleration of 2 m/sec², but there is no 5-kg mass involved here. You could divide the two numbers and get 0.4 m/kg-sec², or 2.5 kg-sec²/m. The second of these has physical significance; you divided a force F by an acceleration a and found a mass $m = F/a = 2.5$ kg-sec²/m $\equiv$ 2.5 slug.

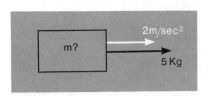

5 kg × 2 m/sec² = 10 n; physical significance?

It is because the terms pound, kilogram and gram are used for units of two different physical quantities that we must use some care in interpreting calculations made with these units. Use of the terms kg-mass and kg-force, or the abbreviations lb and pd, help to keep the difference in mind, but we will no longer make this distinction in our examples because it must be clear in the context whether force or mass is involved.

In general in the examples we will ignore the variation in g and assume its magnitude as exactly 32 ft/sec², or exactly 9.8 m/sec². Then there is no ambiguity in referring to a 5-kg object; it is an object of mass 5 kg on which there is a gravitational force of 5 kg $\equiv$ 49 newtons.

The advantage of working in a consistent system of units is that you do not have to check the units of calculated quantities. If you are working in the mks absolute system of units and calculate a force by any means whatsoever you know that the number calculated will be in newtons, and this is an advantage if you are doing a great many calculations. However, we suggest that while learning how to make calculations it is useful to keep checking the units.

ISOLATION OF A PARTICLE OR A SYSTEM OF PARTICLES

In the last chapter we saw that Newton's law $\mathbf{F} = m\mathbf{a}$ described the motion of a system of particles as well as that of a single particle. The force $\mathbf{F}$ is the **external resultant** force on the system, the mass m is the total mass of the system, and the acceleration **a** is the acceleration of the point in the system called the center of mass. The system of particles can be a number of particles all moving with respect to one another and interacting in complex ways, or can be a number of particles all at rest with respect to one another, as in our idealization of a rigid body.

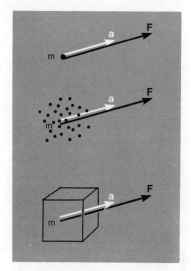

Remember that a particle is a concept. Any system is a particle if the frame of reference in which its motion is described has a large enough scale. Our solar system is a particle in the frame of reference of the universe; the sun and earth and moon are particles in the frame of reference of the solar system; mountains and buildings and men are particles in the frame of reference of the earth; atoms and molecules are particles in the frame in which man makes measurements. A particle is a system where we are not concerned with internal structure; it can be located at a point in the frame of reference. We

Resultant force on a particle and on a system of particles.

can speak of *its* mass, *its* acceleration, and the force on *it*. If we investigate any system with a fine enough probe we find that it does have some sort of structure. We can say that it is made up of still smaller systems that we call particles, until we probe still more deeply, and so on. Whether or not this process can be carried on indefinitely we do not really know. At the present stage of our knowledge the structure of all matter can apparently be described in terms of certain fundamental particles, but just how many fundamental particles there are is still a matter for conjecture and research. Deeper probing has shown that many of the particles we now call fundamental have internal structure. In any case, as we have already mentioned in the last chapter, classical mechanics is not appropriate for description below the atomic level. Atoms and molecules can be treated as particles and their motions described by the methods of classical mechanics. However, in order to deal satisfactorily with the interaction between them, the methods of quantum mechanics must be used, because their internal structure may be altered in these interactions.

Classical mechanics then enables us to describe and predict the motions of systems ranging from atoms to galaxies, sometimes treated as single particles, sometimes as systems of particles. No matter what the system, the basic equation $\mathbf{F} = m\mathbf{a}$ involves the resultant **external** force on the system. This means that in order to use this equation we must be able to distinguish between internal forces and external forces. To do this we mentally *isolate* the system, and draw a force diagram showing only forces acting *on* the system, *not* forces that the system exerts on some other system, and *not* internal forces.

In order to illustrate the isolation of a system, and the use of force diagrams, it will be instructive to consider a system of particles consisting of a rectangular block of metal in a variety of physical situations. We will examine the motion of this system in a frame of reference fixed to the earth, and we will assume that this is an inertial frame of reference, so that Newton's laws can be applied.

A block at rest on a table.

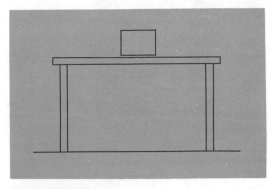

First think of the block resting on a table. The table rests on the floor, the floor is attached to the building that rests on the earth, and so on. There are all sorts of forces we could think about. The atoms in the metal block attract one another, holding the block together in a rigid structure. There are atoms in the table below the block and perhaps they are attracting the atoms in the block—or perhaps there is a repulsive force. Every particle in the universe exerts a gravitational attraction for every other particle, so the block is attracted by the table, the floor, the moon, and so on. You know that the predominant gravitational effect here is a downward force due to the earth. The block does not accelerate down because the table holds it up—and it pushes back down on the table. The air in the room exerts a force on the block, and so does any radiation falling on it. Out of the enormous array of forces acting we must pick out those that act on the block, and are not negligible.

In order to mentally isolate the block it is a good idea to make a diagram of it alone, because if we try to put arrows representing forces on the diagram including the table there is a danger that we will include forces exerted by the block as well as those on the block.

The significant external forces that act on the particles of the block.

You know from experience (meaning experiments have shown) that the only external forces that are important here are the downward pull due to the earth's gravity, acting on all the particles in the block, and the upward force exerted by the table surface on the bottom of the block. These are not single forces, but are forces distributed over the block.

Now think of the block as a **system** of particles, and apply Newton's law $F = ma$. We are observing the block in a frame of reference fixed to the earth, and we are assuming that this is an inertial frame, so that the law can be applied. In this frame the block is at rest, so $a = 0$ and therefore $F = 0$. This tells us the resultant of the gravitational forces acting on the particles throughout the block and the contact forces across the bottom of the block is zero, and that is all. However, suppose for the moment that the table is not there. Then the block would accelerate downward with an acceleration we could measure, the acceleration g due to gravity. The only force acting is the earth's gravity which we call the weight of the block w. Then $F = w$, and $F = ma$ gives $w = mg$.

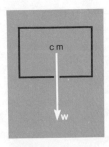

The center of mass moves as though a single force acts at this point.

The weight is distributed over the particles of the system, but remember we showed in the last chapter that **the point called the center of mass of a system moves as though all the mass of the system is at this point, and all the external forces act at this point.** Therefore for the system we can show a single force **w** acting at the center of mass. The position of the center of mass depends only on the distribution of the mass particles; we will show later how to calculate this position for solid objects.

Putting the block back on the table does not affect the force of gravity **w**, but now there is the additional force due to the table. Since all external forces can be considered to act at the center of mass, we can represent the force of the table by a single force **N** at this point. The total force $\mathbf{F} = \mathbf{N} + \mathbf{w} = m\mathbf{a} = 0$, so that $\mathbf{N} = -\mathbf{w} = -m\mathbf{g}$. The symbol **N** is used because the force is normal to the surface of the table.

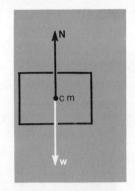

The resultant force on the block is zero.

Instead of thinking of a block resting on a table, think of the block suspended by a string. The force diagram would show the weight **w** and an equal but opposite upward force $\mathbf{T} = -\mathbf{w}$ due to the string. The symbol **T** is used for tension in the string. A spring balance in the string would measure this tension, and therefore the weight of the object. In this case the external force due to the string is not distributed over the body, but acts at a point. There is a single force, whose direction is the direction of the string. The force **T** acts at the center of mass, and therefore the center of mass will be along the line of the string, directly below the point of support. You probably recall that the **center**

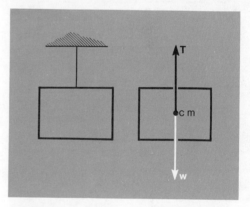

A block suspended by a string.

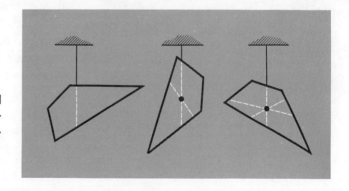

The center of gravity of a solid object can be found by suspending it in different positions.

of gravity of a solid object can be found by suspending it in different positions: it always lies on the line of suspension. The center of gravity is the point at which the total weight of the object can be considered to act as a single force. It might appear that it is identical with the center of mass, but this is not necessarily so, as we will see in a later section. In a uniform gravitational field the two points do coincide.

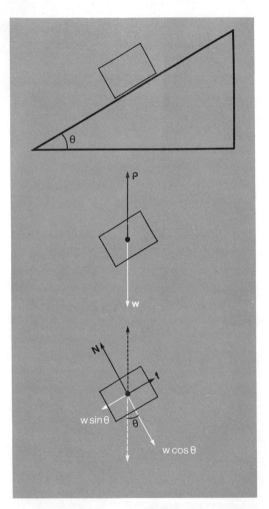

A block at rest on an inclined plane.

Now think about our system of particles, the metal block, in another situation. This time it is at rest on a non-horizontal surface, an inclined plane. The inclination of the plane, the angle it makes with horizontal, is θ. The force diagram for the block is exactly the same as in the two previous examples. There is a downward force **w**, the weight, and an equal and opposite force **P** = −**w** due to the plane. We have called the force due to the plane **P** this time, rather than **N** as in the case of horizontal plane, because here the force **P** is *not* normal to the plane. The block can be maintained at rest only if the plane can exert a force that is not perpendicular to its surface. It is sometimes convenient to think of the force **P** in terms of two components, one perpendicular to the plane called the **normal force N,** and one parallel to the plane that we will call the **frictional force f.** Of course this force may arise because the block is glued on, or nailed on, but it may simply be because of friction between the two surfaces. Note that the force diagram redrawn shows **P** dotted—remember that **P** is **replaced** by its components. It is shown dotted on the diagram only to emphasize that the diagram represents the same situation as before.

The weight **w** can also be resolved into components perpendicular and parallel to the plane, of magnitudes $w \cos \theta$, and $w \sin \theta$. The acceleration **a** of the block is zero, therefore the resultant force **F** on it is zero, and this means that the sum of the force components in any direction is zero.

$$N + w \cos \theta = 0, \qquad f + w \sin \theta = 0$$

These are really vector equations, but since the vectors in each case are in the same line, they can be treated as scalar equations. Essentially we have introduced a rectangular co-ordinate system with axes perpendicular and parallel to the plane. The third axis is in the horizontal direction, so that the axis parallel to the plane is up the plane. You will recall that in discussing vectors in Chapter 5 we pointed out that the term x-component of a vector **A** is used both for the vector $\mathbf{A}_x$ and its magnitude A_x. Equations involving components in a particular direction can be treated as scalar equations.

It is obvious that the larger the inclination of the plane the greater the force of friction required to hold the block in equilibrium, and that at some angle the block will start to slip. We will return to this situation later in discussing frictional forces, but at present will think about what happens when there is *no* frictional force. The term **smooth** is used for a surface that can exert a force only perpendicular to itself, a normal force. There is no such thing as a smooth surface, but the force of friction can be

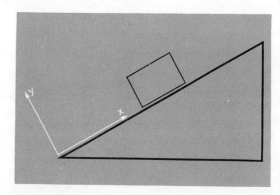

Introduction of a co-ordinate system in order to write component equations.

made quite small by lubrication with various fluids. A gas is a very effective lubricant under some conditions—you are familiar with the nearly frictionless motion of dry ice pucks, for example, where the puck floats on a thin film of carbon dioxide gas.

The metal block on a smooth inclined plane cannot be in equilibrium at rest. (It can of course be instantaneously at rest.) The equation of motion $\mathbf{F} = m\mathbf{a}$ for the system is $\mathbf{N} + \mathbf{w} = m\mathbf{a}$, where **N** is the force exerted by the plane, **w** is the weight, m is the total mass of the block, and **a** is the acceleration of the center of mass of the block. However, rather than using this general vector expression it is more useful to recognize the constraints of the physical situation. The force **N** exists only because the block is on the surface of the plane; if the block left the surface, the force **N** would vanish. We are assuming solid surfaces, so the block cannot sink into the plane. The block is constrained to move on the surface, and therefore the acceleration **a** cannot have a component perpendicular to the plane, in the y-direction. The total acceleration **a** is in the x-direction. The component equations $F_y = ma_y$ and $F_x = ma_x$ are therefore

Force diagram for a block on a smooth inclined plane.

$$N + w \cos \theta = 0 \qquad w \sin \theta = ma$$

We have already seen that the weight w is related to the mass m by $w = mg$, so that

$$mg \sin \theta = ma, \qquad a = g \sin \theta$$

The acceleration of the block does not depend on its mass. This is true whenever the accelerating force on an object is the force of gravity, because this force is proportional to the mass of the object.

TRANSLATION AND ROTATION

Now think of the metal block on the table again, but this time not completely supported. One edge of the block rests along the edge of the table. If the block is released in this position, you know that it will not remain at rest—it will fall. The force **N** exerted by the table would act at the edge, not at the center of

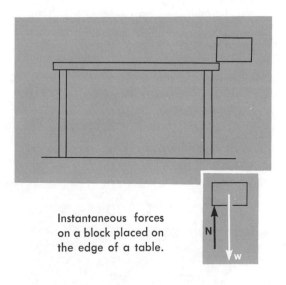

Instantaneous forces on a block placed on the edge of a table.

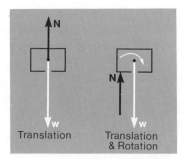

Translation   Translation & Rotation

The force **N** due to the table can be considered to act at the c-of-m as far as acceleration of the c-f-m is concerned. Since **N** does not actually act through the c-of-m, there will be rotation as well as translation produced.

mass. But did we not say earlier that all external forces can be considered to act at the center of mass? What we said (and what we showed in the last chapter) was that the center of mass *moves as though* all the external forces act at this point. As far as the acceleration of the center of mass is concerned, we *can* consider that the force **N** (as well as the weight **w**) acts at the center of mass. The resultant force **w** + **N** is not equal to zero, and will produce a downward acceleration of the center of mass. The fact that the force **N** does not actually act through the center of mass means that the block will start to **rotate** as well. There will be **angular** acceleration about the center of mass as well as linear acceleration (usually just the acceleration) of the center of mass.

The motion of any system of particles in a frame of reference can be thought of as a combination of translation and rotation. In a previous chapter we described the motion of a rolling wheel, for example, and using transformation of the frame of reference showed that the rolling motion could be described by

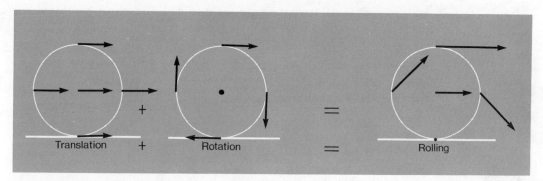

Translation   +   Rotation   =   Rolling

The motion of a rolling wheel can be considered a combination of pure translation and pure rotation.

assuming that every particle of the wheel was moving in pure translation, and additionally assuming that every particle is moving in pure rotation around the center of the wheel. This particular example illustrates the general point: that all motions of systems of particles can be considered translation plus rotation.

In describing the motion of an individual particle the distinction between translation and rotation does not arise, and in this chapter we will restrict ourselves to the motion of individual particles, or to systems of particles where the path of each particle in the frame of reference is the same, that is to systems in **pure translation.** We know how to determine the motion of the center of mass of a system, and we are going to consider at present only situations where the motion of all particles in the system is the same as the motion of its center of mass.

So far the system to which we have applied Newton's law has been a block of metal. In reality this is a complex system of billions of interacting atoms, but we can think of it as a simple system by using the idealization of a rigid body, a system of particles all at rest with respect to one another. In addition we are assuming pure translation, so that the motion of all the particles is the same.

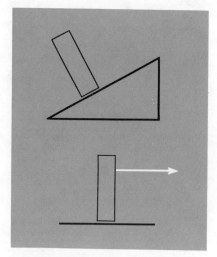

We assume pure translation.

We are not going to worry about whether a block on an inclined plane topples over rather than staying at rest or sliding down the plane, or whether a string attached to a block on a table upsets the block rather than moving it in pure translation. This section is really restricted to what is called **particle dynamics,** even though we use systems of particles in the examples, because we *assume* the same motion for all the particles of the system. Later we will see that whenever the resultant external force on a system acts through the center of mass, pure translational acceleration results. If the resultant force does not act through the center of mass there is both translational and rotational acceleration, although as we have shown the center of mass is always accelerated as though the resultant force acted at this point.

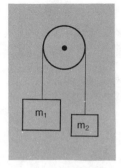

Two masses suspended by an ideal string passing over an ideal pulley.

ISOLATION OF ELEMENTS OF A SYSTEM

Now think about a situation in which two objects of masses m_1 and m_2 are suspended at the ends of a string passing over a pulley free to rotate about a fixed horizontal axle. The objects may be thought of as particles, or as blocks of finite dimensions. We assume that the string is inextensible and perfectly flexible, that the masses of the string and pulley are negligible, and that the pulley is frictionless. None of these conditions is ever completely fulfilled, but this is our model. We could equally well think of the string passing over a smooth (frictionless) horizontal peg. For convenience we will think of the situation where $m_1 > m_2$.

What happens if the masses are released from rest? You know that the heavier mass will accelerate downward and the lighter mass will accelerate upward. You might be tempted to say that there is an unbalanced force ($m_1g - m_2g$), the difference in weights of the objects, acting on a total mass ($m_1 + m_2$) producing an acceleration

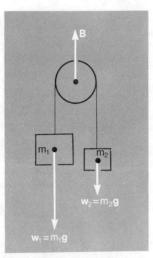

Force diagram for the pulley–string–masses system.

$$a = \left(\frac{m_1 - m_2}{m_1 + m_2}\right) g$$

of the system. But what system is this the acceleration of? It is the magnitude of the upward acceleration of m_2, and of the downward acceleration of m_1, but it is *not* the acceleration of the center of mass of the system consisting of m_1 and m_2. Can we think of m_1 and m_2 as a system of particles? You can see that this is difficult because of the effect of the string: considering the two masses as a system the tension in the string is an **internal** force, but the pulley exerts forces on the string, and how do we take this into account? In order for the forces in the string to be internal forces, we will have to take as the system the masses and string and pulley together. The external forces on this system are the two weights $w_1 = m_1g$ and $w_2 = m_2g$ acting downward and the upward force **B** exerted by the axle holding the pulley. Do we know the magnitude of the force **B**? If we supported the pulley axle by a spring balance, what would its reading be? Would it read the total weight $w_1 + w_2$?

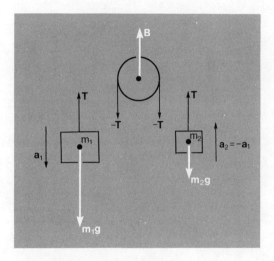

If the two blocks weighed 10 lb and 6 lb, would the balance read 16 lb? Perhaps you can see that it would not. As the larger mass moves down, the smaller mass moves up the same distance, so the center of mass of the system (the "mass-weighted average position") moves down. The center of mass of the system is accelerating downward, and therefore the resultant force $(\mathbf{B} + \mathbf{w_1} + \mathbf{w_2})$ is not zero, and the magnitude of the force **B** is not the total weight. In order to determine **B** we must look at the total system more closely, that is, consider it made up of simpler systems. Separate force diagrams for the pulley and the two masses are shown. The effect of the massless string is to transfer force unchanged from one point to another; the tension acts upward on both masses, and down on both sides of the pulley. If we use **T** to designate the upward force on each mass, the force on each side of the pulley is $-\mathbf{T}$.

Individual force diagrams for the pulley and the two masses.

We will write the equations describing the motions of these systems both in vector form, in which the sign (direction) is automatically included, and later in a form involving only magnitudes. The equation $\mathbf{F} = m\mathbf{a}$ applied to the three systems gives

$$\mathbf{B} + 2(-\mathbf{T}) = 0$$
$$\mathbf{T} + m_1\mathbf{g} = m_1\mathbf{a_1}$$
$$\mathbf{T} + m_2\mathbf{g} = m_2\mathbf{a_2}$$

Because the masses are connected together by the inextensible string passing over the pulley, their accelerations are equal in magnitude but opposite in direction: $\mathbf{a_2} = -\mathbf{a_1}$. Combining this condition with the last two force equations to eliminate **T** and $\mathbf{a_2}$ gives

$$m_1\mathbf{g} - m_2\mathbf{g} = m_1\mathbf{a_1} + m_2\mathbf{a_1} \qquad \text{or} \qquad \mathbf{a_1} = \left(\frac{m_1 - m_2}{m_1 + m_2}\right)\mathbf{g}$$

The acceleration of m_1 is in the same direction as $\mathbf{g}$ if $m_1 > m_2$, in the opposite direction if $m_1 < m_2$.

The force $\mathbf{T}$ can be found from either force equation

$$\mathbf{T} = m_1\mathbf{a}_1 - m_1\mathbf{g} = m_1\left(\frac{m_1 - m_2}{m_1 + m_2}\right)\mathbf{g} - \mathbf{g} = -\left(\frac{2m_1m_2}{m_1 + m_2}\right)\mathbf{g}$$

or $\quad \mathbf{T} = m_2\mathbf{a}_2 - m_2\mathbf{g} = m_2\left(-\frac{m_1 - m_2}{m_1 + m_2}\right)\mathbf{g} - \mathbf{g} = -\left(\frac{2m_1m_2}{m_1 + m_2}\right)\mathbf{g}$

This force is in the opposite direction to $\mathbf{g}$.

From the force equation for the pulley

$$\mathbf{B} = 2\mathbf{T} = -\left(\frac{4m_1m_2}{m_1 + m_2}\right)\mathbf{g}$$

again an upward force.

We can now return to the larger system, made up of the masses and string and pulley, where the tension in the string is an internal force. The total force $(\mathbf{B} + m_1\mathbf{g} + m_2\mathbf{g})$ can be considered to act on the total mass $(m_1 + m_2)$ at the center of mass, giving it an acceleration $\mathbf{a}_c$.

$$\mathbf{a}_c = \frac{\mathbf{B} + m_1\mathbf{g} + m_2\mathbf{g}}{m_1 + m_2} = \left(-\frac{4m_1m_2}{m_1 + m_2}\mathbf{g} + m_1\mathbf{g} + m_2\mathbf{g}\right)/(m_1 + m_2)$$

$$= \left(\frac{m_1 - m_2}{m_1 + m_2}\right)^2\mathbf{g}$$

There is a downward acceleration of the center of mass of the system, of magnitude different from the acceleration of either mass. For this situation there is no reason to be interested in $\mathbf{a}_c$; all of the measurable forces and accelerations have already been calculated. We have focused attention on $\mathbf{a}_c$ in order to emphasize that, while we may speak of "the system of two masses," this is *not* a system that can be isolated in order to apply Newton's law.

If the masses are equal, $m_1 = m_2 = m$, then

$$\mathbf{a}_1 = 0 \qquad \mathbf{a}_2 = 0 \qquad \mathbf{a}_c = 0 \qquad T = mg \qquad B = 2mg$$

These values apply whether the masses are at rest, or are moving uniformly.

If the masses are $m_1 = 10$ lb, $m_2 = 6$ lb, then

$$a_1 = \left(\frac{10 - 6}{10 + 6}\right)g = \tfrac{1}{4}g = 8 \text{ ft/sec}^2 \qquad \text{:using } g = 32 \text{ ft/sec}^2$$

$$T = \left(\frac{2 \times 6 \times 10}{10 + 6}\right)g = 7.5g$$

$$= 7.5 \times 32 \text{ lb-ft/sec}^2 = 240 \text{ pndl}$$

$$= 7.5 \text{ pd}$$

$$B = 2T = 480 \text{ pndl} = 15 \text{ pd}$$

$$a_c = (\tfrac{1}{4})^2g = 2 \text{ ft/sec}^2$$

We assumed that the pulley was of negligible mass. If we do not make this assumption, we cannot assume that the tension in the string on both sides is the same because an unbalanced force is required to accelerate the particles of mass in the pulley. This motion can best be described in terms of angular acceleration, as we saw in discussing the kinematics of rotation. We will return to the dynamics of rotation.

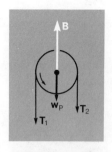

We gave a vector discussion in this example, in which the directions of the various forces and accelerations are automatically included. This is a one-dimensional situation, and the vector description is essentially a scalar description because all components are in the same direction.

An alternative approach to examples of this kind is to write the equations of motion for the **magnitudes** only. This means that **we assume we know the directions of the forces and accelerations.** These are indicated on the diagrams. The symbol T now represents the magnitude of the tension in the string, the symbol a represents the magnitude of the acceleration of m_1 and of m_2.

If the pulley is not of negligible mass, $T_1 \neq T_2$, and $B \neq T_1 + T_2$.

The equations relating magnitudes are

$$B - 2T = 0 \qquad m_1g - T = m_1a \qquad T - m_2g = m_2a$$

and these three equations can be solved to give the three unknown quantities a, T and B as before.

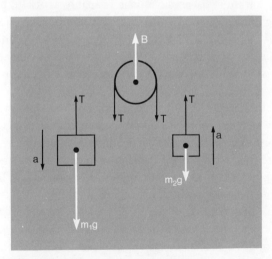

Force diagrams with vectors labelled by their magnitudes only.

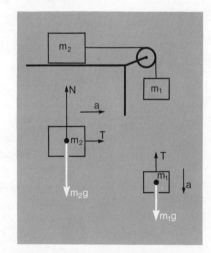

Force diagrams for two blocks moving at right angles to one another.

One reason this approach is useful is that the effect of strings passing around pulleys is to make essentially one-dimensional situations out of what appear to be two-dimensional ones. Think of a mass m_1 suspended by a string passing over a pulley to pull horizontally on a mass m_2 at rest on a smooth table. Naturally the string is inextensible and massless, the pulley frictionless and massless.

Force diagrams for the two masses show the tension T acting on each of them, horizontally on m_2 and vertically on m_1. We *cannot* label both these vectors **T** because they are identical only in magnitude, not in direction. Similarly the accelerations of the masses are the same in magnitude, but at right angles to one another.

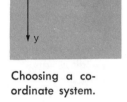

Choosing a co-ordinate system.

It is possible to give a vector description here by using the component relations $F_x = ma_x$, $F_y = ma_y$ for each mass, but we must proceed carefully because of the effect of the string coupling the masses. The component equations apply to a particular choice of co-ordinate system. For m_2 the tension force has a component T only in the x-direction, and the acceleration a component $a_2 = a$ in the same direction. If for m_1 we consider that the acceleration has a component $a_1 = a$ in the y-direction, we must say that the tension force has a component $-T$ in the y-direction. The equations are

	$F_x = ma_x$	$F_y = ma_y$
For m_2:	$T = m_2 a$	$N + m_2 g = 0$
For m_1:	$0 = 0$	$m_1 g + (-T) = m_1 a$

These equations can be solved to give a, T and N in terms of masses m_1 and m_2.

While this method of attack is possible, it is probably as useful to take an approach using magnitudes only. In this case the component equations of motion are $T = m_2 a$, $N - m_2 g = 0$, $m_1 g - T = m_1 a$. The only difference is in the second one: the component equation $N + m_2 g = 0$ *shows* that the forces **N** and m_2**g** are equal but in opposite directions. The magnitude equation $N - m_2 g = 0$ *assumes* that the forces are in opposite directions. This may appear to be a trivial difference, but it is important in attacking any problem to know what different approaches are possible, and what approach you are using. The question of sign may seem insignificant, but it sometimes seems that physicists spend more time trying to get the sign right than anything else.

The motions being described in these examples are in one sense linear motions, because each mass moves in a straight line. If we think of the two masses as moving in the same line, because of the string they have equal accelerations, but the string exerts equal and opposite forces on them. The effect of the pulley is to change the direction of the force between them and this leads to difficulty in using a vector approach.

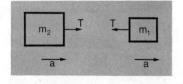

A situation may be described in linear terms even though it is not one-dimensional.

A third example of masses coupled by a string will further illustrate the point. Here m_2 is on a smooth inclined plane, and the string exerting a force on it is parallel to the plane. In order to write component equations, we must choose a co-ordinate system. As far as m_1 is concerned a co-ordinate system with one axis vertical is best, but as far as m_2 is concerned the most appropriate system has axes parallel and perpendicular to the plane. Rather than try to work in a single system, or to relate the signs in the two systems, we write separate component equations in the appropriate system for each mass, using magnitudes only.

We do not know whether the coupled masses will accelerate to the left or the right—this will depend on their relative size and the slope θ. We assume a particular direction, and write the magnitude equations on the basis of this assumption. For example, assume that the acceleration is to the right, meaning that $m_1 g > T$ and $T > m_2 g \sin \theta$. The magnitude component equations are, then

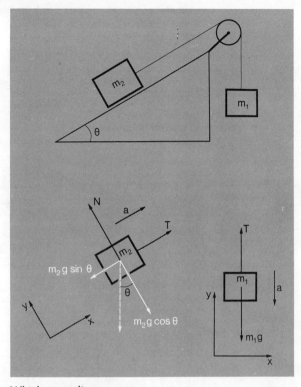

Which co-ordinate system should be used here?

$$N - m_2 g \cos \theta = 0$$
$$T - m_2 g \sin \theta = m_2 a$$
$$m_1 g - T = m_1 a$$

Adding the last two relations, $a = (m_1 - m_2 \sin \theta)/(m_1 + m_2)g$. This will be positive if $m_1 > m_2 \sin \theta$, and the acceleration will be in the assumed direction. If $m_1 < m_2 \sin \theta$ the value of a will be negative, indicating acceleration in the opposite direction. Choosing a direction of motion is equivalent to calling a particular co-ordinate direction positive in a one-dimensional situation.

Example: As a final example of the importance of isolating the elements of a complex system, so that Newton's law can be applied, think of the rather wild system made up of three masses connected by the strings and pulleys shown. One pulley rotates about a fixed axle, the

Will mass 2m accelerate upward or downward?

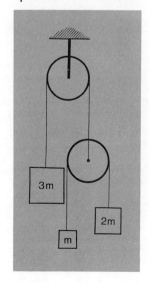

other has its axle suspended at the end of a string. To simplify the algebra we use masses in the ratio 1 : 2 : 3 rather than three masses of arbitrary size. If this system is released from rest it will start to accelerate: the mass $2m$ will start downward, and the mass m upward. This means that the gravitational force on the suspended pulley due to these masses will be less than $3mg$, so that the mass $3m$ will accelerate downward, causing the suspended pulley to accelerate upward, thus changing the accelerations of m and $2m$ relative to the earth frame of reference. All of this will take place instantaneously—there are constant forces on the system, due to gravity and the support of the fixed pulley, and the accelerations will be constant. What are the accelerations? Will mass $2m$ accelerate upward or downward in the earth frame?

We assume that the strings and pulleys are massless and frictionless, so that the magnitude of the tension is the same throughout each string, and label these T_1 for the upper string and T_2 for the lower string. The accelerations of m, $2m$ and $3m$ relative to the earth frame have magnitudes a_1, a_2 and a_3. We assume that these accelerations are in the direction indicated, a_3 downward, a_1 and a_2 upward.

The equations of motion for the three masses using these magnitudes are

$$3mg - T_1 = 3ma_3$$
$$T_2 - mg = ma_1$$
$$T_2 - 2mg = 2ma_2$$

These 3 conditions are not sufficient for a solution for the 5 unknown quantities T_1, T_2, a_1, a_2, a_3. However there are two further relations between these quantities. From the force diagram for the suspended pulley of zero mass, $T_1 = 2T_2$. Considering the relation between the accelerations of three points on this pulley gives a relation between them. The center of the pulley has an acceleration $\mathbf{a}_3$, the point on the left side has acceleration $\mathbf{a}_1$, the same as m, and the point on the right side has acceleration $\mathbf{a}_2$, the same as $2m$. Now think of a frame of reference S' accelerating upward with acceleration $\mathbf{a}_3$. In this frame of reference the motion of the pulley is pure rotation about its center. The left side will have an acceleration $\mathbf{a}_1'$, the right side an acceleration $\mathbf{a}_2' = -\mathbf{a}_1'$. We showed in Chapter 8 that the acceleration transformation between two frames S and S' is $\mathbf{a} = \mathbf{a}' + \mathbf{A}$, where $\mathbf{A}$ is the acceleration of frame S' relative to S. In the earth frame of reference S, then

$$\mathbf{a}_1 = \mathbf{a}_1' + \mathbf{a}_3$$
$$\mathbf{a}_2 = \mathbf{a}_2' + \mathbf{a}_3 = -\mathbf{a}_1' + \mathbf{a}_3$$

Adding these

$$\mathbf{a}_1 + \mathbf{a}_2 = 2\mathbf{a}_3$$

Force diagrams (using magnitudes) for the three masses and the moving pulley.

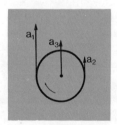

Accelerations of points on the moving pulley in the earth frame of reference.

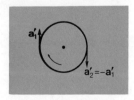

Accelerations of points on the moving pulley in the frame in which its motion is pure rotation.

This vector result is valid no matter what the directions of the accelerations are. The relation between their **magnitudes** depends on the directions assumed. With the directions we have assumed the relation is $a_1 + a_2 = 2a_3$. (If instead we had assumed that mass $2m$ accelerated downward, the relation would be $a_1 - a_2 = 2a_3$.)

There are now 5 relations between the 5 unknown quantities. A little algebra will yield

$$a_1 = \tfrac{7}{17}g \qquad a_2 = -\tfrac{5}{17}g \qquad a_3 = \tfrac{1}{17}g$$
$$T_1 = \tfrac{48}{17}mg \qquad T_2 = \tfrac{24}{17}mg$$

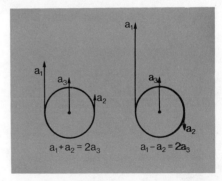

For both cases
$$\mathbf{a}_1 + \mathbf{a}_2 = 2\mathbf{a}_3.$$

The fact that a_2 comes out as a negative number shows that our assumption about its direction was wrong; mass $2m$ actually accelerates downward. The point is that if we make a set of initial assumptions that are consistent with the physical situation (we could not for example assume that all three masses accelerated downward) then any errors made will show up in the results.

Note that the concept of center of mass of the system as a whole is not particularly useful here. What is the acceleration of the center of mass of this system?

CENTER OF MASS

We introduced the concept of center of mass of a system of particles in the last chapter, and discussed its importance in applying Newton's laws to the system. In this chapter we have applied Newton's laws to determine the motion of a block of metal acted upon by the force of gravity in an assortment of different situations. We determined what would happen to the center of mass of the block in each example, and assumed that all the particles in the block would have the same motion. Therefore we were treating the block as a rigid body, a system of particles all at rest with respect to one another.

The center of mass of any system of particles, whether in a rigid body or not, depends only on the masses and relative positions of the particles; we described it as the mass-weighted average position. If the particles are all moving with respect to one another, the position of the center of mass must be specified with respect to some other frame of reference, but if the particles are at rest with respect to one another, as in a rigid body, the position of the center of mass can be specified with respect to the particles themselves.

Example: Think of four masses m, $2m$, $3m$, $4m$ fixed at the corners of a square of side length d. Where is the c-of-m of this system of particles?

The definition of the location of the c-of-m is

$$\mathbf{R}_c = \frac{\sum m_i \mathbf{r}_i}{\sum m_i}$$

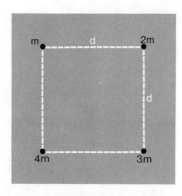

Where is the c-of-m?

relating the displacement $\mathbf{R}_c$ of the c-of-m to the displacements $\mathbf{r}_i$ of the particles, all displacements referred to the same fixed point in some frame of reference. Like all vector relations this is equivalent to three scalar relations, the particular scalar relations depending on the choice of co-ordinate system. The co-ordinates of the c-of-m are

$$X_c = \sum m_i x_i / \sum m_i$$
$$Y_c = \sum m_i y_i / \sum m_i$$
$$Z_c = \sum m_i z_i / \sum m_i$$

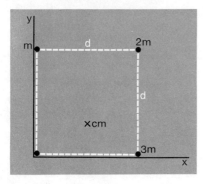

Choosing a suitable co-ordinate system.

A co-ordinate system is chosen in such a way as to simplify the calculation in any particular situation. For the four masses at the corners of a square, the simplest choice is a co-ordinate system with origin at one corner of the square. With the choice shown, the co-ordinates of the masses m, $2m$, $3m$, $4m$ are $(0,d)$, (d,d), $(d,0)$ and $(0,0)$. The c-of-m is at the point (X_c, Y_c) where

$$X_c = \frac{2md + 3md}{m + 2m + 3m + 4m} = \tfrac{1}{2}d$$

$$Y_c = \frac{md + 2md}{10m} = \tfrac{3}{10}d$$

Suppose that the four particles held at the corners of the square are released simultaneously, and are subject only to their mutual gravitational attractions. Their subsequent motion would be enormously complex to work out in detail, but we can predict that they will all end up clustered at the center of mass. This position can be specified in the frame of reference in which the particles were initially at rest.

Calculation of the center of mass of a solid, or of a confined volume of fluid, can be carried out if we make certain assumptions about the system. We know that matter is made up of atoms; if we think of the atoms as particles, the distance between these particles in normal solids and liquids is about 10^{-10} m, and even in gases under normal conditions is about 10^{-8} m, so that it is reasonable to ignore the particle structure and think of matter as a continuous medium. If we confine our attention to homogeneous matter, there will be a constant density ρ throughout the medium. Think of a volume V of matter, divided up into a large number of equal small elements of volume ΔV. Each element ΔV has the same mass $\Delta m = \rho \, \Delta V$. The displacement $\mathbf{r}_i$ of the element from a fixed point O in the frame of reference is different for different elements. (The frame of reference is the frame in which the volume V is at rest; the point O can be inside or outside the volume.) From the definition of center of mass for a system of particles, its displacement is

$$\mathbf{R}_c = \frac{\sum \Delta m \, \mathbf{r}_i}{\sum \Delta m} = \frac{\sum \rho \, \Delta V \, \mathbf{r}_i}{\sum \rho \, \Delta V} = \frac{\sum \mathbf{r}_i \, \Delta V}{\sum \Delta V}$$

where $\sum$ stands for $\sum\limits_{i=1}^{N}$, the sum as i varies from
1 to N, and N is the number of volume elements. If we think of the volume divided into smaller and smaller elements, it becomes more and more accurate to speak of "the" displacement of an element. The volume element ΔV becomes the infinitesimal volume dV, the number N increases indefinitely, and we summarize all this by the integral notation

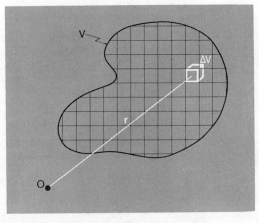

$$\mathbf{R}_c = \frac{\int \mathbf{r} \, dm}{\int dm} = \frac{\rho \int \mathbf{r} \, dV}{\rho \int dV} = \frac{\int \mathbf{r} \, dV}{\int dV}$$

Division of a volume V into equal volume elements ΔV.

where the $\int$ sign must be interpreted as "the integral over the volume V."

This vector equation is equivalent to three scalar equations. The co-ordinates of the center of mass of a homogeneous volume of matter in a particular co-ordinate system are

$$X_c = \frac{\int x \, dV}{\int dV} \qquad Y_c = \frac{\int y \, dV}{\int dV} \qquad Z_c = \frac{\int z \, dV}{\int dV}$$

where again the integration is carried out over the volume of matter.

Many objects have some sort of symmetry: symmetry with respect to a point, meaning that for every element ΔV on one side of the point there is a symmetric one on the opposite side (e.g., a sphere); symmetry with respect to a line, meaning that for every element on one side of the line there is a symmetric one on the opposite side (e.g., a cone); symmetry with respect to a plane, meaning that for every element on one side of the plane there is a symmetric one on the opposite side (e.g., a man, roughly). This means if the point O is chosen at the point, or on the line, or in the plane of symmetry, that for every contribution $\mathbf{r}_i \, \Delta V$ there will be a contribution $-\mathbf{r}_i \, \Delta V$ and therefore $\mathbf{R}_c = 0$. The center of mass will lie at the point O.

Example: Think of a solid cone. We know from symmetry that the c-of-m will lie on the axis. Where on the axis? Choose a co-ordinate system with x-axis along the cone axis, and origin at the base. We do not need to use a volume element $dV = dx \, dy \, dz$ because we know the y and z–co-ordinates of the c-of-m, $Y_c = Z_c = 0$. Instead we use

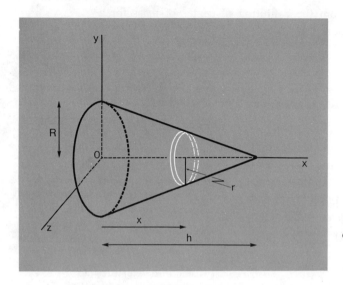

Finding the c-of-m of a solid cone.

as a volume element a uniform slice of the cone perpendicular to the x-axis, of thickness dx. The x–co-ordinate of the c-of-m is given by $X_c = \int x\, dV / \int dV$, and this integration can be performed for the volume element dV because all parts of the element, in the limit, have the same x–co-ordinate. (We really should be using ΔV and Δx instead of dV and dx here, because these elements are not infinitesimal until we integrate, but it is common in physics to use this notation.)

The radius r of this circular slice depends on its position. If the cone has a base of radius R, and height h, then

$$r = R\left(1 - \frac{x}{h}\right)$$

When $x = 0$, $r = R$; and when $x = h$, $r = 0$. As x is varied from 0 to h, the slice moves over the volume of the cone.

The volume of the slice $dV = \pi r^2\, dx$. This assumes that the slice is a cylinder of radius r and height dx, and is accurate in the limit. Using $dV = \pi r^2\, dx = \pi R^2 \left(1 - \frac{x}{h}\right)^2 dx$, the x–co-ordinate of the c-of-m is

$$X_c = \frac{\int x\, dV}{\int dV} = \frac{\pi R^2 \int_0^h x(1 - x/h)^2\, dx}{\pi R^2 \int_0^h (1 - x/h)^2\, dx}$$

Evaluation of the integrals is a mathematical operation. It may be done by consulting a table of integrals, but in this case it can be done directly because all terms are of the form $\int x^n\, dx$. For example,

$$\int_0^h (1 - x/h)^2\, dx = \int_0^h dx - \frac{2}{h}\int_0^h x\, dx + \frac{1}{h^2}\int_0^h x^2\, dx = h - \frac{2}{h}\left(\frac{h^2}{2}\right) + \frac{1}{h^2}\left(\frac{h^3}{3}\right) = \tfrac{1}{3}h$$

The volume of the cone is $V = \int dV = \frac{1}{3}\pi R^2 h$. Evaluation of $\int x\, dV$ gives $\pi R^2(h^2/12)$, and therefore

$$X_c = \frac{\pi R^2(h^2/12)}{\pi R^2(h^2/3)} = \frac{h}{4}$$

The center of mass is on the axis of the cone, one-quarter of its height above the base.

What we have calculated here is really the **centroid** of the volume of the cone. For a volume of homogeneous matter the center of mass is at the centroid of the volume. The relation $\mathbf{R}_c = \int \mathbf{r}\, dV / \int dV$ determines the position of the centroid; if the density ρ is not constant, the center of mass is given by

$$\mathbf{R}_c = \int \mathbf{r}\, dm / \int dm = \int \rho\, \mathbf{r}\, dV / \int \rho\, dV$$

It follows from the general properties of the center of mass that if a body is considered to be made up of several parts, and the locations of the c-of-m's of the parts are known (from symmetry, for example), then the c-of-m of the body as a whole can be determined by treating the parts as particles located at their respective c-of-m's. For example, the c-of-m of a thin metal bar bent into the L-shape shown can be found by thinking of it as two straight rods, one of mass twice that of the other. The c-of-m of each rod is at its geometric center. Choosing a co-ordinate system as indicated, we can think of a mass $2m$ at $(0,l)$ and a mass m at $(l/2,0)$. The c-of-m of the system is at

$$X_c = \frac{2m(0) + m(l/2)}{2m + m} = \frac{1}{6}l$$

$$Y_c = \frac{2m(l) + m(0)}{2m + m} = \frac{2}{3}l$$

It is on the line joining the centers of mass of the two parts. The center of mass of a body does not necessarily lie inside the physical structure.

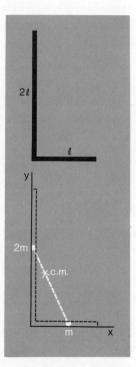

Finding the c-of-m of an L-shaped rod.

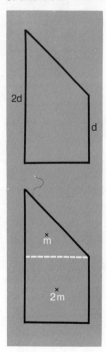

Where is the c-of-m of this metal sheet?

Similarly the center of mass of a flat sheet of metal of the shape shown can be found most easily by thinking of it as a square and a triangle whose mass is half that of the square. The c-of-m of the square is at its center, the c-of-m of the triangle is at its centroid. By thinking of particles of masses $2m$ and m at these points, the c-of-m of the plate can be determined.

CENTER OF MASS AND CENTER OF GRAVITY

We have emphasized that the location of the center of mass of a system of particles depends only on the masses and relative locations of the particles; it is a property of the **system.** Another point that can be defined for a system of particles is the center of gravity. It is not a property of the system, because it is different for the system under different external conditions. We will illustrate this point using a very simple system, an idealized dumbbell, two particles of the same mass m connected by a rigid massless rod. This simple rigid body is symmetric, and its center of mass is at the midpoint of the rod. (This model may appear to be an impractical overidealization for any real system, but it can usefully be used to represent some of the properties of a diatomic molecule.)

The center of gravity of a body is the point at which a single force, equivalent to the gravitational force acting on all the particles making up the body, can be considered to act. Think first of the dumbbell in a **uniform** gravitational field; this means a region in which the gravitational force $\mathbf{w}$ on a particle of mass m is the same at every point. The force $\mathbf{w}$ produces an acceleration $\mathbf{g}$, where $\mathbf{w} = m\mathbf{g}$, and $\mathbf{g}$ is the same at every point. In the uniform field the force $\mathbf{w}$ is the same on

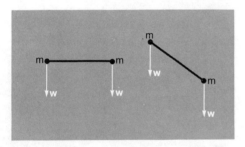

Forces on a dumbbell in a uniform gravitational field.

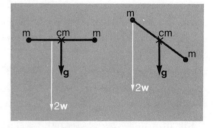

A resultant force **2w** applied at any point produces an acceleration **g** of the c-of-m.

each particle of the dumbbell, and the total force is $2\mathbf{w}$. The c-of-m of the dumbbell moves as though this force acts on the total mass $2m$ at the c-of-m, $2\mathbf{w} = 2m\mathbf{a}_c$. The acceleration of the c-of-m is $\mathbf{a}_c = \mathbf{w}/m = \mathbf{g}$. Note that this does *not* show that the center of mass is the center of gravity of the dumbbell. A single force $2\mathbf{w}$ applied *anywhere* to the dumbbell will give the same acceleration $2\mathbf{w}/2m = \mathbf{g}$ to the center of mass.

The two parallel forces $\mathbf{w}$ on the particles of the dumbbell do not produce rotation of the dumbbell. The acceleration of each particle is the same, and the dumbbell moves in pure translation. Where must a single force $2\mathbf{w}$ be considered to act in order to produce this result? We stated earlier that only if the resultant force acts at the c-of-m will there be pure translation. If we consider that there is only a single force 2w acting, it must act at the c-of-m, and therefore this by definition is the center of gravity.

Now think about the same dumbbell in a non-uniform gravitational field. Suppose, for example, the gravitational forces on the two masses at some

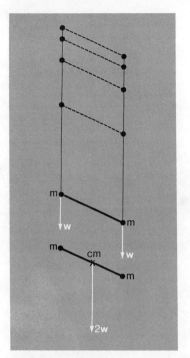

The force **2w** acts at the c-of-m because the motion is pure translation.

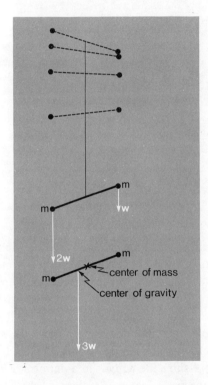

The center of mass and center of gravity do not coincide in a non-uniform field.

instant are in the same direction, but have different magnitudes, say w and 2w. The resultant force 3w will produce an acceleration $a_c = 3w/2m$ of the center of mass of the system, as though a single force 3w acted at the c-of-m. However, we cannot say that the motion is the same as though a single force 3w acted at the c-of-m, because the accelerations of the two masses are different and the system will rotate. If we think of a single force 3w that will produce the same result, it must be considered to act at a point other than the center of mass. This point would be the center of gravity. As the system moves through a non-uniform gravitational field, the forces on each particle will change and the position of the center of gravity will change. The position of this point depends on external conditions, and therefore it is not a property of the system.

You know that the gravitational field of the earth is not uniform—it varies both in magnitude and direction. As a mass is moved around the earth the force on it, directed toward the center of the earth, changes in direction. As it is moved away from the earth, the force on it decreases in magnitude. If we think of a very large dumbbell, the forces on its ends will be parallel if it is lined up with an earth radius (but will not be equal); the forces will be equal if it is perpendicular to a radius (but will not be parallel). In general they will be

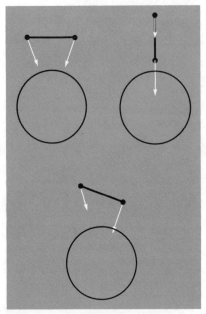

The location of the center of gravity of a large dumbbell depends on its orientation.

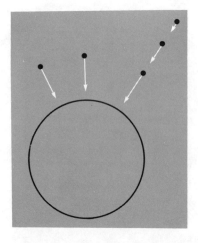

The earth's gravitational field is not uniform.

neither equal nor parallel. The position of the center of gravity will depend on the orientation of the dumbbell. For this reason the notion of a center of gravity is not a very useful one for such an object.

Most bodies are of such a size that it is reasonable to neglect the variations in the gravitational field over the region occupied by the body, that is, to assume the body is in a uniform field. Then the concept of center of gravity, as the point at which the resultant gravitational force acts, is useful but is not really necessary because in a uniform gravitational field the center of mass and center of gravity coincide. Our discussion for the dumbbell can readily be extended to a homogeneous body by considering the body to be made up of a large number of particles. The gravitational force on each particle is proportional to its mass, so the acceleration of each particle is the same, and the body accelerates in pure translation. A single force that would produce this result would have to act at the center of mass.

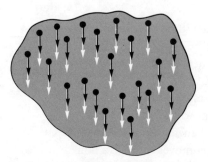

A body in a uniform gravitational field accelerates in pure translation.

A body is said to be falling freely if the only forces acting on it are the gravitational forces of the earth on the particles of the body, and we can equivalently say that the only force on it is its weight acting at its center of gravity. If a freely falling body in a uniform field is rotating, it will continue to rotate uniformly while it is in free fall. The path of its center of mass is that of a particle

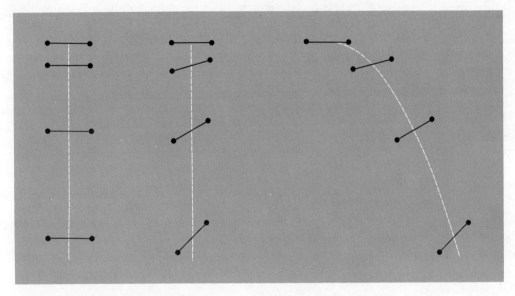

A dumbbell falling in the earth's field
with different initial conditions.

in the field, a parabola as we showed in Chapter 5. The shape of the parabola and the amount of rotation around the center of mass depend on the initial conditions of projection. The diagrams show a dumbbell (1) released from rest, (2) released from rest with an initial spin, (3) projected horizontally with the same initial spin. The positions of the dumbbell are shown for the same equal time intervals in each case.

FORCES OF CONSTRAINT

Application of Newton's law to a particle or system of particles requires mental isolation of the system in order to pick out the forces acting *on* the system. We speak of the system and of everything else, usually referred to as the **surroundings** or the **environment**. We must decide what parts of the environment exert forces on the system that are significant. While all the other particles in the universe exert a gravitational force on the system, we usually assume that for a system near the earth the only significant gravitational force is that due to the earth. There will be a specific force $\mathbf{w} = m\mathbf{g}$ on any mass m near the earth no matter what the motion of the mass is. The force of gravity is the only fundamental force that we have used in the examples in this chapter. The other forces that we have used, those exerted by table tops or strings, are sometimes called **constraint** forces. We cannot state what the value of any constraint force on a mass m will be, because it depends on the motion of mass m, that is on the constraints of the particular situation. If a block of mass m rests on a table, does the table exert a force $\mathbf{N} = -m\mathbf{g}$ on the block? It does if the table is at rest, but it does not if the table is in an elevator that is accelerating upward or downward. If

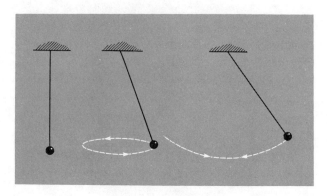

A pendulum bob hanging at rest, moving in a horizontal circle, and oscillating in a vertical plane.

the block hangs at rest at the end of a string, the string exerts a force $\mathbf{T} = -m\mathbf{g}$ on it. If the block is moving in a horizontal circle, a conical pendulum, the string exerts a force on it that is constant in magnitude, but the magnitude is not mg. If the block is swinging in a vertical plane as a pendulum the tension in the string is not constant. If the block is given a push upward, the string stops exerting an upward force on it at all. (One of the better known laws of applied physics is "you can't push a rope.")

We assume that a constraint force is as large as it needs to be to fulfill the conditions of motion assumed. A table holds a block up without collapsing or deforming at all; a string holds a block without stretching or breaking. Of course, real tables and strings do deform; these deformations are dealt with in the parts of physics called the mechanics of deformable bodies, which includes elasticity and plasticity. At present we assume perfectly rigid tables and perfectly flexible inextensible strings, and this is a good model if the forces tending to produce deformation are not too large.

Forces of constraint have their origin in the fundamental electromagnetic interaction binding the atoms in matter together, but we cannot use this fact to calculate their magnitudes—and neither do the measured values of such forces help much in determining interatomic forces. We can increase the tension in a metal wire until it breaks, but the breaking force is much too low to be directly attributable to the breaking of interatomic bonds across the area of the break.

Sometimes the term constraint force is used only for forces that are at right angles to the direction of motion of an object. As we will see when we discuss the concepts of work and energy, such forces can do no work on the object, and therefore can not change its energy. The force exerted by a table on a block sliding on the table can be thought of as having a component **N** perpendicular to the table and a component **f** parallel to the table. Only the second does work on the block, changing its energy. We will *not* restrict the term constraint force to apply only to the force **N**, as is sometimes done, because

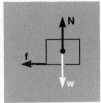

Forces acting on a block sliding on a table.

the force **f** also depends on the motion of the block: it is zero if the block is at rest, and opposes the motion if it is moving. We call it the force of friction.

It is not possible to place limitations on constraint forces in general, but it is possible to make some rough generalizations about the frictional forces that act on moving objects. Experiments show that a solid object moving through a fluid at low speed experiences a retarding force proportional to its speed, or if moving at a high speed a retarding force proportional to the square of its speed. The terms "low" and "high" depend on a number of factors. The retarding frictional force on a solid object sliding on a flat surface turns out to be independent of speed, for a very limited range of low speeds.

THE FORCE OF STATIC FRICTION

We are going to describe here the generalizations, sometimes called the laws of friction, that describe the force between two flat solid surfaces in contact. What does "flat" mean? Think of two blocks of steel with surfaces that have been machined as flat as possible with ordinary milling machines, which means that the surfaces are flat to within a few "thou"—a few thousandths of an inch, or 10^{-2} to 10^{-3} cm. Clearly such surfaces are not flat on the atomic scale, since atoms have dimensions of the order of 10^{-8} cm. By grinding and polishing the surfaces they can be made optically flat, which means that they are flat to within a few wavelengths of light, about 10^{-4} cm. There could still be hills and valleys thousands of atoms in size.

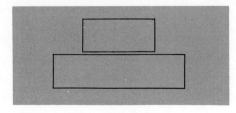

Two flat surfaces in contact. What does "flat" mean? What does "contact" mean?

If the two steel surfaces are flat on the atomic scale, the spacing between atoms across the interface would be about the same as between atoms in the metal, and therefore the forces would be comparable. Moving the surfaces relative to one another would be equivalent to shearing the metal. However, it is not possible to smooth surfaces to this extent. A diagram illustrating the surface irregularities of the best polished surfaces has a scale such that individual atoms can not be indicated. There are a few places where the two surfaces come together and the atoms adhere or weld, but the actual area of contact is much less than the apparent area. What is more, the surfaces are never really clean—there are always oxides or some other contaminant preventing contact between the pure metal surfaces, and these decrease the forces of adhesion.

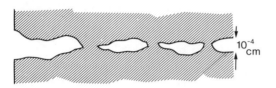

A closer look at two flat surfaces in contact.

Even so, two optically flat surfaces will stick together to some extent due to atomic adhesion. Small polished metal blocks called gauge blocks are manufactured for measuring dimensions. If these blocks are stacked together, it is very difficult to pull them apart; they must be slid apart, and the force required to slide one block off another may be much greater than the weight of the block.

You know that normally if you put two flat surfaces together you cannot detect any attraction at all; the force is negligible compared to other forces such as gravity. These are the kind of flat surfaces we mean when we speak of the laws of friction applied to two flat solid surfaces.

Think of two blocks with such flat surfaces in contact, but not pressed together by any force. What does "contact" mean? It means you push the blocks together, and feel them meet. But if they are not pressed together by any force, their actual area of contact is so small that there is a negligible force of adhesion between them. It requires zero force to pull the blocks apart, it requires zero force to slide one surface across the other.

Are the two surfaces in contact attracted to one another?

Force diagrams for a pair of blocks in contact, and for the blocks individually.

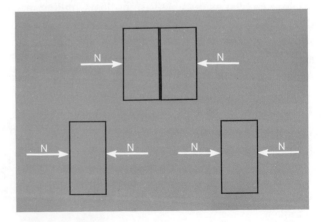

Now apply a pair of forces to push the two blocks together—forces perpendicular to the surface, or normal forces. Each force exerts a force of magnitude N on the surface of the other, so we speak of "the" normal force N as though there were only one, because we can apply Newton's laws only to a single system. For the system of two blocks, the forces exerted by the surfaces on one another is an internal force. For a single block, there is a single force N on the surface. Often the normal force exists because of the force of gravity acting to press one surface against another. However, the normal force is a constraint force. We assume that it is as large as it needs to be, and assume that the block does not collapse under it.

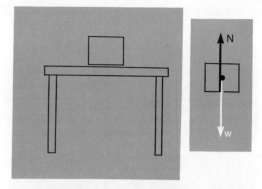

The normal force **N** exerted by the table arises because the force of gravity acts on the block, but the force of gravity is not the normal force on the block.

What happens if we try to slide one surface across the other when there is a normal force? *Because* the blocks are pushed together, a force is required—the force we call the force of friction between the surfaces. It too is a constraint force, because it is as large as it needs to be—up to a point. If we apply a small force F horizontally to a block on a table, the block will remain motionless due to the force of friction f. If F is increased, f increases, and the block still does

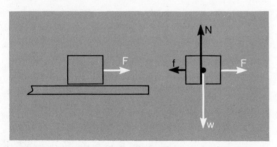

The force of friction **f** depends on the normal force **N** and on the applied force **F**.

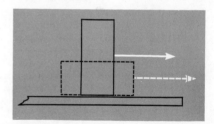

Does the frictional force depend on the area of contact?

not move. However, we cannot increase F indefinitely and have the block remain at rest. The force of friction that will hold the block in static equilibrium has a limiting value f_s. It is clear that this limiting value will depend in some way on the normal force N, since if $N = 0, f_s = 0$. It might also be expected to depend on the area of contact between the two surfaces. Doubling the area of contact for the same normal force would decrease the pressure between the surfaces, and this might be expected to decrease the frictional force—or would the increased area mean more frictional force?

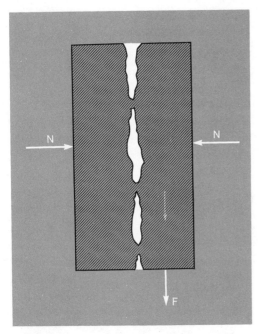

The actual area of contact is approximately proportional to the normal force.

Experiments have shown that for a reasonable range of conditions it can be assumed that f_s is independent of area of contact, and directly proportional to N. This can be understood to some extent by thinking of trying to move the two craggy surfaces past one another on the microscopic scale. The actual area of contact is very small but it will increase as the normal force is increased.

When the surfaces are being pressed together any attempt to slide one on the other brings high spots together—there will be hooking of these peaks as well as some adhesion. If motion is to take place the peaks will have to be sheared off. The process will be complex, but roughly it can be said that the limiting force of friction will be proportional to the actual area of contact, and this area will be proportional to the normal force. The apparent area of contact (the area of the block) does not matter.

THE FORCE OF KINETIC FRICTION

Once motion has been started the force necessary to maintain it at constant speed usually seems to be less; the limiting force of static friction f_s is usually less than the force of kinetic friction f_k between the surfaces once the initial adhesive forces have been overcome.

The force of kinetic friction, like the limiting force of static friction, turns out experimentally to be proportional to the normal force and independent of the area in contact. We will also assume that it is independent of the relative speeds of the two surfaces, although this is only valid for a very limited range of quite low speeds.

These results mean that we can introduce two dimensionless quantities μ_s and μ_k as proportionality constants relating f_s, f_k and N.

$$f_s = \mu_s N$$
$$f_k = \mu_k N$$

These are called the coefficients of static and kinetic friction. Their values depend on the particular pair of surfaces in contact. Like a coefficient of restitution, a coefficient of friction is a joint physical property of a pair of substances.

However, it depends not only on what the substances are, but also on the conditions such as flatness and cleanliness of the surfaces. For metal surfaces machined flat and very clean μ_s can be ~ 0.7, but oxides form rapidly on metals cutting this value in half. For most dry smooth surfaces the coefficients are in the range 0.2–0.5.

Use of the coefficients of friction, either as known experimental numbers or as undetermined constants, enables us to relate the constraint forces we have called normal forces and frictional forces. A surface exerts "a force" on an object, but it is convenient to think of this as two components, one perpendicularly outward from the surface and one parallel to the surface and opposing the motion of the object. Note that the force of static friction is a force between 0 and f_s (as large as it needs to be) in the opposite direction to the direction in which other forces are trying to move the object, and the force of kinetic friction f_k is a force in the opposite direction to the motion of the object. The magnitude and direction of both depend on the particular situation.

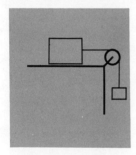

Using a steadily increasing force F to measure f_s and f_k.

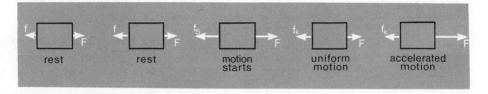

| rest | rest | motion starts | uniform motion | accelerated motion |

Measurement of the coefficients for a block on a surface can be done by applying a steadily increasing horizontal force F, for example by passing a string over a pulley and adding weights. As F increases, f increases, and the block stays at rest. When $F = f_s$, the block starts to move, and it is necessary to decrease F to have it move with constant velocity. This gives f_k. As F increases the unbalanced force of magnitude $(F - f_k)$ produces acceleration of the block. Note that the force F is *not* the weight of the suspended mass if the system is accelerating. (See also diagram top next page.)

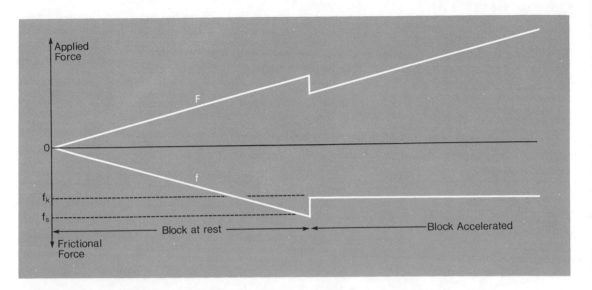

The relation between the applied force F and the frictional force.

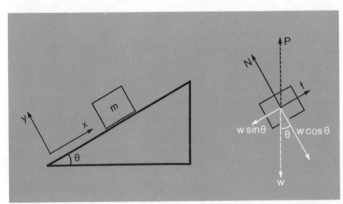

Forces on a block at rest on an inclined plane.

In an earlier section we looked at a block at rest on an inclined plane and pointed out that it was useful to think of the force P exerted by the plane in terms of the two components N and f. In terms of *magnitudes* the component equations $F_x = ma_x$ and $F_y = ma_y$ give $f = w \sin \theta$, $N = w \cos \theta$. Therefore $f/N = \tan \theta$, but this is *not* a coefficient of friction. As the plane angle θ is increased, the normal force decreases and the frictional force increases. At some angle θ_s the block starts to slip. The frictional force f has reached its limiting value f_s. Since $\mu_s = f_s/N = \tan \theta_s$, the plane angle gives the coefficient directly.

At the angle θ_s the block may accelerate down the plane. By decreasing the plane angle a little, an angle θ_k may be found such that if the block is started down the plane with an initial push, it moves down at constant velocity. The equilibrium equations again apply, and therefore $\mu_k = f_k/N = \tan \theta_k$.

Example: Determine the subsequent motion for the system shown. The blocks are initially moving at 4 ft/sec in the direction indicated.

We assume that the string and pulley are ideal, so that there is the same tension T throughout the string. We draw force diagrams for each mass isolated separately, showing the magnitudes of the forces. The angle 37° has the advantage that its sine and cosine are approximately 0.6 and 0.8 (the smaller angle in a 3:4:5 triangle is about 37°). The components of the weight of the 10-lb block perpendicular and parallel to the plane are then $10 \cos \theta = 8$ lb, $10 \sin \theta = 6$ lb. This time we will express all forces in pounds: the symbol T stands for the magnitude of the tension in pounds. There is no acceleration perpendicular to the plane, so the normal force exerted by the plane is equal and opposite to the 8-lb component of the weight; $N = 8$ lb. The block is moving, so the force of kinetic friction $f_k = \mu_k N = 1.6$ lb opposes the motion. We show the frictional force at the surface of the block, but remember we are assuming pure translation and therefore are interested only in the effect of all forces as though they were applied at the center of mass.

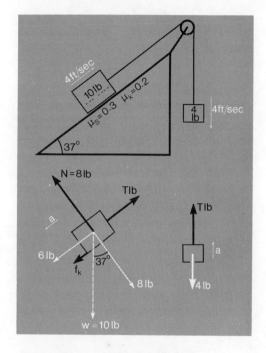

The direction chosen for the acceleration does not matter, as long as we are consistent, but it is worthwhile to try to determine the direction it actually is. If the system was at rest, the tension T would be 4 lb, less than the 6-lb component of weight acting down the plane, so we assume an acceleration in the direction down the plane, in the opposite direction to the motion.

The magnitude equations $F = ma$ for each body, with these assumptions, are

Given initial conditions of motion, to find the subsequent motion.

$$(6 + 1.6 - T)g = 10a \qquad (T - 4)g = 4a$$

The factor $g\,(= 32 \text{ ft/sec}^2)$ converts the unbalanced force in pounds to poundals. Adding these equations

$$3.6g = 14a \qquad a = \frac{1.8}{7}g = 8.2 \text{ ft/sec}^2$$

This is a uniform acceleration in the opposite direction to the initial speed of 4 ft/sec. The system will come to rest in a distance

$$s = \frac{v^2 - v_0^2}{2a} = \frac{0 - 4^2}{-2 \times 8.2} = 0.97 \text{ ft}$$

The system comes to rest after moving about 1 ft. Note that the 4-lb mass is moving downward but accelerating upward. The tension in the string was $T = 4 + 4(a/g) = 4 + 4(1.8/7) = 5.0$ lb.

As long as the forces on the system remain the same, the acceleration is constant. However, the blocks do not start to move in the opposite direction with the same acceleration because one of the forces is friction, and this force always opposes the motion.

If the 10-lb block is moving down the plane, the friction force acts up the plane, and the magnitude equations would be

$$(6 - 1.6 - T)g = 10a \qquad (T - 4)g = 4a$$

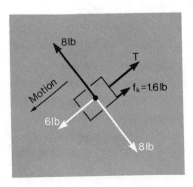

The force of friction always opposes the motion.

giving a different acceleration than when the motion is up the plane. While this would be the acceleration if the system is started down the plane, it is *not* the acceleration here. The blocks come instantaneously to rest —there is no relative motion of the surfaces of the plane and the 10-lb block, and therefore the appropriate force of friction is that of static friction f. The limiting force of static friction is $f_s = \mu_s N = 0.3 \times 8 = 2.4$ lb, but this is *not* the force acting; the force of static friction is only as large as it needs to be. The system will remain at rest with the tension $T = 4$ lb (supporting the 4-lb mass at rest) and a force of friction up the plane on the 10-lb block of $f = 2$ lb.

The block comes to rest and stays in equilibrium.

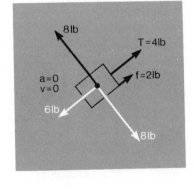

Care must be taken in such a situation not to put $f_s = 2.4$ lb as a force on the system. A little thought will show the sort of inconsistencies that would develop: a force of 2.4 lb up the plane would produce acceleration and motion up the plane, but then the force of friction would act down the plane.

Note that when we refer to the direction of the force of friction this is the direction of the force **on the block.** There will always be a force **on the plane** in the opposite direction. When the system is at rest there is a 2-lb force of friction acting on the plane, down the plane.

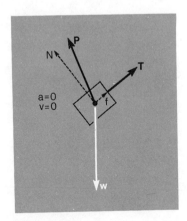

Which forces are forces of constraint?

Note also that the total force exerted by the plane on the 10-lb block is $f + N = P$, a force not equal and opposite to the weight **w**. The block is in equilibrium under forces exerted by three agencies: the force of gravity **w**, the force of the plane **P** and the force of the string **T**. The force of gravity is a fundamental force whose value depends on the mass of the block, not on its motion. The other two are constraint forces that adjust themselves to the constraints of the situation, in this case so that **w** + **P** + **T** = 0.

THE LAWS OF FRICTION

The laws of friction enable us to relate the constraint forces exerted by surfaces, and put certain limitations on them. The laws apply to flat hard surfaces in contact, and may be summarized thus:

1. The force of friction always opposes relative motion of the two surfaces.
2. The force of static friction f varies in magnitude from zero to a maximum f_s: $0 \leq f \leq f_s$.
3. The force of kinetic friction f_k is independent of the relative speed of the surfaces, and may be less than f_s; $f_k \leq f_s$.
4. Both f_s and f_k are proportional to the normal force N pushing the surfaces together, independent of the apparent area of contact. Therefore $f_s = \mu_s N$, $f_k = \mu_k N$, where the coefficients μ_s and μ_k are constant for a particular pair of surfaces.

The laws of friction are sometimes referred to as empirical laws, in contrast to more basic laws such as Newton's laws of motion or of gravitation. Since we regard all the laws of physics as empirical, in the sense that they all have their origin in experiment, we prefer not to make the distinction on this basis, but rather on the basis of range of validity. The laws of friction have a very limited range of validity, while $\mathbf{F} = m\mathbf{a}$ forms the basis of a whole system of mechanics having an enormous range of validity.

FRICTIONAL FORCE IN A FLUID

We have assumed that the force of kinetic friction between solid surfaces is independent of the relative velocity of the surfaces. This is a useful approximation because it enables us to analyze situations that would otherwise be difficult; a block sliding down an inclined plane will have a constant acceleration if the force of friction is constant, otherwise it will not.

It is more realistic to recognize that in general frictional forces **do** depend on velocity. If the velocity dependence is known, then it is possible to analyze the motion. It was mentioned earlier as an experimental fact that an object moving through a fluid at relatively low speeds experiences a retarding force proportional to its speed. We will consider an example with this assumption.

Example: Think of a particle of mass m that falls from rest under the attractive force of gravity mg, and that is acted on by a retarding force proportional to its speed v. We wish to find its speed as a function of time t.

At the initial instant it starts to fall, $t = 0$, the force of gravity, mg, produces a downward acceleration $a = g$. Once it starts to move, however, there will be a retarding force kv, where k is a constant, and the equation of motion in the vertical direction is $mg - kv = ma = m \dfrac{dv}{dt}$.

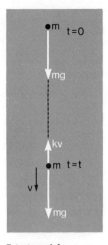

Frictional force on
a particle moving
in a fluid.

The change in speed dv in a time interval dt is given by

$$\frac{m\,dv}{mg - kv} = dt \qquad \text{so} \qquad \int_0^v \frac{m\,dv}{mg - kv} = \int_0^t dt$$

Over a finite time interval $0 \to t$, the speed will change from $0 \to v$. The integration is a mathematical step and we could state the result, but since it is a form which is common we will look at the details.

The basic integral we need was worked out in Chapter 2, and can be found in any table of integrals.

$$\int \left(\frac{1}{x}\right) dx = \ln x + \text{a constant}$$

The integral involving v can be put in this form by multiplying by $(-k/m)$. The denominator is $mg - kv = x$, and the numerator becomes $-k\,dv = dx$.

$$\int_0^v \frac{-k\,dv}{mg - kv} = -\frac{k}{m} \int_0^t dt$$

$$[\ln (mg - kv)]_0^v = -\frac{k}{m}\,[t]_0^t \qquad \ln (mg - kv) - \ln mg = -kt/m$$

$$\ln \frac{mg - kv}{mg} = -\frac{k}{m}\,t \qquad \frac{mg - kv}{mg} = e^{-(k/m)t}$$

Here we have used

$$\ln y = \log_e y = N, \qquad y = e^N$$

$$1 - \frac{kv}{mg} = e^{-(k/m)t}$$

or finally

$$v = \frac{mg}{k}\,(1 - e^{-(k/m)t})$$

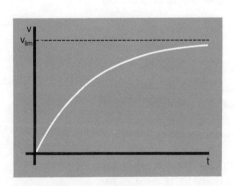

Limiting velocity of a particle
falling through a fluid.

The speed is approaching a **limiting speed** $v_{\lim} = mg/k$ asymptotically. It is said to be approaching it exponentially; note that although v is increasing, it is not increasing exponentially—this would be so if v had the form $v = a\,e^{bt}$.

The series expansion of the exponential function is

$$e^\epsilon = 1 + \epsilon + \epsilon^2/2! + \cdots \cong 1 + \epsilon \qquad \text{for } \epsilon \ll 1$$

Therefore if the retarding frictional coefficient k is small, so that $\dfrac{k}{m}\,t \ll 1$,

$$v \cong \frac{mg}{k}\left[1 - \left(1 - \frac{k}{m}\,t\right)\right] = gt$$

This is the usual expression for "free fall" under gravity.

The limiting speed or velocity is also called the **terminal** velocity.

A falling object must reach a terminal velocity if there is a retarding force increasing with speed, no matter what form the speed dependence takes; only for relatively low speeds is it reasonable to assume a retarding force proportional to the speed and therefore our calculation is not really valid for an object falling through the air.

The form of the velocity dependence is related to the kind of flow of the fluid past the moving object (as the object moves through the fluid, the fluid moves past it). If the flow is streamline (also called laminar or steady flow) the force is different than if the flow is turbulent. The type of flow depends on a number of factors: the speed, shape and size of the object, and the density and viscosity of the fluid.

Example: For a sphere moving through a liquid with streamline flow, the retarding force is given by an empirical expression called Stokes' law: $F_f = 6\pi\eta rv$ where v and r are the speed and radius of the sphere, and η is the viscosity of the liquid. Think of a sphere falling in a liquid under gravity. Since $F_f \propto v$ its speed will increase as we have calculated, approaching a limiting value v_l. However, in the calculation we did not allow for the buoyant force of the fluid. We will determine the limiting velocity for a falling sphere. It will fall at constant speed when the downward force due to gravity F_g is equal to the upward force $F_f + F_b$ due to friction and the buoyant force. Let ρ be the density of the sphere, and d be the density of the liquid. Then $F_g = mg = \frac{4}{3}\pi r^3 \rho g$, and $F_b = \frac{4}{3}\pi r^3 dg$. If $\rho > d$, the sphere will fall down, if $\rho < d$, it will fall up. We are assuming $\rho > d$.

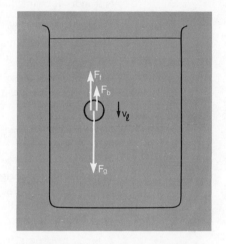

The gravitational, buoyant and frictional forces on a falling sphere.

$$F_f = F_g - F_b$$
$$6\pi\eta r v_l = \tfrac{4}{3}\pi r^3(\rho - d)g$$
$$v_l = \frac{2}{9}\frac{r^2(\rho - d)g}{\eta}$$

To see the size of this, we will put in some numbers. Viscosities are usually given in cgs units: 1 dyne-sec/cm$^2 \equiv$ 1 poise. (You can verify that the dimensions are right.) For water $\eta \sim 0.01$ poise; for many oils $\eta \sim 1$ poise. Think of a metal sphere ($\rho \sim 10$ gm/cm^3) falling in oil ($d \sim 1$ gm/cm^3, $\eta \sim 1$ poise). Then

$$v_l \sim \frac{2}{9}\frac{r^2(10 - 1)980}{1} \sim 2000r^2$$

For $r = 1$ cm, $v_l = 2000$ cm/sec; for $r = 1$ mm, $v_l \sim 20$ cm/sec. It turns out that only for r less than 1 mm is it reasonable to assume streamline flow, and therefore validity of Stokes' law. The criterion for a change from streamline to turbulent flow is a dimensionless quantity called Reynold's number R; in this situation $R = \dfrac{drv}{\eta}$.

Experimentally it is found that for $R < 1$ the flow is streamline, and for $R > 1$ it is turbulent, and somewhere around $R \sim 1$ a transition takes place. For $r = 1$ mm, $R \sim (1 \times 0.1 \times 20)/1 \sim 2$, so this is in the transition region. To ensure streamline flow, we should use smaller spheres.

We have just described a method for measuring the physical property viscosity. By measuring the steady speed as small spheres fall through a liquid, the viscosity can be determined.

Questions for discussion

1. Are the terms **deduction** and **induction** used in physics in the same way as in ordinary conversation?

2. Is an absolute system of units more accurate than a gravitational system of units? Is it more fundamental?

3. Why can the atomic mass unit not be considered an atomic standard of mass?

4. Would it be possible to use different units for gravitational mass than for inertial mass? If so, would it be useful?

5. When we speak of **isolating** a particle (or system) in order to draw a force diagram for it, does this mean we are thinking of removing it from the influence of its surroundings?

6. Two unequal masses are hung at opposite ends of a string passing over a smooth peg. Why is it that we cannot think of the system of two masses as an isolated system?

7. We stated that if a rigid body consists of a number of parts, each with an easily identified center of mass, then the center of mass of the whole body can be found by treating each of the parts as a particle located at its center of mass. Can you prove this using the definition of center of mass?

8. A block rests on a frictionless surface. There is a concave depression in the top surface of the block, and the surface of this "dish" is frictionless. A small block is released at the edge of the dish. What happens to the center of mass of this system during the resulting motion?

9. Center of mass is a property of a system of particles. Why can the center of gravity not be considered a property of the system?

10. For a ship a point called the metacenter is the center of gravity of the water that would have been there if the ship wasn't; that is, it is the center of gravity of the displaced water. Should a ship be designed with its center of mass above, or below, or coinciding with its metacenter?

11. What we have called **forces of constraint** are often called **contact forces.** Do you have any preference? Why?

12. A block is held at rest against a vertical wall by a horizontal force exerted on it. Is the minimum force necessary likely to be equal to, less than or greater than the weight of the block?

13. A bird lands on a clothesline. Is the increase in tension in the line less than, equal to, or greater than the weight of the bird?

14. A sailboat can sail "into the wind," that is move in a direction such that the angle between the direction the boat is moving and the direction the wind is coming from is less than 90°. Can you show on a force diagram for the boat how this is possible? Would it be possible if the boat were sliding on a frictionless surface?

Problems

1. Determine the following ratios of forces, using $g = 9.8$ m/sec^2 = 32 ft/sec^2, and 1 kg = 2.2 lb:

   (a) 1 n/1 kg   (f) 1 pndl/1 lb

   (b) 1 n/1 gm   (g) 1 pndl/1 kg

   (c) 1 n/1 lb   (h) 1 pndl/1 dyne

   (d) 1 n/1 dyne   (i) 1 lb/1 gm

   (e) 1 n/1 pndl   (j) 1 lb/1 dyne

2. Calculate the acceleration in cm/sec^2 of a mass of 3 slugs acted on by a resultant force of 2 kg.

3. Calculate the mass in kilograms which will be accelerated at 20 cm/sec^2 by an unbalanced force of 2 pndl.

4. The **atomic mass unit** is defined by stating that a neutral carbon-12 atom has a mass of exactly 12 amu. The mass of 1 mole (1 gram-molecular-weight) of this isotope is by definition exactly 12 gm. One mole of any substance contains N_0 atoms. The number N_0, Avogadro's number, is determined by experiment to be 6.02×10^{23} atoms/mole. What is the relation between the atomic mass unit and the gram?

5. Two 2-kg masses are suspended by a massless cord passing over two frictionless pulleys as shown.

   (a) If a spring balance of negligible weight is in the cord at A, so that a 2-kg force is exerted on each end of it, does it read 2 kg or 4 kg?

   (b) If a 1-kg mass is hung from the cord at A, what is its acceleration and the acceleration of each of the 2-kg masses the instant after it is released?

   (c) The 1-kg mass is lowered slowly until the system is in equilibrium. What is the angle between the two sections of string at point A?

6. Two pith balls, each of mass 0.2 gm, are given equal electrical charges. Suspended from the same point by threads of equal length, they hang with an angle of 30° between the threads. Determine the electrical repulsive force between them, in dynes and in grams, and the tension in each thread.

7. A 5-kg block rests on a smooth horizontal surface. Calculate the acceleration produced by a force of magnitude 25 n if the force is (a) horizontal, (b) downward at an angle of 60° with the horizontal. (c) What are the accelerations in the two

cases if the surface is not smooth, and there is a coefficient of kinetic friction of 0.4 between block and surface?

8. Estimate the weight of an oil drop one micron (10^{-4} cm) in radius. If the drop is in the space between two parallel metal plates 5 mm apart, with a potential difference of 1000 volts between them, about how many excess electrons ($e = 1.6 \times 10^{-19}$ coul) would it have to carry in order that the electrical force on it would be comparable in size to the gravitational force?

9. A 3000-lb automobile moving at 30 mph is brought to rest in a distance of 60 ft after the brakes are applied. Assuming constant deceleration, and therefore constant forces, calculate the resultant force exerted by the road on the car during deceleration, and the minimum possible value of the coefficient of friction between the tires and the road. Assuming the same retarding force, what distance would be required to bring the car to rest from 60 mph?

10. (a) One end of a spring is fixed to a wall near the floor. A 1-kg mass resting on the floor is pressed against the spring, compressing it. When released it slides 2.2 m along the floor before stopping. Then an unknown mass is pressed against the spring and released. It slides 2.8 m before stopping. What is its mass? Think carefully about all the assumptions you made in your calculations.

(b) A spring is compressed between two blocks resting on a horizontal surface, one of mass 0.5 kg and the other of unknown mass m. When the blocks are released they move in opposite directions, the one of unknown mass moving 2.6 times as far as the other before stopping. Determine m. Did you use conservation of momentum in deducing your result? If you did, did you have to? If you did not, could you have? Did you have to assume that the spring was of negligible mass?

11. A 10-lb stone is suspended by a rope of breaking strength 20 lb. What is the minimum time in which the stone can be raised through a distance of 25 ft, starting from rest?

12. Two 7-lb blocks are suspended at the ends of a weightless string passing over a weightless frictionless pulley whose axle is supported by a spring balance. Each weight is 4 ft off the floor. If a 2-lb weight is added to one of the blocks, how long does it take for this block to reach the floor? What is the reading of the spring balance, in pounds, while the system is in motion?

13. At some instant the block on the plane in the system shown is moving down the plane at 6 ft/sec. Calculate the time it takes to come to rest, and how far it moves. If it starts again, calculate how long it takes to return to its original position and its speed when it gets there. Assume ideal pulley and string, and take $\mu_s = 0.30$, $\mu_k = 0.25$.

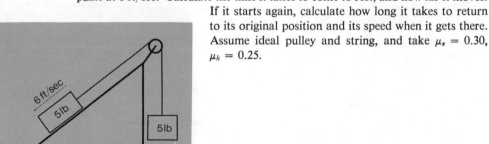

14. Calculate the tension in the cord if the 50-gm mass is released **(a)** if the horizontal surface is smooth, **(b)** if the coefficients of friction between the 70-gm mass and the surface are $\mu_s = 0.4$, $\mu_k = 0.3$. Assume ideal pulleys and string.

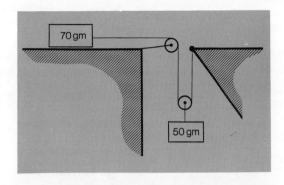

15. A block of wood sits on an inclined plane as the angle θ of the plane with the horizontal is gradually increased. At $\theta = 22°$ the block slips, moving 30 cm down the plane in 1.1 sec. Determine μ_s and μ_k. For what angle should the block slide down at constant velocity if given an initial push?

16. For $F = 4$ kg, calculate the force that the 3-kg block exerts on the 5-kg block in **(a)** and in **(b)**. Take the coefficient of friction (static and kinetic) between blocks and surface, and between the blocks, as 0.3. **(c)** Calculate the maximum value of F for case (b) such that the blocks remain at rest with respect to one another.

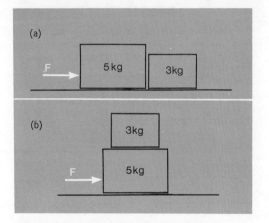

17. A 1-kg block is held at rest against a vertical wall by exerting a horizontal force F on it. The coefficient of static friction between block and wall is 0.4. Determine the minimum value of F, in kilograms, and the corresponding value of the force exerted on the block by the wall.

18. If the angle of an inclined plane is steep enough, it is impossible to push a block up the plane by applying a horizontal force only, no matter how large the force is. Think of a one pound block, with a coefficient of static friction between block and plane of 0.75, and determine the minimum angle θ for which it is impossible to push the block up the plane with a horizontal force F, no matter how large F is. Determine the minimum F that will hold the block at rest on the plane for this angle.

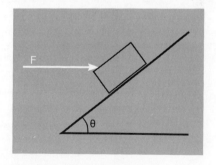

19. **(a)** A projectile is given an initial velocity of 200 ft/sec at an angle of 37° above a horizontal plane. Determine its maximum height above the plane H and its range R.

(b) The projectile is given the same initial speed at the bottom of a smooth ramp. The ramp is 100 ft long and inclined upward at 37°. Again determine H and R.

(c) Suppose the ramp is not smooth, but instead there is a coefficient of kinetic friction between the sliding projectile and the ramp of 0.2. Determine H and R.

20. The earth is about 80 times as massive as the moon, and the moon is at a distance of about 60 times the earth radius. Is the center of mass of the earth–moon system outside or inside the earth? Where?

21. A flat plate is in the form of a right-angled triangle. The sides adjacent to the right angle are of lengths a and b. Determine the position of the c-of-m of the plate.

22. The density of a thin rod varies linearly along the rod, doubling over the length of the rod. Where is the center of mass of the rod?

23. A thin uniform rod is bent into a semicircle of radius R. Determine the position of its center of mass.

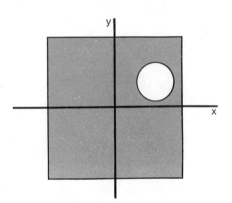

24. (a) A square piece of tin 20 cm on a side has a circular disc of tin cut from the same sheet stuck to it. The diameter of the disc is 6 cm, and in the co-ordinate system indicated the co-ordinates of the center of the disc are $x = 6$ cm, $y = 4$ cm. What are the co-ordinates of the center of mass of the system?

(b) A square piece of tin 20 cm on a side has a circular hole of diameter 6 cm cut in it. In the co-ordinate system indicated the co-ordinates of the center of the hole are $x = 6$ cm, $y = 4$ cm. What are the co-ordinates of the center of mass of the tin?

25. An odd number n identical particles, each of mass m, are placed at equal intervals a distance d apart along a straight line. Choose this line as the x-axis, with origin at the center particle, so that the center of mass of the system is at $x = 0$. Suppose that the particle second from the end, the $(n - 1)$th one, is removed. What is the position of the center of mass of the system now? Show that the result can be obtained by thinking of two **particles,** one of mass nm at the center of mass of the original system, and one of mass $-m$ at the $(n - 1)$th position.

26. Estimate the limiting velocity of fall of a raindrop of radius 0.3 mm, assuming streamline flow of the air. Is the assumption likely to be valid? Take the viscosity of air as 200 micropoises.

27. (a) The viscosity of olive oil (density 0.92 gm/cm³) is determined by releasing plastic spheres (density 1.06 gm/cm³) of radius 2 mm at the top of a tank of oil and measuring the time for the spheres to fall between two levels in the tank 20 cm apart. The average time is 14 sec. Calculate the viscosity in poises assuming streamline flow, and check whether this assumption is reasonable.

(b) The spheres starting from rest will exponentially approach their terminal velocity. Estimate the time required to reach 99% of the terminal velocity. Is it reasonable to assume constant velocity of fall between the two levels?

28. A tiny bubble released at the bottom of a tank of water 20 cm high takes 10 sec to reach the top. Estimate the radius of the bubble, assuming streamline flow. Is this assumption likely to be valid?

10

DYNAMICS OF A PARTICLE
IN A NON-INERTIAL
FRAME OF REFERENCE

In the last chapter we examined motions in a frame of reference fixed to the earth, assumed to be an inertial frame in which Newton's laws may be applied. We could have made transformations into other frames (for example, a frame attached to an accelerated block) but the earth frame was the appropriate one because measurements on the systems described would be made in the earth frame. We now look at examples where measurements might be made in a different frame.

PARTICLE AT REST IN A
UNIFORMLY ACCELERATED FRAME OF REFERENCE

Think about a pendulum suspended from the horizontal ceiling of a train car travelling on a horizontal track, and assume such a well-constructed train and roadbed that there is no vibration. Consider that all of the mass of the pendulum is concentrated in the bob: a particle of mass m is suspended by a massless string.

If the train is at rest, or moving with constant velocity, the pendulum will be observed to hang straight down. (If it is swinging it can be stopped in this position.) The force diagram for the bob would show the downward force of gravity $\mathbf{w} = m\mathbf{g}$ and an upward force exerted by the string $\mathbf{T}$. The particle has no acceleration so $\mathbf{T} + \mathbf{w} = 0$. This description is valid *either* in a frame of reference fixed to the earth **or** in a frame fixed to the train; both are inertial frames, and all inertial frames are dynamically equivalent.

If the train is accelerating the pendulum will not hang straight down. As acceleration begins it will start to swing, and if there is no friction will continue to swing indefinitely. However, for a constant acceleration $\mathbf{a}$ it can be stopped

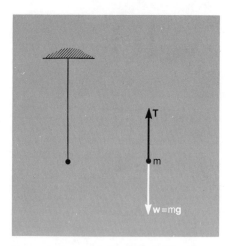

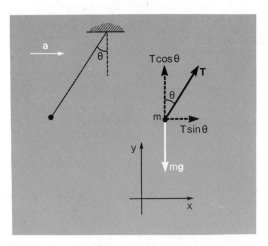

Forces on a pendulum in a train at
rest or moving at constant velocity.

Forces on a pendulum in a train with a constant
acceleration, in the earth frame of reference.

(with respect to the train) to hang at some fixed angle θ with the vertical. First
consider the situation **from the earth frame of reference.** The bob is at rest in
the train, and therefore has the acceleration **a** of the train. The only forces acting
are the weight **w** = m**g** and the tension in the string **T**, and the equation of
motion is **T** + **w** = m**a**. The acceleration **a** is in the horizontal direction (the
train is constrained to move on the track). Choosing co-ordinate axes so that
the x-axis is in the **a** direction and the y-axis is upward, the tension force can be

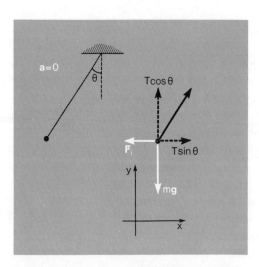

Forces on a pendulum in a train with constant
acceleration, in the train frame of reference.

resolved into x- and y-components $T \sin \theta$ and
$T \cos \theta$. The weight has a component $-mg$ in the
y-direction. The component equations of motion are

$$F_x = ma_x: \qquad T \sin \theta = ma$$
$$F_y = ma_y: \qquad T \cos \theta + (-mg) = m(0)$$

Dividing these two relations gives $\tan \theta = a/g$. The
angle θ is determined by the acceleration.

Now think of the situation **from the train frame
of reference.** In this frame the pendulum bob is at
rest (**a** = 0), hanging at an angle θ with the vertical.
Measurements of the tension T (with a spring
balance in the string for example), the angle θ and
the mass m could be made. Choosing co-ordinate
axes up and to the right, the components of force
$T \sin \theta$, $T \cos \theta$ and $-mg$ could be calculated. It
would be found that $T \cos \theta$ and mg were equal in
magnitude, showing zero acceleration in the vertical

direction, as observed. However, there is also zero acceleration in the horizontal direction, and therefore there must be a horizontal force F_i equal and opposite to the calculated $T \sin \theta$. This force has a component $-F_i$ in the x-direction. The component equations of motion are

$$T \sin \theta + (-F_i) \ = m(0)$$
$$T \cos \theta + (-mg) = m(0)$$

The value of F_i could be calculated. In this frame of reference it is a horizontal force in the direction in which the pendulum is slanting away from the vertical.

The two sets of component equations, one set for the earth frame and one set for the train frame, each describe the same physical situation. Compare them carefully.

	Earth frame	Train frame
$F_x = ma_x$	$T \sin \theta = ma$	$T \sin \theta + (-F_i) \ = 0$
$F_y = ma_y$	$T \cos \theta + (-mg) = 0$	$T \cos \theta + (-mg) = 0$

They are identical if we set $F_i = ma$. The magnitude of the force in the train frame is the same as the magnitude of the mass times the acceleration in the earth frame. But note that $\mathbf{F}_i$ is **not** equal to ma_i. The force $\mathbf{F}_i$ and the acceleration $\mathbf{a}$ are in opposite directions, and therefore the vectors $\mathbf{F}_i$ and ma_i cannot be equal. This is apparent if we consider the vector equation $\mathbf{F} = ma$ in the two frames.

	Earth frame	Train frame
$\mathbf{F} = ma$	$\mathbf{T} + \mathbf{w} = ma$	$\mathbf{T} + \mathbf{w} + \mathbf{F}_i = 0$
	These give $\mathbf{F}_i = -ma$	

In the last chapter we emphasized that Newton's laws of motion are valid only in inertial (non-accelerated) frames of reference, a kind of frame of reference that the laws themselves define. However, we pointed out that the basic relation $\mathbf{F} = ma$ could be applied in an accelerated frame of reference *provided* non-Newtonian forces called inertial forces were introduced. The inertial force on a mass m in a frame of reference with acceleration $\mathbf{a}$ is a force of magnitude ma in the opposite direction to the acceleration, that is a force $-ma$. The force $\mathbf{F}_i$ in the example is such a force. It is a real measurable force in the train, but it does not exist in the earth frame of reference. It is a non-Newtonian force because Newton's Law III does not apply to it—there is no reaction force to it, no equal and opposite force acting on some other body. The force $T \sin \theta$ is not a reaction force because it acts on the same body.

There are reaction forces to the force **T** exerted by the string on the bob, and the force **w** exerted by the earth on the bob. They are a force −**T** exerted *on* the string *by* the bob, and a force −**w** exerted *by* the bob *on* the earth.

We have written and described the vector equations and the component equations of motion, in the two frames of reference, in some detail and with some care because it is important to realize that these two different methods of description are possible. It does not matter which method you adopt, but you must be *consistent*. You must describe the motion *either* in the earth frame, *or* in the train frame, and not mix these two descriptions.

In some earlier examples we showed that it was sometimes convenient to use component equations involving magnitudes only, assuming directions for the forces and accelerations involved rather than letting the directions emerge from the equations. Sometimes it is necessary to do a careful vector treatment in order to get the signs right, sometimes directions are obvious and it is a nuisance to do this. However, no matter what method you are using, you must be careful to decide what frame of reference you are using and be consistent.

To illustrate we will think of a situation where an object is moving in an accelerated frame of reference; the pendulum bob was at rest in the frame of the accelerated train.

PARTICLE IN MOTION IN A
UNIFORMLY ACCELERATED FRAME OF REFERENCE

A block of wood is slid along the floor of the train. If it is given an initial speed of 10 ft/sec it comes to rest after sliding 10 ft when the train is at rest. If the train has an acceleration of 2 ft/sec² in the same direction as the block is moving, how far will it move before coming to rest?

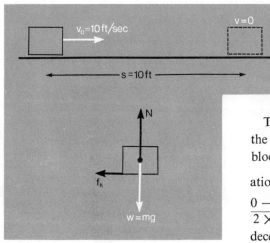

$v_0 = 10\,\text{ft/sec}$

$v = 0$

$s = 10\,\text{ft}$

Motion of a sliding block
in a train at rest.

N

f_k

$w = mg$

The initial information enables us to calculate the coefficient of kinetic friction μ_k between the block and the floor, if we assume that the acceleration is constant. The acceleration is $a = \dfrac{v^2 - v_0^2}{2s} = \dfrac{0 - 10^2}{2 \times 10} = -5$ ft/sec², the minus sign showing a deceleration, or acceleration in the opposite direction to v_0. The unbalanced force producing this acceleration is the force of friction $f_k = \mu_k N = \mu_k mg$, and the equation of motion is

$$\mu_k mg = ma \qquad \text{so} \qquad \mu_k = a/g = 5/32$$

(In writing these relations we have not worried about sign. Since we used $v_0 = 10$ ft/sec, a positive quantity, we have chosen a co-ordinate axis in this direction, and f_k and a are negative. We have used $N = mg$, the relation between magnitudes, rather than the correct component relation $N + mg = 0$.)

This calculation was in the earth frame of reference, the same as that of the train, since the train is at rest. The coefficient μ_k calculated depends on the surfaces of the block and floor, and not on the motion of the train. It is not necessary to calculate the coefficient μ_k explicitly, but it is necessary to assume that the force of friction is constant, independent of the relative velocity of the two surfaces.

You know that if the same experiment was performed in the train moving at a constant velocity $\mathbf{V}$, the same result would be found, but the calculation would depend on the inertial frame of reference used. In the train frame of reference the initial velocity of the block is $\mathbf{v}_0 = 10$ ft/sec, and a calculation identical to the above could be made. However, in the earth frame of reference the initial velocity of the block would be $\mathbf{v}_0 + \mathbf{V}$, and the final velocity $\mathbf{V}$. The **change** in velocity and therefore the acceleration is the same in both frames.

To see explicitly that the calculation gives the same result in the earth frame, suppose that the train is moving with a constant velocity $\mathbf{V}$ ft/sec in the same direction as the block is slid, so that the situation is one-dimensional. In the earth frame of reference the acceleration is $a = -5$ ft/sec^2, and the speed changes from an initial value $v_i = v_0 + V = 10 + V$ ft/sec to a final value

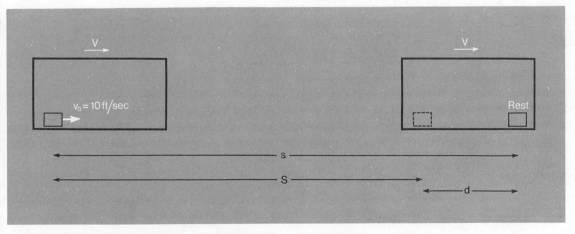

Displacements of the block and a uniformly moving train in the earth frame.

$v_f = V$ ft/sec. The time for the block to come to rest is

$$T = \frac{v_f - v_i}{a} = \frac{V - (10 + V)}{-5} = 2 \text{ sec}$$

In this time the train moves a distance

$$S = VT = 2V \text{ ft}$$

The distance the block moves is

$$s = v_i T + \tfrac{1}{2} a T^2 = (10 + V)(2) + \tfrac{1}{2}(-5)(2)^2 = 10 + 2V \text{ ft}$$

The distance the block moves relative to the ground depends of course on the velocity of the train. The distance the block moves relative to the train is

$$d = s - S = 10 + 2V - 2V = 10 \text{ ft}$$

The point of this calculation is to emphasize that the result is the same, whether calculation is made in the inertial frame of the earth or the inertial frame of the train, but the calculation is not the same in both frames. If you write

$$s = \frac{v^2 - v_0^2}{2a} = \frac{0 - 10^2}{2(-5)} = 10 \text{ ft}$$

you must realize that this is a calculation in the train frame of reference.

Now think about the situation when the train has an acceleration $A = 2$ ft/sec^2 in the same direction as the initial velocity $\mathbf{v}_0$. First we work in the train frame of reference, **now a non-inertial frame.** In this frame in addition to the horizontal force of friction there is an inertial force mA on the block. Since the acceleration **A** is in the same direction as the motion of the block, the inertial force $-m\mathbf{A}$ is in the opposite direction, the same direction as the force of friction. The resultant force decelerating the block is $f_k + mA = \mu_k mg + mA$ and the equation of motion is $\mu_k mg + mA = ma_T$, where a_T is the acceleration of the block in the train frame.

$$a_T = \mu_k g + A = 5 + 2$$
$$= 7 \text{ ft/sec}^2$$

The distance moved by the block in coming to rest is

$$s = \frac{v^2 - v_0^2}{2a} = \frac{0 - 10^2}{2(-7)}$$

$$= 7.1 \text{ ft}$$

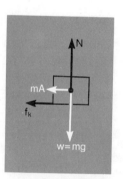

Forces on the sliding block in the non-inertial frame of an accelerated train.

In writing this we have had to recognize that a_T is a deceleration, in the opposite direction to v_0. It is in deciding the direction of the inertial force mA that care must be taken. The component equation written with regard to sign, taking the direction of $\mathbf{v}_0$ as the direction of a co-ordinate axis, is $-\mu_k mg - mA = ma_T$, giving $a_T = -\mu_k g - A = -5 - 2 = -7$ ft/sec^2.

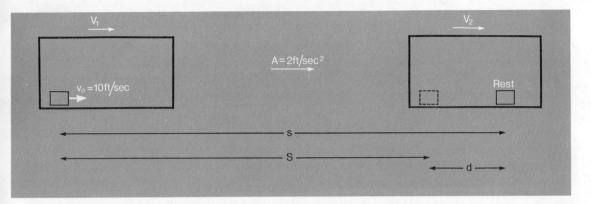

Displacements of the block and the
accelerated train in the earth frame.

Now we will work in the earth frame of reference. In this frame there is no
inertial force. The only horizontal force producing acceleration is the frictional
force, and the acceleration is $a = -5$ ft/sec^2. This time the velocity of the train
is not constant. In the time T sec that it takes the block to come to rest the speed
of the train will change from some initial value V_1 ft/sec to a final value
$V_2 = V_1 + AT = V_1 + 2T$ ft/sec.

The speed of the block changes from an initial value $v_i = v_0 + V_1$ to a final
value $v_f = V_2$. The time it takes is

$$T = \frac{v_f - v_i}{a} = \frac{V_2 - (v_0 + V_1)}{-5} = \frac{(V_1 + 2T) - (10 + V_1)}{-5} = \frac{10 - 2T}{5}$$

Solving for T, $5T = 10 - 2T$, $T = 10/7$ sec. In this time the train moves a
distance

$$S = V_1 T + \tfrac{1}{2} A T^2 = V_1\left(\frac{10}{7}\right) + \frac{1}{2}(2)\left(\frac{10}{7}\right)^2 = \frac{10}{7}V_1 + \frac{100}{49}$$

and the block moves a distance

$$s = v_i T + \tfrac{1}{2} a T^2 = (V_1 + 10)\left(\frac{10}{7}\right) + \frac{1}{2}(-5)\left(\frac{10}{7}\right)^2 = \frac{10}{7}V_1 + \frac{450}{49}$$

The distance the block moves relative to the train is

$$d = s - S = \left(\frac{10}{7}V_1 + \frac{450}{49}\right) - \left(\frac{10}{7}V_1 + \frac{100}{49}\right) = \frac{50}{7} = 7.1 \text{ ft}$$

The result is the same as that calculated using the train frame of reference,
introducing the inertial force. The calculation in the earth frame is messier
because of the unknown velocity of the train. A third way that this problem

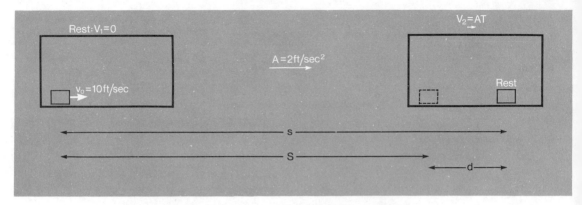

Displacements of the block and the accelerated train in an inertial frame moving at the initial velocity of the train.

can be solved is to work in **an inertial frame that is not the earth frame.** Think of a frame of reference that is moving at a constant velocity V_1, the velocity of the train at the instant the block is released. In this inertial frame the only horizontal force acting is the frictional force, so the acceleration is $a = -5$ ft/sec². In the time T sec that it takes the block to come to rest, the train will acquire a speed $V_2 = AT = 2T$ ft/sec in this frame. The speed of the block changes from $v_i = 10$ ft/sec to $v_f = V_2 = 2T$ ft/sec in this time.

$$T = \frac{v_f - v_i}{a} = \frac{2T - 10}{-5} \qquad T = 10/7 \text{ sec}$$

The distance moved by train and block are

$$S = V_1 T + \tfrac{1}{2}AT^2 = \frac{1}{2}(2)\left(\frac{10}{7}\right)^2 = \frac{100}{49} \text{ ft}$$

$$s = v_i T + \tfrac{1}{2}aT^2 = 10\left(\frac{10}{7}\right) + \frac{1}{2}(-5)\left(\frac{10}{7}\right)^2 = \frac{450}{49} \text{ ft}$$

and the distance moved by the block in the train is

$$d = s - S = \frac{350}{49} = 7.1 \text{ ft}$$

We have worked in three different frames of reference here: a frame fixed to the train, a frame fixed to the earth, and a frame fixed to—to what? The third frame is not fixed to anything. You can if you wish think of it as a frame fixed to a train moving on a parallel track at a constant speed V_1. Measurements made with respect to this train are measurements in the third frame. The point to be emphasized is that motion is always described with respect to a particular frame of reference, and you must be clear in making calculations what frame of reference you are using.

PARTICLE AT REST IN A
UNIFORMLY ROTATING FRAME OF REFERENCE

In the last section we dealt only with one-dimensional situations: the train moved with constant velocity, or with an acceleration in the direction of motion, and the block slid in the same direction. Now think about the train moving on a horizontal curved track. We showed in Chapter 5 that the acceleration **a** can be thought of as having two components, a tangential component $\mathbf{a}_T$ related to change in magnitude of the velocity, and a radial component $\mathbf{a}_R$ related to change in direction of velocity. At any instant the train is moving in a path of radius R, and the magnitude of the radial component of acceleration is $a_R = v^2/R$.

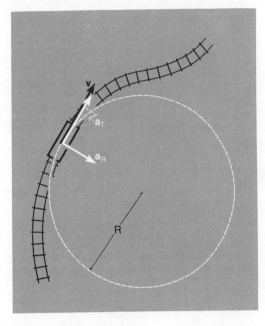

We will next consider the situation where the train moves at constant speed v on a horizontal track around a curve of constant radius R. Then $a_T = 0$ and $a_R = v^2/R$ is constant in magnitude. The train is in uniform circular motion, with respect to the earth frame of reference.

Radial and tangential components of acceleration.

Think about a pendulum hanging in a train moving in this way. It will hang at rest, deflected sideways or outwards, making an angle θ with the vertical. As we showed before, $\tan \theta = a_R/g$, but think about what this means in the two frames

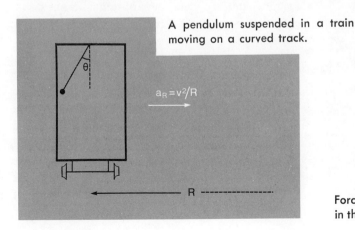

A pendulum suspended in a train moving on a curved track.

$a_R = v^2/R$

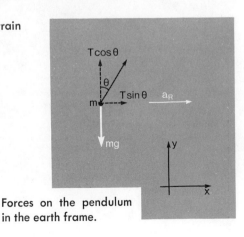

Forces on the pendulum in the earth frame.

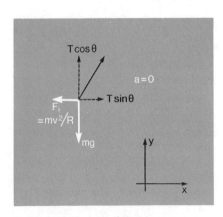

Forces on the pendulum
in the train frame.

of reference. In the earth frame of reference we *cannot* think of a constant acceleration **a** producing a constant angle of deflection θ. The pendulum, like the train, is moving in a circle. A deflection **outward** is west at one time, north a little later. **At any instant** in the earth frame the component equations of motion are $T \sin \theta = ma_R$, $T \cos \theta + (-mg) = 0$, but the co-ordinate system in which these equations apply must be changed from instant to instant. The equation of motion is $\mathbf{T} + \mathbf{w} = m\mathbf{a}_R$ and since $\mathbf{a}_R$ is changing, so is $\mathbf{T}$.

On the other hand, in the train frame the acceleration of the pendulum is not changing—it is zero at every instant. The equation of motion is $\mathbf{T} + \mathbf{w} + \mathbf{F}_i = 0$ and the component equations

$$T \sin \theta + (-mv^2/R) = 0 \qquad T \cos \theta + (-mg) = 0$$

The co-ordinate system in which these apply does not change—it is the same at every instant.

Just what is meant by "the train frame of reference"? While we have stated that it is a frame of reference in which the train is at rest, does this specify it uniquely? Think of a frame of reference S' fixed to the train; it may help to think of a set of rigid rods attached to the train. In this frame of reference the train and pendulum have speed $v' = 0$ and acceleration $a' = 0$. This frame is apparently moving with respect to the earth frame of reference S with both translation and rotation. However, because the train is moving in a circular path of radius R, one point in the S' frame of reference will not be moving in S. A rigid rod fixed on the train at right angles will have one point on it, a distance R from the train, which will not move in S as the train (and S') moves. The frame S' is moving in pure rotation with respect to S, about the fixed point O, the center of the circular track. The frame S' rotates at a constant angular speed ω with respect to S. The speed and acceleration $v' = 0$ and $a' = 0$ in S' transform into $v = R\omega$ and $a = R\omega^2 = v^2/R$ in S.

The train frame of reference here is moving in pure rotation with respect to the earth frame.

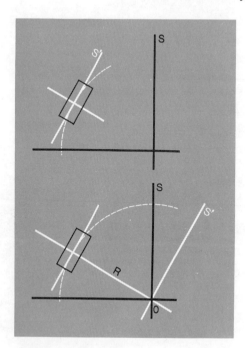

Frame S' in pure rotation
with respect to S.

In the previous train example the train frame moved with pure translation with respect to the earth frame. For motion of the train in general, a combination of the two would be necessary.

CENTRIPETAL AND CENTRIFUGAL FORCES

There are situations where it is simpler to work in a non-inertial frame than an inertial frame. This requires the introduction of inertial forces, and in rotating frames of reference such forces are given special names.

It is in dealing with uniform circular motion of a particle with respect to an inertial frame that a description in a rotating, non-inertial frame is particularly useful. A particle at rest in a frame S' accelerated uniformly in pure translation with respect to an inertial frame S has an acceleration $\mathbf{a}$ in S and $\mathbf{a}' = 0$ in S'. Both $\mathbf{a}$ and $\mathbf{a}'$ are constant. However, if S' is rotating uniformly with respect to S, then $\mathbf{a}' = 0$ is constant but $\mathbf{a}$ is not; it is constant only in magnitude, not in direction. A vector treatment in S' is simpler than in S.

Another reason for a particular interest in rotating frames is that uniform motion in a circle is a common type of motion, while uniformly accelerated motion is not; in the preceding example of the train it would be difficult to maintain a constant linear acceleration for any period of time (in order that the accelerating force F be kept constant, the power supplied $P = Fv$ would have to be continuously increased) but motion of a train around a curve at constant speed is not unusual.

Think of a particle at rest in a frame of reference rotating uniformly with respect to an inertial frame. In the non-inertial frame the inertial force on the particle is called the **centrifugal force.** If the particle is moving in this frame, it is acted upon by an inertial force called the **coriolis force** as well. We will give general expressions for these forces, but first there are some ambiguities of nomenclature that we should try to clear up. These ambiguities arise because motion is different as described in different frames of reference. For example, the term centrifugal force is used for two different things in two different frames of reference. To help distinguish these uses, think about this simple situation. A small block (a particle) slides on a fric-

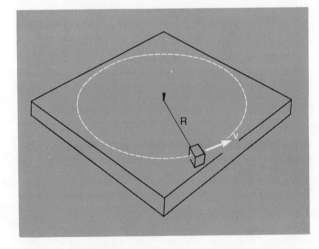

A block sliding in a circle on a smooth table.

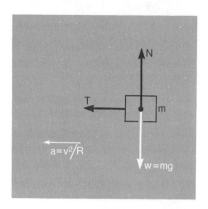

Forces on the block
in the earth frame.

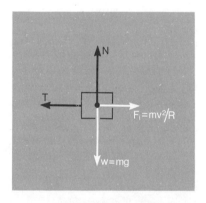

Forces on the block
in the block frame.

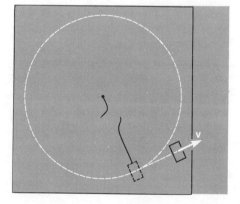

Motion of the block
if the string is cut.

tionless table, constrained to move in a circle of radius R by a massless string looped around a frictionless fixed peg. Given an initial tangential speed v the block will slide forever. It has an acceleration toward the peg of constant magnitude $a = v^2/R$, called the central or centripetal acceleration. The resultant or unbalanced force producing this acceleration is the tension T in the string acting inward on the block. This resultant force $T = mv^2/R$ is called the central or centripetal force. It is *not* an inertial force, but a force that has its origin in matter. It can be a gravitational force or an electric force rather than a contact force as in this example.

This description applies to the earth frame of reference. In a frame of reference attached to the block, meaning a frame rotating about the peg with the same angular speed as the block, the block is at rest. It has no centripetal acceleration in this frame. Nevertheless the force exerted on the block by the string, a real measurable force, is still called the centripetal force. The inertial force in the opposite direction, equal in magnitude to the centripetal force, is called the centrifugal force: $F_i = mv^2/R$. It is a real measurable force too. In this frame of reference it can be said that the centrifugal force balances the centripetal force—or vice versa. Vice versa is probably better, because in this frame of reference the centrifugal force cannot be eliminated. If the string is cut, the centripetal force vanishes, and the centrifugal force produces an outward acceleration. (In the earth frame of reference if the string is cut the block moves in a straight line tangent to the circle with constant velocity $\mathbf{v}$, its instantaneous velocity when the string was cut.) In the block frame of reference the centripetal and centrifugal forces are *not* an action–reaction pair: they both act on the same body, and the centripetal force can be eliminated while the centrifugal force cannot. There is *no* reaction force to the centrifugal force—it is not a Newtonian force.

Ambiguity exists because the term centrifugal force is used sometimes for the reaction to the centripetal force. In *either* frame of reference the string exerts a force T on the block, the centripetal force, and the block exerts an equal and opposite force *on the string*. This force has the same magnitude (mv^2/R) and direction (outward) as the inertial force F_i on the block, and it is this force that is sometimes called the centrifugal force too. It is not a force on the block. If the string is cut, the action–reaction pair disappear. The force F_i remains, in the block frame of reference.

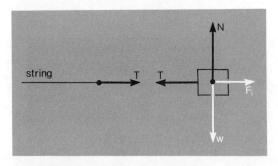

Is the force T on the string the centrifugal force?

The centrifugal force F_i in the block frame of reference does not remain constant after the string is cut, because the block does not stay at rest in this frame. As soon as it starts to move, a coriolis force appears as well. Note that once the string is cut it is no longer appropriate for us to speak of the rotating frame as the block frame of reference, since the block is now moving in this frame of reference.

Use of the terms centripetal and centrifugal is not really necessary and is sometimes confusing, but they are current terms so you might as well learn the different ways that they are used. The term centripetal force is used for the resultant force on an object maintaining it in a circular path; the term centrifugal is used for the inertial force on the object in a rotating frame of reference, and also for the reaction to the centripetal force.

Terms like gravitational force, contact force, or inertial force are used to describe what the *origin* of a force is; the term centripetal force is different—it describes what the force *does*, not what its origin is. It can be any force with its origin in matter—a gravitational force, a contact force, or some combination. For the block on the table, the tension on the string is the centripetal force. For the bob on the pendulum on the train moving around the circular track, the string provides the centripetal force but the total tension is not the centripetal force because the string holds the bob up as well; the component $T \sin \theta$ is the centripetal force. For the moon or any other satellite moving in orbit around the earth, the earth's gravitational attraction is the centripetal force. In particle accelerators such as a cyclotron the centripetal force is a magnetic force; in Chapter 5 we worked out the motion of a charged particle moving at right angles to a magnetic field. In the Bohr model of a hydrogen atom an electron is treated as a particle moving in a circular orbit around a proton, with the electric attraction of the proton the centripetal force.

Think about a small block (a particle) of mass m on the end of a string that is set in motion in a circle of radius R with its plane vertical. (The string is looped

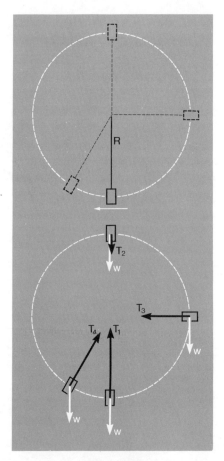

Forces on a block rotating
in a vertical circle.

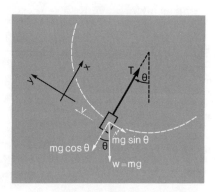

Forces resolved into radial
and tangential components.

around a fixed frictionless horizontal peg.) Its
motion will not be uniform—on its way up, the
force of gravity will slow it down; on its way down,
gravity will speed it up; but if it is moving fast
enough the string will remain taut. What is the
centripetal force? It depends where the block is in
its orbit. At the lowest point the tension T_1 in the
string provides the centripetal force and also holds
the block up; the centripetal force is $T_1 - w$. At the
highest point the centripetal force is the tension in
the string plus the force of gravity $T_2 + w$; if the
speed is low enough that the tension drops to zero
at this point, the centripetal force is completely the
force of gravity w. Only when the string is horizontal is the tension T_3 in the string equal to the
centripetal force. Anywhere on the upper half of
the circle the centripetal force is provided by the
string and gravity, anywhere on the lower half of
the circle the centripetal force is provided by the
string, but is not in general the tension in the string.

The equation of motion in the earth frame of
reference at every instant is $\mathbf{T} + \mathbf{w} = m\mathbf{a}$, where $\mathbf{a}$
is the total acceleration of the block. Only at the
highest and lowest points is this the centripetal
acceleration—at every other point there is a tangential acceleration as well. The component equations
at any instant may be written for a co-ordinate
system with axes in the radial and the tangential
directions. Suppose that the string makes an angle
θ with the downward direction when the instantaneous speed of the block is v. The component
equations for the axes indicated are

$$F_x = ma_x: \quad T - mg \cos \theta = ma_R$$
$$= m(v^2/R)$$
$$= F_{\text{centripetal}}$$
$$F_y = ma_y: \quad -mg \sin \theta = ma_T$$

As θ goes from $0°$ to $180°$, $\sin \theta$ is positive and
a_T is negative, a deceleration; from $180°$ to $360°$,
$\sin \theta$ is negative and the block accelerates. For θ
between $0°$ and $90°$ or between $270°$ and $360°$, $\cos \theta$

is positive and $T = mg \cos \theta + F_{\text{centripetal}}$ is greater than the centripetal force. For θ between 90° and 270°, $\cos \theta$ is negative and T is less than the centripetal force.

This is an example of non-uniform acceleration. The equation of motion could be written in the frame of reference in which the block is at rest, by introducing inertial forces, but this frame would not be rotating uniformly with respect to the earth frame. There would be an inertial force $-ma_R$ (centrifugal force) and inertial force $-ma_T$, both varying in magnitude in the noninertial frame. Probably no simplification in description is provided by such a frame.

While we can write an instantaneous description of the motion here, it is not so easy to write an integrated description dealing with the motion over a time interval. The rate of change of speed for example is given by

$$a_T = dv/dt = -g \sin \theta$$

Can we integrate this equation to find v as a function of time $v(t)$, so that we can determine the change in speed over a finite time interval? To do this we would need to know the relation between v and θ, or between θ and t. The difficulty is that all the quantities T, v, a, and θ change continuously with time. The integration can be done, but the result is complicated.

Some information on what happens over an interval can be determined using the concept of energy. This concept provides no new information, but gives the information in a different form. Energies are so defined that the total energy of the system is constant, independent of time. In this example the block would have kinetic energy and gravitational potential energy, and while the amount of each kind would vary continuously, their sum would be constant. The relation between the speeds v_1 and v_2 at two positions given by angles θ_1 and θ_2 is (you may recall how to show this)

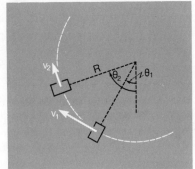

How are v_1 and v_2 related?

$$\tfrac{1}{2}mv_1^2 - mgR \cos \theta_1 = \tfrac{1}{2}mv_2^2 - mgR \cos \theta_2$$

Thus the change in speed $v_1 - v_2$ over a finite interval can be found, but the time required for the change would still not be known. Energy considerations give some information about what happens over an interval, but not complete information. We will discuss this in detail later.

INERTIAL FORCES IN A ROTATING FRAME—
CENTRIFUGAL AND CORIOLIS FORCES

We have digressed to discuss centripetal forces. Let us get back to the question of intertial forces in uniformly rotating frames of reference.

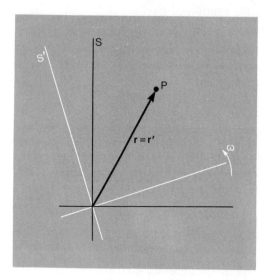

Two frames of reference in pure rotation relative to each other.

We developed in Chapter 7 the transformation relation between two frames of reference S and S' rotating with respect to one another with a constant angular velocity ω. The displacement, velocity and accelerations of a particle P, as measured in the two frames, are related by the general transformation relations

$$\mathbf{r} = \mathbf{r}'$$
$$\mathbf{v} = \mathbf{v}' + \omega \times \mathbf{r}'$$
$$\mathbf{a} = \mathbf{a}' + 2\omega \times \mathbf{v}' + \omega \times (\omega \times \mathbf{r}')$$

We apply this to a situation where S is an inertial frame of reference; than S' cannot be an inertial frame. The acceleration $\mathbf{a}$ of a particle of mass m is produced by a resultant force $\mathbf{F} = m\mathbf{a}$. In the S frame Newton's laws are applicable and this is a force as defined by Newton's laws, a force with its origins in matter, a force exerted by strings or gravity or table tops or whatever.

If we assume that the acceleration $\mathbf{a}'$ is produced by a resultant force $\mathbf{F}' = m\mathbf{a}'$, the relation between $\mathbf{F}$ and $\mathbf{F}'$ is

$$\mathbf{F}' = m\mathbf{a}' = m\mathbf{a} - 2m\omega \times \mathbf{v}' - m\omega \times (\omega \times \mathbf{r}')$$
$$= \mathbf{F} - 2m\omega \times \mathbf{v}' - m\omega \times (\omega \times \mathbf{r}')$$

In order to apply Newton's law of motion $\mathbf{F}' = m\mathbf{a}'$ in frame S' we must add to the force $\mathbf{F}$ an inertial force

$$\mathbf{F}_i = -2m\omega \times \mathbf{v}' - m\omega \times (\omega \times \mathbf{r}')$$
$$= \mathbf{F}_{\text{cor}} + \mathbf{F}_{\text{cf}}$$

The first term in $\mathbf{F}_i$ is called the coriolis force, the second the centrifugal force. This separates $\mathbf{F}_i$ into a force that depends on the velocity $\mathbf{v}'$ of the particle in S', and a force that depends on the displacement $\mathbf{r}'$ of the particle in S'. (This is the displacement from the fixed point O common to the two frames of reference, so $\mathbf{r}' = \mathbf{r}$.) If the particle is at rest in S', then $\mathbf{v}' = 0$, $\mathbf{F}_{\text{cor}} = 0$ and $\mathbf{F}_{\text{cf}} = -m\omega \times (\omega \times \mathbf{r}')$ is constant since ω and $\mathbf{r}'$ are constant. Only if $\mathbf{r}' = 0$ is this force zero. If $\mathbf{v}'$ is not zero, there is a coriolis force as well. Only at the origin O can there be a coriolis force without a centrifugal force.

Another question of nomenclature arises here. The component of acceleration $2\omega \times \mathbf{v}'$ that the particle has in the S frame is called the coriolis acceleration. The component of force $-2m\omega \times \mathbf{v}'$ that has to be used in the S' frame in order to use Newton's law is called the coriolis force. Thus the coriolis force does *not* produce the coriolis acceleration: the terms apply to two different frames of reference. The acceleration $2\boldsymbol{\omega} \times \mathbf{v}'$ in the inertial frame of reference S gives rise to the inertial force $-2m\boldsymbol{\omega} \times \mathbf{v}'$ in the non-inertial frame S'.

Look back to Chapter 7 where we compared the path of a particle moving at constant velocity $\mathbf{v}' = \mathbf{v}_0$ in S' with the path in S. The particle started at the origin and moved radially outward in S'. Its path in S was an Archimedes spiral. We showed that it had a centripetal or central acceleration of steadily increasing magnitude $r\omega^2$, and a sideways or coriolis acceleration of constant magnitude $2\omega v_0$.

If the frame S is an inertial frame, for example the earth frame, then S' is a non-inertial frame— for example a frame attached to a horizontal turn-

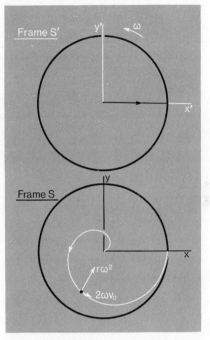

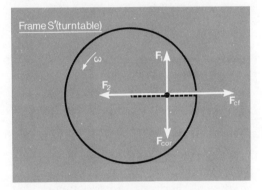

Horizontal forces on you as you are walking at constant velocity out along a radius of a rotating turntable.

Particle moving at constant velocity away from the origin in S' has a spiral path in S.

table rotating at constant angular speed. Think about walking on such a turntable straight out along a radius at a constant velocity $\mathbf{v}_0$. The turntable is rotating counterclockwise, looking from above. There is a constant inertial force $\mathbf{F}_{cor} = -2m\boldsymbol{\omega} \times \mathbf{v}_0$. This is directed to your right. At the instant you are a distance r from the center there is an inertial force $\mathbf{F}_{cf} = -m\boldsymbol{\omega} \times (\boldsymbol{\omega} \times \mathbf{r})$. This is directed away from the center. In order to move at constant velocity in this frame there must be zero resultant force on you, so there must be forces equal and opposite to the two inertial forces. These must be exerted by the floor of the turntable on you, through friction. You will have to walk so that the floor exerts a force $\mathbf{F}_1$ on you to the left, and a force $\mathbf{F}_2$ on you backwards. You of course arrange this by exerting equal and opposite forces on the floor, but remember the force diagram only shows forces on the particle of mass m—in this case, you.

In this example, the vector products involve vectors at right angles to one another, so the magnitude of the product is the product of the magnitudes (see Chapter 4); $F_{cor} = 2m\omega v_0$, $F_{cf} = m\omega^2 r$. With reference to the plane of the page,

Directions of vectors $\boldsymbol{\omega}$, $\mathbf{r}$, $\mathbf{v}_0$, $\mathbf{F}_{cor}$ and $\mathbf{F}_{cf}$.

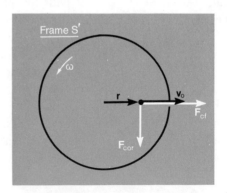

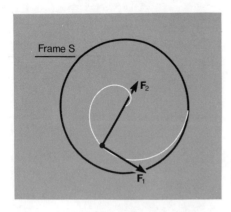

Horizontal forces in the earth frame.

the vector $\boldsymbol{\omega}$ is outward (see Chapter 7). Using the right-hand rule, the vector $\boldsymbol{\omega} \times \mathbf{v}'$ or $\boldsymbol{\omega} \times \mathbf{v}_0$ is upward, and the vector $\mathbf{F}_{cor} = -2m\boldsymbol{\omega} \times \mathbf{v}_0$ is downward. The vector ($\boldsymbol{\omega} \times \mathbf{r}$) is upward, the vector $\boldsymbol{\omega} \times (\boldsymbol{\omega} \times \mathbf{r})$ is to the left, and the vector $\mathbf{F}_{cf} = -m\boldsymbol{\omega} \times (\boldsymbol{\omega} \times \mathbf{r})$ is to the right.

In the S frame of reference, the only horizontal force acting on you is that exerted through friction by the floor of the turntable, with components $\mathbf{F}_1$ and $\mathbf{F}_2$. This unbalanced force produces your eccentric path in the earth frame.

You can turn this situation around by thinking about a puck sliding across a smooth turntable. There is no friction, no horizontal force, and the puck moves with constant velocity in the earth frame of reference S. Can you describe its path in S' if it crosses the center of the turntable?

CALCULATIONS IN
INERTIAL AND NON-INERTIAL FRAMES

In describing the operation of a centrifuge, is it correct to say that particles precipitate because of the centrifugal force? If so, how do we describe the effect in the earth frame of reference, where there is no such force?

We will use three examples of systems in uniform rotation in order to emphasize that they may be described either in the external inertial frame of reference of the earth, or in a non-inertial frame fixed to the system. First we choose an example where you can think of yourself as the particle.

Example 1—Rotating Drum: You may have seen in amusement parks a device which is a large drum rotating about a vertical axis (sometimes the axis can be tilted as well). Passengers stand against the walls of the drum, and when the speed of rotation is large enough the floor is removed, and they stay plastered against the wall by the centrifugal force. Suppose such a drum has a radius of 10 ft, and the minimum coefficient of static friction between a passenger (you) and the wall is 0.3. How fast would the drum have to be rotating before the floor could be safely removed?

As always, we must decide what the system is, and what frame of reference to use. Here the system is you, and we choose a frame of reference fixed to the drum. In this system you are at rest. The forces on you are your weight w down, the inertial force $F_i = mR\omega^2$ away from the center, and the force of the wall. The force of the wall we think of in terms of two components, a normal component N and a frictional component f. Since you are at rest, the resultant force on you is zero $w + F_i + f + N = 0$. However, this vector relation is equivalent to three scalar equations. Choosing co-ordinate axes in the appropriate directions, the component equations are

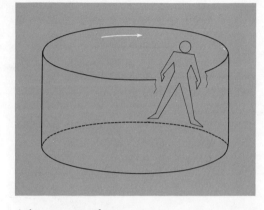

A human centrifuge.

$$w + f = 0 \qquad N + F_i = 0$$

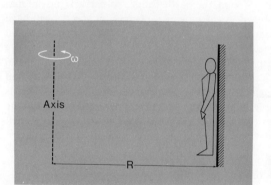

Does the centrifugal force hold you up?

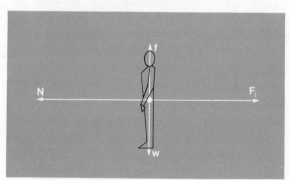

Forces in the rotating frame.

If f is the limiting force of static friction, $f_s = \mu_s N$. Then

$$\mu_s = \frac{f_s}{N} = \frac{w}{F_i} = \frac{mg}{mR\omega^2} = \frac{g}{R\omega^2}$$

The angular speed $\omega = \sqrt{\dfrac{g}{\mu_s R}} = \sqrt{\dfrac{32}{0.3 \times 10}} = 3.3$ rad/sec = 31 rpm. This is the minimum speed: for any larger speed w and f are the same, but F_i and N increase, and f and N are no longer related by the coefficient μ_s. They are constraint forces, as large as they need to be, within certain limits. You can of course work in the inertial frame of reference of the earth equally well—then there is no force F_i.

Example 2—Banking of a Road: A similar situation involves the banking of roads, except that here if a non-inertial frame of reference is used there is no rotating drum to fix it to. We can work in such a frame, in which the car is at rest; we showed earlier in the chapter it is a frame rotating around the center of curvature O with the same angular speed ω as the car.

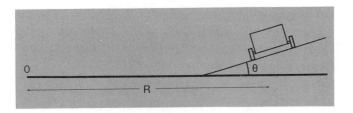

Road banked at angle θ.

Think of a curve of 500-ft radius on a highway on a horizontal plane. The road is properly banked for a speed of 45 mph. If a freezing rain reduced the coefficient of static friction between tires and road to 0.05, what are the maximum and minimum speeds at which the curve can be negotiated?

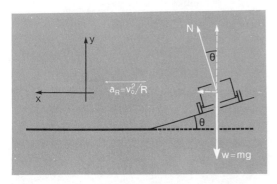

Forces on a car moving at the "correct" speed v_0 around a curve.

This time for variety we will arrange it that we will work in the earth frame, so there is no inertial force F_i. A car moving at a constant speed v will have a centripetal acceleration $a_R = v^2/R$ in the horizontal direction, toward the center of the curve. If the curve is "properly banked" for a speed $v_0 = 45$ mph $= 66$ ft/sec, this means that the force exerted by the road on the car at this speed is a normal force $\mathbf{N}$ only—there is no frictional force necessary. Choosing co-ordinate axes that are instantaneously as shown, the component equations of motion in terms of magnitude only are

$$\sum F_y = ma_y = 0 \quad \text{or} \quad N \cos \theta - mg = 0$$
$$\sum F_x = ma_x \quad \text{or} \quad N \sin \theta = ma_R = mv_0^2/R$$

Dividing, $\tan \theta = \dfrac{v_0^2}{Rg} = \dfrac{66^2}{500 \times 32} = 0.272 \qquad \theta = 15°$

Suppose that the speed is $v > v_0$. Then there must be an additional force inward, and this must be provided by friction. This acts parallel to the road surface. The component equations of motion are

$$N \cos \theta - f \sin \theta - mg = 0$$
$$N \sin \theta + f \cos \theta = ma_R = mv^2/R$$

If the force of friction is its limiting value $f_s = \mu_s N$, the speed v will be the maximum speed without slipping.

Forces on a car moving around a curve at speed $v > v_0$.

Dividing, $\dfrac{N \sin \theta + \mu_s N \cos \theta}{N \cos \theta - \mu_s N \sin \theta} = \dfrac{v^2}{gR}$

or
$$\frac{v^2}{gR} = \frac{\tan\theta + \mu_s}{1 - \mu_s \tan\theta} = \frac{0.272 + 0.05}{1 - 0.05 \times 0.272} = 0.326$$

$$v^2 = 0.326 \times 32 \times 500 = 5220 \qquad v = 72.3 \text{ ft/sec} = 49.3 \text{ mph}$$

For any speed greater than this, the car will slide "outward"—that is, will tend to continue in a straight line, and therefore go outward off the road.

For any speed $v < v_0$, the force of friction will be in the opposite direction—the car will tend to slide in. In the limiting case, with $f_s = \mu_s N$, the result is

$$\frac{v^2}{gR} = \frac{\tan\theta - \mu_s}{1 + \mu_s \tan\theta} = \frac{0.272 - 0.05}{1 + 0.05 \times 0.272} = 0.219$$

$$v^2 = 0.219 \times 32 \times 500 = 3500 \qquad v = 59.1 \text{ ft/sec} = 40.4 \text{ mph}$$

At any speed outside the range $40.4 \rightarrow 49.3$ mph the car cannot make it around the curve.

Example 3—Shape of Surface of a Rotating Liquid:
Still another example of centrifugal forces in a rotating system is provided by thinking about the liquid in a cylinder which is rotated about its axis at a constant angular speed ω. You know that the surface will not be flat—the liquid will pile up around the edges: in the rotating frame of reference, we say this is due to the centrifugal force; in the earth frame of reference, where there is no inertial force, we say the liquid piles up because of Newton's first law—it is trying to move in a straight line.

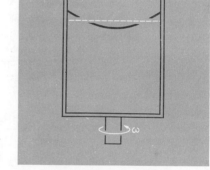

Liquid in a rotating cylinder.

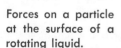

Forces on a particle at the surface of a rotating liquid.

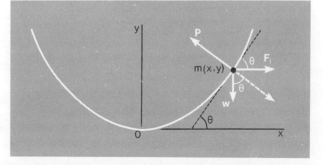

What is the shape of the liquid surface? Is it spherical? To find out, let us work in the non-inertial frame of reference of the rotating cylinder, and fix our attention on a particle of mass m of the fluid, at the surface. Choose a co-ordinate system with y-axis the axis of the cylinder, and origin O at the liquid surface. Think of the particle m in the xy plane, co-ordinates (x, y). There are three forces on m, its weight $\mathbf{w} = m\mathbf{g}$ downward, the centrifugal force $\mathbf{F}_i$ of magnitude $F_i = mx\omega^2$ away from the axis, and a force

P due to the rest of the liquid pushing on it. This force **P** will be normal to the surface; if it were not the particle would move along the surface, and we are describing the equilibrium situation. This means that the resultant of the other two forces **w** and $\mathbf{F}_i$ must also be normal to the surface, in the opposite direction (since $\mathbf{P} + \mathbf{w} + \mathbf{F}_i = 0$). If the tangent to the surface at (x,y) is drawn, making an angle θ with the horizontal, you can see from the diagram that

$$\tan\theta = \frac{F_i}{w} = \frac{mx\omega^2}{mg} = \frac{\omega^2}{g}x$$

The slope of the tangent to a curve at the point (x,y) is by definition the derivative dy/dx at the point

$$\frac{dy}{dx} = \tan\theta = \frac{\omega^2}{g}x$$

or integrating, realizing that ω^2 and g are constants

$$y = \frac{\omega^2}{g}\frac{x^2}{2} + C$$

where C is a constant. We chose axes so that the point $(0,0)$ was on the surface, so $C = 0$. The equation of the line of surface shown is $y = Ax^2$ (where $A = \omega^2/2g$), a parabola. This is not the equation of the three-dimensional surface. The surface is obtained by rotating the parabola about the y-axis, and is a **paraboloid.**

Think of a cylinder 4 cm in diameter. How fast would it have to be rotated in order that the liquid at the circumference is 1 cm higher than the liquid at the center?

Then $x = 2$ cm $y = 1$ cm

$$\omega^2 = \frac{2gy}{x^2} = \frac{2\times 980 \times 1}{4} = 490 \qquad \omega = 22 \text{ rad/sec} = 210 \text{ rpm}$$

Questions for discussion

1. Why are inertial forces also called **fictitious forces?** Why are they not considered to be Newtonian forces? Can the relation $\mathbf{F} = m\mathbf{a}$ be used in a non-inertial frame of reference?

2. Is a **centripetal force** an inertial force? Is it a constraint force? Is it a fundamental force?

3. The term **centrifugal force** is used for an inertial force in a non-inertial frame of reference, and also for a non-inertial force in an inertial frame of reference. In any particular situation, these two forces are of the same magnitude and in the same direction. What is different about them?

4. Does the centripetal force always produce an acceleration? Can you answer without specifying the frame of reference? Does the centrifugal force ever produce an acceleration? Can a centrifugal force exist without a centripetal force? Can a centripetal force exist without a centrifugal force?

5. The centripetal acceleration is produced by the centripetal force, but the coriolis acceleration is not produced by the coriolis force. Is there anything of fundamental significance about this, or is it a matter of nomenclature?

6. Think about the following three pairs of statements. Are they correct? If so, in what frame of reference?

(a) When a pail of water is swung in a vertical circle the water does not fall out when the pail is upside down at the top because (1) the upward centrifugal force is greater than or equal to the downward force of gravity, (2) although the water is accelerated downward by the force of gravity it is moving so fast it doesn't have time to fall out.

(b) (1) Particles in suspension in a fluid are precipitated more rapidly in a centrifuge than they are under gravity because the centrifugal field is stronger than the gravitational field. (2) Particles in suspension are precipitated in a centrifuge because they tend to move in straight lines (the law of inertia) and the force exerted on them by the fluid is not sufficient to make them follow a circular path.

(c) (1) The moon is accelerating toward the earth because the earth exerts an unbalanced force on it, although it doesn't get any closer because it is moving sideways at just the right speed. (2) The earth–moon distance does not change because the moon is in equilibrium under the gravitational pull of the earth and an equal and opposite centrifugal force.

Is it sometimes easier to describe physical situations by introducing inertial forces—and therefore thinking in non-inertial frames of reference?

Problems

The problems in this chapter can be solved either in an inertial or a non-inertial frame of reference. Choose either, but be clear which you are using in each case.

1. A 100-kg man stands on a scale calibrated in kilograms, in an elevator. What does the scale read at an instant the elevator is moving **(a)** up at a constant speed of 5 m/sec, **(b)** up at 5 m/sec with an upward acceleration of 2 m/sec², **(c)** up at 5 m/sec with a downward acceleration (a deceleration) of 2 m/sec², **(d)** down at 5 m/sec with an upward acceleration of 2 m/sec²? **(e)** The man drops his watch from a point 2 m above the elevator floor; how long before it hits the floor, if at the instant he drops it the elevator is moving as in (a), as in (b), and as in (c)? **(f)** What is the displacement of the watch in the earth frame of reference as it falls in each case?

2. A waiter carrying a tray tilts the tray forward if he is accelerating, so that there is no tendency for the glasses on the tray to slip or topple. What is the appropriate relation between the magnitude of his acceleration a and the angle θ of the tray with the horizontal?

3. A coin rests on the turntable of a record player, 4 in. from the center. Assume a coefficient of static friction of 0.5. Will the coin stay on the turntable if it is rotating at 33 rpm? At 78 rpm?

4. Calculate the centripetal force in pounds on a 150-lb man standing at the equator. (Assume the earth is a sphere 4000 miles in radius.) What provides this force? What would be the length of the day if the centripetal force was 150 lb? Would the man then be weightless? (See Chapter 11.)

5. (a) Calculate the centripetal force on the moon, assuming it moves in a circular orbit around the earth, and compare it with the gravitational force exerted on it by the earth. Use: earth mass 5.98×10^{24} kg, moon mass 7.35×10^{22} kg, earth-moon distance 3.85×10^8 m, period 27.3 days, gravitational constant 6.67×10^{-11} m³/kg-sec².

   (b) Calculate the centripetal force on an electron treating it as a particle moving about a nucleus in a circular orbit 1 angstrom unit in diameter, making 4×10^{17} rpm. Compare this with the gravitational force between the nucleus and the electron. Take the electron mass as 9.1×10^{-31} kg and assume a reasonable mass for the nucleus.

6. What is the centripetal force in poundals, and in pounds, on a 200-lb astronaut in an earth satellite in a circular orbit at a height such that $g = 26$ ft/sec²? Is there a centrifugal force as well? Is he weightless? (See Chapter 11.)

7. A physics student, bored by a long railroad journey, suspends a pendulum from the flat horizontal ceiling of his coach and observes the angle it makes with the perpendicular to the ceiling in a variety of circumstances. What angle does he observe if the coach is moving (a) on a horizontal straight track at a constant speed of 30 mph? (b) On a horizontal straight track with a steady acceleration of 3 ft/sec²? (c) Up a grade of 1 in 10 (rise 1 unit for 10 units along the slope) with a deceleration of 3 ft/sec²? (d) Around a horizontal unbanked curve of radius 200 ft at a constant speed of 30 mph?

8. A 10-lb pail of water is swung in a vertical circle of diameter 5 ft. The speed at the top of the path, when the pail is upside down, is 12 ft/sec. What is the centripetal force on the pail? What is producing the centripetal force on the water? What is the minimum speed at the top such that the water stays in the pail? What is producing the centripetal force on the water then?

9. A 200-lb pilot flies in a vertical circle of radius 2000 ft at a constant speed of 250 mph. What is the magnitude of his acceleration, in terms of g? What is the force in pounds exerted on him by the aircraft, at the bottom and at the top of the loop? At this speed, for what radius of loop would he feel "weightless" at the top?

10. At the center of a smooth table 30 in. high there is a small smooth hole. A 4-ft string passes through the hole, with a mass m suspended from its lower end 2 ft below the table top, and an equal mass m fastened to its other end, held at rest on the table top 2 ft from the hole. If this mass were released, how long would it take to reach the hole? Instead it is given a push at right angles to the string. What speed must it be given so that it stays the same distance from the hole? If the string were cut while the system was moving, with what velocity would each mass hit the floor? If the lower mass were pulled down to the floor and held, what would you expect to happen to the speed of the mass on the table? (See Chapter 14.)

11. A cycle track is a circle 100 yd in diameter. (a) If it is not banked, what minimum coefficient of static friction between tires and track is necessary for a speed of 30 mph? (b) At what angle should it be banked for this speed? (c) If it is banked for 30 mph, and the coefficient of static friction is that found in (a), what are the maximum and minimum speeds possible without skidding?

12. A bowl has the shape of a section of a spherical shell of radius 8 in. At its center the depth of the bowl is 4 in. A small marble is placed in the bowl, and the bowl is rotated about its vertical axis at a gradually increasing speed. At what angular speed will the marble no longer stay in the bowl?

13. A package sits on the flat bed of a truck, 6 ft from the open tailgate. The bed of the truck is 4 ft above the road. The coefficients of static and kinetic friction between package and surface are 0.4 and 0.3. In what minimum time can the truck accelerate uniformly to a speed of 30 mph from rest, if the package is not to slip? Suppose the truck accelerates at this rate, but starts with a slight jerk. With what velocity, relative to the road, will the package leave the truck? How far will it have moved horizontally along the road from its original rest position when it hits the road?

14. Masses of 2 kg and 3 kg hang at opposite ends of a string passing over a pulley (massless and frictionless). The pulley is suspended from the ceiling of an elevator by a spring balance. If the system is released from rest, what acceleration would the elevator have to be given in order that the 3-kg mass remain at rest in the earth frame of reference? What would the spring balance read? If the elevator were accelerating upward at 4 cm/sec², what would the spring balance read?

15. A theater uses a revolving stage 30 ft in diameter, rotating at a constant angular velocity. A 100-lb showgirl steps on at one side and by walking along a diameter at a steady speed of 3 ft/sec reaches the opposite side just in time to step off at her original position (with respect to the audience). What is the magnitude of the unbalanced force on her just as she starts across, and as she crosses the center? At what angle with respect to the vertical must she walk at each of these positions?

16. A 2-kg block rests on the smooth floor of a train. A physicist invents a gadget that can exert a constant horizontal force of 0.3 n on the block, always at right angles to the direction of motion of the train, independent of the motion of the block. The train is moving at 10 km/hr (it is a European train) on a straight track when the gadget is applied; 3 sec later the train brakes, coming uniformly to rest in a distance of 20 m. What is the shape of the path of the block on the floor of the train during the deceleration? Determine its displacement on the floor during the first 4 sec of deceleration, assuming it does not hit the wall.

17. A block slides on a smooth horizontal surface, constrained to move in a circle of radius R because it slides against a circular wall. Assume that the coefficient of kinetic friction between the block and the wall is a constant μ. The block at some instant ($t = 0$) has a speed v_0 in its circular path. Derive an expression (in terms of R, μ and v_0) for its speed v at any later time t. Perform a second integration to find the distance S that the block moves in the time $0 \rightarrow t$.

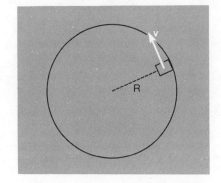

THE EARTH AS
A NON-INERTIAL
FRAME OF REFERENCE

THE MOTION OF THE EARTH

So far we have treated a frame of reference fixed to the earth as an inertial frame, realizing that this is only an approximation. The earth is spinning on its axis and moving in orbit around the sun. We know the period and the radius of both of these roughly circular motions, so we can work out the accelerations involved, relative to an appropriate frame of reference. The earth spins on its axis once every 24 hours, so its period $T_E = 24$ hr $= 24 \times 3600$ sec and its angular frequency or angular speed is $\omega_E = 2\pi/T_E = 7.27 \times 10^{-5}$ rad/sec. Its orbit around the sun has a period $T_s = 1$ yr $= 365 \times 24 \times 3600$ sec, so its angular speed in the sun's frame of reference is $\omega_s = 2\pi/T_s = \omega_E/365 = 2.0 \times 10^{-7}$ rad/sec. Its distance from the sun varies from 91.4 million miles at perihelion to 94.5 million miles at aphelion, with an average distance $R_s = 93 \times 10^6$ miles $= 1.5 \times 10^{13}$ cm. In the sun frame of reference the earth is a particle with a centripetal acceleration of magnitude $a_s = R_s\omega_s^2 = 1.5 \times 10^{13} \times (2.0 \times 10^{-7})^2 = 0.60$ cm/sec^2.

Angular speeds of spin and of orbital motion of the earth.

In a frame of reference in which the earth's axis is at rest, the earth cannot be thought of as a particle. It is approximately a spheroid of polar radius 3951 miles, equatorial radius 3964 miles, so that it is not unreasonable to treat it as a sphere of mean radius $R_E = 3960$ miles $= 6.37 \times 10^8$ cm. In the axis frame of reference a particle at rest at the equator has a centripetal acceleration $a_E = R_E\omega_E^2 = 6.4 \times 10^8 \times (7.3 \times 10^{-5})^2 = 3.4$ cm/sec², while a particle at rest at either pole has zero acceleration.

In Chapter 8 we stated that the best we could do to establish a true inertial frame of reference was to assume that the distant stars established such a frame. Any frame moving at constant velocity relative to this frame will also be an inertial frame. A frame attached to the earth is certainly not such a frame. In addition to its spin on its own axis, it has the acceleration a_s toward the sun, and the sun itself has an acceleration in the frame of the fixed stars.

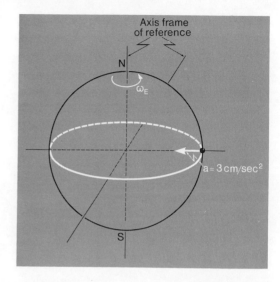

The axis frame of reference.

PARTICLE AT REST AT THE EQUATOR

To see what effect the fact that the earth is not an inertial frame has on measurements made on the earth's surface, we will first **consider that the axis frame of reference is an inertial frame,** in which Newton's laws can be applied. Since $a_s = 0.6$ cm/sec² and $a_E = 3$ cm/sec² are of the same order of magnitude, it might appear that the earth's spin and its orbital motion would have comparable effects, but this is not the case. We will come back to this point.

So far we have been dealing here with the description of motion only, and have not used any dynamical concepts such as force. The only fundamental force we need to consider here is the force of gravity. We are going to investigate what effect the spin of the earth has on the motion of a particle in a number of different situations near the earth's surface. Any particle of mass m near the earth's surface is acted upon by the force of gravitational attraction of the earth, a force we have called the weight **w**, giving the particle an acceleration **g**, where **w** = m**g**, and **g** is the acceleration due to gravity.

We are going to have to be somewhat more precise than we have been before. When we considered that a frame of reference fixed to the earth was an inertial or non-accelerated frame, the only forces that could act in it were forces originating in matter, such as gravitational forces or contact forces; there are no such things as inertial forces in such a frame. If a particle is released near the earth's surface, it is measured to have a certain acceleration **g** downward. "Released" means we exert no forces of constraint on it; the only force on it is the fundamental force of gravity, the force **w** = m**g**. If we hold it at rest by suspending it

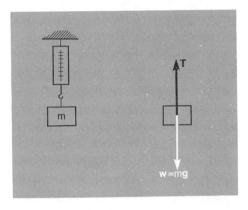

Mass suspended by
a spring balance.

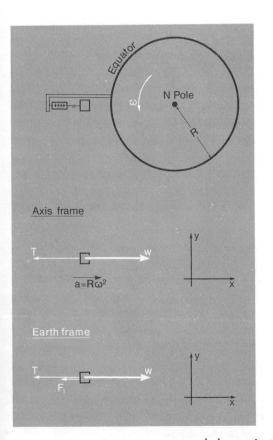

Axis frame

$a = R\omega^2$

Earth frame

Forces on a suspended mass in the
axis frame and in the earth frame.

from a spring balance the upward constraint force
of the spring balance **T** balances the weight:
T + **w** = 0. The reading of the spring balance is
the magnitude of the weight w.

If we recognize the fact that the earth is spinning,
what effect does this have? The force of gravity is
a fundamental force between particles that depends
only on the distance between them, *not* on their
relative motion. The gravitational force between
two particles of masses M and m a distance R apart

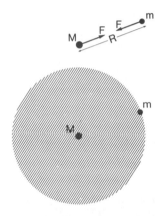

Gravitational force between
a particle and the earth.

has a magnitude $F = GMm/R^2$ where G is a constant called the constant of universal gravitation.
We will show later that a homogeneous sphere
of total mass M acts, as far as its attraction for
masses outside its boundary is concerned, as
though its mass was concentrated at a point at
its center. For the present we will think of the
earth as such a sphere. Then the force of gravity
on a mass m near the surface of the earth is
$w = GMm/R^2$, where R is the radius of the earth.
This force does *not* depend on the relative motion
of M and m, or on the frame of reference used
to describe the motion. The diagram (left) shows
a particle of mass m suspended by a spring balance at the equator. (We are looking down on the

earth from above the north pole, and the size of the mass and balance is some-what exaggerated.) In the axis frame of reference, considered to be an inertial frame, the particle is not at rest, but has a centripetal acceleration **a** of magnitude $a = R\omega^2 = 3.4$ cm/sec². This acceleration keeps changing in direction, so the equation of motion $\mathbf{T} + \mathbf{w} = m\mathbf{a}$ involves vectors changing in direction. How-ever, at any instant a component equation can be written

$$w + (-T) = ma = mR\omega^2$$

In a frame of reference fixed to the earth the particle is at rest. This is not an inertial frame, and there is an inertial force $\mathbf{F}_i = -m\mathbf{a}$ on the particle. The equation of motion is $\mathbf{w} + \mathbf{T} + \mathbf{F}_i = 0$, giving a component equation $w + (-T) + (-F_i) = 0$.

The forces $w = GMm/R^2$, exerted by the earth, and T, exerted by the spring balance, originate in matter and do not depend on the frame of reference. The inertial force F_i exists in one frame, not in the other. In either frame

$$w = T + mR\omega^2$$

showing that the weight is *not* the reading of the spring balance, as we said it was when the earth was considered an inertial frame. If the earth spun faster ω would be larger and T would be smaller because w does not depend on the motion; re-member that T is a constraint force, adjusting itself to be as large as it needs to be.

If ω were large enough, T would become zero. In the axis frame of reference we would say that the particle was moving in a circular orbit with gravity as the centripetal force. In the earth frame of reference we would say—what? We might say that the particle was weightless, or that it was apparently weightless, or that the weight was balanced by the centrifugal force. It all depends on the definition of weight, and that is why we said we must be more precise than be-fore, when the earth was considered an inertial frame. If weight is defined as what the spring balance reads, then the particle is weightless. It is more usual—and more useful—to define weight as the force w exerted by the earth. Some-times a distinction is made by calling w the true weight and T the apparent weight. The normal place to do experiments is on the earth's surface, and the quantity measured is the force T, which depends on the rotation of the earth as well as on the force w.

We will use the term **weight** to mean the gravitational attraction of the earth, the force that would be measured in the earth frame if the earth was not rotating. Note that even if the earth was not rotating, the force w at the surface would not be constant in magnitude, because the earth is not a homogeneous sphere. The expression $w = GMm/R^2$ is based on this assumption, and is only an approxima-tion.

Now how does the acceleration due to gravity **g** enter this description? Accelerations are measured relative to a frame of reference. The acceleration due to gravity is measured in the earth frame of reference. If the earth were not rotating, a particle released at the surface would be subject only to the weight **w**, producing the (true) acceleration due to gravity **g**. The equation of motion is $\mathbf{w} = m\mathbf{g}$. However, the earth *is* rotating, and a particle released at the surface is subject to an inertial force $\mathbf{F}_i$ as well as **w**. The equation of motion is $\mathbf{w} + \mathbf{F}_i = m\mathbf{g}_{\text{obs}}$, where $\mathbf{g}_{\text{obs}}$ is the observed or apparent acceleration due to gravity. The inertial force $\mathbf{F}_i$ is actually a coriolis force (because the particle is moving) as well as a centrifugal force. For the moment we will ignore the coriolis force, and consider that the particle is falling at the equator, so that F_i and w are on the same line in opposite directions and $F_i = mR\omega^2$. Then a component equation of motion can be written

$$w + (-F_i) = mg_{\text{obs}}$$

or $$mg - mR\omega^2 = mg_{\text{obs}}$$

$$g_{\text{obs}} = g - R\omega^2 = g(1 - R\omega^2/g)$$

We have seen that $R\omega^2 = 3.4$ cm/sec², and $g \cong 980$ cm/sec², so the term $R\omega^2/g \cong 3.5 \times 10^{-3}$. The observed acceleration due to gravity differs from the acceleration that would be due to gravity alone by about 0.3% at the equator. The magnitude of the apparent weight $w_{\text{obs}} = mg_{\text{obs}}$ varies by the same amount.

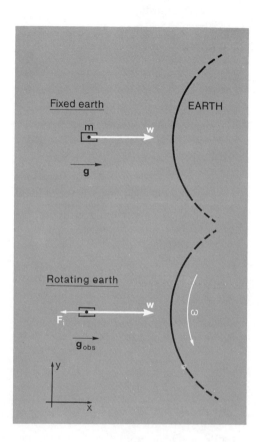

Forces on a falling mass for a fixed earth and a rotating earth.

This description has been made entirely in the earth frame of reference, the frame in which measurements are actually made. We could equally well have deduced this result working in the axis frame of reference, an inertial frame.

If the earth is considered to be a homogeneous sphere then $w = GMm/R^2 = mg$, so that $g = GM/R^2$, a constant that depends on the universal constant G and the mass M and radius R of the earth. Since the earth is not quite a sphere, this expression is an approximation. The value of g_{obs} varies from about 978 cm/sec² at the equator to about 983 cm/sec² at the poles; about half of this variation is due to the rotation of the earth, and the other half is due to a real variation in the force of gravity.

PARTICLE AT REST NOT AT THE EQUATOR

The observed acceleration due to gravity g_{obs}, and the apparent weight vary not only in magnitude but also in direction as we move from the equator to the pole. Think of the situation for a spherical earth, because only then can we speak of the center of the earth. The true acceleration **g** and weight **w** are always directed toward the center but g_{obs} is not.

Pendula at the N pole, at the equator, and at latitude λ.

Think of three pendula hanging at rest (three plumb-bobs), one suspended at the N pole, one at the equator, and one at angle of latitude λ. The one at the N pole hangs "straight down" (i.e., the line of the string passes through the center of the earth) and the tension in the string T is the weight w of the bob. The one at the equator also hangs straight down, but the tension T is not the weight w. The one at latitude λ does not hang straight down, but makes an angle θ with the line through the center of the earth, and tension T is not the weight w. If the line through the center of the earth is called the true vertical, a plumb-line hangs at angle θ with respect to the true vertical. (Note, however, that the notion of true vertical depends on the concept of a truly spherical earth with a "center.")

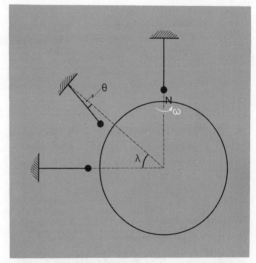

Example: We will work out the angle θ for latitude λ = 45°, so that $\cos \lambda = \sin \lambda = 1/\sqrt{2}$. The particle of mass m is moving in a circle of radius $R \cos \lambda = R/\sqrt{2}$ in the axis frame of reference, so it has a centripetal acceleration $R\omega^2/\sqrt{2}$ in this frame. This means that in the earth frame of reference there is an inertial force $F_i = mR\omega^2/\sqrt{2}$ directed outward. The equation of motion is $\mathbf{T} + \mathbf{w} + \mathbf{F}_i = 0$. Choosing co-ordinate axes in the directions shown, the component equations are

$$(-T \cos \theta) + w + (-F_i \cos \lambda) = 0$$
$$T \sin \theta + (-F_i \sin \lambda) = 0$$

or using

$$w = mg \quad \sin \lambda = \cos \lambda = 1/\sqrt{2}$$
$$\text{and} \quad F_i = mR\omega^2/\sqrt{2}$$

$$-T \cos \theta + mg - mR\omega^2/2 = 0 \quad \text{or} \quad T \cos \theta = mg - mR\omega^2/2$$
$$T \sin \theta - mR\omega^2/2 = 0 \quad \text{or} \quad T \sin \theta = mR\omega^2/2$$

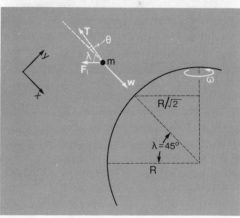

Forces on a pendulum at latitude 45°, in the axis frame.

Dividing, $\tan\theta = \dfrac{R\omega^2/2}{g - R\omega^2/2} = \dfrac{1}{2g/(R\omega^2) - 1} \cong \dfrac{R\omega^2}{2g} = 1.7 \times 10^{-3}$

(We have calculated that $R\omega^2/g \cong 3.5 \times 10^{-3}$; therefore the -1 in the denominator can be neglected with respect to $2g/(R\omega^2) \sim 570$.) Since $\tan\theta \cong \theta$ for small θ, the angle with the true vertical is $\theta = 1.7 \times 10^{-3}$ radians $= 1.7 \times 10^{-3}$ rad $\times 57$ deg/rad $= 0.10°$. For this small angle $\cos\theta = 1 - \theta^2/2 \doteq 1 - (1.5 \times 10^{-6}) = 0.9999985$, and $T = T \cos\theta = mg - mR\omega^2/2 = mg(1 - R\omega^2/2g)$.

At the equator $T = w - mR\omega^2 = mg(1 - R\omega^2/g)$. The tension T differs from the true weight w by 0.3%. At $\lambda = 45°$ the difference is half this.

PARTICLE IN MOTION ON THE ROTATING EARTH

When a particle is at rest in the earth frame of reference, the inertial force on it is the centrifugal force only, but if the particle is moving there is a coriolis force as well. Think of a frame of reference S, an inertial frame fixed to the axis, and a frame S' fixed to the earth, rotating with the angular velocity $\boldsymbol{\omega}$ with respect to S. Displacements in both frames are measured with respect to the center of the earth O, so $\mathbf{r} = \mathbf{r}'$. In the earth frame S' we have shown that there is a centrifugal force $\mathbf{F}_{\mathrm{cf}} = -m\boldsymbol{\omega} \times (\boldsymbol{\omega} \times \mathbf{r})$ and a coriolis force $\mathbf{F}_{\mathrm{cor}} = -2m\boldsymbol{\omega} \times \mathbf{v}'$ where $\mathbf{v}'$ is the velocity of the particle in the earth or S' frame. The force $\mathbf{F}_{\mathrm{cf}}$ is always directed outward from the axis (*not* from the center O) but the direction of $\mathbf{F}_{\mathrm{cor}}$ depends on the direction of $\mathbf{v}'$.

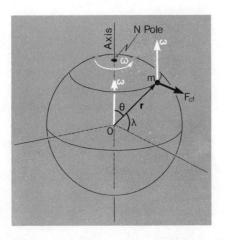

The centrifugal force is always outward from the axis.

For a particle near the earth surface $\mathbf{r}$ is constant in magnitude $|\mathbf{r}| = R$ but the vector $\mathbf{F}_{\mathrm{cf}} = -m\boldsymbol{\omega} \times (\boldsymbol{\omega} \times \mathbf{r})$ depends on the location: $|\boldsymbol{\omega} \times \mathbf{r}| = \omega R \sin\theta = \omega R \cos\lambda$ at latitude λ, so $F_{\mathrm{cf}} = mR\omega^2\cos\lambda$, as we have seen. The magnitude of the centrifugal force is a maximum at the equator, decreasing to zero at the poles.

A particle moving with a velocity $\mathbf{v}'$ toward the center O at some instant is acted upon by a force $\mathbf{F}_{\mathrm{cor}} = -2m\boldsymbol{\omega} \times \mathbf{v}'$ tangent to the parallel of latitude, toward the east. At the equator $\boldsymbol{\omega}$ and $\mathbf{v}'$ would be perpendicular and the magnitude is $F_{\mathrm{cor}} = 2m\omega v'$. Of course this sideways force will accelerate the particle sideways, so that its velocity is no longer straight down, but we can make an approximate calculation of the size of the effect knowing that the coriolis force is small compared to the force of gravity.

A particle released at a point near the earth would accelerate straight down under the force of gravity if the earth were not rotating. In time t it acquires a

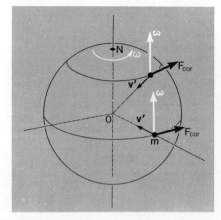

Coriolis force on
a moving particle.

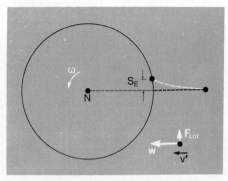

Effect of the Coriolis force on a
particle falling at the equator.

velocity $v' = gt$. If the earth is rotating, at the equator there is an eastward
force $F_{cor} = 2m\omega v' = 2m\omega gt$, *assuming* v' remains at right angles to ω. This
gives an eastward acceleration $a_E = F_{cor}/m = 2\omega gt$. Integrating $a_E = dv_E/dt$,

$$\int_0^{v_E} dv_E = 2\omega g \int_0^t t \, dt$$

giving an eastward velocity $v_E = \omega gt^2$. Integrating again,

$$v_E = \frac{ds_E}{dt} \qquad \int_0^{s_E} ds_E = \omega g \int_0^t t^2 \, dt$$

giving an eastward displacement $s_E = \frac{1}{3}\omega gt^3$.

Example: The leaning tower of Pisa, where Galileo did experiments with falling objects,
is 179 ft high. The time to fall from this height is $t = \sqrt{2s/g} = \sqrt{(2 \times 179)/32} = 3.3$
sec. The eastward deflection (if the tower were at the equator) is $s_E = \frac{1}{3}\omega gt^3 =$
$\frac{1}{3}(7.3 \times 10^{-5})(32)(3.3)^3 \cong 3 \times 10^{-2}$ ft $\cong 0.3$ in.
   The Empire State Building is 1250 ft high. A particle dropped from this height at
the equator would take about 9 sec to fall, with an eastward deflection s_E of about 6 in.
Just before it lands its vertical speed would be nearly 300 ft/sec, and its sideways speed
v_E about 0.2 ft/sec, so the assumption that v', the resultant velocity, remains perpendicular to ω is a very good one.

   At the equator then, a plumb-line hangs straight down but a falling object
does not fall along this line. The eastward shift can be measured, but it is difficult because of the effect of air resistance and because tall buildings sway by
much more than the amount of the shift. Note that the shift is toward the east,
the direction of the earth's turning—the particle lands **ahead** of where it would
if it fell straight down.

THE EFFECT OF THE CORIOLIS FORCE

It is only on a very large scale that the coriolis force produces readily observable effects. The movements of large air masses are influenced by this force, and this causes cyclones to rotate counter-clockwise in the northern hemisphere and clockwise in the southern hemisphere, as can be seen as follows.

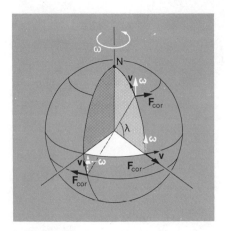

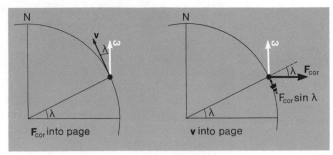

Any particle moving horizontally in the northern hemisphere experiences a sideways Coriolis force to the right.

Direction of Coriolis forces.

A particle moving with velocity **v** (we will drop the prime ['] now) **tangent to the earth's surface** experiences a coriolis force with a component to the right in the northern hemisphere, a component to the left in the southern hemisphere. (At the equator the force is straight up or straight down, and has no sideways component. If **v** is due north or due south at the equator, then $\boldsymbol{\omega} \times \mathbf{v} = 0$ and the coriolis force is zero.) Think of a particle at latitude λ. If **v** is due N (tangentially) then $\mathbf{F}_{cor}$ is due E, with magnitude $F_{cor} = 2m\omega v \sin \lambda$; if **v** is due E, then $\mathbf{F}_{cor}$ is straight out from the axis, with magnitude $F_{cor} = 2m\omega v$, and it has a component south (tangentially) of

$$F_{cor} \sin \lambda = 2m\omega v \sin \lambda$$

A tangential velocity in any direction can be resolved into a N–S and an E–W component, so in general any particle moving tangentially experiences a sideways force of magnitude $2 m\omega v \sin \lambda$. Thus a mass of air moving in any tangential direction experiences a sideways force per unit mass of magnitude $2\omega v \sin \lambda$. Masses of air converging on a low pressure area in the northern hemisphere will be deflected to the right, creating a counter-clockwise vortex. There will be equilibrium when the outward force due to the coriolis force is equal to the inward centripetal force mv^2/R provided by the pressure gradient, that is, there will be circular motion of radius R such that $2\omega v \sin \lambda \sim v^2/R$. For a 20-mph wind ($\sim 30$ ft/sec) at latitude $45°$ the radius of the vortex is of the order of

Counterclockwise rotation of air around a low pressure area.

$$R \sim \frac{v}{2\omega \sin \lambda} \sim \frac{30}{2(7 \times 10^{-5})(0.7)} \sim 3 \times 10^5 \text{ ft} \sim 50 \text{ miles}$$

Nowadays cameras mounted in earth satellites orbiting above the atmosphere provide clear pictures of large-scale atmospheric activity. The radius of an observed vortex is a measure of the wind velocities involved.

THE FOUCAULT PENDULUM

You are probably familiar with a Foucault pendulum, and may have seen one operating at a science museum or at the United Nations building in New York. The name is used for any pendulum used to illustrate the rotation of the earth on its axis, and therefore to show that the earth is not an inertial frame of reference. The pendulum must be suspended in such a way that it can swing freely (or at least with equal freedom) in any plane, and then it can be observed that the plane of vibration gradually changes (unless the pendulum is at the equator). The plane of vibration rotates very slowly, taking at least 24 hours to rotate through one revolution, so the pendulum must oscillate for a long time. If a very long pendulum is used, the period is long, the bob moves slowly, and air resistance (which is roughly proportional to the speed) is minimized. In Foucault's original demonstration at the Paris Pantheon the pendulum was 70 m long, with a period $T_F = 2\pi\sqrt{l/g} = 2\pi\sqrt{70/9.8} \cong 17$ sec. The UN pendulum is about 75 ft long, with a period $T_F = 2\pi\sqrt{75/32} \cong 10$ sec. However, the vibrations of any pendulum ultimately die away due to friction, and demonstration Foucault pendula are sometimes driven, for example, by using an electromagnet to give a push each cycle. If this is done care must be taken not to cheat; that is, the magnetic field must not be allowed to change the plane of vibration.

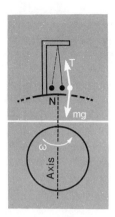

Foucault pendulum
at the N pole.

It is not difficult to see how a Foucault pendulum works if it is at the north pole. Thinking of the axis frame of reference as an inertial frame, the only forces acting are the force of gravity directed toward the center of the earth, and the tension in the supporting string or wire. If the pendulum is deflected from its equilibrium position, both of these have components to restore it to this position. (The main restoring force comes from the tension, since the direction of the force of gravity is essentially unchanged for ordinary amplitudes.) If the pendulum is released there is no sideways force and it will oscillate in a plane. However, this is in the axis frame of reference. In this frame the earth is rotating with an angular speed $\omega = 7.3 \times 10^{-5}$ rad/sec, and it rotates under the pendulum with a period $T_0 = 2\pi/\omega = 24$ hr = 1 day. The direction of rotation is toward the east, counterclockwise looking down from above the north pole.

In the earth frame of reference, the frame in which we observe and measure the motion, the pendulum does not vibrate in a fixed plane. Its plane of vibration rotates in the clockwise direction at an angular speed ω, or with period $T_E = 24$ hr. In the earth frame there is a sideways force, the coriolis force.

We can consider that the motion of the pendulum bob is parallel to the earth surface; that is, the velocity is tangential. At the north pole the coriolis force has a magnitude $F_{cor} = 2m\omega v$, and it deflects the pendulum bob to the right, causing the plane of vibration to rotate clockwise. The speed of the pendulum in its swing is continuously changing (a maximum at the center, zero at the ends of the swing) so the size of the deflecting force keeps changing, but we know that the overall result is to cause the plane of vibration to rotate through one revolution in 24 hr: $T_E = 24$ hr.

A detailed analysis of the motion of a pendulum suspended at a location other than the pole is rather messy, but you can see what the result would be. We showed that any particle moving tangentially with speed v in any direction at latitude λ experiences a sideways force $2m\omega v \sin \lambda$; the sideways force is a maximum at the pole ($\lambda = 90°$) decreasing to zero at the equator. The lower the sideways force, the slower the speed of rotation of the plane of vibration of a Foucault pendulum; at the pole, the angular speed is ω, at latitude λ it is $\omega \sin \lambda$. The time for the plane to rotate through one revolution is $T_E = 24$ hr at the pole, and is $T_\lambda = T_E/\sin \lambda$ at latitude λ. At New York, latitude $40° 48'$, $\sin \lambda = 0.653$, so the time for a revolution of the UN pendulum is $T_\lambda = 24/0.653 = 36.8$ hr.

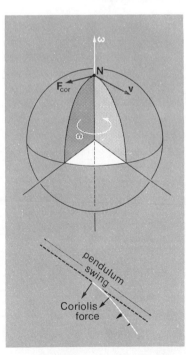

The sideways Coriolis force
changes the plane of swing.

THE EFFECT OF
THE MOTION OF THE EARTH IN ORBIT

We have considered the axis frame of reference to be an inertial frame, and have seen that the spin of the earth has a small but observable influence on measurements made in the earth frame of reference; a pendulum hanging at latitude 45° makes an angle of 0.1° with the direction it would have if the earth were not rotating; the tension in its supporting string is 0.15 % less than it would be if the earth were not rotating; if it is set swinging its plane of vibration rotates with an angular speed of 5×10^{-5} rad/sec, whereas it would stay in a fixed plane if the earth were not rotating. These effects arise because of the spin of the earth at angular speed $\omega_E = 7.3 \times 10^{-5}$ rad/sec, giving a centripetal acceleration at the equator of $a_E = 3.4$ cm/sec², relative to the axis frame.

We know that the axis frame is not really an inertial frame. In the sun frame of reference the earth has an angular speed $\omega_s = 2.0 \times 10^{-7}$ rad/sec, and a centripetal acceleration $a_s = 0.60$ cm/sec², about one-fifth of a_E. It might appear then that this motion would lead to effects about one-fifth as great (on measurements in the earth frame) as the spin motion. However, this is not so. This is because the only fundamental force involved is the force of gravity; all the objects involved in experiments on earth, and the earth itself, are accelerated toward the sun at nearly the same rate.

To see the size of the effect, think of a mass m released near the earth's surface on the side of the earth opposite the sun. In the frame of reference of the sun, considered an inertial frame, the only forces acting on the mass are the gravitational force $w = GM_E m / R_E^2$ exerted by the earth, and gravitational force $F_s =$

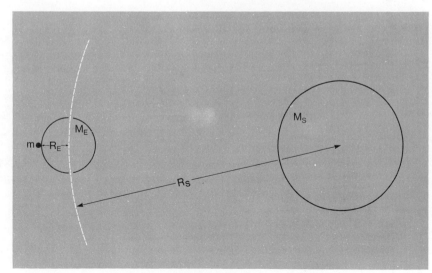

A mass m on the opposite side of the earth from the sun.

$GM_sm/(R_s + R_E)^2$ exerted by the sun. (Note R_s is the radius of the earth's orbit around the sun, not the radius of the sun.) In this position these forces are in the same direction, so the total force accelerating the mass toward the sun is

$$F_s + w = \frac{GM_Em}{R_E^2} + \frac{GM_sm}{(R_s + R_E)^2} \cong \frac{GM_Em}{R_E^2} + \frac{GM_sm}{R_s^2}\left(1 - 2\frac{R_E}{R_s}\right)$$

In the sun frame of reference the earth has an acceleration toward the sun $a_s = GM_s/R_s^2 = 0.6$ cm/sec². To make a transformation to the earth frame of reference we must introduce an inertial force $F_i = -ma_s$, a force in the opposite direction. In the earth frame the total force on the mass is

$$F_s + w - F_i = \frac{GM_Em}{R_E^2} + \frac{GM_sm}{R_s^2}\left(-2\frac{R_E}{R_s}\right)$$

giving it an acceleration

$$a = \frac{F_s + w - F_i}{m} = \frac{GM_E}{R_E^2} + \frac{GM_s}{R_s^2}\left(-2\frac{R_E}{R_s}\right) = g - a_s\left(2\frac{R_E}{R_s}\right)$$

The acceleration in the earth frame is different from the acceleration g due to the earth alone by an amount that depends not on a_s, but on $a_s(2R_E/R_s) \sim 0.6 \times 2 \times 4 \times 10^{-5} \sim 5 \times 10^{-5}$ cm/sec². The acceleration $g \sim 980$ cm/sec², so the correction is a fraction 5×10^{-8} of this.

The effect of the earth's orbital motion is negligible in almost all experimental situations. The effect of the earth's spin is a factor 10^5 larger, but this too can be neglected in most experiments. We can assume that the earth is an inertial frame of reference to an accuracy of better than 1%.

Unless otherwise stated we will continue to assume, as we have done before, that a frame of reference attached to the earth's surface is an inertial frame.

Questions for discussion

1. The earth is not homogeneous, and is not a perfect sphere. Does it have a center of mass? If so, is the gravitational force the earth exerts on an object at its surface a vector pointing directly toward the center of mass? Is the apparent weight of the object a vector pointing directly toward the center of mass?

2. The centripetal acceleration of a particle at the equator is 3.4 cm/sec² toward the center of the earth. The acceleration due to gravity is also directed toward the center of the earth. Since these accelerations are in the same direction, why is the observed acceleration due to gravity **less** than the true acceleration due to gravity?

3. Is the period of oscillation of a Foucault pendulum related to the period of rotation of its plane of vibration? At the equator is the period of rotation of its plane zero or infinity?

4. We once had a rather spirited discussion with a lady tourist in the United Nations building, about the Foucault pendulum. She explained to us very positively that it demonstrated perpetual motion. What would you have said to her?

5. The effect of the coriolis force on a falling object is to make the object land at a point east of where it would have landed if the earth were not rotating. The earth is rotating toward the east, so it can be said the object lands **ahead** of where it would have landed. This may appear to be wrong, based on the following argument: During the time it takes the object to fall the earth will rotate, so the object should land **behind** where it would have if it fell in zero time. What is wrong with this argument?

6. Does the reading of a spring balance depend on where on earth it is used? Does the reading of an equal arm balance depend on where on earth it is used? Does an equal arm balance measure mass, apparent weight, or true weight? Is **weighing** an unambiguous term?

7. For points that are not at the equator, is it reasonable to define the apparent weight of a mass as the tension in a string supporting the mass at rest? Would this weight agree with that determined using various types of scales, to a high degree of accuracy? Suppose the earth were spinning faster, so that the angle θ made by a plumb-line with the true vertical was several degrees. Would it then be better to define apparent weight as the tension T in the string, or as the component $T \cos \theta$ in the direction of the true vertical?

8. It is sometimes suggested that the direction of rotation of water in a bathtub as it drains out is different in the northern hemisphere than in the southern hemisphere. Should it be clockwise or counter-clockwise in the northern hemisphere? Have you noticed whether or not it is?

Problems

1. What is the speed, in the axis frame of reference, of a point on the earth's surface at the equator? What is the speed of a satellite in a circular orbit at a height of 500 miles? Where would a satellite have to be in orbit in order that it could remain at rest with respect to the earth? (See Chapter 24.)

2. If the angle with the true vertical of a plumb-line at latitude 45° were 1.0° rather than 0.10°, what would be the period of the earth's rotation?

3. Suppose that the earth makes 1 rev on its axis in 3 hr rather than 24 hr. A 2-kg mass hangs by a cord at latitude 45°. What angle does the cord make with the true vertical, and what is its tension? What is the apparent weight of the 2-kg mass?

4. If every object at the equator had zero apparent weight, what would be the length of the day? For this condition derive an expression relating the angle of latitude λ to the angle θ a plumb-bob makes with true vertical; derive an expression for tension T in a cord suspending a mass m at latitude λ. What are θ and T for $\lambda = 45°$?

5. Determine the centrifugal force and the coriolis force on a 10-kg mass that is **(a)** at rest at the equator, **(b)** moving straight down at 100 m/sec at the equator, **(c)** moving N at 100 m/sec at the equator, **(d)** moving straight down at 100 m/sec at the N pole, **(e)** moving tangentially at 100 m/sec at the N pole, **(f)** moving straight down at 100 m/sec at latitude 30°, **(g)** moving N tangentially at 100 m/sec at latitude 30°, **(h)** moving E tangentially at 100 m/sec at latitude 30°.

6. What velocity would a particle require at the equator in order that the centrifugal and coriolis forces on it be equal in magnitude and direction?

12

DYNAMICS OF SIMPLE HARMONIC MOTION OF A PARTICLE

In Chapter 5 we described the particular kind of periodic motion called simple harmonic motion. It was motion of a particle P in one-dimension such that the acceleration was proportional to the displacement from a point, and oppositely directed. Choosing the x-axis of a co-ordinate system along the motion, $a = d^2x/dt^2 \propto -x$, or $a + \omega^2 x = 0$. The constant ω is the angular frequency of the SHM, related to the period T and frequency f by $\omega = 2\pi f = 2\pi/T$. The general solution to the differential equation is $x = x_0 \sin(\omega t + \delta)$, where x_0 is the amplitude of the motion and δ is the phase, or phase angle.

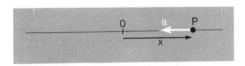

SHM if $a \propto -x$ and motion in one dimension.

DYNAMIC DEFINITION OF SIMPLE HARMONIC MOTION

To discuss the dynamics of SHM we introduce the mass m of the particle, and the force **F** on it. Since **a** is in one-dimension, the resultant force $\mathbf{F} = m\mathbf{a}$ on the particle will be in one-dimension.

Since
$$\mathbf{F} = m\mathbf{a} = -m\omega^2\mathbf{x} = -k\mathbf{x}$$

SHM can be defined dynamically as motion in which there is a **restoring force proportional to displacement.** The constant k is called the **force constant** for the motion.

$$\omega^2 = \frac{k}{m} \qquad \omega = \sqrt{\frac{k}{m}} \qquad f = \frac{1}{2\pi}\sqrt{\frac{k}{m}} \qquad T = 2\pi\sqrt{\frac{m}{k}}$$

The period of vibration depends on the mass m, a property of the **system,** and on the force constant k, a property of the **environment.** For a large m, large inertia, the period is long; for a large k, large restoring force, the period is short.

These remarks encompass the fundamental facts about the dynamics of SHM, but as usual some examples will help to illustrate them.

336

ELASTIC RESTORING FORCES AND IDEAL SPRINGS

We have used and will use the model of a rigid body in describing motion of systems of particles, but there is no such thing; every body is deformed if a force is applied to it—it stretches or twists or bends or compresses. Internal stresses are set up in the body, tending to restore it to its normal shape, and these restoring forces are often the forces producing simple harmonic motion. The amount of deformation of solids is usually small, and that is why the rigid body model is a useful one.

A spring is a solid formed in such a way that it can be deformed a large amount. Locally the deformation is small (the metal wire is twisted a little) but the overall effect is a large deformation.

When a body is deformed it is said to behave with perfect elasticity if three conditions are fulfilled: (1) the deformation is instantaneous, (2) the deformation is completely recoverable, (3) the amount of deformation is proportional to the

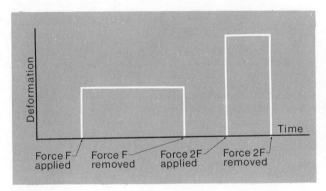

Ideal elastic
behavior.

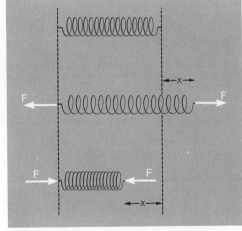

Elongation or compression
of an ideal spring: $x \propto F$.

force applied. A body behaving in this way is said to be Hookian, or to obey **Hooke's law.** While no real solid is perfectly elastic, the behavior of metals is a good approximation for small deformations. An external force F applied to a Hookian spring stretches (or compresses) it an amount x, where $x \propto F$. Thus $F = kx$, where k is a constant for the particular spring, the **spring constant.** Its value depends on the elasticity of the metal and the geometry of the spring.

When the external force F acts on the spring holding it extended, there is an internal force equal in magnitude, because every point in the spring is at rest.

In our examples we will use ideal springs, which are not only Hookian but massless.

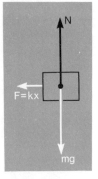

F=kx

N

mg

Forces on the
released mass.

Example: A block of mass $m = 1$ kg rests on a smooth track, attached to the end of an ideal spring whose other end is fixed. A horizontal force of 100 gm is necessary to hold the mass displaced 2 cm from its equilibrium position.

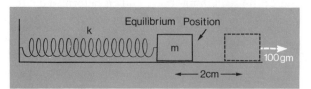

Mass displaced
from an equilib-
rium position.

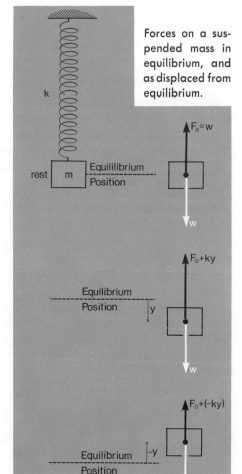

Forces on a sus-
pended mass in
equilibrium, and
as displaced from
equilibrium.

If the block is released, it will vibrate with SHM of amplitude 2 cm about its equilibrium position. The spring constant k is the force constant for the motion: there are other forces on the system (the block) but only the spring exerts a force in the horizontal direction.

The spring constant is $k = F/x = 100/2$ gm/cm $=$ 50 gm/cm $= 5$ kg/m $= 49$ newton/m $= 4.9 \times 10^4$ dyne/cm. Any of these is an appropriate unit for k.

The period of vibration is $T = 2\pi \sqrt{m/k}$. To determine T in seconds we will use a consistent system of units. In mks units $m = 1$ kg, $T = 2\pi \sqrt{1/49} = 2\pi/7$ sec. Check the units.

The displacement of the block as a function of time, referred to the equilibrium position, is

$$x = 2 \sin 7t$$

where x is in cm, t is in seconds.

Think now of the same spring, used to suspend the same block. In the equilibrium position the weight of the block will extend the spring an amount $w/k = 1/5$ kg/(kg/m) $= 0.2$ m $= 20$ cm. We will assume that our ideal spring can stand this large extension, and maintain the same k.

Now suppose the block is drawn down 2 cm and then released. It will vibrate with SHM in the vertical direction. This time both the weight and the spring act in the vertical direction, but the **resultant** force is a restoring force proportional to the displacement y from the equilibrium position. The total force $F_0 + ky$ exerted by the spring is not the restoring force—the spring holds the block up as well as providing the restoring force. The equation of motion is

$$y = 2 \sin 7t$$

where y is in cm, t is in seconds.

Now use the same spring to join two 1-kg masses, free to move in the same smooth track. If the masses are pulled apart 2 cm, and released, what happens? Are the amplitude and period of vibration the same as before, or not? We could answer these questions now, but will wait until the next chapter when we discuss two-particle systems.

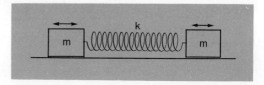

What is the period if both masses vibrate?

GRAVITATIONAL RESTORING FORCES AND THE SIMPLE PENDULUM

The restoring force producing SHM is often an elastic force due to the deformation of solid matter, but it may also be due to the force of gravity. Since the force of gravity always acts in the same direction (in a uniform gravitational field), it might appear that it cannot be a restoring force, and in a way this is

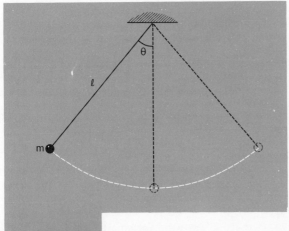

Forces on a pendulum resolved into components in different directions.

true. However, the force of gravity in conjunction with constraint forces can produce a restoring force.

We previously discussed the motion of a small block whirling in a vertical circle at the end of a string. We use this same example, but now do not give the block such a high speed. If the block is held with the string making an angle θ with the vertical, and released, it will vibrate in a plane in periodic motion. The motion is *not* simple harmonic however. There is a restoring force, but the restoring force is not proportional to the displacement, and the acceleration and velocity are not in the same line (the motion is not one-dimensional).

The only forces acting are the weight $\mathbf{w} = m\mathbf{g}$ downward and the tension $\mathbf{T}$ in the string, a constraint force. If we resolve forces in the vertical and horizontal directions, we can think of the force $T \sin \theta$ as a restoring force. If we resolve the forces into components perpendicular and parallel to the string, we can think of the force $w \sin \theta$ as a restoring force.

If the block is considered a particle, and the string considered massless and inextensible (it could be a massless rigid rod) the system is called a **simple pendulum.** As usual there is no such thing, but a good deal about the properties of real pendula can be deduced by thinking about this idealization.

The periodic motion of a pendulum is simple harmonic if the amplitude of vibration is small enough. How small this is depends on the accuracy of measurement required; only for amplitude zero would the motion be exactly simple harmonic.

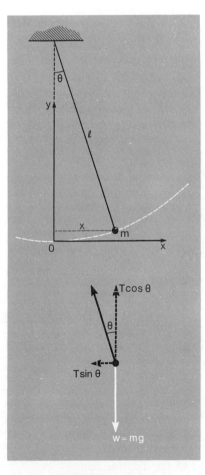

The particle of mass m is constrained to move in a circle, so angular variables θ, ω, α are appropriate for describing the motion, but we will not use these at this point.

Choose co-ordinate axes in the plane of motion, y-axis upward, origin O at the lowest (equilibrium) position of the particle m. The component equations of motion, in terms of magnitudes, are

$$-T \sin \theta = ma_x \qquad T \cos \theta - mg = ma_y$$

Using $\sin \theta = x/l$, and assuming that θ is a small angle so that $\cos \theta = 1$, these become

$$-Tx/l = ma_x \qquad T - mg = ma_y$$

These are valid for small θ no matter how fast the pendulum is moving—even if it has been released with the string horizontal the equations apply when the string is near the vertical. However, we want to approximate one-dimensional motion, which means we want to set $a_y = 0$. The value of a_y depends on the speed; near the center point O it is approximately a centripetal acceleration v^2/l. Only if we assume the speed v is always small can we assume $a_y \cong 0$. This means the amplitude of vibration must be small. If the pendulum is released near O, its speed at every point will be low.

If $a_y = 0$, then $T = mg$ and the component equation in the x-direction becomes

Forces with respect to horizontal and vertical axes.

$$-(mg) \left(\frac{x}{l}\right) = ma_x \quad \text{or} \quad a_x + \frac{g}{l} x = 0 \quad \text{or} \quad \frac{d^2x}{dt^2} + \frac{g}{l} x = 0$$

This is the differential equation of simple harmonic motion, of angular frequency

$$\omega = \sqrt{g/l} \quad \text{and period} \quad T = 2\pi \sqrt{l/g}$$

This has not been a very satisfactory discussion—it was rather messy and imprecise. In Chapter 17 we will tackle this by the methods of rotational dynamics, and obtain the result more elegantly. However, the fact is that the situation is messy, in the sense that the period T of the periodic motion actually depends on the **amplitude** of the motion. A fundamental feature of simple harmonic motion, and a feature that makes it very useful, is that the amplitude and the period (or frequency) are **independent** quantities. In

$$x = x_0 \sin(\omega t + \delta) = x_0 \sin(2\pi t/T + \delta)$$

the angular frequency $\omega = \sqrt{k/m}$ is a property of the system and its surroundings, while the amplitude x_0 depends only on the initial conditions. If you start the system with amplitude x_0, it vibrates with frequency ω no matter what x_0 is.

An exact analysis of the simple pendulum shows that the period T is

$$T = 2\pi\sqrt{l/g} \left[1 + \tfrac{1}{4} \sin^2(\theta_0/2) + (9/64) \sin^4(\theta_0/2) + \cdots \right]$$

where θ_0 is the maximum angular displacement. Only if $\theta_0 = 0$ is the motion exactly simple harmonic—and then there is no motion! However, the period is very close to that for SHM for small amplitudes.

Example: Even for $\theta_0 = 60°$ the error is not large. For this amplitude the term

$$\tfrac{1}{4} \sin^2 \theta_0/2 = \tfrac{1}{4} \sin^2 30° = \tfrac{1}{4}(\tfrac{1}{2})^2 = \tfrac{1}{16}$$

and successive terms are much smaller. The difference between the actual T and the value assuming SHM is about 7%.

If $\theta_0 = 0.2$ rad (about 11°), $\tfrac{1}{4} \sin^2(\theta_0/2) = \tfrac{1}{4}(0.1)^2 = 0.25 \times 10^{-2}$ and the difference is about one-quarter of 1%.

Simple harmonic motion occurs when there is a restoring force F proportional to displacement, $F = -kx$. For the pendulum near O the relation between F and x may be approximated by a linear function with a high degree of accuracy, but it is an approximation. A pendulum whose period is truly independent of its amplitude is said to be isochronous. One way of making an isochronous

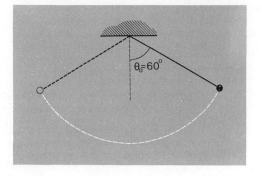

A pendulum with amplitude 60°.

$\theta_0{=}60°$

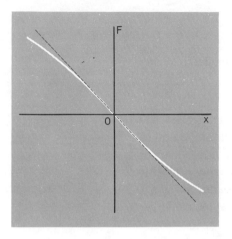

The restoring force on a pendulum
is not proportional to displacement.

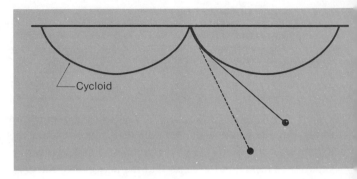

An isochronous
pendulum.

pendulum is to suspend the bob in such a way that the string follows the curve of a cycloid (the path of the bob is then a cycloid too). It can be shown that for this system the period is independent of the amplitude.

GRAVITATIONAL AND INERTIAL MASS

The period of a simple pendulum (or any pendulum swinging under gravity) does not depend on the mass. This is because the force constant k is proportional to the mass, and therefore $\omega = \sqrt{k/m}$ is independent of the mass. The restoring force is

$$T \sin \theta = T \left(\frac{x}{l}\right) \cong \left(\frac{mg}{l}\right) x = kx$$

where $\qquad k = \dfrac{mg}{l} \qquad$ and $\qquad \omega = \sqrt{\dfrac{k}{m}} = \sqrt{\dfrac{mg}{ml}} = \sqrt{\dfrac{g}{l}}$

There is more to this cancellation of the m's than you might think, because actually

$$\omega = \sqrt{\frac{m_g g}{m_i l}}$$

where m_i is the inertial mass, the physical property of a body that represents its resistance to being accelerated, and m_g is the gravitational mass, the physical property of a body that determines its gravitational interaction with the other bodies in the universe. We stated as an experimental fact in Chapter 9 that these two kinds of mass are proportional to one another, or equal to one another if units are appropriately chosen. One kind of experiment that can be done to investigate this is to use identical pendula made of materials of different density. Such experiments were performed by Newton, and have been done by many others, always with the same result: the period is independent of the material (i.e., of the mass) and therefore $m_i \propto m_g$. During the early part of this century a series of experiments were performed by Eotvos using a different kind of pendulum, a torsion pendulum. These extremely sensitive experiments showed that the gravitational and inertial masses of an object were proportional to an accuracy of 1 part in 10^9. More recently (Dicke, 1961) the experiments have been repeated with an accuracy of 1 part in 10^{11}, still with the same result.

From the point of view of classical physics the equivalence of gravitational and inertial mass must be regarded as a remarkable experimental fact, but one that cannot be explained on a theoretical basis. Classically there appears to be no reason why these two properties of an object should be related. It is of course natural to feel that there must be more to this than sheer accident, that there must be some underlying significance to equivalence, and in the view of modern theories of physics there is. The general theory of relativity is basically a theory of gravitation in which equivalence plays a fundamental role.

CONICAL PENDULUM

A **conical pendulum** is a pendulum where the pendulum bob is projected to move in a horizontal circle with a constant speed v, so the string moves around the surface of a cone. The motion of the particle is circular, not simple harmonic, although viewed from the side it appears to be SHM because the projection of circular motion on a diameter is SHM.

This situation is simpler than that of the pendulum vibrating in a plane because the magnitudes of all quantities involved are constant. The component equations of motion, in terms of magnitudes, are

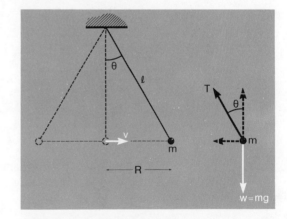

Motion of a conical pendulum.

$$T \sin \theta = ma_x = m(v^2/R)$$
$$T \cos \theta - mg = ma_y = 0$$

Dividing, $\tan \theta = v^2/Rg$. The angular speed of the particle in the circle is

$$\omega = \frac{v}{R}, \quad \text{so} \quad \omega^2 = \frac{v^2}{R^2} = \frac{g \tan \theta}{R}$$

These results are valid for any angle θ. If θ is small, so that

$$\sin \theta = R/l \cong \tan \theta \quad \text{then} \quad \omega^2 = \frac{g}{R}\left(\frac{R}{l}\right) = \frac{g}{l}$$

Same period for
small amplitudes.

and the angular speed of rotation $\omega = \sqrt{g/l}$ is the same as the angular frequency of a simple pendulum. For small amplitudes the period is the same whether the pendulum vibrates in a plane or moves in a circle.

DAMPED AND FORCED VIBRATIONS

Simple harmonic motion is an idealized motion that cannot exist if frictional forces act, because it depends on a resultant restoring force proportional to displacement, independent of direction of motion. If there is a frictional force it opposes the motion, and the resultant cannot be independent of direction.

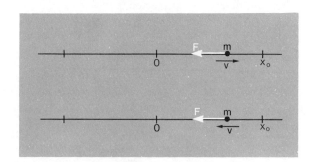

Restoring force independent of direction of motion.

Vibrations left to themselves die away, or are damped. They can be maintained by applying a periodic force to keep them going. We will look briefly here at damped harmonic motion and forced harmonic motion, but this is a topic we will not explore in detail, only give a few results. Think of a particle moving on the x-axis with a restoring force proportional to displacement and a retarding frictional force proportional to velocity. The equation of motion is

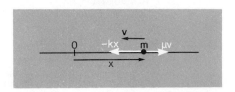

Frictional force
opposes motion.

$$-kx - \mu v = ma$$

where k is a force constant and μ is a frictional constant. This gives

$$m \frac{d^2x}{dt^2} + \mu \frac{dx}{dt} + kx = 0$$

the differential equation for **damped harmonic motion.** The solution $x = x(t)$ of this equation, if the damping term is small, can be shown to be

$$x = x_0 e^{-\lambda t} \cos (\omega t + \delta)$$

where $\lambda = \dfrac{\mu}{2m}$ and $\omega = \sqrt{\dfrac{k}{m} - \lambda^2} = \sqrt{\dfrac{k}{m} - \left(\dfrac{\mu}{2m}\right)^2}$

The motion is periodic, with an amplitude that is decreasing exponentially. The angular frequency ω is less than it would be if $\mu = 0$; friction slows the motion.

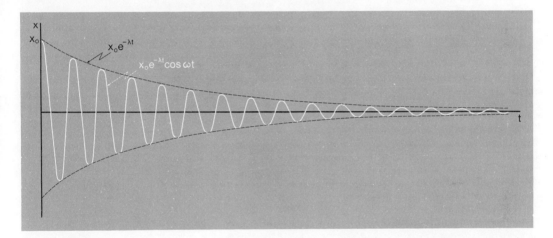

Damped harmonic motion.

The constant $1/\lambda$ is called the time constant, or relaxation time for the system, because it is a measure of how long it takes the vibrations to die away; in a time $t = 1/\lambda$ the amplitude has decreased to $1/e = 1/2.72 = 0.37$, or 37% of its initial value.

If the damping per cycle is small, $\lambda \ll \omega$ and the frequency is close to that of the undamped motion $\sqrt{k/m}$. If the damping is large the motion will not be oscillatory at all, and the solution given is not valid. The displacement will exponentially die away.

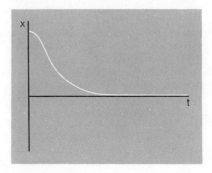

Overdamped motion.

Now suppose that a periodically varying force is applied to m, in the direction of the x-axis, in order to keep the oscillations from dying away. If the force is of the form $F_0 \cos \omega t$ the equation of motion is

$$F_0 \cos \omega t - kx - \mu v = ma \qquad \text{or} \qquad m \frac{dx^2}{dt^2} + \mu \frac{dx}{dt} + kx = F_0 \cos \omega t$$

This is the differential equation for **forced harmonic motion.** The general solution will have a transient term (one that dies away with time) and a steady state term. The steady state part is

$$x = A_\omega \cos (\omega t + \delta)$$

which is simple harmonic motion at the frequency ω of the applied force. The amplitude is

$$A_\omega = \frac{F_0/m}{\sqrt{(\omega - \omega_0)^2 + (\mu \omega/m)^2}}$$

where $\omega_0 = \sqrt{k/m}$, the natural frequency of the system. The shape of the A_ω-vs.-ω graph depends on the degree of damping. If μ is large, the graph is quite flat, but as μ becomes smaller the graph is more sharply peaked in the region near the natural frequency ω_0. The place where the maximum in the graph occurs is called the **resonance** frequency. For small damping it is close to the natural frequency.

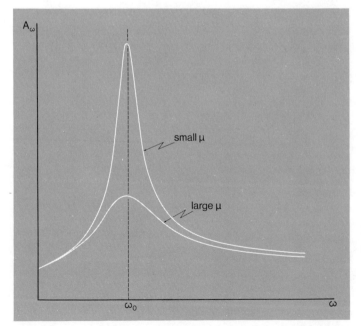

Dependence of the amplitude of forced harmonic motion on the frequency of the applied force.

The equations describing damped and forced harmonic motion are important because they have application to a wide variety of physical situations. We have touched on them here to emphasize that our description of simple harmonic motion is only the beginning of a development of a theory of vibrations.

Questions for discussion

1. Can you give a kinematic, a dynamic, and a geometric definition of simple harmonic motion, and also a differential equation defining it?

2. Is the term **phase** as used in physics the same as is used in ordinary conversation? What do **in phase** and **out of phase** mean? Sometimes phase is expressed as phase angle, in radians or degrees, or sometimes as a time. Since an angle and a time have different dimensions, how is this possible?

3. We gave three conditions for ideal elastic behavior. Do you think these are each equally well fulfilled by real solids?

4. A cord is stretched between two fixed supports. Two masses are suspended by two strings of equal length, tied to the cord at different points. If one of these pendula is started swinging, what would you expect to happen to the other one? Why? Suppose the supporting strings are slightly different in length. What would you expect then?

5. If a uniform spring is cut in half, is the force constant of each half the same as that of the original spring, or half as large or twice as large?

6. For a simple pendulum, is the tension in the string a maximum when the bob is at the end of its swing, or when it is at the center of its swing?

Problems

1. The vertical displacement of a 200-gm mass suspended by a spring is given by $y = 10 \cos (4\pi t + 0.2\pi)$ cm, where t is in sec. (a) State the amplitude, angular frequency, frequency, and period of the motion. (b) State the phase angle in radians and degrees, and the phase in seconds and as a fraction of a period. (c) Determine the displacement, velocity and acceleration of the mass at $t = 0$. (d) Determine the force constant for the motion, and the spring constant for the spring. (e) Determine the ordinate giving the position of the mass if the spring were not extended.

2. The spring constant of a spring is 100 n/m. How much will it be extended if used to suspend a 0.5-kg mass? The mass is pulled down 3 cm and released. Write an equation describing its position as a function of time.

3. A 4-lb weight produces an extension of 0.2 ft of a vertical spring. If the weight is pulled down another 0.1 ft and released, what are the amplitude and frequency of the oscillations? Suppose that gravity could be "turned off" when the weight is at its lowest point. What would the amplitude and frequency be?

4. The top end of a spring of force constant 64 pndl/ft is fixed, and a 0.5-lb mass is fastened to its lower end. The mass is released with the spring unstretched.

How far does it fall? What are the amplitude and frequency of its subsequent motion?

5. A car weighs 3200 lb. When four 200-lb passengers enter the car it rests 1 in. lower on its springs. What is the period of vertical vibrations of the car? If it is travelling on a "washboard" dirt road, with ridges across the road every 6 ft, at what speeds would the up and down motion of the car be most pronounced?

6. A 0.1-kg block is on a smooth 37° inclined plane, held at rest by a spring parallel to the plane, its upper end fixed at the top of the plane. The spring constant is 10 n/m. How much is the spring extended? If the block is pulled 5 cm down the plane, and released from rest, what is the amplitude and period of the resulting motion?

7. (a) Masses are sometimes compared using an inertial balance. This is a platform supported by two flat spring metal strips in such a way that the platform surface vibrates in a horizontal plane. A 1-kg mass placed on the balance makes 20 vibrations in 17 sec. An unknown mass makes 20 vibrations in 13 sec. What is its mass?

(b) Assume that the motion of an inertial balance is simple harmonic, and that the coefficient of static friction between a mass and the platform surface is 0.6. The mass makes 20 vibrations in 10 sec. What is the maximum amplitude with which it can vibrate without slipping?

8. When a boy stands on the end of a diving board it depresses 9 in. Assuming that the weight of the board is negligible, at what frequency should he bounce up and down to get the maximum effect from the board?

9. A mass suspended in equilibrium at the end of an ideal spring extends the spring an amount d. Displaced vertically and released, the mass vibrates. What is the length (in terms of d) of a simple pendulum that vibrates at the same frequency?

10. A cylindrical glass tube, sealed at each end, of outside diameter 2 cm, length 10 cm, and mass 20 gm has an extra 5-gm mass sealed inside one end. Floated vertically in water, what length of tube is immersed? Show that if the tube is pushed down a little and released, and the damping effect of the water can be neglected, the motion is simple harmonic. Determine its period.

11. A long light spring is vertical with its lower end fixed. A 0.5-lb ball placed on its upper end is in equilibrium with the spring compressed 2 in. The ball is then dropped from a point 1 ft above the top of the spring. It falls, hits the spring and compresses it, then bounces back to its original height, falls again and so on. What is the period of its periodic motion? Is it simple harmonic motion? How far is the spring compressed each time it is hit?

12. A wire of length L and of cross section area A being stretched by a force F elongates an amount ΔL. The amount of elongation depends on an elastic "constant" (an elastic modulus) for the material called **Young's modulus** E, defined by $E = \text{stress/strain} = (F/A)/(\Delta L/L) = FL/A (\Delta L)$. For steel, for example, $E \sim 2.1 \times 10^{11}$ n/m².

Determine the force constant k for a steel wire 1 mm in diameter and 10 m long. How much would the wire be stretched in supporting a 1-kg mass? What would be its frequency of vibration if the 1-kg mass were pulled down and released?

13. A 2-lb mass is suspended by a 5-ft cord from the ceiling of a room 7 ft high. A point O on the floor is directly below the point of suspension. The mass is projected into a horizontal circle of radius 3 ft, moving as a conical pendulum. What is the tension in the string? If the cord is cut, how far from the point O will the mass land?

14. Three pendula, each 2 m long, hang in a row. They are all pulled aside, and then released one at a time at 1-sec intervals. Determine the phase difference in degrees between the first and second, and between the first and third.

15. Two simple pendula hang side by side. Assume one to be exactly 1 m long and the other exactly 1.1 m long. They are each pulled sideways and released at the same instant. (a) Determine the periods T_1 and T_2, and $(T_2 - T_1)$ and $(\omega_1 - \omega_2)$, all to three-figure accuracy. (b) What is the phase difference between the pendula after 1 sec? (c) How long before the phase difference is $\pi/2$? π? (Assume g is exactly 9.8 m/sec².)

16. (a) The period of a simple pendulum is 10 sec. If its length increases by 1% due to thermal expansion, what is the change in its period? (b) The magnitude of the acceleration due to gravity g varies by about 0.5% over the earth's surface. What would be the percentage variation in the period of a simple pendulum used at various places on the earth's surface? (c) By forming the logarithm of the expression $T = 2\pi\sqrt{l/g}$, and then differentiating, deduce a general expression relating the fractional change in period $\Delta T/T$ and small fractional changes $\Delta l/l$ and $\Delta g/g$ in the length and the acceleration due to gravity.

17. A mass suspended by a spring and a simple pendulum are both hanging from the ceiling of an elevator. When the elevator is at rest the periods of their respective vibrations are 0.2 sec and 2 sec. What are their periods when the elevator is moving (a) upward at a constant speed of 5 m/sec, (b) upward with a constant upward acceleration of 2 m/sec²?

18. An elevator operator constructs an accelerometer by hanging a mass from a spring, and making a scale showing the displacement of the mass from its equilibrium position. He calibrates the device by measuring that its period of vibration is 1.5 sec when the elevator is at rest. In using it as an accelerometer he suspends the mass in a fluid in order to damp out vibrations. Determine the sensitivity of his calibration scale, in (cm/sec²)/cm. His maximum recorded deflection was 5.6 cm on his scale. What acceleration (in terms of g) did he achieve? Does the damping mechanism affect his calibration?

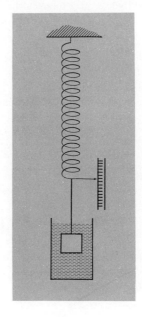

19. A mass hanging on a spring vibrates at a frequency of 2 cps. The mass and spring are placed on a horizontal smooth surface. One end of the spring is fastened to a fixed pivot, and the mass, fastened to the other end of the spring, is started in motion so that it moves in a circle on the surface, making one revolution in 2 sec. The unstretched length of the spring is 25 cm. What is its length during the circular motion? Can the mass move in a circle at 1 rev/sec? At 2 rev/sec?

20. Determine the maximum tension in the supporting cord of a simple pendulum executing SHM, in terms of the weight mg of the bob and the maximum angle θ_0 that the cord makes with the vertical. By what percentage is the tension greater than the weight for a maximum angle of $10°$?

21. Ripples are moving on the surface of a lake at a speed of 1.5 ft/sec. At one instant the equation of the surface profile, in a co-ordinate system with x-axis in the direction of motion of the waves and y-axis perpendicular to the lake, is $y = 0.02 \sin \pi x$ ft, where x is in ft. A particle at the lake surface moves up and down in SHM as the ripples are passing. What is its frequency? Give its vertical displacement as a function of time.

22. The end of a long, horizontal, stretched cord is moved up and down in SHM with an amplitude of 2 cm and a frequency of 20 cps, sending periodic waves along the cord at a speed of 5 m/sec. Suppose that a picture is taken of the cord from the side, "freezing" the motion at an instant when the end of the cord is at the top of its motion. In a co-ordinate system with x-axis along the line of the undisturbed cord, y-axis vertical, and origin at the end, what is the equation of the cord in the picture? Assume that the wave is not damped as it moves along the cord, and is not reflected back from the other end.

23. A small block rests on a smooth table, fastened between two identical springs in a straight line. The outer ends of the springs are fixed to the table, and the springs are unstretched. If the block is displaced at right angles to the springs and released, would you expect the resulting motion to be simple harmonic?

Derive an expression for the restoring force on the block in terms of its sideways displacement y, and the force constant k and unstretched length l of each spring. What does this become for $y \ll l$?

24. (a) Solids are not ideally elastic, but are viscoelastic. Deformation when a force is applied and recovery when it is removed are not completely instantaneous, although recovery may sometimes be complete. A simple model of a solid exhibiting what is called retarded elastic behavior can be formed by thinking of an ideal spring and another ideal element called a dashpot in parallel. The force necessary

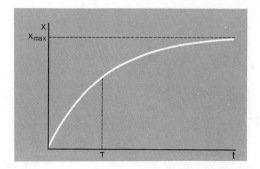

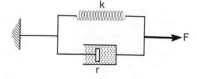

to deform a spring (or the force exerted by it if deformed) is proportional to its extension x; $F = kx$, where k is the spring constant. The force exerted by a dashpot is proportional to the rate of change of extension; $F = r\,dx/dt$, where r is a resistive or viscous constant. A dashpot can be thought of as a piston dragged through a viscous fluid, assuming the force necessary is proportional to the velocity. Just as an ideal spring is a model for ideal (Hookian) elastic behavior, a dashpot is said to be a model for ideal (Newtonian) viscous behavior.

Think what happens if a constant force F is applied to extend the parallel system (a parallel system means that the extension x of each element is the same at any instant). If the spring were alone it would deform to extension $x_{\max} = F/k$ instantly, but a dashpot cannot respond instantly (the force required would be infinite). It retards the deformation. As the deformation increases, the force tending to extend the dashpot decreases because the spring is pulling against the applied force, so the rate of increase of extension x keeps decreasing. At any instant $F = kx + r\,dx/dt$.

Derive an expression for x as a function of t, and show that x approaches $x_{\max}$ exponentially with a retardation (or relaxation) time constant τ. Verify that the dimensions of k and r are consistent with your expression for τ.

For solids the relaxation time is so small that deformations can often be regarded as instantaneous.

(If you have studied transients in electric circuits, you will recognize that this situation is exactly like charging a capacitor with a resistor in series. A capacitor or a spring is an energy storing device, a resistor or a dashpot is an energy dissipating device. If you have not studied electrical transients this electrical analogy won't help—but the mechanical analogy should help when you do!)

(b) The response of solids to mechanical vibrations depends on the frequency of the vibration. The model shown will illustrate this. A periodic force $F = F_0 \sin \omega t$

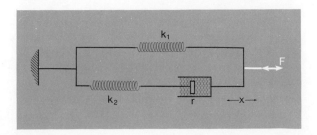

is applied to the system. How would you expect the resulting amplitude of vibration x_0 to depend on the frequency ω? Think what the effect of the dashpot is at low frequencies, and at high frequencies, and sketch a graph showing amplitude of vibration as a function of frequency. At low or high frequencies the response is independent of frequency, but there is frequency dependence in the region around $\omega_0 = 1/\tau$ where τ is the relaxation time for the system. This is called the dispersion region (do you know an optical analogue?). At low and high frequencies the applied force F and the extension x are in phase, but in the dispersion region they are out of phase. This means that energy will be dissipated in the system.

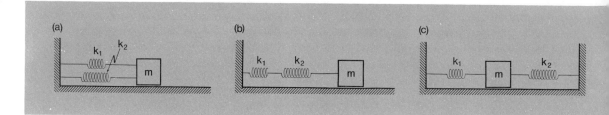

25. The diagrams show a block of mass m resting on a smooth surface, connected in different ways to two ideal springs of different spring constants k_1 and k_2. In **(a)** the springs are in parallel. If the block is displaced to the right, each spring is extended the same amount x, and the total restoring force is $k_1 x + k_2 x$. In **(b)** the springs are in series. If the block is displaced to the right the force extending each spring is the same, F, and the springs extend different amounts $x_1 = F/k_1$, $x_2 = F/k_2$. In **(c)** if the block is displaced one spring gets longer and the other shorter.

For each case find the period T of vibration of the mass m if it is displaced and released, and the force constant k for the system. In (a) does it make a difference if the unstretched lengths of the springs are not the same? In (c) does it make a difference if the springs are stretched when the block is in its equilibrium position?

Dynamics of a system of particles

In Part III we used only the fundamental equation of classical mechanics $\mathbf{F} = m\mathbf{a}$, a relation between the properties of a **system** ($m\mathbf{a} = d\mathbf{p}/dt$) and the effect of the **surroundings** on the system ($\mathbf{F}$). We applied this relation only to a single particle, or to systems of particles all moving in pure translation. The relation is an instantaneous one but in some situations, where the force was constant in magnitude or direction, we could describe motion over a time interval.

The force $\mathbf{F}$ is the resultant external force on the system, including inertial forces if the system is described in a non-inertial frame of reference. We are going to go on now and show that the effect of the surroundings on a system can also be described in other ways: in terms of **torque**, the instantaneous turning effect of a force around an axis, or in terms of **impulse**, the integrated effect of force over time, or in terms of **angular impulse**, the integrated effect of torque over time, or in terms of **work**, the integrated effect of force or torque over space.

The changes produced in a system over a time interval can be described in various ways also: an impulse produces a change in the **linear momentum** of the system, an angular impulse produces a change in the **angular momentum** of the system, and work produces a change in the **energy** of a system.

We are going to give specific definitions to all of these concepts here in Part IV and in Part V. There is really no new physical information contained in these definitions—we are just formulating Newton's law $\mathbf{F} = m\mathbf{a}$ in different terms. There are two basic reasons why it is useful to do this. One is that the law is a differential equation, a description of the effect of a force at an instant of time. The integrated effect over a time interval is sometimes usefully expressed as a sum over time $\int \mathbf{F}\, dt$, but is sometimes more usefully expressed as a sum over space, as the work done by the force in the interval.

The other reason for alternate formulations of the law is related to the concept of a particle. It is important to remember that this *is* a concept; everything acts like a particle in some circumstances, but nothing is really a particle. Any particle turns out not to be a particle if examined closely, so we say that it is made up of other particles, which in turn are made up of other particles, and so on.

We showed in Chapter 8 that the expression $\mathbf{F} = m\mathbf{a} = m\,d\mathbf{v}/dt = d\mathbf{p}/dt$ for a single particle of mass m led to the expression

$$\mathbf{F}_{ext} = d\mathbf{P}/dt = M\,d\mathbf{V}_c/dt = M\mathbf{A}_c$$

for a system of particles of total mass M, total linear momentum $\mathbf{P}$. The center of mass of the system had velocity $\mathbf{V}_c$, acceleration $\mathbf{A}_c$. The center of mass of the system moves as though the resultant external force on the whole system is a single force $\mathbf{F}_{ext}$ acting at the center of mass. The motion of the center of mass can be treated as though the system were a single particle. However, as we showed in Chapter 9, the resultant external force may not act at the center of mass, even though the c-of-m always moves as though it did. Then the force will produce rotation around the c-of-m as well. The concepts of torque and angular momentum are useful in the dynamics of rotation; they are introduced for a single particle, but are useful because there is really no such thing as a single particle.

In Part IV we introduce the instantaneous quantities torque and angular momentum, and also the concepts of impulse and angular impulse, the integrated effects of force and torque over time. Then in Part V we will deal with the integrated effects of force and torque over space.

13

IMPULSE AND

LINEAR MOMENTUM

IMPULSE ON A PARTICLE

The basic equation of motion for a particle of mass m is

$$\mathbf{F} = m\mathbf{a} = m\frac{d\mathbf{v}}{dt} = \frac{d\mathbf{p}}{dt}$$

In general the force is a function of time $\mathbf{F}(t)$. We define the **impulse J** of the force over a time interval $t_1 \rightarrow t_2$ by

$$\mathbf{J} = \int_{t_1}^{t_2} \mathbf{F}\, dt$$

From the equation of motion $\qquad \mathbf{F}\, dt = d\mathbf{p}$

and therefore $\qquad \mathbf{J} = \int_{t_1}^{t_2} \mathbf{F}\, dt = \int_{t_1}^{t_2} d\mathbf{p} = \mathbf{p}_2 - \mathbf{p}_1$

where $\mathbf{p}_1$ is the momentum of the particle at time t_1 and $\mathbf{p}_2$ is its momentum at t_2. The $\int_{t_1}^{t_2} d\mathbf{p}$ means the total change in momentum in the time interval $t_1 \rightarrow t_2$, and this is $\mathbf{p}_2 - \mathbf{p}_1$.

The relation $\mathbf{J} = \mathbf{p}_2 - \mathbf{p}_1$ is an integrated form of Newton's law. The impulse $\mathbf{J}$ depends on $\mathbf{F}(t)$ and on the time interval.

If $\mathbf{F}$ is constant (in magnitude and direction)

$$\mathbf{J} = \int_{t_1}^{t_2} \mathbf{F}\, dt = \mathbf{F} \int_{t_1}^{t_2} dt = \mathbf{F}(t_2 - t_1)$$

If $\mathbf{F}$ is not constant, we can write $\mathbf{J} = \bar{\mathbf{F}}(t_2 - t_1)$ where $\bar{\mathbf{F}}$ is the average force that would produce the same result as the variable force over the time interval.

The units and dimensions of impulse, force times time, are the same as the units of momentum, mass times velocity. The dimensions are MLT^{-1}. The mks units, for example, are kg-m/sec $\equiv$ newton-sec. Of course, impulse can be expressed using any force and time units, for example, as ton-years.

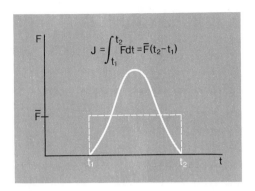

$$J = \int_{t_1}^{t_2} F dt = \overline{F}(t_2 - t_1)$$

An impulsive force.

The definition of impulse is valid for a time interval of any duration. It is particularly useful for describing the effect of a force which varies from zero through a maximum to zero, called an **impulsive force**. If the time interval covers the whole period the force acts, then $J = p_2 - p_1$ gives the total change in momentum produced by the force. This is the sort of force that occurs in collisions, in which case the time interval is usually short and the average force large, and this means that the effect of other forces acting during the collision can be neglected.

Example: Think for example of a 2-oz ball hit by a golf club, acquiring a speed of 100 ft/sec. The magnitude of the impulse is

$$J = p_2 - p_1 = (2)(100) - 2(0) = 200 \text{ oz-ft/sec}$$
$$= 200/16 \text{ lb-ft/sec} = 12.5 \text{ pndl-sec}$$

If the ball and club are in contact for 0.01 sec the average force exerted on the ball is

$$\overline{F} = J/(t_2 - t_1) = 12.5/0.01 \text{ pndl}$$
$$= 1250 \text{ pndl} = 39 \text{ pounds} = 620 \text{ oz}$$

The average force on the ball is over 300 times the weight of the ball, and therefore the fact that the weight acts during the collision does not matter much. This means that we do not have to worry about the direction of the blow, relative to the force of gravity.

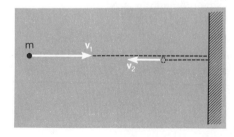

Head-on non-elastic collision with a wall.

Impulse is a vector quantity. In one-dimensional situations this means only that we must be concerned about sign. Think for example of a ball heading straight toward a solid wall with velocity v_1, rebounding with velocity v_2. If we choose a co-ordinate axis perpendicular to the wall, positive direction into the wall, the vector equation $J = p_2 - p_1$ is equivalent to the single scalar equation $J = p_2 - p_1 = mv_2 - mv_1$. If the initial and rebound speeds are 10 m/sec and 8 m/sec, and the ball has a mass of 0.1 kg

$$J = (0.1)(-8) - (0.1)(10) = -1.8 \text{ n-sec}$$

the minus (−) sign showing that the impulse is outward from the wall. (The ball of course exerts an equal and opposite impulse on the wall.)

In Chapter 6 we discussed collisions and defined an elastic collision as one in which no mechanical energy is lost. If the ball makes an elastic collision with the wall this means that its rebound speed equals its initial speed. In this idealized situation for a head-on collision

$$J = -2mv_1 = -2p_1$$

In a completely inelastic collision the ball would not rebound at all: $v_2 = 0$, and $J = -mv_1 = -p_1$.

In general a vector relation represents three scalar relations. Think of a ball making a skew collision with a wall, at an angle θ with the normal to the wall. Suppose that the wall is perfectly smooth, so that it can exert a force only in the normal direction. Choosing axes as shown, in the plane defined by $\mathbf{v}_1$ and the normal, the relation $\mathbf{J} = \mathbf{p}_2 - \mathbf{p}_1$ is equivalent to the two scalar equations

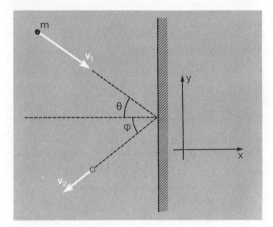

$$J_x = mv_{2x} - mv_{1x} = J$$
$$J_y = mv_{2y} - mv_{1y} = 0$$

Since the wall can exert a force only in the x-direction, $J_y = 0$ and the y-component of velocity is unchanged in the collision. In general energy is lost in the collision, so $|\mathbf{v}_2| < |\mathbf{v}_1|$ and therefore $v_{2x} < v_{1x}$. This would give an angle of reflection φ greater than the angle of incidence θ. However, if the collision is elastic $|\mathbf{v}_1| = |\mathbf{v}_2|$, and since $v_{1y} = v_{2y}$ this means v_{1x} must equal v_{2x} in magnitude. The angle of reflection will be the same as the angle of incidence θ, and $v_{1x} = v_1 \cos \theta$, $v_{2x} = -v_1 \cos \theta$. For an elastic skew collision with a smooth wall

Skew non-elastic collision with a wall.

$$J = -2mv_{1x} = -2mv_1 \cos \theta = -2p_1 \cos \theta$$

Elastic collisions may be approximated by macroscopic objects such as billiard balls, but are of particular interest in considering collisions of gas molecules with one another or with the walls of a container. Collisions of real macroscopic bodies always involve deformation of the bodies and energy transformation into the form of energy we call heat energy. In collisions between molecules, if the molecular speed is not too high, the internal energy state of the molecule is not changed in the collision, and it is an elastic collision.

In the collisions of gas molecules with a wall, we are not as interested in the average force exerted on a molecule by the wall as we are in the average force exerted on the wall by a lot of molecules.

IMPULSE OF A SYSTEM OF PARTICLES

Think of a stream of identical particles each of mass m all traveling with the same velocity $\mathbf{v}$ at right angles to a wall; if the particles are a stream of bullets they will be stopped by the wall, and the impulse on each will be $J = -mv$; if they are a stream of molecules they will bounce back with unchanged speed,

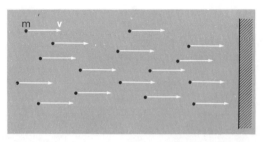

and on each $J = -2mv$. We will assume the latter for the moment. Each particle will exert an impulse $-J = 2mv$ on the wall, and if N of them hit the wall the total impulse on the wall is $J_w = -NJ = 2Nmv$. Suppose that N is the number hitting an area A of the wall in a time interval t.

Then $J_w = \overline{F}_w t$, where $\overline{F}_w$ is the average force on area A of the wall over the time interval t. The average force per unit area of the wall is the pressure p due to the bombardment.

Stream of particles hitting a wall.

$$p = \frac{\overline{F}_w}{A} = \frac{J_w}{At} = \frac{2Nmv}{At} = 2N_0 mv$$

where $N_0 = N/At$ is the particle **flux density,** the number of particles hitting unit area of the wall in unit time.

We can relate the flux density to the number of particles per unit volume in the stream, the **number density** n. Think of unit area of the wall, and a tube of

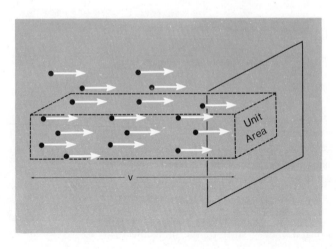

What is the relation between number density n and flux density N_0?

length v (where v is the speed) extending from this area into the particle stream. In unit time all the particles in this tube that are headed toward the wall will hit the unit area: if they are farther away than length v they will not reach the wall.

The volume of the tube is $v \times 1$, and if n is the number density, there are nv particles in the tube. However, only **half** of these will be heading toward the wall—remember that they all rebound with the same speed.

Therefore $N_0 = nv/2$ and $p = 2N_0mv = nmv^2$

Note that if we had assumed an **inelastic** collision at the wall, we would have the same result, because then $p = N_0mv$ but $N_0 = nv$.

If the stream is headed toward a smooth wall at an angle θ with the normal, the impulse per collision is reduced by a factor $\cos \theta$, as we have shown. The pressure is reduced by a factor $\cos^2 \theta$. The second $\cos \theta$ factor arises because the particles hitting unit area come from a tube of smaller volume; the area of the tube is $1 \times \cos \theta$, the volume $v \cos \theta$.

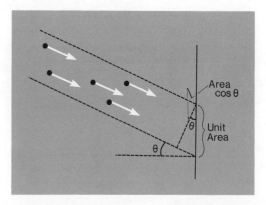

$$p = (N_0 \cos \theta)(2mv \cos \theta) = nmv^2 \cos^2 \theta$$

Now let us think about applying this model to the molecules of a gas bombarding a wall. There will be at least two things different—the molecules do not all travel in a stream in the same direction, and they do not all have the same speed v. What difference will these make?

Area of tube reduced for skew collisions.

If it is assumed that all directions for molecular motion are equally probable, the averaging of the $\cos^2 \theta$ factor over all directions gives a numerical factor $\frac{1}{3}$.

Since such a calculation occurs in many situations, we will do it here, even though it is a digression from our topic, impulse.

For a stream of molecules in the θ direction,

$$p = nmv^2 \cos^2 \theta$$

where n is the number density. If the molecules are moving in all directions, only a fraction of the number n will be coming from the θ direction.

Think of a sphere of radius r with the unit area at its center. We cannot speak of the number of molecules coming from a **fixed** direction θ, only of the number in a **range** θ to $\theta + d\theta$. The fraction of the molecules coming from this direction is, if all directions are equally probable,

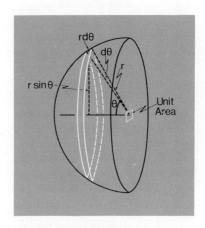

$$\text{Fraction (of } n \text{ in range } \theta \to \theta + d\theta) = \frac{\text{area of ring}}{\text{area of sphere}}$$

where the ring has a width $r\, d\theta$ and a radius $r \sin \theta$ so

$$\text{Fraction} = \frac{2\pi(r \sin \theta)(r\, d\theta)}{4\pi r^2} = \frac{\sin \theta\, d\theta}{2}$$

Fraction of molecules coming from the θ-direction.

However, here we do not want the fraction of these moving in *all* directions in the range $\theta \to \theta + d\theta$, but only the fraction of these moving from the left, that is, from the hemisphere, of area $2\pi r^2$. (The *net* flux at any point in the gas is zero, because there are as many molecules moving in one direction as the other.)

The fraction of n headed from the θ-direction toward the wall is then $\sin\theta\, d\theta$, and the total pressure is the sum of the contributions as θ varies over the hemisphere, from $\theta \to \pi/2$.

$$p = nmv^2 \int_0^{\pi/2} \sin\theta \cos^2\theta\, d\theta = nmv^2 \int_0^{\pi/2} \cos^2\theta[-d(\cos\theta)]$$

$$= nmv^2 \left[-\frac{\cos^3\theta}{3} \right]_0^{\pi/2} = \tfrac{1}{3}nmv^2$$

The resultant pressure of a gas due to molecular bombardment on the walls is

$$p = \tfrac{1}{3}nm\overline{v^2}$$

where $\overline{v^2}$ is the average of the squares of the molecular speeds. In Chapter 3 we described the distribution of molecular speeds as an example of a distribution function.

This has been an example of the kind of calculation that is made in **kinetic theory,** where the concepts of mechanics are applied to the microscopic particles called molecules. We have used it here to introduce the various kinds of averages that are involved: the average (molecular speed)², the average of $\cos^2\theta$ over direction, the average force exerted by a single particle on a wall, the average force exerted by a stream of particles on a wall, the average molecular flux, the average number density. The number of molecules per unit volume n, is not a constant, but an average value: if we count the number of molecules in a particular unit volume, this number will fluctuate as time goes on—fluctuations with time. If at some instant we could count the numbers in unit volumes at various points in a gas, we would find the numbers vary—fluctuations in space.

The size of the fluctuations depends on the numbers involved. Later in this book we will discuss random events, and develop specific expressions for the probabilities involved. We will show that if the average value of a quantity is n, and the fluctuations from this are random events, then the standard deviation is $\sigma = \sqrt{n}$. This means that if a measurement is made of n, there is a 68% chance of it being in the range $n \pm \sqrt{n}$, a 95% chance of it being in the range $n \pm 2\sqrt{n}$, a 99.74% chance of it being in the range $n \pm 3\sqrt{n}$, and so on.

Example: In a gas at standard temperature and pressure (0° C and 1 atmosphere) 1 mole occupies a volume of 22.4 liters. This means that Avogadro's number ($N_A = 6 \times 10^{23}$ molecules/mole) of molecules occupy $22.4l = 22{,}400$ cm³, and the number density is

$$n = 6 \times 10^{23}/2.24 \times 10^4 \sim 3 \times 10^{19} \text{ molecules/cm}^3$$

The standard deviation is $\sigma = \sqrt{n} \sim 10^{10}$ mols/cm³. While this is a large number, it is negligible with respect to n; the relative fluctuations in n are $\sigma/n \sim 1/\sqrt{n} \sim 10^{-10}$. Only if measurements of n could be made to an accuracy of 1 in 10^{10} could fluctuations be detected.

Think of a much smaller volume, of the order of the wavelength of light in size, $\sim 10^3$ angstrom units $\sim 10^{-5}$ cm. The volume is 10^{-15} cm³ and $n \sim 10^4$ molecules per unit volume. Then $\sqrt{n} \sim 10^2$ and the relative fluctuations in n are $\sigma/n \sim 10^{-2}$. If the numbers in such a volume could be counted with an accuracy of 1 in 100, fluctuations could be detected. Such counting cannot be done directly, but there are observable results that depend on this fluctuation. The scattering of light by a gas can be related to these small fluctuations in local density.

MOLECULAR ORIGIN OF FLUID FRICTION

We have wandered from our topic, the impulse exerted on, or by, a single particle, but it is perhaps useful to attempt to tie together some of the threads that we are following through the fabric of physics.

Perhaps we might digress a little further to tie in another thread. In Chapter 9 we stated there is a retarding force on an object moving through a fluid that is proportional to the speed of the object, if the speed is low. We can use the result just obtained to make this plausible, for an object moving through a gas. We have shown that a gas exerts a pressure p on the wall of a container (or any wall in the gas) that is proportional to v^2, the square of the molecular speed. Assume that the speed is the same for all molecules, and they are all moving at right angles to the wall, for simplicity.

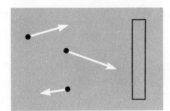

The pressure on a wall is proportional to (molecular speed)².

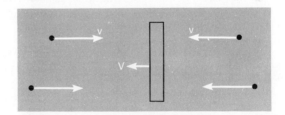

For a moving wall, relative speed is different on the two sides.

Now think of the wall moving through the gas at a speed V which is small compared to v. The relative speed of molecules hitting the front of the wall is $v + V$, while the relative speed of those hitting the back is $v - V$, so there is a pressure difference

$$p_1 - p_2 \propto (v + V)^2 - (v - V)^2 \propto 4vV$$

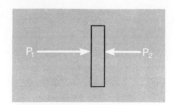

Resultant force opposes motion of a wall.

showing that there is a backward force on the wall proportional to its speed V.

This is a rather rough argument, and there are many factors that should be investigated, such as the effect of molecular collisions with one another; but it gives an idea of the molecular origin of the property of a fluid called viscosity.

IMPULSE ON A SYSTEM OF PARTICLES— CONSERVATION OF LINEAR MOMENTUM

In the first section of this chapter we developed the integrated equation of motion for a single particle $\mathbf{J} = \mathbf{p}_2 - \mathbf{p}_1$, where $\mathbf{J} = \int_{t_1}^{t_2} \mathbf{F}\, dt$. If there is no resultant force $\mathbf{F}$ on the particle in the time interval $\mathbf{J} = 0$ and $\mathbf{p}_1 = \mathbf{p}_2$. This really does not tell us anything that we could not have observed from the instantaneous equation of motion $\mathbf{F} = d\mathbf{p}/dt$. If $\mathbf{F} = 0$, $\mathbf{p}$ is constant, and the motion of the particle is uniform.

The instantaneous equation of motion for a **system** of particles is $\mathbf{F}_{\text{ext}} = d\mathbf{P}/dt$, where $\mathbf{F}_{\text{ext}}$ is the resultant external force on the system and $\mathbf{P}$ is the total momentum of the system $\mathbf{P} = \sum \mathbf{p}_i$. The integrated form of this is

$$\mathbf{J}_{\text{ext}} = \int_{t_1}^{t_2} \mathbf{F}_{\text{ext}}\, dt = \mathbf{P}_2 - \mathbf{P}_1$$

If there is an external force on the system in the time interval $t_1 \rightarrow t_2$, we can use this to determine the change in momentum of the center of mass of the system. However, this is particularly useful in dealing with what happens over an interval when something happens **internally** in the system, but in the interval $\mathbf{F}_{\text{ext}} = 0$. Then $\mathbf{J}_{\text{ext}} = 0$ and $\mathbf{P}_2 = \mathbf{P}_1$; the momentum of the system is the same at the end of the interval as before the interval, and momentum is **conserved.**

The important point here is the choice of the system to which the law of motion is to be applied. We can always choose a system large enough that all the forces are internal, and the total momentum is constant, but this may not be very useful. In the example of a ball hitting a wall, used in the first section, we chose the ball as the system, treating it as a particle. The wall exerted an impulse on the ball, changing its momentum. What system could we choose where the resultant impulse is zero, and the total momentum constant? If we think of the wall as a rigid body attached to the earth, with a total mass M, for the system of earth-wall and ball we can say $\mathbf{J}_{\text{ext}} = 0$ and $\mathbf{P}_2 = \mathbf{P}_1$ over any time interval. Think of a time interval that covers a collision between the ball and the wall

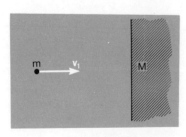

Collision with a wall fixed to the earth.

$$\mathbf{P}_2(\text{ball} + \text{earth-wall}) = \mathbf{P}_1(\text{ball} + \text{earth-wall})$$

$$m\mathbf{v}_2 + M\mathbf{V}_2 = m\mathbf{v}_1 + M\mathbf{V}_1$$

where the velocities are measured in an external inertial frame of reference. Suppose the external frame of reference is one in which the earth was initially at rest, so $\mathbf{V}_1 = 0$. Then $\mathbf{v}_1 - \mathbf{v}_2 = M\mathbf{V}_2/m$. The earth acquires a velocity $\mathbf{V}_2$ in the collision. This relation is really not very helpful. We may know M and m, but $\mathbf{V}_2$ is not a quantity that can be measured, since $M \ggg m$ and $\mathbf{V}_2 \cong 0$.

In analyzing a physical situation an important step is picking out a system such that an application of the law of motion will give useful information.

Suppose that the wall just described is not attached to the earth, but is the wall of a block of wood at rest on a table. Now it is useful to think of the ball–block system. There are external forces on this system, the force of gravity on the ball and block, the force of the table on the block. The question is, during a collision between ball and block are these forces negligible with respect to the **internal** forces, the forces the objects exert on each other? If so, we can say $\mathbf{J}_{\text{ext}} = 0$ over the interval of the collision, and $\mathbf{P}_1 = \mathbf{P}_2$. Whether the external forces are negligible during the collision depends on the particular situation; if, for example, the ball is soft rubber, so that during the impact the block had time to start to move, with friction opposing the motion, then it would not be reasonable to assume conservation of momentum in the collision. If we think of collisions between hard objects, where the time of contact is short and the average force high (recall the golf club and ball) then it is a reasonable assumption.

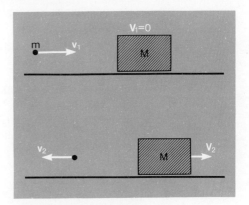

Collision with the wall of a block free to move.

It is impossible to choose a system such that momentum is conserved *absolutely;* there are external forces on every system. On the other hand, it is often possible to choose systems for which conservation of momentum is an excellent approximation.

The ball–block system can of course be treated as two separate systems. The block exerts an impulse $\mathbf{J}$ on the ball, where $\mathbf{J} = \int \mathbf{F}_{\text{block on ball}}\, dt$, and the equation of motion for the ball is

$$\mathbf{J} = m\mathbf{v}_2 - m\mathbf{v}_1$$

At every instant the ball exerts an equal and opposite force on the block $\mathbf{F}_{\text{ball on block}} = -\mathbf{F}_{\text{block on ball}}$ and since the time of contact is common,

$$\int \mathbf{F}_{\text{ball on block}}\, dt = -\int \mathbf{F}_{\text{block on ball}}\, dt = -\mathbf{J}$$

For the block $-\mathbf{J} = M\mathbf{V}_2 - M\mathbf{V}_1 = M\mathbf{V}_2$ since $\mathbf{V}_1 = 0$

Combining the two equations of motion

$$m\mathbf{v}_2 - m\mathbf{v}_1 = \mathbf{J} = -M\mathbf{V}_2 \quad \text{or} \quad m\mathbf{v}_1 = m\mathbf{v}_2 + M\mathbf{V}_2$$

This is simply $\mathbf{P}_1 = \mathbf{P}_2$ for the ball–block system.

Conservation of momentum is useful in any situation where internal forces act over a finite time interval, provided the internal forces are large compared to any external forces acting in the time interval. In Chapter 6 in discussing the Galilean transformation of the frame of reference we introduced the c-of-m frame of reference and used conservation of momentum in some of the examples. These applications were to two-particle systems. We pointed out that conservation of momentum did not determine the result of a collision uniquely, and distinguished between an elastic collision (energy conserved), an inelastic collision (mechanical energy lost), and an explosive collision (mechanical energy increased).

We will look at some further examples of conservation of linear momentum now.

Example 1—Exploding Shell: A shell fired from a gun has a range of 1000 yards. When the shell is at the highest point in its trajectory it explodes into three equal fragments; one goes straight down, another straight up, and the third continues in the original direction of motion. How far from the gun does each fragment land?

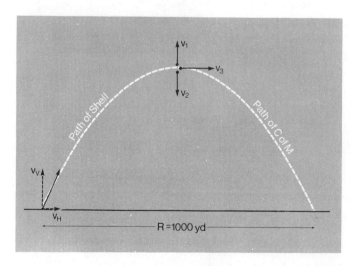

A shell exploding into three fragments.

Recall the symmetric trajectory of a projectile (neglecting air resistance, and assuming **g** constant). The only force acting on the shell is the force of gravity. Considered as a system of particles, it follows the parabolic path shown—both before *and after* the explosion, since the explosion involves only internal forces in the system. The downward part of the path is the trajectory of the c-of-m of the system.

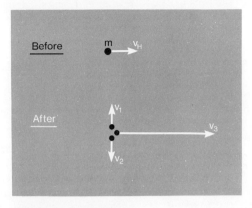

Fragments shot straight up and straight down will land directly below the point of explosion, 500 yd from the gun. Just before the explosion, the shell is moving horizontally with velocity $\mathbf{v}_H$, the horizontal component of the velocity of projection. The momentum is $m\mathbf{v}_H$. The two fragments shot up and down have no momentum in this direction. The vector relation $\mathbf{P}_1 = \mathbf{P}_2$ gives two scalar relations: in the vertical direction

$$0 = \left(\frac{m}{3}\right) v_1 + \left(\frac{m}{3}\right) v_2$$

and in the horizontal direction

$$m v_H = \left(\frac{m}{3}\right) v_3$$

Momentum conserved in the explosion.

The third particle has an initial velocity $v_3 = 3v_H$. In the time it takes to fall, the original shell unexploded would have moved a horizontal distance $R/2$; this particle will move a horizontal distance $3R/2$. Therefore it will be found a total distance $2R = 2000$ yd from the gun.

Although we know $v_1 = -v_2$, we do not know the magnitude of these. Conservation of momentum gives us some restrictions on the motion, but the values of v_1 and v_2 depend on the energy liberated in the explosion.

Example 2—Boys on a Plank: A long 100-lb plank rests on a smooth sheet of ice. Two 50-lb boys are standing on the plank. One walks at a speed of 4 ft/sec (relative to the plank) to the end of the plank and steps off. Then the second does the same. What is the plank's final speed? Would it be the same if they walked off together?

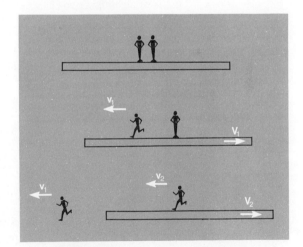

External forces on the system (these are due to gravity and the ice) are all vertical. The only horizontal forces are those exerted by the boys on the plank (and their reactions) and these are internal forces if we choose the boys plus plank as the system. Therefore we can assume conservation of momentum in the horizontal direction. Since all velocities are in the same line, we can use a single scalar relation for $\mathbf{P}_1 = \mathbf{P}_2$

$$0 = m v_1 + M V_1$$

Boys walking off plank in succession.

where m is the mass of the boy moving with velocity v_1, and M is the mass of the other boy and plank moving with velocity V_1; $m = 50$ lb, $M = 150$ lb.

The velocities v_1 and V_1 are velocities in the inertial frame of the earth. We know the velocity of the boy is 4 ft/sec **relative to the plank,** that is, in the plank frame of

reference. Using the transformation

$$v_{\text{earth frame}} = v_{\text{plank frame}} + v_{\text{plank frame re earth}}$$
$$v_1 = 4 + V_1$$

Using the momentum relation

$$0 = 50v_1 + 150V_1, \qquad v_1 = -3V_1$$
$$-3V_1 = 4 + V_1$$
$$V_1 = -1 \text{ ft/sec}$$

This is in the opposite direction to that the boy is moving. His speed relative to the earth is $v_1 = 4 + V_1 = 4 - 1 = 3$ ft/sec. These are the velocities as the boy walks along the plank, and after he steps off. We have chosen the positive direction as the direction the boy is moving.

Now the second boy walks along the plank. His velocity relative to the plank is 4 ft/sec, his velocity relative to the earth is

$$v_2 = 4 + V_2$$

where V_2 is the new velocity of the plank relative to the earth. We can apply conservation of momentum to the old system

$$0 = 50v_1 + 50v_2 + 100V_2$$

or we can deal with a new system, the second boy plus plank, which has an initial momentum $150V_1$

$$150V_1 = 50v_2 + 100V_2$$

No matter which system we use gives, since $v_1 = 3$ ft/sec, $V_1 = -1$ ft/sec,

$$-150 = 50v_2 + 100V_2 = 50(4 + V_2) + 100V_2$$
$$= 200 + 150V_2$$
$$V_2 = -350/150 = -7/3 \text{ ft/sec}$$

The speed of the second boy relative to the ground, both before and after he steps off the plank, is

$$v_2 = 4 + V_2 = 4 - 7/3 = 5/3 \text{ ft/sec}$$

If both boys walked together they would have a velocity relative to the earth of

$$v_3 = 4 + V_3$$

where V_3 is the velocity of the plank. Conservation of momentum gives

$$0 = 100v_3 + 100V_3$$
$$= 100(4 + V_3) + 100V_3$$
$$0 = 4 + V_3 + V_3$$

Boys walking off plank simultaneously.

$$V_3 = -2 \text{ ft/sec} \qquad v_3 = 2 \text{ ft/sec}$$

The plank acquires a speed which is less in this case.

Example 3—Rocket: The example with the boys and the plank was used to lead up to another example, the acceleration of a rocket. There are two features that are common—the mass of the rocket-plus-stored-fuel system decreases as fuel is used, and the fuel particles are ejected at a constant velocity relative to the rocket. However, we can assume for the rocket that the fuel is ejected continuously, rather than "one boy at a time."

For a rocket near the earth it is not realistic to ignore the force of gravity. We will not try to describe the general situation, acceleration through a non-uniform gravitational field. Instead we will look at two limiting cases: the rocket at rest in the earth's field, and the rocket far from the earth.

The rocket has an initial total mass m_0 (payload plus fuel) and it continuously ejects gas particles with a velocity v_0 relative to the rocket.

(a) If the rocket is just above the earth's surface, and the gas is ejected directly downward at a rate such that the rocket remains at rest relative to the earth, derive an expression for the mass m of the rocket as a function of time t. If $v_0 = 2$ km/sec, how long could the rocket stay parked in this position if 50% of the original mass is fuel? If 98% of the original mass is fuel?

(b) If the rocket is in space, essentially free from external forces, derive an expression for the mass m as a function of the speed v the rocket acquires with respect to an initial rest position. To reach a final speed of $4v_0$, what fraction of the initial mass would have to be fuel?

(a) *Rocket at rest in the earth frame of reference:* At any instant its mass is m, and the downward force of gravity on it is mg. It is ejecting particles at a constant velocity $\mathbf{v}_0$ downward; if it ejects particles of total mass dm in a short time dt, the downward impulse on the particles is

$$d\mathbf{J} = \mathbf{v}_0\, dm$$

and there is an upward impulse $-d\mathbf{J} = -\mathbf{v}_0\, dm$ on the rocket. There is an instantaneous upward force on the rocket $\mathbf{F}$ such that $\mathbf{F}\, dt = -\mathbf{v}_0\, dm$, or

$$\mathbf{F} = -\mathbf{v}_0 \frac{dm}{dt}$$

The equation of motion for the rocket is $\mathbf{F} + \mathbf{w} = m\mathbf{a} = 0$, and the component equation in the vertical direction is

$$-v_0 \frac{dm}{dt} + (-mg) = 0 \quad\text{or}\quad \frac{dm}{m} = -\frac{g}{v_0}\, dt$$

The initial mass is m_0 at $t = 0$, and to determine m as a function of time t we can integrate

$$\int_{m_0}^{m} \frac{dm}{m} = -\frac{g}{v_0} \int_{0}^{t} dt$$

What force holds rocket in equilibrium?

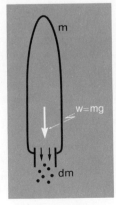

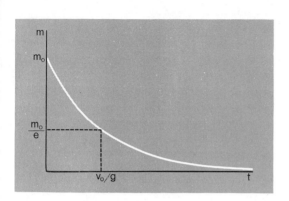

Total mass decreases
exponentially with time.

Using $\int dx/x = \ln x + C$

$$[\ln m]^{m}_{m_0} = -\frac{g}{v_0} [t]^{t}_{0}$$

$$\ln m - \ln m_0 = -gt/v_0$$

$$\ln m/m_0 = -gt/v_0$$

$$m/m_0 = e^{-gt/v_0} \qquad m = m_0 e^{-gt/v_0}$$

The mass decreases exponentially, with a time constant v_0/g. The larger v_0, the longer the fuel will last. For $v_0 = 2$ km/sec, $v_0/g = 2000/9.8$ sec $= 204$ sec.

If 50% of the original mass is fuel, the fuel is exhausted when $m = 0.5m_0$. The rocket can park for a time

$$t = \frac{v_0}{g} \ln \frac{m_0}{m} = 204 \ln 2 = 204 \times 0.69$$

$$= 141 \text{ sec} = 2.3 \text{ min}$$

If 98% of the original mass is fuel, the fuel is exhausted when $m = m_0/50$. The time parked is

$$t = 204 \ln 50 = 204 \times 3.9$$
$$= 800 \text{ sec} = 13 \text{ min}$$

You can see that maintaining a rocket at rest, sitting on its exhaust, is not possible for very long periods of time.

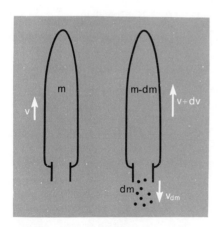

Rocket in space at time t
and at time $t + dt$.

(b) *Rocket in space:* When the rocket was at the earth's surface, we could not assume conservation of momentum for the rocket because of the external force of gravity. Note that the system to which we applied the equation of motion was the rocket plus stored fuel, and did not include the ejected fuel, so that the system had a continuously decreasing mass. We will use the same system for the rocket in space, but now we can use conservation of momentum. We will describe the motion in a frame of reference in which the rocket was initially at rest, $v = 0$, with its total mass m_0. At some later time it will have reached a velocity v, and its mass will have decreased to m. During the next short interval of time it will eject a quantity of fuel dm, and increase its velocity by dv. From conservation of momentum

$$mv = (m - dm)(v + dv) + v_{dm}\, dm$$

The velocity v_{dm} is the velocity of the mass dm in the initial inertial frame of reference

$$v_{dm} = \text{Vel. of } dm \text{ re rocket} + \text{Vel. of rocket re inertial frame}$$
$$= v_0 + (v + dv)$$

Therefore

$$mv = (m - dm)(v + dv) + (v_0 + v + dv)\, dm$$
$$= mv - v\, dm + m\, dv - dm\, dv + v_0\, dm + v\, dm + dm\, dv$$

or

$$0 = m\, dv + v_0\, dm$$

Note that this is the same result that would be obtained if we applied conservation of momentum in an inertial frame in which the rocket is at rest at the beginning of the interval. Then

$$0 = (m - dm)\, dv + (v_0 + dv)\, dm$$
$$= m\, dv + v_0\, dm$$

Integrating

$$\int_{m_0}^{m} \frac{dm}{m} = -\frac{1}{v_0} \int_{0}^{v} dv$$

$$\ln \frac{m}{m_0} = -\frac{v}{v_0} \qquad m = m_0 e^{-v/v_0}$$

If the rocket reaches a speed $v = 4v_0$, its mass will be

$$m = m_0 e^{-4} = 0.0183 m_0 = m_0/55$$

and the fraction of its original mass that was fuel is

$$\frac{m_0 - m}{m_0} = 1 - \frac{m}{m_0} = 1 - 0.0183 = 0.982$$

If $v_0 = 2$ km/sec, 98% of the rocket would have to be fuel if it is to reach a speed of 8 km/sec.

Note that if **all** the fuel is ejected at once, with a velocity v_0 relative to the rocket, the speed reached by the rocket cannot be greater than v_0. If mass m_f of fuel is ejected, conservation of momentum gives

$$0 = (m_0 - m_f)v + m_f v_f$$
$$= (m_0 - m_f)v + m_f(v_0 + v)$$
$$= m_0 v + m_f v_0$$

where v and v_f are the velocities of rocket and fuel in the initial frame of reference.

$$v = -\frac{m_f}{m_0} v_0$$

The greater the fraction of the total mass that is fuel, the closer the ratio m_f/m_0 is to unity, and the closer v is to v_0 (in magnitude) though it is always less than v_0.

Questions for discussion

1. Is the term **average force** unambiguous? Does **average** always require elucidation?

2. Can Newton's Law III be stated in terms of impulse?

3. A rifle is fired while clamped in a vise, and while held in the hands. Is the speed acquired by the bullet the same in each case?

4. A sand glass is balanced on an equal-arm balance while the sand is running through. Does it remain balanced after the sand has stopped?

5. Does a propeller aircraft propel itself by pulling itself through the air like a swimmer in water, or by throwing the air backwards, or what? Does a rocket push on its exhaust, or does the exhaust push on the rocket?

6. Why are spacecraft sent up using multi-stage rather than single-stage rockets?

Problems

Some problems involving conservation of momentum were used in Chapters 6 and 7 to illustrate transformations of the frame of reference.

1. A 5-lb ball is projected straight up from ground level, reaching a height of 16 ft. The ball is accelerated by a spring gun whose muzzle is at ground level; the gun exerts a constant force F through a vertical distance of 1 ft on the ball to accelerate it.

(a) Determine F in pounds. (b) What impulse is exerted on the earth by the ball as it is being accelerated? (c) After the ball leaves the gun, what impulse does it exert on the earth (1) in the interval it is on its way up? (2) in the interval it is on its way down? (3) over the whole interval it is in the air? (d) When the ball lands it rebounds straight up to a height of 4 ft. What impulse did it exert on the earth during the collision? (e) The collision lasted for 0.001 sec. What average force did the ball exert on the earth during the collision? (f) If the ball is allowed to bounce until it comes to rest, what is the total impulse it has exerted on the earth from the time its motion began?

2. A golfer can hit a 2-oz golf ball a maximum distance of 200 yd, excluding the roll of the ball after it lands. What impulse does this require? Neglect air resistance, and assume that the ball is given the same initial speed at any angle of projection.

3. A 4-oz baseball moving horizontally at 60 ft/sec is hit at home plate. It rises a maximum height of 36 ft and is caught at the same height that it was hit, 240 ft straight out from the plate. What impulse did the bat exert on the ball? Neglect air resistance.

4. What impulse is required to reverse the velocity of a proton (1.67×10^{-27} kg) moving at one-tenth the speed of light? What force would be required to do this in 1 microsec? What is the strength of the electric field necessary? Would it be difficult to produce such a field?

5. A particle moving with momentum $2\mathbf{i} + 3\mathbf{j}$ kg-m/sec is acted on by an impulse $\mathbf{J}$, changing its momentum to $3\mathbf{i} - 2\mathbf{j}$ kg-m/sec. Determine $\mathbf{J}$, and the angle through which the particle turned.

6. A 3-lb mass moving with a velocity $2\mathbf{i} + 2\mathbf{j}$ ft/sec is acted on by an impulse $\mathbf{J} = -2\mathbf{i} + 3\mathbf{k}$ pndl-sec. Determine the new velocity of the particle, and the angle through which it turned.

7. A machine gun fires 5-gm bullets at 600 m/sec. If it is fired at a rate of 200 rounds per minute directly into a block of wood, and the bullets become embedded in the wood, what is the average force exerted on the block? If the block has a mass of 5 kg and rests on a smooth surface, and the stream of bullets is horizontal, approximately how long will it take to move the block 10 m? Why is your answer approximate?

8. A 50-gm ball moving at 200 cm/sec hits a wall at an angle of 30° with the normal to the wall, and rebounds at an angle of 40° with the normal. Calculate the impulse exerted on the wall in the impact **(a)** if the wall is smooth, **(b)** if the speed of the ball after impact is 120 cm/sec.

9. (a) A falling ball bounces on a hard surface. The maximum upward force exerted on the ball is 5 lb, and the duration of contact is 0.1 sec. Calculate the impulse on the ball and the average force exerted on it during the collision, assuming that the force varies with time in each of the four ways indicated below. (Note that in (4) it is not necessary to integrate if you are careful about the units of area.)

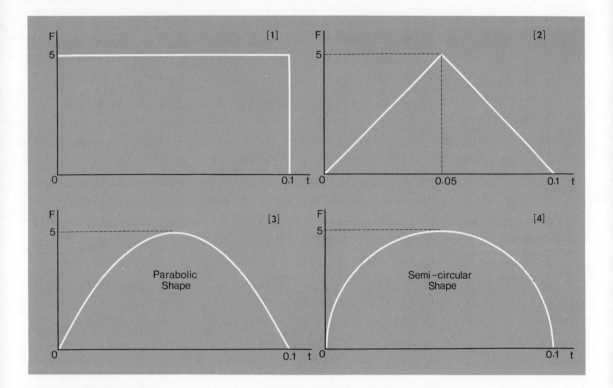

(b) The ball in (a) has a mass of 0.5 lb and is dropped from a height of 4 ft. Calculate the rebound height corresponding to the four force variations assumed.

10. A 50-lb, 12-ft boat is at right angles to a pier, with one end touching the pier. A 100-lb boy at the opposite end of the boat walks toward the pier. If there were no resistance of the water, how far from the pier would he be when he got to the other end of the boat? Does it matter where the center of mass of the boat is?

11. A 2-kg wooden block rests on a floor. The coefficient of kinetic friction between block and floor is 0.3. The speed of a 3-gm bullet is found by firing it horizontally into the center of the block. If the block slides 8 cm, what is the speed of the bullet? Why should it be fired into the center of the block? If it had bounced back with nearly its initial speed (made an elastic collision with the block) how far would the block have slid?

12. Two figure skaters, a 160-lb man and a 120-lb woman, approach one another, the man moving south at 15 ft/sec, the woman east at 20 ft/sec. The man lifts the woman off the ice when they meet, but unfortunately sits down in the process. With what velocity do they start to slide?

13. Two particles of mass $m_1 = 3$ units and $m_2 = 2$ units are moving in the same plane at velocities $\mathbf{u}_1 = 4\mathbf{i} - \mathbf{j}$ m/sec, $\mathbf{u}_2 = 2\mathbf{i} + 3\mathbf{j}$ m/sec. They interact with one another, and after this collision the velocity of m_2 is $\mathbf{v}_2 = 5\mathbf{i}$ m/sec. Determine $\mathbf{v}_1$ **(a)** by working in the inertial frame in which the velocities are stated, **(b)** by working in the center-of-mass frame of reference as follows: determine $\mathbf{p}_1$ and $\mathbf{p}_2$ and $\mathbf{v}_{cm} = (\mathbf{p}_1 + \mathbf{p}_2)/(m_1 + m_2)$, then $(\mathbf{v}_2)_{cm} = \mathbf{v}_2 - \mathbf{v}_{cm}$ and $(\mathbf{p}_2')_{cm}$; $(\mathbf{p}_1')_{cm} = -(\mathbf{p}_2')_{cm}$ gives $(\mathbf{v}_1)_{cm}$ and $\mathbf{v}_1 = (\mathbf{v}_1)_{cm} + \mathbf{v}_{cm}$. **(c)** Determine the angle through which each particle is scattered. **(d)** Is the collision elastic?

14. A hockey puck sliding along the ice hits an identical puck at rest. The first puck continues to slide after the collision, at half its original speed and deflected 30° from its original direction. In what direction does the second puck move? Is the collision elastic? What is the maximum angle through which the first puck could be deflected?

15. Three 2000-lb automobiles are suspended by three cranes above a railroad track, spaced at equal intervals. A 5-ton flat car is rolling along the track at an initial speed of 6 ft/sec. The automobiles are dropped onto the flat car in succession. Assuming the flat car rolls without friction, what is its final speed? Would it make a difference if the automobiles were all dropped onto the flat car at the same time?

16. A train with open freight cars passes under a hopper from which coal falls straight down into the cars at a constant rate of 25 tons per minute. What additional horizontal force in pounds must the engine exert on the train in order to keep it moving at a constant speed of 6 mph as the coal is being loaded?

17. A spring gun fires putty pellets horizontally. It can fire 3 pellets each of mass m in succession, each at the same speed v_0 if the gun is clamped in a vise. It can also fire a single pellet of mass $3m$ at the same speed if clamped. A cart of mass $3m$ is free to move on a smooth straight horizontal track. The gun is clamped on the track, pointing toward the cart at rest. Choose a co-ordinate axis in this direction. Assume pellets fired at the cart hit it and stick to it. **(a)** Determine the velocity acquired by the cart if it is hit by a single pellet of mass $3m$ fired from the gun. **(b)** Determine the velocity acquired by the cart if it is hit by three pellets (each of mass m) in succession. **(c)** Determine the velocity of the third pellet relative to the cart just before it hits it.

Now suppose that the gun is mounted on the cart, pointing toward its previous position on the track. The total mass of cart, gun and pellets is adjusted to be $6m$ (so 50% of the load is fuel), and the cart is initially at rest. **(d)** Determine the velocity acquired by the cart if the gun fires a single pellet of mass $3m$. **(e)** Determine the velocity acquired by the cart if the gun fires three pellets, each of mass m, in succession, and **(f)** determine the velocity of the third pellet fired, relative to the track.

18. A rocket is in space "at rest." It accelerates by ejecting particles at a constant speed v_0 relative to the rocket. What is its velocity (relative to the rest frame of reference) when the velocity of its exhaust is zero in the rest frame? What fraction of its original mass remains at this instant?

19. A rocket of initial total mass m_0 is accelerated vertically upward from the earth's surface by ejecting mass downward at a rate dm/dt with an exhaust speed v_0. **(a)** What is the rate of mass ejection required to support the rocket and **(b)** what is the total rate required to give it an initial upward acceleration of magnitude g? **(c)** If the mass is 20 tons and the exhaust speed 2000 ft/sec, determine the initial rate of mass ejection in tons/sec and the initial upward thrust in tons. What is the upward impulse over the first second in ton-sec, and the approximate velocity after 1 sec?

20. In this chapter we showed that the pressure produced by a gas on the wall of a container due to molecular collisions is $p = \frac{1}{3}nm\overline{v^2}$. This "kinetic theory" calculation took into account the fact that the molecules move in all directions, and involved an integration. The result can be obtained by a simplified argument without integrating. Since the velocity of each molecule can be resolved into three mutually perpendicular components, think of the molecules as all moving in three perpendicular directions, parallel and perpendicular to the wall being considered. There are equal numbers of molecules moving in any direction, so with this model there are one-sixth of them moving toward the wall at any instant, or per unit volume a number $n/6$ heading in this direction. Assuming the molecules all move at the same speed v, the number hitting unit area of the wall in unit time is $nv/6$. The change in momentum per collision (the impulse) is $2mv$, so the pressure on the wall is

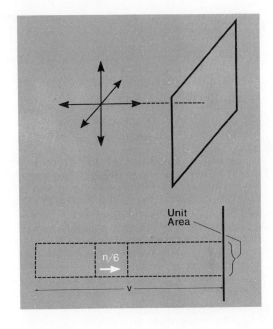

$$p = (2mv)(nv/6) = \tfrac{1}{3}nmv^2$$

The simple argument gives the same result as integrating over all directions of motion, but the fact that there is precise agreement, including the numerical factor 1/3, must be regarded as fortuitous. To see why, think about the number (call it N) of molecules hitting unit area in unit time—this is called the flux density of the molecules. According to the simple model, $N = nv/6$. Instead of using this model, do a calculation that takes into account all directions of motion, using the fact we worked out that a fraction $\sin\theta\, d\theta/2$ came from a direction in the range θ to $\theta + d\theta$. You will find that the flux density is $N = nv/4$, a numerical factor of 1/4 rather than 1/6. Simple kinetic theory models are useful in order to find dependence on molecular parameters, but cannot be expected to give correct numerical factors.

If the distribution of molecular speeds is taken into account, the molecular flux density in a gas is found to be $n\bar{v}/4$, where $\bar{v}$ is the average molecular speed.

14

ANGULAR MOMENTUM

ANGULAR MOMENTUM OF A PARTICLE

Think of a particle of mass m moving in an inertial frame of reference; at any instant it has a velocity $\mathbf{v}$, a momentum $\mathbf{p} = m\mathbf{v}$. With respect to an arbitrary fixed point O in the frame of reference it has a displacement $\mathbf{r}$. The velocity is $\mathbf{v} = d\mathbf{r}/dt$, but the velocity $\mathbf{v}$ and momentum $\mathbf{p}$ do *not* depend on what fixed point O is used as a reference point; velocity involves **change** in displacement.

We define a property of the particle called **angular momentum** or sometimes **moment of momentum** by

$$\mathbf{l} = \mathbf{r} \times \mathbf{p} = m\mathbf{r} \times \mathbf{v}$$

This is a vector quantity, the vector product of the displacement $\mathbf{r}$ and momentum $\mathbf{p}$. Its magnitude is $rp \sin \theta$, where θ is the angle between the two vectors, and it will be at right angles to the plane defined by the two vectors, in a direction determined by the right-hand rule. In the diagram, if $\mathbf{v}$ and $\mathbf{r}$ are in the plane of the page, $\mathbf{l}$ is straight out from the page.

This property of the particle, unlike the momentum $\mathbf{p}$, *does* depend on what reference point O is used.

The angular momentum of a particle takes on a particularly simple form **if the particle is moving in a circular path,** and point O is chosen as the center

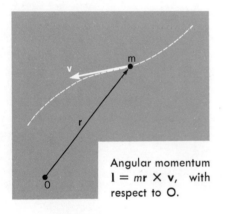

Angular momentum $\mathbf{l} = m\mathbf{r} \times \mathbf{v}$, with respect to O.

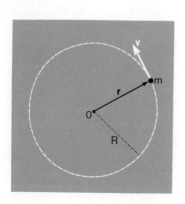

Angular momentum $\mathbf{l} = mR^2\omega$, with respect to O.

of the circle. Then **r** and **v** are always at right angles, and in the same plane, and **l** has a constant direction perpendicular to the plane; this is the same direction as the angular velocity $\boldsymbol{\omega}$ of the particle, with respect to the point O. The velocity $\mathbf{v} = \boldsymbol{\omega} \times \mathbf{r}$ is a vector in the plane, with magnitude $v = R\omega$, where R is the radius of the circular path. The vector $\mathbf{l} = \mathbf{r} \times \mathbf{p} = m\mathbf{r} \times \mathbf{v}$ is a vector perpendicular to the plane, with magnitude $l = mRv = mR^2\omega$. Thus in this special case

$$\mathbf{l} = mR^2\boldsymbol{\omega}$$

The quantity $I = mR^2$ is called the **moment of inertia** or **rotational inertia** of the particle with respect to the center of the circle O. It relates the angular momentum and angular velocity in the same way that mass or inertia relates linear momentum and velocity; $\mathbf{l} = I\boldsymbol{\omega}$, $\mathbf{p} \doteq m\mathbf{v}$. Since $\mathbf{l}$ and $\boldsymbol{\omega}$ are vectors in the same direction, I is a scalar. Note, however, that **this is only true for a particle moving in a circle**—otherwise the angular velocity $\boldsymbol{\omega}$ of the particle with respect to point O and its angular momentum $\mathbf{l}$ with respect to O are *not* in the same direction, and we do not have this simple relation between $\mathbf{l}$ and $\boldsymbol{\omega}$.

If a particle moves in a circular path at **constant speed** v, then $\boldsymbol{\omega}$ is constant in magnitude as well as in direction, and $\mathbf{l} = I\boldsymbol{\omega}$ is constant. Do not confuse the symbol l, the angular momentum (a vector) with the symbol I, the moment of inertia (a scalar).

TORQUE AND ANGULAR IMPULSE ON A PARTICLE

We will find the concept of angular momentum particularly useful in describing the rotation of a particle or system of particles about an axis through the point O, but the definition of $\mathbf{l}$ is general—there is no axis involved. In general as time goes on **both r** and **p** will change, producing changes in $\mathbf{l} = \mathbf{r} \times \mathbf{p}$. The rate of change of $\mathbf{l}$ with time can be found by differentiating. A vector product can be differentiated in the same way as the product of two scalar quantities, but the order must not be changed

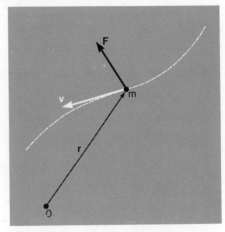

$$\frac{d\mathbf{l}}{dt} = \frac{d}{dt}(\mathbf{r} \times \mathbf{p}) = \frac{d\mathbf{r}}{dt} \times \mathbf{p} + \mathbf{r} \times \frac{d\mathbf{p}}{dt}$$

$$= \mathbf{v} \times \mathbf{p} + \mathbf{r} \times \mathbf{F}$$

The vectors **v** and **p** are parallel, so the first term is zero. The rate of change of momentum $d\mathbf{p}/dt$ is, using Newton's law, equal to the resultant force **F** exerted on the particle by its surroundings. In general the force will not be in the **p** or **r** directions, nor in the plane defined by these vectors.

Torque $\boldsymbol{\tau} = \mathbf{r} \times \mathbf{F}$ on the particle, with respect to O.

We define the quantity $\mathbf{r} \times \mathbf{F}$ as the **torque** or **moment of force** on the particle with respect to the point O, a vector quantity: $\boldsymbol{\tau} = \mathbf{r} \times \mathbf{F}$. Then

$$d\mathbf{l}/dt = \boldsymbol{\tau}$$

This relates the rate of change of angular momentum, a property of the particle, to the torque, the effect of the surroundings on the particle.

We have shown that the instantaneous equation of motion $\mathbf{F} = d\mathbf{p}/dt$ is sometimes more useful in the integrated form

$$\mathbf{J} = \int_{t_1}^{t_2} \mathbf{F}\, dt = \mathbf{p}_2 - \mathbf{p}_1$$

where $\mathbf{J}$ is the impulse, the integrated effect of the force over the interval $t_1 \rightarrow t_2$.

Similarly over a time interval the instantaneous relation $\boldsymbol{\tau} = d\mathbf{l}/dt$ can be integrated to give

$$\int_{t_1}^{t_2} \boldsymbol{\tau}\, dt = \mathbf{l}_2 - \mathbf{l}_1$$

where $\int_{t_1}^{t_2} \boldsymbol{\tau}\, dt$ is called the **angular impulse.**

It is particularly useful when the force $\mathbf{F}$ is impulsive, acting only for a short interval of time, so that the displacement $\mathbf{r}$ of the particle does not change appreciably during the interval.

Then $$\int \boldsymbol{\tau}\, dt = \int \mathbf{r} \times \mathbf{F}\, dt = \mathbf{r} \times \int \mathbf{F}\, dt = \mathbf{r} \times \mathbf{J}$$

These alternative methods of stating the physical content of Newton's law are useful in certain circumstances, as we will show.

ANGULAR MOMENTUM OF A PARTICLE ACTED ON BY A CENTRAL FORCE

Think now of a particle moving under the influence of a **central force.** This means that the **resultant** force on the particle always acts directly toward (or

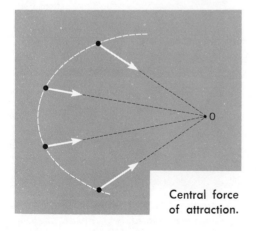

Central force
of attraction.

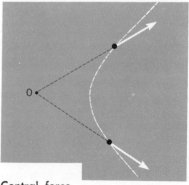

Central force
of repulsion.

directly away from) a fixed point in the frame
of reference. The particle might be a block on a
smooth table sliding under the influence of an elastic band looped around a fixed peg, or the moon
or some other satellite moving under the influence
of the earth's gravity (directed toward the center
of the earth, a fixed point in the earth frame of
reference), or a proton moving under the influence
of the repulsive electrical force of an atomic nucleus
(i.e., being scattered by the nucleus).

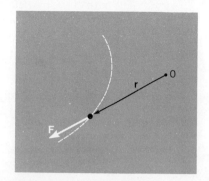

The torque with respect to
the center of force is zero.

If the fixed point that is the center of force is chosen as the fixed point O from which displacement $\mathbf{r}$
is measured, $\mathbf{r}$ and $\mathbf{F}$ are parallel or antiparallel
vectors, and torque $\tau = \mathbf{r} \times \mathbf{F} = 0$. The force
may be attractive or repulsive, and its magnitude may depend on the distance
r in any way ($F \propto 1/r^2$, or $F \propto r$, for example).

Since $\tau = d\mathbf{l}/dt = 0$, the angular momentum $\mathbf{l}$ of the particle is constant,
independent of time. We say that its angular momentum is conserved—but
remember, angular momentum depends on the choice of reference point;
angular momentum with respect to the center of force O is conserved.

A particle moving under the influence of a central
force is said to be moving in a central force field.
The motion is confined to a plane, the plane defined
by the vectors $\mathbf{r}$ and $\mathbf{p}$ (or $\mathbf{v}$) at any instant, because
there is no force component to accelerate it out of
the plane. The vector $\mathbf{l} = \mathbf{r} \times \mathbf{p}$ is constant in magnitude and direction, the direction perpendicular
to the fixed plane. Its magnitude can be expressed
in a number of ways; in terms of r and p and the
angle φ between them, or the component $v_\perp$ of $\mathbf{v}$
perpendicular to $\mathbf{r}$, or the angular speed ω with
respect of O:

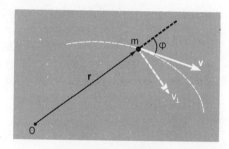

Angular momentum $l = mr^2\omega$,
with respect to O, where O is
the center of force.

$$l = rp \sin \varphi \qquad\qquad : p = mv$$
$$= mrv \sin \varphi = mrv_\perp \qquad : v_\perp = v \sin \varphi$$
$$= mr^2\omega = I\omega \qquad\qquad : v_\perp = r\omega$$

In this case, as for a particle in circular motion, the vector ω and the vector $\mathbf{l}$
are in the same direction, and we can introduce the scalar moment of inertia
$I = mr^2$. However, here it is not a constant, because the distance r can change
with time.

$$\mathbf{l} = mr^2\omega = I\omega$$

The path of the particle is not necessarily a closed orbit, but this is one possibility if the central force is one of attraction. The orbit may be circular, if the particle is given the right initial conditions; then I and ω are constant. In general, however, motion under a central force, while confined to a plane, is not circular.

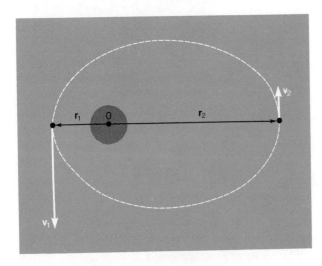

Closed elliptic orbit under an inverse-square central force.

We will show later that the path of an earth satellite (or any particle moving in a closed orbit under an inverse-square force) is an ellipse, with the center of the earth at one focus. The speeds and distances at the farthest point (apogee) and nearest point (perigee) are related by $r_1 v_1 = r_2 v_2$ since $l = mr v_{\perp} = $ constant for any point in orbit, and at these two points $v_{\perp}$ is the total speed v, because $\mathbf{v}$ and $\mathbf{r}$ are at right angles.

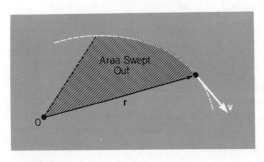

Sweeping out an area in space.

The angular speed ω of a particle is also the angular speed of the straight line joining the particle and the center of force O. As the particle moves this line moves through space, and we speak of it as sweeping out an area of space. It is usually said that the radius vector $\mathbf{r}$ sweeps out the area, but this is rather loose. The vector $\mathbf{r}$ is a quantity whose direction is that of the line and whose magnitude represents the length of the line in some units, but it is not the line itself. The vector $\mathbf{r}$ is defined as **change** in position, and its location in the frame of reference does not matter.

We will show that the rate at which area is swept out is constant. Think of the particle at some instant t, and a short time later $t + \Delta t$. In this time the radius vector has changed from $\mathbf{r}_1$ to $\mathbf{r}_2 = \mathbf{r}_1 + \Delta\mathbf{r}$, rotating through an angle $\Delta\theta$.

The area ΔA swept in time Δt is the area shown.
The area of a triangle is $\frac{1}{2}$ (Base)(Altitude) and
the altitude is approximately $r_1 \Delta\theta$: $\Delta A = \frac{1}{2}r_2 r_1 \Delta\theta$.
The rate at which area is swept out is

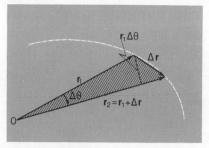

$$\frac{dA}{dt} = \lim_{\Delta t \to 0} \frac{\Delta A}{\Delta t} = \lim_{\Delta t \to 0} \frac{1}{2}r_2 r_1 \frac{\Delta\theta}{\Delta t} = \frac{1}{2}r^2\omega$$

$$= \frac{l}{2m} = \text{constant}$$

Area of triangle
$\Delta A \cong \frac{1}{2}r_1 r_2 \ \Delta\theta.$

In the limit the lengths r_1 and r_2 become equal,
and $\Delta\theta/\Delta t$ becomes the angular speed ω. We
showed before that $l = mr^2\omega$.

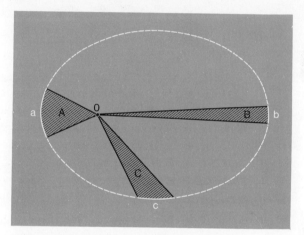

Equal areas in
equal times for
elliptic orbit.

The fact that the rate at which area is swept out is constant is sometimes
expressed by saying that equal areas are swept out in equal times—remember
Kepler's second law for planetary motion? The three areas A, B, C are equal if
the same time is required to travel each path segment a, b, c.

Remember, we have not yet shown that the orbit of an earth satellite is an
ellipse; we need to use an inverse-square central force to show this. We have
shown that when a particle moves under a central force of any kind the angular
momentum of the particle with respect to the center of force is constant, and the
rate at which area is swept out by the radius vector is constant.

ANGULAR MOMENTUM OF A SYSTEM OF PARTICLES

We have defined angular momentum l for a single particle, and shown that the
torque τ on the particle is related to the angular momentum by $\tau = dl/dt$. We
now extend these ideas to a **system** of particles. The particles may be fixed in a
rigid body, or be moving relative to one another.

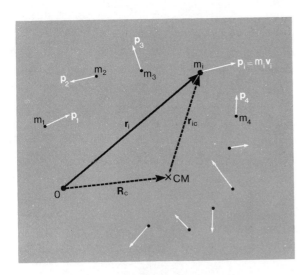

Center of mass of a
system of particles.

In a particular inertial frame of reference at some instant, each particle has a velocity $\mathbf{v}_i$, a momentum $\mathbf{p}_i = m\mathbf{v}_i$, and a displacement $\mathbf{r}_i$ with respect to a fixed point O in the frame of reference. The system will have a center of mass, with displacement $\mathbf{R}_c$ with respect to O, and moving with velocity $\mathbf{V}_c$.

Each particle has angular momentum $\mathbf{l}_i = \mathbf{r}_i \times \mathbf{p}_i$ with respect to point O, and the total angular momentum of the system is defined as the vector sum of these over all the particles. We write this, and then add and subtract the quantity $\mathbf{R}_c \times \mathbf{p}_i$ from each term:

$$
\begin{aligned}
\mathbf{L} = \sum \mathbf{l}_i &= \sum \mathbf{r}_i \times \mathbf{p}_i \\
&= \sum (\mathbf{r}_i \times \mathbf{p}_i - \mathbf{R}_c \times \mathbf{p}_i + \mathbf{R}_c \times \mathbf{p}_i) \\
&= \sum (\mathbf{r}_i - \mathbf{R}_c) \times \mathbf{p}_i + \sum \mathbf{R}_c \times \mathbf{p}_i \\
&= \sum \mathbf{r}_{ic} \times \mathbf{p}_i + \mathbf{R}_c \times \sum \mathbf{p}_i \\
&= \mathbf{L}_c + \mathbf{R}_c \times \mathbf{P}
\end{aligned}
$$

This separates the angular momentum of the system with respect to the point O into two terms. The first term $\mathbf{L}_c = \sum \mathbf{r}_{ic} \times \mathbf{p}_i$ is the angular momentum of the system with respect to its center of mass, and it does *not* depend on the choice of fixed point O. The second term $\mathbf{R}_c \times \mathbf{P}$ involves the total linear momentum $\mathbf{P} = \sum \mathbf{p}_i$ of the system. We showed in Chapter 8 that the total momentum $\mathbf{P}$ is the product of the total mass $M = \sum m_i$ and the velocity of the center of mass $\mathbf{V}_c$. Therefore the second term is $\mathbf{R}_c \times \mathbf{P} = M\mathbf{R}_c \times \mathbf{V}_c$, the angular momentum of the center of mass with respect to the point O.

So far we have simply described the system at some instant, in terms of the angular momenta instead of other quantities. As time goes on the particles will move around and change velocity both because of their mutual interactions, and because of external forces (the influence of the surroundings of the system). The center of mass will also move around and accelerate, in general. The quantities $\mathbf{L}$, $\mathbf{L}_c$, $\mathbf{R}_c$ and $\mathbf{P}$ will all change with time.

For each particle the rate of change of angular momentum is $d\mathbf{l}_i/dt = \boldsymbol{\tau}_i$, where $\boldsymbol{\tau}_i$ is the resultant torque on the ith particle; $\boldsymbol{\tau}_i = \mathbf{r}_i \times \mathbf{F}_i$, where $\mathbf{F}_i$ is the resultant force on the ith particle.

For the system the rate of change of angular momentum is $d\mathbf{L}/dt = \sum d\mathbf{l}_i/dt = \sum \boldsymbol{\tau}_i$. The quantity $\sum \boldsymbol{\tau}_i$ is the sum of the torques on all the particles, whether arising from internal or external forces. If we assume that Newton's Law III is valid, and that the internal forces are central forces, then the internal torques cancel out in this sum, and it becomes the resultant torque due

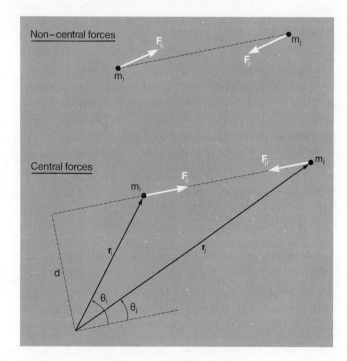

Torques due to central interaction forces cancel in pairs.

to external forces, the effect of the surroundings on the system. To see this, think of two masses m_i and m_j. Law III says that if m_j exerts a force $\mathbf{F}_{ij}$ on m_i, then m_i exerts a force $\mathbf{F}_{ji} = -\mathbf{F}_{ij}$ on m_j. This does *not* mean that these forces necessarily are in the same line. We assume that they are; this assumption is valid for most interactions, and the result turns out to be valid even for non-central internal forces. With this assumption the forces $\mathbf{F}_{ij}$ and $\mathbf{F}_{ji}$ lie on the line joining m_1 and m_2, and all vectors in the diagram are in the same plane—say the plane of the page. The magnitude of the torque $\tau_{ij} = \mathbf{r}_i \times \mathbf{F}_{ij}$ is $\tau_{ij} =$

$r_iF_{ij}\sin\theta_i = F_{ij}d$. The magnitude of $\tau_{ji} = r_j \times F_{ji}$ is $\tau_{ji} = r_jF_{ji}\sin\theta_j = F_{ji}d = F_{ij}d$. The vector τ_{ij} points straight into the page. The vector τ_{ji} is a vector of equal length pointing straight out, as you can verify with the right hand rule. Therefore $\tau_{ij} = -\tau_{ji}$, and they cancel in the sum $\sum \tau_i$.

Since all the internal torques cancel out in pairs the sum $\sum \tau_i = \tau_{\text{ext}}$, the resultant **external** torque on the system of particles. Therefore

$$\tau_{\text{ext}} = \frac{d\mathbf{L}}{dt}$$

for the system. This relates a property of the system, the rate of change of total angular momentum, to the influence of the environment τ_{ext}.

This relation is similar to $\mathbf{F}_{\text{ext}} = d\mathbf{P}/dt$ relating the external force and the rate of change of total linear momentum of a system of particles. If the resultant force is zero, the total momentum $\mathbf{P}$ is constant, and the center of mass moves at a constant velocity $\mathbf{V}_c = \mathbf{P}/M$.

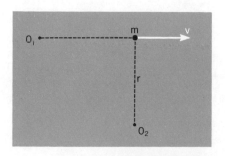

Angular momentum depends on a fixed reference point.

If the resultant torque on a system is zero, the total angular momentum $\mathbf{L}$ of the system is constant. Remember, however, that torque and angular momentum are specified with respect to an arbitrary fixed point. A particle (or a system) can have angular momentum $l = 0$ with respect to a point O_1, but angular momentum $l = mvr$ with respect to a different point O_2.

The total angular momentum $\mathbf{L}$ of a system with respect to an arbitrary fixed point can be divided into two terms, as we showed; $\mathbf{L} = \mathbf{L}_c + \mathbf{R}_c \times \mathbf{P}$. The first term is the angular momentum of the system with respect to the center of mass, the second is the angular momentum of the c-of-m with respect to the arbitrary fixed point, as though all the mass were at the c-of-m.

For a single particle the mass is concentrated at a point; all the mass is at the center of mass, and $\mathbf{L}_c = 0$. However, as we have pointed out, a particle is just a concept. It may be possible to treat a system as a particle for most considerations, and yet have to take into account its angular momentum with respect to its c-of-m. This is called the **spin angular momentum,** or sometimes just the spin.

ANGULAR MOMENTUM IN
A NON-INERTIAL FRAME OF REFERENCE

The relation $\tau_{\text{ext}} = d\mathbf{L}/dt$ was derived for an inertial frame of reference; we assumed Newton's law III, which is not valid in a non-inertial frame of reference. The external torque τ_{ext} and angular momentum $\mathbf{L}$ are referred to a fixed point O in the frame of reference. However, the relation is also valid in a non-inertial frame of reference **if the reference point is the center of mass.**

We can use Newton's law $\mathbf{F} = d\mathbf{p}/dt$ in a non-inertial reference frame which has an acceleration $\mathbf{A}$ (with respect to an inertial frame) if we introduce an inertial force $-m\mathbf{A}$ on every particle of mass m. In general $d\mathbf{L}/dt = \sum \tau_i$, where τ_i is the resultant torque on the ith particle. If the center of mass is the reference point, $d\mathbf{L}_c/dt = \sum \tau_{ic}$.

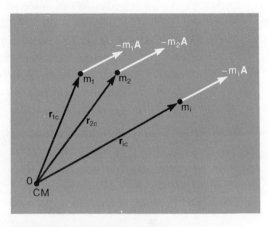

We showed before that $\sum \tau_i$ due to internal torques was zero, assuming Newton's law III and central forces, so that $\sum \tau_i = \tau_{\text{ext}}$, the resultant external force. But if the reference frame is not inertial, we cannot make this assumption. There will be an inertial force $-m_i\mathbf{A}$ on each particle, and there will *not* be an equal and opposite force on some other particle to compensate for it. When we form the sum $\tau_i = \sum \mathbf{r}_i \times \mathbf{F}_i$ there will be a contribution $-\sum \mathbf{r}_i \times (m_i\mathbf{A}) = -\sum m_i\mathbf{r}_i \times \mathbf{A}$ that is due to these forces, in general. However,

Inertial forces on particles in a non-inertial frame.

remember the definition of center of mass. With reference to an arbitrary fixed point in the frame of reference, its displacement is $\mathbf{R}_c = \sum m_i\mathbf{r}_i/\sum m_i$. Therefore if displacements are referred to the center of mass $\mathbf{R}_c = 0$, and $\sum m_i\mathbf{r}_{ic} = 0$. This means that the resultant torque due to inertial forces, $-\sum m_i\mathbf{r}_{ic} \times \mathbf{A}$, is zero, and we can take $\sum \tau_i$ as the resultant **external** torque, as before. In a non-inertial frame this is only valid if the reference point is the c-of-m, so we denote the torque by $(\tau_{\text{ext}})_c$.

The relation $(\tau_{\text{ext}})_c = d\mathbf{L}_c/dt$ applies in *any* frame of reference, inertial or not. This fact is very useful, because it means that we can divide the motion of a system of particles into two parts, motion of the c-of-m and motion about the c-of-m, and deal with them separately.

So far the definitions and results involving angular momentum have been general. Now we can examine a number of examples of systems of particles. First we make some estimates about the solar system.

ANGULAR MOMENTUM OF THE SOLAR SYSTEM

On the scale of the solar system the bodies in the system can be treated as particles—or can they? Can we calculate the total angular momentum of the solar system assuming that the sun and planets act as particles, or is it necessary to take the spin angular momentum into account? In other words, is the spin angular momentum negligible?

We will make an estimate for the planet we know best, the earth. The sun exerts a central force on the earth. This means that the angular momentum of the earth with respect to the sun would be constant if no other forces acted on it. Of course there are other forces on it, the gravitational force due to all the other bodies in the universe, particularly the other planets. We know that the effect of the sun is the dominant one, however, since the earth moves in orbit around the sun. The effect of the other planets is to perturb the orbit a little.

We will estimate the angular momentum of the earth with respect to the sun from our knowledge of the motion. The calculation is made in a frame of reference in which the center of the sun is at rest, and is the fixed point O. The

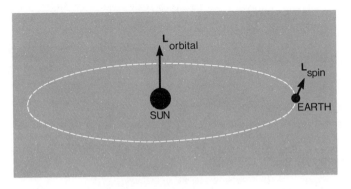

Spin and orbital angular momentum of the earth.

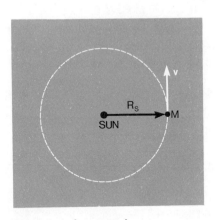

Estimation of magnitude of $\mathbf{L}_{\text{orbital}}$.

angular momentum of the earth is

$$\mathbf{L} = \mathbf{L}_c + \mathbf{R}_c \times \mathbf{P} = \mathbf{L}_{\text{spin}} + \mathbf{L}_{\text{orbital}}$$

We want to calculate whether or not the first term, the spin angular momentum, is negligible with respect to the second. The second term is the angular momentum due to the motion in orbit around the sun, the orbital angular momentum. This term can be estimated reasonably accurately by assuming the orbit is a circle: the distance to the sun varies from 1.47×10^{11} to 1.52×10^{11} m, a variation of 3%, so we assume a constant radius $R_s = 1.5 \times 10^{11}$ m. The mass of the earth is $M = 6.0 \times 10^{24}$ kg. The angular speed in orbit is $\omega_s = 2\pi$ rad/year $= 2.0 \times 10^{-7}$ rad/sec.

$$
\begin{aligned}
L_{\text{orbital}} \cong R_s M V &= R_s M (R_s \omega_s) = M R_s^2 \omega \\
&= (6.02 \times 10^{24})(1.5 \times 10^{11})^2 (2.0 \times 10^{-7}) \text{ kg-m}^2/\text{sec} \\
&= 2.7 \times 10^{40} \text{ kg-m}^2/\text{sec}
\end{aligned}
$$

The vector $\mathbf{L}_{\text{orbital}}$ is perpendicular to the plane of the orbit.

To estimate $\mathbf{L}_{\text{spin}}$ we cannot treat the earth as a particle. It is a roughly spherical distribution of mass spinning about its axis with an angular speed $\omega_E = 2\pi$ rad/day $= 7.3 \times 10^{-5}$ rad/sec. We will see later how to calculate $\mathbf{L}_{\text{spin}}$ for such a distribution, but we can put an upper limit on it by assuming that all the mass is concentrated in a ring at the equator. Each particle of mass is the same distance $r_i = R_E$ from the center of mass, and moves with the same speed $v_i = R_E\omega_E$, where $R_E = 6.4 \times 10^6$ m, the radius of the earth. The angular momentum of each particle with respect to the c-of-m O is $l_i = \mathbf{r}_i \times \mathbf{p}_i = m_i\mathbf{r}_i \times \mathbf{v}_i$. Each l_i has the same direction, the direction of $\boldsymbol{\omega}_E$, and magnitude $l_i = m_ir_iv_i = m_iR_E^2\omega_E$. The total spin angular momentum is

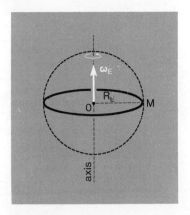

Estimation of magnitude of $\mathbf{L}_{\text{spin}}$.

$$\mathbf{L}_{\text{spin}} = \sum m_iR_E^2\omega_E = R_E^2\omega_E \sum m_i = MR_E^2\omega_E$$

since $\sum m_i = M$, the total mass of the earth. This is a vector in the axial direction, of magnitude

$$L_{\text{spin}} = (6.0 \times 10^{24})(6.4 \times 10^6)^2(7.3 \times 10^{-5}) \text{ kg-m}^2/\text{sec}$$
$$\sim 2 \times 10^{34} \text{ kg-m}^2/\text{sec}$$

This gives an upper limit for L_{spin} because we have assumed each particle of mass is farther from the axis than it actually is. The result is a factor 10^6 smaller than L_{orbital}, and therefore is negligible. The total angular momentum of the earth with respect to the sun is $\mathbf{L} = \mathbf{L}_{\text{orbital}}$. In the sun frame of reference the earth can be treated as a particle from the point of view of both its size and its contribution to the total angular momentum. In Chapter 16 we will point out that fundamental "particles" in atomic systems have a spin angular momentum that cannot be neglected.

Note that if L_{spin} is not negligible we cannot simply add the magnitudes L_{orbital} and L_{spin}. The vector $\mathbf{L}_{\text{orbital}}$ is perpendicular to the plane of the orbit, but the earth spins on an axis tilted with respect to the perpendicular to the plane by about 23°. The total angular momentum is the vector sum $\mathbf{L}_{\text{orbital}} + \mathbf{L}_{\text{spin}}$.

The total angular momentum of the solar system, with respect to the center of the sun, is 3.2×10^{43} kg-m²/sec, and 98% of this is orbital angular momentum of the planets. The largest contribution comes from the planet Jupiter, about 60% of the total; the earth contributes less than 0.1%. The spin angular momentum of the sun itself contributes about 2%.

Is the total angular momentum of the solar system constant? To answer this question we have to think of a frame of reference external to the system, and specify a fixed point in this frame. The total angular momentum is $\mathbf{L} = \mathbf{L}_c + $

$\mathbf{R}_c \times \mathbf{P}$. If we choose a frame of reference in which the center of mass is at rest, and specify this as the fixed point, then $\mathbf{R}_c = 0$, and $\mathbf{L} = \mathbf{L}_c$. The resultant external torque $(\tau_{\text{ext}})_c$ with respect to the center of mass is $(\tau_{\text{ext}})_c = d\mathbf{L}/dt = d\mathbf{L}_c/dt$. If $(\tau_{\text{ext}})_c = 0$, then $\mathbf{L}_c$ is constant. To decide whether this is so we would have to determine where the center of mass of the solar system is, and then calculate what the external torque is. Conversely if $\mathbf{L}_c$ is measured and found to be constant we know that $(\tau_{\text{ext}})_c$ is constant. It turns out that the center of mass of the solar system is quite close to the center of the sun, so that $\mathbf{L}_c$ is close to the value we have given, and it turns out that the value is constant, showing that $(\tau_{\text{ext}})_c$ due to other star systems is negligible. However, a detailed analysis of a ten-particle system is very complex. We will examine instead, in the next chapter, a two-particle system.

Questions for discussion

1. Is angular momentum a property of a particle (like linear momentum) or is it a joint property of the particle and its surroundings (like center of gravity)?

2. For a particle moving in a circle, is the angular momentum with respect to the center of the circle necessarily constant? For a particle moving in a central force field, but not moving in a circle, is the angular momentum with respect to the center of force necessarily constant?

3. For a particle moving at constant velocity, is the angular momentum with respect to any fixed point a constant? Does a line joining the particle and the fixed point sweep out area at a constant rate?

4. For a particle of mass m moving in a central force field, the rate at which area is swept out by a line joining the particle and the force center is $dA/dt = l/(2m)$, where l is the magnitude of the angular momentum. Since angular momentum is a vector $\mathbf{l}$, does this mean that area can be considered to be a vector?

5. A particle is moving in a circle on a smooth table, at the end of a string tied to a pivot at the center of the table. Is there an external resultant force on the particle? Is there an external resultant torque on the particle? Is its velocity constant? Is its angular velocity constant? Is its momentum constant? Is its angular momentum constant? In answering these questions, did you ask "angular momentum with respect to what point?" in order to be able to answer?

6. We have used a massless, inextensible, perfectly flexible string as a model for real strings, in order to exert forces of constraint in various ways. Think of the ideal string as a row of particles. What are the properties of this system of particles? Another useful model is a massless rigid rod. Considered as a row of particles, what are the properties of the particles of this system? What can an ideal rod do that an ideal string cannot, and vice versa?

7. In order for an object to be in static equilibrium, is it sufficient to have zero resultant force on it? Is it sufficient to have zero resultant torque on it? Can you think of examples to illustrate your answers?
What are the conditions necessary for static equilibrium of a particle, and of a

system of particles? Are these conditions also sufficient—that is, do they guarantee static equilibrium?

8. In the center of mass frame of reference of the solar system, is the angular momentum of the sun negligible? Can the sun be treated as a particle in this frame?

9. Are the names **moment of inertia** and **rotational inertia** reasonably descriptive for the quantity mR^2 for a particle? Would you expect that rotational inertia should be mR?

Problems

The material introduced in this chapter forms the basis for the next five chapters, and in these chapters the principles will be developed further and examples worked out. Some of the problems in this chapter and the next may be solved more readily after the next few chapters have been read. They serve here to some extent as a preview, although only principles introduced in this chapter are necessary for their solution. If you find them difficult, go on and come back to them later.

1. What are the dimensions, in terms of M, L and T, of torque, angular momentum, angular impulse, and moment of inertia? What are the units for each of these in mks, cgs and fps units?

2. A particle P of mass m moves at a constant velocity $\mathbf{v}$. What is the magnitude of its angular momentum l with respect to a fixed point O that is a distance d from the line of motion of the particle? At what rate does the line OP sweep out area?

3. A particle of mass m has at some instant a velocity $\mathbf{v}$, and a displacement $\mathbf{r}$ with respect to a fixed point O. Choose a co-ordinate system with origin at O, and state the components of angular momentum (l_x, l_y, l_z) in terms of the co-ordinates of the particle (x, y, z) and its components of velocity (v_x, v_y, v_z). The component l_x is called the x-component of angular momentum with respect to the point O, or the component of angular momentum with respect to the x-axis. Are these equivalent statements? Can a particle have an angular momentum with respect to a line rather than a point?

4. A particle of mass m moves in a circle on a smooth table, tied to fixed pivot O by an ideal string of length r. At an instant when its speed is v a horizontal force $\mathbf{F}$ is applied to it, at right angles to the string. The force acts for an infinitesimal time Δt, so it can be considered to remain perpendicular to the string. State the magnitude of the impulse J, and use $J = \Delta p$ to express the change in speed Δv in terms of F, m and Δt. What is the magnitude of the torque τ exerted on m about

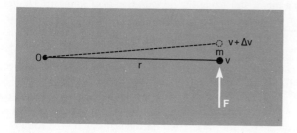

the point O? What is the angular impulse? Use $\tau \, \Delta t = \Delta l$ to express the change in angular speed $\Delta \omega$ in terms of F, m, r and Δt. Is $\Delta v = r \, \Delta \omega$?

The point of the exercise is to emphasize that the same calculation can be performed in different ways. In working with rotating systems it is often more convenient to use variables such as angular momentum but it is never essential.

5. An earth satellite in a circular orbit 1000 miles above the earth's surface has a speed of 16,000 mph. Assume that the earth is a sphere of radius 4000 miles. Suppose that the same satellite is put into a non-circular orbit with the same angular momentum (with respect to the center of the earth). In this orbit the maximum and minimum distances above the earth are 1900 miles and 500 miles. What are the maximum and minimum speeds of the satellite? Would you guess that the period in this orbit would be the same, or greater, or less, than the period in the circular orbit? (See Chapter 24.)

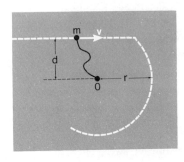

6. A particle of mass m is sliding at a constant velocity v on a smooth table, on a line a distance d from a fixed point O. An ideal string of length r $(r > d)$ connects the particle to a pivot at O. When the particle is a distance r from O, its path becomes a circle. Is its angular momentum l the same before and after it makes a "collision" with the string? If not, what exerted a torque to change it? Determine the speed of the particle in its circular path.

7. Determine the magnitude of the torque about the point indicated due to the force (or forces) specified in each of the following situations.

(a) A uniform cantilever beam is horizontal, one end embedded in a wall. The projecting part of the beam weighs 200 lb and is 12 ft long. Determine the torque due to the weight, about the point where the beam enters the wall. Why doesn't the beam fall?

(b) A tree weighing 12,000 pounds grows at an angle. Its center of gravity is 30 ft from the ground and displaced sideways 5 ft from the center of the base. Determine the torque about the center of the base due to the weight.

(c) A lathe is driven by a moving belt looped around a pulley 8 in. in diameter. The tension in the belt on one side of the pulley is 60 lb, the tension on the other side is 20 lb. Determine the torque exerted by the belt about the center of the pulley. Does it matter whether or not the belt is slipping on the pulley?

(d) A housewife opens a jar by squeezing the lid with a pair of tongs, exerting an inward force of 30 lb on each side of the lid. When she turns the tongs she exerts a tangential force of 20 lb on each side of the lid. The lid is 3 in. across. Determine the torque she exerts about the center of the lid. Does the jar open?

(e) One end of a 2-kg rod is pivoted at a wall. The rod projects straight out from the wall, supporting a 10-kg sign. One end of a cable 6 m long is fixed to the rod 2 m out from the wall, and the other end is fixed to the wall directly above the pivot. The tension in the cable is 100 newtons. Determine the torque exerted by the cable about the pivot. Is this torque exerted on the wall, or on the rod?

8. An ideal string passes through a smooth hole in a smooth table. A mass m is suspended from the lower end, and an equal mass m fastened to the other end is sliding in a circle of 2-ft radius on the table top. **(a)** What is the speed of the mass on the table? **(b)** What is its speed if the lower mass is pulled down 1 ft and held? **(c)** By what factor does the tension in the string change when the lower mass is pulled down? **(d)** If the lower mass is released, will the upper one return to its original orbit?

9. A rigid body is a system of particles all at rest with respect to one another. A rigid body at rest in a frame of reference, then, is a system of particles at rest. This means that the resultant force on the body is zero, since its momentum is constant (zero), and the resultant torque on the body is zero, since its angular momentum is constant (zero). Since all the particles are at rest, the resultant torque about any point is zero (if the frame of reference is an inertial frame). The conditions necessary for static equilibrium of a rigid body in an inertial frame of reference are therefore $F_{ext} = 0$, $\tau_{ext} = 0$.

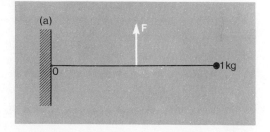

(a) One end of a massless rigid rod 1 m long is pivoted at a point O at a wall, and a particle of mass 1 kg is fixed at the other end. What vertical force **F** at the midpoint of the rod will keep the system at rest in a horizontal position?

(b) What would these forces be if the rod was not massless, but was uniform and had a mass of 0.5 kg?

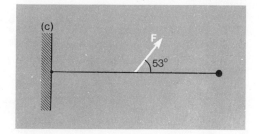

(c) Determine the force **F** and the pivot force if the rod is massless and the force is applied at the midpoint upward at an angle of 53° to the rod.

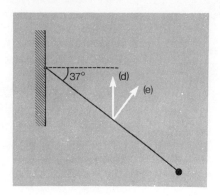

(d) Determine the vertical force **F** and the pivot force to hold the rod at an angle of 37° below the horizontal.

(e) Determine the force **F** and the pivot force if the rod is held at 37° below the horizontal, and the force **F** is at right angles to the rod.

10. A uniform rod 12 ft long and weighing 20 lb is pivoted at a wall at one end and carries a 50-lb weight at the other. The rod is held horizontal by a cable of breaking strength 150 lb, fastened to the rod 9 ft from the wall and to the wall a distance d above the pivot. Determine the minimum distance d, and the corresponding force exerted by the pivot on the rod.

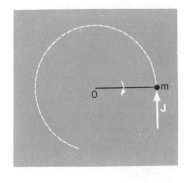

11. A 20-gm particle is moving in a circle of radius 30 cm on a smooth table, held in its path by a massless rigid rod pivoted at the center O of the circle, and moving with an angular speed of 6 rad/min.

(a) Determine the magnitude of the momentum of the particle, and the magnitude of its angular momentum with respect to O.

(b) The particle is brought to rest suddenly by its being struck a head-on blow of impulse **J**. Determine the magnitude of this impulse, and of the angular impulse with respect to O.

(c) Suppose that the system is brought suddenly to rest by a horizontal blow at the center of the rigid rod, at right angles to the rod. Determine the magnitude of the impulse of this blow. Note that when this blow is struck there will be an impulse in reaction to it at the pivot O, and we would have to take this into account in using $\mathbf{J} = \Delta\mathbf{p}$. However, this reactive impulse at O does not produce an angular impulse about O, and therefore the change in angular momentum of the system about O is equal to the angular impulse of the blow about O.

(d) Suppose that the rod is struck a horizontal blow at the center of the rod, at an angle of 30° to the rod. Determine the magnitude of the impulse necessary to stop the motion.

(e) Instead of being struck a blow, suppose that the system makes a collision with another particle. Another 20-gm particle is at rest on the smooth table, on the circular path of the first one. After the collision the particles stick together. Determine the angular speed of the system after the collision. Do you think you can use conservation of linear momentum, or of angular momentum, or either? **(f)** Suppose that the second 20-gm particle is at rest on the table 15 cm from O. When the rigid rod hits it, it sticks to the rod. Determine the angular speed after collision in this case. Here you cannot assume conservation of linear momentum. Why?

(g) Finally, suppose that the second 20-gm particle is at rest on the table 15 cm from O, but when hit by the rod it rebounds, sliding across the table at a speed of 2 cm/sec. Determine the angular speed of the rotating system after the collision.

12. The dynamic relation $\mathbf{F} = d\mathbf{p}/dt = m\,d\mathbf{v}/dt = m\mathbf{a}$ (if m is constant) is sometimes in rotational situations less convenient than its rotational equivalent $\boldsymbol{\tau} = d\mathbf{l}/dt = I\,d\omega/dt = I\alpha$ (if I is constant). Think of a 2-lb particle connected by an ideal string 3 ft long to a pivot fixed to a wall at O. The particle is held straight out from the wall and released.

(a) Determine the magnitudes, the instant after it is released, of the resultant force on the particle, the resultant torque on it about O, its acceleration, and its angular acceleration.

(b) Think about the situation after the particle has fallen to the point where the string makes an angle of 30° with the horizontal. Now it is more difficult to determine the resultant force on it, because the string exerts a force on it that depends on the speed. In order to find the speed, it would be necessary to integrate because $a = dv/dt$ is not constant. However, the tension in the cord does not exert a torque on the particle about the point O, and therefore the resultant torque about O can be stated, and the angular acceleration about O determined. What is it? Use it to determine the tangential component of acceleration a_T, and note that the result is $g \cos 30°$. Is the radial component of acceleration $g \sin 30°$? (We will look again at this situation in later chapters.)

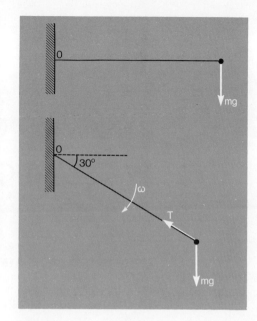

15

DYNAMICS OF A
TWO-PARTICLE SYSTEM

RIGID TWO-PARTICLE SYSTEM WITH NO EXTERNAL FORCE

In order to examine the dynamics of a system of particles in detail, we choose the simplest system we can by using the minimum number of particles greater than one. We will think first of two interacting particles a constant distance apart. The model is two particles of masses m_1 and m_2 connected by a rigid massless rod of length R. This can represent a number of different systems to some degree of approximation: the sun and earth, or the earth and moon, or a diatomic molecule, or two blocks connected by a string and rotating on a table or thrown into the air.

We assume initially that there are *no* external forces acting on the system. This means we are describing the system in an inertial frame of reference—otherwise there would be inertial forces. The resultant force and the resultant torque on the system are both zero, $\mathbf{F}_{\text{ext}} = 0$ and $\tau_{\text{ext}} = 0$, and the total momentum $\mathbf{P}$ and angular momentum $\mathbf{L}$ are constant. The system may be at rest (see the diagram at the top of the next page), or moving with pure translation, or pure rotation, or a combination of rotation and translation—all with respect to the inertial frame of reference. The center of mass of the system if it is not at rest is moving with a constant velocity $\mathbf{V}_c = \mathbf{P}/M = \mathbf{P}/(m_1 + m_2)$. We can make a transformation to the frame in which the c-of-m is at rest, the c-of-m frame, and it will be an inertial frame. If the system is moving with pure translation, both particles will be at rest in the c-of-m frame.

Note, however, that if the system is rotating with respect to an inertial frame, then it is not possible to find an inertial frame in which **either** particle is at rest. From the point of view of kinematics, the description of the motion, each particle can be thought of as moving in a circle of radius R around the other (see the diagram on the next page). That is, we can choose a frame of reference in which m_1 is at rest, and m_2 rotates in a circle. However, this cannot be an

Motions of a rigid
two-particle system.

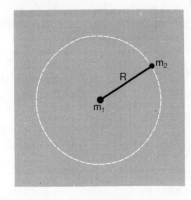

Is m_2 moving in a
circle, or is m_1?

inertial frame. The force $\mathbf{F}_{21}$ exerted on m_2 by m_1 through the rod is the centripetal force holding it in a circular path. There will be an equal and opposite force $\mathbf{F}_{12} = -\mathbf{F}_{21}$ on m_1, and since there are no external forces this would accelerate it and it could not be at rest. The only way it can be at rest is if there is an inertial force to balance the force $\mathbf{F}_{12}$, in which case the frame is not an inertial frame.

If the system is rotating, the only point in the system that can be at rest in an inertial frame (in *any* inertial frame) is the center of mass. Thus while we can choose an inertial frame in which $\mathbf{P} = 0$, we cannot choose an inertial frame in which $\mathbf{L} = \mathbf{L}_c + \mathbf{R}_c \times \mathbf{P}$ is zero. The spin angular momentum $\mathbf{L}_c$ is the minimum value it can take on.

We will consider the motion now in the c-of-m frame of reference, so that it is pure rotation. Each particle moves in a circle about the c-of-m at constant speed. If we choose the c-of-m as the fixed point O from which displacement is measured, the angular momentum is $\mathbf{L}_c = \sum \mathbf{r}_i \times \mathbf{p}_i = m_1\mathbf{r}_1 \times \mathbf{v}_1 + m_2\mathbf{r}_2 \times \mathbf{v}_2$. Both $\mathbf{r}_1 \times \mathbf{v}_1$ and $\mathbf{r}_2 \times \mathbf{v}_2$ are vectors in the same direction, perpendicular to the plane of motion.

$$L_c = m_1 r_1 v_1 + m_2 r_2 v_2$$
$$= (m_1 r_1^2 + m_2 r_2^2)\omega$$
$$\mathbf{L}_c = I\boldsymbol{\omega}$$

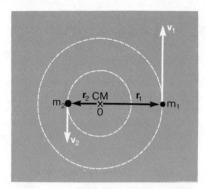

Motion in the c-of-m frame of reference.

The vector $\boldsymbol{\omega}$ is the angular velocity of the **system,** the angular velocity of either particle with respect to O: $\mathbf{v}_1 = \boldsymbol{\omega} \times \mathbf{r}_1$, $\mathbf{v}_2 = \boldsymbol{\omega} \times \mathbf{r}_2$. You can verify that it is also the angular velocity of either particle with respect to the other. It is a vector in the same direction as $\mathbf{L}_c$, and therefore (as for a single particle moving in a circle) there is a scalar quantity relating $\mathbf{L}_c$ and $\boldsymbol{\omega}$. The quantity $I = m_1 r_1^2 + m_2 r_2^2$ is the moment of inertia for the two-particle system.

Recalling the definition of the center of mass, you know that the magnitudes of r_1 and r_2 are related by $m_1 r_1 = m_2 r_2$. Using this, and the fact that $r_1 + r_2 = R$, a little algebra will show that

$$I = m_1 r_1^2 + m_2 r_2^2 = \left(\frac{m_1 m_2}{m_1 + m_2}\right) R^2 = \mu R^2$$

where μ is the **reduced mass** of the system, introduced in Chapter 6.

The angular momentum of the system is

$$\mathbf{L}_c = \mu R^2 \boldsymbol{\omega}$$

the same as though there was a single particle of mass μ a distance R from the center O. Examine what happens if one particle is a great deal more massive than the other. Suppose that $m_1 \ggg m_2$.

$$\mu = \frac{m_1 m_2}{m_1 + m_2} = \frac{m_1 m_2}{m_1(1 + m_2/m_1)} = m_2(1 + m_2/m_1)^{-1} \cong m_2(1 - m_2/m_1)$$
$$R = r_1 + r_2 = m_2 r_2/m_1 + r_2 = r_2(1 + m_2/m_1)$$

As $m_2/m_1 \to 0$, $\mu \to m_2$, $R \to r_2$, $r_1 \to 0$ and $\mathbf{L}_c \to m_2 r_2^2 \boldsymbol{\omega}$. The total angular momentum becomes associated with the less massive particle. Of course for any finite mass ratio, both particles are moving in circles. The massive m_1 has the smaller radius r_1, and $m_2 r_2^2 \ggg m_1 r_1^2$.

Example: Consider the earth–moon system:

$$\frac{m_2}{m_1} = \frac{m_{\text{moon}}}{m_{\text{earth}}} = \frac{7.3 \times 10^{22} \text{ kg}}{6.0 \times 10^{24} \text{ kg}} = 1.2 \times 10^{-2}$$

The earth–moon distance is $R = 240{,}000$ miles.

$$R = r_2(1 + m_2/m_1) = r_2(1 + 1.2 \times 10^{-2}) \cong r_2$$
$$r_1 = m_2 r_2/m_1 \cong m_2 R/m_1 = 1.2 \times 10^{-2} R \cong 3000 \text{ miles}$$

The radius of the earth is $R_E \cong 4000$ miles, so the earth–moon system rotates around a center of mass that is about a thousand miles inside the earth's surface, but is *not* the center of the earth.

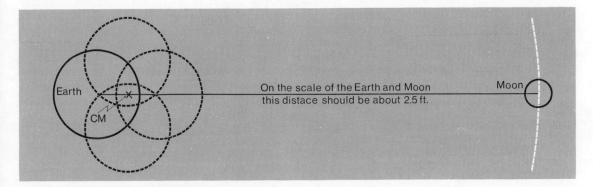

Earth

CM

On the scale of the Earth and Moon
this distace should be about 2.5 ft.

Moon

Motion of earth–moon system,
with respect to the c-of-m.

For the sun–earth system the mass ratio is much smaller, 3×10^{-6}, so the distance of the c-of-m from the center of the sun is $r_1 \cong m_2 R/m_1 = (3 \times 10^{-6})(92 \times 10^6$ miles$) \cong 300$ miles. The sun is about 0.4 million miles in radius.

NON-RIGID TWO-PARTICLE SYSTEM
WITH NO EXTERNAL FORCE

So far we have considered the two-particle system with R constant, and with $\mathbf{F}_{\text{ext}} = 0$, $\tau_{\text{ext}} = 0$. Suppose that the external force and torque are zero, but R is not constant. Again we can choose the center of mass frame of reference as an inertial frame. Since $\tau_{\text{ext}} = 0$, the angular momentum $\mathbf{L}_c$ is constant. Now, however, the angular momentum of the individual particle can vary, only the sum $\mathbf{l}_1 + \mathbf{l}_2$ is constant. If the force of interaction between the particles is a central force (like gravity, or the tension in a string joining the particles) the motion will be in a plane because there is no component of force out of the plane. Then the angular momenta $\mathbf{l}_1$ and $\mathbf{l}_2$ of the particles will always be in the same direction as $\boldsymbol{\omega}$, the angular velocity of the system, and the total momentum

$$\mathbf{L}_c = \mathbf{l}_1 + \mathbf{l}_2 = I\boldsymbol{\omega} = (m_1 r_1^2 + m_2 r_2^2)\boldsymbol{\omega} = \mu R^2 \boldsymbol{\omega} = \text{constant}$$

This time the moment of inertia I and the angular velocity $\boldsymbol{\omega}$ are not constant, but $I\boldsymbol{\omega}$ is constant; if I increases, $\boldsymbol{\omega}$ must decrease.

Example: Think of two blocks joined by a string set sliding around their center of mass on a smooth table top. The string has a length R and the angular velocity is $\boldsymbol{\omega}$. Now

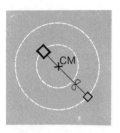

What happens when the slip knot slips?

suppose there is a slip knot in the string, and the length of the string changes to $2R$. What happens to ω? Since $\mathbf{L}_c = I\omega = \mu R^2\omega$ is constant, and μ does not change, $R^2\omega$ is constant. The initial and final values are related by $R_i^2\omega_i = R_f^2\omega_f$, so

$$\omega_f = \left(\frac{R_i}{R_f}\right)^2 \omega_i = \left(\frac{R}{2R}\right)^2 \omega_i = \tfrac{1}{4}\omega_i$$

The angular velocity is reduced by a factor 4. Note that the mass ratio does not influence this result—it is the same for any pair of masses. Note also that the tension T in the string does not enter the calculation—it is an internal force. We leave it to you to show that the magnitude of the tension is $T = m_1 r_1 \omega^2 = m_2 r_2 \omega^2 = \mu R \omega^2$, and to determine what happens to the tension when the string length changes from R to $2R$. The tension is the central force between the particles.

In this example we used conservation of angular momentum to relate two steady states of the system; in the initial state each particle is moving in a circle at constant speed, and in the final state each particle is moving in a circle at constant speed. In the more realistic situation of a central force whose magnitude varies continuously with distance R, the motion of each particle will vary continuously, but always in such a way that the total angular momentum is conserved.

We showed in discussing the angular momentum of a single particle that its angular momentum in a central force field is constant—but this is its angular momentum with respect to the center of force. We stated that the path of an earth satellite is an ellipse, with the earth at one focus. This is the path with respect to the earth frame of reference. With respect to an external frame of

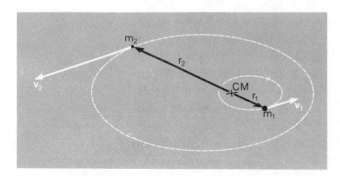

Motion of a non-rigid two-particle system, with an inverse-square attractive interaction.

reference, in which the c-of-m is at rest, both earth and satellite move in elliptical orbits around the center of mass. In this frame of reference $\mathbf{P} = m_1\mathbf{v}_1 + m_2\mathbf{v}_2 = 0$, and $\mathbf{L}_c = \mu R^2\omega = \mu(r_1 + r_2)^2\omega = $ constant. The angular momentum of the individual particles is not constant. If the satellite is the moon, the angular momentum of the earth is not negligible, but for man-made satellites $m_1 \gg m_2$ and $\mathbf{L}_c = m_2 r_2^2\omega$ to a high degree of accuracy.

SIMPLE HARMONIC MOTION OF
A TWO-PARTICLE SYSTEM

In Chapter 12 we discussed the dynamics of simple harmonic motion for a single particle. A mass m sliding in a smooth track, connected to the end of a spring of force constant k, vibrated with an angular frequency $\omega = \sqrt{k/m}$, or period $T = 2\pi\sqrt{m/k}$. We asked the question: If two masses are connected by the spring, and are pulled apart and released, are the period and amplitude of the motion the same as for a single mass? We can now deal with this question.

Is the frequency
the same for the
two systems?

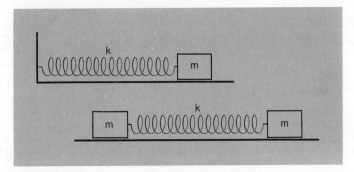

We will not assume that the two masses are equal. If the masses are released from rest, the c-of-m is initially at rest and will remain at rest since the spring is an internal force for the two-particle system. (Otherwise we can work in the

Masses released simul-
taneously from rest,
with springs extended.

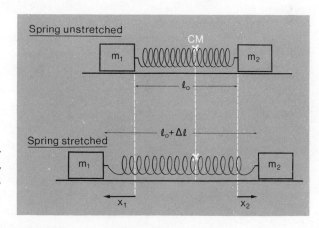

c-of-m frame of reference.) If the spring is stretched an amount Δl, it exerts a restoring force $F = k\,\Delta l$ on each mass. The ratio of distances of each mass from the c-of-m are the inverse of the mass ratio, and the extra extensions are in the same ratio since the c-of-m remains at rest; that is

$$m_1 x_1 = m_2 x_2 \qquad \text{or} \qquad x_2/x_1 = m_1/m_2$$
$$\Delta l = x_1 + x_2 = x_1 + m_1 x_1/m_2 = (m_1 + m_2) x_1/m_2$$

The restoring force on m_1 is

$$F = k \, \Delta l = k \left(\frac{m_1 + m_2}{m_2} \right) x_1$$

Thus the force constant for m_1 is $k\,[(m_1 + m_2)/m_2]$ and its angular frequency is

$$\omega = \sqrt{\frac{\text{force constant}}{m_1}} = \sqrt{\frac{(m_1 + m_2)}{m_1 m_2} k} = \sqrt{\frac{k}{\mu}} \qquad \text{and } T = 2\pi \sqrt{\frac{\mu}{k}}$$

where μ is the reduced mass of the two-particle system. A similar argument shows that ω for m_2 is the same.

If the two masses are equal, $m_1 = m_2 = m$, the reduced mass is $\mu = m/2$, and $\omega = \sqrt{2k/m}$, $T = 2\pi\sqrt{m/2k}$. The period is $1/\sqrt{2}$ times that of a single mass vibrating under the influence of the spring.

TRANSLATION, ROTATION AND VIBRATION

The motion of our two-particle system in general can be divided into three parts: **translation**, **rotation** and **vibration**. At any instant each particle has a single position, velocity and acceleration, but it is convenient to think of the motion as though the whole system was in translation, with the velocity and acceleration of the c-of-m, and with rotation and vibration with respect to the c-of-m superposed.

A diatomic molecule such as H_2 can be reasonably represented by such a model. However, while we can think of a molecule of hydrogen gas as a dumbbell moving through space, spinning and vibrating, the methods of quantum physics tell us that there are certain limitations on this motion; for example, the molecule cannot rotate with any arbitrary frequency but only at certain permitted frequencies. These stationary states or quantum states are usually expressed in terms of energy— the atom has certain rotational energy levels, and certain vibrational energy levels.

As hydrogen gas is excited, for example by heating it, the molecules move around more rapidly and in collisions with each other the energy states may

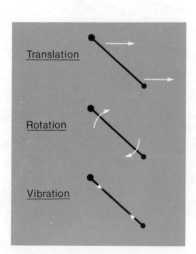

Translation

Rotation

Vibration

Motions of a non-rigid two-particle system.

change, and radiation may be emitted. A study of the radiation by the methods of spectroscopy gives information about the structure of the molecules—the moment of inertia, and the force constant for the interaction between the atoms.

The motion of systems of more than two particles can also be thought of as translation plus rotation plus vibration. We are restricting ourselves to a two-particle system because the basic features of the motion are represented, and we can work out the details for such a system. Mostly we are using the rigid body model because vibrations can complicate the picture considerably. Think of just a three-particle system, a triatomic molecule such as H_2O. The H atoms can vibrate with respect to the O atom, but this is not the only kind of vibration of the system—there can be torsional or flexural vibrations of various types as well. Even this apparently simple system can lead to a rather messy analysis.

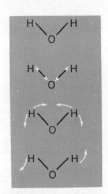

The modes of vibration of a three-particle system may be complex.

DYNAMICS OF A RIGID DUMBBELL

We have studied the motion of a two-particle system under the conditions $\mathbf{F}_{ext} = 0$, $\tau_{ext} = 0$; there were *no* external forces on the system, so there could be no external torques on the system. (It is possible to have $\mathbf{F}_{ext} = 0$, $\tau_{ext} \neq 0$.) We wish to examine the effect of external forces and torques on a system now. We use as a model two particles connected by a massless rigid rod, and it will be convenient to use particles of equal mass, so that the center of mass is at the center of the rod. The model is an idealized dumbbell. Each particle has mass m, and the length of the rod is R. The total mass is $M = m + m = 2m$. The reduced mass is $\mu = mm/(m + m) = m/2$. The moment of inertia with respect to the c-of-m is $I = \mu R^2 = mR^2/2 = MR^2/4 = M(R/2)^2$; the moment of inertia is the same as that of a single mass M a distance $R/2$ from the c-of-m. If the dumbbell is rotating with an angular velocity ω about its center of mass, its angular momentum is $\mathbf{L}_c = I\omega$.

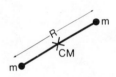

A rigid dumbbell.

Think of the dumbbell at rest on a smooth table. There is zero resultant force on it, although there are vertical forces on it; the downward force of gravity is balanced by the normal force due to the table. We will think of additional forces applied only in the horizontal plane, so acceleration will occur only in this plane.

Think first of a single horizontal force $\mathbf{F}$ applied at the center of mass of the dumbbell. It will produce an acceleration $\mathbf{A}_c = \mathbf{F}/M$ of the c-of-m. If the force $\mathbf{F}$ is constant, the acceleration is constant. The torque τ_{ext} is the resultant torque on the system due to external forces; it must be calculated with respect to a fixed point O in the frame of reference. If we choose O as the initial position of the

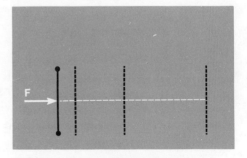

The unbalanced force at the c-of-m produces linear acceleration only.

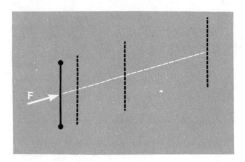

The acceleration is in the direction of the force.

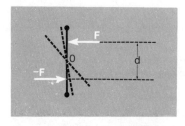

A symmetric couple produces angular acceleration only.

c-of-m, then $(\tau_{\text{ext}})_c = \mathbf{r} \times \mathbf{F} = 0$ because $\mathbf{r} = 0$. Even after the dumbbell moves off this will be so. Since $(\tau_{\text{ext}})_c = d\mathbf{L}_c/dt$, the angular momentum with respect to the c-of-m is constant. The stick was not rotating initially, so it will not start to rotate; if it had been rotating, it would continue to rotate with the same angular speed. We showed the force $\mathbf{F}$ at right angles to the rod at the c-of-m, but this is not necessary. A resultant force at the c-of-m in any direction will produce pure translational acceleration of the system in that direction.

Now think of horizontal forces $\mathbf{F}$ and $-\mathbf{F}$, equal in magnitude but opposite in direction, and *not* in the same line, but a distance d apart. Assume the forces are applied at right angles to the rod, symmetrically with respect to the center O. The resultant force on the system is $\mathbf{F}_{\text{ext}} = \mathbf{F} + (-\mathbf{F}) = 0$, and the c-of-m of the system will remain at rest. The resultant torque on the system τ_{ext} is not zero, no matter what point is chosen as a reference point. With respect to the c-of-m O, $(\tau_{\text{ext}})_c = \mathbf{r}_1 \times \mathbf{F} + \mathbf{r}_2 \times (-\mathbf{F})$, where $\mathbf{r}_1$ and $\mathbf{r}_2$ are the displacements of the points on the rod at which $\mathbf{F}$ and $-\mathbf{F}$ are applied. Both $\mathbf{r}_1 \times \mathbf{F}$ and $\mathbf{r}_2 \times (-\mathbf{F})$ are vectors in the same direction (out of the page in the diagram) and with equal magnitude since $r_1 = r_2 = d/2$. The magnitude of the torque is $(\tau_{\text{ext}})_c = \mathbf{F}(d/2) + F(d/2) = Fd$, and $(\tau_{\text{ext}})_c$ is at right angles to the plane of the table.

Since $(\tau_{\text{ext}})_c = d\mathbf{L}_c/dt$, the angular momentum with respect to the c-of-m $\mathbf{L}_c$ is changing. For the dumbbell $\mathbf{L}_c = I\omega$ where I, the moment of inertia, is constant. Therefore $d\mathbf{L}_c/dt = I\,d\omega/dt = I\alpha$ where α is the angular acceleration about the center of mass.

$$(\tau_{\text{ext}})_c = I\alpha$$

This system is in pure rotation around the c-of-m O. The resultant torque (about O) is equal to the moment of inertia (about O) times the angular acceleration (about O). This is the rotational equivalent of Newton's law $\mathbf{F} = m\mathbf{a}$ for this particular case. If the forces $\mathbf{F}$ and $-\mathbf{F}$ are kept the same magnitude and kept at right angles to the rod as it starts to rotate, the torque $(\tau_{\text{ext}})_c$ will be constant in magnitude and direction, and the angular acceleration will be constant.

The pair of forces $\mathbf{F}$ and $-\mathbf{F}$ a distance d apart is called a **couple.** We showed the forces were applied symmetrically with respect to O, but this was *not neces-*

sary—the torque about the c-of-m is the same
no matter where they are applied. If they are ap-
plied as shown the vectors $\mathbf{r}_1 \times \mathbf{F}$ and $\mathbf{r}_2 \times (-\mathbf{F})$
are in the same direction (out of the page) but
are not equal in magnitude: $|\mathbf{r}_1 \times \mathbf{F}| = F(d - x)$,
$|\mathbf{r}_2 \times (-\mathbf{F})| = Fx$. The magnitude of the torque
is $(\tau_{\text{ext}})_c = F(d - x) + Fx = Fd$ as before. If
the forces are both applied on the same end of the
rod, the vectors $\mathbf{r}_1 \times \mathbf{F}$ and $\mathbf{r}_2 \times (-\mathbf{F})$ are in opposite directions, and again the magnitude is $(\tau_{\text{ext}})_c =$
$F(d + x) - Fx = Fd$. It may be hard to accept
that such a pair of forces produces pure rotation
around the center O. Try it by pushing on a meterstick lying on a table, remembering the forces are
equal in magnitude. The magnitude $(\tau_{\text{ext}})_c = Fd$
whether or not the forces are applied at right angles
to the rod. If they make an angle θ with the rod,

$$
\begin{aligned}
(\tau_{\text{ext}})_c &= |\mathbf{r}_1 \times \mathbf{F}| + |\mathbf{r}_2 \times (-\mathbf{F})| \\
&= r_1 F \sin \theta + r_2 F \sin \theta \\
&= F(r_1 + r_2) \sin \theta \\
&= Fd
\end{aligned}
$$

A couple always produces pure rotational acceleration around the c-of-m of the system; since the
resultant force on the system is zero, the c-of-m is
not accelerated.

Now think of a single horizontal force $\mathbf{F}$ applied
to the system at some point other than the c-of-m.

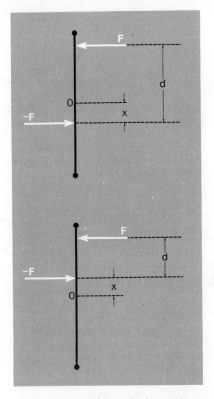

A couple applied anywhere
produces angular acceleration about the c-of-m.

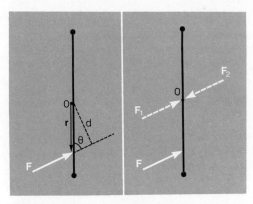

The effect of the single force **F** is the
same as that produced by **F**, $\mathbf{F}_1$ and $\mathbf{F}_2$.

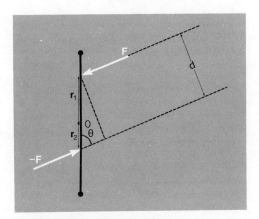

The magnitude of a couple depends on the distance between
the two anti-parallel forces.

How does the system move? The resultant force on the system is $\mathbf{F}$, and the c-of-m accelerates as though this force were applied at the c-of-m, with an acceleration $\mathbf{A}_c = \mathbf{F}/M$. Now, however, there is a torque $(\tau_{\text{ext}})_c = \mathbf{r} \times \mathbf{F}$, of magnitude $(\tau_{\text{ext}})_c = rF \sin \theta = Fd$, producing acceleration around the c-of-m.

It is helpful to introduce two forces $\mathbf{F}_1$ and $\mathbf{F}_2$ acting at the c-of-m, $\mathbf{F}_1 = \mathbf{F}$ and $\mathbf{F}_2 = -\mathbf{F}$. This pair of forces has a resultant zero, and resultant torque zero, but serves to illustrate that we can separate the total motion of the dumbbell into two parts. The force $\mathbf{F}_1$ produces pure translational acceleration of the dumbbell. The forces $\mathbf{F}$ and $\mathbf{F}_2$ form a couple of magnitude Fd, producing pure rotational acceleration of the dumbbell around its center of mass. We can think of the system as moving with pure translation, with rotation about the c-of-m superposed.

If the force $\mathbf{F}$ is constant (in magnitude and direction) and the point of application is not changed, then the acceleration of the c-of-m is constant (although the angular acceleration about the c-of-m may not be), but this is an unlikely situation. A more realistic situation is for the dumbbell to be acted upon by a force for a short time, an impulsive force; this would be the case, for example, if the dumbbell represents a diatomic molecule, and another molecule makes a collision with it.

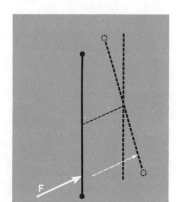

Does a constant force produce constant linear and angular accelerations?

We have used the simplest possible example of a system of particles to make a number of points about motion. The model was simple so that you could readily visualize the motion, but the results are general because we did not at any point use the fact that the body was a dumbbell. The dumbbell is a simple rigid body, and the results, which are based on the concepts developed in this chapter, **apply in general to the motion of rigid bodies.** We will summarize them, and then consider some more examples.

SUMMARY OF RIGID-BODY DYNAMICS

1. Static equilibrium or uniform motion: $\mathbf{F}_{\text{ext}} = 0$, $(\tau_{\text{ext}})_c = 0$. If, in a particular frame of reference, the resultant external force and the resultant external torque on a system are both zero, then the total linear momentum $\mathbf{P}$ and the total angular momentum $\mathbf{L}$ are constant. The system is moving uniformly (in translation, or rotation, or both) or is at rest. If it is at rest it is said to be in static equilibrium, and $\tau_{\text{ext}} = 0$ about *any* fixed point in the frame of reference.

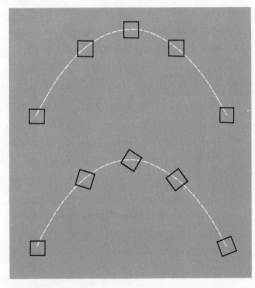

A rigid body may be moving, even though the resultant force and torque are both zero.

Conversely, if a system is in uniform motion (or at rest) then the resultant force and torque on it are zero.

2. Translational acceleration: $\mathbf{F}_{\text{ext}} \neq 0$, $(\tau_{\text{ext}})_c = 0$. If the external forces on a system have a resultant which is a single force acting at the center of mass of the system, then $\mathbf{L}_c = $ constant, and the system has a translational acceleration only. The system may be moving with pure translation, or may be rotating uniformly about the center of mass.

3. Rotational acceleration: $\mathbf{F}_{\text{ext}} = 0$, $(\tau_{\text{ext}})_c \neq 0$. If the external forces on a system have a zero resultant which is a couple, then $\mathbf{P} = $ constant, and the

For a pulley accelerating about a fixed axis, is there a resultant force? A resultant torque? A couple?

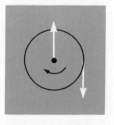

A projectile may or may not be rotating.

system has a rotational acceleration about the center of mass only. The center of mass may be moving uniformly, or be at rest.

4. Both translational and rotational acceleration: $\mathbf{F}_{\text{ext}} \neq 0$, $(\tau_{\text{ext}})_c \neq 0$. The motion can be considered as though the whole system had a pure translational acceleration, with rotational acceleration about the center of mass superposed.

PURE ROTATION ABOUT A FIXED AXIS ≡ PURE TRANSLATION PLUS ROTATION ABOUT C-OF-M

Before going on to other systems, there are a few more points that can be made using our dumbbell model.

First, think of the dumbbell on the smooth table again, but this time its motion is restricted; a smooth pin passes through the massless rod and sticks into the table, forming an axle about which the dumbbell can rotate. The pin is not at the c-of-m O, but a distance $R/4$ from it. A horizontal blow (impulsive force) of impulse $\mathbf{J}$ is applied to one of the masses as shown, at right angles to the rod. We will show that the resulting motion can be considered as *either* pure rotation about the pin $\mathbf{P}$, *or* as translation plus rotation about the c-of-m.

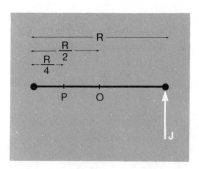

A dumbbell pivoted at P, given an impulsive blow J.

After the blow is struck both particles will be moving in circles around the point P, with total angular momentum

$$L_P = l_1 + l_2 = m_1 r_1 v_1 + m_2 r_2 v_2 = m r_1^2 \omega + m r_2^2 \omega$$
$$= I_P \omega_P$$

where ω_P is the angular speed with respect to P, and I_P is the moment of inertia with respect to P. (Note that $\mathbf{L}_P$ and $\boldsymbol{\omega}_P$ are vectors in the same direction, so we can introduce the scalar moment of inertia.)

$$I_P = m r_1^2 + m r_2^2 = m(R/4)^2 + m(3R/4)^2 = \tfrac{5}{8} m R^2$$

and

$$\tau_P = \frac{d\mathbf{L}_P}{dt} = \frac{d}{dt}(I_P \boldsymbol{\omega}_P) = I_P \frac{d\boldsymbol{\omega}_P}{dt}$$

The impulse $\mathbf{J} = \int \mathbf{F}\, dt$ will give an angular impulse about the pin P. Since $\mathbf{J}$ is at right angles to the rod, $\tau_P = \mathbf{r} \times \mathbf{F}$ has a magnitude $\tau_P = \tfrac{3}{4} RF$

and

$$\int \tau_P \, dt = \int \tfrac{3}{4} RF \, dt = \tfrac{3}{4} R \int F \, dt = \tfrac{3}{4} RJ$$

If the rod is initially at rest, the blow will give it an angular velocity ω_P where

$$\int \tau_P \, dt = \int I_P \, d\omega_P = I_P \omega_P$$

$$\tfrac{3}{4} RJ = \tfrac{5}{8} m R^2 \omega_P \qquad \omega_P = \tfrac{6}{5} \frac{J}{mR}$$

Now let us see if we can get the same result by thinking of the motion as translation plus rotation around the c-of-m, the midpoint of the dumbbell O.

As far as motion of the system as a whole is concerned, the impulse **J** can be considered to act at the c-of-m, but note that this is *not* the only horizontal impulse acting on the system. Because the impulse **J** acts, **there is an impulse exerted by the pin J**$_P$. We did not have to consider this in dealing with the motion as pure rotation around P, because the force involved has no torque about P.

We can find **J**$_P$ because we know the velocity acquired by the c-of-m,

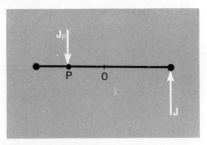

Reactive impulse at the pivot.

$$v_c = \left(\frac{R}{4}\right) \omega_P = \left(\frac{R}{4}\right)\left(\frac{6}{5}\frac{J}{mR}\right) = \frac{3}{10}\frac{J}{m}$$

The total mass of the system is $M = 2m$, so the c-of-m acquires a momentum

$$Mv_c = 2mv_c = 2m\left(\frac{3}{10}\frac{J}{m}\right) = \tfrac{3}{5}J$$

This is a vector in the same direction as the original impulse **J**. The change in momentum is equal to the **total** impulse $\mathbf{J} + \mathbf{J}_P$

$$\tfrac{3}{5}\mathbf{J} = \mathbf{J} + \mathbf{J}_P \qquad \mathbf{J}_P = -\tfrac{2}{5}\mathbf{J}$$

The pin exerts an impulse in the opposite direction to that applied.

The velocity $\mathbf{v}_c$ is acquired by every point in the rod, considered to move in pure translation. However, there is rotation around the c-of-m superposed.

Both **J** and **J**$_P$ exert an angular impulse around the c-of-m in the same direction, of total magnitude

$$J\left(\frac{R}{2}\right) + \tfrac{2}{5}J\left(\frac{R}{4}\right) = \tfrac{3}{5}JR$$

The moment of inertia with respect to the c-of-m is $I_c = mR^2/2$ so the angular velocity ω_c acquired about the c-of-m is given by

$$\tfrac{3}{5}JR = I_c\omega_c = \tfrac{1}{2}mR^2\omega_c$$

$$\omega_c = \frac{6}{5}\frac{J}{mR}$$

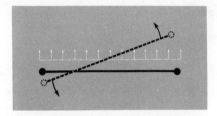

Pure translation plus rotation about the c-of-m equivalent to pure rotation about the pivot.

The point P will have a linear velocity v_P with respect to O:

$$v_P = \frac{R}{4}\,\omega_c = \left(\frac{R}{4}\right)\left(\frac{6}{5}\frac{5}{mR}\right) = \frac{3}{10}\frac{J}{m}$$

This is of the same size as its translational speed, and in the opposite direction, so point P stays at rest. You can see that the speed of P with respect to O is the same as the speed of O with respect to P.

It is simpler in this example, with a fixed axis, to consider the motion as one of pure rotation, but we have shown that it can also be considered as translation plus rotation about the center of mass.

MOMENT OF INERTIA AS A SCALAR PROPERTY

In order to show that the concept of moment of inertia as a scalar must be used with some care, we will modify our simple dumbbell. In addition to the massless rigid rod of length R connecting the two particles, we introduce another massless rod BB. This rod is vertical, and its ends are held in frictionless bearings. The rigid rod of the dumbbell is welded at its midpoint to the rod BB, *either* at right angles *or* at an angle θ. The rigid system is free to rotate about the vertical axis BB, and we consider both systems when rotating at a constant angular velocity ω.

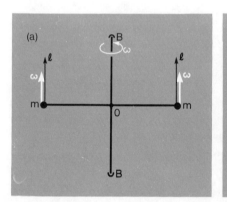

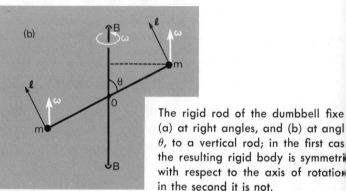

The rigid rod of the dumbbell fixe (a) at right angles, and (b) at angl θ, to a vertical rod; in the first cas the resulting rigid body is symmetri with respect to the axis of rotatio in the second it is not.

When the rods are at right angles, the situation is essentially the same as when the dumbbell is rotating on the smooth table. Each mass moves in a circle of radius $r = R/2$ at a constant speed $v = r\omega$ with angular momentum

$$\mathbf{l} = \mathbf{r} \times \mathbf{p} = m\mathbf{r} \times \mathbf{v} = mr^2\omega$$

since $\mathbf{l}$ is in the same direction as ω. The total angular momentum $L = \mathbf{l} + \mathbf{l} = 2mr^2\omega = I\omega$, where I is the moment of inertia; $I = 2mr^2 = mR^2/2$. Since $\mathbf{L}$ is constant (in magnitude and direction), $\tau_{\text{ext}} = d\mathbf{L}/dt = 0$. The bearings exert no torque on the system—they simply hold it up. The system is said to be in **dynamic equilibrium**—there are no variable external forces on it.

When the rods are not at right angles, but at an angle θ, the vectors $\mathbf{l}$ are *not* in the same direction as ω. Each mass moves in a circle of radius $r \sin \theta$ at a constant speed $v = (r \sin \theta)\omega$, with angular momentum $\mathbf{l} = \mathbf{r} \times \mathbf{p} = m\mathbf{r} \times \mathbf{v}$. The magnitude of the angular momentum of each particle is $l = mrv = mr^2\omega \sin \theta$, and of the system is $L = 2mr^2\omega \sin \theta$, but we *cannot* say $\mathbf{l} = mr^2 \sin \theta\omega$, or

$L = 2mr^2 \sin \theta \omega$. The angular momentum is constant in magnitude, but not in direction. The vector **L**, at right angles to the rod *mm*, makes an angle $(90 - \theta)$ with the *BB* axis, rotating around it with the motion called precession. There is an external torque $\tau_{\text{ext}} = d\mathbf{L}/dt$ which is constant in magnitude but not in direction. The bearings exert a sideways force on the rod *BB*, as well as holding it up. These forces $\mathbf{F}_B$ and $-\mathbf{F}_B$ provide a couple on the system. If you think of describing the motion in the frame of reference rotating with the system, there is an outward centrifugal force on each mass. These

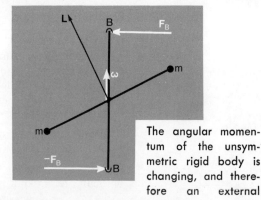

The angular momentum of the unsymmetric rigid body is changing, and therefore an external torque must be acting.

form a couple, tending to line the rod *mm* up at right angles to the axis *BB*. This couple must be balanced by the couple produced by the bearings.

Since $\mathbf{L} \neq$ (a scalar quantity) $\boldsymbol{\omega}$, we cannot introduce the moment of inertia I as a scalar quantity. Only in certain symmetric situations is there a scalar factor relating **L** and **ω**. In general, moment of inertia must be considered to be a more complex quantity called a tensor.

It is beyond our scope, but it can be shown that for any rigid body, of any shape, there are three mutually perpendicular axes passing through the center of mass, called the principal axes of the body, which have the property that if the body is rotating about any one of these axes, or axes parallel to them, its angular momentum and angular velocity are in the same direction, so they are related by a scalar factor. For a body with axes of symmetry, the principal axes are the symmetry axes. We will restrict ourselves to dealing with the rotations of symmetric bodies about axes parallel to the axes of symmetry, so that we can treat moment of inertia as a scalar quantity. In the next chapter we will show that this is the case.

Questions for discussion

1. Does the moon move around the earth or does the earth move around the moon? From a kinematic point of view, can you say both are correct? From a dynamic point of view, can you say neither is correct?

2. Can you list the various guises in which "$\mathbf{F} = m\mathbf{a}$" has appeared so far?

3. Why do you suppose **reduced mass** is so called?

4. Why does a diver curl up for certain dives?

5. A block on the end of a string is rotating uniformly on a smooth table. Is the system in dynamic equilibrium?

6. What is meant by **static equilibrium**? By **dynamic equilibrium**?

7. When car wheels are "balanced" are they balanced for static or dynamic equilibrium?

Problems

1. A non-existent metal called nomium, used in physics problems, has zero density, is completely rigid, and has a thermal expansion coefficient much higher than that of real materials. A drum major's baton consists of a nomium rod with a mass m at each end. He throws it into the air, rotating at 90 rpm. While in the air a passing laser beam hits it, causing its length to increase 50%. Determine its new rate of rotation, and also the factor by which the tension in the rod has changed.

2. In an external frame of reference, by how much would the earth shift as a 1000-kg satellite at 1000 km above the earth moved from one side of it to the other?

3. Two stones weighing 0.5 kg and 0.2 kg are attached to the ends of a string 1 m in length. A slip knot is tied in the string so that the length between the stones is 0.4 m. The stones are thrown upward in such a way that each stone is rotating around the other with an angular speed of 60 rad/sec. While the stones are in the air the slip knot becomes undone. **(a)** Calculate the tension in the string in kg before and after the knot becomes untied. **(b)** Use the expression $\frac{1}{2}mv^2$ to determine the kinetic energy of the stones before and after the knot slips. (Later we will introduce rotational kinetic energy, but you can use translational kinetic energy here.) What do you think has happened to the kinetic energy that disappeared?

4. Two ice blocks of masses 1 kg and 3 kg are attached to the ends of a spring of spring constant 300 n/m, and resting on a floor. What is the reduced mass of the system? Drawn apart and released, with what period will each mass vibrate?

5. Two blocks of masses 3 lb and 1 lb rest in a straight smooth horizontal trough, joined by a massless uniform spring. Drawn 2 in. apart and released, the blocks vibrate with a period of 2 sec. **(a)** Determine the spring constant, and the amplitude of vibration of each block. **(b)** At an instant when the spring is at its maximum extension a pin is passed through the center of the spring and into the surface of the trough. Determine the motion of each block after this.

6. (a) Two blocks of masses 1 kg and 2 kg are joined by an ideal spring of spring constant 200 n/m. With the spring unstretched the blocks are 25 cm apart at rest on a smooth table. The blocks are pulled apart and pushed at right angles to one another so that the system rotates with a constant distance l between the masses, making one revolution in 0.8 sec. Determine the length l. **(b)** Suppose that the system was set rotating with a vibration superposed. What would be the period of this vibration? Would the angular speed of rotation be constant as before?

7. A 6-in.-diameter pulley is free to rotate about a fixed horizontal axle. A 4-ft rod with a 10-lb lead ball at each end is attached symmetrically to the face of the pulley.

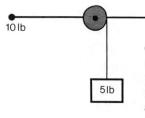

One end of a cord is fixed to the pulley edge, the cord is wound several times around the pulley, and a 5-lb weight is suspended from it. Assuming that all masses except those given are negligible, and neglecting friction, determine the acceleration of the 5-lb mass, the angular acceleration of the dumbbell, the tension in the cord, and the force exerted on the axle. Is there a couple acting on the rotating system? How long would it take the 5-lb weight to descend 4 ft, starting from rest? This is an effective way of producing a small and easily measured acceleration that is related to the acceleration due to gravity, and therefore such a system can be used to measure g. (Assume g is exactly 32 ft/sec^2 here.)

8. A light 60-cm rod with 200-gm lead pellets at each end lies on a table. Two threads are looped about the rod, 30 cm apart, and each is pulled with a 50-gm force perpendicular to the rod, in opposite directions. Making the necessary idealizations, calculate the initial acceleration of each end of the rod **(a)** if the threads are placed symmetrically as shown, **(b)** if one thread is at the center of the rod, and the other is at one end. **(c)** Suppose that the threads are passed over the smooth edges of the table and a 50-gm weight is suspended from each. What would the results for (a) and (b) be?

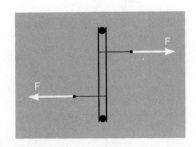

9. Two 0.5-lb particles joined by a massless rod 2 ft long are at rest on a smooth table. A horizontal force **F** of magnitude 5 pndl is applied to the system. Determine the magnitudes of the initial acceleration a of the center of mass and of the initial angular acceleration α about the c-of-m, **(a)** if **F** is perpendicular to the rod at its center, **(b)** if **F** is perpendicular to the rod at one end, **(c)** if **F** is 6 in. from the center, at 30° to the rod.

10. Two 200-gm particles joined by a massless rigid rod 1 m long are at rest on a smooth table. The system is struck a horizontal blow of impulse **J** whose magnitude is 10,000 dyne-sec. Determine the position of the system 2 sec after the blow is struck **(a)** if **J** is perpendicular to the rod at its center, **(b)** if **J** is perpendicular to the rod 20 cm from its center, **(c)** if **J** is at an angle of 30° with the rod, 20 cm from its center.

11. Two 0.2-kg particles joined by a massless rigid rod 1 m long are at rest on a smooth table. **(a)** A 0.1-kg particle sliding on the table at right angles to the rod with a speed of 0.8 m/sec hits the rod 0.2 m from its center and rebounds with a speed of 0.2 m/sec in the opposite direction. Determine the position of the rod 2 sec after the collision (compare part (b) of the previous question). **(b)** The 0.1-kg particle again slides on the table at right angles to the rod, hitting it 0.2 m from its center, but this time the particle moves at 1 m/sec and sticks to the rod when it hits. Determine the position of the system 2 sec after the collision. Note that the mass, center of mass, and moment of inertia of the system have changed.

12. A system of two 0.1-lb particles connected by a massless rigid rod 1 ft long is thrown with an initial velocity of 12 ft/sec at 45° above the horizontal, and spinning at 60 rpm. At the top of its trajectory it is struck a blow that reverses both its linear momentum and its angular momentum. Determine the impulse **J** of the blow, and its point of application on the rod.

13. A 0.1-kg particle and a 0.3-kg particle joined by a rigid massless rod 2 m long are at rest on a smooth table. An ideal string is tied to the rod and extends horizontally, at right angles to the rod, passing over an ideal pulley at the edge of the table to suspend a 0.2-kg mass. **(a)** Determine where the string must be tied to the rod so that the system moves in pure translation, and find its acceleration. **(b)** Determine the magnitudes of the initial accelerations of each of the three masses if the string is tied to the center of the rod.

16

DYNAMICS OF ROTATION
OF A RIGID BODY

ANGULAR MOMENTUM OF
A SYMMETRIC RIGID BODY

In discussing the total angular momentum of the solar system we estimated the spin angular momentum of the earth by assuming that all of its mass was concentrated in a ring at the equator. We now make a better calculation, assuming that the earth is a rigid body, and is a perfect sphere. Most of the discussion of this section will apply to *any* rigid body that has an axis of symmetry, and only at the end will we limit ourselves to a sphere. However, we give the discussion using a spherical earth as an example so that you have a definite rigid

A rigid body with symmetry with respect to an axis.

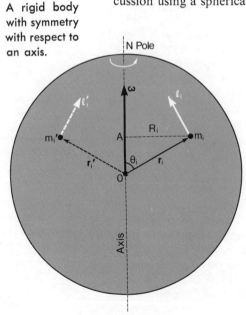

body to visualize. We wish to determine $\mathbf{L}_{\text{spin}} = \sum \mathbf{r}_i \times \mathbf{p}_i = \sum m_i \mathbf{r}_i \times \mathbf{v}_i$, where $\mathbf{r}_i$ is the displacement of the particle of mass m_i from the center of mass O, the center of the earth. We will consider that the earth is a perfectly spherical rigid body, rotating with an angular velocity $\boldsymbol{\omega}$ about its axis. Then each particle of the earth has the same angular velocity. A particle with displacement $\mathbf{r}_i$ rotates in a circle of radius $r_i \sin \theta_i = R_i$, where θ_i is the angle between $\mathbf{r}_i$ and $\boldsymbol{\omega}$ (the axis direction), and R_i is the distance of the particle from the axis. The velocity is $\mathbf{v}_i = \boldsymbol{\omega} \times \mathbf{r}_i$ with a constant magnitude $v_i = \omega r_i \sin \theta_i = \omega R_i$. The angular momentum of m_i with respect to the fixed point A on the axis has a magnitude $m_i R_i v_i = m_i R_i^2 \omega$. This would be a vector in the $\boldsymbol{\omega}$ direction, but note that it is *not* the angular momentum $\mathbf{l}_i$ with respect to the center of mass O, it is just the **component** of $\mathbf{l}_i$

410

parallel to the axis. In the diagram think of a particle m_i in the plane of the page. The velocity $\mathbf{v}_i$ is directly into the page, and $\mathbf{l}_i = \mathbf{r}_i \times \mathbf{p}_i$ has the direction shown, not the $\boldsymbol{\omega}$ direction. Each mass m_i will have an $\mathbf{l}_i$ in a different direction. However, an important simplification arises here because we are considering a body that is **symmetrical with respect to the axis.** For the particle m_i there will be another particle m_i' on the opposite side of the axis, with a velocity directed out of the page, and an angular momentum $\mathbf{l}_i'$ as indicated. The magnitude of $\mathbf{l}_i$ and $\mathbf{l}_i'$ will be the same, and the tilt with respect to the axis will be the same. The components **parallel** to the axis will be in the **same** direction, the components **perpendicular** to the axis will be in **opposite** directions. Thus when the vector sum $\sum \mathbf{l}_i$ is found, the perpendicular components will cancel out and only the parallel components will contribute to the sum.

We showed that the magnitude of the parallel component of $\mathbf{l}_i$ is

$$m_i r_i v_i \sin \theta_i = m_i R_i v_i = m_i R_i^2 \omega$$

so

$$L_{\mathrm{spin}} = \sum l_i = \sum m_i R_i^2 \omega = \left(\sum m_i R_i^2\right)\omega$$

and since this is a vector in the $\boldsymbol{\omega}$ direction

$$\mathbf{L}_{\mathrm{spin}} = \left(\sum m_i R_i^2\right)\boldsymbol{\omega} = I\boldsymbol{\omega}$$

where again we have introduced the scalar quantity $I = \sum m_i R_i^2$, the moment of inertia.

For a continuous distribution of mass, as we can assume for the earth, the sum is replaced by an integral, exactly as we did in Chapter 9 in finding the position of the center of mass for continuous mass distributions.

$$I = \sum m_i R_i^2 \rightarrow \int R^2 \, dm$$

where the integral is taken over the body. Note that R is the distance **from the axis,** not the distance from a fixed point.

So far we have said nothing that restricted our discussion to the rotation of a sphere; the essential thing we have assumed is **symmetry** with respect to the axis through the c-of-m. (Remember that if a rigid body has symmetry the c-of-m will lie on the axis of symmetry.)

In order to apply the results of this discussion to a sphere, we would have to evaluate the quantity $I = \int R^2 \, dm$ for a spherical mass distribution. We will show later some examples of this kind of calculation. For a sphere of mass M, radius R, the moment of inertia about its axis is $I = \frac{2}{5} MR^2$. Therefore the calculation of spin angular momentum of the earth before using $L_{\mathrm{spin}} = MR_E^2 \omega_E$ was a factor $\frac{5}{2}$ too high. A more accurate result is

$$L_{\mathrm{spin}} = \tfrac{2}{5} M_E R_E^2 \omega_E = 6.9 \times 10^{33} \text{ kg-m}^2/\text{sec}$$

The earlier rough calculation of course was adequate to show that L_{spin} is negligible with respect to L_{orbital}.

ROTATION ABOUT AN AXIS PARALLEL TO AN AXIS OF SYMMETRY—THE PARALLEL-AXIS THEOREM

Now instead of thinking of a sphere rotating about an axis C through the center of mass, think of one rotating about a parallel axis A, a distance R_0 away: the axis A may or may not pass through the body, but the body is in **pure rotation** around this axis. All points in the body have the same angular velocity ω_A around this axis.

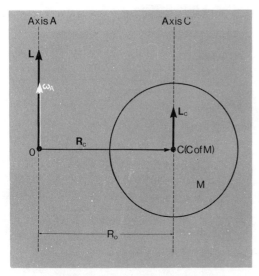

We showed previously that the angular momentum of any system of particles with respect to any fixed point O is $\mathbf{L} = \mathbf{L}_c + \mathbf{R}_c \times \mathbf{P}$, where $\mathbf{L}_c$ is the angular momentum with respect to the center of mass, and $\mathbf{R}_c \times \mathbf{P}$ is the angular momentum of the center of mass with respect to O.

If we choose the fixed point O on the axis A, then $\mathbf{R}_c \times \mathbf{P} = M\mathbf{R}_c \times \mathbf{V}_c = MR_0^2\omega_A$ because the velocity of the c-of-m $\mathbf{V}_c$ is at right angles to the vector $\mathbf{R}_c$, so $\mathbf{V}_c = \omega_A \times \mathbf{R}_c$ has a magnitude $R_0\omega_A$, and a direction at right angles to $\mathbf{R}_c$.

We have already shown that $\mathbf{L}_{\text{spin}} = \mathbf{L}_c = I_c\omega_c$, where I_c is the moment of inertia with respect to axis C, and ω_c is the angular velocity with respect to axis C. But observe that $\omega_c = \omega_A$: if the point C has a speed $R_0\omega_A$ *into* the page, with respect to O, the point O has a speed $R_0\omega_c = R_0\omega_A$ *out* of the page, with respect to C.

A rigid body in pure rotation about an axis parallel to an axis of symmetry.

We then have that the angular momentum with respect to the axis A is

$$
\begin{aligned}
\mathbf{L}_A &= \mathbf{L}_c + \mathbf{R}_c \times \mathbf{P} \\
&= I_c\omega_A + MR_0^2\omega_A \\
&= (I_c + MR_0^2)\omega_A \\
&= I_A\omega_A
\end{aligned}
$$

Again there is a scalar factor relating angular momentum $\mathbf{L}_A$ and angular velocity ω_A, and we can introduce the moment of inertia I_A as a scalar quantity. We can show that $I_A = \sum m_i R_{iA}^2$ where R_{iA} is the distance of the particle of mass m_i from the A axis, but we do not need this because I_A is expressed in terms of I_c.

$$I_A = I_c + MR_0^2$$

This relation is called the **parallel-axis theorem** for moment of inertia; the moment of inertia about any axis is equal to the moment of inertia about a parallel axis through the center of mass plus the mass times the distance between the axes squared. Note, however, that we have shown this only for axes of symmetry, where we can use moment of inertia as a scalar.

INTRINSIC ANGULAR MOMENTUM OF FUNDAMENTAL PARTICLES

We have shown that as far as its motion with respect to the sun is concerned, the earth can be treated as a particle; it looks like a particle in the frame of reference of the solar system, and its spin angular momentum is negligible with respect to its orbital angular momentum. In dealing with the particles of atomic or nuclear physics, this turns out not to be so. Objects that otherwise can be treated like particles have a spin angular momentum that is not negligible. A proton, for example, can in some senses be considered to be a particle but it has a spin angular momentum that must be taken into account in calculating the total angular momentum of atomic systems and also in considering its interaction with other particles.

What is spinning to give a proton its spin angular momentum? Is a proton made up of a distribution of smaller particles? We have pointed out that at the sub-atomic level classical mechanics does not provide an appropriate description of motion—instead we need to use quantum mechanics. The concept of a particle as an entity that can be precisely located in space and time must be given up, so that while we continue to use the term "particle" in quantum mechanics it does not have the same connotation as in classical mechanics. Questions like "what is spinning?" lose their meaning. Instead we recognize as an experimental fact that the fundamental particles have a spin angular momentum, and treat this as an **intrinsic** property of the particle, like mass, without necessarily trying to visualize something rotating. Just as all protons seem to have the same mass, all protons seem to have the same angular momentum. What is more, all electrons and all neutrons have this same angular momentum as well. It certainly seems then that we must treat spin angular momentum as an intrinsic or fundamental property of the fundamental particle.

The spin angular momentum for fundamental particles is usually expressed in units of $\hbar = h/2\pi$, where h is Planck's constant: $\hbar = 1.05 \times 10^{-34}$ joule-sec. You can verify that the dimensions are the same as those for angular momentum mvr. The quantity $\hbar$ is sometimes called a natural unit of angular momentum, just as the electronic charge e is called a natural unit of electric charge. The spin angular momentum of the fundamental particles, of atoms, and of molecules, always appears in half-integral multiples of $\hbar$. For example, a proton has spin $\frac{1}{2}$, meaning that its spin angular momentum is $\hbar/2 = 0.5 \times 10^{-34}$ kg-m^2/sec.

The spin of an electron or a neutron is also $\frac{1}{2}$. The other fundamental particles (neutrinos and the various kinds of mesons) have spins of $\frac{1}{2}$ or zero.

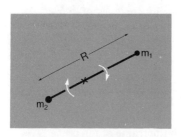

A rigid rotator model for a diatomic molecule.

While we cannot ask meaningfully what is rotating to give a proton its spin, we can sometimes usefully think of a molecule as a system of particles rotating. A diatomic molecule, for example, can be represented by a model of two point masses m_1 and m_2 (the atoms) a constant distance R apart, where R is the interatomic spacing ~ 1 Å. This rigid rotator model does not represent all aspects of molecule motion—it does not allow for vibration of the atoms with respect to one another—but it does represent the rotational motion. We will estimate the frequency of rotation of such a molecule.

Diatomic gas molecules such as H_2, O_2, N_2, HCl consist of particles (atoms) of mass $m \sim 10^{-26}$ kg. The moment of inertia of a rigid rotator about its center of mass we have shown to be

$$I = \mu R^2 = mR^2/2 \sim (10^{-26} \text{ kg})(10^{-10} \text{ m})^2/2 \sim 10^{-46} \text{ kg-m}^2$$

and its spin angular momentum is $L = I\omega$. Using $L \sim \hbar \sim 10^{-34}$ joule-sec gives

$$\omega = L/I \sim 10^{-34}/10^{-46} \sim 10^{12} \text{ rad/sec}$$

or frequency $\qquad\qquad f = \omega/2\pi \sim 10^{11}$ cycles/sec

The only way this motion can be detected is if it changes. If a molecule is made to emit radiation, and if its angular momentum can only take on certain values (is quantized in half-integral multiples of $\hbar$), then the frequency of the radiation corresponding to changes in angular momentum (and corresponding changes in energy) will be in the frequency region $\sim 10^{11}$ cps. This is in the microwave region of the electromagnetic spectrum, corresponding to radiation of wavelength of the order of millimeters:

$$\lambda = c/f \sim (3 \times 10^8 \text{ m/sec})/(10^{11} \text{ sec}^{-1}) \sim 3 \times 10^{-3} \text{ m} \sim 3 \text{ mm}$$

Microwave spectroscopy shows that there are transitions in excited diatomic gases in this spectral region, and these are attributed to changes in rotation of the molecules.

The frequency of radiation emitted due to changes in vibrational energy levels is much higher, $\sim 10^{14}$ cps, corresponding to radiation in the infrared region of the spectrum.

The rigid rotator model we have used in this discussion is based completely on classical mechanics concepts, even though we used some of the results of quantum mechanics in estimating the frequencies. Such a model, like the Bohr mechanistic model of the hydrogen atom, enables us to visualize atoms and molecules in classical terms, but it should be emphasized that such models have no validity from the point of view of quantum mechanics. It can be argued that maintaining these classical models inhibits a proper understanding of atomic systems as described from a quantum mechanics standpoint.

CALCULATION OF MOMENTS OF INERTIA OF SYMMETRIC RIGID BODIES

We have shown that the concept of moment of inertia as a scalar quantity must be used with some care. However, we have established that if we restrict ourselves to considering rigid bodies with an axis of symmetry, and consider only rotations about axes parallel to the axis of symmetry, then there is a scalar relation between $\mathbf{L}$ and $\boldsymbol{\omega}$, $\mathbf{L} = I\boldsymbol{\omega}$. Before going on to rigid body dynamics we will calculate the moment of inertia for certain common shapes. This is not really physics—the physics is the part we have already done. Calculation of $I = \int R^2 \, dm$ is a mathematical step that we could omit, simply quoting the results, but probably some practice in such calculations is useful.

Our calculations are based on assuming rigid bodies with a continuous, uniform mass distribution, as for the calculation of center of mass. In general, even if we require the moment of inertia with respect to an axis not passing through the c-of-m, it is simpler to calculate the moment of inertia about the axis of symmetry, and use the parallel-axis theorem.

Example 1—Rigid Rod: Think first of a one-dimensional rigid body, a rigid rod of mass m, length l. This is a reasonable approximation for any object, such as a meterstick, whose length is large compared to its cross sectional dimensions. Let the element of mass dm be a slice across the rod, of thickness dx and a distance x from the center of mass C. The assumption is that all particles in this mass element are the same distance from an axis, at right angles to the rod, through C. Use ρ for the **linear density** of the rod, assumed constant; $\rho = m/l$, the mass per unit length. Then $dm = \rho \, dx$ and

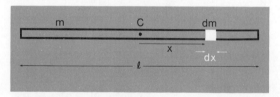

Moment of inertia of a thin uniform rod about an axis perpendicular to the rod through its center.

$$I_c = \int R^2 \, dm = \int x^2 \rho \, dx = \rho \int_{-l/2}^{l/2} x^2 \, dx = \rho[x^3/3]_{-l/2}^{l/2}$$

$$= \frac{\rho}{3}\left[\left(\frac{l^3}{8}\right) - \left(-\frac{l^3}{8}\right)\right] = \frac{\rho}{12} l^3 = \tfrac{1}{12}ml^2$$

The integration $\int R^2 \, dm$ is to be performed as the mass element dm is moved over the whole body, which means in this case that x ranges from $-l/2$ to $l/2$.

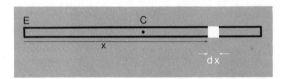

Moment of inertia of a thin uniform rod about an axis perpendicular to the rod through one end.

We could calculate the moment of inertia about an axis through the end of the rod, at right angles, measuring x from the end of the rod, and changing the limits

$$I_E = \rho \int_0^l x^2 \, dx = \tfrac{1}{3}\rho l^3 = \tfrac{1}{3}ml^2$$

The same result is obtained using the parallel-axis theorem:

$$I_E = I_c + m\left(\frac{l}{2}\right)^2 = \tfrac{1}{12}ml^2 + \tfrac{1}{4}ml^2 = \tfrac{1}{3}ml^2$$

Example 2—Ring: The moment of inertia of a ring with respect to an axis through its center of mass at right angles to its plane (an axis of symmetry) is

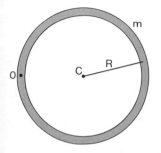

Moment of inertia of a thin ring about an axis perpendicular to its .plane through its center.

$$I_c = \int R^2 \, dm = R^2 \int dm = mR^2$$

assuming that the ring is of negligible thickness.

The moment of inertia about a parallel axis at the circumference is

$$I_0 = I_c + mR^2 = 2mR^2$$

These results are valid no matter how wide the ring is, as long as it is uniform in width; the diagram could represent the end of a pipe of indeterminate length.

Example 3—Rod or Disc or Solid Cylinder: The diagram represents a thin flat disc of thickness l, or the end of a solid cylinder of length l. The axis is the axis of symmetry of the cylinder. The element of mass dm is the tube of radius r, length l and thickness dr. Its circumference is $2\pi r$, and its volume $(2\pi r)(dr)(l)$, in the limit as $dr \to 0$, so $dm = 2\pi \rho l r \, dr$ where ρ is the density of the material: $m = \rho \times$ total volume $= \rho \pi R^2 l$.

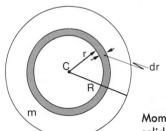

Moment of inertia of a solid rod about its axis.

$$I_c = \int r^2 \, dm = 2\pi \rho l \int_0^R r^3 \, dr = 2\pi l R^4/4 = \tfrac{1}{2}mR^2$$

In addition to the parallel-axis theorem, there is another useful general theorem concerning moments of inertia. This is called the **perpendicular-axis theorem,** and applies only to a **lamina,** or thin uniform plane sheet of matter. The diagram shows a lamina, with a co-ordinate system such that the x- and y-axes are in the plane of the lamina, the z-axis at right angles to it. The moment of inertia with respect to the x-axis is $I_x = \int y^2 \, dm$. Similarly $I_y = \int x^2 \, dm$. Now note that

$$I_x + I_y = \int y^2 \, dm + \int x^2 \, dm$$
$$= \int (x^2 + y^2) \, dm = \int r^2 \, dm$$
$$= I_z$$

since $\int r^2 \, dm$ is the moment of inertia with respect to an axis through O at right angles to the plane, or the z-axis.

The perpendicular-axis theorem says that the sum of the moments of inertia about two perpendicular axes in the plane of a lamina is equal to the moment of inertia about an axis perpendicular to the plane.

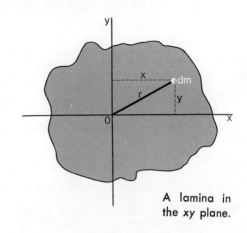

A lamina in the xy plane.

Example 4—Flat Disc: The perpendicular-axis theorem enables us to determine the moment of inertia of a disc about a diameter without integrating. Thinking of symmetric axes as shown, we know $I_x = I_y$ from symmetry, and $I_z = \frac{1}{2}mR^2$ as we showed before.

$$I_x + I_y = 2I_x = I_z = \tfrac{1}{2}mR^2$$
$$I_x = \tfrac{1}{4}mR^2$$

This is the moment of inertia about any diameter.

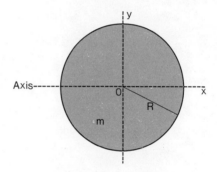

Moment of inertia of a flat disc about a diameter.

Example 5—Thick Rod: Using the two theorems facilitates the calculation of moments of inertia. Think of a thick rod, and an axis at right angles to it through its center C. The element of mass dm is a slice at right angles to the rod axis, of thickness dx, mass $dm = \rho \pi R^2 \, dx$. Its moment of inertia with respect to its own diameter is $\frac{1}{4}dm \, R^2$,

Moment of inertia of a thick rod about an axis perpendicular to its axis, through its center.

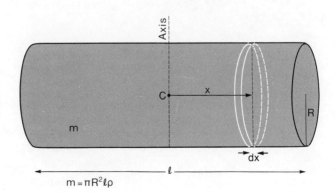

$m = \pi R^2 \ell \rho$

as shown for a disc, and with respect to the axis through C is, using the parallel-axis theorem, $\frac{1}{4}dm\,R^2 + x^2\,dm$. The total moment of inertia is

$$I_c = \frac{1}{4}R^2\int dm + \rho\pi R^2\int_{-l/2}^{l/2} x^2\,dx = \frac{1}{4}mR^2 + \frac{1}{12}ml^2$$

If $R \ll l$, the value becomes that for a thin rod; if $l \ll R$, the value becomes that for a thin disc.

Example 6—Thin Shell: For bodies of spherical symmetry it may be more useful to use an angle as the variable. Think of a spherical shell of uniform **area density** ρ: $m = (4\pi R^2)\rho$. The element of mass is a ring whose plane is perpendicular to the axis, of radius $r = R\sin\theta$. Then

$$dm = (2\pi r)(Rd\theta)(\rho)$$

and the moment of inertia of this ring about the axis is $dm\,r^2 = 2\pi\rho R^4\sin^3\theta\,d\theta$. To integrate it is helpful to write $\sin^3\theta = \sin\theta(1 - \cos^2\theta)$

$$I_c = 2\pi\rho R^4\left[\int_0^\pi \sin\theta\,d\theta + \int_0^\pi \cos^2\theta\,d(\cos\theta)\right]$$

$$= 2\pi\rho R^4\{[-\cos\theta]_0^\pi + [\cos^3\theta/3]_0^\pi\}$$

$$= 2\pi\rho R^4[-(-1-1) + \frac{1}{3}(-1-1)]$$

$$= \frac{8}{3}\pi\rho R^4 = \frac{2}{3}mR^2$$

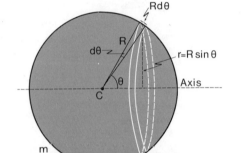

Moment of inertia of a thin spherical shell about a diameter.

Example 7—Solid Sphere: A solid sphere may be thought of as made up of concentric spherical shells. A shell of radius r, thickness dr, density ρ has a mass

$$dm = 4\pi r^2\,dr\,\rho$$

and a moment of inertia about a diameter of

$$\frac{2}{3}dm\,r^2 = \frac{8}{3}\pi\rho r^4\,dr$$

The moment of inertia of the solid sphere is

$$I_c = \frac{8}{3}\pi\rho\int_0^R r^4\,dr = \frac{8}{15}\pi\rho R^5 = \frac{2}{5}mR^2$$

This result was used previously for the earth.

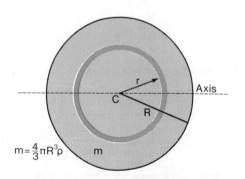

Moment of inertia of a solid homogeneous sphere about a diameter.

In all these examples the moment of inertia with respect to an axis through the c-of-m has the form: $I =$ a numerical factor $\times$ mass of body $\times$ (a dimension of the body)^2, where the numerical factor depends on the shape of the body. Sometimes the numerical and dimension factors are combined by writing $I =$

mk^2, where k is the **radius of gyration.** The body acts as though all of its mass were concentrated at a distance k from the axis. For a solid cylinder with respect to its axis, $k = R/\sqrt{2}$; for a solid sphere $k = \sqrt{\frac{2}{5}}R$. The advantage of using k is that bodies of different shapes can be described using the same general expression $I = mk^2$.

THE ROTATIONAL ANALOGUE OF F = ma: $\tau = I\alpha$

We have shown that the external torque on a system of particles and the total angular momentum of the system are related in general by $\tau_{\text{ext}} = d\mathbf{L}/dt$.

If we consider the motion of rigid bodies with axes of symmetry, and deal only with rotations about axes parallel to these axes, the angular momentum is related to the angular velocity by $\mathbf{L} = I\boldsymbol{\omega}$ where I is a scalar constant. Then

$$\tau_{\text{ext}} = \frac{d\mathbf{L}}{dt} = \frac{d(I\boldsymbol{\omega})}{dt}$$

$$= I\frac{d\boldsymbol{\omega}}{dt} = I\boldsymbol{\alpha}$$

This is the rotational analogue of the fundamental equation of dynamics, $\mathbf{F} = m\mathbf{a}$, expressed in variables more appropriate for dealing with rotation.

If a rigid body is rotating about a **fixed** axis, then every particle in it rotates in a circle about this axis; the angular velocity vector has a fixed direction in the frame of reference (the axis direction). An external torque that would change this direction is balanced by whatever is providing the fixed axis. Therefore τ_{ext}, $\boldsymbol{\omega}$ and $\boldsymbol{\alpha}$ are all vectors in the same line, and the situation is really a one-dimensional one—the rotational analogue of one-dimensional translation. The vector character of the variables means only that we must have regard for sign. We will look at a few examples.

Example 1—Accelerated Flywheel: A 100-lb cylindrical flywheel 2 ft in diameter is mounted on a smooth axle. A cord is wrapped several times around the wheel, and pulled with a constant force of 5 lb. How long will it take for the wheel to reach a speed of 180 rpm? How many turns of string were necessary?

The wheel has a moment of inertia with respect to its axis of $I = \frac{1}{2}MR^2 = \frac{1}{2} \times 100 \times 1^2 = 50$ lb-ft². The force acts tangentially to the wheel, so the torque with respect to the axis $\tau = \mathbf{r} \times \mathbf{F}$ has a magnitude $\tau = FR = 5$ lb-ft. Note that we are using the pound as both a unit of force and of mass. We will work in absolute British units; then we convert the force to poundals: $\tau = FR = (5 \times 32) \times (1) = 160$ pndl-ft.

The angular acceleration is

$$\alpha = \tau/I = 160/50 \text{ sec}^{-2} = 3.2 \text{ rad/sec}^2$$

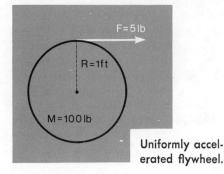

F=5lb

R=1ft

M=100lb

Uniformly accelerated flywheel.

To reach a speed of 180 rpm = 3 rev/sec = 6π rad/sec the time required is

$$t = \frac{\omega - \omega_0}{\alpha} = \frac{6\pi}{3.2} = 5.9 \text{ sec}$$

The angle turned through in this time is

$$\theta = \left(\frac{\omega_0 + \omega}{2}\right)t = \frac{6\pi}{2} \times 5.9 \text{ radians} = \tfrac{3}{2} \times 5.9 \text{ revs} = 8.9 \text{ revolutions}$$

The cord will have to be wrapped at least 9 times around the wheel.

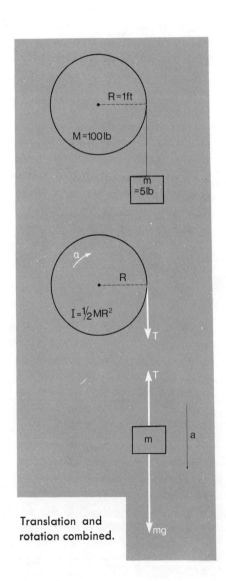

Translation and
rotation combined.

Whatever is pulling on the string has moved $S = R\theta = 8.9 \times 2\pi \times 1 = 56$ ft, and is moving with a speed $v = R\omega = 1 \times 6\pi = 19$ ft/sec ~ 13 mph. This is not a very realistic situation, in general.

One way in which a constant force is exerted is by gravity. Think of the same wheel, with its smooth axle horizontal, and a 5-lb weight suspended from the cord wound around it.

It might at first appear that the force is the same as before, and therefore also the acceleration. The force *is* the same, the 5-lb force of gravity on the 5-lb mass, but the system being accelerated is *not* the same, because the mass itself is being accelerated. The tension in the string is T poundals, and this is not 160 pndl as before.

Here we have a translational and a rotational system combined, and it is useful to separate them.

For the 5-lb mass the equation of motion (in terms of magnitudes) $F = ma$ is

$$5g - T = 5a$$

For the flywheel the equation $\tau = I\alpha$ is

$$TR = I\alpha = (\tfrac{1}{2}MR^2)\alpha$$
$$T = \tfrac{1}{2}MR\alpha$$

It might appear that we have three unknowns T, a, and α, with only two equations, but there is one other relation; the tangential acceleration of the wheel is the same as the acceleration of the string, and of mass m. Therefore, $a = R\alpha$ and $T = \tfrac{1}{2}MR\alpha = \tfrac{1}{2}Ma = 50a$.

Combining with the equation $5g - T = 5a$ gives $a = g/11 = 2.9$ ft/sec², $T = 50g/11$ pndl = $50/11$ lb = 4.5 lb. Note that the results do not depend on the radius of the wheel, only on its mass and shape.

We have not shown the force exerted on the wheel by gravity, or by the smooth axle, because neither exerts a torque on the wheel. Since the wheel's c-of-m is at rest, the resultant force on it is zero, and the force upward due to the axle F_a is equal in magnitude to the downward force $Mg + T$. Note that while the resultant force on the wheel is zero, there is a resultant **couple** on the system, a couple of magnitude TR. We pointed out previously that whenever a system is in pure rotation about its center of mass there is a resultant couple acting on it.

It is of course not possible to have a completely frictionless axle. There will always be a retarding torque due to friction. Suppose that our flywheel at some instant is rotating at 180 rpm, and is observed to come to rest in 5 min. Assuming that the acceleration is constant, $\omega_0 = 180$ rpm $= 6\pi$ rad/sec, $t = 300$ sec

$$\alpha = \frac{\omega - \omega_0}{t} = \frac{0 - 6\pi}{300} = -\pi/50 \text{ rad/sec}^2$$

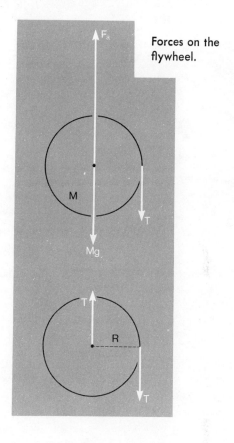

Forces on the flywheel.

the negative sign indicating the deceleration. The frictional torque causing this deceleration is

$$\begin{aligned} \tau_{fr} &= I\alpha = 50 \times \pi/50 \text{ lb-ft}^2/\text{sec}^2 \\ &= \pi \text{ pndl-ft} = \pi/32 \text{ lb-ft} \end{aligned}$$

If the axle is a shaft 1 in. in radius, the frictional force around the circumference would be

$$\begin{aligned} F_{fr} &= \tau_{fr}/r \\ &= (\pi/32)/(1/12) \\ &= 0.12 \text{ lb} \end{aligned}$$

Frictional force tangential, opposing motion.

This is the value of the single force applied at the radius distance that would produce the frictional torque.

The frictional torque may of course not be constant, but depend on the speed of rotation, in which case the calculations made give average values of α, τ_{fr} and F_{fr}.

Example 2—Falling Pivoted Stick: Now think about a rigid body that is rotating about a fixed axis that is not through its center of mass. A hole O is drilled near one end of a 500-gm meterstick, and the stick suspended from a fixed pin passing through the hole. It is drawn sideways and held horizontal by a finger at the other end. We will determine the force exerted by the pin on the stick before it is released, and just after it is released, and the acceleration of the free end of the stick just after it is released. When the stick is at rest in the horizontal position the resultant force on it is zero, so in magnitude $F_1 + F_2 = w$. The resultant torque about its center of mass (or any other point) is also zero, so $F_1(l/2) = F_2(l/2)$ (in magnitude) or $F_1 = F_2$. The pin exerts a force $F_1 = w/2 = 250$ gm on the stick before

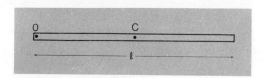

Thin uniform stick pivoted at O, released from rest.

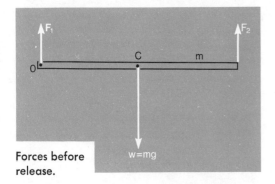

Forces before
release.

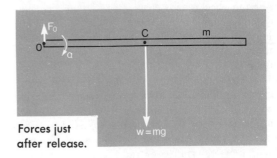

Forces just
after release.

it is released. After it is released there is pure rotation about the pin O. The weight provides an initial torque about O of $\tau_0 = w(l/2)$. The stick has a moment of inertia about O of $I_0 = \frac{1}{3}ml^2$. The angular acceleration about O is

$$\alpha = \frac{\tau_0}{I_0} = \frac{wl/2}{ml^2/3} = \frac{3}{2}\frac{mgl}{ml^2} = \frac{3}{2}\frac{g}{l}$$

The free end of the stick has an initial acceleration of

$$a_{\text{end}} = l\alpha = \tfrac{3}{2}g$$

This acceleration is greater than that of free fall under gravity; if a small object is sitting on the end of the stick before it is released, the end of the stick will accelerate away from it.

The force exerted by the pin F_0 does not enter the calculation, because it exerts no torque about O. However, we can find its value because we know the acceleration of the center of mass C of the stick.

$$a_c = \left(\frac{l}{2}\right)\alpha = \left(\frac{l}{2}\right)\left(\frac{3}{2}\frac{g}{l}\right) = \tfrac{3}{4}g$$

This is related to the resultant force $\mathbf{F}_0 + \mathbf{w}$ by

$$\mathbf{F}_0 + \mathbf{w} = m\mathbf{a}_c = \tfrac{3}{4}m\mathbf{g}$$
$$\mathbf{F}_0 = \tfrac{3}{4}m\mathbf{g} - m\mathbf{g} = -\tfrac{1}{4}m\mathbf{g} = -\tfrac{1}{4}\mathbf{w}$$

The force due to the pin just after release is an upward force of magnitude one-quarter the weight, or 125 gm. As the free end is released, the force at O drops from $w/2$ to $w/4$.

As we showed before (for the dumbbell) the motion can be treated as pure translation plus rotation about the center of mass. The *whole* stick can be considered to have a downward acceleration $a_c = 3g/4$. There will be an acceleration around the c-of-m due to the torque $F_0(l/2)$, of angular acceleration

$$\alpha_c = \frac{\tau_c}{I_c} = \frac{F_0(l/2)}{ml^2/12} = \frac{6F_0}{ml} = \frac{6(mg/4)}{ml} = \frac{3}{2}\frac{g}{l}$$

The angular acceleration of O about C is the same as the angular acceleration of C about O. The downward acceleration of the point O of $a_c = 3g/4$ (considering the whole stick to be in translation) is compensated by the upward acceleration due to rotation around the c-of-m, $a_0 = (l/2)\alpha_c = 3g/4$, and the point O stays at rest.

All of this discussion applies only to the instant just after release of the stick, because the accelerating torque is not constant. The torque wd about O keeps decreasing because the length of the moment arm d keeps decreasing. At the instant the stick swings through the vertical position, the torque is zero. Because the acceleration is continuously changing we cannot readily integrate to find the time it takes for the stick to move a finite distance, or find its velocity at any point. We will see in Part V that the concept of energy is useful in finding the velocity.

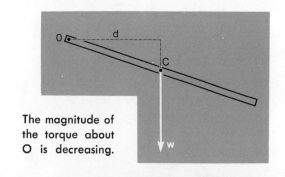

The magnitude of the torque about O is decreasing.

Think of the stick at the instant it is at 45° with the horizontal. The torque about O is

$$\tau_0 = w\left(\frac{l}{2}\sin 45°\right) = mgl/2\sqrt{2}$$

$$\alpha = \frac{\tau_0}{I_0} = \frac{mgl/2\sqrt{2}}{ml^2/3} = \frac{3}{2\sqrt{2}}\frac{g}{l}$$

$$a_c = \frac{l}{2}\alpha = \frac{3}{4\sqrt{2}}g$$

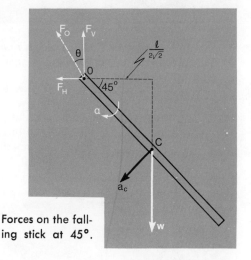

Forces on the falling stick at 45°.

This acceleration of the c-of-m is tangential to the circular path of C. It can be resolved into vertical and horizontal components $a_{cV} = a_c \sin 45°$, $a_{cH} = a_c \cos 45°$, both of the same magnitude

$$a_{cV} = a_{cH} = \tfrac{3}{8}g$$

In the horizontal direction $F_H = ma_{cH} = \tfrac{3}{8}mg$. In the vertical direction $w - F_V = ma_{cV} = \tfrac{3}{8}g$, so $F_V = \tfrac{5}{8}mg$. The resultant of these is

$$F_0 = \sqrt{F_H^2 + F_V^2} = 0.73\ mg$$

at an angle θ with the vertical: $\tan \theta = F_H/F_V = 3/5$, $\theta = 31°$.

Note that **this is not the total force exerted on the stick by the pin.** This would be the total force if the stick had just been released at the 45° angle, at the instant it started to move. However, if it is moving at the 45° position, then the tangential acceleration a_c is *not* the only acceleration of the center of mass. If the stick has an angular velocity ω with respect to O, then C has a radial acceleration (toward O) of magnitude $a_{cR} = (l/2)\omega^2$. This means that the pin must exert a force $F_R = ma_{cR} = ml\omega^2/2$ in the radial direction, as well as the force F_0 already calculated. The magnitude of F_R will depend on ω, which depends on where the stick was released. We will see in Part V that we can relate changes in gravitational potential energy to changes in rotational kinetic energy to find ω. If the stick is released while horizontal, we would have $mg(l/2\sqrt{2}) = I_0\omega^2/2$, and this would determine ω and hence F_R.

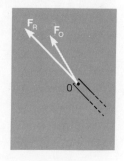

The pivot must also supply the centripetal force.

Example 3—Uniformly Rotating Pivoted Stick: In order to emphasize the presence of the central force, we will think of an example where there is no tangential acceleration. Think of the stick on a smooth table, rotating about a smooth fixed pin O at a

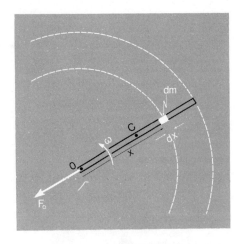

Centripetal force on a
uniformly rotating stick.

constant speed ω. The forces due to gravity and the table in the vertical direction balance out, and the only horizontal force on the stick is that exerted by the pin F_0. It is the central or centripetal force. We will show directly that the total centripetal force is the same as though all the mass of the stick were concentrated at the center of mass C.

Think of an element of the stick of length dx, mass $dm = \rho\, dx$, where ρ is the linear density of the rod $\rho = m/l$. The element dm moves in a circle of radius x with angular speed ω, so the centripetal force on it is $dm\, x\omega^2 = \rho\omega^2 x\, dx$. The resultant centripetal force F_0 is the sum of these forces as x goes from 0 to l.

$$F_0 = \rho\omega^2 \int_0^l x\, dx = \rho\omega^2 l^2/2 = m\omega^2(l/2)$$

Thus the centripetal force is the same as if the mass m were concentrated a distance $l/2$ from the axis—that is, at the center of mass.

We did *not* have to show this directly. For *any* system $\mathbf{F}_{\text{ext}} = m\mathbf{A}_c$; the resultant external force gives the center of mass an acceleration as though all the mass were concentrated at this point. We know here that the center of mass has an acceleration $a_c = (l/2)\omega^2$ and therefore the resultant force is $m(l/2)\omega^2$. The force is constant in magnitude, but not in direction—it is always in the line of the stick.

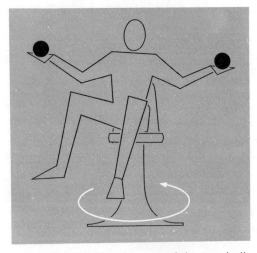

What happens if the iron balls
are moved in toward the axis?

Example 4—Rotating Chair: You may have seen demonstrations on angular momentum involving a chair free to rotate about a vertical axis. In one example, a volunteer seated in the chair is given two iron balls which he holds with arms outstretched, and set rotating slowly. He is told to pull the iron balls in to his chest— and finds himself rotating much more rapidly. Stretching his arms out again he returns to his original speed (if friction is small). We will estimate how much his speed will change.

Assuming that the bearings on the chair are frictionless, there can be no external torque about the vertical axis, so $\tau_{\text{ext}} = d\mathbf{L}/dt = 0$, and the total momentum $\mathbf{L}$ of the man-plus-chair-plus-iron-balls system is constant. If we can define a moment of inertia for the system, $I\omega$ is constant. We will assume enough axial symmetry so that we can use a moment of inertia. The moment of inertia is changed when the iron balls are drawn in, and therefore ω is changed; the angular momentum $I_1\omega_1$ before is the same as $I_2\omega_2$ after.

To estimate the change in ω, assume that the man and chair have a constant moment of inertia I_0, and treat the iron balls as particles of mass m, initially each a distance r_1 from the axis, finally a distance r_2 from the axis. Then $I_1 = I_0 + 2mr_1^2$, $I_2 = I_0 + 2mr_2^2$.

If man and chair are approximated by a 150-lb cylinder 1 ft in diameter, $I_0 = \frac{1}{2}MR^2 = \frac{1}{2} \times 150 \times (\frac{1}{2})^2 \sim 20$ lb-ft². Using $m = 10$ lb, $r_1 = 3$ ft and $r_2 = 0$ (the iron balls held at the axis), $I_1 = 20 + 20(3)^2 = 200$ lb-ft², $I_2 = 20$ lb-ft². $\therefore \omega_2/\omega_1 = I_1/I_2 = 10$. The angular speed is increased by a factor 10. If the volunteer is rotating sedately at 5 rpm with his arms extended, he will rotate at 50 rpm when he draws his arms in. We will see later that he has done work in pulling the balls in, increasing the kinetic energy of the system.

This example illustrates the dominant effect of the r in mr^2; moving the two 10-lb masses has a large effect on the 170-lb system.

Example 5—Rotating Chair with Spinning Wheel: In order to emphasize that angular momentum is a vector quantity, think of another experiment with the rotating chair. This time the volunteer sits on the chair at rest, holding the axle of a spinning wheel. The wheel, moment of inertia I_w, is spinning in the horizontal plane with angular velocity ω_w. The angular momentum $\mathbf{L}_w = I_w\omega_w$ is a vector in the vertical direction.

What happens if the volunteer turns the wheel over, so that its angular momentum is in the opposite direction? He will have to exert a torque on the wheel to do this, but this is an internal torque in the system of man plus wheel. There is no external torque about the chair axis, so the total angular momentum is constant.

What happens if the spinning wheel is inverted?

Initially the chair and man were at rest, so the initial angular momentum $\mathbf{L}_1$ is that of the wheel alone: $\mathbf{L}_1 = \mathbf{L}_w$. After the wheel has been inverted, its angular momentum is $-\mathbf{L}_w$, and therefore the man and chair must have an angular momentum $\mathbf{L}_0 = I_0\omega_0$ such that

$$\mathbf{L}_1 = \mathbf{L}_2 \qquad \mathbf{L}_w = \mathbf{L}_0 + (-\mathbf{L}_w)$$
$$\mathbf{L}_0 = 2\mathbf{L}_w \qquad \text{or} \qquad I_0\omega_0 = 2I_w\omega_w$$

(All angular velocities are expressed with respect to the frame of reference of the earth. The angular speed ω_w cannot be changed, assuming the wheel has frictionless bearings.)

A bicycle wheel with its rim weighted with a 20-lb strip of lead would have a moment of inertia $I_w \sim mr^2 \sim 20 \times 1^2 \sim 20$ lb-ft². Using $I_0 \sim 20$ lb-ft² as before, the man acquires an angular speed $\omega_0 = (2I_w/I_0)\omega_w = 2\omega_w$. If the wheel was originally rotating at 10 rpm, the man will be rotating at 20 rpm after he inverts it. If he inverts it again, he will come to rest—approximately, since there is some friction.

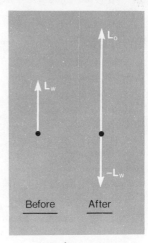

Angular momenta in the earth frame.

Example 6—Man Walking on a Free Turntable: As in translational situations, velocities are sometimes more conveniently measured with respect to a non-inertial frame of reference than an inertial frame. Think of a massive 1000-lb turntable 10 ft in radius, free to rotate about a vertical axis through its center. If a 150-lb man steps on to the turntable at rest, and walks around the edge with a speed of 5 ft/sec **relative to the turntable,** what is his speed relative to the earth?

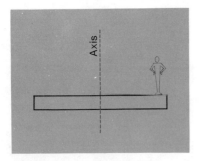

A man walking around the circumference of the turntable.

Treating the turntable as a disc of uniform thickness, it has a moment of inertia $I_0 = \frac{1}{2}MR^2 = \frac{1}{2} \times 1000 \times 10^2 = 5 \times 10^4$ lb-ft², relative to the axis. Treating the man as a point particle at the rim, he has a moment of inertia $I_m = mR^2 = 150 \times 10^2 = 1.5 \times 10^4$ lb-ft², relative to the same axis.

The man plus turntable system is initially at rest, total angular momentum zero. If the system is free to rotate about the vertical axis, this means there can be no external torque about this axis, and the angular momentum remains zero.

$$0 = I_0\omega_0 + I_m\omega_m$$

where ω_0 and ω_m are the angular velocities of turntable and man with respect to the axis. These are in the **earth** frame of reference. We know the velocity of the man in the turntable frame of reference; his speed is $v'_m = 5$ ft/sec, his angular velocity relative to the axis is ω'_m of magnitude $\omega'_m = v'_m/R = 5/10 = 0.5$ rad/sec.

We must make a transformation of velocity.

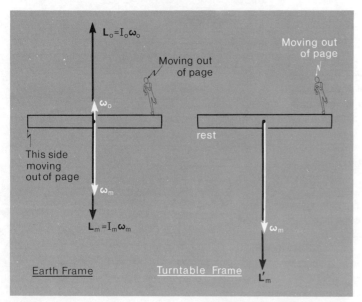

Angular momenta and angular velocities in two frames of reference.

$$\omega_{\text{man re earth}} = \omega_{\text{man re turntable}}$$
$$+ \ \omega_{\text{turntable re earth}}$$
$$\omega_m = \omega'_m + \omega_0$$

Using this result

$$0 = I_0\omega_0 + I_m(\omega'_m + \omega_0)$$
$$= (I_0 + I_m)\omega_0 + I_m\omega'_m$$
$$\omega_0 = -\frac{I_m}{I_0 + I_m}\,\omega'_m$$
$$\omega_m = -\frac{I_0}{I_m}\,\omega_0 = \frac{I_0}{I_0 + I_m}\,\omega'_m$$
$$v_m = R\omega_m = \frac{I_0}{I_0 + I_m}\,v'_m$$
$$= \frac{5 \times 10^4}{6.5 \times 10^4} \times 5$$
$$= 3.8 \text{ ft/sec}$$

In the earth frame of reference, the man and turntable have equal and opposite angular momenta so that the total is zero. The angular velocities are in opposite directions, with magnitudes in the ratio I_0/I_m.

In the turntable frame of reference, only the man has an angular momentum; $\mathbf{L}'_m = I_m\omega'_m = I_m(\omega_m - \omega_0)$. The angular momentum is constant, and therefore there is no external torque about the axis.

$$\tau'_{\text{ext}} = d\mathbf{L}'_m/dt = 0$$

Although there is no external torque about the vertical axis, there *are* external horizontal forces on the man in this frame of reference. (The horizontal forces between the turntable and his feet are internal forces.) This is a frame of reference rotating with angular velocity ω_0 with respect to an inertial frame, and this means that there are inertial forces on any mass m in the frame; there is a centrifugal force $-m\omega_0 \times (\omega_0 \times \mathbf{r})$, which depends on the displacement $\mathbf{r}$ from the axis, and a coriolis force $-2m\omega_0 \times \mathbf{v}'$ which depends on the velocity $\mathbf{v}'$ of the mass in the frame. You can verify that the centrifugal force is outward, away from the axis, and the coriolis force is inward, toward the axis. Therefore neither exerts a torque about the axis.

Since the motion is circular the magnitudes of the inertial forces are $F_{cf} = mR\omega_0^2$, $F_{\text{cor}} = 2m\omega_0v'$. You can calculate ω_0 and determine that $F_{cf} = 0.6$ lb, $F_{\text{cor}} = 5.4$ lb. The floor of the turntable would have to exert horizontal forces to balance these, as well as hold the man up. He would have to lean at an angle that depends on both the speed of the turntable, and his own speed.

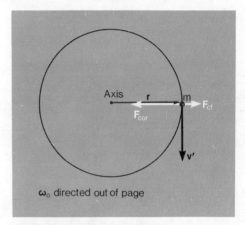

ω_0 directed out of page

Inertial forces on the man in the turntable frame of reference.

Example 7—Man at Rest on a Uniformly Rotating Turntable: In order to separate the two inertial forces and their effects, let us think of a slightly different situation. We have the same turntable but this time it is not rotating freely. It is driven by a motor at a constant angular speed $\omega_0 = 0.5$ rad/sec—no matter what the antics of the man on it. Think first of him standing still at the edge, $R = 10$ ft from the axis. At what angle must he lean, and what is the minimum coefficient of friction between his feet and the turntable floor?

In the earth frame of reference the only forces on the man are his weight, acting at his center of mass C (center of gravity) and the force of the floor acting on his feet. If the turntable is at rest, the force due to the floor is a force $\mathbf{N}$ vertically upward, passing through his center of mass; there is zero resultant force on him, and zero resultant torque on him. When the turntable is rotating he has an acceleration $a_R = R\omega_0^2$ in the horizontal direction toward the axis. The equations of

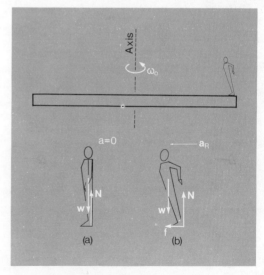

Forces on a man standing on the turntable (a) at rest, and (b) rotating uniformly.

motion with respect to co-ordinate axes in the vertical and horizontal directions are (using magnitudes only) at any instant

$$N = w = mg$$
$$f = ma_R = mR\omega_0^2$$

The horizontal force f exerted by the floor may be exerted by having a lip on the turntable edge, or by nailing the man's shoes to the floor; however, let us assume it is a frictional force. If f were the limiting force of static friction,

$$\mu_s = \frac{f}{N} = \frac{R\omega_0^2}{g} = \frac{10 \times 0.5^2}{32}$$
$$= 0.078$$

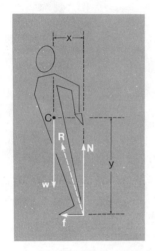

Forces in the earth frame of reference.

Therefore if the coefficient of static friction is this size or larger, the man will not slip off.

He will fall off nevertheless unless he leans toward the center. The force **f** exerts a torque about his center of mass C, producing rotation about C unless there is a torque to balance it. The only other force that can do this is **N**. The torque Nx must balance the torque fy about C. The man must lean at an angle θ so that his c-of-m is displaced inward an amount x.

$$\tan \theta = \frac{x}{y} = \frac{f}{N} \qquad \text{since } Nx = fy$$

To look at this another way, this simply means that the resultant force **R** exerted by the floor must pass through the c-of-m, so that there is no torque about C. In this example $\tan \theta = 0.078$, $\theta = 0.078$ rad $= 4.5°$.

In the turntable frame of reference the man is at rest. In addition to the forces **w** and **R**, there is the centrifugal force F_{cf} of magnitude $mR\omega_0^2$ acting away from the center of the turntable. In magnitude $N = w = mg$ and $f = F_{cf} = mR\omega_0^2$, since the resultant force in any direction is zero. The man is in static equilibrium in this frame of reference, and the resultant torque about any point is zero; with respect to the feet for example, $wx = F_{cf}y$, giving $\tan \theta = x/y = F_{cf}/w = R\omega_0^2/g$. Note that in the earth frame the resultant torque about the man's feet is not zero.

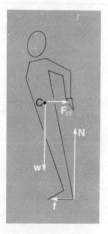

Forces in the turntable frame of reference.

Example 8—Man Walking on Uniformly Rotating Turntable: Now suppose that the man instead of standing at the edge of the turntable walks around the rim. He can walk in the same direction as the rotation ω_0, or the opposite direction (as in the last example). Suppose first that he walks with a speed of 5 ft/sec (relative to the turntable) in the *same* direction; then his speed relative to the ground is 10 ft/sec, since the rim of the turntable has a speed $R\omega_0 = 10 \times 0.5 = 5$ ft/sec.

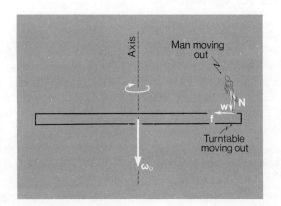

Forces on a man walking around the circumference of a uniformly rotating turntable, in the earth frame.

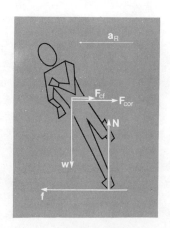

Forces on the man in the turntable frame.

In the earth frame of reference, the force diagram is the same as before, but now the man has a horizontal acceleration toward the axis of magnitude

$$a_R = v^2/R = R\omega^2 = R(2\omega_0)^2 = 4R\omega_0^2$$

since his angular speed ω is twice that of the turntable ω_0. As before, the minimum coefficient of friction is

$$\mu_s = \frac{f}{N} = \frac{4R\omega_0^2}{g} = 4 \times 0.078$$

and $\tan\theta = 4 \times 0.078 = 0.31, \qquad \theta = 18°$

He must lean at an angle more than four times as large as to stand still.

In the frame of reference of the turntable (*not* his frame of reference since he is moving) there is the same outward centrifugal force $F_{cf} = mR\omega_0^2$ as before, and also an *outward* coriolis force of magnitude $F_{cor} = 2m\omega_0 v' = 2mR\omega_0^2$, using $v' = R\omega_0$ since his speed v' relative to the turntable is the same as the speed $R\omega_0$ of the rim relative to the earth.

In this frame he is moving in a circle of radius R with speed v', and therefore has a central acceleration $a_R = (v')^2/R = R\omega_0^2$. The equation of motion in the horizontal direction, using magnitudes only, is

$$f - F_{cf} - F_{cor} = ma_R = mR\omega_0^2$$

or $$f = F_{cf} + F_{cor} + mR\omega_0^2 = 4mR\omega_0^2$$

as determined in the earth frame.

Suppose that he walks with a speed of 5 ft/sec in the *opposite* direction to that of the rim, so that he is at rest relative to the ground. He will not have to lean inward or outward. In the turntable frame of reference there will be an outward centrifugal force $mR\omega_0^2$, and an *inward* coriolis force $2mR\omega_0^2$, the resultant of these providing the acceleration $R\omega_0^2$ toward the center in this frame. In the earth frame there are no horizontal forces or accelerations.

Questions for discussion

1. Is moment of inertia of a particle calculated with respect to a point, or with respect to a line? Is moment of inertia of a rigid body calculated with respect to a point, or with respect to a line?

2. To calculate the moment of inertia of a rigid body of mass m with respect to some axis, is it useful to think of a single particle of mass m at the center of mass? Is there any point at which a single particle of mass m could be placed to give the same moment of inertia?

3. Is it more difficult for you to accept **intrinsic angular momentum** as a property of a particle than it is to accept **mass** as an intrinsic property? Do you know what causes a particle to have mass?

4. Moment of inertia is a property of a body that describes the rotational inertia of the body with respect to a particular axis. Can it be defined for an axis making any direction with respect to the body?

5. What kind of symmetry must a body have in order that its moment of inertia with respect to all axes passing through its center of mass is the same? What kind of symmetry must it have in order that its moment of inertia with respect to all axes passing through its center of mass, and lying in a single plane, is the same?

6. Is the perpendicular-axis theorem for moment of inertia valid for rigid bodies in general, or for a particular kind of rigid body? Is the parallel-axis theorem applicable to rigid bodies in general? Is it valid for axes in any direction with respect to the body?

7. A professor is holding two heavy spheres at arms' length while demonstrating conservation of angular momentum using a rotating chair. He tires, and lets go of the spheres, which fall to the floor. Does his angular speed change, and if so does he speed up or slow down? Is the angular momentum of the system changed? Is angular momentum conserved?

Problems

1. A thin rod of mass m is bent into a complete circle of radius R. What is the moment of inertia of this ring **(a)** about an axis along a diameter, **(b)** about an axis tangent to the ring?

2. **(a)** Determine the moment of inertia of a hollow circular cylinder of mass m, inner radius R_1 and outer radius R_2, about its axis. **(b)** Express the result in terms of $\Delta R = R_2 - R_1$, and note the result for $\Delta R \ll R_2$. **(c)** For what ratio $\Delta R / R_2$ can the cylinder be assumed to have the moment of inertia of a cylinder of infinitesimal thickness, to 1% accuracy?

3. Determine the moment of inertia of a square sheet of metal of mass m, side D, about **(a)** an axis through its center of mass parallel to an edge, **(b)** an axis through its center of mass perpendicular to its plane.

4. A piece of sheet metal of mass m is a square of side D with a circular hole cut in it. The hole is symmetric in the square, and is one-half the area of the whole square. Determine the moment of inertia of the piece about an axis perpendicular to its plane through its center.

5. The walls, top and bottom of a cubical box of side 2 ft and weight 18 lb are all made from the same plywood. **(a)** Calculate the moment of inertia of the empty box about an axis through its center of mass and parallel to an edge. **(b)** The box is balanced on one edge on a floor. If disturbed slightly, what is the magnitude of the angular acceleration of its center of mass just after the box is disturbed, and just before its face hits the floor, assuming the edge does not slip on the floor?

6. We have emphasized that the motion of fundamental particles like the proton cannot be described by the methods of classical mechanics, so questions like "What is spinning to give a proton its angular momentum $\hbar/2$?" have little significance. However, as an exercise, assume that a proton ($m = 1.67 \times 10^{-27}$ kg) can be treated as a sphere about the size of the atomic nucleus, $\sim 10^{-14}$ m. How fast would the sphere be spinning? What would its density be? (This is the density of "nuclear matter.")

7. A rigid body of mass m has a moment of inertia $I = mk^2$ about an axis through its center of mass, where k is its radius of gyration with respect to this axis. The body is rotating around a parallel axis a distance h from the axis through the c-of-m. How far would a single particle of mass m have to be placed from this axis in order to have the same rotational inertia as the body?

8. The moment of inertia of a 12-cm-diameter tin disc about an axis through its center perpendicular to its plane is 2000 gm-cm². Determine the moment of inertia of a rectangular piece 10 cm by 14 cm cut from the same sheet of tin, about an axis through its center perpendicular to its plane.

9. A thin metal rod of mass m is bent into a semicircle of radius R. Determine its moment of inertia about an axis through its center of mass and perpendicular to its plane.

10. Determine the moment of inertia of a solid circular cone of base radius R, mass M, about its axis.

11. A gyroscope wheel has almost all of its mass in the shape of a torus, or donut. This is the shape obtained by rotating a circle of radius a, with center a distance b from the axis, about the axis. **(a)** Determine the volume of a torus. **(b)** Calculate the mass of the wheel if $a = 1$ cm, $b = 2$ cm and it is made of metal of density 10 gm/cm³. **(c)** Calculate the moment of inertia of the wheel assuming that all its mass is concentrated in a ring of radius $b = 2$ cm. Will this estimate be too high or too low? **(d)** Determine the actual moment of inertia of the torus about its axis.

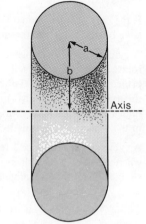

Torus cross section

12. We used a dumbbell model extensively in Chapter 15 in order to examine the behavior of rigid bodies using a simple two-particle system. The ideal dumbbell was two particles ("mass points") each of mass m separated by a fixed distance R (a massless rigid rod). To see the extent to which this system approximates a real system, make the following calculations. **(a)** Determine the diameter of a lead sphere of mass 1 kg (density of lead 11.3 gm/cm³). **(b)** Calculate the moment of inertia of such a lead sphere about an axis through its center of mass. **(c)** Think of two such spheres with their centers 20 cm apart (this is less than four times the diameter of each) and calculate the moment of inertia of this system about the line joining the centers, and about an axis through the center of mass of the system at right angles to the line joining the centers. **(d)** As far as rotation is concerned, what percentage error is made in treating this system as two 1-kg particles connected by a massless rod 20 cm long? **(e)** Think of a lead rod 1 cm in diameter between the two spheres. Calculate its mass, its moment of inertia about its axis, and about an axis through its center of mass at right angles to its length. Do these contribute substantially to the total mass and moment of inertia of the system?

13. A thin rod, similar to a billiard cue, of mass m and length l has a linear density that varies uniformly along the rod, its value at one end being twice that at the other. **(a)** Determine the position of its center of mass with respect to the light end. **(b)** Determine its moment of inertia about an axis perpendicular to its length, at the light end. **(c)** Determine its moment of inertia about an axis through its center of mass, perpendicular to its length.

14. The turntable of a record player has a moment of inertia about its axis of 0.2 lb-ft². It is coasting at 33 rpm when a 12-in., 2.5-oz record drops on it. What is its angular speed now? Ignoring frictional torque, what constant torque in oz-in. would have to be applied to bring it back to 33 rpm in 2 sec?

15. A cylindrical cage 4 ft in diameter is at rest, free to rotate about a vertical axis through its center. A mouse, initially asleep at the edge of the cage, starts to run around the circumference. He runs at a speed of 10 ft/sec with respect to the cage. To a cat sitting outside the cage the mouse is moving at 2 ft/sec. The cat estimates the mouse mass to be 2 oz; what does he estimate for the moment of inertia of the cage about its axis?

16. If the earth contracted so that its diameter was 200 m less, what effect would this have on the length of the day?

17. A cylindrical wooden wheel 40 cm in radius and of mass 1.5 kg is at rest, free to rotate about a fixed axis. Determine the angular speed it acquires if hit by a 200-gm projectile moving at 300 m/sec on a line at right angles to the axis and 20 cm from the axis, assuming that **(a)** the projectile passes right through the wheel and continues in its original direction at half its speed, **(b)** the projectile becomes embedded in the wheel, 10 cm radially inside its edge.

18. A cylindrical grindstone 1 ft in diameter and weighing 80 lb is rotating at 300 rpm when a 2-lb chip flies off its edge. What happens to the angular speed of the grindstone? Determine its angular momentum before and after the chip flies off.

19. A steel rod is 4 ft long. How fast can it be rotated about an axis through its center and perpendicular to it, if the stress at its center is not to exceed the elastic limit for steel, about 6×10^4 lb/in.²? (If a stress above the elastic limit is applied to a metal, the metal may deform permanently, or "flow.")

20. A metal hatch cover is a 90-lb solid circular disc 2 ft in diameter. It is hinged at one edge, and locked by a sliding bolt at the other. Its plane is horizontal, and it opens downward. If the sliding bolt is removed, what is the acceleration of the outer edge of the hatch, and the force exerted by the hinge, immediately afterward?

21. A man steps on to a platform free to rotate about a vertical axis on frictionless bearings. He carries a wheel by its axle, with the axis vertical. The wheel has a moment of inertia about its axis of 10 lb-ft², and is spinning at 40 rpm. The moment of inertia of man and platform about the vertical axis of the platform is about 25 lb-ft². Estimate the angular speed of the man and platform if the man **(a)** turns the wheel through 180° so that its spin is in the opposite direction, **(b)** brings the wheel to rest by holding his hand on the rim. Assume that the axes of the platform and the wheel are coincident. (Why does this matter?) **(c)** Estimate the angular speed of the man if he rotates the wheel 90° from its original position, so that its axle is horizontal. Assume its center is on the axis of the platform. Can you visualize the forces he has to exert to hold the wheel in this position? (See Chapter 19.)

22. An ideal string passes over a cylindrical pulley of mass 200 gm and radius 2 cm, free to rotate about a horizontal axis. Masses of 300 gm and 400 gm are attached to the ends of the string. Determine the magnitude of the acceleration of the masses and the tensions in the string.

23. A 0.3-kg meterstick is pivoted at one end and hanging at rest. **(a)** Calculate the initial acceleration of its lower end if a force of 2 n is applied to it at right angles at its center. **(b)** Calculate the initial speed of its lower end if it is struck a blow of impulse 2 n-sec at right angles at its center. **(c)** Calculate the initial speed of its lower end if a 0.4-kg particle moving horizontally at 5 m/sec hits the stick at its center and (1) is brought to rest by the collision, (2) sticks to the stick.

24. The moment of inertia of a pulley is measured as follows. The pulley rotates on a fixed horizontal axis, and the distance from the axis to the bottom of the pulley groove is 10 cm. A thread is wound several times around the pulley so that it does not slip, and a 7-gm weight is tied to its end. The weight is released from rest and falls 2 m to the floor, taking 2 sec to fall. Once the weight hits the floor the thread falls off the pulley. The pulley continues to rotate for 10 sec more before stopping. Determine its moment of inertia about its axis, assuming that the frictional torque on the pulley is constant throughout its motion.

25. A flywheel has an axle of radius 2 in. It is mounted with its axle horizontal, supported by bearings at each end. A cord is wound around the axle and a mass m tied to the end of the cord. The system is released from rest, and the time t for the mass to descend 4 ft to the floor is measured. For $m = 10$ lb, $t = 4.8$ sec, and for $m = 20$ lb, $t = 2.6$ sec. Determine the moment of inertia of the flywheel about its axis, and the frictional torque acting on it, assuming this torque is constant.

17

DYNAMICS OF
SIMPLE HARMONIC MOTION
OF A RIGID BODY

The last chapter dealt with rotation of a rigid body about a fixed axis parallel to an axis of symmetry (so that we could use a scalar moment of inertia). The motion of a pendulum is rotation about a fixed axis, and can be described by the methods we have developed. However, if the amplitude of vibration is small we have the particular kind of motion called simple harmonic motion. One important feature of SHM is that **the period of vibration is independent of the amplitude of vibration.**

SIMPLE PENDULUM

In Chapter 12 we described the idealization called a **simple pendulum,** a particle of mass m connected to a fixed point by an inextensible massless string or rod of length l. We showed that for small amplitudes of vibration the motion was SHM with period $T = 2\pi\sqrt{l/g}$. We will look at this model again, using the concepts of rotational dynamics.

The particle is moving in a circle of radius l about the fixed point O. We have shown that the particle has a moment of inertia $I_0 = ml^2$ with respect to O, and angular momentum $I_0\omega = ml^2\omega$ about O. The torque about O is

$$\tau_0 = \frac{d\mathbf{L}_0}{dt} = ml^2\frac{d\omega}{dt} = ml^2\alpha$$

The only forces acting on the particle are its weight $\mathbf{w}$ and tension $\mathbf{T}$ in the supporting rod or string. The force $\mathbf{T}$ is directed toward O, and therefore has no torque about O. The torque due to $\mathbf{w}$ has magnitude $mgl \sin \theta$ about O, and its direction is always such as to decrease the angle θ.

The magnitude of the angular acceleration α is $\alpha = d^2\theta/dt^2$. If the vector $d\theta$ is out of the plane of the page, the vector τ_0 is into the plane of the page, so the scalar equation of motion is

$$-mgl \sin \theta = ml^2\alpha = ml^2 \frac{d^2\theta}{dt^2}$$

or
$$\frac{d^2\theta}{dt^2} + \frac{g}{l} \sin \theta = 0$$

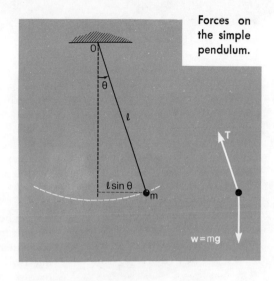

Forces on the simple pendulum.

There have been no approximations made so far, and this is not the differential equation of SHM. It is the equation of SHM **provided** $\sin \theta = \theta$. Then it has the form

$$\frac{d^2\theta}{dt^2} + \omega^2\theta = 0 \qquad \text{where} \qquad \omega^2 = \frac{g}{l}$$

The relation $\sin \theta = \theta$ is valid only for $\theta = 0$, but it is an excellent approximation up to $\theta = 0.1$ rad $\sim 6°$, as we have seen. The motion is not precisely in a straight line for finite amplitudes, but nearly so.

$$h = l - l \cos \theta = l(1 - \cos \theta)$$
$$= l(1 - \sqrt{1 - \sin^2 \theta})$$
$$\cong l[1 - (1 - \tfrac{1}{2} \sin^2 \theta)]$$
$$= \tfrac{1}{2}l \sin^2 \theta = \tfrac{1}{2}l \left(\frac{x}{l}\right)^2 = \tfrac{1}{2}\frac{x^2}{l}$$

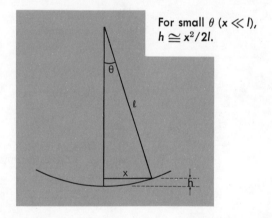

For small θ $(x \ll l)$, $h \cong x^2/2l$.

For a pendulum 1 m long, with a maximum sideways displacement $x = 10$ cm, $\theta = 0.1$ and $h = \tfrac{1}{2} \times 10^2/100 = 0.5$ cm $= 5$ mm.

PHYSICAL PENDULUM

There is no such thing as a simple pendulum, a particle suspended by a massless inextensible rod. We now think of a rigid body free to rotate about a fixed point O, called the point of suspension or **center of suspension,** which is other than the center of gravity G. Such a pendulum is called a **compound pendulum** or a **physical pendulum.** Since we are assuming a rigid body it is not a real pendulum, but is a better approximation than a simple pendulum.

We will not specify the shape of the rigid body, but we will assume that it has some sort of symmetry, such that we can use a scalar moment of inertia about an axis through G, or a parallel axis through O, and will consider vibrations about such an axis. A flat plate of any shape, for example, is considered to be

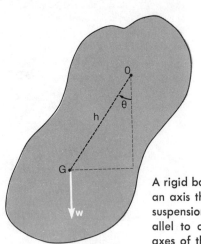

vibrating about an axis perpendicular to the plate.

The only external forces acting on the rigid body are the weight **w**, which may be considered to be a single force acting at the c-of-m G, and the force due to whatever is providing the axis at O. Only the force of gravity exerts a torque about O. The magnitude of the torque for an angular displacement θ is $mgh \sin \theta$ where h is the distance between the points O and G (or parallel axes through these points).

A rigid body oscillating about an axis through the center of suspension O; this axis is parallel to one of the principal axes of the body.

By an argument similar to that used for the simple pendulum, the scalar equation of motion is

$$-mgh \sin \theta = I_0 \alpha = I_0 \frac{d^2\theta}{dt^2}$$

where I_0 is the moment of inertia about the axis through O.

$$\frac{d^2\theta}{dt^2} + \frac{mgh}{I_0} \sin \theta = 0$$

Provided the oscillations are small enough so that $\sin \theta = \theta$, the motion is SHM with

$$\omega^2 = \frac{mgh}{I_0} \qquad \text{or} \qquad T = 2\pi \sqrt{\frac{I_0}{mgh}}$$

We can put this in another form by using the parallel axis theorem

$$I_0 = I_G + mh^2$$
$$= mk^2 + mh^2 = m(k^2 + h^2)$$

where k is the radius of gyration about the c-of-m, defined earlier.

We then have an expression for the period that does not depend on the mass, only on the distribution of mass, or shape of the body.

$$T = 2\pi \sqrt{\frac{m(k^2 + h^2)}{mgh}} = 2\pi \sqrt{\frac{h + k^2/h}{g}} = 2\pi \sqrt{\frac{L}{g}}$$

The quantity $L = h + k^2/h$ is called the length of the equivalent simple pendulum.

Example: For a simple pendulum the mass m is concentrated at a point, the c-of-m: $k = 0, L = h = l$.

For a thin rod suspended at one end

$$I_G = \tfrac{1}{12}ml^2 \qquad \text{so} \qquad k = l/\sqrt{12}$$

and $h = l/2$

$$L = h + k^2/h = \frac{l}{2} + \left(\frac{l^2}{12}\right)\left(\frac{2}{l}\right) = \tfrac{2}{3}l$$

A simple pendulum 67 cm long has the same period as a meter stick suspended at one end.

For a ring hung on a nail, vibrating in its own plane, $h = R$ and $k = R$.

$$L = h + k^2/h = R + R^2/R = 2R$$

The period is the same as that of a simple pendulum of length equal to the ring diameter. What if the oscillations were at right angles to this?

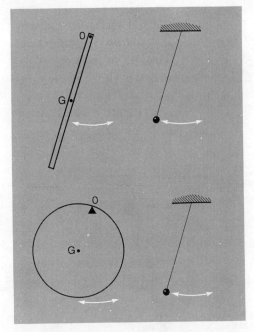

Length of the equivalent simple pendulum for a rod and for a hoop.

CENTER OF OSCILLATION

The point S, a distance $OS = h + k^2/h$ from the point O, is called the **center of oscillation** corresponding to the center of suspension O. It has the property that if the pendulum is suspended about an axis through S the period is the same as when it is suspended at O.

$$T = 2\pi \sqrt{OS/g} \qquad \text{about } O \text{ or } S$$

This is a useful result, because if we can find the two points O and S for a body the period depends *only* on the distance between them, not on the shape of the body. Thus an accurate measurement of this length and an accurate measurement of the corresponding period can be used to determine an accurate value

Relation between the center of suspension O and the center of oscillation S.

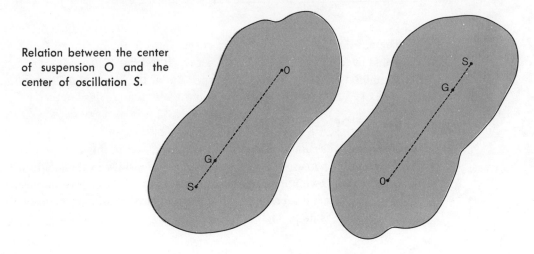

of the acceleration due to gravity g. A device called a **Kater pendulum** is used for such measurements; knife edges are fixed at two points on the pendulum, and an adjustable mass is moved on the pendulum until the period is the same for suspension by either set of knife edges.

A thin uniform rod that can be pivoted at various points is called a **bar pendulum.** The period T plotted as a function of pivot position is the symmetric curve shown; at the center of the bar, $T = \infty$.

$$T = 2\pi\sqrt{L/g} \qquad L = h + (l^2/12)/h$$

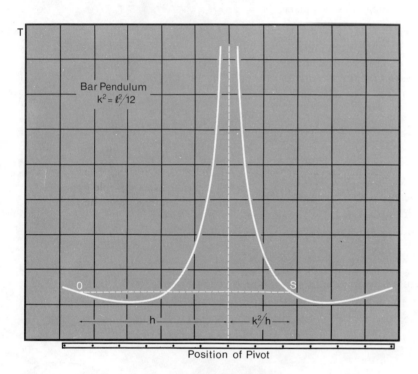

Bar Pendulum
$k^2 = l^2/12$

Period of a bar pendulum as a function of pivot position.

The position for minimum period corresponds to the minimum L. This can be found by forming dL/dh and setting it equal to zero. Show that for a meter stick the minimum period occurs for suspension at the 21-cm and 79-cm points.

CENTER OF PERCUSSION

The point S has another interesting property, and in this context is also called the **center of percussion.** If the body receives a blow at this point, it starts to rotate about O with pure rotational acceleration, that is there is no reaction at O. If the pendulum is a baseball bat, the center of percussion is the place to hit the ball so there is no "sting" on the hands.

Think of the rigid body (a baseball bat?) hanging from a pin through O, at rest. It is struck a horizontal blow of impulse $\mathbf{J} = \int \mathbf{F}\, dt$ a distance y away from O. The torque about O has a magnitude Fy, and the angular impulse a magnitude
$$\int \tau\, dt = \int Fy\, dt = y \int F\, dt = Jy.$$

The angular impulse produces a change in angular momentum. The stick, initially at rest, will start to rotate about O with angular velocity ω where

$$Jy = I_0 \omega$$

and the c-of-m will acquire a linear velocity

$$v_c = h\omega = \frac{Jyh}{I_0} = \frac{Jyh}{m(k^2 + h^2)}$$

and momentum

$$mv_c = \frac{Jyh}{k^2 + h^2}$$

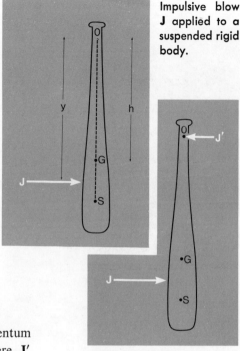

Impulsive blow $\mathbf{J}$ applied to a suspended rigid body.

Impulsive reaction $\mathbf{J}'$ at the pivot.

in the horizontal direction. This is the change in momentum produced by the total horizontal impulse $\mathbf{J} + \mathbf{J}'$, where $\mathbf{J}'$ is the reactive impulse at the pin when the blow $\mathbf{J}$ is struck. We are interested in finding y such that the impulse $\mathbf{J}' = 0$. Then

$$J = mv_c = \frac{Jyh}{k^2 + h^2} \qquad \text{or} \qquad y = \frac{k^2 + h^2}{h} = h + k^2/h$$

This shows that the center of percussion is the same as the center of oscillation S. Only if the impulse $\mathbf{J}$ acts on a line through S will there be no reaction at O.

If a meter stick suspended from a pivot at one end is struck a horizontal blow at the 67-cm mark, there will be no reaction at the pivot. Similarly if a meter stick lying on a smooth table is struck a blow at right angles at the 67-cm mark it will start to move **initially** in pure rotation about its end. What is its subsequent motion?

TORSION PENDULUM

In discussing the dynamics of simple harmonic motion in Chapter 12, we pointed out that the restoring force is often an elastic force due to the deformation of solid objects. We have used an ideal spring to provide a restoring force in some of the examples of vibration in one dimension.

Application of a torque to a solid object such as a rod twists the rod, and there are internal forces that provide torques that tend to restore the rod to its undeformed condition.

Suppose that a torque τ applied about the axis of a rod twists one end of the rod through an angle θ with respect to the other end. If the rod is behaving with ideal elasticity, the deformation θ will be proportional to the applied torque τ.

$$\tau \propto \theta \qquad \text{or} \qquad \tau = C\theta$$

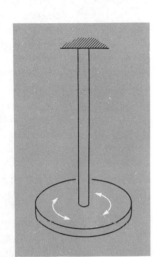

A rod twist-ed through angle θ.

where C is called the **torque constant** for the rod. It is the rotational analog to the force constant k for a spring or wire stretched in one dimension.

Now think of a rigid body with axial symmetry suspended by a wire or rod so that the axis of symmetry coincides with the axis of the rod. If the rigid body is twisted away from its equilibrium position, the rod will exert a torque to restore it, and vibrations will take place. Such a system is called a **torsion pendulum.** If the rod is behaving with ideal elasticity, so that the restoring torque is proportional to the angular displacement of the rigid body, the motion of the rigid body is called **angular simple harmonic** motion (or rotational SHM).

Rotational vibra-tion of a torsion pendulum.

We assume that the mass of the suspending rod is negligible with respect to that of the suspended body, so that no torque is required to accelerate the mass particles in the rod; this is equivalent to assuming massless springs, as we did for SHM. Then we can write the scalar equation of motion for rotation about the axis of the system

$$-C\theta = I_0\alpha = I_0\frac{d^2\theta}{dt^2}$$

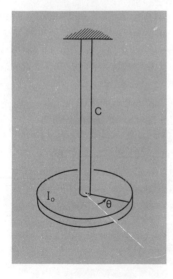

Angular displace-ment θ from equi-librium.

where C is the torque constant for the rod, I_0 is the moment of inertia of the rigid body about its axis. Written in the form

$$\frac{d^2\theta}{dt^2} + \frac{C}{I_0}\theta = 0$$

the equation is identical in form to the equation for linear SHM

$$\frac{d^2x}{dt^2} + \omega^2x = 0$$

with the angular displacement θ as a variable instead of the linear displacement x.

The solution is $\theta = \theta_0 \sin(\omega t + \delta)$ where θ_0 is the amplitude of the angular SHM, δ is the phase constant, and ω is the angular frequency

$$\omega = \sqrt{C/I_0} \qquad T = 2\pi\sqrt{I_0/C}$$

The amplitude is not necessarily small, as it must be for a gravity pendulum to execute SHM. For rods or wires made of many materials $\tau \propto \theta$ for quite large angles.

It might appear that the vibrations of a gravity pendulum are really angular SHM, not linear SHM, since the motion is circular. However, since the motion is only simple harmonic for infinitesimal displacements it can be called either with equal validity.

The torsion pendulum is a device used in a variety of scientific instruments, because it can be used to measure extremely small torques or forces. By using as a suspension a fine filament, for example a quartz fiber, the torsion constant can be very small. It can be measured by measuring the period of vibration of the system; in some instruments the period may be several minutes.

You may be familiar with the Cavendish experiment to measure the gravitational constant G, by measuring minute changes in torque when two iron balls are shifted in position with respect to a small dumbbell suspended as a torsion pendulum. The torsion pendulum is also used in the galvanometer, a sensitive instrument for measuring current.

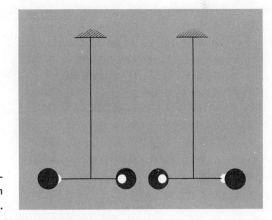

Use of the torsion pendulum in the Cavendish gravitation experiment.

The measurement of small forces in laboratories on earth is difficult because of the masking effect of gravity. The torsion pendulum takes advantage of the properties of matter to balance out this force; a very thin fibre can be strong enough to hold up a body of reasonable mass (and moment of inertia I_0) and yet be twisted by an infinitesimal torque.

Problems

1. A hula hoop 3 ft in diameter is suspended by a finger. What is the period of small oscillations **(a)** in the plane of the hoop, **(b)** at right angles to the plane?

2. A Foucault pendulum is 75 ft long and swings with an amplitude of 3 ft. What is the variation in the height of its bob as it swings?

3. A punching bag is suspended by a pivot at its surface. Assuming the bag is a spherical shell of diameter 1 ft, what is its period of oscillation if pushed sideways a little?

4. A solid metal ball suspended by a wire is often treated as a simple pendulum of length l, where l is the distance from the point of support of the wire to the center of the ball. If the ball radius is r, what ratio of r/l is necessary in order that the difference between l and the length of the equivalent simple pendulum is less than 1%? For this value of r/l, what is the % error in the period if it is calculated assuming a simple pendulum of length l? For $l = 1$ m, what radius of ball corresponds to this error?

5. A small hole is drilled in a circular sheet of plywood of radius R. Where should the hole be drilled so that the period of small oscillations of the sheet about a fixed nail through the hole is a minimum? What is the length of the equivalent simple pendulum?

6. A small hole is drilled in a meter stick and the stick is suspended from a nail through the hole. **(a)** If the hole is near the end of the stick, what is the period of small vibrations? **(b)** Where should the hole be drilled for the minimum period of vibration? What is this period?

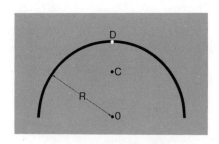

7. A thin uniform rod of mass M is bent into a semicircle of radius R.

(a) Determine its moment of inertia about an axis through the center O, perpendicular to the plane of the semicircle.

(b) Determine its moment of inertia about a parallel axis through the center of mass C, a distance $2R/\pi$ from O.

(c) Determine its moment of inertia about a parallel axis through D, the midpoint of the rod.

(d) If the rod is hung from a nail at D, what is the period of small oscillations in the plane of the semicircle? Compare the result to that for a complete circular ring of the same radius.

8. A small block sits at the bottom of a smooth hemispherical bowl of radius R. If the block is displaced sideways a small amount and released, what is the period of the resulting oscillation? How does it compare with the period of a simple pendulum of length R? Suppose the bowl is not smooth, so that a small marble rolls back and forth at the bottom of the bowl without slipping. Would you expect its period to be greater than, equal to, or less than that of the sliding block? (See next chapter.)

9. A 0.5-kg meter stick can rotate about a fixed pivot at one end. It is drawn aside and released, reaching its vertical position with an angular speed of 5 rad/sec. It is struck a horizontal blow of impulse **J** that brings it to rest in this vertical position. **(a)** Determine **J**, and its point of application, if there is no horizontal reaction at the pivot. Determine **J** and the horizontal reaction **J′** at the pivot if the blow is struck **(b)** 10 cm higher than in (a), **(c)** 10 cm lower than in (a).

10. The rate of a clock is controlled by a physical pendulum made of a single kind of metal. The clock is adjusted to run accurately at one temperature, but is used in a house at a higher temperature so that the dimensions of the pendulum change by 0.02%. What effect does this have on the rate of the clock, in seconds per day? Does the shape of the pendulum make any difference? Can you think of a way to construct a pendulum whose period would be independent of temperature?

11. (a) The center of percussion of a baseball bat is determined by drilling a hole through the handle at about where the hands would be, and suspending it from a nail. The period of oscillation is 1.6 sec. How far is the center of percussion from the hole? **(b)** The bat weighs 30 oz, and it is found by balancing it that the center of gravity is 20 in. from the hole. What is its moment of inertia with respect to an axis through the hole? **(c)** The bat is suspended from the nail, and struck a horizontal blow of impulse 30 pndl-sec (about that of hitting a baseball) at its center of mass. Determine the initial angular speed of the bat, the initial speed of its center of mass, and the horizontal reactive impulse at the pivot.

12. (a) A torsion pendulum oscillates with angular frequency ω_0 and angular amplitude θ_0. Express its displacement as $\theta = \theta_0 \sin \omega_0 t$, and determine the magnitudes of the tangential and radial components of acceleration a_T and a_R of a point on the pendulum bob a distance r from the axis, as functions of time. What are the maximum values of these components? Is the resultant acceleration of the point greater than the larger of these during any part of the cycle?

(b) The bob of a torsion pendulum is a flat disc, oscillating with a period of 1 sec and an angular amplitude of 60°. A small block is placed on the disc. Assuming a coefficient of static friction between block and disc of 0.4, how far from the axis of rotation can the block be placed without slipping? Is it more likely to slip at the mid-point or at the ends of its path?

13. The balance wheel of a watch oscillates with a period of 0.5 sec and an angular amplitude of $\pi/4$ rad. Assuming that its motion is angular SHM, what is its maximum angular speed and acceleration? If it is 1 cm in diameter, what is the maximum speed and acceleration of a point on its edge? Does the point have its maximum acceleration at the mid-point or at the ends of the motion?

14. The moment of inertia of an object that has reasonable symmetry with respect to an axis, but a shape that would make it difficult to calculate the moment of inertia (for example a toothed wheel from a gear box) can be measured using a torsion pendulum. A circular metal disc of mass m, radius R, is suspended by a wire fixed to its center, with its plane horizontal, and the period T_1 of torsional oscillations is measured. Then the object of unknown moment of inertia I (about its axis of symmetry) is placed symmetrically on the disc (sitting on the disc if the object has a hole at its center, or glued to the bottom of the disc if not) and the period of torsional oscillations T_2 is measured. What is I in terms of the known quantities?

15. The torque constant of a circular rod (or a wire) can be expressed in terms of the geometry of the rod and the elastic constant of the material called the shear modulus or rigidity modulus G. For a rod of length L, radius R, the torque constant is $C = \pi G R^4/2L$. (Note that the resistance of the rod to twisting depends inversely on its length, as you might guess, but depends on the fourth power of the diameter, as might not be so readily apparent.) For steel the shear modulus G is about 8×10^{10} n/m².

(a) Think of a steel rod 1 m long clamped at one end, and with a pipe wrench twisting the other. Using the wrench, a force of 20 kg is exerted at right angles to the rod axis, 30 cm from the axis. Estimate the angle through which the end of the rod is twisted if the rod has (1) a radius of 1 cm, (2) a diameter of 1 cm.

(b) A steel wire 10 m long and 0.2 mm² in cross section supports a 10-kg solid sphere of radius 10 cm. Calculate the period of torsional vibrations of the sphere.

16. (a) A bob for a torsion pendulum to be used in a Cavendish experiment is made by fixing two 0.04-gm lead balls to the ends of a very thin stiff wire 8 cm long. This dumbbell is suspended from its center by a long slender quartz fiber. The

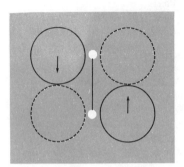

period of torsional oscillations is found to be 15 min. Determine the torsion constant of the fiber, in dyne-cm/rad.

(b) To see the size of the effect observed, think about the change in torque as two lead spheres are moved as indicated. Each sphere has a radius of 4 cm and a mass of 3 kg. They are placed so the center of each is 5 cm from the nearer small ball. What is the force between a sphere and the nearer ball? ($G = 6.7 \times 10^{-8}$ cm³/gm-sec².) What is the resultant torque, and the change in torque as the spheres are moved? Through what angle will the dumbbell be rotated by this torque?

(c) The effect is observed by fastening a small mirror to the fiber at the dumbbell, and reflecting a beam of light from it to form a spot on a scale 2 m away. How far will the spot move as the spheres are moved?

What difficulties can you envisage in undertaking this experiment?

18

DYNAMICS OF
RIGID BODY MOTION IN
TWO DIMENSIONS

We used earlier the two-particle rigid body to distinguish four different situations for the resultant force $\mathbf{F}_{ext}$ and the resultant torque about the c-of-m $(\tau_{ext})_c$ for any rigid body:

1. $\mathbf{F}_{ext} = 0$, $(\tau_{ext})_c = 0$:$\mathbf{P}$ constant, $\mathbf{L}_c$ constant
2. $\mathbf{F}_{ext} \neq 0$, $(\tau_{ext})_c = 0$:$\mathbf{L}_c$ constant, translational acceleration
3. $\mathbf{F}_{ext} = 0$, $(\tau_{ext})_c \neq 0$:$\mathbf{P}$ constant, rotational acceleration
4. $\mathbf{F}_{ext} \neq 0$, $(\tau_{ext})_c \neq 0$:translational and rotational acceleration

In the last two chapters we have been looking at examples of type (3). Before going on to type (4) we will look at one or two examples of static equilibrium of a rigid body.

STATIC EQUILIBRIUM

If all particles in a rigid body are at rest in a frame of reference, the body is in static equilibrium; $\mathbf{F}_{ext} = 0$ and $(\tau_{ext})_c = 0$. However, since every point in the body is at rest, $\tau_{ext} = 0$ about *any* fixed point in the reference frame, not just the c-of-m. You have probably studied statics, but we will do one example in order to emphasize that forces and torques are vector quantities.

Example: A uniform 20-lb ladder 10 ft long leans against a smooth wall, with a 100-lb boy standing 2 ft from the top. If the coefficient of static friction between ladder and floor is 0.5, what is the maximum distance out from the wall the foot of the ladder can be placed?
   The system to which we will apply the laws of motion is the ladder. It exerts a force

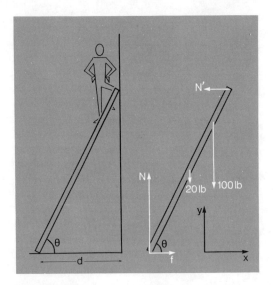

Ladder in static equilibrium.

of 100 lb on the boy to hold him up, so he exerts a force of 100 lb down, 2 ft from the top. The ladder is uniform, so the force of gravity on it is a force of 20 lb at its center, 5 ft from the end. The floor exerts a force which we will describe in terms of an upward normal component N and a sideways frictional component f. This force will oppose the tendency of the ladder to move, so it will be toward the wall. Since the foot of the ladder is as far out as possible the frictional force has its maximum value $f = \mu_s N = 0.5N$. The wall exerts a force N' normal to itself, since it is a smooth wall.

The vector relation $\mathbf{F}_{ext} = 0$ is equivalent to three scalar relations. Choosing a co-ordinate system with axes vertical and horizontal and at right angles to the plane of the diagram, only two of these give information.

$$(F_{ext})_x = 0 \qquad f + (-N') = 0$$
$$(F_{ext})_y = 0 \qquad N + (-20) + (-100) = 0$$

These give $N = 120$ lb, $f = 0.5N = 60$ lb, $N' = f = 60$ lb. The vector relation $\tau_{ext} = 0$ is equivalent to three scalar relations. Choosing any axis at right angles to the plane of the diagram, all forces give torques (about the axis) in the plane of the diagram, and a single scalar equation includes all the information. It is convenient to choose the axis so that the torques due to some of the forces are zero. For an axis at the foot of the ladder

$$(20)(5 \cos \theta) + (100)(8 \cos \theta) + (-N')(10 \sin \theta) = 0$$
$$100 \cos \theta + 800 \cos \theta - 600 \sin \theta = 0$$

$$9 \cos \theta = 6 \sin \theta \qquad \tan \theta = 1.5 \qquad \theta = 56.3°$$

The maximum distance of the foot of the latter from the wall is

$$d = 10 \cos \theta = 10 \times 0.55 = 5.5 \text{ ft}$$

STATIC EQUILIBRIUM IN AN ACCELERATED FRAME OF REFERENCE

We have already given one example of an object in static equilibrium in an accelerated frame of reference (the man standing on the edge of a turntable) but we give another here, where the frame of reference has a linear acceleration.

Example: A cylindrical drum, full of nitroglycerine, sits upright on the floor of a truck. The truck is traveling at a velocity of 30 mph, the cylinder is 5 ft high and 2 ft in diameter, and the coefficient of static friction between drum and truck floor is 0.5. What is the minimum time in which the truck can be stopped, if the drum is not to slide or tip?

The minimum time will be achieved if the acceleration is uniform since then the forces can have their limiting values at all times. We assume that the c-of-m C of the

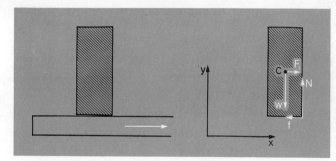

Forces on a drum
in the non-inertial
frame of reference
of a truck.

drum is at its geometric center. We will use the frame of reference of the truck, a non-inertial reference frame. In this frame, the drum is to be in static equilibrium. We assume that the acceleration is such that the drum is just about to tip forward. Then the force exerted by the floor will be at the front edge of the drum.

The acceleration a is backward (a deceleration) so the inertial force $\mathbf{F}_i = -m\mathbf{a}$ is forward. The component equations of motion are

$$(F_{\text{ext}})_x = 0 \qquad F_i + (-f) = 0 \qquad \text{or} \qquad f = F_i = ma$$
$$(F_{\text{ext}})_y = 0 \qquad N + (-w) = 0 \qquad \text{or} \qquad N = w = mg$$
$$(\tau_{\text{ext}})_c = 0 \qquad (2.5)(f) + (1)(-N) = 0 \qquad \text{or} \qquad N = 2.5f, f = 0.4N$$

Since $f_{\max} = \mu_s N = 0.5N$, the force of friction is less than the limiting force, and the drum will not slip for this acceleration.

$$a = \frac{f}{m} = \frac{0.4N}{m} = \frac{0.4mg}{m} = 0.4g = 12.8 \text{ ft/sec}^2$$

In the earth frame of reference, this is the maximum deceleration of the truck. The time it takes to slow from $v_0 = 30$ mph $= 44$ ft/sec to $v = 0$ is

$$t = \frac{v - v_0}{a} = \frac{0 - 44}{-12.8} = 3.5 \text{ sec}$$

Under the circumstances, it would probably be advisable to allow a little extra time, just in case the assumptions made were not quite valid.

The calculation can of course be made totally in the earth frame of reference. Then the situation is not one of static equilibrium, but of pure translational acceleration; $\mathbf{F}_{\text{ext}} \neq 0$, but $(\tau_{\text{ext}})_c = 0$. Note that in the truck frame of reference $\tau_{\text{ext}} = 0$ about any axis, but this is not so in the earth frame.

Forces on the
drum in the
earth frame.

EXAMPLES OF TRANSLATION AND ROTATION
UNDER CONSTANT UNBALANCED FORCES

We now look at some examples involving translational and rotational acceleration.

$$\mathbf{F}_{\text{ext}} = \frac{d\mathbf{P}}{dt} = M\frac{d\mathbf{V}_c}{dt} = M\mathbf{A}_c$$

We can determine the motion of the c-of-m from the resultant external force.

$$(\tau_{\text{ext}})_c = \frac{d\mathbf{L}_c}{dt}$$

$$= I_c \frac{d\omega_c}{dt} = I_c \boldsymbol{\alpha}_c \qquad \textbf{if symmetry}$$

We can determine the motion around the c-of-m provided we consider only rigid bodies with an axis of symmetry, and situations where the rotation is about the axis of symmetry, or a parallel axis. We will consider only such situations, and in this chapter will consider only examples involving motion in two dimensions.

Example 1—Rolling Without Slipping: We first consider examples where there is a simple relationship between linear and angular quantities. We showed in Chapter 6 that for a rigid body with cylindrical symmetry rolling without slipping along a straight line

$$S = R\theta \qquad v = R\omega \qquad a = R\alpha$$

relating the linear displacement, velocity and acceleration of the body (i.e., of the center of the body) and the angular displacement, velocity and acceleration about the center.

Think about such an object rolling down an inclined plane of angle θ. The only forces acting are the weight $\mathbf{w}$, downward at the center of mass (the center of symmetry C) and the force due to the plane which we resolve into components $\mathbf{N}$ and $\mathbf{f}$. Note that the plane cannot be smooth, because then the object would slip and we are assuming rolling without slipping. The force f opposes the motion.

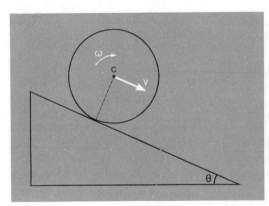 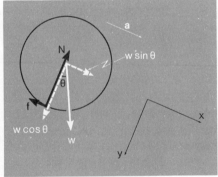

Forces on a rigid body rolling down an inclined plane.

Choosing axes as indicated, and computing torques about an axis through the c-of-m in the z-direction (into page), the equations of motion are

$$
\begin{aligned}
(F_{\text{ext}})_x &= ma & mg \sin \theta + (-f) &= ma \\
(F_{\text{ext}})_y &= 0 & mg \cos \theta + (-N) &= 0 \\
(\tau_{\text{ext}})_c &= I_c\alpha & fR &= I_c\alpha
\end{aligned}
$$

These relations are valid whether or not the object is slipping. I_c is the moment of inertia of the rigid body about an axis through its c-of-m; $I_c = mk^2$, where k is the radius of gyration.

If there is rolling without slipping $a = R\alpha$. Then

$$f = \frac{mk^2}{R}\alpha = \frac{mk^2}{R^2}a$$

and

$$mg\sin\theta = ma + f = ma\left(1 + \frac{k^2}{R^2}\right)$$

$$a = \frac{g\sin\theta}{1 + k^2/R^2}$$

A body sliding down a frictionless plane has an acceleration $g\sin\theta$. For bodies rolling down this acceleration is reduced by a factor that depends on the shape.

For a ring, hoop, or open cylinder $I_c = mR^2$, $k = R$ and

$$a = \tfrac{1}{2}g\sin\theta$$

For a solid cylinder or disc $I_c = \tfrac{1}{2}mR^2$, $k = R/\sqrt{2}$ and

$$a = \tfrac{2}{3}g\sin\theta$$

For a ball or solid sphere $I_c = \tfrac{2}{5}mR^2$, $k = \sqrt{2/5}\,R$ and

$$a = \tfrac{5}{7}g\sin\theta$$

This motion can be considered as pure rotation around an instantaneous axis, as we saw in Chapter 6. The line of contact between the body and the plane is instantaneously at rest, and we can apply the general relation $\tau_{\text{ext}} = dL/dt = I_{IA}\alpha$, where I_{IA} is the moment of inertia about this axis. Using the parallel axis theorem, $I_{IA} = I_c + mR^2 = m(k^2 + R^2)$.

The equation of motion using this axis is

$$mgR\sin\theta = I_{IA}\alpha = m(k^2 + R^2)\left(\frac{a}{R}\right)$$

or

$$a = \frac{g\sin\theta}{1 + k^2/R^2}$$

as before. Although this may appear to be a simpler way to deal with this motion, the first method is better because it is more general.

As the plane angle is increased the normal force N is decreased and the frictional force f necessary to maintain rotation is increased. For some angle the force f will reach its limiting value, and for larger angles the body will slide as it moves down the plane; it will have both a translational acceleration $a = g\sin\theta - f/m$ and a rotational acceleration $\alpha = fR/(mk^2)$ but they will *not* be related by $a = R\alpha$. However, the frictional force will be related to the normal force $f = \mu_k N$, where μ_k is the coefficient of kinetic friction.

Example 2—Falling Spool: A similar situation involves a Yo-yo or spool suspended by strings wound around an axle. The body will fall with an acceleration that depends on its shape.

If the axle, of radius r, is small then the force of the suspension T can be considered to be vertical. The scalar equations of motion are

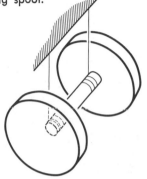
A falling spool.

$$(F_{ext})_y = Ma \qquad Mg + (-T) = Ma$$
$$(\tau_{ext})_c = I_c\alpha \qquad Tr = I_c\alpha$$
$$= Mk^2\alpha$$

Since the strings are wound around the axle, $a = r\alpha$

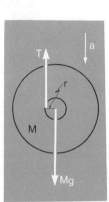

so $\qquad T = Mk^2\alpha/r = Mk^2a/r^2$

and $\qquad Mg = Ma + T = Ma(1 + k^2/r^2)$

$$a = \frac{g}{1 + k^2/r^2} \qquad T = \frac{Mg}{1 + r^2/k^2}$$

A Yo-yo or similar spool is designed to have a large moment of inertia about its axis, so $k^2 \gg r^2$. This means that $T \cong Mg$ and $a \ll g$.

Forces on the falling spool.

Example 3—Slipping or Rolling? Think of a spool with a thick axle. If you pull gently on a cord wound around this axle, at an upward angle as shown, will the spool roll away from you, unwinding the cord, or toward you, winding the cord up, or will it slip?

You can see that the answer will depend on the angle. Think of the line of contact between spool and floor as an instantaneous axis. Depending whether the line of action of force **P** passes above or below this axis, the string will wind up or unwind. If it passes through the line of contact, there is no torque and the spool slips, no matter how gently you pull—if it moves at all.

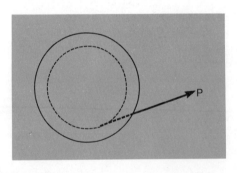

Which way does the spool roll?

The spool may roll toward you, away from you, or not at all.

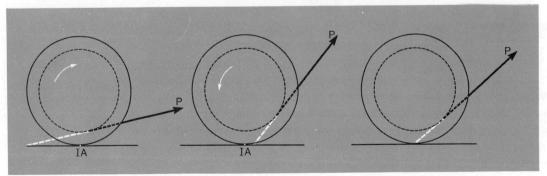

Example 4—Slipping and Rolling: A bowling ball is thrown down an alley in such a way that initially it is in pure translation (i.e., is slipping without rolling) at a speed v_0. At what speed (in terms of v_0) will it start to roll without slipping? How far will it have moved for reasonable values of μ_k and v_0?

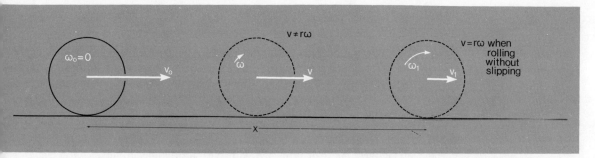

$$v \neq r\omega$$

$$\omega_0 = 0 \qquad v_0$$

$$\omega \qquad v$$

$$v = r\omega \text{ when rolling without slipping}$$

$$\omega_1 \qquad v_1$$

A bowling ball initially slipping without rolling ends up rolling without slipping.

The force of friction f gives a deceleration a, causing v to **decrease**, but produces a torque fr which gives an angular acceleration α, causing ω to **increase**.

As long as the ball is slipping, the force of friction is $f = \mu N$, assumed constant, where μ is the coefficient of kinetic friction.

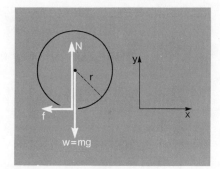

Forces on the ball, whether slipping or rolling.

$$
\begin{aligned}
(F_{\text{ext}})_y = 0 &\quad \text{gives} \quad N + (-mg) = 0 \\
(F_{\text{ext}})_x = ma &\quad \text{gives} \quad -f = ma \\
(\tau_{\text{ext}})_c = I_c\alpha &\quad \text{gives} \quad fr = I_c\alpha = \tfrac{2}{5}mr^2\alpha
\end{aligned}
$$

$$a = -\frac{f}{m} = -\frac{\mu N}{m} = -\frac{\mu mg}{m} = -\mu g$$

$$\alpha = \frac{5}{2}\frac{fr}{mr^2} = \frac{5}{2}\frac{\mu N}{mr} = \frac{5}{2}\frac{\mu g}{r}$$

$$v = v_0 + at = v_0 - \mu gt \qquad \text{:decreasing } v$$

$$\omega = \omega_0 + \alpha t = 0 + \frac{5}{2}\frac{\mu gt}{r} \qquad \text{:increasing } \omega$$

After some time t_1, the velocity v will have decreased and angular velocity ω will have increased until the condition $v = r\omega$ for rolling without slipping is fulfilled.

$$
\begin{aligned}
v_1 = r\omega_1 &= \tfrac{5}{2}\mu gt_1 \\
&= v_0 - \mu gt_1
\end{aligned}
$$

$$v_0 = \tfrac{7}{2}\mu gt_1 \qquad t_1 = \frac{2}{7}\frac{v_0}{\mu g}$$

The velocity after this time is

$$v_1 = v_0 - \mu gt_1 = v_0 - \tfrac{2}{7}v_0 = \tfrac{5}{7}v_0$$

This result does not depend on the value of μ, but of course the lower μ is the longer it will take for the velocity to drop to this value, and the further it will move. The distance it will move is

$$x = \frac{v_1^2 - v_0^2}{2a} = \frac{(\frac{5}{7}v_0)^2 - v_0^2}{-2\mu g} = \frac{12}{49}\frac{v_0^2}{\mu g}$$

For reasonable values of v_0 and μ try $v_0 = 16$ ft/sec, $\mu = 0.3$. Then

$$x = \frac{12}{49}\frac{16^2}{0.3 \times 32} = 6.5 \text{ ft}$$

Once the ball has reached the velocity v_1 it will continue to roll at constant velocity, if we assume that ball and floor are perfectly rigid bodies. The friction force will drop to zero; the two surfaces in contact are not moving with respect to one another, and there is no force trying to move them with respect to one another. The resultant force and torque (re c-of-m) on the ball are both zero.

For real bodies there is some deformation of the two surfaces and a small retarding force called the force of rolling friction.

Think about the same ball projected with pure translation up an inclined plane. Again the force of friction will act to decrease v and increase ω until the ball starts to roll without slipping. At this point the force of friction will reverse itself; the force of gravity will decrease v, and in order to decrease ω the force of static friction between the two surfaces will have to act up the plane.

IMPULSIVE FORCE ON A RIGID BODY

The integrated form of the equations of motion for a rigid body are

$$\mathbf{J}_{ext} = \int \mathbf{F}_{ext}\,dt = \mathbf{P}_2 - \mathbf{P}_1$$

$$\mathbf{r}_c \times \mathbf{J}_{ext} = \int (\tau_{ext})_c\,dt = \mathbf{L}_{c2} - \mathbf{L}_{c1}$$

In the second relation we have assumed an impulsive force of short duration, so that the system does not have time to move during the blow. The torque with respect to the c-of-m is

$$(\tau_{ext})_c = \mathbf{r}_c \times \mathbf{F}_{ext}$$

where $\mathbf{r}_c$ is the displacement of the point of application of $\mathbf{F}_{ext}$ with respect to the c-of-m. If it is assumed that the system does not have time to move, $\mathbf{r}_c$ does not change during the time the force is applied and the angular impulse $\int (\tau_{ext})_c\,dt = \int \mathbf{r}_c \times \mathbf{F}_{ext}\,dt = \mathbf{r}_c \times \int \mathbf{F}_{ext}\,dt = \mathbf{r}_c \times \mathbf{J}_{ext}$.

Example: Think of a ball resting on a smooth surface, struck a horizontal blow whose line of action is a distance y above the c-of-m. Then the magnitude of the angular impulse is $|\mathbf{r}_c \times \mathbf{J}_{ext}| = yJ$.

Initially $\mathbf{P}_1 = 0$, $\mathbf{L}_{c1} = 0$. The blow will give the ball a velocity $\mathbf{v}$ and an angular velocity $\boldsymbol{\omega}$ about the c-of-m. The scalar equations of motion, with respect to appropriate axes (think about what axes) are

$$J = P_2 = mv \qquad yJ = L_{c2} = I_c\omega = \tfrac{2}{5}mR^2\omega$$

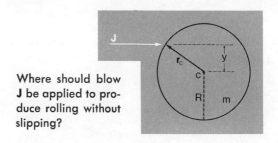

The linear velocity depends on the impulse, the angular velocity depends on the point of application as well; if $y = 0$, the ball moves off in pure translation.

With what value of y would the ball roll without slipping? Then v and ω will be related by $v = R\omega$.

$$\frac{J}{m} = R\left(\frac{5}{2}\frac{yJ}{mR^2}\right) \qquad \text{or} \qquad y = \tfrac{2}{5}R$$

Where should blow **J** be applied to produce rolling without slipping?

If a billiard ball is struck by the cue at a height 7/10 of the ball diameter above the table, the ball will roll without slipping; struck higher than this it will have top-spin, struck lower it will have back-spin. Of course a billiard table is not frictionless. If the horizontal force of friction is small compared to the size of the forces in the impulsive blow, as it usually is, the equations we have written are valid. The effect of friction will be to decrease the values of v and ω after the ball starts to move.

Note that the value $y = \tfrac{2}{5}R$ corresponds to the center of percussion with respect to the bottom of the ball. Struck at this point there is no horizontal reaction at the table, and it does not matter if the table is smooth or not. You can verify that this is consistent with the definition of center of percussion given before for suspended bodies.

COLLISION WITH A RIGID BODY

If two rigid bodies collide, or a particle collides with a rigid body, the forces between the two bodies are internal forces as far as the total system is concerned. As is the case for particle collisions, the size of the internal forces in the collision are often so large that it is reasonable to assume that the external forces on the system are negligible during the collision, so that the external impulse is zero. Then

$$\mathbf{J}_{ext} = \mathbf{P}_2 - \mathbf{P}_1 = 0 \qquad \mathbf{P}_1 = \mathbf{P}_2$$
$$\mathbf{r}_c \times \mathbf{J}_{ext} = \mathbf{L}_{c2} - \mathbf{L}_{c1} = 0 \qquad \mathbf{L}_{c1} = \mathbf{L}_{c2}$$

The total linear momentum is conserved, and the total angular momentum with respect to the c-of-m is conserved, in the collision.

Example: Think of a 500-gm meterstick at rest on a smooth table. A 200-gm ball of putty sliding on the table hits the end of the stick and sticks to it. Where is the system 1 sec after the collision?

The system is the putty ball and meter stick together. Initially only the ball is moving, after collision both are moving in the frame of reference of the table.

Choosing a co-ordinate system with an axis in the original direction of motion of the ball, the relation $\mathbf{P}_1 = \mathbf{P}_2$ gives the single scalar relation

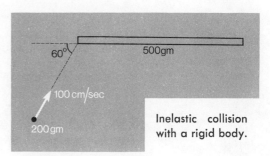

Inelastic collision with a rigid body.

$$200 \times 100 = (500 + 200)v_c$$
$$v_c = 200/7 = 28.6 \text{ cm/sec}$$

where $\mathbf{v}_c$ is the velocity of the center of mass in the initial direction. Note that this is the c-of-m of the **system,** not just of the meterstick. Treating the ball of putty as a particle, the position of the c-of-m of the system after impact, with respect to the end of the stick, is

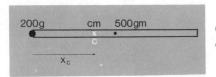

Center of mass of a system.

$$x_c = \frac{\sum m_i x_i}{\sum m_i}$$

$$= \frac{(200)(0) + (500)(50)}{200 + 500} = 35.8 \text{ cm}$$

In 1 sec the c-of-m will move 28.6 cm in the original direction of motion of the ball.

The initial angular momentum with respect to the point C is that of the particle

$$\mathbf{L}_{c1} = \mathbf{r}_c \times \mathbf{p}$$

or $L_{c1} = mvr = 200 \times 100 \times 35.8 \sin 60°$
$$= 6.20 \times 10^5 \text{ gm-cm/sec}$$

Angular momentum re the c-of-m.

The final angular momentum is $\mathbf{L}_{c2} = I_c \boldsymbol{\omega}_c$ where $I_c = I_{\text{stick}} + I_{\text{putty}}$. We know the moment of inertia of a stick about its center of mass, $I = (1/12)Ml^2$, and we use the parallel axis theorem to find it about C.

$$I_c = \frac{1}{12} \times 500 \times 100^2 + 500 \times 14.2^2 + 200 \times 35.8^2 = 7.74 \times 10^5 \text{ gm-cm}^2$$

The angular velocity $\boldsymbol{\omega}_c$ after collision has a magnitude

$$\omega_c = \frac{L_{c1}}{I_c} = \frac{6.20 \times 10^5}{7.74 \times 10^5} = 0.80 \text{ rad/sec}$$

In 1 sec the system rotates through 0.80 rad = 46° about its c-of-m.

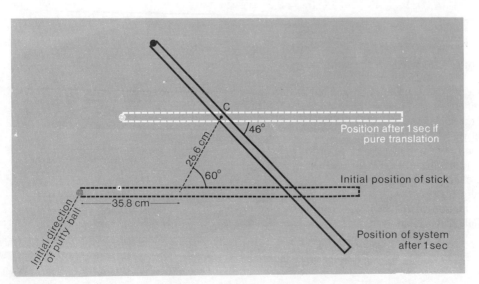

Translation and rotation combined.

46° / Position after 1 sec if pure translation

26.6 cm

60°

Initial position of stick

35.8 cm

Position of system after 1 sec

Initial direction of putty ball

Problems

1. The center of gravity of a racing car is 2 ft above the road and its width is 6 ft (i.e., its wheels are 6 ft apart). **(a)** How fast would it be able to go around an unbanked curve of 200 ft radius without tipping? Why can't it do it? **(b)** If it traveled around the same curve at 45 mph, what fraction of its weight would be on its inside wheels and what minimum coefficient of friction would be required?

2. A uniform wooden cylinder 1 ft in diameter and 3 ft long sits on end on a flat board. The coefficient of static friction between them is 0.35. One end of the board is slowly lifted. Will the cylinder slip first or tip first? At what angle?

3. **(a)** We worked out an example of static equilibrium. A uniform 20-lb ladder 10 ft long rested against a smooth wall, with a 100-lb boy standing 2 ft from the top. With a coefficient of static friction of 0.5 between ladder and floor, the base of the ladder could be placed 5.5 ft from the wall without slipping. Would you expect that the position of the boy on the ladder would matter, since his weight acts straight down no matter where he is? Work out the maximum distance of the base of the ladder from the wall if the boy is 2 ft from the bottom, instead of 2 ft from the top.

   (b) If the base of the ladder is placed 6 ft from the wall, how far up the ladder can he go before it slips?

   (c) Suppose the wall is not smooth, and there is a coefficient of static friction of 0.5 between ladder and wall. Now what is the maximum distance out of the base, if the boy is 2 ft from the top? Can you solve this without assuming that the force of static friction is at its maximum value at both top and bottom of ladder? Is this a justifiable assumption?

4. A Yo-yo consists of two cylindrical discs 5 cm in diameter, each of mass 20 gm, joined symmetrically by a short rod 0.7 cm in diameter. A light string is wound around the rod. If the end of the string is held fixed and the Yo-yo released, what is its downward acceleration and how long does it take to fall 0.5 m from rest?

5. A spherical 9-in.-diameter bowling ball is placed between two parallel rails that have a slope of 2°. The distance between the rails is such that the center of the ball is $\frac{1}{2}$ in. above its instantaneous axis of rotation on the rails. Calculate the time it takes to roll 6 ft along the rails, starting from rest, and its linear and angular speeds after this time.

6. In the system shown the cylinder of radius R, moment of inertia about its axis $MR^2/2$, has a narrow groove around its center, providing an axle of radius $R/2$. A light cord is wound around the axle, leaves horizontally and passes over an ideal pulley to support a mass $M/2$. The cylinder rolls on the surface without slipping. Calculate the downward acceleration of the suspended mass, and the minimum coefficient of static friction required between cylinder and surface, if **(a)** the cord passes under the axle as shown so that it winds up as the system moves, **(b)** the cord passes over the axle so that it unwinds as the system moves (assume the pulley is in a position such that the cord leaves the axle horizontally). (See drawing at top of p. 456.)

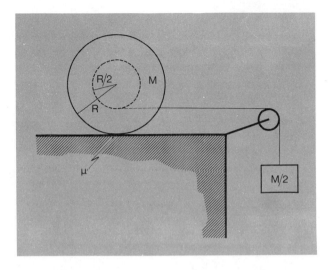

7. A cylindrical cement lawn roller of mass 100 lb and radius 1 ft is being towed behind a truck, so that a horizontal force F is applied to its axle. The coefficients of static and kinetic friction with the road are both 0.5. (a) What is the maximum F such that the roller will roll without slipping? (b) If $F = 200$ lb, how far does the roller move while it makes one revolution? Does it matter whether it is the first revolution or not?

8. A meterstick resting on a smooth table is struck a horizontal blow at right angles to its length at the 10-cm mark. What point on the stick remains initially at rest?

9. (a) A small sphere of radius r is released near the bottom of a hemispherical bowl of radius R, and rolls without slipping toward the center. When it is at a point on the bowl where the slope is θ, what is the magnitude of its acceleration? (b) Express its acceleration in terms of the horizontal displacement x of its center from the equilibrium position at the bottom of the bowl. (c) What is the period of oscillation of the sphere as it rolls back and forth, if the amplitude is small? (d) Compare the period of a small sphere that rolls without slipping to that of a small block that slides without friction in a bowl of the same radius.

10. (a) A solid sphere rolls down an inclined plane. The coefficient of static friction between sphere and plane is μ_s. Determine the relation between μ_s and θ_m, where θ_m is the maximum slope the plane can have such that the sphere rolls without slipping. (b) A solid sphere rolls down a plane inclined at 53°. The coefficients of static and kinetic friction between sphere and plane are 0.35 and 0.30. If it is rolling without slipping it will move a distance $2\pi R$ down the plane in making one complete revolution. By what factor is this distance increased here?

11. A boy throws a hoop forward along a road, keeping its plane vertical and giving it a backward spin as he throws. Depending on the relation between the initial linear and angular speeds, and the coefficient of friction, the hoop may stop and fall over, or stop and roll back to him, or stop spinning backward and start rolling forward without slipping. Suppose that the hoop radius is 2 ft, the coefficient of kinetic friction between hoop and road is 0.5, and the initial forward speed is 16

ft/sec. Analyze the subsequent motion if the initial backwards spin is at **(a)** 16 rad/sec, **(b)** 8 rad/sec, **(c)** 4 rad/sec.

12. (a) A billiard cue hits a ball a horizontal blow of impulse **J** at the center of the ball, giving it an initial velocity of 4 m/sec. The coefficient of kinetic friction between the ball and the felt of the billiard table is 0.6. How far does the ball move before it starts to roll without slipping? **(b)** Suppose the same horizontal blow is struck at a distance $0.4R$ below the center, where R is the ball radius. Now how far does the ball move before it starts to roll without slipping?

13. A bowling ball is thrown up a plane inclined at 37°, with an initial velocity v_0 up the plane, moving in pure translation. The coefficient of kinetic friction between ball and plane is 0.5. Calculate the speed (in terms of v_0) with which the ball returns to its initial position. Assume no deformation of surfaces ("rolling friction") when the ball is rolling without slipping.

14. A quantum mechanical description of a diatomic molecule shows that its angular momentum is $\sqrt{n(n+1)}\,\hbar$, where $\hbar = h/2\pi = 1.05 \times 10^{-34}$ joule-sec, and n is an integer, so the smallest non-zero angular momentum is $\sqrt{2}\,\hbar$. We will indicate a classical calculation to see what effect a collision producing a change in angular momentum might have on the speed of a molecule. This model is unrealistic but it will give an idea of the orders of magnitude involved.

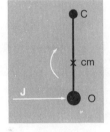

Think of a carbon monoxide molecule as two particles (the C and O atoms, masses 12 and 16 amu) separated by a fixed distance 1.13 angstrom units. Suppose the molecule has angular momentum $\sqrt{2}\,\hbar$. Another molecule collides with it, leaving its angular momentum unchanged in magnitude but reversed in direction. Assume the effect of the collision is to exert an impulse **J** on the oxygen atom at right angles to the angular momentum, and determine the effect of this impulse on the translational speed of the molecule. Do the calculation in the c-of-m frame of reference of the molecule, where its c-of-m is initially at rest.

19

DYNAMICS OF
RIGID BODY MOTION IN
THREE DIMENSIONS

The motion of a rigid body in general is described completely by the two relations

$$\mathbf{F}_{\text{ext}} = \frac{d\mathbf{P}}{dt} \qquad (\boldsymbol{\tau}_{\text{ext}})_c = \frac{d\mathbf{L}_c}{dt}$$

The two vector equations represent six scalar equations. So far we have considered only examples involving rotations confined **to a plane** (to two dimensions) in an inertial frame of reference. This meant that the vector relation involving torque and angular momentum could be represented by a single scalar equation in an appropriate co-ordinate system; the vector character of the angular quantities meant only that they were treated as scalar quantities that could be positive or negative. In all the examples each particle in the rigid body moved in a circle in a fixed plane in the c-of-m frame of reference, and there were no external forces or impulses tending to move it out of the plane.

It is beyond the scope of this volume to deal with motion of a rigid body in three dimensions in general. This is a complex and difficult subject, and volumes have been devoted to it. However, we will give an approximate analysis of one type of motion, in order to provide some understanding of such motions as that of a gyroscope or a spinning top. These motions are fascinating in themselves, but perhaps more importantly have application in understanding the motions of fundamental particles. We have pointed out that a fundamental particle has an intrinsic spin angular momentum. Associated with this there is an intrinsic magnetic moment, as though the particle were a tiny loop of electric current. The motion of such a particle in a magnetic field is similar to the motion of a spinning top in the earth's gravitational field.

LIMITATION: SPIN SPEED LARGE *RE* PRECESSION SPEED

We will as before consider the motion of a rigid body spinning about an axis of symmetry so that $\mathbf{L}_c = I_0 \boldsymbol{\omega}_0$ and

$$(\tau_{\text{ext}})_c = \frac{d\mathbf{L}_c}{dt} = I_0 \frac{d\boldsymbol{\omega}_0}{dt} = I_0 \boldsymbol{\alpha}$$

In the examples so far the resultant torque, and angular acceleration $\boldsymbol{\alpha}$, have been in the same line as $\boldsymbol{\omega}_0$, and therefore $\boldsymbol{\omega}_0$ has changed in **magnitude,** not in direction. Now we consider examples where $\boldsymbol{\alpha}$ is always at right angles to $\boldsymbol{\omega}_0$ so $\boldsymbol{\omega}_0$ changes in **direction,** not in magnitude. This motion is analogous to the motion of a particle in a circle at constant speed; in uniform circular motion the velocity $\mathbf{v}$ is constant in magnitude but continuously changing in direction, because the acceleration $\mathbf{a}$ is always at right angles to it.

We showed in Chapter 8 that if the acceleration $\boldsymbol{\alpha}$ of a rigid body is at right angles to its angular velocity $\boldsymbol{\omega}_0$, the body rotates at an angular velocity Ω about an axis perpendicular to $\boldsymbol{\omega}_0$ and $\boldsymbol{\alpha}$, in the motion called **precession.** The rigid body has a new angular velocity $\boldsymbol{\omega} = \boldsymbol{\omega}_0 + \boldsymbol{\Omega}$. The magnitudes are related by $\alpha = \omega_0 \Omega$ in this special case.

If the acceleration $\boldsymbol{\alpha}$ is produced by an external torque that is constant in magnitude, and always at right angles to $\boldsymbol{\omega}_0$, then α, ω_0 and Ω are constant in magnitude. We are going to look at such examples, and we are going to **assume that the angular speed of spin ω_0 is very high compared to the angular speed of precession** Ω. This means that we will be able to assume that total angular momentum of the system is $\mathbf{L}_c = I_0 \boldsymbol{\omega}_0$, neglecting rotation about other axes.

GYROSCOPE WHEEL WITH CENTER OF MASS AT REST

We will think of a spinning system in which the center of mass remains at rest, for example a gyroscope in a gimbal mounting. The supporting frame allows rotation of the wheel about three mutually perpendicular axes. The gyroscope wheel spins on bearings $B_1 B_2$. It can be rotated about an axis at right angles, $B_3 B_4$, and about a vertical axis B_5. Assume that the bearings are frictionless. The system is symmetric so that the wheel can be set at rest in any position. There is no torque on the

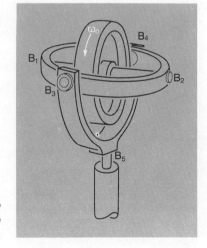

A gyroscope free to rotate about three perpendicular axes.

wheel no matter what frame of reference it is in. If it is spinning the axis will always point in a fixed direction in some external inertial frame of reference.

The system of particles (rigid body) is the wheel and axle, total mass M, moment of inertia I_0 about its axis, angular momentum $\mathbf{L}_c = I_0 \boldsymbol{\omega}_0$. The center of mass is at the center of the wheel, a distance d from either bearing B_1 or B_2.

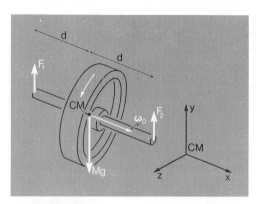

The gyroscope spinning about a fixed horizontal axis.

Think first of the frame at rest, the wheel spinning about a fixed horizontal axis. Then $\mathbf{P} = 0$ and $\mathbf{L}_c = I_0 \boldsymbol{\omega}_0 = $ constant, so $\mathbf{F}_{\text{ext}} = d\mathbf{P}/dt = 0$ and $(\boldsymbol{\tau}_{\text{ext}})_c = d\mathbf{L}_c/dt = 0$. The forces acting are those exerted by the bearings $\mathbf{F}_1$ and $\mathbf{F}_2$, and the weight $M\mathbf{g}$.

In the co-ordinate system indicated (with origin at the c-of-m), the equations of motion in terms of magnitudes are (all forces in the y-direction, and taking torques around the z-axis through the c-of-m)

$$F_1 + F_2 - Mg = 0$$
$$F_1 d - F_2 d = 0$$

giving $F_1 = F_2 = Mg/2$. The bearings support the wheel equally.

Now think about the spinning wheel also rotating with a constant velocity Ω about the vertical axis; the axle rotates in the horizontal plane. If the wheel were *not* spinning, no external torque would be required to maintain this rotation. However, when the wheel is spinning there is a torque required

$$(\boldsymbol{\tau}_{\text{ext}})_c = d\mathbf{L}_c/dt$$

Note that when the wheel is rotating with angular velocity Ω as well as angular velocity $\boldsymbol{\omega}_0$ its angular momentum $\mathbf{L}_c$ is not $I_0 \boldsymbol{\omega}_0$. The angular momentum

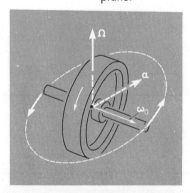

The gyroscope axis rotating in the horizontal plane.

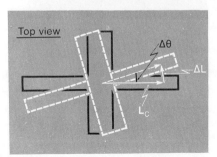

Top view

$$\Delta L \cong L_C \, \Delta\theta$$

$$(T_{\text{ext}})_C = \lim_{\Delta t \to 0} \frac{\Delta L_C}{\Delta t}$$

$$\cong L_C \lim_{\Delta t \to 0} \frac{\Delta\theta}{\Delta t}$$

$$= L_C \, \Omega$$

$$\cong I_0 \omega_0 \, \Omega$$

$$\cong I_0 \alpha$$

The gyroscope equation assuming $\omega_0 \gg \Omega$.

vector L_c will not be in the same direction as ω_0. However, we are restricting ourselves to the approximation where $\omega_0 \ggg \Omega$. Then we can assume that the total angular momentum L_c is essentially the spin angular momentum $I_0\omega_0$. This remains constant in magnitude, but changes in direction, rotating in the horizontal plane.

Note also the **direction** of the external torque $(\tau_{ext})_c$. It is *not* a torque about the vertical axis, but about the horizontal axis B_3B_4 perpendicular to the axis of spin. If we tried to rotate the wheel in the horizontal plane by applying sideways forces at B_3 and B_4 (as we would do if the wheel were not spinning) we would find that the axle turned out of the horizontal plane, reacting at right angles to what it does if it is not spinning. To rotate the axle in the horizontal plane we would have to press down on B_2, decreasing F_2, or lift up on B_1, increasing F_1, so that there is a torque about the B_3B_4 axis.

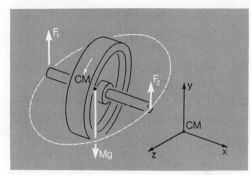

Forces on the gyroscope with two bearings.

Again we can refer to a co-ordinate system with origin at the c-of-m, with directions as indicated. This is a co-ordinate system in the inertial frame of reference, not one rotating with the axle. In this system, in terms of magnitudes, the equations of motion are:

$$(F_{ext})_y = 0 \qquad \text{gives} \qquad F_1 + F_2 - Mg = 0$$
$$[(\tau_{ext})_c]_z = I_0\alpha \qquad \text{gives} \qquad F_1d - F_2d = I_0\alpha = I_0\omega_0\Omega$$

or solving for F_1 and F_2

$$F_1 = \frac{Mg}{2} + \frac{I_0\omega_0\Omega}{2d} \qquad F_2 = \frac{Mg}{2} - \frac{I_0\omega_0\Omega}{2d}$$

From instant to instant the co-ordinate system in which these relations apply will change, but the magnitudes of the forces are constant for the particular values of ω_0 and Ω.

You can see that for a particular relationship between the angular speeds, the force F_2 will become zero; if $Mg = I_0\omega_0\Omega/d$, then $F_2 = 0$ and $F_1 = Mg$. The wheel is completely supported by the bearing at B_1, and the bearing at B_2 could be removed. If the frame is rotating at an angular speed Ω greater than that determined by this relation, then the bearing at B_2 would exert a downward force.

The important point here is that a **continuing** resultant torque must be applied to produce a constant angular speed Ω for the system. The situation is similar to that for a single particle; a continuing centripetal force must be applied to produce a constant angular speed of rotation for a particle.

The angular momentum of a spinning body provides it with a rotational inertia, or resistance to change in its spin direction. You know that a bullet leaving

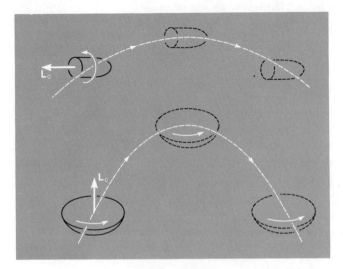

The spin angular momentum of a projectile (such as a bullet or a flying saucer) is constant, neglecting the external torque due to the air.

a rifle is made to spin about its axis (by the rifling, spiral grooves in the barrel) so that it does not tumble as it moves along its trajectory. Similarly rockets or flying saucers may be given stability by spinning them about an axis of symmetry. If there is no external torque, the spin angular momentum vector maintains a fixed direction in an inertial frame of reference.

A gyrocompass is a gyroscope mounted so that its axis of spin is always kept in a horizontal plane, but is free to rotate in this plane. It will always line up in the north–south direction due to the rotation of the earth.

GYROSCOPE WHEEL WITH CENTER OF MASS IN ROTATION

Now think about the wheel and axle again, but this time supported by a single **fixed** bearing at *B*, at one end of the axle. If the wheel is not spinning, and is re-

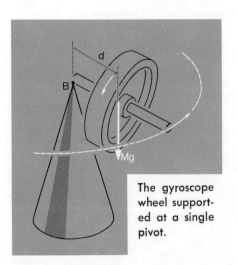

The gyroscope wheel supported at a single pivot.

leased in a horizontal position, it will fall—that is, it will rotate about *B* in a vertical plane, because of the torque *Mgd* acting about the fixed point *B*.

However, when the wheel is spinning the torque *Mgd* is at right angles to the angular momentum $\mathbf{L}_c$, and this will tend to produce rotation about *B* in a horizontal plane. If the wheel is moving in a horizontal circle with an appropriate angular velocity Ω about a vertical axis through *B*, there will be a steady state of motion. The difference between this example and the previous one is that here the c-of-m of the system is not at rest, so $\mathbf{P} \neq 0$. The c-of-m will be moving in a circle of radius d about B, and the bearing will have to exert a horizontal centripetal force as well as a vertical force. With respect to the fixed point B in the inertial frame of reference, the total

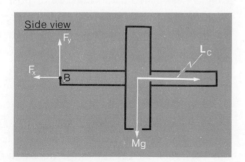

Forces on the gyroscope
with a single bearing.

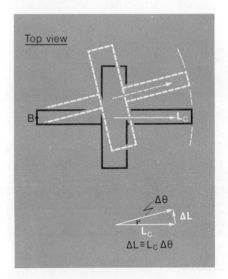

The wheel has spin and orbital angular momentum with respect to pivot B.

angular momentum is the sum of the spin angular momentum and the orbital angular momentum

$$L_B = L_c + R \times P$$

where R is the displacement of the c-of-m from B. Again we assume that the spin speed ω_0 is very high, so that the orbital term is negligible. Then the angular momentum is $L_B = L_c = I\omega_0$, constant in magnitude but rotating about the point B with the constant angular velocity Ω. The rate of change of angular momentum about B is

$$\lim_{\Delta t \to 0} \frac{\Delta L}{\Delta t} \cong L_c \lim_{\Delta t \to 0} \frac{\Delta \theta}{\Delta t} = L_c \Omega = I_0 \omega_0 \Omega$$

In a co-ordinate system in the inertial frame with origin at B, with axes as indicated, the equations of motion are:

$$(F_{\text{ext}})_y = 0 \qquad \text{gives} \qquad F_y - Mg = 0$$
$$(F_{\text{ext}})_x = Ma_x \qquad \text{gives} \qquad F_x = Ma_x = M\Omega^2 d$$
$$(\tau_{\text{ext}})_{\text{about } z\text{-axis}} = I_0 \omega_0 \Omega \qquad \text{gives} \qquad Mgd = I_0 \omega_0 \Omega$$

The angular speed of precession is

$$\Omega = \frac{Mgd}{I_0 \omega_0}$$

Note that we have *assumed* the steady state condition in our examples, that is we have assumed that the wheel is rotating about the vertical axis with the appropriate constant angular speed Ω without considering how it got into this state. In order to achieve this smooth precessional motion in a horizontal circle it would be necessary to start the motion with the appropriate Ω. If the spinning wheel is simply released from the horizontal position it will not have this motion. The tip of the axle *will* start to fall when released from the horizontal position. This rotation about the z-axis would require a torque about the y-axis, but there is no such torque if the bearing is frictionless, so the motion cannot be maintained. The wheel moves in the opposite direction to the missing torque, or sideways, giving motion around the y-axis. The speed acquired turns out to be greater than the steady precessional speed and the tip of the axle rises to its original level, then falls again. Superposed on the steady motion of precession there are vertical vibrations called **nutation.** The path of the tip of the axle (or

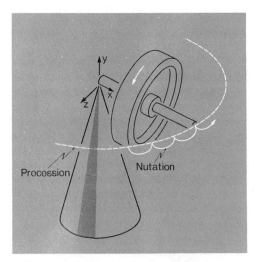

Nutation and precession.

the c-of-m) is a cycloid. For very high spin speeds ω_0 the motion of nutation is rapid and may not be apparent. In the absence of friction the motion of nutation would continue, but the effect of friction (present in any real system) is to damp out this motion, leaving the steady motion of precession. However, when this does happen the axis of the wheel will not be quite horizontal. Because of the rotation about the y-axis there is a small component of angular momentum in the y-direction (upward). This is equal in magnitude to the component of the spin angular momentum in the y-direction (downward). The initial total angular momentum was horizontal, and the final total angular momentum is horizontal. Of course, if the wheel is started with the appropriate angular speed Ω, by applying external torques, the axle can rotate in the horizontal plane.

This qualitative discussion has given some notion of the details of the complex motion of the spinning system, and you can perhaps see why we have not attempted an accurate quantitative discussion.

Spinning tops with fixed pivot.

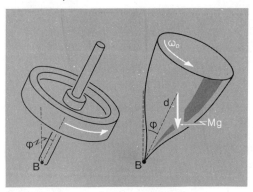

SPINNING TOP

As a final example, think of the situation where the tip of the axle of the spinning wheel is in a fixed bearing at B, but the axle is not horizontal. The axle is inclined at an angle φ with the vertical. This is the example of the spinning top, except that for a top in general the tip is free to move on a horizontal surface.

The torque about fixed point B is $Mgd \sin \varphi$, where d, as before, is the distance between B and the c-of-m. As before we assume the orbital angular momentum is negligible, so the total angular momentum is essentially the spin angular momentum $\mathbf{L}_c = I_0\omega_0$. We consider the steady state situation where the axis of the top is rotating around the vertical axis at a constant angular velocity Ω.

The angular momentum has a constant vertical component $L_c \cos \varphi$, and a horizontal component $L_c \sin \varphi$ that is constant in magnitude but rotates at an angular velocity Ω. The rate of change of angular momentum about B is

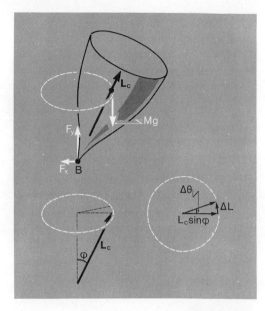

$$\lim_{\Delta t \to 0} \frac{\Delta L}{\Delta t} \cong L_c \sin \varphi \lim_{\Delta t \to 0} \frac{\Delta \theta}{\Delta t} = L_c\Omega \sin \varphi$$

In a co-ordinate system in the inertial frame with origin at B, the equations of motion are:

$(F_{\text{ext}})_y = 0$ gives $F_y - Mg = 0$

$(F_{\text{ext}})_x = Ma_x$ gives $F_x = M\Omega^2 d \sin \theta$

$(\tau_{\text{ext}})_{\text{about } z\text{-axis}} = L_c\Omega \sin \varphi$ gives $Mgd \sin \varphi = L_c\Omega \sin \varphi = I_0\omega_0\Omega \sin \varphi$

Analysis of the spinning top.

The appropriate angular speed of precession is

$$\Omega = Mgd/I_0\omega_0$$

as in the previous example where the axis of spin was horizontal. The angular speed Ω is **independent** of the angle φ. No matter what the angle of tilt of the top is, the angular speed of precession is the same, for a particular top (particular M, I_0, d) and a particular speed of spin ω_0.

In each of the examples we have used, you can see that $\Omega \propto 1/\omega_0$; the higher the speed of spin, the lower the speed of precession for a given torque, and the more valid our assumption that the spin angular momentum about the axis is the total angular momentum.

Note that if a top is set spinning on a **smooth** surface, the surface cannot exert the horizontal centripetal force F_x, and the tilted top would precess around a vertical axis through the c-of-m. The actual motion of a top depends on frictional torques as well as the torque due to gravity, but we will not explore these fascinating motions further.

PRECESSION OF MAGNETIC DIPOLE IN A MAGNETIC FIELD

We stated earlier that the motion of a spinning top in the gravitational field is similar to that of a fundamental particle in a magnetic field. We are not really in a position to discuss this motion here, because we have not developed the necessary background in electromagnetic theory, but some comments should be made because there are important applications in present-day research; you may have heard of nuclear magnetic resonance (NMR) or electron or proton magnetic resonance. We will simply make a number of unsupported statements.

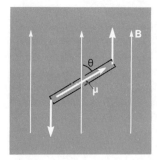

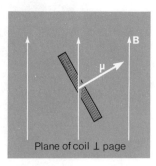

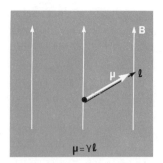

Torque on a magnet $\tau = \mu \times B$ in a magnetic field.

Torque on a current loop in a magnetic field.

Torque on a particle with intrinsic magnetic moment μ in a magnetic field.

A magnet, for example a compass needle, that is free to rotate will line up with an external magnetic field. There is a torque $\tau = \mu \times B$ on the magnet, where μ is called the magnetic dipole moment of the magnet (it is the "strength" of the magnet). The torque of magnitude $\tau = \mu B \sin \theta$ is zero when μ and B are parallel.

A loop of wire carrying a current, for example the coil of a galvanometer, that is free to rotate will line up with its plane perpendicular to an external magnetic field. There is a magnetic moment μ normal to the plane of the loop, and a torque $\tau = \mu \times B$. Magnitude μ depends on the current and area of the loop.

We pointed out earlier that the fundamental particles have an intrinsic spin angular momentum l, a property of the particle; for electrons, protons and neutrons the magnitude of l is $\frac{1}{2}\hbar$. Such particles also have a magnetic moment $\mu = \gamma l$ where γ is a scalar constant. (For a free electron it is the charge-to-mass ratio $\gamma = e/m$.) Thus a fundamental particle in a magnetic field B will experience a torque $\tau = \mu \times B$ tending to line it up with the field, but it will not line up because of the spin angular momentum. Instead it will precess around the field direction at an angular speed Ω, usually called in this case the precession frequency. By an argument similar to that for the spinning top, you can see that the magnitude of Ω is given by

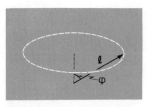

The angular momentum vector of a particle precesses around the field direction.

$$\Omega = \frac{\mu B \sin \varphi}{l \sin \varphi} = \gamma B$$

again independent of the angle made with the field direction.

The importance of this relation is that the precession frequency Ω can be measured in a magnetic field of known strength B, and therefore the quantity γ can be calculated; this is a property of the particle—of a fundamental particle, or of an atomic nucleus. The measurement can be made because the strength of the magnetic field, unlike that of the gravitational field, can be varied. Alternating magnetic fields are produced by alternating electric currents. In spin resonance experiments a small alternating field $B_0 \sin \omega t$ is applied at right angles to the main field $\mathbf{B}$, and the frequency ω is varied, with particles in the field. When $\omega = \Omega$ resonance occurs; it is possible to tell this from the response of the electric circuits providing the alternating field, just as it is possible for you to tell from the feel of a swing when you are pushing it at the resonant frequency.

The magnetic moment μ related to the spin angular momentum I can be thought of as arising because the spinning particle is a spinning sphere of electric charge, or current loop. However, note that there may be a magnetic moment even when the particle has no **net** electric charge.

A proper description of spin and magnetic moment of atomic and nuclear particles requires the use of quantum mechanics, but the notion of precession around the field direction remains a useful one.

GENERAL MOTION IN THREE DIMENSIONS

At the beginning of this book we remarked that motion could be complicated, and suggested you think about a tennis racquet thrown through the air, wobbling and twisting as it went. We have gone as far as we are going to in describing motion, and *still* have not reached the point where we can explain the wobbling tennis racquet in detail. This is because we have restricted ourselves to considering rigid bodies rotating about a single axis of symmetry (principal axis), or, in this last section, to examples where the speed of rotation about an axis of symmetry is so high that we can assume the total angular momentum is approximately equal to the spin angular momentum about the axis of symmetry. (See the two diagrams at the top of the next page.)

If a racquet is thrown with a spin about any one of the three axes indicated (one perpendicular to the page) the motion as it flies through the air is smooth; the c-of-m will follow a parabolic path, and there will be a smooth rotation about an axis through the c-of-m. The direction of this axis will remain fixed, in the external frame of reference. There is zero external torque, and the angular momentum $\mathbf{L}_c$ is constant. For spin about these axes, $\mathbf{L}_c = I_c \boldsymbol{\omega}_c$, where I_c is the appropriate moment of inertia, and $\boldsymbol{\omega}_c$ remains constant as the motion goes on.

If the racquet is thrown with an initial spin about any other axis, the motion will not be smooth. The total angular momentum $\mathbf{L}_c$ is constant, but there is *not* the simple equation $\mathbf{L}_c = I_c \boldsymbol{\omega}_c$ relating the angular momentum $\mathbf{L}_c$ and the angular velocity $\boldsymbol{\omega}_c$ by a scalar factor. The angular velocity $\boldsymbol{\omega}_c$ is not in general

Symmetry axes (principal axes) of a tennis racquet.

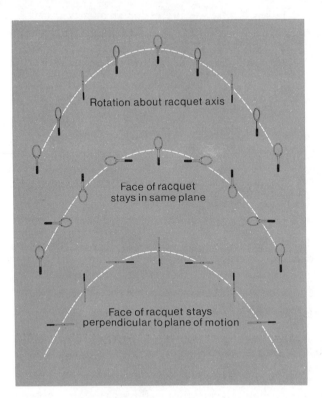

Rotation about racquet axis

Face of racquet stays in same plane

Face of racquet stays perpendicular to plane of motion

Smooth motion for rotation about a principal axis.

in the same direction as the angular momentum $\mathbf{L}_c$. At every instant the racquet has an angular velocity $\boldsymbol{\omega}_c$ that is precessing around the $\mathbf{L}_c$ direction; $\boldsymbol{\omega}_c$ is constant neither in magnitude or direction. It can be related to $\mathbf{L}_c$ by introducing moment of inertia as a tensor quantity.

COMPONENT EQUATIONS OF MOTION
WITH NO EXTERNAL FORCE

We can summarize the general equations for rotational motion of a rigid body in three dimensions, without developing these in detail. We consider the situation where there is no resultant external force $\mathbf{F}_{\text{ext}} = 0$; then the c-of-m frame of reference is an inertial frame, and we describe the motion in this frame, referring displacements $\mathbf{r}_i$ of any particle to the c-of-m as a fixed point in the frame of reference.

The total angular momentum is

$$\mathbf{L} = \sum m_i \mathbf{r}_i \times \mathbf{v}_i$$

At any instant every particle has the same instantaneous angular velocity $\boldsymbol{\omega}$ about an axis through the c-of-m (we drop the subscript c for now).

Then
$$\mathbf{v}_i = \boldsymbol{\omega} \times \mathbf{r}_i$$

and
$$\mathbf{L} = \sum m_i \mathbf{r}_i \times (\boldsymbol{\omega} \times \mathbf{r}_i)$$

Using the vector identity

$$\mathbf{A} \times (\mathbf{B} \times \mathbf{C}) = \mathbf{B}(\mathbf{A}\cdot\mathbf{C}) - \mathbf{C}(\mathbf{A}\cdot\mathbf{B})$$

this becomes
$$\mathbf{L} = \sum m_i \left[\boldsymbol{\omega} r_i^2 - \mathbf{r}_i(\mathbf{r}_i\cdot\boldsymbol{\omega}) \right]$$

which means that in a particular co-ordinate system in the inertial frame the angular momentum has components of the form

$$L_x = \omega_x \sum m_i r_i^2 - \omega_x \sum m_i x_i^2 - \omega_y \sum m_i x_i y_i - \omega_z \sum m_i x_i z_i$$

with similar expressions for the y- and z-components.

A set of inertial coefficients, or moments of inertia, is defined by

$$I_{xx} = \sum m_i (r_i^2 - x_i^2)$$
$$I_{xy} = -\sum m_i x_i y_i$$
$$I_{xz} = -\sum m_i x_i z_i$$

and with similar expressions for the quantities in L_y and L_z we have

$$L_x = I_{xx}\omega_x + I_{xy}\omega_y + I_{xz}\omega_z$$
$$L_y = I_{yx}\omega_x + I_{yy}\omega_y + I_{yz}\omega_z$$
$$L_z = I_{zx}\omega_x + I_{zy}\omega_y + I_{zz}\omega_z$$

The inertial coefficients are terms in the matrix

$$\begin{pmatrix} I_{xx} & I_{yx} & I_{zx} \\ I_{xy} & I_{yy} & I_{zy} \\ I_{xz} & I_{yz} & I_{zz} \end{pmatrix}$$

This quantity can be described as a tensor, and $\mathbf{L}$ and $\boldsymbol{\omega}$ are then said to be related by this tensor, rather than by a scalar moment of inertia as in the examples we have considered. These inertial coefficients depend on the mass distribution of the rigid body *and on time* because they depend on the instantaneous orientation of the body with respect to the co-ordinate axes, which are fixed in the inertial frame. Note that the diagonal terms can be thought of as moments of inertia about the respective axes, for example

$$I_{xx} = \sum m_i (r_i^2 - x_i^2) = \sum m_i (y_i^2 + z_i^2)$$

which is the sum of the products of each mass and the square of its distance from the x-axis. The sum of the diagonal terms is

$$I_{xx} + I_{yy} + I_{zz} = 2 \sum m_i r_i^2$$

which is independent of the orientation of the body relative to the co-ordinate axes.

The off-diagonal terms are symmetric; that is, $I_{xy} = I_{yx}$, etc. Depending on symmetry, these terms may disappear; for example, if a body is symmetrical with respect to the yz plane, for every mass m_i at (x_i, y_i, z_i) there will be a mass m_i at $(-x_i, y_i, z_i)$ and $I_{xy} = 0$.

For every rigid body there is a particular set of axes, called the principal axes, such that all the off-diagonal terms are zero. Only the diagonal terms remain: $I_{xx} = I_1$, $I_{yy} = I_2$, $I_{zz} = I_3$. If at any instant we choose co-ordinate axes (in the inertial frame) in the direction of the principal axes of the body, the relation between $\mathbf{L}$ and $\boldsymbol{\omega}$ becomes less complex

$$L_1 = I_1\omega_1 \qquad L_2 = I_2\omega_2 \qquad L_3 = I_3\omega_3$$

If the body is rotating about a principal axis, then only one of these component equations will be a non-zero equation, and $\mathbf{L}$ and $\boldsymbol{\omega}$ will be parallel. This is the situation we have considered mostly in this book.

The inertial coefficients take on a simple form for the principal axes, a set of axes fixed in the rotating body and therefore a non-inertial frame. The general equation of motion $(\tau_{\text{ext}})_c = \dfrac{d\mathbf{L}_c}{dt}$ is valid in an inertial frame, so it is convenient to make a transformation of the reference frame by the methods discussed in Chapter 7.

If $\mathbf{L}$ is the angular momentum in the **rotating** frame the transformation is

$$\left(\frac{d\mathbf{L}}{dt}\right)_{\text{inertial frame}} = \left(\frac{d\mathbf{L}}{dt}\right)_{\text{rotating frame}} + \boldsymbol{\omega} \times \mathbf{L}$$

and therefore the equation of motion is

$$(\tau_{\text{ext}})_c = \frac{d\mathbf{L}}{dt} + \boldsymbol{\omega} \times \mathbf{L}$$

where $\mathbf{L}$ is referred to the rotating frame. Choosing co-ordinate axes in the rotating frame in the directions of the principal axes of the body, the component equations take the form

$$\tau_1 = \left(\frac{d\mathbf{L}}{dt}\right)_1 + (\boldsymbol{\omega} \times \mathbf{L})_1 = \frac{dL_1}{dt} + \omega_2 L_3 - \omega_3 L_2$$

$$= I_1 \frac{d\omega_1}{dt} + \omega_2 I_3 \omega_3 - \omega_3 I_2 \omega_2$$

$$= I_1 \frac{d\omega_1}{dt} + (I_3 - I_2)\,\omega_2\omega_3$$

where τ_1 is the instantaneous component of torque in the direction of axis 1 of the rotating body. The three relations

$$\tau_1 = I_1 \frac{d\omega_1}{dt} + (I_3 - I_2)\,\omega_2\omega_3$$

$$\tau_2 = I_2 \frac{d\omega_2}{dt} + (I_1 - I_3)\,\omega_1\omega_3$$

$$\tau_3 = I_3 \frac{d\omega_3}{dt} + (I_2 - I_1)\,\omega_1\omega_2$$

are called the Euler equations. These equations of motion refer to axes (principal axes) fixed in the rotating body.

A detailed solution of the Euler equations for motion under arbitrary torques of a rigid body of arbitrary shape may still be difficult, since there are three simultaneous equations to solve. We will look at one simple example. Think of a body with no external torque ($\tau_1 = \tau_2 = \tau_3 = 0$) and with symmetry about one axis, so that $I_1 = I_2 \neq I_3$. This is the case of the symmetric top, set spinning about an arbitrary axis and released in force-free space.

Since $I_1 = I_2$, from the third Euler equation ω_3 is constant. The speed of spin about the axis of symmetry is constant. The other two equations become

$$\frac{d\omega_1}{dt} + \Omega\omega_2 = 0 \qquad \frac{d\omega_2}{dt} - \Omega\omega_1 = 0$$

where $\Omega = [(I_3 - I_1)/I_2] \omega_3 = [(I_3 - I_2)/I_1] \omega_3$ is a constant. These equations are satisfied if $\omega_1 = A \cos \Omega t$, $\omega_2 = A \sin \Omega t$, where A is a constant. This means that the component of the angular velocity $\boldsymbol{\omega}$ that is perpendicular to axis 3 rotates with a constant angular speed Ω. The top, spinning about its axis of symmetry with speed ω_3, will wobble (precess) with frequency Ω. The total angular momentum of the top is constant, but the angular velocity is not constant; the components of angular velocity and of angular momentum keep changing with time.

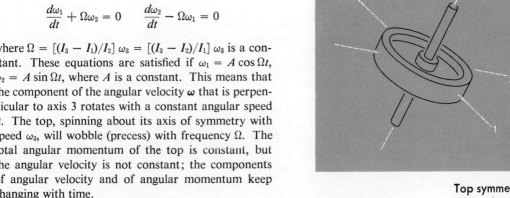

Top symmetric about the "3" axis.

This example has been used because of its interest in connection with the motion of the earth. For a perfect sphere $I_1 = I_2 = I_3$, and if $\tau = 0$ the Euler equations show that $\boldsymbol{\omega}$ = constant. However, the earth is not a sphere (the major difference is the flattening at the poles) and therefore it wobbles as it spins on its axis. The predicted period of the precessional wobble is about 300 days, while the observed period is over 400 days. The difference is attributed to the fact that the earth is not rigid, and provides a means of estimating the degree of rigidity of the earth.

QUESTIONS FOR DISCUSSION

1. In uniform circular motion of a particle its linear momentum $\mathbf{p}$ is constant in magnitude but changing uniformly in direction; the centripetal force $\mathbf{F} = d\mathbf{p}/dt$ is constant in magnitude but changing in direction. In the rotational analogue, the angular momentum $\mathbf{L}$ of a rigid body is constant in magnitude but changing uniformly in direction, and the resultant torque $\boldsymbol{\tau} = d\mathbf{L}/dt$ is constant in magnitude but changing in direction. Is this relation exact or an approximation? What assumption did we make in explaining the motion of a gyroscope or top? Why did we make it?

2. The effect of gyroscopic action is often unexpected, because when a torque is applied there is a reaction at right angles to what we expect. However, sometimes we learn to automatically compensate. Think about riding a bicycle. Suppose you turn the front wheel to the left. What does the wheel tend to do because of its spin? How do you compensate?

3. When an aircraft powered by a single propeller rotating clockwise (as seen from behind) is turned to the left does the nose of the aircraft tend to rise or to fall?

4. Can you visualize how to use a weight in mounting a gyroscope so the gyroscope axis always remains in a horizontal plane, but is free to rotate about a vertical axis?

5. A massive spinning wheel can be used for a stabilizing effect on a ship. Mounted with its axis at right angles to the ship, what is its effect when the ship tends to roll from side to side?

6. Think of looking down on a spinning top which is tilted at an angle and precessing. Is the precession in the same direction as the spin or the opposite direction?

7. Think of a top spinning in a frictionless bearing at its tip, but subject to air friction. As its spin speed decreases due to this, does its speed of precession increase or decrease or stay the same? Does its angle of tilt increase or decrease or stay the same?

8. Think of spinning a saucer shaped object on a horizontal non-smooth surface, so there is a frictional torque acting on it. Can you explain why such an object tends to "rise up" and spin on its edge? You may have seen a "tippy-top"; at rest this top sits on a hemispherical base, but when spun it turns over and spins on its narrow top. Would you expect it to perform on a frictionless surface? (This top has been the topic of several articles in physics journals.)

9. Can you flip a coin without rotating it around a principal axis? How can you tell if you have?

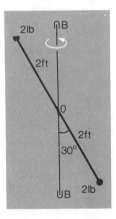

Problems

1. Two massless rigid rods are welded at an angle of 30° as shown. The ends of one rod are held in fixed frictionless bearings B, and the other rod carries two 2-lb particles, each 2 ft from the intersection O. The system is rotating around the axis BB at 200 rpm. **(a)** Determine the magnitude L of the angular momentum $\mathbf{L}$ of the system with respect to a fixed point in the frame of reference at O. **(b)** Determine the magnitude τ of the torque $\boldsymbol{\tau} = \boldsymbol{\omega} \times \mathbf{L}$ about O. **(c)** Perform a calculation in the non-inertial frame of reference in which the particles are at rest, and find the magnitude of the torque about O that is produced by the centrifugal forces on the particles. **(d)** What is the magnitude of the torque about O exerted on the system by the bearings?

2. A conical pendulum is one in which the pendulum bob moves in a horizontal circle, its supporting cord making a constant angle with the vertical. We used it in Chapter 12 as an example of periodic motion. To the extent that the pendulum is ideal (that is, that the bob is a particle of mass m and the string is massless) the motion is that of a single particle, and direct application of the basic dynamic relation $\mathbf{F} = d\mathbf{p}/dt$ is possible. The motion can equally well be analyzed with the rotational equivalent $\boldsymbol{\tau} = d\mathbf{l}/dt$. In using this dynamic relation all quantities must be referred to a fixed point in the frame of reference. For the conical pendulum the fixed point may be chosen as the center of the circle O_1; then the vectors $\mathbf{r}_1$, $\mathbf{p} = m\mathbf{v}$, and the resultant force $\mathbf{F}$ lie in the horizontal plane; the vector $\mathbf{l} = \mathbf{r}_1 \times \mathbf{p}$ is at right angles to the plane and $\boldsymbol{\tau} = \mathbf{r}_1 \times \mathbf{F} = 0$; there is no resultant torque on the particle and its angular momentum is constant. In terms of the vector $\boldsymbol{\omega}$, $\mathbf{l} = mr_1^2\boldsymbol{\omega} = I\boldsymbol{\omega}$.

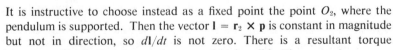

It is instructive to choose instead as a fixed point the point O_2, where the pendulum is supported. Then the vector $\mathbf{l} = \mathbf{r}_2 \times \mathbf{p}$ is constant in magnitude but not in direction, so $d\mathbf{l}/dt$ is not zero. There is a resultant torque $\boldsymbol{\tau}$ on the system. Verify that the relation $\boldsymbol{\tau} = d\mathbf{l}/dt$ is valid. The vector $\mathbf{l}$ precesses around the vertical direction with an angular speed ω. What is the direction of $\boldsymbol{\omega}$? What is the relation between $\boldsymbol{\tau}$, $\boldsymbol{\omega}$ and $\mathbf{l}$? Can we use $\mathbf{l} =$ (a scalar) $\boldsymbol{\omega}$ and therefore introduce a scalar moment of inertia?

3. Assume a bicycle wheel weighs 3 lb and has a diameter of 2 ft, and estimate the magnitude of its angular momentum when a cyclist is moving at 15 mph. If he turns the wheel through 30° in $\frac{1}{5}$ sec, what magnitude of torque (in lb-ft) is necessary?

4. A gyroscope wheel has a mass of 400 gm and a moment of inertia about its axis of 1600 gm-cm². It is mounted symmetrically in a gimbal mounting so there is no torque on it. It is set spinning at 3000 rpm with its axis horizontal. The distance between the bearings at B_1 and B_2 at the ends of its axle is 12 cm. A 50-gm mass m is suspended from the frame bearing at B_2. Determine the time for the system to make one revolution about its vertical axis, and the upward forces exerted by the bearings at B_1 and B_2 on the axle. In the diagram, will B_2 move into the page or out of the page?

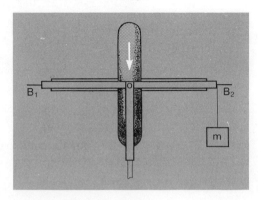

5. A weighted bicycle wheel has a mass of 20 lb and a moment of inertia about its axis of 20 lb-ft². It is set spinning at 180 rpm by holding it against a rubber disc on a motor. The wheel is mounted on an axle supported on a single pivot 6 in. from the center of the wheel. What sideways speed does the wheel have to be started with in order to rotate about a vertical axis through the pivot with its axle horizontal? Is the spin speed much greater than the precessional speed?

6. For a free electron the ratio between the spin angular momentum $l = \hbar/2$ and the magnetic dipole moment μ is the charge-to-mass ratio e/m. (a) What is the mks unit of magnetic moment? (b) What is the precession frequency of a free electron in a magnetic field of flux density $B = 2$ weber/m², using this model?

7. (a) Show that for a symmetric top spinning on a pivot the spin speed ω_0 and the precessional speed Ω are related by $\omega_0 \Omega = K$, where K is a constant that depends on the mass distribution of the top but not on its mass. Work out K for (b) a solid sphere of radius R spinning on a short thin rod embedded in its surface, (c) a solid cylinder of radius R spinning on a thin rod

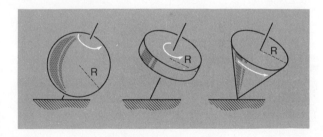

of length such that the distance from the pivot to the center of the cylinder is R, (d) a solid circular cone of radius R, height h, spinning upside down on its tip. (From problems in earlier chapters the center of mass of the cone is $h/4$ from the base, and $I = 0.3MR^2$.) In this case express K in terms of the ratio $r = h/R$, and the radius R. (e) Work out Ω corresponding to a spin speed of 900 rpm (15 rev/sec) for $R = 10$ cm for the sphere and cylinder, and for $R = 10$ cm, $r = 1$ and $r = 5$ for the cone. Note that a very high spin speed is necessary if the assumption $\omega_0 \gg \Omega$ is to be valid.

The concept of energy

V

In analyzing any physical situation it is desirable to have all possible tools available, but so far we have not developed and exploited one of the physicist's most useful tools, the concept of energy. This is because we wanted to emphasize that a great deal could be said in mechanics without this concept. Sometimes so much stress is placed on it (physics is often called the study of matter and energy) that it appears to have some sort of special status as a basic attribute of nature. This is a possible point of view, but we prefer to emphasize that it is one of the concepts man finds useful in attempting to describe nature—a very useful concept, but nonetheless a man-made one.

We have distinguished between fundamental physical quantities (the starting points in our description of nature, given operational definitions) and derived physical quantities (defined in terms of other physical quantities). What is chosen as fundamental is arbitrary; usually in mechanics we choose *mass*, *length* and *time*. Then all other quantities in mechanics, including energy, are derived quantities, with dimensions expressible in terms of M, L and T.

While we are going to give explicit definitions for certain kinds of mechanical energy, **it is not possible to give a definition of energy in general.** We cannot answer the general question, often asked by students, "What is energy?" We had a somewhat similar situation in trying to describe what we meant by a particle. The notion of a particle has been an extremely useful one, one which has permeated our whole discussion of mechanics, and yet we could not give a simple (or even a complex) general definition of a particle. Everything can be treated as a particle under certain circumstances, yet nothing is really a particle.

It is sometimes argued that the most important and fruitful concepts are those to which it is impossible to attach a well-defined meaning, and this certainly has force when we think of the importance of the particle and energy concepts.

We concluded our introduction of the particle concept by saying "you know what we mean by a particle" and we can similarly say "you know what we mean by energy." Neither statement is true; what is meant is these are, in a general way, familiar concepts. The importance of the energy concept rests on the fact that energy is conserved, and we have pointed out the value of conserved quantities in attempting to describe nature. What we must consider is precisely **what** is conserved, under what circumstances? While we cannot give a general definition of energy, we can precisely define various kinds of energy: kinetic, gravitational, elastic, electical, magnetic, chemical, nuclear, thermal, and so on.

We do not use the term energy by itself, but always as the energy **of** something: of a particle, a system of particles, a lump of coal, or of an electromagnetic field, or whatever; in general, then, the **energy of a system.** Energy is a property of a system, like mass or charge or linear momentum, but there are different kinds of energy, so the term in a sense includes a variety of properties of the system.

As before in mechanics, we are interested here in the relation of a system to surroundings (or environment). Energy can be transferred between a system and its surroundings in various ways; if there is no transfer of energy, then the energy of the system is constant, or conserved. Within the system there may be transformations between the various kinds of energy, but the total energy is constant. We **define** the various kinds of energy in such a way that this is so.

A system that cannot exchange energy with its surroundings is called an **isolated** system, and so by definition the statement of conservation of energy applies to such a system; the total energy of an isolated system is constant. The idea of an isolated system is itself an idealization—no system can be completely isolated from its surroundings, and therefore conservation of energy is an approximation. However, just as conservation of linear momentum is an excellent approximation under certain conditions, so conservation of total energy is an excellent approximation under certain conditions.

Conservation of energy is such a useful tool in analyzing physical situations that where it was found to be violated in terms of existing definitions of energy it has been reinstated by appropriately redefining the forms of energy. The most striking example of this is found in Einstein's relativistic mechanics.

We are going to restrict ourselves in Part V to the kind of energy called **mechanical energy,** which includes kinetic energy and potential energy. As we shall see there are conditions under which it is reasonable to assume conservation of mechanical energy for a system, but it must be kept in mind that there may be other forms of energy as well.

Energy, as we have stated, is a property of a system. This property can only change if there is a transfer of energy between the system and its surroundings (other systems), but usually we do not use the term energy for energy in transit between systems. Just as we distinguish between impulse (the effect of the surroundings) and change in linear momentum (the change in a property of the system produced by the impulse) we distinguish between **work** (the effect of the surroundings) and change in energy (the change in a property of the system produced by the work). Work is the term used for one form of energy transfer between systems. In Part V this is the only kind of energy transfer with which we will be concerned, but later, in discussing thermodynamics, we will introduce another kind of energy transfer, called **heat flow.**

20

THE WORK–ENERGY RELATION
FOR A PARTICLE

WORK AND KINETIC ENERGY FOR
MOTION IN ONE DIMENSION

We begin by thinking about the motion of a single particle along a straight line. In this one-dimensional situation the vector quantities displacement, velocity, acceleration and force can be treated as scalars. This will serve to introduce (or to recall) the definitions of work and kinetic energy, but the importance of the energy concept really only becomes apparent when we consider motion in two or three dimensions, because much of its usefulness depends on the fact that it is a scalar quantity, not a vector quantity.

Think of a particle of mass m that at some instant ($t = t_1$) has a velocity $\mathbf{v}_1$. A force $\mathbf{F}$ acts on the particle, in the same line as $\mathbf{v}_1$ (parallel or anti-parallel). This is the only force on the particle, or is the resultant force on it.

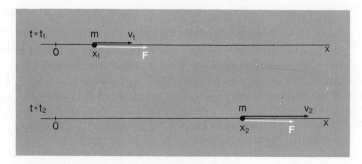

Particle in motion
in one dimension.

At a later instant ($t = t_2$) the particle will have a velocity $\mathbf{v}_2$ in the same line as $\mathbf{v}_1$. Choosing a co-ordinate system with one axis (the x-axis) along the line of the motion, we can treat all of the quantities involved as scalars.

477

Suppose first that **F** is constant in magnitude as well as in direction. Then the acceleration **a** is constant, and we can use the results found previously for uniformly accelerated motion.

$$v_2 = v_1 + a(t_2 - t_1) = v_1 + \frac{F}{m}(t_2 - t_1)$$

$$v_2^2 = v_1^2 + 2a(x_2 - x_1) = v_1^2 + 2\frac{F}{m}(x_2 - x_1)$$

These may be rearranged thus:

$$F(t_2 - t_1) = mv_2 - mv_1$$
$$F(x_2 - x_1) = \tfrac{1}{2}mv_2^2 - \tfrac{1}{2}mv_1^2$$

The first is the impulse–momentum relation $J = p_2 - p_1$ discussed before. The integrated effect of the force acting over a time interval is to change the linear momentum of the particle. The effect of the **surroundings** is related to a change in the **system.**

The second relation expresses the effect of the surroundings (whatever is providing the force) in a different way. Instead of the force times the time interval, the left side is the force times the displacement in the time interval. The right side gives the change of the property $\tfrac{1}{2}mv^2$ of the particle in the time interval. We define a quantity called **work done by the force** F by $W_{1\to2} = F(x_2 - x_1)$, and a quantity called **kinetic energy of the particle** by $K = \tfrac{1}{2}mv^2$. Then the relation is

$$W_{1\to2} = K_2 - K_1$$

The definitions are made so that the work done by the force (the effect of the surroundings) is equal to the change in kinetic energy of the particle (a change in a property of the system).

If the force **F** is not constant in magnitude as well as in direction, we cannot use the equations for uniformly accelerated motion, but the definitions can be extended to give the same relationship. If **F** is constant in direction, but not in magnitude, then F depends on time $F(t)$ or on displacement $F(x)$. The instantaneous equation of motion for the particle is

$$F = ma = m\frac{dv}{dt}$$

or integrating over the interval

$$\int_{t_1}^{t_2} F\, dt = \int_{v_1}^{v_2} m\, dv = mv_2 - mv_1$$

and as before $\qquad\qquad J = p_2 - p_1$

since we defined impulse as $\qquad J = \int_{t_1}^{t_2} F\, dt$

From the previous definition of work done by the force $W_{1\to2} = F(x_2 - x_1)$ the work done ΔW by a force acting over a small displacement Δx is $\Delta W = F \Delta x$, if the interval is small enough so the force can be considered constant over this distance. Using the equation of motion

$$\Delta W = F \Delta x = m \frac{\Delta v}{\Delta t} \Delta x = m \Delta v \frac{\Delta x}{\Delta t} = mv \Delta v$$

Over a small displacement Δx, F may be considered constant.

or integrating over the interval

$$W_{1 \to 2} = \int_{x_1}^{x_2} F \, dx = \int_{v_1}^{v_2} mv \, dv = \tfrac{1}{2}mv_2^2 - \tfrac{1}{2}mv_1^2$$
$$= K_2 - K_1$$

If F is constant, $W_{1 \to 2} = \int_{x_1}^{x_2} F \, dx = F \int_{x_1}^{x_2} dx = F(x_2 - x_1)$ as before.

WORK AND KINETIC ENERGY FOR MOTION IN THREE DIMENSIONS

So far we have stressed the similarity between the impulse–momentum equation $J = p_2 - p_1$ and the work–energy equation $W = K_2 - K_1$, different ways of relating the effect of the surroundings to changes of the system. Now we note that there is a fundamental difference between these. The equation $J = p_2 - p_1$ is really a relationship between **vector** quantities; we have been able to treat it as a scalar equation here because we have considered only motion in one dimension.

For the motion of a particle in general the equation of motion is

$$\mathbf{F} = m \frac{d\mathbf{v}}{dt} = \frac{d\mathbf{p}}{dt}$$

or integrating over a time interval

$$\mathbf{J} = \int_{t_1}^{t_2} \mathbf{F} \, dt = \int_{\mathbf{p}_1}^{\mathbf{p}_2} d\mathbf{p} = \mathbf{p}_2 - \mathbf{p}_1$$

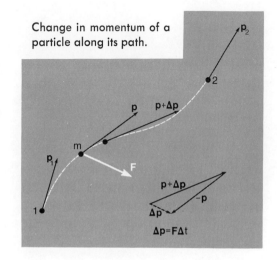

Change in momentum of a particle along its path.

This vector equation represents three scalar equations: $J_x = p_{2x} - p_{1x}$, etc. We have been looking at the situation where only one of these is a non-zero equation.

The definition of impulse $\mathbf{J} = \int \mathbf{F} \, dt$ means that the resultant impulse is the vector sum of the infinitesimal impulses $\mathbf{F} \, dt$. At any instant a particle has momentum $\mathbf{p}$. A short time Δt later it has a momentum $\mathbf{p} + \Delta \mathbf{p}$ where $\Delta \mathbf{p} = \mathbf{F} \Delta t$. The change in momentum is a vector in the same direction as the applied force **F**, and the sum of the vectors **F** Δt over the whole interval $(t_2 - t_1)$ gives the total change in momentum $\mathbf{p}_2 - \mathbf{p}_1$.

We know what it means to multiply the vector quantity force **F** by the scalar quantity time Δt; the result is a vector quantity in the same direction.

What does it mean to multiply the vector quantity force by another vector quantity, displacement? We know one way to answer this question. In Chapter 14 we defined the quantity called torque τ acting on a particle by $\tau = \mathbf{r} \times \mathbf{F}$. The vector product or cross product of two vectors is a third vector at right angles to the plane defined by the other two. Torque is an **instantaneous** quantity; its value depends on the instantaneous force **F** on the particle, and the instantaneous displacement **r** of the particle from a fixed point O in the frame of reference.

The quantity work is also defined as the product of a force and a displacement, but it differs from torque in two fundamental ways: it is a **scalar,** and it is defined **over an interval.**

We do not refer to the work done on the particle at some instant, but rather to the work done over an interval. In a time interval Δt, the work done ΔW depends on the force **F** (which can be considered constant if the time interval is short enough) and on the **change** in displacement of the particle $\Delta \mathbf{r}$ in the interval.

In order to make ΔW a scalar quantity, we use the definition of scalar or dot product, given in the earlier description of vectors.

$$\Delta W = \mathbf{F} \cdot \Delta \mathbf{r}$$

or over the total interval

$$W_{1 \to 2} = \int_{\mathbf{r}_1}^{\mathbf{r}_2} \mathbf{F} \cdot d\mathbf{r}$$

Examine what this means for the motion of the particle in the time interval Δt. At the beginning of the interval the velocity is **v**, after time Δt it is **v** + Δ**v**. The velocity has changed in magnitude and direction, due to the impulse **F** Δt. The force **F** can be resolved into two components $F \cos \theta$ in the **v** direction and $F \sin \theta$ perpendicular to the

Torque on a particle at a point in its path $\tau = \mathbf{r} \times \mathbf{F}$.

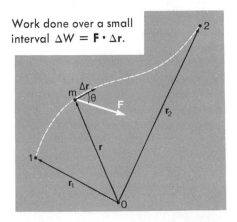

Work done over a small interval $\Delta W = \mathbf{F} \cdot \Delta \mathbf{r}$.

Work done is related to change in magnitude of v.

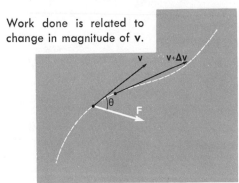

$\mathbf{v}$ direction; the impulse $F \cos \theta \, \Delta t$ will change the **magnitude** of $\mathbf{v}$, the impulse $F \sin \theta \, \Delta t$ will change the **direction** of $\mathbf{v}$.

The scalar product is defined to be

$$\Delta W = \mathbf{F} \cdot \Delta \mathbf{r} = F \, \Delta r \cos \theta$$
$$= (F \cos \theta) \, \Delta r$$

Thus the calculation of work done is related to the change in magnitude of $\mathbf{v}$, not to the change in direction of $\mathbf{v}$. This is precisely what is wanted in order to be able to define the quantity $K = \frac{1}{2}mv^2$ for the particle, a scalar property that depends on the speed v of the particle, but not on its direction of motion. This can be seen as follows:

The displacement in Δt is $\Delta \mathbf{r} = \mathbf{v} \, \Delta t$, and therefore

$$\mathbf{F} \cdot \Delta \mathbf{r} = \mathbf{F} \cdot \mathbf{v} \, \Delta t$$
$$= \mathbf{F} \, \Delta t \cdot \mathbf{v}$$
$$= m \, \Delta \mathbf{v} \cdot \mathbf{v}$$

From the definition of the scalar product, $\mathbf{v} \cdot \mathbf{v} = v^2$. Therefore a change $\Delta(v^2)$ can be written

$$\Delta(v^2) = \Delta(\mathbf{v} \cdot \mathbf{v})$$
$$= \Delta \mathbf{v} \cdot \mathbf{v} + \mathbf{v} \cdot \Delta \mathbf{v}$$
$$= 2 \, \Delta \mathbf{v} \cdot \mathbf{v}$$

(We showed in discussing vectors that the commutative law holds for the scalar product, so $\Delta \mathbf{v} \cdot \mathbf{v} = \mathbf{v} \cdot \Delta \mathbf{v}$.)

We can write the work done over the small interval then as

$$\Delta W = \mathbf{F} \cdot \Delta \mathbf{r} = m \, \Delta \mathbf{v} \cdot \mathbf{v}$$
$$= (m/2) \, \Delta(v^2)$$

or over the whole interval

$$W_{1 \to 2} = \int_{\mathbf{r_1}}^{\mathbf{r_2}} \mathbf{F} \cdot d\mathbf{r} = \frac{m}{2} \int_{v_1}^{v_2} d(v^2) = \tfrac{1}{2}mv_2^2 - \tfrac{1}{2}mv_1^2 = K_2 - K_1$$

The work done by the force over the interval, an integrated quantity, is related to the kinetic energy, an instantaneous quantity. Both are scalar quantities; the kinetic energy of a particle of mass m moving with velocity $\mathbf{v}$ is $K = \frac{1}{2}mv^2$ no matter whether the particle is moving up, down or sideways. While the value of K does not depend on the direction of motion in the frame of reference, it does depend on the frame of reference used to describe the motion, because the magnitude of $\mathbf{v}$ depends on the frame of reference.

Evaluation of the work done

$$W = \int_{\mathbf{r_1}}^{\mathbf{r_2}} \mathbf{F} \cdot d\mathbf{r}$$

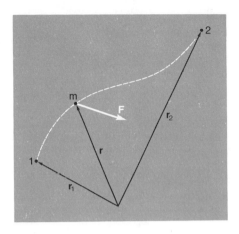

Work done depends on
the path from 1 to 2.

involves the determination of what is called a **line
integral.** The result depends on the path of the
particle at it moves from position 1 to position 2.
We are going to see that under certain circumstances the result depends only on the end points,
and not on the path.

POWER

We have emphasized that work done $W_{1\to 2} = \int_{r_1}^{r_2} \mathbf{F} \cdot d\mathbf{r}$ refers to an interval; W
is the work done by the force $\mathbf{F}$ as the displacement of the particle changes from
$\mathbf{r_1}$ to $\mathbf{r_2}$, which takes place in some time interval $(t_2 - t_1)$.

It is convenient to introduce a quantity called **power,** the work done divided
by the time. The average power over the interval is

$$\bar{P} = \frac{W_{1\to 2}}{(t_2 - t_1)}$$

Over a short time interval Δt the force $\mathbf{F}$ can be considered constant. The work
done is $\Delta W = \mathbf{F} \cdot \Delta \mathbf{r}$ and the average power is

$$\bar{P} = \frac{\Delta W}{\Delta t} = \mathbf{F} \cdot \frac{\Delta \mathbf{r}}{\Delta t}$$

In the limit as $\Delta t \to 0$, $\dfrac{\Delta \mathbf{r}}{\Delta t} \to \mathbf{v}$, and the **instantaneous power** is

$$P = \frac{dW}{dt} = \mathbf{F} \cdot \mathbf{v}$$

Note carefully that this is an instantaneous quantity, but **not an instantaneous
property of the particle.** It does depend on a property of the particle, its velocity
$\mathbf{v}$, but it also depends on the force $\mathbf{F}$. Power is the rate at which work is being
done by whatever is exerting the force $\mathbf{F}$ on the particle.

If $\mathbf{F}$ is the *only* force acting on the particle, the work–energy relation states
that the work done ΔW is equal to the change in kinetic energy ΔK, so

$$P = \frac{dK}{dt}$$

UNITS OF WORK, ENERGY, AND POWER

Work is defined as the product of force and displacement, so the unit of work may be any force unit times any length unit, for example newton-meter, kilogram-meter, foot-pound, ton-mile, and so on.

So far we have defined only one form of energy, kinetic energy of a particle. Since it has been so defined that the work done on the particle is equal to the change in kinetic energy of the particle, the units of work and kinetic energy are the same. We are going to have to define other forms of energy, in order to have conservation of energy, and the units of these other forms will have to be the same also. You can verify from any of the equations involving work or energy that the dimensions of work or energy are ML^2T^{-2}.

In the **systems** of units we have described, special names are given to certain units of work. In the mks system the unit is

$$1 \text{ newton-m} \equiv 1 \text{ kg-m}^2/\text{sec}^2 \equiv 1 \text{ joule}$$

In the cgs system the unit is

$$1 \text{ dyne-cm} \equiv 1 \text{ gm-cm}^2/\text{sec}^2 \equiv 1 \text{ erg}$$

In the British absolute system the unit of work is the foot-poundal, and in the British gravitational (or engineering) system it is the foot-pound.

There are two special names used for power:

$$1 \text{ joule/sec} \equiv 1 \text{ watt}$$
$$550 \text{ ft-lb/sec} \equiv 1 \text{ horsepower (hp)}$$

These are sometimes used to provide other names for units of work:

$$1 \text{ watt-sec} \equiv 1 \text{ joule}$$
$$1 \text{ kilowatt-hour (kwh)} = 10^3 \text{ watts} \times 3600 \text{ sec}$$
$$\equiv 3.6 \times 10^6 \text{ joules}$$

The relationship between the various units can be worked out:

$$1 \text{ joule} = 10^7 \text{ ergs} \qquad 1 \text{ hp} = 746 \text{ watts} \qquad \text{etc.}$$

Some units for work or energy have an historical origin. For example, one form of energy transfer is heat flow, and a unit called the **calorie** was originally defined as the heat energy that had to be transferred to raise the temperature of 1 gram of water through 1 Celsius degree. Since the amount of energy necessary is different at different temperatures (because the specific heat capacity of water is not quite constant) the "15° calorie" was defined as the heat necessary to change the temperature of 1 gram of water from 14.5° C to 15.5° C, and the "mean calorie" was defined as 1/100 of the heat necessary to change 1 gm of water from 0° to 100° C.

During the last century experiments were performed (by Joule and many others) to measure "the mechanical equivalent of heat," that is to measure the relationship between the units of work (e.g., the joule) and of heat (e.g., the calorie). Once it became accepted that these were different units for the same physical quantity, such experiments became equivalent to measuring the relationship between the yard and the meter. Today, just as the yard is defined in terms of the meter, the calorie is **defined** in terms of the joule; 1 calorie $\equiv 4.184$ joules.

In some fields a common energy unit is the kilocalorie, originally defined as the energy necessary to heat 1 kg of water through 1 Celsius degree. This unit is also called the Calorie: 1 kilocalorie $\equiv$ 1 Cal $\equiv 10^3$ cal. Sometimes the terms gram-calorie and kilogram-calorie are used for the *calorie* and the *Calorie*, but this is a dangerous convention because the dimensions are wrong.

In atomic and nuclear physics the most common unit is the electron volt (ev) or multiples such as kev (10^3 ev), Mev (10^6 ev), and Bev (10^9 ev). Instead of using Bev for billion electron volts (10^9 ev) it is usual to use Gev (prefix "giga-" for gigantic), in order to avoid the confusion that arises because the term billion is used differently in different parts of the world. In the United States, for example, a billion is a thousand million, while in Great Britain a billion is a million million. An electron volt is the energy acquired by an electron (or any other particle with the fundamental charge e) accelerated by a potential difference of 1 volt. Since the charge is $e = 1.6 \times 10^{-19}$ coulomb, and the work done on a particle in falling through a potential difference of V volts $\equiv V$ joules/coulomb, is eV,

$$1 \text{ ev} = 1.6 \times 10^{-19} \text{ coulomb} \times 1 \text{ joule/coulomb} = 1.6 \times 10^{-19} \text{ joule}$$

This unit is useful because atomic energies (the kinetic energy of an atom in a gas at normal temperature, or the energy required to ionize an atom, etc.) are of the order of ev. The energies of particles released in nuclear reactions are of the order of Mev, and of particles accelerated by modern particle accelerators may be of Bev. Note that an energy of 1 billion electron volts = 1 Bev = 10^9 ev = 1.6×10^{-10} joule = 1.6×10^{-3} erg, a very small amount of energy.

It is not uncommon in nuclear physics or in fundamental particle physics to use mass units as units of energy. You are probably familiar with the Einstein mass–energy relationship $E = mc^2$ that emerges from the special theory of relativity. In this equation c, the speed of light, is a universal constant $c = 3 \times 10^8$ m/sec. Therefore the energy equivalent of 1 kg of mass is $E = 9 \times 10^{16}$ joules. It is more useful to know the energy equivalent of 1 atomic mass unit (amu). Atomic and nuclear masses are measured in amu, based on the mass of one atom of the C^{12} isotope of carbon as 12 amu. (The amu was originally defined as the mass of one atom of the O^{16} isotope of oxygen. With the new definition, based on carbon-12, it is referred to as the **unified** atomic mass unit, and often given the symbol u rather than amu.)

One **gram molecular weight** of C^{12} (or Avogadro's number of atoms, $N_0 = 6.02 \times 10^{23}$ molecules/mole) has a mass of 12 gm, so the mass of one C^{12} atom is $12/N_0$ gm, and

$$1 \text{ amu} = \frac{1}{12}\left(\frac{12}{N_0}\right) \text{gm} = \frac{1}{6.02 \times 10^{23}} \text{gm} = 1.66 \times 10^{-24} \text{ gm}$$

The energy equivalent of 1 amu is then

$$1.66 \times 10^{-24} \times (3 \times 10^{10})^2 = 1.5 \times 10^{-3} \text{ erg} = 1.5 \times 10^{-10} \text{ joule}$$
$$= 931 \text{ Mev}$$

Just as energies are sometimes expressed in terms of the equivalent mass, they may be expressed in terms of the equivalent temperature. When a particle is said to have an "energy of 10^4 °K" it means that the particle has an energy equal to the average kinetic energy of particles in a gas in equilibrium at a temperature of 10^4 °K. This average KE we will later show to be $\frac{3}{2}kT$, where k is Boltzmann's constant: $k = 1.38 \times 10^{-16}$ erg/K°. It is conventional to ignore the numerical factor $\frac{3}{2}$ (~ 1) since we are referring to average values, and refer to **thermal energy** kT. The thermal energy corresponding to a temperature of 10^4 °K is

$$E = 1.38 \times 10^{-16} \times 10^4 = 1.38 \times 10^{-12} \text{ erg} \cong 1 \text{ ev}$$

The thermal energy corresponding to room temperature ~ 300 °K is

$$E = 1.38 \times 10^{-16} \times 300 \sim 5 \times 10^{-14} \text{ erg} \sim 0.03 \text{ ev}$$

APPLICATION OF THE WORK–ENERGY RELATION
FOR A PARTICLE

We have defined the **kinetic energy of a particle** $K = \frac{1}{2}mv^2$, a property of the particle, and defined **work done by a force** $W = \int \mathbf{F} \cdot d\mathbf{r}$, one method of describing the effect of a force over an interval.

The **work–energy relation** $W_{1 \to 2} = K_2 - K_1$ is an integrated form of the instantaneous law of motion $\mathbf{F} = m\mathbf{a}$. Just as $\mathbf{F}$ as used in this law is the resultant force on the particle, the force used in evaluating $W_{1 \to 2}$ in the work–energy relation is the resultant force. Note, however, that the definition of work done by a force applies to any force acting. If there are several forces $\mathbf{F}_1, \mathbf{F}_2, \cdots$, acting, the work done by any one of them is

$$(W_i)_{1 \to 2} = \int_{\mathbf{r}_1}^{\mathbf{r}_2} \mathbf{F}_i \cdot d\mathbf{r}$$

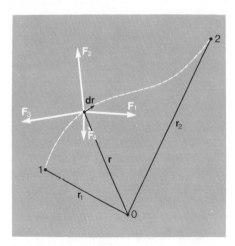

Each force does work on the particle; the net work done is equal to the change in kinetic energy.

It is the **net** work

$$W_{1\to2} = \sum (W_i)_{1\to2}$$

that is equal to the change in kinetic energy of the particle in the interval. Work is a scalar quantity, and it is sometimes easier to determine this sum than it is to determine the resultant force from the vector sum $\mathbf{F} = \sum \mathbf{F}_i$.

These definitions contain no new information, but simply express the content of Newton's law in a different form, a form that is useful under certain conditions. In order to see this it is necessary to look at specific situations. We will look at some examples which could be analyzed completely with the use of Newton's law, and therefore where the work–energy relation is not necessary. Then we will go on to examples where we cannot apply Newton's law directly, but can obtain some information using the work–energy relation. Sometimes a direct application of Newton's law is possible but difficult, and the required result can be obtained more readily using the work–energy relation.

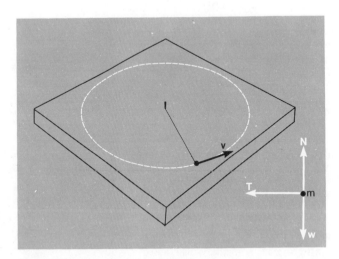

Particle in uniform circular motion.

Example 1—Uniform Circular Motion: First think of a particle moving in a circle on a smooth horizontal table, held by a string looped over a smooth peg. The forces on the particle are its weight $\mathbf{w}$, the normal force of the table $\mathbf{N}$, and the tension in the string $\mathbf{T}$. The resultant force is the tension $\mathbf{T}$, the centripetal force providing the centripetal acceleration as the particle moves in its circular path. The work done over any interval $W = \int \mathbf{T} \cdot d\mathbf{r} = 0$, because the force $\mathbf{T}$ is always at right angles to the motion of the particle, that is at right angles to the infinitesimal displacement $d\mathbf{r}$. Therefore $W = K_2 - K_1 = 0$, and the kinetic energy of the particle is constant. Since $K = \frac{1}{2}mv^2$, and the speed v is constant, this result is no surprise.

Forces of constraint such as the tension $\mathbf{T}$ that are at right angles to the motion at every instant are sometimes called **no-work** forces.

Think of a satellite moving around the earth, held in orbit by the gravitational pull of the earth. If the orbit is circular the force of gravity is the centripetal force, it does no work on the satellite and the kinetic energy of the satellite is constant. If the orbit

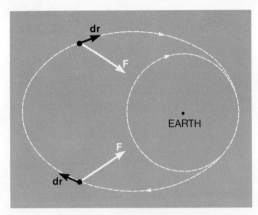

Circular and elliptic orbits of a satellite.

is not a circle, then work is done by the force of gravity. Sometimes $\mathbf{F} \cdot d\mathbf{r}$ is positive, and the kinetic energy of the satellite is increasing; sometimes $\mathbf{F} \cdot d\mathbf{r}$ is negative, and the kinetic energy of the satellite is decreasing. We will return to this example and examine it more carefully later.

Example 2—Free Fall Under Gravity: Now think of a particle released near the earth's surface. Neglecting the buoyancy and resistance of the air, the only force on it is the constant force $\mathbf{w}$. The particle will fall straight down. Choosing a co-ordinate system with y-axis vertically downward, and origin at the point of release of the particle, the work done by the force $\mathbf{w}$ as the particle moves down through a displacement y is

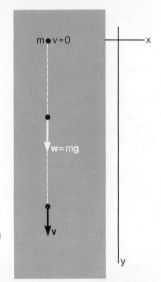

$$W_{0 \to y} = \int \mathbf{w} \cdot d\mathbf{r} = \int_0^y mg \, dy = mgy$$

and the work–energy relation gives

$$W_{0 \to y} = mgy = K_2 - K_1 = \tfrac{1}{2}mv^2$$

The initial kinetic energy $K_1 = 0$, and the kinetic energy after falling a distance y is $K_2 = \tfrac{1}{2}mv^2$, where v is the speed. The result $v = \sqrt{2gy}$ is familiar because we know how to deal with motion with constant acceleration.

Particle falling from rest.

Example 3—Sliding Down a Straight Track: Now think of the particle sliding down a smooth straight track of slope θ, length s. In addition to the force $\mathbf{w}$ there is also the constraint force $\mathbf{N}$. However, this is a "no-work" force since it is at right angles to the motion of the particle $\int \mathbf{N} \cdot d\mathbf{r} = 0$. The weight $\mathbf{w}$ has a constant component $w \sin \theta$ in the direction of motion, so the work done by the force of gravity is

Particle on a smooth straight track.

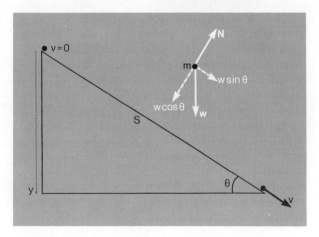

$$W = \int \mathbf{w} \cdot d\mathbf{r} = \int mg \sin \theta \, dr = mg \sin \theta \int_0^s dr$$

$$= mg \sin \theta \, s = mgy$$

where y is the vertical displacement of the particle.

The work–energy relation gives

$$W_{0 \rightarrow s} = mgy = K_2 - K_1 = \tfrac{1}{2}mv^2$$

The speed $v = \sqrt{2gy}$ of the particle at the bottom of the track is the same as if it had fallen straight down through the same vertical displacement. Note, however, that the **time** to fall is not the same.

Since the acceleration is constant, again we could have analyzed this situation using the basic law of dynamics $\mathbf{F} = m\mathbf{a}$.

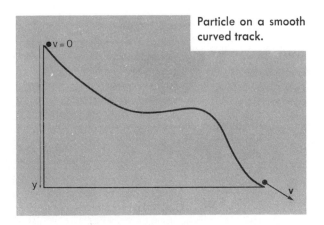

Particle on a smooth curved track.

Example 4—Sliding Down a Non-straight Track: Now think of the particle sliding down a smooth track that is not straight. The acceleration will not be constant, but will depend on the slope of the track at each point. However, the final result is the same as before, as can be seen from the work–energy relation. The force $\mathbf{N}$ on the particle varies in magnitude, depending on the slope, but is always at right angles to the motion of the particle, and therefore

$$\int \mathbf{N} \cdot d\mathbf{r} = 0$$

The force $\mathbf{w}$ is a constant force downward; in a coordinate system with y-axis downward, this force has only a y-component $w_y = mg$. The displacement $\Delta \mathbf{r}$ of the particle in time Δt will have components $\Delta x, \Delta y, \Delta z$, and the work done by $\mathbf{w}$ in this time is

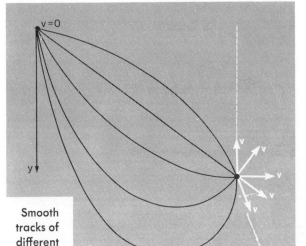

Smooth tracks of different shapes.

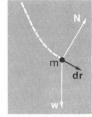

The normal force does zero work.

$$\Delta W = \mathbf{w} \cdot \Delta \mathbf{r} = \mathbf{w}_x \, \Delta x$$
$$+ \, \mathbf{w}_y \, \Delta y$$
$$+ \, \mathbf{w}_z \, \Delta z$$
$$= mg \, \Delta y$$

so that the work done depends only on the y-displacement

$$W = \int \mathbf{w} \cdot d\mathbf{r} = mg \int_0^y dy = mgy = K_2 - K_1$$

$$= \tfrac{1}{2}mv^2$$

For a smooth track of any shape the speed v at the bottom depends only on the vertical displacement. The **direction** of **v**, and the **time** to traverse the track, depend on the shape of the track. If **v** is straight up, the particle will rise to its initial height.

The result $mgy = \frac{1}{2}mv^2$ gives the speed $v = \sqrt{2gy}$. This is the same as the speed acquired by a particle in falling a distance y from rest with a constant acceleration **g**, but note that here the acceleration of the particle is *not* **g**. In the expression $v = \sqrt{2gy}$ the symbol g represents a number (32 ft/sec², or 9.8 m/sec²), *not* the acceleration of the particle.

This example illustrates the kind of situation in which the work–energy relation is useful because a detailed analysis would be difficult.

Example 5—Motion of a Projectile: The work done by a force may be positive or negative. Think of a particle that is projected at some angle upward, given an initial kinetic energy $K_1 = \frac{1}{2}mv_1^2$. We can determine its kinetic energy $K_2 = \frac{1}{2}mv_2^2$ at any later time as a function of its vertical displacement y. This time for variety we choose a co-ordinate system with y-axis upward, and origin at the initial point of projection. In this co-ordinate system the force **w** has only a y-component $w_y = -mg$ and therefore

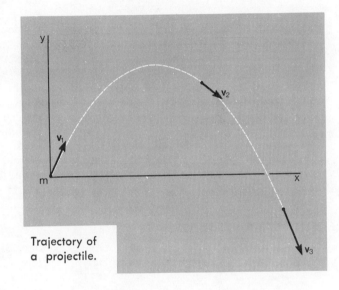

Trajectory of a projectile.

$$W_{0 \to y} = \int \mathbf{w} \cdot d\mathbf{r} = -mg \int_0^y dy = -mgy$$
$$= K_2 - K_1 = \frac{1}{2}mv_2^2 - \frac{1}{2}mv_1^2$$

If y is positive (the particle is higher than its point of projection) the force **w** has done negative work on the particle, and $K_2 < K_1$.

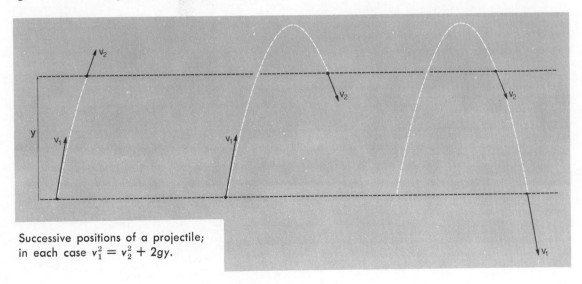

Successive positions of a projectile; in each case $v_1^2 = v_2^2 + 2gy$.

If y is negative, the net work done by **w** is positive, and $K_2 > K_1$.
The work–energy relation

$$-mgy = \tfrac{1}{2}mv_2^2 - \tfrac{1}{2}mv_1^2 \quad \text{or} \quad v_1^2 = v_2^2 + 2gy$$

relates the speeds v_1 and v_2 at displacements 0 and y, independent of the direction of motion.

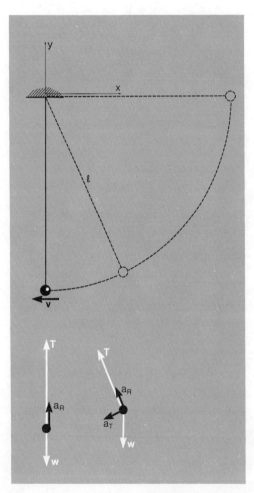

Forces on a falling pendulum.

Example 6—Falling Pendulum: The work–energy relation provides certain information about the motion, but not complete information. A complete analysis of the motion requires the application of the basic law **F** − m**a**. Sometimes we can determine what we want to know without doing this.

For example, think of a simple pendulum that is released from rest from the horizontal position. Suppose we wish to find the tension T in the supporting string at the instant the bob is in the lowest position. It is possible to work out the motion in detail, but as we have pointed out before this is not simple because the acceleration is not constant. We find that using the work–energy relation we can find the required tension without a detailed solution.

The forces acting are the tension **T** and the weight **w**, and in general there will be a tangential acceleration a_T and a radial acceleration a_R of the bob. However, at the lowest point the string is vertical and there is no tangential acceleration. The radial acceleration is directed upward, with magnitude $a_R = v^2/l$ where v is the speed at this instant. The equation of motion **T** + **w** = m**a** involves only vectors in the vertical direction. In a co-ordinate system as indicated the y-component equation is

$$T + (-mg) = ma_R = mv^2/l$$

The tension **T** is a no-work force, since it is at right angles to the motion. The work done by the force **w** as the particle moves from displacement 0 to displacement y is

$$W = \int \mathbf{w} \cdot d\mathbf{r} = -mg \int_0^y dy = -mgy$$

At the lowest point, $y = -l$, and the work–energy relation gives

$$W = mgl = K_2 - K_1$$
$$= \tfrac{1}{2}mv^2 - 0$$

Therefore the tension T at the lowest point is

$$T = mg + mv^2/l = mg + (2mgl)/l = 3mg = 3w$$

The tension is three times the weight of the bob. The string provides the centripetal force $2w$ as well as holding up the bob.

This result has been obtained without working out the time for the pendulum to fall.

Example 7—Work Done by the Force of Friction: So far the only forces we have used in the examples are the force of gravity, assumed to be a constant force, and no-work forces such as normal forces. This is because the calculation of work done by a force $\int \mathbf{F} \cdot d\mathbf{r}$ is simple if the force is constant, or is at right angles to the motion. The force of kinetic friction is another kind of force for which the work done can be calculated readily, because we have assumed that this force is independent of speed. The force of friction is always in the opposite direction to the direction of motion of the particle, and therefore the work done by the force of friction $\int \mathbf{f}_k \cdot d\mathbf{r}$ is always negative, tending to decrease the kinetic energy of the particle. Think of a block slid along a table with an initial speed v, coming to rest after sliding a distance d.

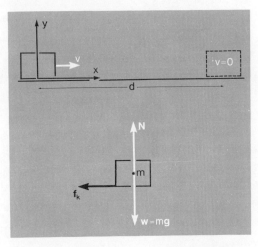

Sliding block on a non-smooth horizontal plane.

The resultant force on the block is the frictional force $\mathbf{f}_k$ opposing its motion. In the co-ordinate system indicated

$$W = \int \mathbf{f}_k \cdot d\mathbf{r} = -\int_0^d f_k \, dx$$
$$= -f_k d = K_2 - K_1$$
$$= 0 - \tfrac{1}{2}mv^2$$

The energy of the block has decreased to zero because of the negative work done by the force of friction on the block. Later we will say that the kinetic energy of the block has become heat energy of—of what? This is the key question. We must always be clear in mechanics what **system** we are talking about. At present we are applying the work–energy relation to a particle. When we extend our ideas of work and energy to apply to systems of particles, we will find it useful to define other kinds of energy. For the moment the block is treated as a particle—that is, as a rigid body with all particles moving in pure translation.

Introducing the coefficient of kinetic friction μ_k

$$f_k = \mu_k N = \mu_k mg$$

so $$\tfrac{1}{2}mv^2 = f_k d = \mu_k mgd \qquad \text{or} \qquad v^2 = \mu_k gd$$

from measurements of v and d, the coefficient μ_k can be determined.

Think now of a block projected up an inclined plane, coming instantaneously to rest a distance d up the plane, then sliding back to its starting point. Again we can describe the situation completely using $\mathbf{F} = m\mathbf{a}$, but let us examine what information the work–energy relation provides. On the way up the plane the work done on the block by the force of gravity $\mathbf{w}$ is $-mgh$ (where $h = d \sin \theta$ is the vertical displacement) and the work done by the force of friction is $-f_k d$. The work–energy relation gives

$$W = K_2 - K_1$$
$$-mgh - f_k d = 0 - \tfrac{1}{2}mv_1^2$$

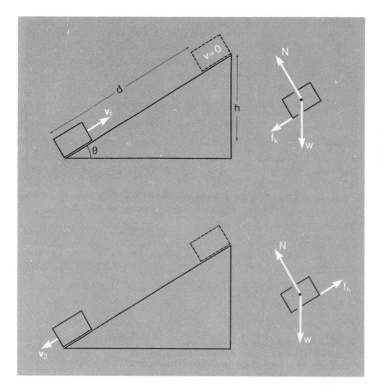

Block slid up
a non-smooth
inclined plane.

On the way down the plane the work done by friction is again $-f_k d$ but the work done by the weight is $+mgh$. The work–energy relation gives

$$W = K_2 - K_1$$
$$mgh - f_k d = \tfrac{1}{2}mv_2^2 - 0$$

Adding the two equations $-2f_k d = \tfrac{1}{2}mv_2^2 - \tfrac{1}{2}mv_1^2$

showing that the net loss in kinetic energy of the block is equal to the net work done by the force of friction (a negative amount of work). Using the coefficient of friction, $f_k = \mu_k N = \mu_k mg \cos \theta$, giving

$$4\mu_k gd \cos \theta = v_1^2 - v_2^2$$

If $\mu_k = 0$ the plane is "smooth" and $v_2 = v_1$.

Example 8—Work Done by a Spring. We will look at one example where the force on the particle is not constant, the one-dimensional motion of a particle connected to an ideal spring.

A small block (a particle) rests on a smooth horizontal track, connected by a spring of spring constant k to a fixed point. The spring exerts a force parallel to the track if the particle is displaced from its equilibrium position. We will use a co-ordinate system with origin at the equilibrium position, and x-axis along the track. Then the spring exerts a force $F_s = -kx$ on the particle when its displacement is x.

First think of pulling the block slowly (so that $K \cong 0$) by applying a horizontal force $\mathbf{F}$, keeping this force just large enough to keep extending the spring. Then $F = +kx$ at any point. The work done by the force $\mathbf{F}$ in giving the block a displacement x_0 is

$$W_{0 \to x_0} = \int \mathbf{F} \cdot d\mathbf{r} = \int_0^{x_0} kx \, dx = \tfrac{1}{2}kx_0^2$$

This is not the net work done on the block. The force $\mathbf{F}_s$ does work $-\tfrac{1}{2}kx_0^2$ on it in the same interval (the forces $\mathbf{N}$ and $\mathbf{w}$ do no work on it) and the net work is zero.

Now think about what happens if the force $\mathbf{F}$ is removed when the displacement is x_0. The force $\mathbf{F}_s$ is unbalanced, producing acceleration toward the origin. The only work done on the block is done by the force $\mathbf{F}_s$. As the block moves from x_0 to 0 this work is

$$W_{x_0 \to 0} = \int \mathbf{F}_s \cdot d\mathbf{r} = -\int_{x_0}^0 kx \, dx = [-\tfrac{1}{2}kx^2]_{x_0}^0 = \tfrac{1}{2}kx_0^2$$

Applying the work–energy relation to this interval

$$\tfrac{1}{2}kx_0^2 = K_2 - K_1 = \tfrac{1}{2}mv_0^2 - 0$$

At the origin the block has speed v_0, and therefore will keep moving, compressing the spring. The spring will do negative work on the block, and its kinetic energy will decrease until it comes to rest with displacement $-x_0$ such that

$$-\tfrac{1}{2}k(-x_0)^2 = 0 - \tfrac{1}{2}mv_0^2$$

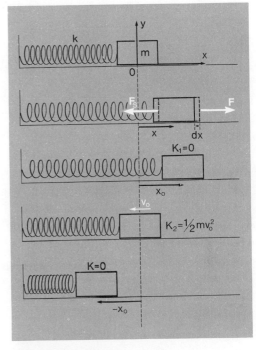

Motion of a block connected to a spring.

The block will keep oscillating to and fro between the limits $-x_0 \to x_0$ as the spring does positive and negative work on it alternately.

NUMERICAL EXAMPLES

Example 1: A 1-kg block on a smooth surface connected to the end of a spring vibrates with a period of 2 sec. If the block is not connected to the spring, but is pressed against it, compressing it 1 cm, and released from rest, what speed does it acquire?

The period of the block–spring system, assuming the spring is of negligible mass, is

$$T = 2\pi \sqrt{\frac{m}{k}} \qquad \text{so} \qquad k = m\frac{4\pi^2}{T^2} = 1 \times \frac{4\pi^2}{2^2} \, kg/sec^2$$

$$= \pi^2 \text{ newton/m}$$

The block vibrates in SHM.

The work done by the spring as its compression changes from x to 0 is

$$W = \tfrac{1}{2}kx^2 = \tfrac{1}{2}\pi^2 \times (10^{-2})^2 \text{ newton/m} \times m^2$$
$$= 10^{-4}\pi^2/2 \text{ joule}$$

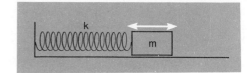

Since the surface is smooth, the spring force is the only force doing work on the block: $W = K_2 - K_1$. $K_1 = 0$, and $K_2 = \frac{1}{2}mv^2$, where v is the speed acquired.

$$v = \sqrt{\frac{2K_2}{m}} = \sqrt{\frac{2W}{m}} = \sqrt{\frac{2 \times 10^{-4}\pi^2}{2 \times 1}}$$
$$= 10^{-2}\pi \text{ m/sec} = 3.14 \text{ cm/sec}$$

Note that the mass m of the block does not have to be known.

$$\tfrac{1}{2}mv^2 = \tfrac{1}{2}kx^2 = \tfrac{1}{2}\left(m\,\frac{4\pi^2}{T^2}\right)x^2$$

$$v = \frac{2\pi x}{T} = \frac{2\pi \times 10^{-2}}{2} \text{ m/sec} - \pi \text{ cm/sec}$$

Example 2: A 4-kg ball hangs at the end of a wire 5 m long. A force F is applied to push the ball sideways. This force is kept horizontal, and is increased slowly from 0 to 3 kg, so that the ball is displaced slowly. Calculate the work done by the force F.

The kind of process suggested here is called a **quasistatic process.** It is assumed that the force F is increased slowly enough that the ball is always in equilibrium under the influence of the three forces $\mathbf{T}$, $\mathbf{F}$ and $\mathbf{w}$. It has a negligible acceleration, and acquires a negligible kinetic energy.

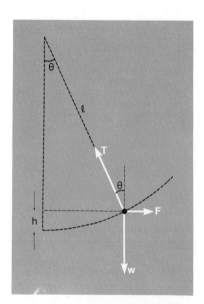

At any angular displacement θ the component equations of motion are

$$F + T\sin\theta = 0 \qquad w + T\cos\theta = 0$$

or dividing

$$F = w\tan\theta$$

The work done by the force $\mathbf{F}$, $W = \int \mathbf{F}\cdot d\mathbf{r}$, will depend on the component $F\cos\theta$ of the force that is along the tangent to the circular path, the direction of motion. Distance along the arc dr is related to change in angular displacement $d\theta$ by $dr = l\,d\theta$, where l is the radius of the circle (the length of the wire).

As the angular displacement increases from 0 to θ the work done by $\mathbf{F}$ is

$$W = \int \mathbf{F}\cdot d\mathbf{r} = \int F\cos\theta\,dr = \int (w\tan\theta)\cos\theta(l\,d\theta)$$

$$= wl\int_0^\theta \sin\theta\,d\theta = wl(-\cos\theta)_0^\theta = wl(1 - \cos\theta)$$

$$= wh$$

Forces on a pendulum bob in equilibrium.

where $h = l - l\cos\theta$ is the vertical distance moved by the ball.

The tension $\mathbf{T}$ is a no-work force, since it is at right angles to the motion. The kinetic energy of the ball does not change $K_2 = K_1 = 0$. The work done by gravity as the ball rises through a height h is $W = -wh = -mgh$. The net work, the sum of the work done by the force F and the work done by gravity, is zero.

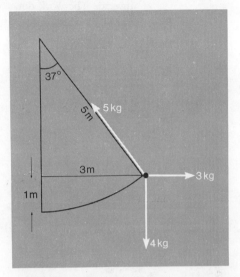

Forces at the final position.

For $w = 4$ kg the final value of F is 3 kg and the final angle is $\tan \theta = F/w = 3/4$, $\theta = 37°$. The height h is $h = l(1 - \cos \theta) = 5(1 - 0.8) = 1$ m, and the work done by F is

$$\begin{aligned} W &= wh = 4 \times 1 \text{ kg-m} \\ &= 4 \times 9.8 \text{ newton-m} \\ &= 39 \text{ joules} \end{aligned}$$

The work done by the force of gravity is -39 joules.

Example 3: An electron is accelerated by a potential difference of 1000 volts in the electron gun of a cathode ray tube. Determine the resultant kinetic energy and speed of the electron.

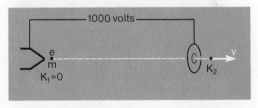

A 1000-volt electron gun.

A potential difference of 1000 volts between two points means that an amount of work $W = 1000$ joules/coulomb is done by the electric force on any charge moved from one point to the other. Assuming that the electron is initially at rest, $K_1 = 0$, and assuming that no force except the electric force acts on it, it acquires energy $K_2 = W$ in the electron gun.

The work done is $W = qV$, where q is the charge in coulombs and V is the potential difference. Here q is the electron charge $e = 1.6 \times 10^{-19}$ coulomb

$$K_2 = 1000 \text{ electron-volts} \quad \text{(recall the definition)}$$

or

$$\begin{aligned} K_2 &= 1000 \times 1.6 \times 10^{-19} \text{ joule/coul} \times \text{coul} \\ &= 1.6 \times 10^{-16} \text{ joule} \end{aligned}$$

The electron mass is $m = 9 \times 10^{-31}$ kg, and its speed is

$$v = \sqrt{\frac{2K_2}{m}} = \sqrt{\frac{2 \times 1.6 \times 10^{-16}}{9 \times 10^{-31}}} = 1.9 \times 10^7 \text{ m/sec}$$

This is less than 10% of the speed of light (3×10^8 m/sec) and this means that a non-relativistic (or classical) calculation is adequate.

Example 4: A 500-gm ball falls 1 m onto a rigid surface, rebounding to a height of 0.8 m. How much work is done by the force of gravity on it as it falls? As it rises? Does the force exerted by the rigid surface do any work on the ball?

The force of gravity on the ball is $F = mg = 0.5 \times 9.8 \text{ kg-m/sec}^2 = 4.9$ newtons, downward. As it falls its displacement is downward, as it rises its displacement is upward. The work done by gravity on it as it falls is $W = 4.9 \times 1$ newton-m $= 4.9$ joules, and as it rises is $W = -4.9 \times 0.8$ newton-m $= -3.9$ joules. These are the works done by gravity no matter what other forces act. If the force of air friction can be neglected, the force of gravity is the only force acting as the ball falls or rises, and the work–energy relation $W = K_2 - K_1$ then says that its kinetic energy just before it hits the rigid surface is 4.9 joules, and just after it leaves the rigid surface is 3.9 joules.

This does *not* mean that the force exerted by the rigid surface does 1 joule of work on the ball. If the surface is completely rigid (undeformed in the collision) it does no **net** work on the ball at all; it will do negative work as the ball is decelerated ($\mathbf{F}_s$ and $d\mathbf{r}$ in opposite directions) and an equal amount of positive work as the ball is accelerated upward. The surface exerts a net upward **impulse** $\mathbf{J} = \int \mathbf{F}_s \, dt$ but does no net work.

Then what force acting on the ball did the work that decreased its kinetic energy from 4.9 to 3.9 joules?

Much of the next few chapters will be devoted to answering this question. There is *no* force on the ball that did the work to decrease its kinetic energy—that is, no external force. A ball is not a particle, but a system of particles and the work–energy relation $W = K_2 - K_1$ we derived for a particle does not work for a system of particles, in general. While it sometimes can be applied (as for the falling ball) it is necessary to do so with care. As the ball falls it is assumed that it is behaving as a rigid body; every particle in it is moving in the same way. When it hits the rigid surface it is deformed, and internal changes occur.

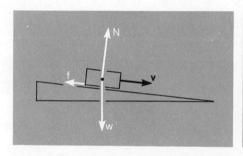

What happens to the kinetic energy in an inelastic collision?

Example 5: A 2000-lb automobile coasts down a grade of 1-in-10 at 30 mph. What horsepower is required to drive it up the same hill at the same speed?

A grade of 1-in-10 means that the height increases by 1 unit for each 10 units along

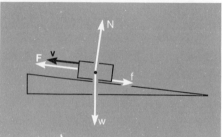

Forces on a car moving down and moving up the slope.

the slope, so $\sin \theta = 0.1$. When the car is coasting at constant speed down the slope, the resultant force on it is zero. The component of the gravitational force down the plane is equal to the retarding force of friction up the plane.

$$f = mg \sin \theta = 0.1 \, mg$$

Moving up the plane at the same speed, the friction force has the same magnitude but now acts down the plane, in the same direction as the component of the weight. There will have to be an applied force F up the plane of magnitude

$$F = f + mg \sin \theta = 0.2 \, mg$$

This force is exerted by the plane on the car (because the driving wheels exert a force on the plane in the opposite direction). With $w = 2000$ lb, $v = 30$ mph $= 44$ ft/sec, 1 hp $= 550$ ft-lb/sec, the power necessary is

$$
\begin{aligned}
P = \mathbf{F} \cdot \mathbf{v} &= Fv = 0.2 \, mgv \\
&= 0.2 \, wv \\
&= 0.2 \times 2000 \times 44 \text{ ft-lb/sec} \\
&= \frac{0.2 \times 2000 \times 44}{550} \text{ hp} = 32 \text{ hp}
\end{aligned}
$$

This is the rate at which work must be done on the car. This work is done by the engine, but the power produced by the engine will be greater than this because of energy losses in transmission between the engine and the wheels.

Note that in this example the work–energy relation has not appeared explicitly, because we used force instead. We could equally well have said that the kinetic energy of the car as it moves down the slope is constant, and therefore the net work done on it is zero. In moving a distance s the work done by the force of gravity is $smg \sin \theta$, and this must equal the negative work done by the force of friction $-fs$

$$W_{\text{net}} = smg \sin \theta - fs = 0$$

In moving up the plane both the force of gravity and the force of friction do negative work, so there must be another force F doing positive work.

$$W_{\text{net}} = Fs - smg \sin \theta - fs = 0$$

Example 6: A train traveling at 60 mph picks up water at a rate of 3000 gal/min from a trough between the rails. What additional force (in tons) and additional horsepower is required? The train must exert a force forward on the water to change its speed from 0 to v, and there will be an equal force backward on the train.

Fix your attention on a particle of water of mass Δm, which in some time Δt has its speed changed from 0 to v. Its change in momentum is $v \, \Delta m$, and the impulse producing this change is $F \, \Delta t$.

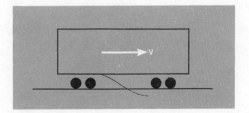

Train car scooping up water continuously.

$$F \, \Delta t = v \, \Delta m \qquad F = v \frac{\Delta m}{\Delta t}$$

The quantity $\Delta m/\Delta t$ is the rate at which water is being picked up, a constant.

$$\frac{\Delta m}{\Delta t} = \rho \frac{\Delta V}{\Delta t} \qquad \text{where } \rho \text{ is density, } V \text{ is volume}$$

$$= \rho \times 3000 \text{ gal/min}$$
$$= \rho \times 50 \text{ gal/sec} \qquad (\rho = 10 \text{ lb/gal for water})$$
$$= 500 \text{ lb/sec}$$

At the speed $v = 60$ mph $= 88$ ft/sec, the force forward on the water is

$$F = v\frac{\Delta m}{\Delta t} = 88 \times 500 \text{ ft-lb/sec}^2 = 44{,}000 \text{ pndl}$$

$$= 1380 \text{ lb} = 0.69 \text{ ton}$$

There is an extra retarding force of 0.69 tons on the train while it is picking up water. The extra power required is

$$P = Fv = v^2\frac{\Delta m}{\Delta t} = 88^2 \times 500 \text{ ft-lb}^2/\text{sec}^2$$

$$= 88^2 \times 500 \text{ ft-pndl/sec}$$

$$= \frac{88^2 \times 500}{32} \text{ ft-lb/sec}$$

$$= \frac{88^2 \times 500}{32 \times 550} \text{ hp} = 220 \text{ hp}$$

We used the impulse–momentum relation $J = p_2 - p_1$ here, and not the work–energy relation $W = K_2 - K_1$. Why?

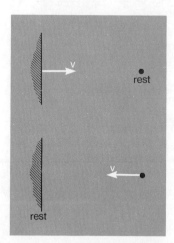

Motion is relative.

The kinetic energy acquired by the mass Δm in the time Δt is $\frac{1}{2}(\Delta m)v^2$, and the rate at which the kinetic energy of the water is increasing is $\frac{1}{2}(\Delta m/\Delta t)v^2$. If the work–energy relation is applicable, this is the rate at which work is being done, the power P. It is one-half that calculated before.

Again the work–energy relation cannot be applied because although we have talked about a particle of water, we really do not have a single particle, but a system of particles. The force F is an external force on the system of particles. The forces on an individual particle arise from other particles around it, not from the force F.

Some insight may be obtained here by thinking of the process as a collision; a particle of water collides with the train, and ends up moving with the train. A moving wall hitting a particle at rest is equivalent to a particle hitting a fixed wall.

If the particle sticks to the wall, the collision is inelastic, and energy is lost; only if the particle bounces back with the same speed is the collision elastic.

The water picked up by the moving train sloshes around, ultimately coming to rest ("sticking to the train") and in this process energy is lost.

Questions for discussion

1. An elementary definition of work is that it is force times distance. Why is this definition inadequate?

2. When work is done by a force on a body, does this necessarily produce a change in the kinetic energy of the body?

3. When you hold a heavy object at arm's length at rest, are you doing work on it? When you hold a heavy object at arm's length and walk at a steady speed on a level road, are you doing work on it?

4. When a truck travels along a straight level road at constant speed, what external forces are doing work on it? What external forces are acting on it but not doing work on it? At what rate is work being done on it?

5. Work is defined to be a scalar quantity. Does this mean that it cannot be negative? Can the kinetic energy of a particle be negative?

6. Does the work done by a force depend on the co-ordinate system used to calculate it? Does it depend on the frame of reference in which it is calculated? Does the kinetic energy of a particle depend on the frame of reference in which its motion is described?

7. Is the instantaneous power developed by a force acting on a particle a property of the particle, or of its surroundings, or both?

8. The work–kinetic energy relation and the impulse–momentum relation for a particle are both integrated forms of the basic instantaneous dynamic relation $F = ma$. How are they the same as one another, and how are they different?

9. Does the gravitational force of the earth on the moon do work on the moon? Does the gravitational force of the moon on the earth do work on the earth?

10. When a charged particle enters the earth's atmosphere from space, what forces do you think will do work on it—the force of gravity, the force due to air resistance, the force due to the earth's magnetic field?

11. Do you think work can be done by a centripetal force? Do you think work can be done by inertial forces such as centrifugal and coriolis forces?

12. A force that depends on position acts for a certain time through a certain displacement. Is the force averaged over the time interval necessarily the same as the force averaged over the displacement interval?

Problems

1. (a) A 100-lb block rests on a smooth floor. A constant force **F** of magnitude 60 lb is applied to it, moving it 10 ft along the floor. Determine the work done by **F** if it is (1) horizontal, (2) at 30° downward from the horizontal, (3) at 30° upward from the horizontal.

(b) The same block is on the floor and the same force **F** is applied, but between block and floor there are coefficients of static and kinetic friction of 0.35 and 0.3. What is the work done by **F** in the three cases as in (a)?

(c) Determine the kinetic energy of the block after it has moved the 10 ft for each of the three cases in (b).

2. A 0.1-kg ball falls freely from rest. What work in joules has been done on it by the force of gravity after it has fallen 5 m? What is its kinetic energy at this point? What is its rate of change of kinetic energy in watts at a point a distance y meters below its starting point? What is its rate of change of kinetic energy with height at any point?

3. A horse pulls a cart around a circular track $\frac{1}{2}$ mile in circumference, exerting a constant horizontal force of magnitude 25 lb on the cart and trotting at a steady 15 mph. In making one complete circuit of the track, what is the work done by the horse on the cart and the impulse exerted by the horse on the cart? At what rate is the horse doing work on the cart? At what rate are frictional forces doing work on the cart?

4. The coefficient of kinetic friction between a 2-kg block and an inclined plane is 0.25. The block is sliding down the plane at a constant speed of 0.4 m/sec. At what rate in watts is the force of gravity doing work on the block, and at what rate is the force of friction doing work on the block?

5. (a) A 10-kg block hangs by a rope 6 m long. It is drawn slowly sideways by a horizontal force and held so that it has been raised 1 m. Calculate the work done W by the horizontal force, and the force F required to hold it in its displaced position, if the horizontal force is applied (1) at the lower end of the rope, (2) at the midpoint of the rope. (b) The same block is drawn aside and held so that its sideways displacement is 1 m. Calculate W and F for the two cases again.

6. A 2000-lb car is accelerated uniformly from rest to 30 mph in 10 sec. What is the average power (in hp) required? Determine the instantaneous power P (in hp) as a function of time t (in sec).

7. A train flat car is moving at a constant speed of 2 ft/sec. A 160-lb box, initially at rest on the flat car, is pushed by a constant resultant horizontal force F of 4 lb in the direction the train is moving. (a) Over the first 3 sec the force acts, find the work done W and the magnitude of the impulse J of the force in the interval, as determined in (1) the train frame of reference, (2) the earth frame of reference. (b) Calculate W and J for the force in the interval that it takes to move the box 6 ft (1) in the train frame of reference, (2) in the earth frame of reference.

8. A ball of mass m hangs by a cord of length l from a fixed point. It is set in motion in a vertical circle. What is the work done on it by gravity as it moves from the bottom to the top of the circle? What is the difference between its kinetic energy K_1 at the bottom and K_2 at the top? What is the difference between the tension T_1 in the cord at the bottom and the tension T_2 at the top? What is the minimum breaking strength of the cord, in terms of the weight of the ball?

9. A 0.5-gm insect starts to slide at the edge of a hemispherical bowl of radius 15 cm, and reaches the center of the bowl with a speed of 80 cm/sec. How much work was done on the insect by the force of gravity? Assuming he is relaxing and enjoying the slip, how much work was done by the force of friction? What was the average force of friction over the distance of the slide?

10. A particle hangs at rest at the end of a string. Compare the amount of work that must be done on the particle to set it swinging in a vertical plane, with maximum

angle of the string with the vertical 60°, to the amount of work that must be done on it to start it moving as a conical pendulum with the string making a constant angle of 60° with the vertical.

11. A tube for launching a projectile vertically is in the shape of a quarter-circle of 50-ft radius, with its lower end horizontal and its upper end vertical. The projectile is given an initial speed of 200 ft/sec into the bottom of the tube. (a) If the inside of the tube is smooth, how high does the projectile rise above the top of the tube? (b) If the tube is not smooth, and the projectile rises to a height of 450 ft above the top of the tube, how does the average frictional force over the length of the tube compare with the weight of the projectile? Is it possible for it to be larger than the weight? What is the sideways force on the tube (in terms of the weight of the projectile) just before the projectile leaves it?

12. An ideal spring is horizontal. One end is fixed and the other connected to a 0.5-kg block at rest on a smooth table. The block is moved, extending the spring 2 cm. When the block is released, oscillations take place at a frequency of 5 cps. Consider the interval from the instant the block is released until it reaches its equilibrium position. Calculate the work done by the spring on the block in this interval. What is the average force exerted by the spring on the block in this interval? (Note that there are two different answers, depending on whether the average is taken over time or over displacement.)

13. An ideal spring is vertical, its lower end fixed. A 0.2-kg ball is lowered on to its upper end, depressing the end 2 cm. (a) How much work is done on the spring in compressing it? (b) The ball is pushed down a further 4 cm and held. How much work is done on the spring? What downward force on the ball is required to hold it in this position? (c) The ball is released. How high does it rise above the position of the uncompressed end of the spring?

14. (a) The engine of a car traveling at a steady 30 mph on a level road transmits a power of 20 hp to the driving wheels. What is the retarding force of friction on the car? (b) Assuming that the retarding frictional forces are proportional to the speed, what power must be transmitted to the wheels at 60 mph?

15. A block of mass 0.5 kg is at rest on a smooth horizontal surface. A horizontal force F is applied to it. This force is constant in direction, and decreases linearly with time from $F = 2n$ at $t = 0$ to $F = 0$ at $t = 10$ sec. (a) Determine the impulse J exerted by F over the 10-sec interval. (b) Determine the speed v_0 of the block at the end of the interval. (c) Determine the kinetic energy K_0 of the block at the end of the interval. (d) Determine the work done W by the force F over the interval. (e) Integrate to find the speed of the block as a function of time, and integrate again to find its displacement as a function of time. Determine its displacement x_0 at the end of the interval. (f) Determine W directly by integrating $dW = F\,dx = Fv\,dt$. (g) State the average force over the time interval, and the average force over the displacement interval, and note that they are different.

16. A particle is at rest on the x-axis of a co-ordinate system at $x = 10$ cm. At this point there is a resultant force F on it toward the origin, of magnitude 50 dyne. Calculate the work done by F as the particle moves from $x = 10$ cm to $x = 1$ cm if the force is always directed toward the origin, assuming that (a) F is inversely proportional to x^2, (b) F is inversely proportional to x. Before you work it out, in which case do you think the work done will be larger?

17. A small block of mass m is sliding in a circle of radius r_1 on a smooth table, held by an ideal string that passes from the block to a smooth hole in the center of the table, and held from below with a force F_1. The speed of the block is v_1, the angular speed ω_1, and the kinetic energy K_1.

(a) The string is pulled down by increasing the force F, until the block is moving in a circle of radius $r_2 = r_1/2$. Determine ω_2 in terms of ω_1, v_2 in terms of v_1, F_2 in terms of F_1, and K_2 in terms of K_1. What is the work done W on the block by the force F, in terms of the initial kinetic energy K_1?

(b) Obtain the work done by assuming that the force F is increased slowly (quasi-statically) so that at every instant $F = mr\omega^2$ and $W = \int F \, dr = \int_{r_1}^{r_2} mr\omega^2 \, dr$. Use the fact that $l = mr^2\omega$ is constant in order to integrate. Is the result for W valid only if the force is increased slowly?

(c) Suppose the initial conditions are the same, but instead of the ideal string passing through the hole it is fixed to a peg projecting out of the table. As the block rotates, the string becomes wound around the peg, continuously decreasing the radius of the orbit. At the instant that $r_2 = r_1/2$, determine K_2, v_2, ω_2, T_2. Is the string doing work on the block?

18. (a) A cylinder of radius R rotates about a fixed axis. A string is fastened to the cylinder and wound around it several times. The string is pulled at right angles to the cylinder axis by a constant force $\mathbf{F}$. As the cylinder speeds up the string will have to be pulled faster to keep the force constant. At the instant the string is moving with velocity $\mathbf{v}$, the rate at which the force $\mathbf{F}$ is doing work is $P = \mathbf{F} \cdot \mathbf{v} = Fv$. Express this in terms of the torque τ exerted by the force $\mathbf{F}$ and the instantaneous angular speed ω of the cylinder.

(b) An automobile engine is turning over at 1200 rpm and developing 60 hp. What is the torque on the crankshaft?

(c) The torque constant for a rod of length L and radius R is $C = \pi G R^4/2L$ where G is the shear modulus of the material. For steel $G \sim 1.7 \times 10^9$ lb/ft². What is the torque constant for a steel shaft 1 ft in length and of 1-in. diameter? By how much would the shaft be twisted if rotating at 1200 rpm and transmitting 60 hp?

21

MECHANICAL ENERGY OF
A PARTICLE

We said that the concept of energy is particularly useful because it is a conserved quantity, but so far this aspect of its usefulness has not been apparent. The work–energy relation $W_{1\to2} = K_2 - K_1$ for a particle tells us that if $W_{1\to2} = 0$, $K_2 = K_1$; the kinetic energy of the particle is constant, or conserved over the interval for which $W_{1\to2} = 0$. If this is all there were to conservation of energy it would not be a very exciting or important notion. It is when we come to think about describing systems of interacting particles that the idea of conservation of energy becomes useful.

A similar situation existed in applying the impulse–momentum relation $\mathbf{J} = \int \mathbf{F}\, dt = \mathbf{p}_2 - \mathbf{p}_1$. Applied to a single particle, this states that if the impulse on the particle is zero over some interval of time, its momentum is constant in this interval. However, this result follows directly from $\mathbf{F} = m\mathbf{a}$; if $\mathbf{F} = 0$, $\mathbf{a} = 0$ and $\mathbf{v}$ (or $\mathbf{p}$) is constant. The conservation of momentum principle only became useful when we looked at systems of particles. In situations such as collisions where it can be assumed that there is a negligible external impulse on the system over some interval, the total momentum $\mathbf{P}$ of the system is constant over the interval. The momentum $\mathbf{P}_1 = \sum \mathbf{p}_i$ at the start is the same as the momentum $\mathbf{P}_2 = \sum \mathbf{p}_i$ at the end of the interval. Due to internal interactions in the system the momentum of an individual particle $\mathbf{p}_i$ may change in the interval, but the sum $\sum \mathbf{p}_i$ is constant.

The impulse–momentum relation $\mathbf{J} = \int \mathbf{F}\, dt = \mathbf{p}_2 - \mathbf{p}_1$ for a particle also applies to a system of interacting particles $\mathbf{J}_{\text{ext}} = \int \mathbf{F}_{\text{ext}}\, dt = \mathbf{P}_2 - \mathbf{P}_1$, **but the work–energy relation $W_{1\to2} = K_2 - K_1$ does not.** Think of a system of interacting particles that are all released from rest at the same instant. After release there are no external forces on the system, $\mathbf{F}_{\text{ext}} = 0$, and the work done on the system $W = \int \mathbf{F}_{\text{ext}} \cdot d\mathbf{r} = 0$ for any interval. The total kinetic energy of the system $K = \sum K_i$ since kinetic energy is a scalar quantity. Initially each $K_i = 0$ and the sum $K_1 = 0$. Due to their mutual interaction the particles will accelerate in

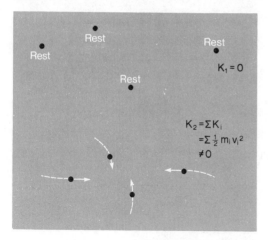

A system of interacting particles released from rest will acquire kinetic energy.

some way, and therefore after an interval the sum $K_2 \neq 0$. Therefore the work–energy relation cannot be applied to the system.

Conservation of energy for a system of particles does not emerge from the work-energy relation in the same way that conservation of momentum emerged from the impulse-momentum equation. This is because the internal momentum of a system cancels out, but internal kinetic energy does not.

What we want to do is define another kind of energy, in addition to kinetic energy, in such a way that we can say the total energy of a system is constant if there is no work done on the system by external forces. We will see that the kind of energy we can define depends on the kind of interaction force there is between the particles of the system. We will call the energy potential energy, but unlike kinetic energy (which is always $\frac{1}{2}mv^2$) there are different kinds of potential energy, depending on the force.

There are some subtleties in the development of the concept of potential energy, as you will see. Perhaps this is one reason why classical mechanics developed for two centuries after Newton without the idea of conservation of energy, even though in Newton's time a property mv^2 called **vis viva** was recognized as being a useful quantity in describing motion.

We said that the introduction of potential energy is necessary in order to have conservation of energy for **systems** of particles, but we are going to begin by looking at the motion of a **single** particle, and see if we can find some quantity that remains constant as the particle moves.

Remember that the forces acting on a particle have their origin in other bodies, due to the gravitational or electrical or nuclear interaction between the particle and the particles of the other bodies. We find that under certain conditions it is possible to describe the effects of other bodies (the surroundings) by defining a property **of the particle** called potential energy.

After we establish how to define potential energy for a single particle, we will come back in a later chapter to the question of energy of a system of particles. We are going to spend some time on the notion of potential energy of a single particle, and this is necessary because there is no such thing as a single particle!

ELASTIC POTENTIAL ENERGY

Recall the example of the block on a smooth track, connected by an ideal spring to a fixed support. Think about the work done on the block by the spring as the block moves between any two displacements x_1 and x_2, its corresponding speeds being v_1 and v_2.

$$W_{1\to2} = \int_{x_1}^{x_2} \mathbf{F}_s \cdot d\mathbf{r} = -\int_{x_1}^{x_2} kx\,dx = \left[-\frac{kx^2}{2}\right]_{x_1}^{x_2} = \tfrac{1}{2}kx_1^2 - \tfrac{1}{2}kx_2^2$$

$$= K_2 - K_1 = \tfrac{1}{2}mv_2^2 - \tfrac{1}{2}mv_1^2$$

This can be rearranged to give

$$\tfrac{1}{2}mv_1^2 + \tfrac{1}{2}kx_1^2 = \tfrac{1}{2}mv_2^2 + \tfrac{1}{2}kx_2^2$$

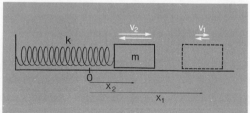

This shows that the quantity $(\tfrac{1}{2}mv^2 + \tfrac{1}{2}kx^2)$ is the same for the two positions of the block and, since these were any two positions, that this quantity is the same for any position; it is an invariant for the motion, or a constant of the motion. We can call this quantity "energy."

Are x and v related?

The energy **of what?** The term $\tfrac{1}{2}mv^2$ is the kinetic energy of the block, and the term $\tfrac{1}{2}kx^2$ depends on the spring. Remember we showed that in extending a spring an amount x, work $W = \tfrac{1}{2}kx^2$ had to be done by an external force, so we can say that energy is stored in the spring, potentially available, and define the **elastic potential energy** of the spring by

$$U(x) = \tfrac{1}{2}kx^2$$

where $U(x)$ has been written to emphasize that the elastic potential energy U is a function of the spring elongation x.

Now if we define the **mechanical energy** E of the spring–block system by

$$E = K + U = \tfrac{1}{2}mv^2 + \tfrac{1}{2}kx^2$$

we can say that the mechanical energy of the block–spring system is constant.

Assigning the elastic potential energy to the spring seems reasonable here, but think about the motion of a particle that is acted upon by a restoring force $F = -kx$, **but there is no spring.** A spring is a macroscopic device, with some useful practical applications, but its main interest in the study of physics is as a model. Analysis of the mass–spring system helps us to visualize and understand simple harmonic motion, the motion that occurs whenever there is a restoring force proportional to displacement. Whenever a particle is displaced a small amount from a position of stable equilibrium, this is the kind of motion that will result. For example, an atom in a crystal lattice in a solid can be considered to vibrate about its lattice site with this motion. It is held in place by the electro-magnetic interaction with other atoms, and this interaction provides the restoring force if it is displaced.

Idealized crystal lattice.

If there is no spring (with spring constant k), but simply a force $F = -kx$ (where k is a force constant), acting on the particle, we can as before define the

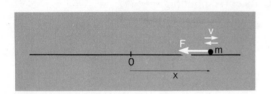

A restoring force does not require a spring.

elastic potential energy $U = \frac{1}{2}kx^2$ and mechanical energy

$$E = K + U$$
$$= \frac{1}{2}mv^2 + \frac{1}{2}kx^2$$

Now there is no spring to assign the energy U to, and we say arbitrarily that **the particle** has potential energy U and total mechanical energy $E = K + U$.

The assignment of energy to some entity is a matter of definition. We want to define energies in such a way that the total energy of a system is constant; in a way, keeping track of the energy then becomes a kind of bookkeeping, and the books must always balance. As in bookkeeping, there is at the outset some choice as to what you label things—you may decide to put an item under "overhead," or "operating expense"—the important thing is not to put it under both.

For a spring–block system the quantity $\frac{1}{2}kx^2$ can be considered to be a property of the spring, because it involves the spring constant k and the spring extension x. On the other hand, it depends on the displacement x of the block, so we can instead call it a property of the block for the particular situation where the block is subject to a restoring force of force constant k. Thus we can refer to the **elastic potential energy of the block,** where this energy, unlike its kinetic energy, depends on its environment. Potential energy of an object in general has to do with **the location of the object relative to something else.**

The equation of motion $\mathbf{F} = m\mathbf{a}$, or its integrated form $W_{1\to2} = K_2 - K_1$, describes the effect of the surroundings on the block in terms of resultant force $\mathbf{F}$ or the work this force does on the block $W = \int \mathbf{F} \cdot d\mathbf{r}$. The equation $E = K + U$ is also an equation of motion, where the effect of the surroundings is described by the potential energy U. **The potential energy depends on the kind of force acting.**

Example: You can see that the equation of motion

$$E = K + U = \frac{1}{2}mv^2 + \frac{1}{2}kx^2$$

gives the equation of motion for simple harmonic motion we derived before. Differentiate with respect to time.

$$\frac{dE}{dt} = \frac{1}{2}m\left(2v\frac{dv}{dt}\right) + \frac{1}{2}k\left(2x\frac{dx}{dt}\right)$$

Since E is constant, $\dfrac{dE}{dt} = 0$. Also $v = \dfrac{dx}{dt}$, $a = \dfrac{dv}{dt} = \dfrac{d^2x}{dt^2}$ so the equation is

$$mv\frac{d^2x}{dt^2} + kxv = 0 \qquad \text{or} \qquad \frac{d^2x}{dt^2} + \frac{k}{m}x = 0$$

This is the differential equation of simple harmonic motion, with angular frequency $\omega = \sqrt{k/m}$.

GRAVITATIONAL POTENTIAL ENERGY

We have emphasized that we label the kind of potential energy we assign to a
particle by the kind of force acting on the particle. Look at another example.
A particle moves near the earth's surface under conditions where the only force
that does work on it is the constant force of gravity $\mathbf{w} = m\mathbf{g}$. The particle may

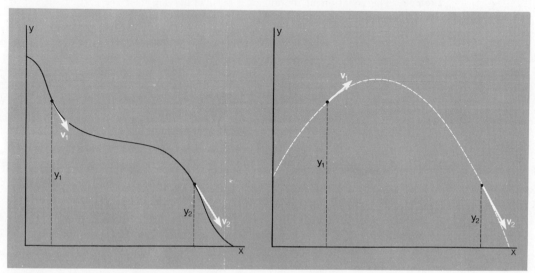

Similar energy considerations apply to a particle sliding
on a smooth surface, or moving as a projectile.

be sliding on a smooth surface, or moving as a projectile. In a co-ordinate
system with y-axis vertically upward the force $\mathbf{w}$ has only a y-component $w_y = -mg$. As the particle moves from a y-displacement y_1 to y_2, its speed changing
from v_1 to v_2, the work done by gravity is

$$W = \int \mathbf{w} \cdot d\mathbf{r} = -mg \int_{y_1}^{y_2} dy = -mg(y_2 - y_1)$$
$$= K_2 - K_1 = \tfrac{1}{2}mv_2^2 - \tfrac{1}{2}mv_1^2$$

This can be rearranged to give

$$\tfrac{1}{2}mv_1^2 + mgy_1 = \tfrac{1}{2}mv_2^2 + mgy_2$$

showing that the quantity $(\tfrac{1}{2}mv^2 + mgy)$ is constant as the particle moves, since
the two points were any two points on the path. Again we can call this quantity
the mechanical energy E of the particle if we define

$$U(y) = mgy$$

as the **gravitational potential energy of the particle.** Note that this quantity involves the mass m of the particle, the magnitude of the acceleration g that any object has near the earth's surface due to the earth's gravity, and the height y that the particle is above an arbitrary horizontal plane in the earth frame of reference. Thus this is a joint property of the particle and the earth, but we call it a property of the particle—again a matter of bookkeeping.

Example: The equation of motion of a particle moving near the earth's surface in terms of energy is

$$E = K + U = \tfrac{1}{2}mv^2 + mgy = \text{constant}$$

Differentiating with respect to time gives

$$\frac{dE}{dt} = mv\frac{dv}{dt} + mg\frac{dy}{dt} = 0$$

or

$$v\frac{dv}{dt} + g\frac{dy}{dt} = 0$$

This time we *cannot* say $v = \dfrac{dy}{dt}$ as in the one-dimensional example of the particle vibrating in simple harmonic motion. In general $v = [(dx/dt)^2 + (dy/dt)^2 + (dz/dt)^2]^{1/2}$. Only in the special case of a particle moving along a straight line parallel to the y-axis so that $dx/dt = dz/dt = 0$ can we say $v = dy/dt$, and then the equation of motion becomes $dv/dt + g = 0$. In this special case the particle has an acceleration $a = a_y = dv/dt = -g$, an acceleration g downwards.

CONSERVATIVE FORCES

We have formed two different ways of saying the same thing. As a particle moves from point 1 to point 2 we can say that the work done by the force of gravity is $W_{1 \to 2} = -mg(y_2 - y_1)$, and using the work–energy relation this is equal to the change in kinetic energy $K_2 - K_1$. Equivalently we can say that the total mechanical energy $E = K + U = \tfrac{1}{2}mv^2 + mgy$ is constant, so at the points 1 and 2

$$E_1 = E_2 \quad \text{or} \quad K_1 + U_1 = K_2 + U_2$$
$$K_2 - K_1 = U_1 - U_2$$
$$= mg(y_1 - y_2)$$

The change in potential energy over the interval of $1 \to 2$ is

$$U_2 - U_1 = mg(y_2 - y_1) = -W_{1 \to 2}$$

What is different about the two approaches? The essential thing is that we have introduced an **instantaneous** property of the particle, U, instead of

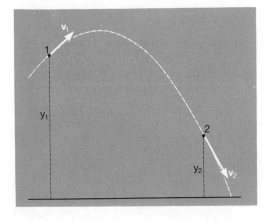

Total mechanical energy constant.

the quantity W, defined over an interval. Since W depends on the instantaneous force $\mathbf{F}$ on the particle, $W_{1\to2} = \int_1^2 \mathbf{F}\cdot d\mathbf{r}$, what difference does this make? The difference arises because while you can always calculate the work done by a force, you *cannot* always define a corresponding potential energy. It is possible to define a potential energy **only if the work done by the force is independent of the path.** Remember that $W_{1\to2} = \int_1^2 \mathbf{F}\cdot d\mathbf{r}$ is a line integral, its value depending on the path of the particle as it moves from point 1 to point 2. For certain kinds of forces, the value does not depend on the path, but only on the end points. Such forces are called **conservative forces,** because then it is possible to define a potential energy and introduce conservation of mechanical energy.

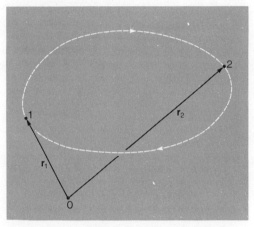

To see why it is necessary to have work done independent of path in order to be able to define potential energy, think of a particle moving in a closed path. Points 1 and 2, specified by displacements $\mathbf{r}_1$ and $\mathbf{r}_2$ from a fixed point O in a frame of reference, are any two points on the path. If the resultant force on the particle is $\mathbf{F}$, the work done on it as it moves from 1 to 2 is $W_{1\to2} = \int_{\mathbf{r}_1}^{\mathbf{r}_2} \mathbf{F}\cdot d\mathbf{r}$, and the work done on it as it moves from 2 to 1 is

$$W_{2\to1} = \int_{\mathbf{r}_2}^{\mathbf{r}_1} \mathbf{F}\cdot d\mathbf{r} = -\int_{\mathbf{r}_1}^{\mathbf{r}_2} \mathbf{F}\cdot d\mathbf{r} \overset{?}{=} -W_{1\to2}$$

Particle in a closed path.

In general $W_{2\to1}$ is *not* equal to $-W_{1\to2}$, because $\int_{\mathbf{r}_1}^{\mathbf{r}_2} \mathbf{F}\cdot d\mathbf{r}$ depends on the path, and therefore the net work done by the force over the closed loop is $W_{1\to2} + W_{2\to1} \neq 0$. Then it would make no sense to try to define a total energy $E = K + U$ for the particle that was a constant of the motion. However, if the work done is independent of the path, the net work done over the closed loop is zero, and we can define $E = K + U$ as a constant of the motion. At the points 1 and 2,

$$E_1 = E_2 \quad \text{or} \quad K_1 + U_1 = K_2 + U_2$$

or
$$K_2 - K_1 = -(U_2 - U_1)$$

By the work–energy relation, $W_{1\to2} = \int_{\mathbf{r}_1}^{\mathbf{r}_2} \mathbf{F}\cdot d\mathbf{r} = K_2 - K_1$

so
$$U_2 - U_1 = -W_{1\to2} = -\int_{\mathbf{r}_1}^{\mathbf{r}_2} \mathbf{F}\cdot d\mathbf{r}$$

The change in potential energy associated with a force is the negative of the work done by the force.

This shows how to define potential energy in general, but note that it can only be done if the force **F** is a conservative force, which means that

$$W_{1\to2} = \int_{r_1}^{r_2} \mathbf{F}\cdot d\mathbf{r}$$

is independent of path, or equivalently

$$\oint \mathbf{F}\cdot d\mathbf{r} = 0$$

where $\oint$ is a symbol meaning integration around a closed path.

THE NON-CONSERVATIVE FORCE OF FRICTION

So far we have defined potential energy for two kinds of forces, the constant force **w** due to gravity near the earth surface, and the one-dimensional restoring force $F = -kx$. The non-conservative force with which we will be concerned mostly is the force of friction; since this force **f** always opposes motion, **f** and $d\mathbf{r}$ are always in opposite directions, $\int \mathbf{f}\cdot d\mathbf{r}$ is always a negative quantity, and it is impossible to have $\oint \mathbf{f}\cdot d\mathbf{r} = 0$. For any particle or system where there are frictional forces acting it is impossible to have conservation of mechanical energy. This does *not* mean that we cannot use the idea of potential energy associated with the other forces acting.

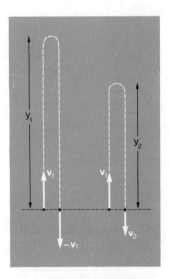

If air resistance is considered, $y_2 < y_1$ and $v_2 < v_1$.

Think, for example, of a particle shot straight up near the earth with an initial velocity v_1. Neglecting air friction we can say that it will rise to a height y_1 above its initial position, where

$$\tfrac{1}{2}mv_1^2 = mgy_1$$

This assumes conservation of mechanical energy

$$\text{Loss in } K = \text{Gain in } U$$

When the particle returns to its initial position, there will have been no net change in U, and therefore no net change in K, and its speed is again v_1.

If air friction is considered, the particle will lose mechanical energy on the way up, and will come to rest at a height $y_2 < y_1$. At this point the mechanical energy is

$$mgy_2 = \tfrac{1}{2}mv_1^2 - (\text{loss in mechanical energy due to friction on way up})$$

On the way down the particle will continue to lose mechanical energy. When it reaches its initial position the net change in potential energy will be zero, and

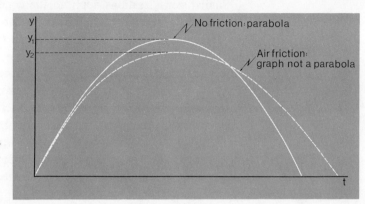

Displacement–time graphs for a projectile shot vertically upward.

the speed will be less than the initial value, $v_2 < v_1$.

$$\tfrac{1}{2}mv_2^2 = \tfrac{1}{2}mv_1^2 - \text{(loss in mechanical energy due to friction on round trip)}$$

Note that the speed at any point on the downward path is less than the speed at the same point on the upward path. The displacement–time graph is symmetric (a parabola) in the absence of friction, but is not symmetric if friction is appreciable.

If the force of friction is constant the work done by this force is the same on the way up as on the way down, and the round trip loss is twice the one-way loss in mechanical energy; we looked at an example earlier, for a block sliding up and down an inclined plane. However, if the frictional force depends on the speed, as it does in general, the energy loss on the way up will be greater than it is on the way down.

When we speak of "energy loss" here we mean of course a loss in the kind of energy we have defined, mechanical energy. We can maintain the concept of conservation of energy by defining a new kind of energy to take care of the "loss," and you know that we do this by defining thermal energy. We will come back to this later, but we should note here that we will have to distinguish between macroscopic systems (made up of very large numbers of particles) and microscopic systems (individual particles, such as atoms). The concept of thermal energy applies to a macroscopic system. At the microscopic level we identify the kinetic energy of individual atoms as giving rise to what we call thermal energy at the macroscopic level. Thus **the kind of energy defined depends on the kind of system considered.** At the macroscopic level keeping the books on energy balanced requires the definition of many different kinds of energy, such as thermal energy and chemical energy. At the microscopic level fewer kinds of energy are necessary, in order to keep the books straight. Chemical energy for example turns out to be a combination of kinetic energy of electrons and electric potential energy of atoms.

Similar considerations apply to the concept of force. At the macroscopic level we use contact forces and frictional forces, but we have stated that the only fundamental forces are the gravitational, the electromagnetic and the nuclear interactions. From the point of view of classical mechanics, all the fundamental forces are conservative, and therefore a potential energy can be associated with each. If we confine our attention to systems involving only fundamental forces, then, we can say that there really is no such thing as a non-conservative force, and mechanical energy is conserved. It is only at the macroscopic level that we must be concerned about the non-conservative force of friction. However, all of our direct experience is with macroscopic systems, where mechanical energy is not conserved and therefore where we need the concept of friction.

THE RELATION BETWEEN POTENTIAL ENERGY AND CONSERVATIVE FORCE

We have seen how potential energy U can be defined in such a way that the total mechanical energy $E = K + U$ of a particle is conserved. Now we will explore the relation between force and potential energy more fully.

We showed that when a conservative force $\mathbf{F}$ acts on a particle a potential energy U can be associated with the particle, defined by

$$U_2 - U_1 = -\int_{\mathbf{r}_1}^{\mathbf{r}_2} \mathbf{F} \cdot d\mathbf{r}$$

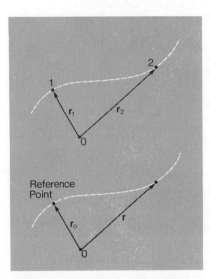

This defines only **differences** in potential energy, which means there is an arbitrary zero for potential energy. We can set $U_1 = 0$ and call U_2 **the** potential energy U of the particle, meaning its potential energy with respect to the arbitrary position 1. The potential energy of a particle at a point is the negative of the work done in moving the particle from an arbitrary reference position to the point.

$$U(\mathbf{r}) = -\int_{\mathbf{r}_0}^{\mathbf{r}} \mathbf{F} \cdot d\mathbf{r} \quad \text{(any path from } \mathbf{r}_0 \text{ to } \mathbf{r})$$

Note that $U(\mathbf{r})$ means that U is a function of **position** in the frame of reference, specified by $\mathbf{r}$, but U is not a vector quantity. In a particular co-ordinate system $U(\mathbf{r})$ means $U(x,y,z)$.

We have had two examples: (1) $U(y) = mgy$ for a particle near the earth surface, acted on by the constant force $\mathbf{w} = m\mathbf{g}$. The frame of reference is the earth, and y is the vertical displacement with respect to an arbitrary fixed horizontal reference

Since only potential energy difference is defined, it is necessary to choose an arbitrary reference point in order to talk about "the" potential energy.

plane in this frame. (2) $U(x) = \frac{1}{2}kx^2$ for a particle moving in one-dimension, acted on by a restoring force $\mathbf{F} = -k\mathbf{x}$. The frame of reference is one in which the center of force is at rest, and $\mathbf{x}$ is the displacement with respect to this point.

In the first example the force is constant, independent of position, and in the second we know the force as a function of position $F(x)$. This suggests the following possibility: we have seen that potential energy is a function of position $U(\mathbf{r})$, so perhaps a conservative force is one that is a function of position $\mathbf{F}(\mathbf{r})$; this would mean that the force on a particle is uniquely specified at any point in the frame of reference. It turns out that in one-dimension this is the case; a conservative force is one that is a unique function of position $F(x)$. However, in three-dimensional situations this is not true; the fact that the force is a unique function of position $\mathbf{F}(\mathbf{r})$ is a necessary but not sufficient condition that it be a conservative force. That is, a force must be a unique function of position in order to be conservative, but the fact that it is does not guarantee that it is conservative. We cannot specify, therefore, whether or not a force is conservative except by the criterion $\oint \mathbf{F} \cdot d\mathbf{r} = 0$, or the equivalent statement that $\int_1^2 \mathbf{F} \cdot d\mathbf{r}$ is independent of path.

There are certain difficulties that arise in relating U and $\mathbf{F}$. This is because one is a scalar quantity, the other a vector, and in general one vector quantity is equivalent to three scalars. These difficulties are not apparent if we confine our attention to one-dimensional situations, because then we are interested only in a single component of the force $\mathbf{F}$.

We have seen how to find U if we know $\mathbf{F}$. Can we go the other way, and find $\mathbf{F}$ if we know U? First think about one-dimensional situations, where $\mathbf{F}$ can be treated as a scalar quantity $F(x)$. For any two points the definition of potential energy gives

$$U(x_2) - U(x_1) = -\int_{x_1}^{x_2} F\, dx$$

Potential energy in one dimension.

The change in potential energy dU corresponding to an infinitesimal displacement dx is therefore

$$dU = -F\, dx \qquad \text{or} \qquad F = -\frac{dU}{dx}$$

Note that

$$-\int_{x_1}^{x_2} F\, dx = +\int_{x_1}^{x_2} \frac{dU}{dx}\, dx = \int_{x_1}^{x_2} dU = U(x_2) - U(x_1)$$

Elastic potential energy.

The force corresponding to the elastic potential energy $U = \frac{1}{2}kx^2$ is

$$F = -\frac{dU}{dx} = -kx$$

as it should be.

The force corresponding to the gravitational potential energy $U = mgy$ is

$$F = -\frac{dU}{dy} = -mg$$

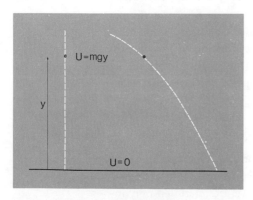

Gravitational potential energy; motion not in one dimension.

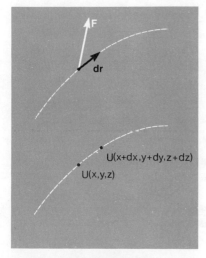

Work done = −(change in potential energy).

How did we know we should differentiate with respect to y? This is a valid result for a particle moving in one-dimension, in a co-ordinate system with y-axis upward. The force $\mathbf{w} = m\mathbf{g}$ has a component $-mg$ in the y-direction. However, the result applies to a particle with any trajectory near the earth's surface. Why?

In one dimension, the relation $F = -dU/dx$ tells us that the force F depends on the rate of change of potential energy U with position; that is, the value of F at a point depends not only on the value of U at the point, but depends also on its value at nearby points. In three dimensions, U is a function of position $U(x,y,z)$ and its rate of change of position may be different in different directions. How can we form a vector from this scalar quantity? A clue is found by looking at the scalar product $\mathbf{F}\cdot d\mathbf{r}$ used to calculate work done. In a particular co-ordinate system (x,y,z) the vector $\mathbf{F}$ has components (F_x, F_y, F_z), the infinitesimal displacement $d\mathbf{r}$ has components (dx, dy, dz), and

$$\mathbf{F}\cdot d\mathbf{r} = F_x\,dx + F_y\,dy + F_z\,dz$$

The infinitesimal change in potential energy dU in the interval is

$$dU = dU_x + dU_y + dU_z$$

$$= \left(\frac{\partial U}{\partial x}\right)dx + \left(\frac{\partial U}{\partial y}\right)dy + \left(\frac{\partial U}{\partial z}\right)dz$$

where $(\partial U/\partial x)$ is the rate of change of U with position in the x-direction. It is written $\partial U/\partial x$ rather than dU/dx because it is a **partial derivative** of the function U; its value is found by differentiating $U(x,y,z)$ with respect to x, treating y and z as constants. Sometimes this is emphasized by writing $(\partial U/\partial x)_{y,z}$. The term $(\partial U/\partial x)\,dx$ in dU is the rate of change of U with x, multiplied by the change in x, or the change dU_x in the x-component of U.

The relation between the change in U and the work done is $dU = -\mathbf{F}\cdot d\mathbf{r}$ and therefore the components are related by

$$F_x = -\frac{\partial U}{\partial x} \qquad F_y = -\frac{\partial U}{\partial y} \qquad F_z = -\frac{\partial U}{\partial z}$$

The force $\mathbf{F}$ corresponding to the potential U is then determined

$$\mathbf{F} = F_x\mathbf{i} + F_y\mathbf{j} + F_z\mathbf{k}$$
$$= -\mathbf{i}\frac{\partial U}{\partial x} - \mathbf{j}\frac{\partial U}{\partial y} - \mathbf{k}\frac{\partial U}{\partial z} \qquad \text{(i,j,k unit vectors)}$$
$$= -\operatorname{grad} U = -\nabla U$$

For notation we have introduced the **gradient operator** grad or ∇ (read "del")

$$\operatorname{grad} \equiv \nabla \equiv +\mathbf{i}\frac{\partial}{\partial x} + \mathbf{j}\frac{\partial}{\partial y} + \mathbf{k}\frac{\partial}{\partial z}$$

It is an instruction how to operate on a scalar quantity to produce a vector quantity. It can be shown that the direction of the vector produced is that of the maximum rate of increase of the scalar.

We have stated how to find $\mathbf{F}$ given U in a particular Cartesian co-ordinate system, but remember that the result is independent of the co-ordinate system. The direction of the vector $\mathbf{F} = -\operatorname{grad} U$ is that of the maximum rate of **decrease** of the scalar U.

In the example of a particle moving near the earth surface, $U = mgy$. The potential energy is independent of the x– and z–co-ordinates, and therefore the corresponding force has a y-component only

$$\mathbf{F} = -\mathbf{j}\frac{\partial U}{\partial y} = -\mathbf{j}mg$$

This force is downward, the direction of the maximum rate of decrease of U.

EXACT AND INEXACT DIFFERENTIALS

We have said that the work done by a force is $W_{1\to2} = \int \mathbf{F}\cdot d\mathbf{r}$, and that if the force is conservative there is a related potential energy U such that $U_2 - U_1 = -W_{1\to2} = -\int \mathbf{F}\cdot d\mathbf{r}$, or such that $dU = -\mathbf{F}\cdot d\mathbf{r}$. We have avoided using the

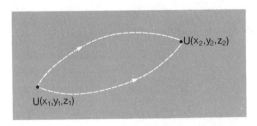

There is no function of position W(x,y,z).

notation dW for the work done over an infinitesimal interval; we have *not* used $dW = \mathbf{F} \cdot d\mathbf{r}$, and $dU = -dW$. This is because in general there is no function of position $W(x,y,z)$ of which dW is the differential. In general the work done by a force depends on the path, and not just on the end points. Only if the force is conservative does the work depend only on the end points, and then we can define the potential energy U, a function of position $U(x,y,z)$.

The mathematical way of distinguishing between these two kinds of quantities is to call dU an **exact** differential and dW an **inexact** differential. For notation it may be written dW to show that it is different; dW means the work done over an infinitesimal interval, but that there is not a corresponding function W.

$$\int_1^2 dU = U_2 - U_1 \qquad : \text{result independent of path}$$

$$\int_1^2 dW \neq W_2 - W_1 \qquad : \text{result depends on path}$$

CENTRAL FORCES

In an earlier chapter we stated what is meant by a **central force** and showed that the angular momentum of a particle with respect to the center of force is conserved. A central force is one that always acts directly toward (or directly away from) a fixed point O in the frame of reference, so that the force $\mathbf{F}$ and the radius vector $\mathbf{r}$ are parallel or anti-parallel vectors. The magnitude of F may depend on

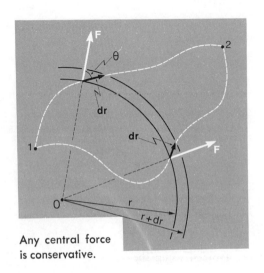

Any central force is conservative.

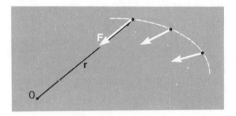

A central force.

the distance r in any way ($F \propto r$, or $F \propto 1/r^2$, etc.).

Any central force is conservative. To see this, think of a particle moving from point 1 to point 2 along any path. Think of the particle as its **distance** from point O changes from r to $r + dr$. Its actual displacement $d\mathbf{r}$ will depend on its path, but the work done $F \cdot d\mathbf{r}$ does not because

$$\mathbf{F} \cdot d\mathbf{r} = F \, dr \cos \theta = F \times (\text{projection of } d\mathbf{r} \text{ in the } \mathbf{F} \text{ direction})$$

The magnitude F is the same at distance r for any path, and the projection of $d\mathbf{r}$ in the $\mathbf{F}$ (or radial) direction is the same for any path, so $\int_1^2 \mathbf{F} \cdot d\mathbf{r}$ is independent of the path and the force is conservative.

It can also be seen that for a central force the potential energy of a particle at all points equidistant from the center of force O is the same. Points 1 and 2 are any two points equidistant from O: $r_1 = r_2$. The work done by F as the particle is moved along the circular arc joining them is 0 because $\mathbf{F}$ and $d\mathbf{r}$ are always at right angles, and since the force is conservative this is true for any path.

$$U(r_2) - U(r_1) = - \int_{r_1}^{r_2} \mathbf{F} \cdot d\mathbf{r} = 0 \qquad \text{if} \qquad r_1 = r_2$$

This means that the potential energy, which in general is a function of position $U(\mathbf{r})$, for a central force is a function of r only, $U(r)$.

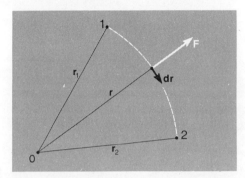

For a central force
$U(\mathbf{r}) = U(r)$.

POTENTIAL ENERGY FOR AN INVERSE-SQUARE FORCE

The form of $U(r)$ will depend on the kind of central force. The most important kind of central force is the inverse-square force of the gravitational or electrostatic interaction. The gravitational force of attraction between two particles depends on their masses

$$F = G \frac{m_1 m_2}{r^2}$$

where G is the gravitational constant. The electrostatic force between two particles depends on their electric charges

$$F = K \frac{q_1 q_2}{r^2}$$

where K is the Coulomb constant. This force may be attractive or repulsive, depending on the sign of the charges.

At present we are considering the motion of a single particle with respect to a fixed center of force. In order to show both its magnitude and its direc-

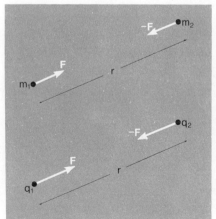

The gravitational and electrostatic interactions are inverse-square central forces.

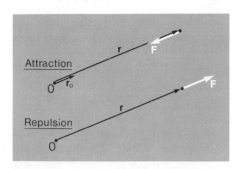

$F = Cr/r^3 = Cr_0/r^2$; for attraction C is negative, for repulsion C is positive.

The change in potential energy is the same for both paths.

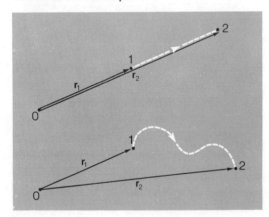

tion, an inverse-square central force can be written

$$F = \frac{C}{r^3} r \quad \text{or} \quad F = \frac{C}{r^2} r_0$$

where r_0 is a unit vector in the r direction and C is a constant. If C is positive, F and r are in the same direction and the force is repulsive. If C is negative, F and r are in opposite directions and the force is attractive.

We will calculate the change in potential energy $U_2 - U_1$ as a particle is moved from displacement r_1 to displacement r_2. We take r_1 and r_2 in the same direction, and use as a path the straight line joining them. This makes the calculation simple, and we have already showed that for any central force the result depends only on the distances r_1 and r_2.

Along the straight radial path

$$F \cdot dr = \frac{C}{r^2} r_0 \cdot dr = \frac{C}{r^2} dr$$

since r_0 and dr are parallel vectors.

$$U_2 - U_1 = -\int_1^2 F \cdot dr = -\int_{r_1}^{r_2} \frac{C}{r^2} dr$$

$$= \left[\frac{C}{r} \right]_{r_1}^{r_2} = C \left(\frac{1}{r_2} - \frac{1}{r_1} \right)$$

It is usual to choose the arbitrary zero of potential energy for the particle far removed from the center O, that is to set $U_1 = 0$ for $r_1 = \infty$. Then the potential energy corresponding to the inverse-square force is

$$U(r) = \frac{C}{r}$$

We should be able to verify this result by finding the force using

$$F = -\text{grad } U$$

$$= -i \frac{\partial U}{\partial x} - j \frac{\partial U}{\partial y} - k \frac{\partial U}{\partial z}$$

and this is possible by using $r^2 = x^2 + y^2 + z^2$, but this is not the best way to do it. Since the potential energy is expressed in terms of the single co-ordinate r, it is more appropriate to express the gradient operator in terms of spherical co-ordinates. Then the only non-zero term will be the r-component

$$F_r = -\frac{\partial U}{\partial r} = -\left[\frac{\partial}{\partial r}\left(\frac{C}{r}\right)\right] = \frac{C}{r^2}$$

so the force is $\mathbf{F} = \mathbf{r}_0(C/r^2)$. The maximum rate of change of the potential energy U occurs in the radial direction.

MOTION IN THE GRAVITATIONAL FIELD OF A FIXED PARTICLE

As an example of how energy considerations may be used to analyze motion, we examine the motion of a particle of mass m under the influence of the gravitational force due to a particle of mass M at the fixed point O in the frame of reference.

$$\mathbf{F} = \frac{C}{r^2}\mathbf{r}_0 = -G\frac{Mm}{r^2}\mathbf{r}_0 \quad \text{so} \quad C = -GMm$$

The potential energy of mass m is

$$U(r) = -\frac{GMm}{r}$$

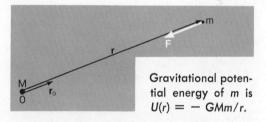

Gravitational potential energy of m is $U(r) = -\ GMm/r$.

This is always negative, because we have chosen the zero of potential energy at $r = \infty$. The work done by the gravitational force on m in bringing it up to a distance r from the fixed mass M is $+$ GMm/r, and the corresponding potential energy is $-GMm/r$.

If m is released at ∞ (i.e., far from M) it will fall toward M with continuously increasing speed v (and kinetic energy $\frac{1}{2}mv^2$) and continuously decreasing potential energy. Its mechanical energy $E = K + U = \frac{1}{2}mv^2 - GMm/r$ is **zero,** because at $r = \infty$, $v = 0$. The speed at any distance r is $v = \sqrt{2GM/r}$.

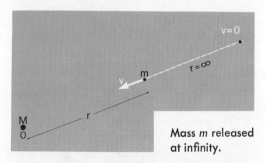

Mass m released at infinity.

If m is released at a finite distance r_1 from M, again it will fall straight toward M. Its mechanical energy is

$$E = \tfrac{1}{2}mv^2 - \frac{GMm}{r} = -\frac{GMm}{r_1}$$

Its speed at any distance r is

$$v = \sqrt{2GM\left(\frac{1}{r} - \frac{1}{r_1}\right)}$$

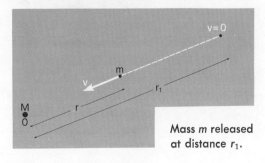

Mass m released at distance r_1.

Whenever the particle is released from rest, or projected initially straight toward M or away from M, its motion will be confined to one dimension. Then a knowledge of the single quantity E (determined by the initial conditions) is

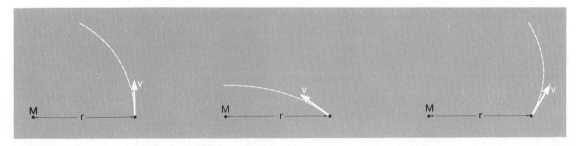

The same energy equation describes each case.

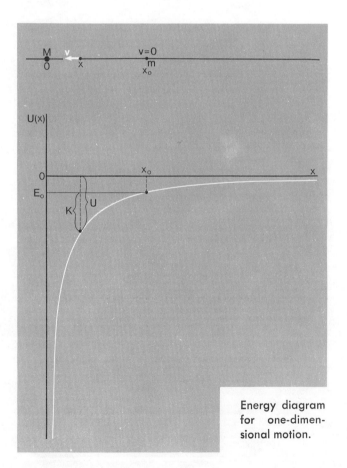

Energy diagram for one-dimensional motion.

all that is necessary to describe the motion completely.

This is not the case unless the motion is in one dimension. Each of the situations shown is described by the same energy equation

$$E = \tfrac{1}{2}mv^2 - \frac{GMm}{r} = \text{constant}$$

but the motions are not the same. A knowledge of the energy tells **something** about the motion, but not everything.

In one dimension the speed and displacement of the particle involve a single co-ordinate. Choosing a co-ordinate system with the x-axis along the line of the motion

$$r = x \quad \text{and} \quad v = \frac{dx}{dt}$$

$$E = K + U = \tfrac{1}{2}m\left(\frac{dx}{dt}\right)^2 - G\frac{Mm}{x}$$

This equation involves two variables x and t, and constants E, G, M, m. It can be solved to find x as a function of time $x(t)$, and the motion is therefore completely described.

A diagram in which $U(x)$ is plotted as a function of x, called an **energy diagram,** is useful in describing the motion. A particle released at x_0 has a constant total energy $E_0 = U(x_0) = -GMm/x_0$ shown by the horizontal line on the graph. At any other displacement $x < x_0$ the energy E_0 is partly kinetic and partly potential. In a way the particle can be thought of as sliding down the potential curve, but there are dangers in using this analogy, as we shall see later. Note that the kinetic energy K is always a positive quantity; U is negative, so $E = K + U$ can be positive or negative, but E is always less negative than U. The horizontal line representing the constant mechanical energy E only exists *above* the potential energy line in an energy diagram. If $E < 0$, the particle is **bound.** If $E \geq 0$ the particle is not bound; it can escape from the force center. If it is shot straight out from a distance r_0 from the center, what is the minimum speed it would have to be given in order not to fall back? This is the escape speed corresponding to this value of r.

For motion in general, in three dimensions, the speed v does not involve a single co-ordinate.

$$v^2 = \left(\frac{dx}{dt}\right)^2 + \left(\frac{dy}{dt}\right)^2 + \left(\frac{dz}{dt}\right)^2$$

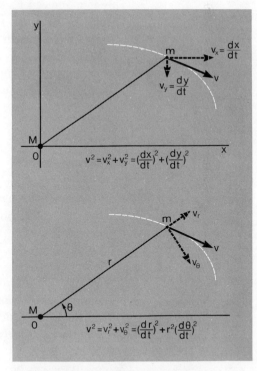

The complete description of motion requires a knowledge of $x(t), y(t), z(t)$ and the single energy condition is not sufficient to determine these. We showed before that motion under a central force is confined to a plane. Choosing a co-ordinate system with xy plane in the plane of the motion, the speed involves only two co-ordinates

$$v^2 = \left(\frac{dx}{dt}\right)^2 + \left(\frac{dy}{dt}\right)^2$$

Since the potential energy in a central force field involves the distance r from the center of force, it is more appropriate to use polar co-ordinates, expressing the speed v in terms of its radial component $v_r = dr/dt$, describing changes in **magnitude** of the displacement **r,** and its tangential component

$$v_\theta = r\omega = r\frac{d\theta}{dt}$$

describing changes in the **direction** of **r.** The energy equation

Components of velocity in Cartesian and in polar co-ordinates.

$$E = K + U = \tfrac{1}{2}m\left(\frac{dr}{dt}\right)^2 + \tfrac{1}{2}mr^2\left(\frac{d\theta}{dt}\right)^2 - \frac{GMm}{r}$$

involves the variables r, θ and t and constants, and is not sufficient to determine $r(t)$, $\theta(t)$.

However, we know another constant of the motion for motion under a central force. We know that the angular momentum of the particle with respect to the center of force O is constant.

$$\mathbf{L} = \mathbf{r} \times \mathbf{p} = m\mathbf{r} \times \mathbf{v} = \text{constant}$$

In magnitude $L = mrv_\theta = mr^2\omega = mr^2\,(d\theta/dt) = \text{constant}$. (Earlier we used l for the angular momentum of a single particle, and L for the angular momentum of a system of particles. We now change to use $\mathbf{L}$ for the single particle.)

There are now two equations involving the three variables r, θ and t, and this is sufficient to describe the motion completely.

The θ-term can be eliminated from the E-equation using the L-equation $L = mr^2\,(d\theta/dt)$.

$$E = \tfrac{1}{2}m \left(\frac{dr}{dt}\right)^2 + \tfrac{1}{2}\frac{L^2}{mr^2} - \frac{GMm}{r}$$

This equation can be solved to find $r(t)$, and the result used in the L-equation to find $\theta(t)$. We are not going to perform these integrations. What we are interested in at present is just what part of the total information is contained in the energy statement. In a later chapter we will use the L- and E-equations to eliminate the time t, and find r as a function of θ, $r(\theta)$, the equation of the path.

The energy equation involves the r–co-ordinate and its derivative dr/dt.

$$E = \tfrac{1}{2}m \left(\frac{dr}{dt}\right)^2 + U_1(r)$$

where
$$U_1(r) = \tfrac{1}{2}\frac{L^2}{mr^2} - \frac{GMm}{r}$$

$U_1(r)$ is called the **equivalent one-dimensional potential energy**, by analogy to the one-dimensional motion described by

$$E = \tfrac{1}{2}m \left(\frac{dx}{dt}\right)^2 + U(x) \qquad U(x) = -\frac{GMm}{x}$$

A graph of $U_1(r)$ can be used to visualize the limitations on the motion for different values of L and E.

The curve $U_1(r)$ corresponds to a particular value of L. The particle must move so that $E \geq U_1(r)$.

At the energy E_0, only one value of r is possible: $r = r_0 = \text{constant}$. Although $dr/dt = 0$ the kinetic energy is *not* zero.

$$E_0 = U_1(r_0) = \tfrac{1}{2}\frac{L^2}{mr_0^2} - \frac{GMm}{r_0} = K + U$$

The particle is moving in a circle of radius r_0.

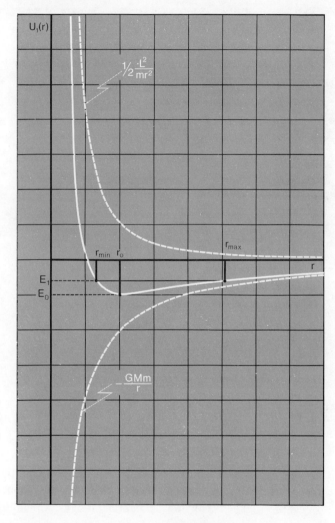

$U_1(r)$

$\frac{1}{2}\frac{\cdot L^2}{mr^2}$

r_{min} r_0

r_{max}

E_1
E_0

r

$-\frac{GMm}{r}$

Energy diagram for equivalent one-dimensional potential energy.

For a higher energy E_1, the particle moves in the region between the minimum and maximum distances r_{min} and r_{max} from the force center (diagram p. 524).

The term $\frac{1}{2}(L^2/mr^2)$ in the equivalent one-dimensional potential $U_1(r)$ is sometimes called the centrifugal potential energy. The force related to any potential energy in a central field is given by $F = -(dU/dr)$. Here $U_1 = \frac{1}{2}(L^2/mr^2) - GMm/r$ and the corresponding force would be

$$F_1 = -\frac{dU_1}{dr} = \frac{L^2}{mr^3} - \frac{GMm}{r^2} = mr\omega^2 - \frac{GMm}{r^2}$$

The second term is the inward force of gravity. The first term looks like an outward force of magnitude $mr\omega^2$. In the non-inertial frame of reference fixed

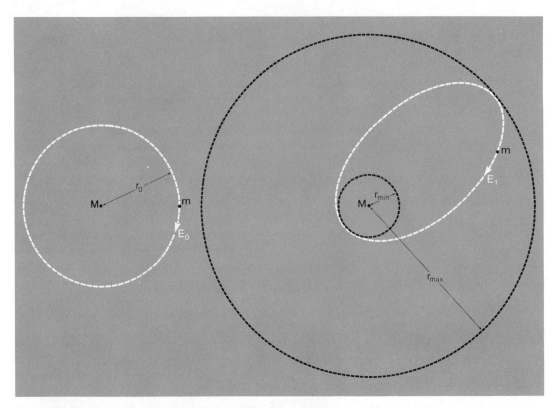

Orbits for the same angular momentum L but different
energies E_0 (circular orbit) and E_1 ($E_1 > E_0$).

to the moving particle m there is an outward force $mr\omega^2$, the inertial force called
the centrifugal force. However, in the inertial frame of reference in which M is
fixed, there is no such force on m—the only force on it is the gravitational force.
The "centrifugal potential energy" is really part of the kinetic energy, the part
due to change in direction of the radius vector $\mathbf{r}$. It is artificially considered
part of the potential energy so that the radial motion can be treated as a one-
dimensional motion.

Questions for discussion

1. Is the energy equation $E = K + U$ an instantaneous description of motion like the
   dynamic relation $\mathbf{F} = m\mathbf{a}$, or a description that applies to an interval like the impulse–momentum or work–energy relation?

2. When we say that a particle has a certain potential energy, this is its potential
   energy referred to some arbitrary position—that is, there is an arbitrary zero in
   potential energy. Is there an arbitrary zero in the definition of kinetic energy?

3. In an oscillating spring-and-block system, is it a legitimate question to ask whether it is **really** the block or the spring that has the potential energy?

4. In analyzing the motion of a single particle, is the energy equation $E = K + U$ more useful than the work–energy relation $W = K_2 - K_1$? Do these relations have the same physical content?

5. Several central forces in different directions act on the same particle. Is the resultant a conservative force?

6. Does the adjective "conservative" used to define certain kinds of forces have a political analogy?

7. Is the term "inexact differential" used for quantities like dW a well-chosen term? Would "indeterminate" be a better adjective?

8. Why is the vector operator ∇ called the gradient?

9. A spring is compressed between the jaws of a clamp. Clamp and spring are then dropped in acid. What happens to the elastic potential energy as they dissolve?

10. After Chapter 5 you were asked to think about a ball thrown straight up into the air and caught at the same height, and asked if the time spent in the air on the way up was greater than, the same as, or less than the time spent on the way down. What did you answer? Does the answer depend on whether or not you assume the frictional retarding force is independent of speed?

11. If a particle is to remain in orbit around a center of force, how must its kinetic energy be related to its potential energy?

Problems

1. The electron mass is 9.1×10^{-31} kg and the proton mass is 1836 times greater. An electron has a kinetic energy of 2 kev. What is its speed? What is the speed of a proton with the same energy? What is the speed of a proton with the same momentum as the electron?

2. In order for the classical expression for kinetic energy $K = \frac{1}{2}mv^2$ to be valid for a particle, the speed v cannot be close to the speed of light $c = 3 \times 10^8$ m/sec. For most purposes classical mechanics is sufficiently accurate for speeds up to $0.1c$. Determine the kinetic energy of **(a)** an electron, **(b)** a proton with $v = 0.1c$. Express the energies in electron volts. Through what potential differences, in volts, can **(c)** an electron, **(d)** a proton be accelerated, and still be treated classically?

3. A 10-ton freight car moving at 3 mph hits a spring buffer, compressing it 6 in., and then rebounds at the same speed. Calculate the impulse exerted on the car by the spring, the work done on the car by the spring, the elastic potential energy at the instant the spring is fully compressed, and the spring constant.

4. A seaside cliff is 400 ft high. A projectile is shot over the water from the top of the cliff, with an initial speed of 500 ft/sec. Neglecting air resistance, with what speed does it hit the water? Does the angle of projection matter? Is the maximum range on the water achieved for a projection angle of 45°?

5. A ball hangs from a fixed point by a cord 5 ft long. The ball is displaced sidways so it is 3 ft from the vertical line through its rest position, and released. Determine its speed when it reaches its rest position. What would you calculate its speed to

be if you assume this is a simple pendulum of length 5 ft in simple harmonic motion of amplitude 3 ft?

6. A spring with spring constant 800 n/m is vertical, its lower end fixed. A 2-kg ball is dropped from a point 1 m above the free end of the spring. Calculate the distance the ball falls before coming instantaneously to rest, and the elastic potential energy at this instant.

7. There is a coefficient of kinetic friction of 0.2 between a 3-kg box of sand and the table on which it rests. A 5-gm bullet moving horizontally at 300 m/sec at right angles to the end of the box hits the end at the center and penetrates 10 cm before stopping. (a) Determine how far the box moves on the table. (b) Determine the kinetic energy of the bullet before impact, and of the bullet and box just after impact. (c) In order to determine the speed of the box after impact you assumed conservation of linear momentum (or did you assume conservation of energy?). This means you assumed that external impulses were negligible during the collision. Show that this assumption is justifiable by calculating the magnitude of the impulse the box and bullet exert on one another, and comparing the impulse due to friction in the time interval of the collision.

8. A 5-lb block and a 3-lb block are tied to opposite ends of an ideal string that passes over an ideal pulley fixed to a wall. The system is released from rest with the 5-lb block 2 ft off the floor. With what speed will it hit the floor (assuming the other block doesn't hit the pulley first)? Note that you can obtain the result without analyzing the motion in detail using $\mathbf{F} = m\mathbf{a}$.

9. The velocity of a bullet can be measured by firing it horizontally into a box of sand suspended as a pendulum. This arrangement is called a ballistic pendulum.

   A 10-lb box of sand is suspended by four parallel wires 20 ft long attached to the corners of the box. A 0.2-oz bullet is fired horizontally into the box, becoming embedded, and the box swings 8 in. backward. Calculate the speed of the bullet before impact, thinking carefully about the assumptions you are making. What fraction of the mechanical energy is lost in the impact? Do you think the bullet is likely to melt during the collision? (The specific heat capacity of lead is 0.03 cal/gm-C°, and the melting point of lead is 327°C.)

10. A block is projected up a 37° inclined plane with an initial speed v. When it returns to its initial position its speed is $\frac{3}{4}v$. Determine the coefficient of kinetic friction between block and plane.

11. A careless fly lands on his back on top of a smooth bowling ball of radius R. He twitches, and therefore starts to slip from this point of unstable equilibrium. Through what vertical distance does he move before losing contact with the surface of the ball?

12. A simple pendulum 5 ft long hangs close to a wall. The bob is drawn sideways, parallel to the wall, so that it is 3 ft from a vertical axis through its rest position, and is released from this position. There is a nail in the wall directly below the pivot point of the pendulum, so that as the pendulum reaches its vertical position its string hits the nail. Determine the distance from the vertical axis (on the opposite side from that of release) where the bob comes instantaneously to rest if the nail is (a) 2.5 ft below the pivot, (b) 4 ft below. (c) What is the highest the nail can be, if the string is to wind around the nail, but the string does not go slack?

13. A small block slides in the smooth track shown. Determine the minimum starting height h (in terms of R) such that the block will stay in contact with the track for its full length. **(b)** The block is released with $h = 2R$. Determine the height above the reference level that it leaves the track, and maximum height reached, in terms of R.

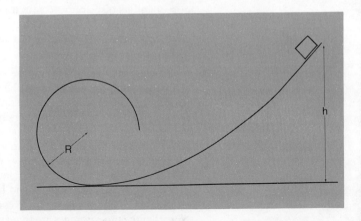

14. A particle of mass m falls through a viscous fluid. There is a retarding force on it of kv, where v is its speed and k is a viscous constant for the particle. When it is falling at its terminal velocity, at what rate is it losing mechanical energy?

15. A ball dropped on a floor from a height of 1 m rebounds to a height of 81 cm. What is the coefficient of restitution for the impact? What fraction of its mechanical energy does the ball lose in the impact? Assuming the coefficient of restitution is constant, what fraction of the ball's mechanical energy is left after 10 bounces? How many bounces before it has less than 1 % of its mechanical energy left?

16. **(a)** A 0.8-kg block is on a smooth table, vibrating in SHM of amplitude 5 cm at the end of a horizontal ideal spring of force constant 200 n/m. Determine its maximum kinetic energy and its maximum elastic potential energy.

(b) The same spring is used to suspend the same block, and the block is oscillating vertically with amplitude 5 cm. Determine the kinetic energy, the elastic potential energy, and the gravitational potential energy of the block (1) at the midpoint, (2) at the highest point, (3) at the lowest point in its motion. Choose the zero of elastic potential energy as you did in (a), that is, assume the elastic potential energy is zero when the spring is unstretched, and take the reference level for gravitational potential energy as the equilibrium position of the block. Check that the total energy at each point is the same.

17. A particle is vibrating in simple harmonic motion, with displacement $x = x_0 \sin \omega t$. **(a)** Express its speed v at any displacement x in terms of ω, x_0 and x. **(b)** When its displacement is $x_0/2$, determine the fraction of its mechanical energy E that is potential energy U and the fraction that is kinetic energy K. **(c)** Determine its displacement when its energy is half kinetic and half potential.

18. We showed by differentiating the energy equation for SHM with respect to time that the differential equation for SHM resulted. Express the speed $v = dx/dt$ as a function of x, and integrate to obtain x as a function of t. (From integral tables $\int dx/\sqrt{a^2 - x^2} = \text{arc sin}\,(x/a)$, where a is a constant.)

19. A 0.1-kg block is on a 37° inclined plane. The coefficient of kinetic friction between block and plane is 0.2. The block is attached to the lower end of a spring of spring constant 10 n/m. The spring extends up the plane, and its upper end is fixed to the plane. The block is released from rest from the position where the spring is

unstretched. **(a)** Determine an expression relating the speed v of the block (in m/sec) and its displacement x (in m) down the plane from its initial position. **(b)** For what x does the block reach its maximum speed? **(c)** How far does it move down the plane before coming to rest? **(d)** How close to its initial position does it come on its return trip?

20. A particle is moving in SHM on the x-axis: $x = x_0 \sin \omega t$. **(a)** Sketch an x–t graph and a v–t graph for one cycle of the motion. **(b)** Sketch a potential energy–time $(U$–$t)$ graph and a kinetic energy–time $(K$–$t)$ graph for one cycle of the motion. Is the period for these energies the same as the period for the motion? **(c)** Sketch a potential energy–displacement $(U$–$x)$ graph and a kinetic energy–displacement $(K$–$x)$ graph for the interval $-x_0$ to x_0. **(d)** The average energy over an interval is the area under the graphs you have drawn, divided by the width of the interval. Determine the average kinetic and potential energies $\overline{K}$ and $\overline{U}$ with respect to time, over one cycle, and determine $\overline{K}$ and $\overline{U}$ with respect to displacement over one cycle. Express these in terms of the force constant k and the amplitude x_0 of the motion. Note that the time averages are the same, but the displacement averages are not. In both cases, however, the sum is the constant total mechanical energy $E = kx_0^2/2$.

21. The elongation ΔL of a wire of length L and a cross sectional area A when stretched by a force F is given by $\Delta L = FL/EA$, where E is the elastic constant of the material called Young's modulus. For steel, $E = 2.1 \times 10^{11}$ n/m². **(a)** Determine the force constant k for a steel wire 1 mm in diameter and 10 m long. **(b)** How much is the wire stretched when used to suspend a 2-kg ball? **(c)** How much elastic potential energy is stored in the wire? **(d)** If the ball is drawn sideways until the wire is horizontal, and released, what is the extension of the wire at the bottom of the swing? **(e)** Do you think the wire would be permanently stretched? (The elastic limit for steel is about 4×10^8 n/m².)

22. The potential energy for any inverse-square force is $U(r) = C/r = C(x^2 + y^2 + z^2)^{-1/2}$ in a particular co-ordinate system. Show directly by forming $F_x = -\partial U/\partial x$, etc., that $\mathbf{F}$ is an inverse-square force in the radial direction.

23. A particle of mass m is moving in orbit under the gravitational attraction of a fixed particle of mass M. **(a)** Show that if the particle is moving in a circular orbit of radius r_0, the kinetic energy K_0 and the potential energy U_0 (referred to a zero at infinity) are related by $U_0 = -2K_0$. Express the total energy E_0 for this orbit in terms of K_0, and in terms of U_0, and in terms of the angular momentum L_0. **(b)** Now suppose that the particle is moving in an orbit with the same angular momentum L_0, but a total energy $E_1 = E_0/2$. Note that this is a higher energy, because E is negative. Determine the maximum and minimum distances r_{max} and r_{min} that the particle will be from the fixed particle in this orbit, in terms of r_0. Determine the maximum value of the ratio $-K/U$ in this orbit. What is the limiting value of this ratio if the particle is to be in a closed orbit?

24. We stated that in one-dimensional situations if a force is a unique function of position $F(x)$ then the force is conservative, but that this is not true in general. As a simple example, use the force $\mathbf{F} = x\mathbf{i} + xy\mathbf{j}$, a force specified at every point in the x–y plane. Calculate the work done by this force on a particle as the particle is moved from the origin (0,0) to the position (1 m, 1 m), first if the particle is moved along the x-axis and then up the line $x = 1$, then if the particle is moved up the y-axis and along the line $y = 1$. The result depends on the path, so the force is not conservative.

22

FORCE, FIELD, POTENTIAL ENERGY AND POTENTIAL

There are a number of different ways that the interaction between particles or systems of particles can be described. We will use the gravitational interaction to discuss these, but the terms introduced apply to other interactions as well.

The concept of force as the basis of interaction between particles is fundamental in classical dynamics; particles exert equal and opposite forces on one another. You can't have a force on one particle without having a force on the other. Sometimes it is convenient to separate whatever is producing the force (a particle or system of particles) from whatever the force is acting on. This is done using the concept of a **field**. We have used this term casually up to now, to describe the region around a particle where it influences other particles, but now we give it precise definition.

FIELD DUE TO A PARTICLE

Think of a particle of mass M fixed in a frame of reference (or with a frame of reference fixed to it). It will exert a force

$$\mathbf{F} = -G\frac{Mm}{r^2}\mathbf{r}_0$$

on a particle of mass m at a point P that has a displacement $\mathbf{r} = r\mathbf{r}_0$ from M.

Whether or not there is a particle at point P, there is said to be a field $\mathbf{E}_P$ at the point

$$\mathbf{E}_P = -G\frac{M}{r^2}\mathbf{r}_0$$

This vector quantity is called the gravitational

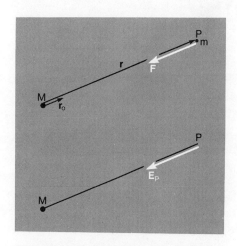

If there is a gravitational force on a particle at P there is a gravitational field at P, whether the particle is there or not.

529

field strength or **field intensity** at point P. If there is a mass m at P, the force on it is

$$\mathbf{F} = m\mathbf{E}_P$$

that is, the field strength is the force per unit mass on any mass at P. We can think of the region around M as full of vectors, all pointing toward M and of length $\propto 1/r^2$. This is the gravitational field $\mathbf{E}$ around M. Sometimes con-

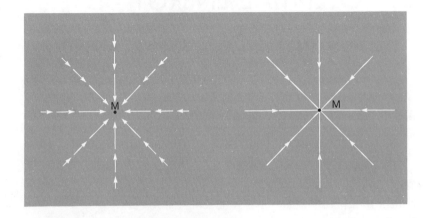

Representation of the field by vectors and by field lines.

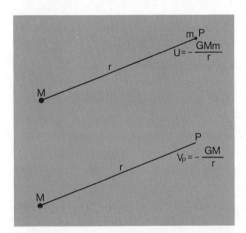

If a particle at P has gravitational potential energy there is a gravitational potential at P, whether the particle is there or not.

tinuous lines called field lines are drawn showing the direction of the field.

Instead of describing the effect of M on m in terms of force $\mathbf{F}$, we can say that at point P the mass m has potential energy

$$U = -\frac{GMm}{r}$$

and whether or not there is a mass at P, there is a **potential** V_P at the point

$$V_P = -\frac{GM}{r}$$

Just as field is the force per unit mass, potential is the potential energy per unit mass of a particle at P.

$$U = mV_P$$

Instead of the vector field $\mathbf{E}$ around M, we can think of a scalar field V. We cannot represent this scalar field by lines showing direction—a scalar has no direction so instead we use the concept of an **equipotential surface**. The potential V is in general a function of position $V(x,y,z)$, and $V(x,y,z) = $ constant is the equation of a surface. For the potential $V = -GM/r$ the equipotential surfaces are concentric spheres.

Since force and potential energy of a particle at any point are related by

$$\mathbf{F} = -\operatorname{grad} U$$

the vector and scalar fields are related by

$$\mathbf{E} = -\operatorname{grad} V$$

This means that the field $\mathbf{E}$ is always in the direction of maximum decrease of potential V. There is zero change of potential along an equipotential surface, and a maximum change at right angles to the surface, so that the field lines are always at right angles to (orthogonal to) the equipotential surfaces. This is obvious for the example of the field produced by a single mass M, but can be shown to be true in general.

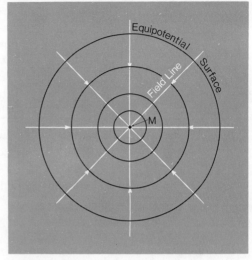

Relation between field lines and equipotential surfaces for the gravitational field of a single particle.

FIELD DUE TO A FIXED DISTRIBUTION OF PARTICLES

We have described the concepts of field and potential for the specific example of the gravitational field produced by a single particle of mass M, but the concepts apply to any situation involving a system of particles all at rest with respect to one another. This restriction is necessary because we are considering only **static fields**, where the field is a function of position, but not of **time**. If there are a number of particles m_1, m_2, $\cdots$, fixed in a frame of reference, and a point P in the frame has displacements $\mathbf{r}_1$, $\mathbf{r}_2$, $\cdots$, from these particles, the superposition principle (discussed previously) is an assumption that the resultant effect on a particle at point P is the sum of the individual effects due to the particles m_i; the force $\mathbf{F}_1$ due to m_1 is the same whether the other masses are present or not.

This means that the field at P is

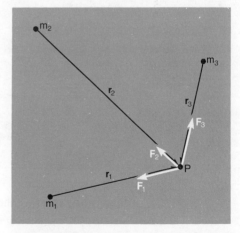

The resultant field at P is the vector sum $\Sigma\, \mathbf{E}_i$ and the resultant potential at P is the scalar sum $\Sigma\, V_i$.

$$\mathbf{E}_P = \sum \mathbf{E}_{iP} = -\sum \frac{Gm_i}{r_i^3}\,\mathbf{r}_i = -G\sum \frac{m_i}{r_i^3}\,\mathbf{r}_i$$

Note that the magnitude of each term is Gm_i/r_i^2; using the vector $\mathbf{r}_i$ in the numerator to specify the direction of the field due to m_i requires an extra r_i in the denominator. Here this is more convenient than the unit vector representation.

The potential at P due to the masses is

$$V_P = -\sum \frac{Gm_i}{r_i} = -G \sum \frac{m_i}{r_i}$$

Determination of the scalar sum for V_P is in general an easier task than evaluation of the vector sum $\mathbf{E}_P$, where direction must be considered. The relation $\mathbf{E} = -\text{grad } V$ can be used to find $\mathbf{E}$ if V is known. For the field due to a continuous mass distribution, as in a rigid body, the sum can be replaced by an integral

$$V_P = -G \int \frac{dm}{r}$$

where r is the distance of the point P from the element of mass dm, and the integration is carried out over the rigid body.

In a two-dimensional diagram only equipotential lines can be shown. The lines for two particles of equal mass are shown; the equipotential surfaces are

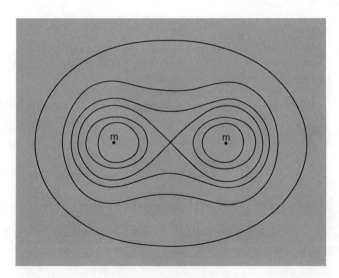

Equipotential lines
for two particles of
equal mass.

obtained by rotating the figure around the horizontal line joining the particles. The force on a particle at any point is at right angles to the equipotential lines. They are like contour lines showing points of equal altitude on a map; the steepest gradient at a point is at right angles to the lines, and the closer the lines are together the steeper the gradient is.

Example: The concept of potential (or potential energy) can be used to make calculations when a complete
solution of the equation of motion would be messy,
as we have seen. Two particles of mass M are fixed a
distance D apart, and a third particle of mass m is
released at point 1, a distance D from both masses.
From symmetry it will follow the path shown, but its
acceleration will vary in magnitude because the force
on it is not constant. Let us find its speed v at point 2,
half-way between the two fixed particles, where the
force on it becomes zero.

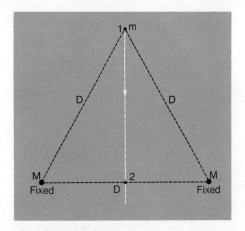

$$V_1 = -\frac{GM}{D} - \frac{GM}{D} = -2\frac{GM}{D}$$

$$V_2 = -\frac{GM}{D/2} - \frac{GM}{D/2} = -4\frac{GM}{D}$$

The use of symmetry plus
energy considerations.

The potential difference is $V_2 - V_1 = -2\dfrac{GM}{D}$

and the potential energy difference for the mass m at the two points is $U_2 - U_1 = -(2GM/D)m$. From conservation of mechanical energy

$$E_1 = E_2 \quad \text{or} \quad K_1 + U_1 = K_2 + U_2$$

or

$$K_2 - K_1 = -(U_2 - U_1) = \frac{2GMm}{D}$$

$$K_1 = 0, \qquad K_2 = \tfrac{1}{2}mv^2 \qquad v = \sqrt{4GM/D}$$

This result does not depend on the size of mass m, but the **time** to make the trip does.
Any particle acquires the same speed in falling through the potential difference, but a
more massive particle would take longer to fall.

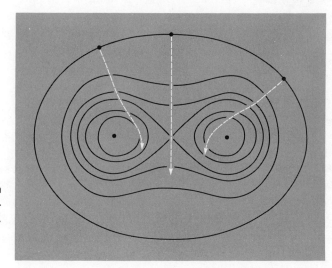

In general motion
is not in the direc-
tion of field lines.

Although in this example the particle moves along a field line, this is not generally true; the field line gives the direction of the force on the particle, *not* the direction of motion of the particle. If the particle is released at any point in the field it will accelerate initially in the field direction, but its subsequent path depends on its velocity as well as the force on it. Only for situations of simple symmetry can we tell what the path is without solving the equations of motion.

GRAVITATIONAL FIELD OF A SPHERE

Several times we have said that the earth acts, as far as its gravitational attraction for other bodies is concerned, as though all of its mass M was concentrated at a point at its center. This fact, first worked out by Newton, is clearly very important for all calculations involving the force of gravity and we are now in a position to show that it is so.

We start by working out the potential due to a thin spherical shell of uniform area density σ: the shell, area $4\pi R^2$, has mass $M = 4\pi\sigma R^2$. We will find the potential at a point P, distance D from the center of the shell O, both for P inside and outside the shell. As an element of mass dm we take a ring in the

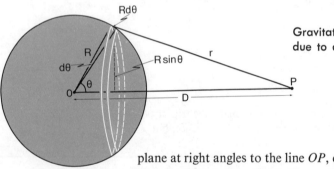

Gravitational potential at P due to a spherical shell.

plane at right angles to the line OP, determined by the angles θ and $\theta + d\theta$ at O. Every point on this ring is the same distance r from the point P (in the limit) and therefore the potential at P due to this mass is

$$dV_P = -G\frac{dm}{r}$$

The ring has radius $R \sin \theta$ and width $R\,d\theta$, so its mass is

$$dm = 2\pi(R \sin \theta)(R\,d\theta)\,\sigma = 2\pi R^2\sigma \sin\theta\,d\theta = \frac{M}{2}\sin\theta\,d\theta$$

and $$dV_P = -\frac{GM}{2}\frac{\sin\theta\,d\theta}{r}$$

As the mass element is moved across the shell, θ and r both vary, but they are related by

$$r^2 = R^2 + D^2 - 2RD\cos\theta$$

Differentiating with respect to θ

$$2r\frac{dr}{d\theta} = 2RD \sin \theta \qquad \text{or} \qquad r\,dr = RD \sin \theta\,d\theta$$

giving $\qquad dV_P = -\frac{GM}{2RD}\,dr \qquad \text{and} \qquad V_P = -\frac{GM}{2RD}\int dr$

Now we must distinguish between the situation where P is outside the shell, or inside the shell, because the results are different.

P—Outside shell: Then $D > R$, and r varies from $D - R$ to $D + R$ as the ring is moved from one side of the shell to the other.

$$V_P = -\frac{GM}{2RD}\int_{D-R}^{D+R} dr$$

$$= -\frac{GM}{2RD}[(D+R) - (D-R)] = -\frac{GM}{D}$$

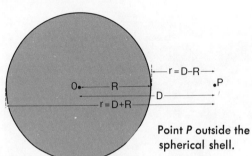

Point P outside the spherical shell.

This is the same as though a particle of mass M was at a distance D from P. A spherical shell acts as though all its mass is concentrated at its center, as far as its gravitational effect at points outside it is concerned. The field $\mathbf{E}_P$ will have magnitude GM/D^2 and be directed toward O.

P—Inside shell: Then $D < R$, and r varies from $R - D$ to $R + D$ as the ring is moved from one side of the shell to the other

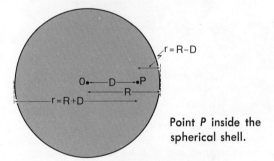

Point P inside the spherical shell.

$$V_P = -\frac{GM}{2RD}[(R+D) - (R-D)] = -\frac{GM}{R}$$

This is **constant**. The potential is the same at every point inside the sphere. This means that the field, which depends on the rate of change of potential with position, is zero at every point inside the shell. There is no force on a particle inside the shell. You can see that this is plausible by thinking of the forces on a particle m due to the areas A_1 and A_2 (and corresponding masses m_1 and m_2) intercepted by a cone meeting the surface of the shell on opposite sides of the particle. The area A_1 is proportional to r_1^2, but the force F_1 due to it decreases as $1/r_1^2$, so the force depends only on the cone angle. Similarly the force F_2 due

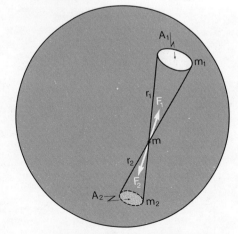

The gravitational field is zero inside a spherical shell.

to A_2 depends only on the cone angle, so the forces are equal and opposite. For every m_1 there is a corresponding m_2, and the net force on the particle is zero.

A solid sphere can be considered to be made up of a number of concentric thin shells, and therefore the potential and field at any point **outside** the surface of the sphere are the same as if the total mass were concentrated at the center. It is not necessary that the density be homogeneous throughout the sphere, but the density at all points equidistant from the center must be the same. The density may vary with distance from the center, as it does for bodies such as the earth.

For points **inside** a solid sphere, we know that the field due to shells of greater radius is zero, and the field due to shells of lesser radius is the same as if the mass were concentrated at the center. If the density varies with radius, this variation would need to be known to find the field at any point. If the sphere is homogeneous, the field is directly proportional to the distance from the center r, because the effective mass involved is proportional to r^3, and the force decreases as $1/r^2$. To show this explicitly: If the density ρ is constant, the total mass of the sphere is $M = \frac{4}{3}\pi r^3 \rho$. Therefore $M_r/M = r^3/R^3$, and the magnitude of the field at P is

For points inside a homogeneous solid sphere $E_p \propto r$.

$$E_P = G\,\frac{M_r}{r^2} = G\,\frac{Mr^3}{R^3 r^2} = G\,\frac{M}{R^3}\,r = E_{\text{surface}}\left(\frac{r}{R}\right)$$

Gravitational potential and gravitational field of a spherical shell and of a homogeneous sphere.

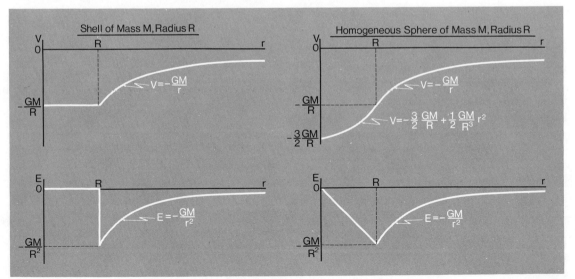

and since the field is toward the center, $E_P = -(GM/R^3)\,\mathbf{r}$. The diagrams show the potential V and the field E as a function of distance from the center r for a spherical shell and for a homogeneous solid sphere.

Example: A particle of mass m is a distance D from the end of a thin uniform rod of length L, mass M, and is on the same line as the axis of the rod. If the gravitational attraction between the two is considered to be the same as that between two particles of masses m and M, how far apart would the particles be?

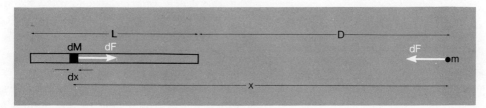

Gravitational force between
a rod and a particle.

Only for spherical objects can the mass be considered to act at the center, so we cannot say that the two particles would be a distance $D + L/2$ apart. If the rod has a linear density (mass per unit length) ρ its total mass is $M = \rho L$ and the mass of an infinitesimal length dx is $dM = \rho\,dx$. The force of gravitational attraction between dM and m is $dF = G(m\,dM/x^2)$ and the resultant force is the sum as x varies from D to $D + L$.

$$F = \int dF = \int \frac{Gm\,dM}{x^2} = Gm\rho \int_D^{D+L} \frac{dx}{x^2} = Gm\rho \left[-\frac{1}{x} \right]_D^{D+L}$$

$$= Gm\rho \left[\frac{1}{D} - \frac{1}{D+L} \right] = Gm\rho \left[\frac{L}{D(D+L)} \right] = G \frac{Mm}{D(D+L)}$$

The gravitational force between two particles of masses M and m a distance R apart is $F = G(Mm/R^2)$, so $R^2 = D(D + L)$. To replace the rod by a particle, it would have to be a distance $R = \sqrt{D(D + L)}$ from the particle of mass m.

This result depends on D as well as L; there is no unique position in the rod where its mass can be said to act. If $D = L$, $R = \sqrt{2}L$. For $D \gg L$, $R \cong D$; the rod acts like a particle as far as points far away are concerned. For $D \ll L$, $R \cong \sqrt{DL}$; if $D = 0.01L$, $R = 0.1L$. As $D \to 0$, $R \to 0$ and $F \to \infty$.

FIELD OF AN INFINITE FLAT PLATE

As another example of the field due to a distribution of mass, we will determine the field due to a flat plate which is infinite in extent. This example is of importance in situations involving electrostatic fields, but we will work it out for the gravitational case and translate it later into electrical terms. We assume

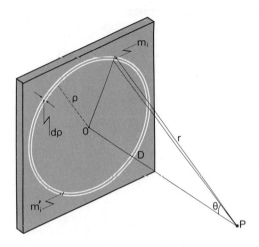

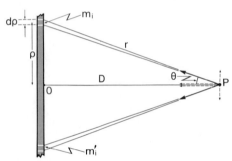

The field at P produced by the infinite thin plate can be determined by considering the field due to a ring of radius ρ, and width $d\rho$.

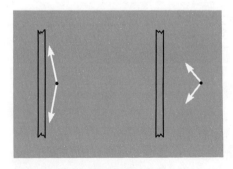

The field is independent of distance from the plate.

the flat plate is uniform in density and thickness, so it has a constant **area density** σ. We wish to find the field at a point P, distance D from the plate. We will calculate the field, not the potential this time. (Later you will see why.)

Think of the effect of a ring of radius ρ, width $d\rho$, centered on the point O where the perpendicular from P meets the plate. A particle m_i on this ring produces a field Gm_i/r^2 at P, directed toward m_i. But there will be an identical particle m_i' on the other side of the ring, and the components of the field parallel to the plate due to these two particles will cancel out, leaving only the components perpendicular to the plate to add up. Thus we can say that the field at P due to the whole ring, of mass dm, has magnitude

$$dE_P = G\, dm \cos\theta/r^2$$
$$= GD\, dm/r^3 \qquad \text{(since } \cos\theta = D/r\text{)}$$

The mass of the ring is $dm = (2\pi\rho)(d\rho)(\sigma)$

but $\qquad \rho^2 + D^2 = r^2 \qquad$ so $\qquad \rho\, d\rho = r\, dr$

and $\qquad\qquad dm = 2\pi\sigma r\, dr$
$$dE_P = 2\pi GD\sigma(dr/r^2)$$

The total field E_P is found by adding the effect of all such rings as r goes from D to ∞.

$$E_P = 2\pi GD\sigma \int_D^\infty \frac{dr}{r^2} = 2\pi GD\sigma \left[-\frac{1}{r} \right]_D^\infty = 2\pi G\sigma$$

(Perhaps you see why we did not use potential here. We would have found ourselves trying to find

$$V_P = -2\pi G\sigma \int_D^\infty dr$$

which would have given ∞ when we integrated. The difficulty arises because of our choice of the zero of potential.) The field at P is $E_P = 2\pi G\sigma$, a **uniform** field directed toward the plate. The fact that the field is independent of the distance D from the plate may be surprising—it might be expected to be stronger near the plate. Near the plate some of the mass is closer, but much of the effect

of the plate is cancelled out. Further out more of the plate is effective in producing the field, and the result is that the distance does not matter.

Note that this is not the same result as found for points inside a spherical
shell, where the potential was constant and the field was zero. Here the field
is constant and the potential is not: $V_P \propto D$. If there are two parallel plates
with the same area density σ, the field between them would be zero.

There is really no such thing as an infinite plate, and the result obtained
applies to a region near a large plate, so that D is small compared to the dimensions of the plate. Even so, this example is not very useful as far as gravitational
situations are concerned, because gravitational forces are only important if one
of the bodies involved is astronomical in size—a planet, a moon or a star.

Now translate this into an electrical situation. The basis of our discussion
of field and potential was the gravitational attraction between masses

$$F = G\frac{Mm}{r^2}$$

The Coulomb law for force between two charges Q and q is

$$F = \frac{1}{4\pi\epsilon_0}\frac{Qq}{r^2}$$

an attractive or a repulsive force depending on whether Q and q are opposite
or the same kinds of charge. The reason for calling the constant $1/4\pi\epsilon_0$ rather
than just C or K or k you will see later, in electromagnetic theory.

In complete analogy with the gravitational case, electric field is defined as
force per unit charge. The field at q due to Q has a magnitude

$$E = \frac{F}{q} = \frac{1}{4\pi\epsilon_0}\frac{Q}{r^2}$$

Similarly electric potential energy $U = \pm(1/4\pi\epsilon_0)(Qq/r)$ and potential $V = \pm(1/4\pi\epsilon_0)(Q/r)$ are defined. (There is an additional factor that must be considered because the force can be repulsive as well as attractive, leading to posi-
tive as well as negative energies.)

The results we have found for gravitational situations can be translated then
by replacing the constant GM by $Q/4\pi\epsilon_0$. For the infinite plate, this means
that the gravitational field $E = 2\pi G\sigma$ becomes an electric field

$$E = \frac{\sigma}{2\epsilon_0}$$

where σ is the **charge** per unit area of the plate. The force on a charge in the
field will be toward the plate, or away from the plate, depending on the kind
of charge. Now think of two plates, one carrying a positive charge and the
other a negative charge, the amount of charge per unit area being the same for

Field between two parallel plates with equal and opposite charges.

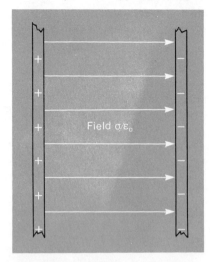

Field σ/ε_0

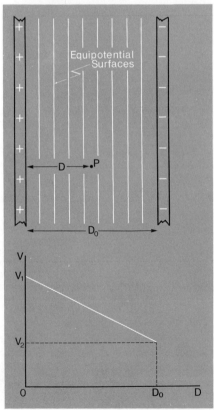

Equipotential Surfaces

The variation in electric potential between the charged plates.

each. This is a familiar and important kind of device, a capacitor or condenser. It can be used to store electric charge because the sets of opposite charges hold themselves together.

At any point outside the plates the field is zero, because the fields due to the plates cancel. However in the region between the plates they combine to produce a resultant uniform field

$$E = \frac{\sigma}{\epsilon_0}$$

The plates of a real capacitor of course are not infinite in size, and at the edges of the plates there will be a region where the field is not uniform. This discussion ignores these "edge effects" and is valid in the region where the field is uniform. The direction of the field is defined to be the direction of the force on a **positive** charge, that is from the plate carrying a positive charge (the positive plate) to the one carrying a negative charge. The equipotential surfaces are planes parallel to the plates, and the potential V changes uniformly between the plates. The field is in the direction of maximum decrease in potential, $\mathbf{E} = -\operatorname{grad} V$, so the potential decreases in moving from the positive to the negative plate: $V = -(\sigma/\epsilon_0)D$ where D is distance from the positive plate. Then

$$E = -\frac{\partial V}{\partial D} = \frac{\sigma}{\epsilon_0}$$

The potential difference between the plates, a distance D_0 apart, is $V_1 - V_2 = (\sigma/\epsilon_0)D_0$. Remember that the zero of potential is arbitrary, and our interest is always in potential (or potential energy) **differences** in applying the concept of conservation of energy. A particle with positive charge q released at the positive plate will "fall" to the negative plate. Its mechanical energy $E = K + U$ is constant (if no forces except the electric force act on it), so $K_1 + U_1 = K_2 + U_2$.

$$K_2 - K_1 = U_1 - U_2 = q(V_1 - V_2)$$

Since $K_1 = 0$, the particle reaches the negative plate with kinetic energy $K_2 = q(V_1 - V_2)$. If the potential difference is measured in volts ($\equiv$ joules/coulomb) and charge in coulombs, the energy is in joules.

ENERGY DIAGRAMS

In general potential energy is a function of position $U(x,y,z)$. We have shown that it is possible sometimes to express it in terms of a single co-ordinate: $U = U(x)$ for one-dimensional motion, $U = U(r)$ for central fields. Then we can draw an energy diagram, as discussed earlier, and this may be helpful in describing possible motions.

An energy diagram is a graph of the potential energy U as a function of a single co-ordinate. If it is assumed that the only force acting on the particle is that due to the conservative force field, for which the potential energy U has been defined, then the mechanical energy $E = K + U$ is a constant. It can be represented by a horizontal line on the energy diagram, but the line only exists in the region where $E > U$, because the kinetic energy K is never negative.

Here we will discuss energy diagrams for the potentials we have defined. You will note that the terms **potential curve** and **potential energy curve** are used somewhat synonymously; they are not the same thing, but they have the same shape, since $U(r) = mV(r)$.

Motion Under a Linear Restoring Force—$F = -kx$, $U = \frac{1}{2}kx^2$: The potential energy graph is a parabola (see the diagrams on the following page). The mechanical energy of the particle at any displacement x is

$$E = \tfrac{1}{2}mv^2 + \tfrac{1}{2}kx^2 = \text{constant}$$

Corresponding to any energy E_0, the particle is confined to move in the region $-x_0$ to x_0, where $E_0 = \frac{1}{2}kx_0^2$; such a particle is said to be **bound**. The larger the energy, the larger its amplitude of oscillation, but it cannot escape. In real situations of course, the force law $F = -kx$ would only be valid within certain limits.

Sometimes in using such a diagram the potential energy curve is thought of as a frictionless track on which the particle is sliding under the influence of gravity. This gravitational analogy helps to visualize the motion, but care must be taken not to take the picture too literally. To see exactly what is involved in the analogue, think of a block m oscillating on a smooth horizontal track under the influence of a spring, and an identical block oscillating on a smooth parabolic track in the vertical plane. The blocks are released with the same initial displacement x_0, and the strength of the spring k and slope of the parabolic track are such that the potential energy graph $U(x)$ vs. x is the same for each. The equation of the track is $y = Kx^2$. Corresponding to displacement x_0,

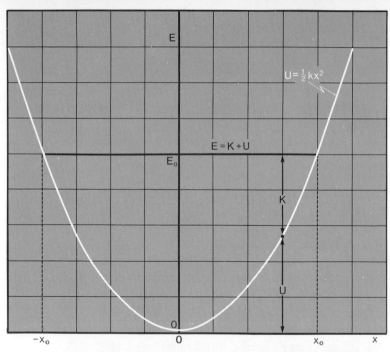

Energy diagram for simple harmonic motion.

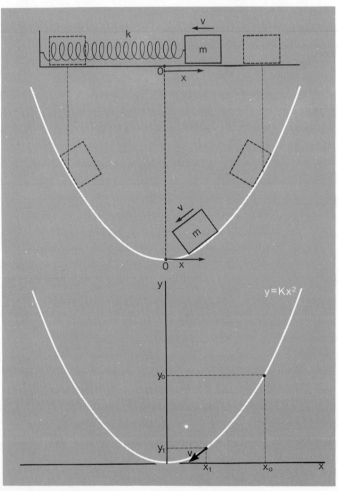

Gravitational analogue of SHM in one dimension.

the potential energy (relative to the center point) is

$$U = mgy_0 = mgKx_0^2$$

and this must be the same as $U = \frac{1}{2}kx_0^2$ for the other block, so $2mgK = k$. For the particle on the parabolic track, released at x_0, the speed v at any other displacement x_1 is given by

$$\frac{1}{2}mv^2 = mg(y_0 - y_1) = mgK(x_0^2 - x_1^2)$$
$$= \frac{1}{2}k(x_0^2 - x_1^2)$$

and this is the same as the kinetic energy of the other block at the same displacement. Both masses have the same speed at the same displacement. Note however, that the motion of the block on the parabolic track is *not* simple harmonic motion, and its projection on the x-axis is *not* simple harmonic motion either. Its kinetic energy at any point is

$$\frac{1}{2}mv^2 = \frac{1}{2}m(v_x^2 + v_y^2) = \frac{1}{2}k(x_0^2 - x^2)$$

The projection of the motion on the x-axis would be simple harmonic if $\frac{1}{2}mv_x^2 = \frac{1}{2}k(x_0^2 - x^2)$, but this is not the case. Only if the y-component of kinetic energy is negligible can the motion be considered to be approximately simple harmonic. This would be so for oscillations of small amplitude, or for a very flat parabolic track.

The periods of the two motions are not the same. The period of the mass connected to the spring is $T = 2\pi\sqrt{m/k}$, independent of its amplitude of oscillation. The period of the block in the parabolic track depends on the amplitude.

The analog of the one-dimensional oscillation is a two-dimensional motion

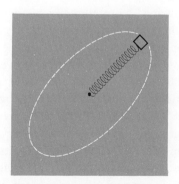

Two-dimensional motion of a block held by a spring.

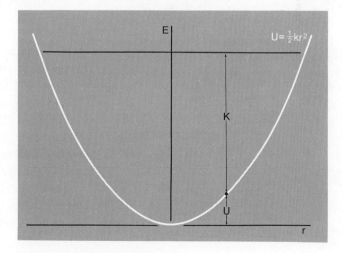

Energy diagram for two-dimensional motion.

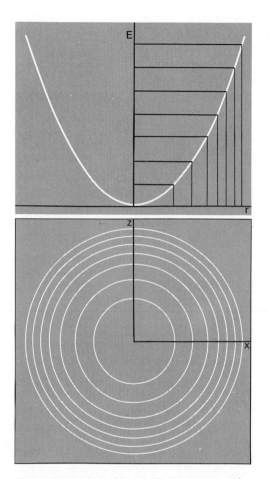

Equipotential lines for equal energy intervals are lines an equal distance apart on the energy diagram, and are concentric circles projected on the xz plane (the plane of the table).

under gravity. In a similar way, there is a three-dimensional gravitational analog for two-dimensional motion. Suppose that a block is on a smooth table, connected by a spring to a fixed pin. The block is given a push sideways, moving in orbit around the pin under the influence of the central force $\mathbf{F} = -k\mathbf{r}$, where $\mathbf{r}$ is displacement from the pin. Its elastic potential energy will be $U = \frac{1}{2}kr^2 = \frac{1}{2}k(x^2 + z^2)$ where the x– and z–co-ordinate axes are in the plane of the table. The energy diagram showing $U(r)$ will look like the previous one, but now we cannot think of it as a frictionless track, except in the special case of the block moving straight toward the pin, or away from it. The diagram is really a cross section of a potential **surface,** the paraboloid that would be obtained by rotating the curve around the E-axis. Let us draw the equipotential energy lines on the x–z plane for equal energy intervals. The lines become more closely spaced the farther out they are from the center, corresponding to a steeper gradient or stronger force.

We pointed out in discussing equipotential surfaces that equipotential lines are like contour lines, showing positions of equal elevation on a map. We treat them literally as contour lines in making a gravitational analog of the motion. The paraboloid that is obtained by rotating the parabola $y = Kx^2$ around the y-axis is thought of as a smooth bowl. A block shot sideways with just the right speed will move in a circle, both its kinetic energy and its gravitational potential energy remaining constant. This is the analog of the block pushed sideways on the table with just the right speed to move in a circle; both its kinetic energy and its elastic potential energy will remain constant.

If the block is not given the right speed to move in a circular orbit its path will be complex, whether we think of the block on the table or the analogue, but it always moves so that $E = K + U$ is constant. For the block on the table, $U = \frac{1}{2}kr^2$, and the motion is confined to the xz plane. In the analogue, $U = mgy$ and the motion is confined to the three-dimensional surface of the paraboloid.

While the analogue is a mental device to help visualize the motion, it some-

times is useful to make an actual model. Frictionless surfaces are hard to come by, but a marble
rolling in a parabolic bowl moves freely enough
that a reasonable impression of the possible orbits
is gained. Looking straight down on the bowl from
above, the motion is seen in two dimensions, and it
must be kept in mind that this is not the true two-
dimensional motion. However, for orbits that do
not depart too much from circles the vertical component of velocity v_y is small and the overhead view
gives a reasonable approximation to the true motion.

Motion Under an Attractive Inverse-Square Force—
$U = -K/r$: We will describe this in terms of the
gravitational interaction, but it applies equally well
to a charged particle moving in the field of a particle with the opposite charge.

The mechanical energy of a particle of mass m
moving in the field of a particle of mass M fixed in

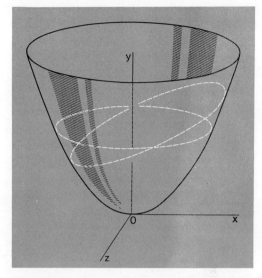

A parabolic bowl provides a gravitational
analogue for the two-dimensional motion.

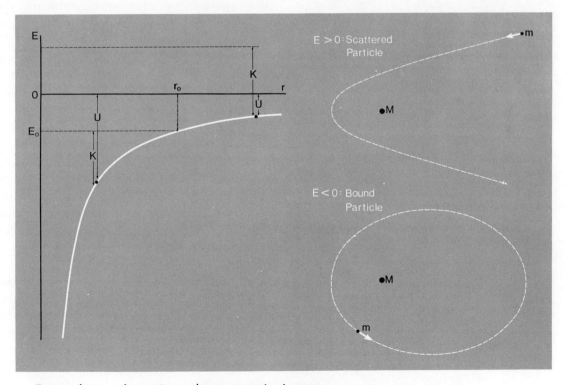

Energy diagram for motion under an attractive inverse-
square force; the particle may be scattered or bound.

an inertial frame is $E = K + U = \frac{1}{2}mv^2 - GMm/r$. This can be positive or negative, and this means that the particle can be bound or unbound.

If $E > 0$, $K > U$, a particle approaching the force center speeds up, reaches a maximum speed when closest to the center, and then escapes—unless it hits whatever is providing the force. The particle is **scattered**; its path is changed by the interaction, but it is not trapped or bound.

If $E < 0$, $K < U$, the particle is bound. Its maximum distance from the force center corresponding to energy E_0 is r_0, where $E_0 = -GMm/r_0$. It will only reach this distance if moving straight out from the center.

For the parabolic potential the zero of potential energy was taken at the origin, the center of force, while here it is taken at infinity. A particle released

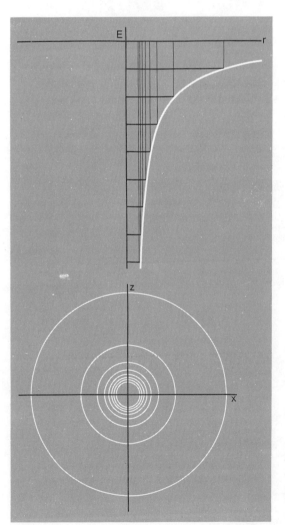

from rest anywhere in the field will move straight toward the force center, "sliding down" the potential energy curve, theoretically with ever-increasing kinetic energy. The zero of potential energy cannot be chosen at $r = 0$. Of course, for any real system whatever is providing the field will not be localized as a particle at a point. If the force center is the earth, for example, the incoming particle will hit the earth. Often the zero of potential energy is transferred to the earth surface for this situation.

While the field is three-dimensional here, the orbit of any particle moving freely in the field is in a plane. We pointed out in discussing central forces that the path of a particle moving under a central force is always in a plane because there is no force tending to accelerate it out of the plane. The orientation of the plane is determined by the initial conditions of projection of the particle.

This means again that we can use an analogue in the one-dimensional gravitational field near the earth. This may seem a little odd; we can replace the three-dimensional gravitational field by a one-dimensional gravitational field, and the two-dimensional orbit becomes a path on a three-

Equipotential lines for equal energy intervals shown on the energy diagram and projected in the plane of motion of the particle.

dimensional surface! For the three-dimensional field the equipotential surfaces are concentric spheres. In the plane of motion of the particle, these will be equipotential lines. As for the parabolic potential, we plot these for equal energy differences. This time the lines become closer together at the center.

In the diagram we have chosen the xz plane in the plane of motion of the particle. If we treat the equipotential lines as contour lines, we can visualize a hyperbolic surface with its axis in the y-direction. Thinking of this as a real surface, with its axis vertical, the paths of particles sliding freely on it represent the paths of the particles in the three-dimensional field. The energy equation $E = \frac{1}{2}mv^2 - GMm/r$ becomes translated into

$$E = \tfrac{1}{2}mv^2 + mgy$$

with the restriction that the particle moves on the surface formed by rotating a curve $xy = -K$ around the y-axis.

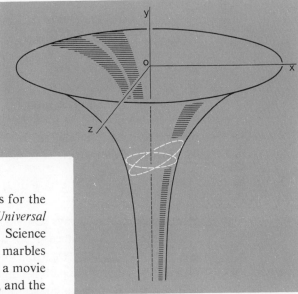

A hyperbolic bowl provides a gravitational analogue for motion under an attractive inverse-square force.

We have used a hyperbolic bowl like this for the description of satellite orbits in a film, *Universal Gravitation*, made as part of the Physical Science Study Committee course. The paths of marbles projected into the bowl were recorded with a movie camera looking straight down on the bowl, and the film was run in slow motion. Given just the right sideways speed, a marble would move in a circular orbit. (The gradual degeneration of the orbit due to friction is an indication of what happens to a satellite due to the earth's atmosphere.) Given a sideways speed that is a little lower, the marble would fall inward, speeding up and moving fast near the center, and slowing down as it moved back out. The path viewed from overhead looked like the elliptic orbit of an earth satellite, but as we have pointed out this is only roughly true, a good approximation if the vertical component of velocity v_y at any point is not too large. Clearly an overhead view does not give a good picture of the motion of a particle released from

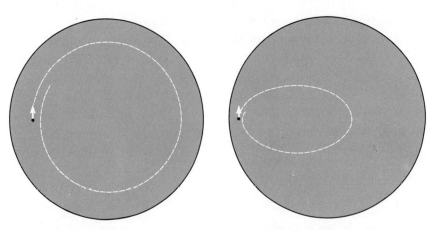

Looking down on the bowl, the motion of a rolling marble approximates the motion of a satellite provided the marble stays approximately in the same horizontal plane.

rest at the edge of the bowl; initially it speeds up, but as it approaches the center, moving straight down, it appears to slow down.

It is the **actual** motion on the surface that is the analogue of motion in the inverse-square field, not the two-dimensional projection of it.

Motion Under a Repulsive Inverse-Square Force: $U = K/r$: This is the kind of potential there would be for a particle of electric charge q moving in the field of another particle of charge Q, where Q and q are the same kind of charge. The energy of the particle is

$$E = K + U = \tfrac{1}{2}mv^2 + \frac{1}{4\pi\epsilon_0}\frac{Qq}{r}$$

Here the particle is always scattered. If it is heading straight toward the force center, the closest distance it can approach corresponding to energy E_0 is r_0, given by $E_0 = (1/4\pi\epsilon_0)(Qq/r_0)$. Otherwise its distance of closest approach r_1 is greater. At point P the path is tangent to the radius $\mathbf{r}$ from the center; the potential energy is a maximum and the kinetic energy a minimum (but not zero).

The distance D, the distance of closest approach of the particle if it is undeflected by the field, is called the **impact parameter** for the collision. We can relate r_0, r_1 and D using the fact that the energy E is constant, and also the angular momentum $\mathbf{l} = \mathbf{r} \times \mathbf{p}$ with respect to the force center is constant.

Let the velocity of the particle when it is far away from the force center be $\mathbf{v}_0$. Then $E_0 = \tfrac{1}{2}mv_0^2$ is its kinetic energy, and if headed straight at the force center the energy becomes completely potential at the distance r_0.

$$E_0 = \tfrac{1}{2}mv_0^2 = \frac{1}{4\pi\epsilon_0}\frac{Qq}{r_0}$$

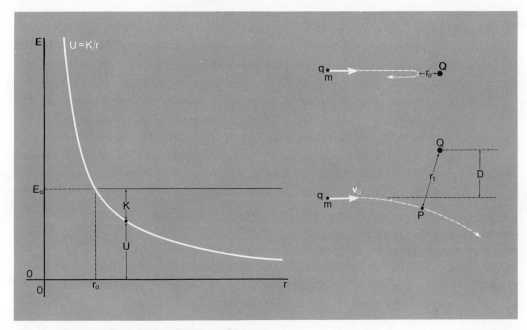

Energy diagram for motion under a repulsive inverse-
square force; the particle is always scattered.

If the particle has an impact parameter D, its angular momentum $\mathbf{l} = \mathbf{r} \times \mathbf{p}$
has magnitude mv_0D, since D is the perpendicular distance from the line of $\mathbf{v}_0$
to the force center. At the point P the velocity has its minimum value $\mathbf{v}_{min}$,
and this is at right angles to the displacement $\mathbf{r}_1$ from the center.

Therefore
$$l = mv_0D = mv_{min}r_1$$

The energy relation at P gives

$$E_0 = \tfrac{1}{2}mv_0^2 = \tfrac{1}{2}mv_{min}^2 + \frac{1}{4\pi\epsilon_0}\frac{Qq}{r_1}$$

or using the previous relations

$$\tfrac{1}{2}mv_0^2 = \tfrac{1}{2}m\left(\frac{v_0D}{r_1}\right)^2 + \tfrac{1}{2}mv_0^2\left(\frac{r_0}{r_1}\right)$$

which gives
$$r_1^2 = D^2 + r_0r_1$$

If $D = 0$, $r_1 = r_0$; this is a head-on collision. If $D \gg r_0$, then $r_1 \cong D$;
the particle is deflected very little in the interaction if the impact parameter
is large.

The gravitational analogue for this example is a hyperbolic hill. Marbles
rolled toward the hill are scattered, the amount of scattering depending on the

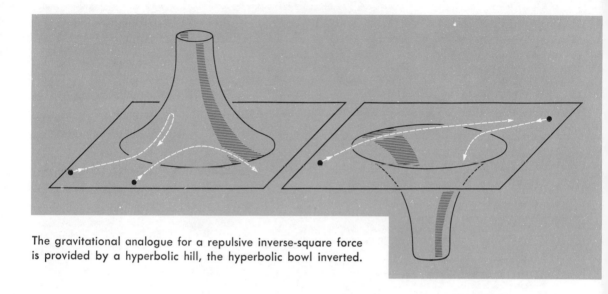

The gravitational analogue for a repulsive inverse-square force is provided by a hyperbolic hill, the hyperbolic bowl inverted.

initial energy and the impact parameter. This hill is just the bowl of the previous example turned upside down. For the bowl (or potential well) the particles may be scattered or captured.

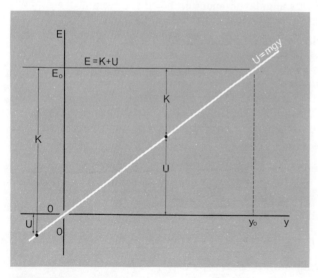

Energy diagram for motion in a uniform field.

Motion in Uniform Field: $U = mgy$: The potential energy graph for a particle in a uniform field is a straight line. The electric field between the plates of a parallel-plate capacitor is uniform, and the gravitational field near the earth is approximately so.

The energy is $E = \frac{1}{2}mv^2 + mgy$. The maximum height of the particle corresponding to energy E_0 is y_0, where $E_0 = mgy_0$, but this does not necessarily mean the particle will reach this height; if projected horizontally, for example, it never rises above its point of projection.

The line in the graph can be regarded as a straight track in the vertical plane only for one-dimensional motion. For motion under gravity in general, the line can be thought of as a side view of a smooth inclined plane.

Generalized Potential: We have described energy diagrams for a particle moving in fields precisely specified in simple mathematical terms, in order to illustrate the use of these diagrams. Real physical systems are sometimes well represented by these functions, sometimes not so well represented. A potential energy diagram gives a useful picture of an interaction, even though it may not be possible to write the potential as a simple function of r, $U(r)$. The diagram

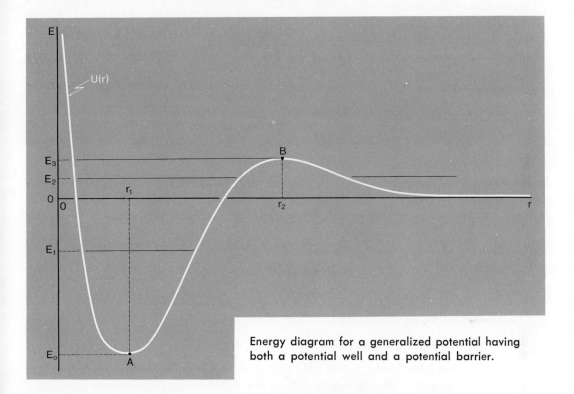

Energy diagram for a generalized potential having both a potential well and a potential barrier.

illustrates the potential for a particle that is repelled from the force center O for large distances $r > r_2$, attracted for intermediate distances $r_1 < r < r_2$, and repelled strongly if $r < r_1$. The diagram has both a **potential well** around r_1 and a **potential hill** or **potential barrier** around r_2. Point A is a point of stable equilibrium; a particle displaced from this point will be attracted back to it, so it will oscillate if moving in one dimension, or more generally will move in an orbit with maximum and minimum displacement determined by the potential curve. It is bound as long as $E < E_3$. A particle with energy E_2, $0 < E_2 < E_3$, may be bound or not, but a particle with energy $E_1 < 0$ is always bound. Point B is a point of unstable equilibrium; a particle displaced from this point falls away from it.

The position of the horizontal axis is arbitrary, chosen so that the potential energy is zero for infinite distance. The axis could be chosen to pass through point A; that is, set $E = 0$ for $r = r_1$. Then all energies would be positive.

A particle released from rest near the position of stable equilibrium A will oscillate in one dimension. No matter what the shape of the potential is, this motion is simple harmonic if the displacement is small enough. To see this choose a co-ordinate axis (an x-axis) along the direction of the one-dimensional vibration, and shift the origin of the energy curve to the point A; that is, plot $U(x)$ instead of $U(r)$, with $x = r - r_1$. It is the same curve, but the variable is now the displacement from the equilibrium position.

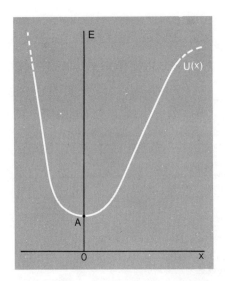

Shifting the origin so that the position variable is displacement from the position of stable equilibrium.

Any function can be represented by a series of the form

$$U(x) = C_0 + C_1x + C_2x^2 + C_3x^3 + \cdots$$

if enough terms are used. The C's are constants for a particular curve.

The force on the particle at any point is

$$F = -\frac{\partial U}{\partial r}$$

$$= -\frac{dU}{dx} \quad \text{(for one-dimensional motion)}$$

$$= -C_1 - 2C_2x - 3C_3x^2 - \cdots$$

Since A is a point of equilibrium, $F = 0$ at $x = 0$ and therefore $C_1 = 0$.

$$F = -2C_2x - 3C_3x^2 - \cdots$$

No matter what the relative size of the coefficients C_2, C_3, $\cdots$, it is always possible to choose x small enough that all the terms in the series are negligible with respect to the first term, and up to this value of x

$$F = -2C_2x = -kx$$

This is simple harmonic motion with force constant $k = 2C_2$

Since $$\frac{d^2U}{dr^2} = \frac{d^2U}{dx^2} = 2C_2 + 6C_3x + \cdots$$

the value of the force constant k can be found by forming d^2U/dr^2 and setting $r = r_1$, where r_1 is the position of the minimum in the $U(r)$ graph. This is symbolized by writing

$$k = \left(\frac{d^2U}{dr^2}\right)_{r=r_1}$$

Square-Well Potential: This is a potential of very simple shape. It can be thought of as representing the potential energy of a particle in a one-dimensional box, bouncing back and forth between perfectly elastic walls at $-x_0$ and x_0. In the range $-x_0 \rightarrow x_0$, $U(x) = U_0$, a negative constant. Outside this range

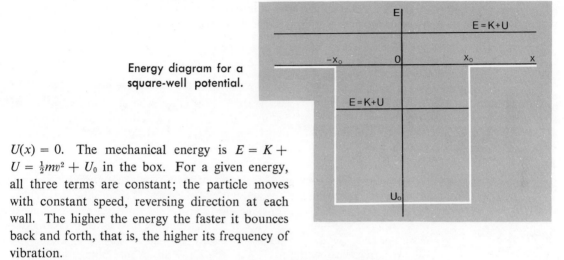

Energy diagram for a square-well potential.

$U(x) = 0$. The mechanical energy is $E = K + U = \frac{1}{2}mv^2 + U_0$ in the box. For a given energy, all three terms are constant; the particle moves with constant speed, reversing direction at each wall. The higher the energy the faster it bounces back and forth, that is, the higher its frequency of vibration.

This potential is convenient because the potential energy is not a continuous function of position. It is of interest because it serves as a simple example of a potential in quantum mechanics. A description of the motion in terms of quantum mechanics instead of classical mechanics shows that the energy of the particle in the box is quantized. This means that the energy can take on only certain allowed values, and therefore the particle can bounce back and forth only with certain allowed frequencies.

Later we will use another energy diagram, that for a diatomic molecule, but first we must establish what we mean by energy of a **system** of particles.

Questions for discussion

1. In a region where a particle would experience a force we say that there is a force field—a vector field. We can instead say that there is a potential at any point in the region—a scalar field. In the region around a hot object you would measure different temperatures at different points. You can say that there is a temperature field in the region. Is this a vector or a scalar field? In a fluid flowing steadily (streamline flow) the velocity of each particle that passes a particular point is the same. This can be described as a velocity field in the fluid. Is it a vector or a scalar field? Can you think of other examples of vector or scalar fields? Why is the term field used?

2. What is the advantage of representing a vector field by continuous lines? What is the advantage of using a number of short vectors?

3. The potential energy of a particle is the same at every point on an equipotential surface. Is the force on it at every point the same? Is the magnitude of the force on it at every point the same?

4. A particle with no resultant force on it and at rest is said to be in equilibrium. Depending on what happens if the particle is disturbed, the particle is said to be in stable, unstable, or neutral equilibrium. With the generalized potential curve that we used, where would a particle be in each of these three states?

Problems

1. Calculate the period of a particle that moves in an orbit close to the surface of a homogeneous sphere of density 5 gm/cm^3, assuming that the gravitational attraction of the sphere is the only force acting on the particle. Use $G = 6.67 \times 10^{-8}$ cm^3/gm-sec^2.

2. Two identical thin uniform rods, each of length L, are dropped by a careless space walker. At some instant they are located in the same line, with a distance L between their nearer ends. Estimate the percentage error made in calculating the gravitational force between them by treating them as particles, with their masses acting at their centers. The approximation can be improved by treating each rod as two halves, or better yet as four quarters. This last gives quite a good estimate, so you can use it in estimating the error. Can you verify this by integrating to determine the force?

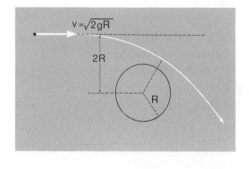

3. A meteor is approaching the earth, with an impact parameter $2R$, where R is the earth radius (i.e., if the meteor continued in a straight line it would pass the earth at a distance $2R$ from the center, or a height R above the surface). When the meteor is a large distance from the earth its speed is $\sqrt{2gR}$, where g is the magnitude of the acceleration due to gravity at the earth's surface (this is the same as the escape speed for a particle launched at the earth's surface). (a) How close to the surface of the earth will the meteor come? (b) For what value of the impact parameter would the meteor graze the surface of the earth (neglecting air resistance)?

4. (a) Determine the gravitational potential at points inside a spherical shell of density ρ, inside and outside radii R_1 and R_2.

(b) Determine the potential inside a homogeneous sphere of mass M, radius R, as a function of the distance from the center r. Verify that the field is given by $\mathbf{E}_p = -GM\mathbf{r}/R^3$.

5. In the famous α-particle scattering experiments of Geiger and Marsden (1911) which helped to establish the Rutherford nuclear model of the atom, α-particles having a kinetic energy of 7.68 Mev (from radioactive polonium) were scattered from a thin

gold foil (for gold the atomic number is 79; that is, there is a positive charge on a gold nucleus of 79e).

(a) Calculate the distance of closest approach r_0 for a head-on collision between an α-particle and a gold nucleus. This gives an upper limit for the "size" of the nucleus. Assume the nucleus remains at rest (i.e., work in a frame of reference fixed to the nucleus, and assume it is an inertial frame). Use the constant in the Coulomb law as $1/(4\pi\epsilon_0) = 9 \times 10^9$ n-m^2/coul^2.

(b) Calculate the distance of closest approach for an α-particle with an impact parameter of 5×10^{-14} m.

6. A 1-gm particle moving in one-dimension with a kinetic energy of 1 joule is bound in a square potential well 1 m wide. What is its frequency of vibration?

7. A small block rests on a smooth table, fastened between two identical ideal springs in a straight line. The springs, each of spring constant k and unstretched length l, are unstretched and the outer end of each is fixed to the table at points $(-l,0)$ and $(l,0)$ in a co-ordinate system with x-axis along the line of the springs, y-axis at right angles (and on the table), and origin at the rest position of the block. (a) Write an expression $U(x,y)$ for the elastic potential energy of the block in terms of its displacement from its rest position. (b) Let $y = 0$ in $U(x,y)$, and find $F_x = -dU/dx$, giving the restoring force for displacements along the x-axis. If the block is displaced and released, is the motion simple harmonic? (c) Let $x = 0$ and find $F_y = -dU/dy$, giving the restoring force for displacements along the y-axis. If the block is displaced and released, is the motion simple harmonic? Is it periodic? What is F_y if $y \ll l$?

23

ENERGY OF
A SYSTEM OF PARTICLES

KINETIC ENERGY OF
A SYSTEM OF PARTICLES

So far we have confined our attention to the motion of a single particle, and
talked about "its" kinetic energy and "its" potential energy, an energy that can
be defined for it if it is in a conservative field. However, we introduced potential
energy by pointing out that it was necessary in order to apply the idea of conservation of energy to a system of particles, be-
cause the work–energy relation $W_{1 \to 2} = K_2 - K_1$
does not apply to a system of particles. If two particles are released from rest, and there are no external forces acting on them, then no work is done on
the system but the kinetic energy will increase because of the interaction of the particles.

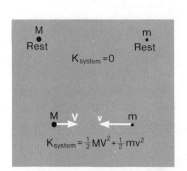

Two interacting particles
released from rest will acquire kinetic energy.

Before discussing the potential energy of the
system, we will say a little more about the kinetic
energy of the system. You remember we showed
in dynamics that the motion of a system of particles can be divided into two parts, motion of the
particles with respect to the center of mass, and
motion of the center of mass as though all the mass
were at this point. This indicates that the kinetic
energy of the system can be divided this way. We will show explicitly that this
is so. This means we are going to compare the motion as described in an external
frame of reference to the motion as described in the center of mass frame.

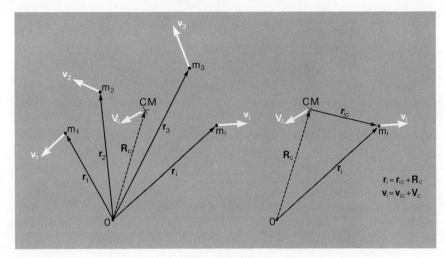

The velocities of a system of particles with respect to the center of mass.

The kinetic energy of the system with respect to the frame of reference in which O is a fixed point is

$$
\begin{aligned}
K &= \tfrac{1}{2} \sum m_i v_i^2 = \tfrac{1}{2} \sum m_i \mathbf{v}_i \cdot \mathbf{v}_i \\
&= \tfrac{1}{2} \sum m_i (\mathbf{v}_{ic} + \mathbf{V}_c) \cdot (\mathbf{v}_{ic} + \mathbf{V}_c) \\
&= \tfrac{1}{2} \sum m_i \mathbf{v}_{ic} \cdot \mathbf{v}_{ic} + \tfrac{1}{2} \sum m_i \mathbf{V}_c \cdot \mathbf{V}_c + \sum m_i \mathbf{v}_{ic} \cdot \mathbf{V}_c \\
&= \tfrac{1}{2} \sum m_i v_{ic}^2 + \tfrac{1}{2} (\sum m_i) V_c^2 + (\sum m_i \mathbf{v}_{ic}) \cdot \mathbf{V}_c \\
&= K_c + \tfrac{1}{2} M V_c^2
\end{aligned}
$$

where K_c is the kinetic energy of the system in the c-of-m frame of reference $K_c = \tfrac{1}{2} \sum m_i v_{ic}^2$, M is the total mass of the system $M = \sum m_i$, and V_c is the speed of the c-of-m with respect to the external frame of reference. The sum $\sum m_i \mathbf{v}_{ic}$ is zero by the definition of center of mass.

The result $K = K_c + \tfrac{1}{2} M V_c^2$ is valid at any instant. If both frames of reference are inertial frames they are related by a constant velocity $\mathbf{V}_c$, and the term $\tfrac{1}{2} M V_c^2$ is constant, but the relation is valid whether or not the frames are inertial frames.

POTENTIAL ENERGY OF A TWO-PARTICLE SYSTEM

In order to discuss the interaction between two particles we will use the gravitational interaction, so that we can write specific expressions for the force and energy, but the discussion is applicable to any central force.

Think about two particles of masses M and m, both initially at rest. The gravitational force between them has magnitude $F = GMm/r^2$, where r is the distance between them. If mass M is **held** at rest, and mass m moved from position 1 to position 2 along two different paths, we have shown that the work done by the force F is the same along each path. Therefore the force is conservative,

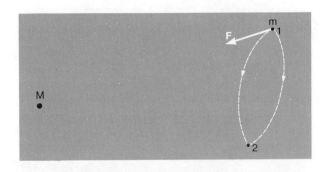

Mass *m* moved 1 → 2
along two paths.

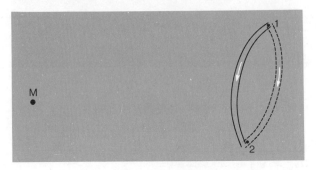

Smooth tubes visualized
to define the paths.

and we can define a potential energy $U = -GMm/r$ for mass m. If the force F is the *only* force doing work on m, we have conservation of energy and its speed at point 2 is the same for either path.

Of course, if F is the only force acting on m it will not follow an arbitrary path. However, we can visualize it sliding in fixed frictionless tubes between points 1 and 2. The constraint forces exerted by the walls of a tube can do no work on m, so its speed at 2 is the same for any smooth tube, if m is released at point 1.

Now suppose that mass M is *not* held fixed. When m is allowed to move from point 1 to point 2 along two different paths (tubes) the work done by the force

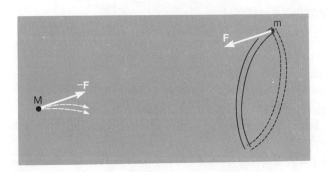

If *M* is not fixed, its motion
depends on the motion of *m*.

F on it will *not* be the same, because the way that M moves (and therefore the force it exerts on m) will be different in the two cases. Does this mean that the force of gravity is not a conservative force here, and we cannot introduce a potential energy?

This paradox is resolved if we remember that potential energy is energy of **position**. This means position relative to something else, that is, **position in a particular frame of reference.**

In a frame of reference in which M is at rest, we say that m has a potential energy $U = -GMm/r$, meaning that an amount of work GMm/r is done by the force of gravity F to bring mass m up to a distance r from mass M.

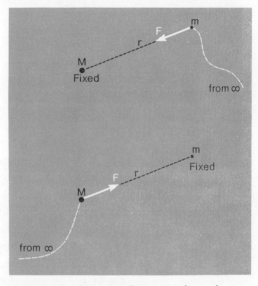

In a frame of reference in which m is at rest, we say that M has a potential energy $U = -GMm/r$, meaning that an amount of work GMm/r is done by the force of gravity F to bring mass M up to a distance r from mass m. Thus we refer to the potential energy of m with respect to M, or the potential energy of M with respect to m, and **this is the same quantity.**

The potential energy of the two-particle **system** due to the gravitational interaction is $-GMm/r$, where r is the distance between the two particles. Whether this energy is assigned to one particle or to the other or to both is a matter of choice— **choice of the frame of reference** in which the motion is described.

Assignment of potential energy depends on the choice of reference frame.

The point of defining potential energy is to have conservation of energy $E = K + U = $ constant (for conservative systems). In a frame of reference in which M is at rest (a frame fixed to M) its kinetic energy is always zero and changes in both kinetic energy and potential energy are associated with mass m. If no forces except the force due to M act on m, its mechanical energy E is constant.

$$E = \tfrac{1}{2}mv^2 - GMm/r$$

where v is the speed of m and r is its distance from the point where M is at rest in the frame of reference.

In a frame of reference fixed to m the changes in both kinetic energy and potential energy are associated with mass M. If no other forces except the force due to m act on M, its mechanical energy E is constant.

$$E = \tfrac{1}{2}MV^2 - GMm/r$$

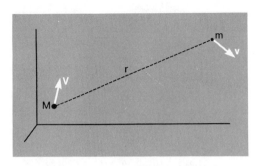

In a reference frame in which M and m are both moving, the potential energy is a property of the two-particle system.

where V is the speed of M and r is its distance from the point where m is at rest in the frame.

If neither M nor m is fixed in the frame of reference, the potential energy $-GMm/r$ cannot be associated uniquely with either particle. It is not a unique function $U(x,y,z)$ of the position of either particle, and therefore as far as the individual particles are concerned the force of gravity between them is not acting as a conservative force. We can, however, consider the **two-particle system,** for which the force of gravity between the particles is an internal force. If there are no external forces on the system, its mechanical energy E is constant.

$$E = \tfrac{1}{2}MV^2 + \tfrac{1}{2}mv^2 - GMm/r$$

where V and v are the speeds of M and m at any instant and r is their distance apart at the same instant. The potential energy $-GMm/r$ is a mutual property of both particles, a property of the **system.**

We defined a central force earlier as one that acts directly toward (or away from) a fixed point in a frame of reference, and this is not the kind of force that is acting on either particle if both particles are moving in a frame of reference. An equivalent definition of a central force recognizes that forces act between particles; a central force between two particles is one whose magnitude depends only on the distance between them and whose direction is along the line joining them. By choosing a frame of reference fixed to one of the particles the argument given earlier shows that any central force must be conservative.

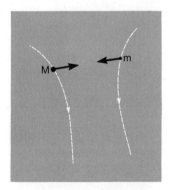

The gravitational force is independent of the frame of reference only if it is assumed to be an instantaneous interaction.

We should emphasize again one of the fundamental assumptions of classical mechanics; we are assuming **instantaneous** action-at-a-distance forces. If we assume that the force between mass M and mass m depends only on the distance between them, and not on their velocity or acceleration, this means there must be instantaneous communication between them. The force depends only on where they *are* at any instant, not how they got there. If there were any time delay in the "signals" between them, this would not be possible.

This assumption means the gravitational force between two particles has a magnitude GMm/r^2, independent of any frame of reference, and we can define a corresponding potential energy $-GMm/r$.

However, the assignment of this potential energy to one particle or the other, or to both, does depend on the frame of reference.

ENERGY IN INERTIAL AND
NON-INERTIAL FRAMES OF REFERENCE

We stated that in a frame of reference fixed to mass M all of the energy (kinetic and potential) is associated with mass m, and its energy is

$$E = \tfrac{1}{2}mv^2 - GMm/r = \text{constant}$$

Does the reference frame in which this applies have to be an inertial frame?

Before dealing with this question, think about the following question. The two particles M and m are held at rest in an inertial frame, a distance r_0 apart. Mass m is released, and then the only force acting on it is the gravitational attraction of M. When m reaches a distance r_1 from M its speed is v_0. Suppose

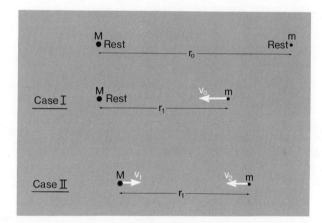

Is the relative velocity the same in both cases?

that instead of just releasing m, both M and m are released simultaneously. When they are a distance r_1 apart, they have speeds v_1 and v_2. The question is this: is the relative speed $(v_2 - v_1)$ the same as v_0, the relative speed at this distance when only m is released?

In a frame of reference fixed to M the conditions for the two cases are similar; in both cases m is released at distance r_0 away, and falls to a distance r_1 away from M. Is the motion the same in both cases? If it is, the relative speed would be v_0 in both cases.

In order to deal with as simple a situation as possible, we will work this out for the symmetric case where the masses are equal $M = m$, although we continue to label them M and m for identification. We also choose the particular distance $r_1 = r_0/2$; the distance between the particles is halved.

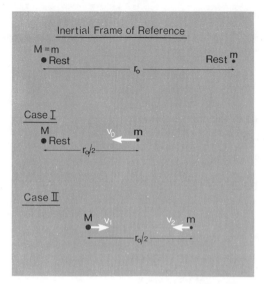

Motion in the inertial
frame of reference.

Because the particles were initially at rest, and the only force after they are released acts along the line joining them, the motion is along the line, confined to one dimension.

In the inertial frame of reference in which the particles are initially at rest, the energy equation for Case I, where M is fixed, is

$$E = -\frac{GMm}{r_0} = \tfrac{1}{2}mv_0^2 - \frac{GMm}{r_0/2}$$

so

$$\tfrac{1}{2}mv_0^2 = \frac{GMm}{r_0}$$

For Case II, where both particles can move, the speeds of the particles will be the same from symmetry $v_2 = v_1$.

$$E = -\frac{GMm}{r_0} = \tfrac{1}{2}mv_1^2 + \tfrac{1}{2}mv_1^2 - \frac{GMm}{r_0/2}$$

so $\quad 2(\tfrac{1}{2}mv_1^2) = \dfrac{GMm}{r_0} \quad$ and $\quad v_1^2 = \dfrac{v_0^2}{2}$

The **relative** speed of the particles is

$$v_{\mathrm{rel}} = 2v_1 = 2(v_0/\sqrt{2}) = \sqrt{2}v_0$$

That is, the relative speed is **greater** in this case. This is not a surprising result, because the same force acts on both particles and if both can move they are both accelerated and come together more quickly than if one is held fixed.

Now think about Case II in the frame of reference fixed to M. The gravitational force on m due to M is $F = GMm/r^2$, the corresponding gravitational energy of m with respect to M is $U = -GMm/r$, but the mechanical energy $E = K + U = \tfrac{1}{2}mv^2 - GMm/r$ **is not constant.** This energy is constant **only if no force except the gravitational force is doing work on m.**

There is another force doing work on m in this frame of reference. The frame of reference is fixed to M, and M has an acceleration $\mathbf{a}$ at every instant with respect to the inertial frame. Therefore there is an inertial force $\mathbf{F}_i = -m\mathbf{a}$ on mass m. This force is in the same direction as the gravitational force F_{grav} due to M, and the resultant force $F_{\mathrm{grav}} + F_i$ produces a larger acceleration and higher speed at any point than if mass M is fixed in the inertial frame as in Case I.

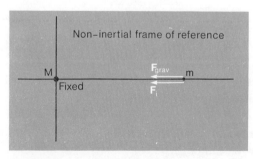

Forces on m in the non-inertial
frame of M in Case II.

We can use the work–energy relation $W_{1 \to 2} = K_2 - K_1$ in the non-inertial frame if we include the work done by the inertial force $\mathbf{F}_i$.

In the inertial frame mass M has an acceleration $a = F/M = Gm/r^2$ toward the right when the particles are a distance r apart. This means that in the non-inertial frame there is an inertial force $F_i = ma = GMm/r^2$ toward the left; here r is the displacement of m from M, a fixed point. The force $\mathbf{F}_i$ and the displacement $\mathbf{r}$ are in opposite directions, so the work done by $\mathbf{F}_i$ as the mass m moves from r_0 to $r_0/2$ is

$$W_i = \int \mathbf{F}_i \cdot d\mathbf{r} = -\int_{r_0}^{r_0/2} F_i \, dr = -GMm \int_{r_0}^{r_0/2} \frac{dr}{r^2} = GMm \left[\frac{1}{r}\right]_{r_0}^{r_0/2} = \frac{GMm}{r_0}$$

The work done by the gravitational force F_{grav} in the same interval is

$$W_{\text{grav}} = -(U_2 - U_1) = -\left(-\frac{GMm}{r_0/2} + \frac{GMm}{r_0}\right) = \frac{GMm}{r_0}$$

so the net work done in the interval

$$W = W_i + W_{\text{grav}} = 2\frac{GMm}{r_0} = K_2 - K_1$$

The initial kinetic energy, at $r = r_0$, is $K_1 = 0$, and at $r_0/2$ the kinetic energy is $K_2 = \frac{1}{2}mv_{\text{rel}}^2$, where v_{rel} is the speed of m with respect to M at this point.

$$2\frac{GMm}{r_0} = \frac{1}{2}mv_{\text{rel}}^2$$

If only mass m was released (Case I) the speed v_0 was determined by

$$\frac{GMm}{r_0} = \frac{1}{2}mv_{\text{rel}}^2$$

so
$$v_{\text{rel}} = \sqrt{2}v_0$$

This is the same result for the relative speed of the two particles as calculated in the inertial frame. The calculation can be made in the non-inertial frame provided the work done by the inertial force is taken into account.

We have emphasized throughout this book that any equation of motion applies to a particular **system,** and applies in a particular **frame of reference.** This example demonstrates this for an equation of motion in the form $K + U =$ constant (E). In the inertial frame where both particles are moving it is possible to have conservation of energy only for the two-particle system, not for the particles individually.

For the two-particle system we can work out the motion of one particle by fixing a frame of reference to the other particle and introducing the inertial force, but this method will not work if there are more than two particles moving relative to one another. In general to avoid this difficulty we use conservation of

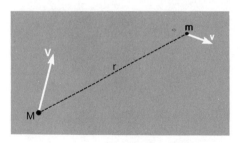

If the only forces acting are due to the mutual interaction of the particles, then E is constant in any inertial frame of reference.

energy only in inertial frames of reference, where the only forces are "body forces," forces due to other bodies.

If two particles are moving under the influence of their mutual gravitational attraction, and other forces on the particles are negligible, then the statement of conservation of energy is

$$E = \tfrac{1}{2}MV^2 + \tfrac{1}{2}mv^2 - GMm/r = \text{constant}$$

where the value of the constant E is determined by the initial conditions. This equation is valid **only in an inertial frame of reference**. This may be the center of mass frame, or any frame moving at constant velocity with respect to it.

In a frame moving at constant velocity $\mathbf{V}_0$ with respect to the c-of-m frame, the energy can be written

$$E = (\tfrac{1}{2}MV_c^2 + \tfrac{1}{2}mv_c^2) + \tfrac{1}{2}(M + m)V_0^2 - G\frac{Mm}{r} = \text{constant}$$

where V_c and v_c are the speeds of the particles in the c-of-m frame.

In the c-of-m frame $MV_c + mv_c = 0$, so the ratio of the kinetic energies is

$$\frac{\tfrac{1}{2}MV_c^2}{\tfrac{1}{2}mv_c^2} = \frac{M}{m}\left(-\frac{m}{M}\right)^2 = \frac{m}{M}$$

If $M \gg m$, this ratio approaches zero. Most of the kinetic energy—and therefore most of the potential energy—is associated with mass m. This is the situation for the motion of the earth–sun system, or the system of the earth and an earth satellite. Conservation of energy really applies to the pair of masses in the c-of-m frame of reference, but it is a good approximation to treat a frame of reference fixed to the more massive particle as an inertial frame, and assume conservation of energy for the less massive particle. Potential energy is always a mutual property, but under some circumstances it can be treated as a property of a single particle.

Later we will return to the two-particle system, and see how some aspects of its motion can be described in terms of an equivalent single particle.

MECHANICAL ENERGY OF A SYSTEM OF PARTICLES

The mechanical energy of a system of two particles, acted on only by the force of their mutual gravitation, is

$$E = \tfrac{1}{2}MV^2 + \tfrac{1}{2}mv^2 - GMm/r = \text{constant}$$

While we have indicated that this result is plausible, we have not really proved it. We prove now that the mechanical energy is constant for an isolated two-particle system with any conservative central force between the particles. The proof can be extended to include any number of particles.

We wish to show that the mechanical energy

$$E = K + U = (\tfrac{1}{2}m_1v_1^2 + \tfrac{1}{2}m_2v_2^2) + U$$

is constant, that is, that $dE/dt = 0$. Using $v^2 = \mathbf{v}\cdot\mathbf{v}$

$$\frac{d(v^2)}{dt} = \mathbf{v}\cdot\frac{d\mathbf{v}}{dt} + \frac{d\mathbf{v}}{dt}\cdot\mathbf{v} = 2\mathbf{v}\cdot\frac{d\mathbf{v}}{dt}$$

so

$$\frac{dK}{dt} = m_1\mathbf{v}_1\cdot\frac{d\mathbf{v}_1}{dt} + m_2\mathbf{v}_2\cdot\frac{d\mathbf{v}_2}{dt}$$

$$= \mathbf{v}_1\cdot\mathbf{F}_{12} + \mathbf{v}_2\cdot\mathbf{F}_{21}$$

where $\mathbf{F}_{12}$ (force on m_1 due to m_2) $= d\mathbf{p}_1/dt = m_1(d\mathbf{v}_1/dt)$ and $\mathbf{F}_{21}$ (force on m_2 due to m_1) $= m_2(d\mathbf{v}_2/dt)$. For any interaction $\mathbf{F}_{21} = -\mathbf{F}_{12}$

$$\frac{dK}{dt} = \mathbf{v}_1\cdot(-\mathbf{F}_{21}) + \mathbf{v}_2\cdot\mathbf{F}_{21} = \mathbf{F}_{21}\cdot(\mathbf{v}_2 - \mathbf{v}_1)$$

$$= \mathbf{F}_{21}\cdot\mathbf{v}_{21}$$

where $\mathbf{v}_{21} = \mathbf{v}_2 - \mathbf{v}_1$ is the velocity of m_2 relative to m_1.

The vector $\mathbf{r}$ is the displacement of m_2 relative to m_1. For a central force, $\mathbf{F}_{21}$ is along the line joining the particles, and it has a magnitude $F_{21} = -dU/dr$, where U is the potential energy of m_2 with respect to m_1 (and therefore the potential energy of the two-particle system). The scalar product $\mathbf{F}_{21}\cdot\mathbf{v}_{21}$ is $F_{21} \times$ (component of $\mathbf{v}_{21}$ along the $\mathbf{r}$ direction) $= F_{21}(dr/dt)$. It depends on the rate of change of magnitude of $\mathbf{r}$, not on the rate of change of direction of $\mathbf{r}$. You can recognize $\mathbf{F}_{21}\cdot\mathbf{v}_{21}$ as the rate at which the force $\mathbf{F}_{21}$ is doing work on m_2.

$$\frac{dK}{dt} = \mathbf{F}_{21}\cdot\mathbf{v}_{21} = F_{21}\frac{dr}{dt} = -\frac{dU}{dr}\frac{dr}{dt} = -\frac{dU}{dt}$$

Therefore $dE/dt = dK/dt + dU/dt = 0$, and mechanical energy E is constant.

We emphasize the conditions under which $E = $ constant is valid:

1. The system is isolated; there are no external forces on the two-particle system.

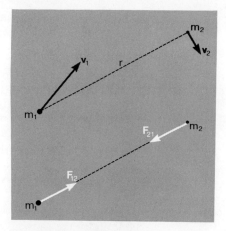

Two-particles with a central force of interaction.

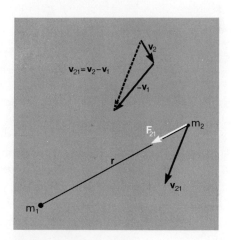

The motion of m_2 with respect to m_1.

2. The motion is described in an inertial frame of reference. Otherwise we could not assume the only forces on the particles were due to one another— there would be inertial forces. Note that the potential energy U is the same in any inertial frame, since it depends only on the relative positions of the particles. The kinetic energy K depends on the particular inertial frame chosen. We showed that $K = K_c + \frac{1}{2}MV_0^2$, where K is the kinetic energy in an inertial frame moving with velocity $\mathbf{V}_0$ with respect to the center-of-mass frame, K_c is the kinetic energy in the c-of-m frame, and M is the total mass $M = \sum m_i$. The kinetic energy has its minimum value in the c-of-m frame.

3. The force between the particles is a conservative central force. Actually the result is valid for any conservative force, but our proof assumes a central force, as in the gravitational or electrostatic interaction.

The result can be extended to a system with any number of interacting particles, under the same assumptions. For example, for a system of particles of masses $m_1, m_2, \cdots$, with only the gravitational interaction between them

$$E = K + U = \sum_i \tfrac{1}{2}m_i v_i^2 - \sum_{i,j(i<j)} G\frac{m_i m_j}{r_{ij}} = \text{constant}$$

The potential energy U involves the sum over all pairs of particles. For example, for three particles there would be three terms $-G[(m_1 m_2/r_{12}) + (m_1 m_3/r_{13}) + (m_2 m_3/r_{23})]$. For four particles there would be six terms, involving the six inter-particle distances r_{12}, r_{13}, r_{14}, r_{23}, r_{24}, r_{34}.

The fact that the result can be extended to any number of particles depends on the superposition assumption (that the interactions are independent of one another, and therefore the resultant effect is the sum of the individual effects). Kinetic energy is a property of an individual particle, and the resultant kinetic energy is the sum of the individual kinetic energies. Potential energy is a property of a pair of particles, and the resultant potential energy is the sum of the potential energies for each pair of particles.

WORK–ENERGY RELATION FOR A SYSTEM OF PARTICLES

The development of the concept of mechanical energy has taken some time, so we summarize what we have done.

We began a discussion of potential energy by pointing out that the work–energy relation $W_{1 \to 2} = K_2 - K_1$ for a particle could not be applied to a system of particles. This relation was an integrated form of the basic law of motion $\mathbf{F} = m\mathbf{a}$, and the work done $W_{1 \to 2}$ is the resultant work due to all forces acting on the particle.

We divided forces into two classes, conservative forces and non-conservative forces, and then could divide the work done in an interval into two parts, work done by conservative forces and work done by non-conservative forces.

$$W_{1\to2} = (W_{1\to2})_c + (W_{1\to2})_{Nc}$$

The work $(W_{1\to2})_c$ done by conservative forces is independent of the path taken by the particle, depending only on the end points, and this enabled us to define potential energy U for the particle by

$$(W_{1\to2})_c = -(U_2 - U_1)$$

and the work–energy relation

$$W_{1\to2} = (W_{1\to2})_{Nc} + (W_{1\to2})_c = K_2 - K_1$$

became

$$\begin{aligned}(W_{1\to2})_{Nc} &= (K_2 - K_1) + (U_2 - U_1)\\ &= (K_2 + U_2) - (K_1 + U_1)\\ &= E_2 - E_1\end{aligned}$$

where $E = K + U$ is called the mechanical energy of the particle. If there are no non-conservative forces acting on the particle, $(W_{1\to2})_{Nc} = 0$ and $E_2 = E_1$. This is conservation of mechanical energy for a single particle.

A conservative force on a particle is a force that depends on position only, not on time, so that we can only assign potential energy to a particle if it is moving in a static force field. Since all forces on a particle are due to other particles, this means that when we talk about potential energy of a particle we are assuming that all other particles that are exerting forces on it are fixed. If two particles are moving, we cannot speak of the potential energy of either one due to the other, but only of the mutual potential energy of the pair, or system.

The important thing about the concept of mechanical energy is that the relation $(W_{1\to2})_{Nc} = E_2 - E_1$ does apply to a system of particles.

The mechanical energy of an isolated conservative system of particles is constant. "Isolated" means that there are no external forces doing work on the system, "conservative" means that the internal forces, the forces between the particles, are conservative so $(W_{1\to2})_{Nc} = 0$.

If there *are* external forces doing work on a system of particles, then the mechanical energy is not constant.

$$W_{ext} = E_2 - E_1$$

This is a work–energy relation that is valid for a system of particles (a conservative system), *or* for a single particle. It is comparable to the impulse–momentum relation $\mathbf{J}_{ext} = \mathbf{P}_2 - \mathbf{P}_1$ for a system of particles.

The work done by internal forces in the system is included under E (provided the system is conservative). For a single particle, there are no internal forces; the only kind of energy the particle can have is kinetic energy, and the general work–energy relation reduces to $W_{ext} = K_2 - K_1$, where W_{ext} simply means all the work done on the particle. There is no "internal" for a particle—this is the idealization that defines a particle.

The work done by external forces on a system of particles may be due to conservative or non-conservative forces. We will use as an example a ball falling through the air near the earth surface. A ball is really a complex system of interacting particles. What can we say about its motion from an energy point of view?

A ball released from rest, with air resistance.

Example: The ball of mass M is released from rest and falls with pure translation. Its downward speed after falling a distance y is V. The external work done by the force of gravity downward is positive, $W_{ext} = Mgy$. Since gravity is a conservative force, we can define a corresponding potential energy, and say that there is a loss in overall potential energy.

There is a force of friction opposing the motion. The work done by this non-conservative force is negative. We can write $W_{ext} = -Q$, where Q is a positive quantity.

The general work–energy relation is then

$$E_2 - E_1 = \sum W_{ext} = Mgy - Q$$

In the inertial frame of reference of the earth, the initial mechanical energy of the ball (treated as a system of particles) is

$$E_1 = (K_c)_1 + (U_{int})_1$$

where $(K_c)_1$ is the sum of the kinetic energies of the particles in the ball, with respect to the center of mass which is initially at rest in the earth frame, and $(U_{int})_1$ is the internal potential energy due to the interaction of the particles of the ball.

When the ball has a speed V with respect to the earth frame, its mechanical energy is

$$E_2 = (K_c)_2 + \tfrac{1}{2}MV^2 + (U_{int})_2$$

The term $\tfrac{1}{2}MV^2$ in the kinetic energy is due to the motion of the center of mass. The internal kinetic and potential energies are not necessarily the same as at the start of the motion.

Suppose the ball is treated as a rigid body. Then all the particles are fixed at rest with respect to one another by the internal forces, so $(K_c)_1 = (K_c)_2 = 0$, $(U_{int})_1 = (U_{int})_2 =$ constant, and $E_2 = E_1 + \tfrac{1}{2}MV^2$.

The work–energy relation is

$$\tfrac{1}{2}MV^2 = Mgy - Q$$

The ball acts as though it were a single particle of mass M, losing an amount Q of mechanical energy in the interval. With the rigid body model we have to say that this energy is "lost," because we have no way of assigning it.

Of course, a ball is not a rigid body, and the work–energy relation in general is

$$[(K_c)_2 + (U_{int})_2] - [(K_c)_1 + (U_{int})_1] + \tfrac{1}{2}MV^2 = Mgy - Q$$

which can be written

$$(E_c)_2 - (E_c)_1 + Q = Mgy - \tfrac{1}{2}MV^2$$

where E_c is the mechanical energy with respect to the center of mass: $E_c = K_c + U_{int}$. This quantity E_c, the sum of the internal kinetic energies and interaction energies, is called the **internal energy** of the system of particles.

The right side of the equation ($Mgy - \frac{1}{2}MV^2$) is the decrease in **macroscopic** mechanical energy of the ball; an amount Q has been lost. The left side of the equation can be interpreted by saying that the energy Q has become part of the **microscopic** mechanical energy, or internal energy.

We have said that from the point of view of classical mechanics the fundamental forces between particles are considered to be conservative, and therefore that the energy of any system of particles is mechanical energy (kinetic plus potential) if the system is described in microscopic terms. In dealing with macroscopic "particles" such as the falling ball, mechanical energy disappears. In order to use the concept of conservation of energy at the macroscopic level, we must define other forms of energy such as thermal energy. A frictional force (a macroscopic concept) acts on the falling ball, and the work done by this force becomes thermal energy Q. At the microscopic level this form of energy is not necessary. The energy Q is mechanical energy of the microscopic particles of the system.

When the internal energy of a system increases by an amount Q both the kinetic and potential energies of the particles may change. An increase in the kinetic energy may change the distance between particles (thermal expansion) and therefore the potential energy of interaction.

The terms **thermal energy** and **heat energy** are sometimes used interchangeably. The energy of a system of gas molecules moving randomly in a container is mechanical energy from a microscopic view, but is called thermal energy or heat energy macroscopically. We use the term thermal energy, and restrict the term "heat" to heat **transfer.** The internal energy of the system of gas molecules can be changed either by external forces doing work W on the system, or by energy transferred by bringing the system into contact (thermal contact) with another system at a different temperature. This kind of energy transfer we call a heat flow Q, and thus restrict the term "heat" to energy in transit between systems.

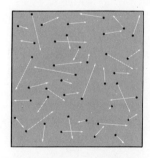

What kind of energy do the gas molecules have?

If heat Q flows into a system, and the system does work W, the change in internal energy of the system is

$$E_2 - E_1 = Q - W$$

This is the first law of thermodynamics.

Thus the thermal energy of a system can change either because of work done on (or by) the system, or because of heat transferred to (or from) the system.

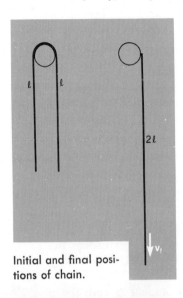

Initial and final positions of chain.

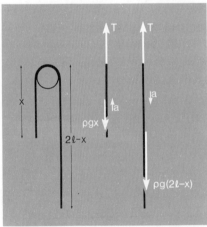

Motion analyzed by considering the chain segments on each side separately.

Example: A thin flexible uniform chain 16 ft long hangs over a smooth peg in unstable equilibrium. If it starts to slip, what is its speed at the instant it leaves the peg?

If we assume that the chain can be treated as a system of particles such that there are no internal energy losses as it moves, we can assume conservation of mechanical energy for the macroscopic system.

Let the chain length be $2l$, and mass be m. Initially the c-of-m of the system is a distance $l/2$ below the peg, and the kinetic energy is zero. At the instant the chain leaves the peg the c-of-m is a distance l below the peg, and the speed is v_f. Assuming conservation of mechanical energy for the system, $mg\,[l - (l/2)] = \tfrac{1}{2}mv_f^2$

$$v_f = \sqrt{gl} = \sqrt{32 \times 8} = 16 \text{ ft/sec}$$

In order to see the simplification made by the use of energy considerations, we also work out the result using the basic dynamic relation $\mathbf{F} = m\mathbf{a}$. We use ρ as the mass per unit length of chain: $m = 2l\rho$.

We write the equations of motion for the sides of the chain, at the instant there is a length x on one side of the peg, length $(2l - x)$ on the other. The tension in the chain at the peg has magnitude T.

$$T - \rho gx = \rho xa$$
$$\rho g(2l - x) - T = \rho(2l - x)a$$

Adding these

$$2\rho g(l - x) = 2\rho la \quad \text{or} \quad a = \left(\frac{l - x}{l}\right)g$$

Acceleration a is related to speed v and position x by

$$a = \frac{dv}{dt} = \frac{dv}{dx}\frac{dx}{dt} = -\frac{dv}{dx}v$$

The speed is $v = -(dx/dt)$ because x decreases as v increases.

$$a = -v\frac{dv}{dx} = \left(\frac{l - x}{l}\right)g \qquad g\left(\frac{l - x}{l}\right)dx = -v\,dv$$

As x goes from l to 0, v goes from 0 to v_f.

$$g\int_l^0 \left[\frac{l - x}{l}\right]dx = -\int_0^{v_f} v\,dv \qquad g\left[x - \frac{x^2}{2l}\right]_l^0 = -\left[\frac{v^2}{2}\right]_0^{v_f}$$

$$g\left[0 - \left(l - \frac{l^2}{2l}\right)\right] = -\frac{v_f^2}{2} \qquad -\frac{gl}{2} = -\frac{v_f^2}{2} \qquad v_f = \sqrt{gl}$$

The energy equation gives this result directly because it is an integrated form of the equation of motion.

Is the assumption that there are no internal energy losses in the chain made in the dynamic solution?

Example: The 500-lb hammer of a pile driver drops 10 ft onto a 1000-lb pile, driving it 6 in. into the ground. What is the average force exerted by the ground on the pile as it moves down? This appears to be a simple physical situation, but an analysis of it raises some interesting questions.

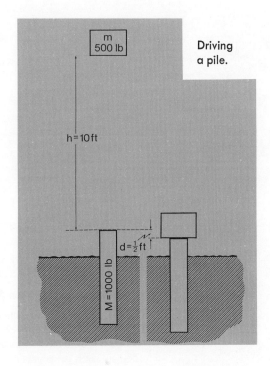

Driving a pile.

For the falling hammer it is reasonable to assume conservation of mechanical energy. Its loss in potential energy is equal to its gain in kinetic energy: $mgh = \frac{1}{2}mv^2$, where v is its speed just before it hits the pile.

For the pile moving downward mechanical energy is certainly not conserved. It comes to rest, and all of its mechanical energy has become thermal energy of the pile and surrounding earth.

What about the intervening stage, the collision between the hammer and pile? Can we assume conservation of linear momentum, or conservation of mechanical energy, or both, or neither?

Suppose we assume that there is no loss in mechanical energy in the collision. The loss in potential energy of the hammer in falling h ft is mgh, and the loss in potential energy of the hammer and pile in moving down d ft is $(M + m)gd$. This net loss in mechanical energy of the hammer–pile system is equal to the work done by the external force in bringing it to rest: $W_{ext} = E_2 - E_1$.

If F is the average upward force exerted by the earth, the work done is $W_{ext} = Fd$

$$Fd = mgh + (M + m)gd$$

$$F = mg\frac{h}{d} + (M + m)g$$

$$= \left[500 \times \frac{10}{1/2} + 1500 \right] 32 \text{ pndl}$$

$$= 10,000 + 1500 \text{ lb}$$

The term $(M + m)g$ or 1500 lb is the upward force necessary to support the weight of the hammer–pile system. There is an additional 10,000 lb necessary to stop it moving.

Here we did not have to consider the collision at all. We assumed no mechanical energy loss, that is we assumed the kinetic energy of the hammer just before collision $\frac{1}{2}mv^2$ is equal to the kinetic energy of the hammer–pile system just after collision: $\frac{1}{2}mv^2 = \frac{1}{2}(M + m)V^2$, where V is the speed just after collision.

We know that there is mechanical energy loss in the collision. We are assuming that the hammer and pile stick together after collision, and energy is not conserved in such a non-elastic impact.

Now let us see what the result is if we assume conservation of linear momentum in the collision: $mv = (M + m)V$. The mechanical energy that must be dissipated, or equal to the external work done, is the kinetic plus potential energy of the hammer–pile system after collision.

$$Fd = \tfrac{1}{2}(M + m)V^2 + (M + m)gd$$

$$= \frac{1}{2}\frac{m^2}{(M + m)}v^2 + (M + m)gd \qquad\qquad V^2 = \frac{m^2}{(m + M)^2}v^2$$

$$= \frac{m^2}{(M + m)}gh + (M + m)gd \qquad\qquad mgh = \tfrac{1}{2}mv^2$$

$$F = \frac{m^2g}{(M + m)}\frac{h}{d} + (M + m)g$$

$$= \tfrac{1}{3}mg\frac{h}{d} + (M + m)g \qquad\qquad \frac{m}{M + m} = \frac{1}{3}$$

$$= \left[\frac{1}{3} \times 500 \times \frac{10}{1/2} + 1500\right] 32 \text{ pndl}$$

$$= \frac{1}{3} \times 10{,}000 + 1500 \text{ lb}$$

This calculation shows the extra stopping force only one-third as large as before.

Can we assume conservation of momentum? The assumption is based on the impulse–momentum relation $\mathbf{J} = \mathbf{P}_2 - \mathbf{P}_1$. If the external impulse $\mathbf{J} = \int \mathbf{F}_{\text{ext}}\,dt$ is zero, $\mathbf{P}_2 = \mathbf{P}_1$. Are the external forces negligible in comparison with the internal forces (between pile and hammer) during the time of the collision? This will depend on the properties of the materials involved—their hardness, their elastic and plastic properties. The collision process is complex; the region near the faces of the pile and hammer in contact will be compressed, and this will be transmitted as a wave through the material.

If the upward impulse $\mathbf{J}$ on the hammer–pile system is not negligible during collision, this means that $\mathbf{P}_2$ will be less than $\mathbf{P}_1$, the speed V will be less than that calculated, and the corresponding average force F would appear to be less. But this would be the average force after the collision is over—that is, after hammer and pile have stopped moving relative to one another. But there is also the upward force **during** collision that must be taken into account in determining the overall average force on the pile as it moves down.

The best we can do here is to assume conservation of momentum in the collision. Some of the mechanical energy is dissipated internally in the impact, and the remaining mechanical energy is dissipated as the pile moves down.

As the mass of the hammer is increased, the proportion of the energy dissipated internally decreases. For $m \ggg M$

$$F = \frac{m^2g}{M + m}\frac{h}{d} + (M + m)g \cong mg\frac{h}{d} + (M + m)g$$

the result found assuming conservation of mechanical energy in collision. For example, for $m = 10M$, $m/(m + M) = 1/1.1 \cong 0.9$, so the extra retarding force is 90% of the value calculated assuming conservation of mechanical energy in impact.

THE EQUIVALENT SINGLE PARTICLE—REDUCED MASS

Classical dynamics is based on the assumption that forces act between particles, and therefore we keep coming back to the two-particle system as the basic dynamical system.

We wish to show that the motion of a two-particle system can be replaced by the motion of a single particle—an equivalent particle of reduced mass μ. We showed this much earlier, in discussing kinematics, for motion in one-dimension, and we showed in dynamics that the angular momentum of a two-particle system with respect to the center of mass is $\mathbf{L} = \mu r^2 \boldsymbol{\omega}$.

As before, in order to write an explicit expression for the potential energy, we use the gravitational interaction, but the result is valid for any central force between the particles.

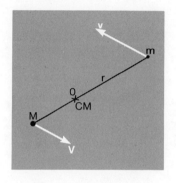

Center of mass of a two-particle system.

We assume there are no external forces on the system, and describe the motion in the center-of-mass frame of reference. This is an inertial frame because there are no external forces.

The energy of the system is

$$E = K + U = \tfrac{1}{2}MV^2 + \tfrac{1}{2}mv^2 - G\frac{Mm}{r}$$

The potential energy U depends only on the relative distance r between the particles. We want to express the kinetic energy in terms of the relative speed v_{rel} of the particles, rather than in terms of the absolute speeds V and v in the c-of-m frame.

In the c-of-m frame, $M\mathbf{V} + m\mathbf{v} = 0$, so the relative velocity is

$$\mathbf{v}_{\text{rel}} = \mathbf{v} - \mathbf{V} = \mathbf{v} + \frac{m}{M}\mathbf{v} = \frac{m+M}{M}\mathbf{v}$$

$$= -\frac{M}{m}\mathbf{V} - \mathbf{V} = -\frac{m+M}{m}\mathbf{V}$$

$$K = \tfrac{1}{2}MV^2 + \tfrac{1}{2}mv^2 = \tfrac{1}{2}M\left(\frac{m}{m+M}\right)^2 v_{\text{rel}}^2 + \tfrac{1}{2}m\left(\frac{M}{m+M}\right)^2 v_{\text{rel}}^2$$

$$= \tfrac{1}{2}\frac{mM}{m+M}v_{\text{rel}}^2 = \tfrac{1}{2}\mu v_{\text{rel}}^2$$

This expresses the kinetic energy in terms of the reduced mass of the system, $\mu = mM/(m+M)$. The kinetic energy is the same as that of a particle of mass μ moving with speed v_{rel} with respect to the center of mass.

The mechanical energy is

$$E = \tfrac{1}{2}\mu v_{\text{rel}}^2 - GMm/r = \text{constant}$$

This expression involves only the relative speed v_{rel} and relative separation r of the particles, but it is *not* independent of the frame of reference. It is valid in the c-of-m frame. In any other inertial frame, moving with constant velocity V_0 with respect to the c-of-m frame, there will be an additional constant term in the energy equation

$$E = \tfrac{1}{2}\mu v_{rel}^2 + \tfrac{1}{2}(M + m)V_0^2 - GMm/r = \text{constant}$$

This is an equation of motion, and any equation of motion applies only in a particular frame of reference.

The equation of motion in the c-of-m frame

$$E = \tfrac{1}{2}\mu v_{rel}^2 - GMm/r = \text{constant}$$

has precisely the same form as the equation of motion for a particle of mass m moving under the influence of a mass M fixed in an inertial frame

$$E = \tfrac{1}{2}mv^2 - GMm/r = \text{constant}$$

Particles released from rest move in one dimension.

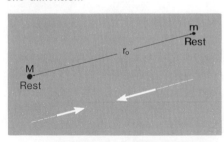

This was discussed in an earlier section (Motion in the gravitational field of a fixed particle, Chapter 21) and the same comments can be made here.

If the particles are simultaneously released from rest a distance r_0 apart, the motion will be in one dimension. Choosing an x-axis along the line of motion, $r = x$ and $v_{rel} = dx/dt$.

$$E = -\frac{GMm}{r_0} = \tfrac{1}{2}\mu \left(\frac{dx}{dt}\right)^2 - G\frac{Mm}{x}$$

This equation involves only two variables x and t. It can be solved (integrated) to find the relative position x as a function of time t, and the motion is completely described.

If the particles are given initial speeds so that they move in circular orbits around one another, their relative separation r is constant, and $dr/dt = 0$, but the relative speed $v_{rel} \neq 0$.

In general the speed v_{rel} of the equivalent particle varies due to changes in magnitude of the relative displacement $\mathbf{r}$, or due to changes in the direction of $\mathbf{r}$.

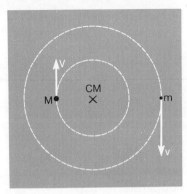

Particles given appropriate initial velocities stay a constant distance apart.

$$v^2 = \left(\frac{dr}{dt}\right)^2 + r^2 \left(\frac{d\theta}{dt}\right)^2$$

$$K = \tfrac{1}{2}\mu \left(\frac{dr}{dt}\right)^2 + \tfrac{1}{2}\mu r^2 \left(\frac{d\theta}{dt}\right)^2$$

The motion is confined to a plane. The angular momentum **L** of the system with respect to the c-of-m is constant, of magnitude $L = \mu r^2 \omega = \mu r^2 (d\theta/dt)$. This can be used to eliminate the θ term in the energy.

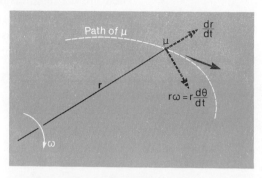

$$E = K + U$$

$$= \tfrac{1}{2}\mu \left(\frac{dr}{dt}\right)^2 + \tfrac{1}{2}\frac{L^2}{\mu r^2} - G\frac{Mm}{r} = \text{constant}$$

$$= \tfrac{1}{2}\mu \left(\frac{dr}{dt}\right)^2 + U_1(r)$$

In general the speed of the equivalent particle changes in magnitude and direction.

where $$U_1(r) = \tfrac{1}{2}\frac{L^2}{\mu r^2} - G\frac{Mm}{r}$$

is the equivalent one-dimensional potential energy.

Energy diagrams showing $U(x)$ (for one-dimensional motion) and $U_1(r)$ can be used to visualize the possible motions of the equivalent particle, exactly as for the motion of a single particle.

Note that there are **three** conserved quantities for the two-particle system when there are no external forces acting on it, and the interaction force is a central force. They are the linear momentum **P**, the angular momentum **L** with respect to the center of mass, and the mechanical energy E. It is usually convenient to describe the motion in the c-of-m frame of reference, so that **P** = 0. For motion confined to one dimension **L** = 0 as well, and E is the only constant necessary to describe the motion. Otherwise the motion is in a plane, and E and L are the constants of the motion, their values determined by the initial conditions.

If the mass of one particle is much larger than that of the other, $M \gg m$, the reduced mass is

$$\mu = \frac{Mm}{M + m} = \frac{m}{1 + m/M} \cong m$$

Then it is a good approximation to think of the inertial c-of-m frame and the frame of reference fixed to mass M as coinciding.

The energy and angular momentum are associated with mass m. The equations of motion become

$$L = mr^2\left(\frac{d\theta}{dt}\right) = \text{constant}$$

$$E = \tfrac{1}{2}mv^2 - GMm/r$$

$$= \tfrac{1}{2}m\left(\frac{dr}{dt}\right)^2 + \tfrac{1}{2}\frac{L^2}{mr^2} - \frac{GMm}{r}$$

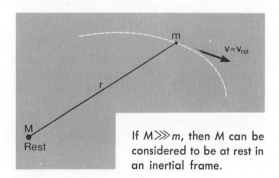

If $M \gg m$, then M can be considered to be at rest in an inertial frame.

These are the relations discussed before for motion about a fixed mass M.

In dealing with an actual situation involving two particles it is possible to work out the details assuming one of the particles is at rest. The results can be modified to take relative motion into account by replacing m by the reduced mass μ.

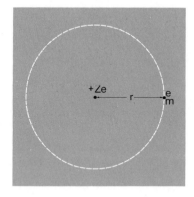

Bohr model for a single electron atom.

Example: You may have studied the Bohr theory of the atom, in which the electrons are assumed to be particles moving around the nucleus like the planets around the sun, with the electrical attraction replacing the gravitational attraction. For a single electron, charge $-e$, mass m, moving in orbit around a fixed nucleus of charge $+Ze$ (Z = atomic number) the Coulomb force is $F = K[(Ze)(e)/r^2]$ and the energy is

$$E = \tfrac{1}{2}mv^2 - \frac{KZe^2}{r}$$

In the Bohr theory only certain circular orbits are permitted, those in which the angular momentum of the electron is quantized in integral multiples of a constant $\hbar$.

$$L = mvr = n\hbar = nh/2\pi$$

This means that only certain values of the energy E are possible

$$E = -\frac{2\pi^2 mZ^2K^2e^4}{n^2h^2} = -\frac{E_0}{n^2}$$

where E_0 is a constant. These energy levels can be used to explain some of the observed features of atomic spectra.

This is a two-particle system, and the nucleus is not really fixed. The motion of the nucleus is taken into account by replacing the electron mass m by the reduced mass μ in the energy. The mass of the nucleus is about 1840 m even for a hydrogen atom, so the correction is small. Nevertheless, there is a measurable difference in the spectra produced by ordinary hydrogen and by heavy hydrogen (the isotope of hydrogen that has twice the mass because there is a neutron as well as a proton in the nucleus). This difference is accounted for by the difference in reduced mass.

The Bohr theory is now only of historical interest, as one of the steps in the development of quantum mechanics. The picture of an atom with an electron in a well-defined orbit is not a valid one from the point of view of quantum mechanics. The existence of well-defined energy levels for an atom arises in quantum mechanics on a different basis than from arbitrary quantization of angular momentum.

THE DIATOMIC MOLECULE

An atom is electrically neutral; the positive charge on the nucleus balances the negative charge of the electrons, so two atoms at a distance are not attracted or repelled by an inverse-square force. On the other hand we know that there are forces between them because they combine to form molecules and solids. Some idea of the forces between atoms in general can be gained by thinking about two atoms bound together, forming a diatomic molecule. When two atoms combine to form a diatomic molecule, the interatomic distance or bond length r_0 is of the order of 1 angstrom unit $\sim 10^{-10}$ m. This is about the same as the atomic diameter, and it may seem unreasonable to think of this as the interaction between two particles. However, the mass of the atoms is concentrated in the nuclei, and we can think of the outer electronic structure as providing the interaction between these nuclei and represent the interaction on an energy diagram. The distance r is the distance between the atomic nuclei, and the potential energy $U(r)$ is the mutual potential energy of the pair. The energy $U(r)$ is electric potential energy because it arises from the electrical interaction, but it is not of the form $U(r) = \pm(K/r)$ because it is not the interaction between two point charges.

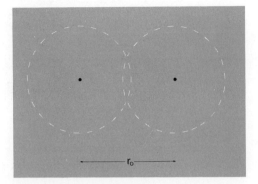

Is a diatomic molecule a two-particle system?

There will be a minimum in the $U(r)$ curve at the bond length $r = r_0$; this is a position of stable equilibrium. The particles repel one another for distances much closer than this (matter does not collapse) and also the force between the atoms decreases rapidly to zero for distances much greater than this. It is these considerations that lead to the general shape of curve indicated.

There are different ways that this curve can be represented mathematically. One is to use two exponential functions. Another is to assume an inverse-power function such as

$$U(r) = \frac{A}{r^{12}} - \frac{B}{r^6}$$

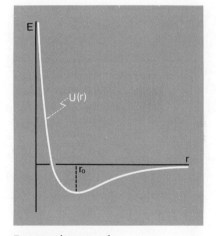

Energy diagram for a diatomic molecule.

where A and B are positive constants for a particular pair of atoms. The first term represents a very short range repulsive force, the second a somewhat longer range attractive force. The exponents (^{12}) and (^{6}) have been found by experiment to be about right.

The aim of experiments is to find a suitable form for the potential (and then

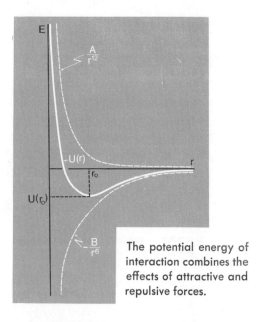

The potential energy of interaction combines the effects of attractive and repulsive forces.

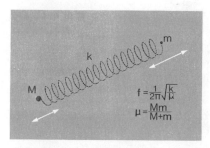

Interaction visualized as a "spring" joining the atoms.

to find an explanation for this form). A particular form is assumed, and experiments done to see if the form is satisfactory. What sort of experiments? You cannot examine a diatomic molecule under a microscope, or measure the force between the atoms with a spring balance. However, certain properties can be measured, not for individual molecules but for groups of molecules, and the assumption made that the molecules are all the same.

Three properties that can be determined by the techniques of chemistry and physics are the bond length r_0, the dissociation energy (or binding energy) $D = -U(r_0)$ and the molecular force constant $k = (d^2U/dr^2)_{r=r_0}$. The frequency of vibration of the molecule is $f = (1/2\pi)\sqrt{k/\mu}$, where μ is the reduced mass and k is the molecular force constant. This frequency can be measured, and therefore k determined.

We will use the potential $U(r) = (A/r^{12}) - (B/r^6)$ to show that there is a relationship between r_0, D and k. The experimental determination of these is then a check on the form of the potential.

$$\frac{dU}{dr} = -12\,\frac{A}{r^{13}} + 6\,\frac{B}{r^7}$$

$$\frac{d^2U}{dr^2} = 156\,\frac{A}{r^{14}} - 42\,\frac{B}{r^8}$$

At $r = r_0$, $dU/dr = 0$

$$-12\,\frac{A}{r_0^{13}} + 6\,\frac{B}{r_0^7} = 0 \qquad r_0^6 = \frac{2A}{B}$$

$$U(r_0) = \frac{A}{(r_0^6)^2} - \frac{B}{r_0^6} = A\left(\frac{B}{2A}\right)^2 - B\left(\frac{B}{2A}\right) = -\frac{B^2}{4A}$$

The energy that must be supplied to separate the atoms completely, the dissociation energy, is $D = -U(r_0) = B^2/4A$.

We showed previously that a force constant can always be defined for oscillations about a point of stable equilibrium, if the amplitude of oscillation is small enough.

$$k = \left(\frac{d^2U}{dr_0^2}\right)_{r=r_0} = \frac{1}{r_0^2}\left(156\,\frac{A}{r_0^{12}} - 42\,\frac{B}{r_0^6}\right)$$

$$= \frac{1}{r_0^2}\left(39\,\frac{B^2}{A} - 21\,\frac{B^2}{A}\right) = \frac{18}{r_0^2}\frac{B^2}{A} = 72\,\frac{D}{r_0^2}$$

If measured values of the properties k, D and r_0 do not satisfy this relation, this is an indication that the form assumed for the potential is not satisfactory.

The interaction between the atoms in a diatomic molecule has been described in terms of the potential energy of interaction rather than in terms of force, although of course there is a related force

$$F = -\frac{dU}{dr} = 12\frac{A}{r^{13}} - 6\frac{B}{r^7}$$

This is because, as we have said, atomic systems should be described using quantum mechanics, not classical mechanics. In quantum mechanics it turns out to be more appropriate to think in terms of energy than in terms of force.

A quantum mechanical treatment of the diatomic molecule shows that only certain energies of vibration (quantized states) are possible, while classically any energy is possible.

An atom in a solid, occupying a lattice site, is interacting with all the atoms around it and not just one other atom as in the diatomic molecule, but a study of the two-particle interaction is a first step in understanding the behavior of solids. Think for example of the thermal expansion of solids; an elementary atomic explanation is to say that at higher temperatures the particles vibrate with larger amplitude about their lattice sites, and therefore, require more space. This picture is inadequate because it is impossible to explain the fact that some solids contract when heated (for example ice in the range 0–4°C).

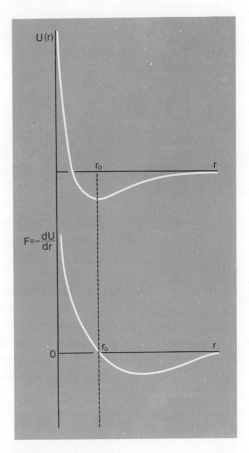

Force and potential energy are related.

A better explanation is provided by referring to the two-particle potential curve. For any value of the vibrational energy the distance r between the atoms varies between certain limits, and the mean distance is the average of these, the midpoint of the line on the energy diagram. For higher energies (higher temperatures of the macroscopic system) this mean distance will become larger or smaller depending on the shape of the potential. (See diagram next page.) If the well in the potential curve is symmetric, like that of a harmonic oscillator for example, the mean distance will not depend on the energy at all.

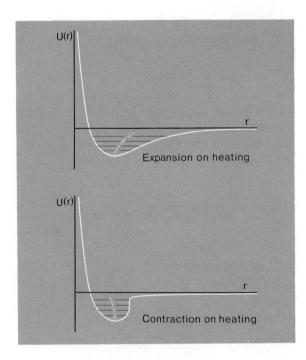

Whether a material expands or contracts on heating depends on the shape of the interaction energy curve.

The potential for an atom in a solid must have some features in common with the two-particle potential. There is an equilibrium position for the atom, and therefore a minimum in the potential, and vibrations of small amplitude about this position are approximately simple harmonic. However, in order to understand thermal expansion it is necessary to realize that the vibrations cannot be completely simple harmonic.

Problems

1. Two particles of masses m and $2m$, acted upon only by their mutual gravitational attraction, are a constant distance d apart. In terms of G, m and d, determine **(a)** the kinetic energy of the system, **(b)** the additional energy that would be required to separate the particles completely.

2. Two particles of masses m and M, subject only to the gravitational force of each other, are a constant distance R apart. State the kinetic energy K and the magnitude of the angular momentum L of this system in terms of R, the angular speed ω, and the reduced mass μ. Note the form of K and L for $M \ggg m$.

3. The self-energy of a body is the work done in bringing the particles of the body together, assuming they are initially an infinite distance apart. **(a)** Determine the gravitational self-energy of three identical particles, each of mass m, fixed at the corners of an equilateral triangle of side D. **(b)** Determine the gravitational self-energy of four identical particles, each of mass m, fixed at the corners of a square of side D.

4. A chunk of glass sitting on a smooth table spontaneously breaks into two pieces, one twice the mass of the other. The smaller piece is observed to slide across the table at 2 ft/sec. What is the other piece doing? Which piece has the larger kinetic energy? What can you deduce about the original piece of glass?

5. (a) Three particles, each of mass m, are released at the corners of an equilateral triangle of side D. No force except the gravitational interaction between the particles acts on them. Calculate the speed of each particle (in terms of G, m, D) when the distance between them has become $D/2$. (b) If there are four identical particles released at the corners of a square of side D, what is the speed of each when they form a square of side $D/2$? (c) In either case, what is the speed when the particles come together?

6. Two blocks, A of mass m and B of mass $2m$, are on a smooth table. They are held with a spring compressed between them, and released. Determine the ratios of their momenta, their velocities, and their kinetic energies after the "explosion."

7. A "particle" of mass 6 gm is moving freely in space at a speed of 3 cm/sec. It explodes into three fragments of masses 1, 2 and 3 gm. In a co-ordinate system with x-axis in the direction of motion of the original particle the velocity of the 1-gm fragment is $v_1 = 3i + 4j$ cm/sec and the velocity of the 2-gm fragment is $v_2 = 2i - 3j + 2k$ cm/sec. Determine the velocity of the third fragment, and calculate the energy produced in the explosion. Does it make a difference in calculating this energy if you work in the center-of-mass frame of reference?

8. A common piece of apparatus used in physics lecture demonstrations (and also popular as an "executive toy") is the "educated spheres." It consists of a number (often six) of identical steel balls hung as pendula so that they are touching one another in a line and all move in the same vertical plane. They are called educated because they can count: pull back one and release it—when it hits the others one bounces off the other end; do the same with two—released together, two come off the other end. It even works with 4 or 5, which may mean the spheres can subtract as well as count.

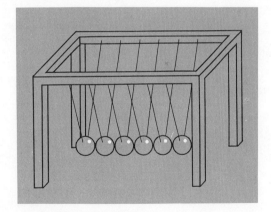

Show that to explain the behavior it is necessary to assume conservation both of linear momentum *and* of kinetic energy for the collisions.

The system only works if the collisions are approximately elastic, as they are for steel spheres. Can you guess what would happen if the collisions were not elastic? If you have a model on your desk, try putting a little gum between the spheres.

9. In radioactive materials the atomic nucleus is unstable and occasionally spontaneously emits a particle or particles. Some energy (nuclear energy) stored in the nucleus becomes kinetic energy of the particles, and to conserve momentum the nucleus may recoil. In addition, some energy may be given off in the process as electromagnetic radiation (called photons, or gamma rays, or gamma particles). The energetic particles produced in radioactive decay (electrons or β-particles,

and helium nuclei or α-particles) can be detected and measurements of their energy provide information about the nucleus.

If the speeds involved are not too large, the nuclear "explosions" of radioactivity can be described by the classical expressions for momentum and energy we have developed. Suppose for example that a nucleus of mass 218 amu decays to produce an α-particle, mass 4 amu. The track of the α-particle is observed in a cloud chamber. There is a magnetic field applied in this region, and the curvature of the track is measured. Suppose from such measurements the kinetic energy of the α-particle is found to be 6.7 Mev. What would be the kinetic energy of the recoil nucleus? What would be the energy released in the reaction? Note that it is not necessary to convert the units.

10. In the Bohr model of the atom, the radius of the first orbit (the ground state of the atom) is 0.53 angstrom units, and energy of the electron is -13.6 ev (an energy of 13.6 ev is required to ionize the atom). An "atom" of positronium is formed when an electron and a positron form a bound system. (A positron has a charge $+e$, the charge of a proton, and the mass of the electron.) What would you guess the distance between the pair in the ground state to be, and the ionization energy to be? Note that in the hydrogen atom the reduced mass is very nearly the electron mass, but this is not so for positronium.

11. A thin flexible uniform chain 4 ft long is held at rest with 2 ft of its length on a smooth table, and 2 ft hanging over the edge. The table top is 4 ft off the floor. If the chain is released, with what speed does the lower end hit the floor?

The result can be found most readily by using conservation of mechanical energy, but you can instead integrate the force equation. In order to find the time to fall, it would be necessary to integrate again. You may wish to try it as an exercise in integration. In a co-ordinate system with y-axis downward and origin at the table top, the position y of the end of the chain and its downward speed v are related by $g(y^2 - 4) = 4v^2$.

Setting $v = dy/dt$, you find the time to fall is determined by $\int_2^4 (y^2 - 4)^{-1/2}\, dy = \sqrt{g/4} \int_0^t dt$. The integral on the left side may be worked out, or found in a table of integrals.

12. The potential energy of interaction between two nucleons is believed to be represented reasonably well by

$$U(r) = -(r_0/r)U_0 e^{-r/r_0}$$

where r is the separation between the nucleons, $r_0 \sim 1.5 \times 10^{-15}$ m, and $U_0 \sim 50$ Mev. **(a)** Determine the expression for the force between the nucleons $F(r)$. **(b)** In order to get an idea of the magnitude involved, compute $F(r_0)$ in newtons. **(c)** The force decreases rapidly with separation because of the exponential term. Determine the ratio $F(10r_0)/F(r_0)$.

24

MOTION IN THE EARTH'S
GRAVITATIONAL FIELD

GRAVITATIONAL FIELD OF THE EARTH

We showed earlier that a solid sphere of mass M of uniform density (or with density that is a function of radial distance only) acts like a particle of mass M at the center of the sphere, as far as the gravitational effect at points outside it is concerned. For many purposes this is an adequate model for the earth.

The field at a point P is

$$\mathbf{E}_P = -\frac{GM}{r^3}\mathbf{r}$$

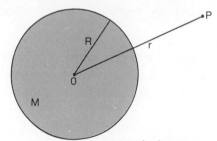

and the force on a mass m at P is

$$\mathbf{F} = m\mathbf{E}_P$$

giving the mass m an acceleration

$$\mathbf{a} = \mathbf{F}/m = \mathbf{E}_P$$

An idealization of the earth.

but this is the acceleration that we call the acceleration due to gravity $\mathbf{g}$.

That is, the field strength (the force per unit mass) and the acceleration due to gravity at P are the same quantity

$$\mathbf{g} = -\frac{GM}{r^3}\mathbf{r} \quad \text{or in magnitude} \quad g = \frac{GM}{r^2}$$

At the earth's surface the magnitude of the field is constant (assuming a spherical earth of radius R)

$$g_0 = \frac{GM}{r^2} \quad \text{and therefore} \quad g = \left(\frac{R}{r}\right)^2 g_0 \quad \text{(for } r \geq R\text{)}$$

In terms of height above the earth surface h

$$g = \left(\frac{R}{R+h}\right)^2 g_0 = \left(1 + \frac{h}{R}\right)^{-2} g_0$$

For points near the earth's surface $h \ll R$ and

$$g \cong \left(1 - 2\frac{h}{R}\right) g_0$$

We showed earlier that if the density is assumed constant the field **inside** a solid sphere is proportional to r.

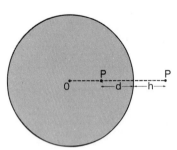

$$g = \left(\frac{r}{R}\right) g_0 \qquad \text{for } r < R$$

In terms of depth d below the surface

$$g = \left(\frac{R-d}{R}\right) g_0 = \left(1 - \frac{d}{R}\right) g_0$$

The acceleration (or field strength) is a maximum at the earth surface, decreasing at twice the rate if you move outward as it does if you move inward, for points near the surface.

The dependence of g on height and on depth.

The potential at point P outside the earth is

$$V_P = -\frac{GM}{r}$$

This refers to a zero of potential at infinity. In dealing with motion near the earth surface it is sometimes more convenient to choose the zero of potential at the earth's surface, at $r = R$ rather than at $r = \infty$.

The difference in potential between any two points at distances r_1 and r_2 from the center O is

$$V_2 - V_1 = -\frac{GM}{r_2} - \left(-\frac{GM}{r_1}\right)$$

If we set $V_1 = 0$ for $r_1 = R$

$$V_2 = -\frac{GM}{r_2} + \frac{GM}{R}$$

With this choice of zero, *the* potential V at distance r becomes

$$V = -\frac{GM}{r} + \frac{GM}{R} = \frac{GM}{R}\left(1 - \frac{R}{r}\right) = Rg_0\left(1 - \frac{R}{r}\right)$$

In terms of height h above the surface

$$V = Rg_0\left(1 - \frac{R}{R+h}\right) = Rg_0\left[1 - \left(1 + \frac{h}{R}\right)^{-1}\right]$$

For points near the surface $h \ll R$ and

$$V \cong Rg_0 \left[1 - \left(1 - \frac{h}{R} \right) \right] = g_0 h$$

The potential energy of a mass m near the surface is

$$U = mV = mg_0 h$$

This is the result that we found before, assuming a **uniform** field $g_0 =$ constant near the earth surface.

TRAJECTORY OF A PARTICLE IN
THE GRAVITATIONAL FIELD OF THE EARTH

In the equation of motion $E = \frac{1}{2}mv^2 + U$ for a particle moving in a conservative force field, force and acceleration have been eliminated by introducing the concept of energy; the mechanical energy E is a constant of the motion. The energy equation is an integrated form of the instantaneous equation of motion $\mathbf{F} = m\mathbf{a}$, but it does not provide a complete solution of the dynamical situation. This would require another integration, eliminating v, in order to give the position of the particle as a function of time. A complete description of the motion means that we know $\mathbf{r}(t)$ or $x(t)$, $y(t)$, $z(t)$.

It is sometimes possible to perform an integration that provides the equation of the path or trajectory of the particle $F(x,y,z) = 0$. This is not a complete description of the motion, in that the time the particle is at any point on the path is not known, but can be very useful.

We are going to find the equation of the trajectory of a particle moving in the gravitational field of the earth; this includes the motion of long range projectiles, the motion of earth satellites, and the motion of particles such as comets that are not bound to the earth.

As is always the case in describing any real physical situation, there are a number of assumptions made, of varying degrees of validity.

1. We assume that the earth can be treated as a solid sphere of mass M and radius R as discussed in the previous section.
2. We assume that the effect of all other bodies (the moon, sun and other planets) can be neglected—that is, that we have an ideal two-particle interaction. There are no external forces on the two-particle system and therefore we can assume conservation of linear momentum, conservation of angular momentum, and conservation of mechanical energy for the system.
3. We assume that the interaction force between the particles is the gravitational force only, a conservative force. The effect of air friction is neglected—a good assumption for points far enough from the earth's surface, but not if the trajectory comes near the surface.

4. We assume that the mass m of the particle in orbit is small enough compared to the mass M of the earth that the center of mass of the two-particle system coincides with the center of the earth. Then the earth is at rest in the inertial center-of-mass frame, and we can associate all of the energy and angular momentum with the particle m. This assumption is *not* essential; the development could equally well be given in terms of the equivalent particle of mass $\mu = Mm/(M + m)$, but it is easier to visualize the motion if we think of only one of the masses as moving in the inertial frame.

Example 1—Circular Orbit: Before dealing with the general trajectory, look at the familiar situation where the path is a circular orbit. If the particle is in a circular orbit it is constant distance r_0 from the center of the earth, moving with a constant speed v_0. The centripetal force is the gravitational force

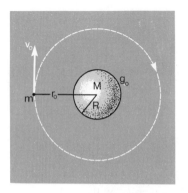

$$G\frac{Mm}{r_0^2} = mg = m\left(\frac{v_0^2}{r_0}\right) \qquad v_0^2 = gr_0 = \frac{GM}{r_0}$$

where g is the acceleration due to gravity at this height.

$$g = \left(\frac{R}{r_0}\right)^2 g_0$$

The time to complete one revolution, or period of the orbit is

$$T_0 = \frac{2\pi r_0}{v_0}$$

Satellite in a circular orbit.

so

$$T_0^2 = \frac{4\pi^2 r_0^2}{v_0^2} = \frac{4\pi^2 r_0^3}{GM} = \frac{4\pi^2 r_0}{g} = \frac{4\pi^2 r_0^3}{g_0 R^2}$$

The result $T_0^2 \propto r_0^3$ is one of Kepler's laws of planetary motion. We will see that it applies to non-circular orbits as well, but instead of a fixed distance r_0 there will be some sort of an average distance.

The energy in the circular orbit, choosing the zero of potential energy at infinity, is

$$E = K + U$$

$$= \tfrac{1}{2}mv_0^2 - G\frac{Mm}{r_0}$$

$$= \tfrac{1}{2}G\frac{Mm}{r_0} - G\frac{Mm}{r_0} = -\tfrac{1}{2}G\frac{Mm}{r_0} = -\tfrac{1}{2}mgr_0 = -\tfrac{1}{2}\frac{mg_0R^2}{r_0}$$

The kinetic energy and potential energy are both constant, and the magnitude of the kinetic energy is half that of the potential energy (with this choice of the zero of potential).

Example 2—Escape Speed: If the particle m is given an initial speed $v_i > v_0$ at the same height r_0, it will travel farther and farther from the earth as v_i is increased. For some speed v_e, the escape speed, it will escape entirely. The kinetic energy required is

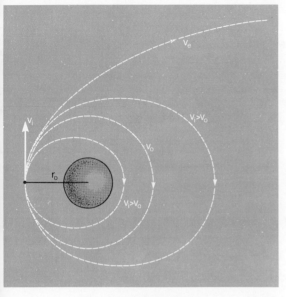

Trajectories for different initial speeds.

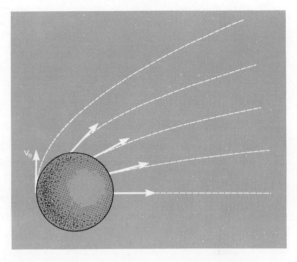

Given the escape speed v_e a particle will escape no matter what its direction of projection.

$$\tfrac{1}{2}mv_e^2 = G\frac{Mm}{r_0} \qquad v_e = \sqrt{\frac{2GM}{r_0}} = \sqrt{2}\, v_0$$

The escape speed is $\sqrt{2}$ times the speed in a circular orbit at the same height. Note that the direction of projection does not matter (as long as the particle does not hit the earth).

At the earth's surface

$$v_0 = \sqrt{GM/R} = \sqrt{g_0 R} = \sqrt{32 \times 4000 \times 5280} \text{ ft/sec}$$
$$= 2.6 \times 10^4 \text{ ft/sec} = 1.8 \times 10^4 \text{ miles/hr}$$
$$= 4.9 \text{ miles/sec}$$

$$v_e = \sqrt{2}\, v_0 = 6.9 \text{ miles/sec}$$

Of course a particle launched at this speed at the surface would neither go into orbit nor escape because of air resistance.

We know that motion under a central force takes place in a plane (since the angular momentum is constant) so by choosing a co-ordinate system with one axis perpendicular to the plane the equation of the path involves only two co-ordinates $F(x,y) = 0$. Since the motion is about a fixed center of force it is convenient to use polar co-ordinates, with origin at the center of force, and determine $F(r,\theta) = 0$.

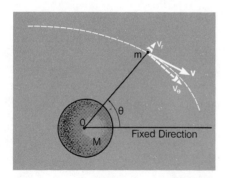

Radial and tangential components of velocity.

With the assumptions we have made, the angular momentum L of the particle with respect to the center O, and the mechanical energy E are constants of the motion.

$$L = mr^2 \left(\frac{d\theta}{dt} \right) = \text{constant}$$

$$E = K + U = \tfrac{1}{2}mv^2 - G\frac{Mm}{r}$$

$$= \tfrac{1}{2}mv^2 - mg_0R^2/r = \text{constant}$$

The time dependence can be eliminated by using the angular momentum.

$$v^2 = v_r^2 + v_\theta^2 = \left(\frac{dr}{dt} \right)^2 + r^2 \left(\frac{d\theta}{dt} \right)^2 = \left(\frac{dr}{d\theta} \right)^2 \left(\frac{d\theta}{dt} \right)^2 + r^2 \left(\frac{d\theta}{dt} \right)^2$$

$$= \left[\left(\frac{dr}{d\theta} \right)^2 + r^2 \right] \left(\frac{d\theta}{dt} \right)^2 = \left[\left(\frac{dr}{d\theta} \right)^2 + r^2 \right] \frac{L^2}{m^2r^4}$$

Then

$$E = \tfrac{1}{2} \left(\frac{dr}{d\theta} \right)^2 \frac{L^2}{mr^4} + \tfrac{1}{2} \frac{L^2}{mr^2} - \frac{mg_0R^2}{r}$$

or

$$\frac{L}{\sqrt{2m}} \frac{1}{r^2} \left(\frac{dr}{d\theta} \right) = \pm \sqrt{E + \frac{mg_0R^2}{r} - \frac{L^2}{2mr^2}}$$

which has the form

$$\frac{c}{r^2} \left(\frac{dr}{d\theta} \right) = \pm \sqrt{a + \frac{b}{r} - \frac{c^2}{r^2}}$$

where $a = E$, $b = mg_0R^2$, and $c = L/\sqrt{2m}$ are constants. This is a differential equation involving the variables r and θ. It is convenient to replace the variable r by a new variable, $u = 1/r$. Then

$$\frac{du}{d\theta} = -\frac{1}{r^2} \left(\frac{dr}{d\theta} \right)$$

and the differential equation in terms of u and θ is

$$c \left(\frac{du}{d\theta} \right) = \pm \sqrt{a + bu - c^2u^2}$$

This integral can be found in tables, and the solution can be verified by differentiation.

$$u = \frac{1}{r} = \frac{b}{2c^2} - \frac{\sqrt{b^2 + 4ac^2}}{2c^2} \cos \theta$$

You may recognize this as the equation for a conic section in polar co-ordinates. A conic is the locus of a point that moves so that its distance from a fixed point

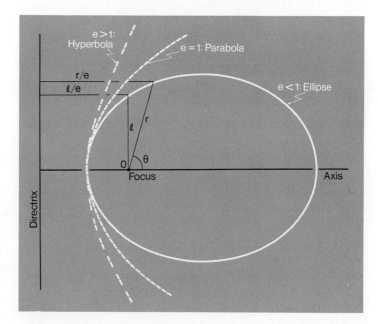

For any conic section the distance from a fixed point (the focus) is equal to a constant times the distance from a fixed line (the directrix).

(the focus) is equal to a constant (the eccentricity e) times the distance from a fixed line (the directrix).

From the diagram

$$\frac{r}{e} = \frac{l}{e} + r \cos \theta$$

so

$$r = \frac{l}{1 - e \cos \theta} \qquad \frac{1}{r} = \frac{1}{l} - \frac{e}{l} \cos \theta$$

The type and shape of the conic is determined by the two constants e and l, the eccentricity and the semi–latus-rectum.

The path of the particle in the earth field is a conic with the center of the earth at the focus. The constants are

$$l = \frac{2c^2}{b} = \frac{L^2}{m^2 g_0 R^2}$$

$$e = \frac{l\sqrt{b^2 + 4ac^2}}{2c^2} = \frac{\sqrt{b^2 + 4ac^2}}{b} = \sqrt{1 + 4ac^2/b^2} = \sqrt{1 + \frac{2EL^2}{m^3 g_0^2 R^4}}$$

The total energy E can be positive or negative. If $E < 0$, $e < 1$ and the particle is bound, moving in an elliptic orbit. If $E > 0$, $e > 1$ and the particle moves in a hyperbolic path past the earth. The energy $E = 0$ is the transition between an open and closed path; $e = 1$, the path is a parabola.

Projectiles: A particle launched at the earth surface with an initial velocity v_1 has energy (neglecting air resistance)

$$E = \tfrac{1}{2}mv_1^2 - mg_0R^2/R = \tfrac{1}{2}mv_1^2 - mg_0R$$

If $v_1 = \sqrt{2g_0R}$, $E = 0$, and the particle escapes on a parabolic path, its speed dropping to zero at infinity. This is the minimum escape speed v_e.

If $v_1 > \sqrt{2g_0R}$, $E > 0$, and the particle escapes on a hyperbolic path.

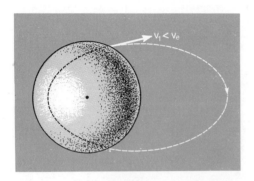

If $v_1 < \sqrt{2g_0R}$, $E < 0$, and the path is an ellipse. The orbit will bring the particle back to the earth unless the velocity v_1 is tangent to the surface, and is greater than $\sqrt{g_0R}$. Otherwise the particle is a projectile. The path of a projectile in a **uniform** gravitational field you will recall is a parabola. If the variation in g is taken into account the path is an ellipse.

The trajectory of a long-range projectile is an ellipse.

Clearly one cannot put a satellite into orbit by giving it all its energy at the earth surface. The only orbit possible is one that skims the surface—and this is only possible if air resistance is ignored. The speed is such that the satellite would burn up very quickly.

Instead rocket engines are used to supply energy after the satellite is above the atmosphere. Remember, however, we are considering the orbit after the engine has stopped—the satellite is "falling freely" after being inserted into orbit.

Satellite Orbits: We will write the eccentricity e in terms of the speed v_P of the satellite at its position of closest approach, or perigee P. (For an ellipse in general the terms pericenter and apocenter are used for the near point and far point. For orbits around the earth, they are perigee and apogee; for orbits around the sun, perihelion and aphelion.) At perigee or apogee the velocity is at right angles to the radius, so

Satellite in an elliptic orbit.

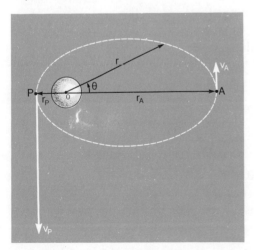

$$L = mv_Pr_P = mv_Ar_A$$

Using g at height r_P as $g_P = (R/r_P)^2g_0$

$$l = \frac{L^2}{m^2g_0R^2} = \frac{v_P^2}{g_P}$$

The equation of the path is $r = l/(1 - e\cos\theta)$. At the perigee, $\theta = \pi$, so

$$r_P = \frac{l}{1+e} \qquad e = \frac{l}{r_P} - 1 = \frac{v_P^2}{g_P r_P} - 1$$

You can verify that the previous expression for e gives this result.

If $v_P = \sqrt{g_P r_P}$, $e = 0$; this is the circular orbit discussed before.

If $v_P = \sqrt{2 g_P r_P}$, $e = 1$; this is the parabolic escape case. The path will be a closed orbit with this point as perigee if $\sqrt{g_P r_P} \leq v_P < \sqrt{2 g_P r_P}$. Note that at apogee $\theta = 0$, so

$$r_A = \frac{l}{1-e}$$

which approaches infinity as e approaches unity.

Period of Orbit: For a circular orbit of radius r_P the period is

$$T_0 = 2\pi \sqrt{\frac{r_P}{g_P}}$$

The period for an elliptic orbit with this perigee distance will be greater, because the particle speed is always less than it is at perigee, and it has farther to go.

The period for the elliptic orbit can be determined without knowing the position of the particle as a function of time, because as we showed in discussing angular momentum, the radius r sweeps out area at a constant rate $dA/dt = L/2m$.

The area of an ellipse is

$$A = \frac{\pi l^2}{(1 - e^2)^{3/2}}$$

$$= \pi a \sqrt{al}$$

$$= \pi a b$$

where a and b are the lengths of the semi-major axis and the semi-minor axis.

The rate at which area is swept out can be expressed in terms of l

$$\frac{dA}{dt} = \frac{L}{2m} = \frac{v_P r_P}{2}$$

$$= \frac{r_P \sqrt{l g_P}}{2} = \frac{R \sqrt{l g_0}}{2}$$

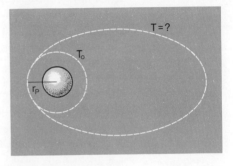

What is the period of the elliptic orbit?

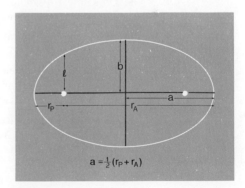

$a = \frac{1}{2}(r_P + r_A)$

Parameters of an ellipse.

so the time to sweep out the total area of the ellipse, the period T, is

$$T = \frac{A}{(dA/dt)} = \frac{\pi a \sqrt{al}}{R\sqrt{lg_0}/2} = 2\pi \frac{a}{R}\sqrt{\frac{a}{g_0}}$$

Therefore $T^2 \propto a^3$. The length of the semi-major axis is the average of the maximum and minimum distance of the satellite $a = \frac{1}{2}(r_P + r_A)$.

This period is not the period measured with respect to the rotating earth. The motion was described in an inertial reference frame in which the earth is treated as a fixed particle. The period is the sidereal period, measured with respect to the stars.

Questions for discussion

1. Does the gravitational force between two particles depend on whether or not there is matter between them? You may know about electric "shielding" of electric circuits; can gravitational shielding be arranged?

2. The earth is not homogeneous, its density being greater in the interior than it is at the surface. Assuming it is radially symmetric, does this change the variation in g with height? with depth?

3. Does the effect of the earth's rotation increase, decrease or not change the escape speed for a projectile launched from the earth's surface? Is the binding energy of a mass on the earth's surface the same as, greater than, or less than it would be if the earth were not rotating?

4. Do you know Kepler's three laws of planetary motion? Were they proposed before or after Newton's theory of gravitation?

5. Does an earth satellite stay in a plane passing through the center of the earth? If so, is it the same center for all orbits?

6. Is the total mechanical energy of a satellite positive or negative? Can you answer unambiguously?

7. Is the speed of a satellite at a point half-way between perigee and apogee (i.e., at the end of the semi-minor axis of the elliptic orbit) the arithmetic average of the speeds at perigee and apogee?

8. As a satellite enters the earth's atmosphere gradually in a nearly circular orbit, it starts to lose some of its mechanical energy. Can you explain why this causes it to speed up, rather than slow down? Does its angular momentum increase, decrease, or stay constant?

Problems

1. Assuming the earth is a homogeneous sphere of radius R, determine the weight in pounds of a man of mass 200 lb when he is (a) at a height $R/2$ above the earth's surface, (b) at the bottom of a vertical hole of depth $R/2$.

2. Determine the acceleration due to gravity on the surface of the moon (in terms of g_0 for the earth) and the escape speed from the moon (in terms of v_e from the earth). Use moon mass as $1/81$ of earth mass, moon radius as $1/3.67$ of earth radius.

3. In terms of the earth radius R and the magnitude of the acceleration due to gravity at the earth's surface g_0, determine the energy per unit mass required to put a satellite into a circular orbit at a height R above the earth's surface.

4. For orbits close to the earth's surface the work done to raise a satellite is less than the work done to put it into a circular orbit (once it has been raised). For orbits farther out, the opposite is true. At what height (in terms of the radius R) is a satellite where the two are equal?

5. (a) Determine the binding energy in joules of an 80-kg mass at rest on the earth's surface. Use $R = 6.4 \times 10^3$ km and ignore the rotation of the earth. **(b)** Determine the binding energy of an 80-kg earth satellite in a circular orbit of height R. **(c)** In an inertial frame of reference fixed to the earth axis, in which the earth is rotating, what is the kinetic energy of the 80-kg mass at rest on the earth? Is the assumption in (a) justified?

6. Suppose that the earth is a homogeneous sphere of radius R. Think of a straight smooth hole joining any two points on the earth's surface. Show that an object dropped into the hole will execute simple harmonic motion between the two points, with a period T_0 that is the same as the period of a satellite in an orbit just above the earth's surface. Note that the hole is not necessarily along a diameter. Verify that the period T_0 is also the period of a simple pendulum of infinite length (i.e., a pendulum for which $l \gg R$).

7. An object is dropped from a height $R/2$, where $R = $ earth radius $= 4000$ miles. **(a)** Neglecting air resistance, with what speed does it hit the earth? **(b)** What error is made if you assume g is constant at its value g_0 at the surface? **(c)** What error is made if you assume g is constant at the arithmetic average value between g_0 and g at height $R/2$? **(d)** Estimate the time to fall from this height.

You can, if you wish, perform an integration to find the time to fall. Find an expression giving v^2 as a function of r (where r is distance from the center of the earth) and use $v = -dr/dt$.

8. Suppose the moon, for some unlikely reason, stopped in its orbit. It would fall. With what speed would it hit the earth? About how long do you think it would take to fall?

9. (a) For a satellite in a circular orbit to be synchronous (i.e., have the same period of rotation as the earth) where does it have to be? **(b)** In order to maintain a 10-kg satellite in a circular synchronous orbit at a height above the earth's surface equal to the earth's radius, what constant force would have to be applied to it, in addition to the force of gravity? Would this force be doing work on the satellite?

10. Two satellites of equal mass are in circular orbits, satellite A at height R and satellite B at height $2R$ above the earth's surface (earth radius R). Determine the ratio of their mechanical energies E_A/E_B, choosing the zero of potential **(a)** at infinity, **(b)** at the surface of the earth.

11. A satellite is raised to a height equal to the earth's diameter above the earth's surface. **(a)** What horizontal speed v_1 must it be given to go into a circular orbit, and what is the period in this orbit? (Express speed in terms of $v_0 = \sqrt{g_0 R} = 4.9$

miles/sec, and period in terms of $T_0 = 2\pi\sqrt{R/g_0} = 84$ min.) **(b)** It is projected into orbit at this height with the speed v_1 at an angle of 30° above the horizontal. Determine its perigee and apogee distances (in terms of R), the eccentricity of its orbit, and the period of its orbit.

12. A projectile is fired from the surface of the earth at an angle of 45° with an initial speed of 5200 ft/sec $= 0.2v_0 = 0.2\sqrt{Rg_0}$. Ignoring air resistance, determine the maximum height it reaches above the earth surface, in terms of the earth radius R, **(a)** treating it as a projectile fired over a horizontal plane in a uniform vertical gravitational field g_0, **(b)** treating its orbit by the methods in this chapter, thereby taking the spherical shape of the earth and the variation in g into account. Why are the two results different by a factor of approximately two?

13. **(a)** In the absence of air resistance a projectile launched at the earth surface with speed $v_0 = \sqrt{Rg_0}$ horizontally becomes a satellite at the earth's surface. If launched with speed v_0 vertically how high would it go? **(b)** The projectile is launched at speed v_0 at an angle of 60° with the vertical. Determine its maximum height above the earth's surface (in terms of R), its speed at this point (in terms of v_0), and the distance away from its launch point that it lands, measured along the earth's circumference.

14. The first Vanguard Satellite, launched on March 17, 1958, had a mass of 3.25 lb and entered into orbit with minimum and maximum distances from the earth of 404 and 2466 miles. Assume a fixed spherical earth of radius 3960 miles and determine **(a)** the time (hours) for one orbit, **(b)** the energy (ft-lb) required to raise the satellite to a height of 404 miles, **(c)** its speed (mph) at this height, **(d)** its kinetic energy (ft-lb) at this point, **(e)** the smallest speed (mph) with which, at this height, it could enter a closed orbit around the earth if there were no air resistance.

25

KINETIC ENERGY OF ROTATION

Think about a block that slides down a smooth inclined plane, reaching the bottom with a speed v_1, and of a ball that rolls without slipping down a plane of the same slope and length as the first, reaching the bottom with a speed v_2. Would you expect to find $v_2 = v_1$, $v_2 > v_1$, or $v_2 < v_1$? Your instincts may give you the right answer, but it is usually safer to work it out.

We showed in Chapter 18 that any object such as a sphere, cylinder, or hoop of radius r and radius of gyration k (where $I_0 = mk^2$) rolling without slipping down a plane of slope θ has an acceleration down the plane of magnitude

$$a = \frac{g \sin \theta}{1 + k^2/r^2}$$

This is less than the acceleration $g \sin \theta$ of the block on the smooth plane, so the speed v_2 acquired in the same displacement S is less than v_1.

In terms of energy, the kinetic energy $\frac{1}{2}mv_1^2$ of the block is greater than the kinetic energy $\frac{1}{2}mv_2^2$ of the ball, assuming equal masses for the block and ball. The work done by the force of gravity (or decrease in gravitational potential energy) is $\int \mathbf{w} \cdot d\mathbf{r} = mgh$, the same for each.

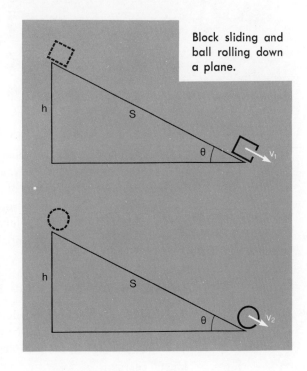

Block sliding and ball rolling down a plane.

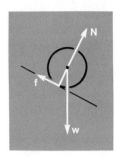

Forces on the
rolling ball.

There is a force of friction on the rolling ball (otherwise it would slide like the block), so it might appear that there is negative work done by this force, making the kinetic energy of the ball less. However, this is not so, because if we assume that the plane and the ball are rigid bodies the friction force does no work. The friction force acts on the ball at the point of contact with the plane, a point that is instantaneously at rest since the ball is rolling without slipping. It is the force of static friction between the surfaces (but not necessarily the limiting force of static friction). The work done is $\int \mathbf{f} \cdot d\mathbf{r} = 0$ because $d\mathbf{r} = 0$; there is no displacement of the particle to which the force $\mathbf{f}$ is applied.

The acceleration $a = g \sin \theta / (1 + k^2/r^2)$ of the rolling body produces a speed v (we will drop the subscript 2) at the bottom of the plane, where $v^2 = 2aS$. We rearrange the equations, multiplying by the mass m of the ball.

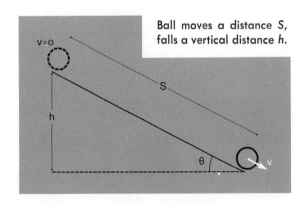

Ball moves a distance S,
falls a vertical distance h.

$$a = \frac{g \sin \theta}{1 + k^2/r^2}$$

$$= \frac{v^2}{2S}$$

$$gS \sin \theta = \frac{v^2}{2} \left(1 + \frac{k^2}{r^2}\right)$$

$$mgS \sin \theta = \tfrac{1}{2}mv^2 + \tfrac{1}{2}mk^2 \left(\frac{v^2}{r^2}\right)$$

$$mgh = \tfrac{1}{2}mv^2 + \tfrac{1}{2}I_0\omega^2$$

The loss in potential energy of the ball mgh is seen to be equal to the gain in kinetic energy $\tfrac{1}{2}mv^2$ plus a similar term $\tfrac{1}{2}I_0\omega^2$ involving the moment of inertia of the ball about the center of mass ($I_0 = mk^2$) and its angular speed $\omega = v/r$. In order to have conservation of energy for the rigid body, we define $\tfrac{1}{2}mv^2$ as the **translational kinetic energy** of the ball, and $\tfrac{1}{2}I_0\omega^2$ as the **rotational kinetic energy** of the ball. The translational kinetic energy is less than that of the sliding block because some of the potential energy has become rotational kinetic energy.

KINETIC ENERGY OF A RIGID BODY

The concept of rotational kinetic energy is useful because we can use variables such as v and ω that refer to the motion of the system of particles **as a whole**. The kinetic energy of the **individual** particles in the ball is $\tfrac{1}{2}m_iv_i^2$, and the total kinetic energy is

$$K = \sum \tfrac{1}{2}m_iv_i^2$$

We showed earlier that the kinetic energy of any system of particles can be written

$$K = \sum \tfrac{1}{2}m_i v_i^2 = \sum \tfrac{1}{2}m_i v_{ic}^2 + \tfrac{1}{2}MV_c^2$$
$$= K_c + \tfrac{1}{2}MV_c^2$$

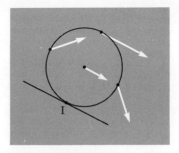

Pure rotation about instantaneous axis I.

where K is the kinetic energy in a particular frame of reference, K_c is the kinetic energy in the center-of-mass frame of reference, M is the total mass $M = \sum m_i$, and $\mathbf{V}_c$ is the velocity of the center of mass with respect to the external frame of reference.

For a rigid body we label the term $\tfrac{1}{2}MV_c^2$ as the translational kinetic energy, and K_c the rotational kinetic energy. The speed v of the ball on the plane is of course the speed of its center of mass.

In dynamics we dealt with the motion of a rigid body in general. Here we will restrict ourselves to **rotations about an axis of symmetry of the body** (so that we can define a scalar moment of inertia) and we will consider only **rotations about an axis having a fixed direction in the frame of reference** (so that the angular velocity ω can change in magnitude, but not in direction). With these restrictions the kinetic energy with respect to the center of mass,

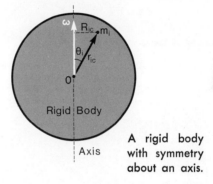

A rigid body with symmetry about an axis.

or rotational kinetic energy, takes a simple form. For a rigid body each particle has the same angular velocity ω at any instant. The velocity $\mathbf{v}_{ic} = \mathbf{r}_{ic} \times \omega$ has a magnitude $v_{ic} = r_{ic}\omega \sin \theta_i = R_{ic}\omega$, where R_{ic} is the distance from an axis of rotation through the center of mass.

$$K_c = \tfrac{1}{2} \sum m_i v_{ic}^2 = \tfrac{1}{2} \sum m_i R_{ic}^2 \omega^2 = \tfrac{1}{2}\omega^2 \sum m_i R_{ic}^2 = \tfrac{1}{2}I_0 \omega^2$$

where I_0 is the moment of inertia with respect to an axis through the center of

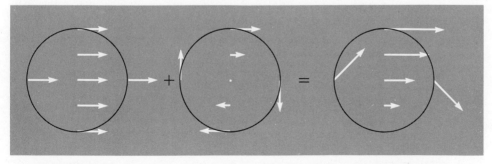

Pure translation plus rotation about the c-of-m is equivalent to pure rotation about the instantaneous axis, for a body rolling without slipping.

mass, as defined before. The total kinetic energy of a rigid body

$$K = K_{\text{trans}} + K_{\text{rot}} = \tfrac{1}{2}mv^2 + \tfrac{1}{2}I_0\omega^2$$

separates the energy into two parts, as though every particle were moving in pure translation with speed v, and every particle was rotating around the c-of-m with speed ω.

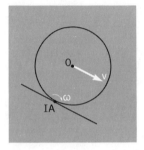

All the kinetic energy can be considered rotational kinetic energy, with respect to the instantaneous axis, for a body rolling without slipping.

In the special case of an object that is rolling without slipping the linear and angular speeds are related by $v = r\omega$, although in general they are unrelated. For the sphere rolling down the inclined plane

$$K = \tfrac{1}{2}mv^2 + \tfrac{1}{2}I\omega^2 = \tfrac{1}{2}mv^2 + (\tfrac{2}{5}\,mr^2)\left(\frac{v^2}{r^2}\right)$$

$$= \tfrac{7}{10}mv^2$$

This can be interpreted as energy of rotation with respect to the point of contact, an instantaneous axis.

$$I_{IA} = I_0 + mr^2 = \tfrac{2}{5}mr^2 + mr^2 = \tfrac{7}{5}mr^2$$
$$K_{IA} = \tfrac{1}{2}I_{IA}\omega^2 = \tfrac{7}{10}mr^2\omega^2 = \tfrac{7}{10}mv^2$$

WORK–ENERGY RELATION FOR A SYMMETRIC RIGID BODY IN ROTATION ABOUT A FIXED AXIS

We established a general work–energy relation for *any* system of particles

$$W_{\text{ext}} = E_2 - E_1$$

The energy $E = K + U$, the sum of the kinetic energies of the particles $K = \sum K_i$, and the internal potential energy of the system, due to interactions between the particles (assuming a conservative interaction).

For a rigid body the particles are all at rest with respect to one another, and therefore the internal potential energy is a constant, unchanged by external work done on the system. Therefore the work–energy relation for a rigid body is

$$W_{\text{ext}} = K_2 - K_1$$

As we have just seen the kinetic energy can be expressed as kinetic energy of translation (as though every particle was moving with the same speed as the center of mass) plus kinetic energy of rotation.

$$K = \sum K_i = K_{\text{trans}} + K_{\text{rot}}$$

For a rigid body in pure rotation about a fixed axis through the center of mass (we are dealing only with rotation about an axis of symmetry of the rigid body, and any axis of symmetry passes through the c-of-m) the work–energy relation becomes

$$W_{\text{ext}} = (K_{\text{rot}})_2 - (K_{\text{rot}})_1$$

It will be useful to verify this result for a rotating rigid body, in order to recall some of the concepts of rotational dynamics.

A wheel of radius R, and moment of inertia I_0, is mounted on a fixed smooth axle through its center along the wheel axis. A cord is wound around the circumference and pulled with a force $\mathbf{F}$; the force is tangential to the wheel and fixed in direction, but not necessarily constant in magnitude. The force $\mathbf{F}$ produces a torque $\boldsymbol{\tau} = \mathbf{R} \times \mathbf{F}$ of magnitude $\tau = RF$ about the center O.

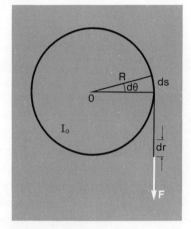

Linear and circular motion related.

The work done by the external force $\mathbf{F}$ in an interval is $W = \int \mathbf{F} \cdot d\mathbf{r}$ where $d\mathbf{r}$ is the infinitesimal displacement along the tangent. Since $\mathbf{F}$ and $d\mathbf{r}$ are parallel, $W = \int F\,dr$. As the string moves a distance dr, a point on the circumference of the wheel moves a distance $ds = dr$, and the wheel turns through an angle $d\theta$, where $ds = R\,d\theta$. Therefore

$$W = \int F\,dr = \int FR\,d\theta = \int \tau\,d\theta$$

This expresses the work done in terms of the rotational variables torque and angular displacement rather than in terms of linear variables, for the particular case we are considering. A more general argument would show that the work done is the scalar product $W = \int \boldsymbol{\tau} \cdot d\boldsymbol{\theta}$.

The torque is related to the angular acceleration and angular velocity by the equation of motion

$$\tau = I_0 \alpha = I_0 \frac{d\omega}{dt}$$

$$W = \int \tau\,d\theta = \int I_0 \frac{d\omega}{dt}\,d\theta = I_0 \int d\omega \frac{d\theta}{dt} = I_0 \int \omega\,d\omega$$

If the angular speed changes from ω_1 to ω_2 over an interval, the work done over the interval is

$$W = I_0 \int_{\omega_1}^{\omega_2} \omega\,d\omega = \tfrac{1}{2}I_0\omega_2^2 - \tfrac{1}{2}I_0\omega_1^2 = (K_{\text{rot}})_2 - (K_{\text{rot}})_1$$

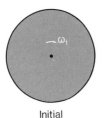 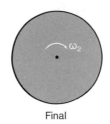

Change in angular speed over a finite interval.

Initial   Final

In the example the only torque exerted on the wheel is that due to the cord wound around the rim. The work done would be positive, and the rotational kinetic energy would increase. A frictional torque acting on the wheel would do negative work on it, decreasing its rotational energy.

A spring is a device for storing energy; when the spring is deformed, elastic potential energy is stored. A capacitor is a device for storing energy; when it is charged, electric potential energy is stored. A flywheel is also a device for storing energy, where the energy is stored in the form of kinetic rather than potential energy. It is used in many kinds of machines for storing energy during part of a cycle of motion. Of course, kinetic energy is stored in any moving object, but translational kinetic energy is not stored at a particular site.

The rate at which energy can be added to or withdrawn from a flywheel depends on the torque applied and angular speed. The power at any instant is

$$P = \frac{dW}{dt} = \tau \frac{d\theta}{dt} = \tau\omega$$

To withdraw energy at a constant rate it would be necessary to increase the retarding torque τ as the speed ω decreased.

KINETIC ENERGY OF AN ISOLATED ROTATING SYSTEM

The expression $K_{\text{rot}} = \frac{1}{2}I_0\omega^2$ is valid for any system of particles that is symmetric with respect to a fixed axis of rotation, whether or not the system is a rigid body. If the particles can move, the moment of inertia $I_0 = \sum m_i R_i^2$ can change.

For an **isolated** rotating system of particles, there is no external torque and no external work and therefore the angular momentum **L** and the mechanical energy E are constant (for a conservative system). The magnitude of the angular momentum is $L = I_0\omega$, so $K_{\text{rot}} = L^2/2I_0$, where L is a constant. If the moment of inertia of the system decreases the kinetic energy of rotation increases. This means the potential energy must decrease, since $E = K + U$ is constant. (If the system is not conservative, the energy may come from other internal sources, but remember that as far as classical mechanics is concerned every system is conservative if examined in fine enough detail.)

In discussing angular momentum we used as an example two blocks joined by a string sliding on a smooth table around their center of mass. The string, length R, has a slip knot in it and the length changes to $2R$. The angular momentum $L = I\omega = \mu R^2 \omega$ is constant, so when the knot slips

$$\mu R^2 \omega_i = \mu (2R)^2 \omega_f$$

where ω_i and ω_f are the initial and final angular speeds. The angular speed is reduced because the moment of inertia is increased: $\omega_f = \frac{1}{4}\omega_i$. The rotational kinetic energy is decreased.

$$\frac{K_f}{K_i} = \frac{\frac{1}{2}I_f\omega_f^2}{\frac{1}{2}I_i\omega_i^2} = \left(\frac{4}{1}\right)\left(\frac{1}{4}\right)^2 = \frac{1}{4}$$

What happens to this energy? The string provides the internal force for the system, and from a macroscopic point of view this is not a conservative force. The blocks make an inelastic collision when they fly out and are brought to rest by the string. The energy becomes thermal energy of the string and blocks, and they would heat up. From a microscopic point of view the energy becomes mechanical energy of the particles of the string and blocks.

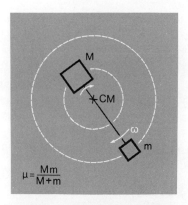

Does the energy change if the length of the string changes?

Suppose now that we introduce an ideal spring joining the blocks, as well as the string. Originally the spring is unextended, and the system is set rotating with speed ω_i. Then the string is cut. As the blocks move apart the rotational kinetic energy will decrease and the potential energy will increase, but the angular momentum and mechanical energy will be constant. The system will not come to equilibrium at some constant lower speed ω_f, but will overshoot, decreasing the kinetic energy and increasing the potential energy too much. Then the spring force will be greater

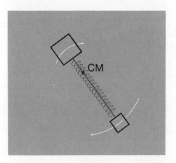

If the string joining the blocks is cut while the system is rotating, will the system rotate at a new angular speed? at a constant angular speed?

than the centripetal force required for stable circular orbits and the blocks will start to come back together again. The system will oscillate as it rotates, and the angular speed of rotation ω will increase and decrease alternately, with the frequency of the vibrational motion. This model indicates the complex motion of any isolated two-particle system with a conservative force of interaction.

Example: In a demonstration of conservation of angular momentum a man is sitting in a chair rotating about a vertical axis. He is holding two 10-lb iron balls 3 ft from the axis of rotation, turning at 5 rpm. He moves the iron balls in to the axis, and speeds up to a speed ω_2. Taking the moment of inertia of man and chair about the axis as $I_0 = 20$ lb-ft², assumed constant, calculate ω_2 and the work done by the man in moving the iron balls inward.

We discussed this example in Chapter 16. Treating the iron balls as particles, each of mass m, the moment of inertia changes from

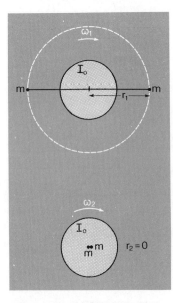

$$I_1 = I_0 + 2m_1^2 = 20 + 2 \times 10 \times 3^2$$
$$= 200 \text{ lb-ft}^2$$
to
$$I_2 = I_0 + 2mr_2^2 = 20 + 0 = 20 \text{ lb-ft}^2$$

There are no external torques on the systems, so angular momentum is conserved.

$$I_1\omega_1 = I_2\omega_2 \qquad \omega_2 = \frac{I_1}{I_2}\omega_1 = 10 \times 5 = 50 \text{ rpm}$$

The kinetic energy is increased by a factior

$$\frac{K_2}{K_1} = \frac{\frac{1}{2}I_2\omega_2^2}{\frac{1}{2}I_1\omega_1^2} = \left(\frac{I_2}{I_1}\right)\left(\frac{\omega_2}{\omega_1}\right)^2 = \frac{I_1}{I_2} = 10$$

The initial speed is

$$\omega_1 = 5 \text{ rpm} = \frac{5 \times 2\pi}{60} \text{ rad/sec} = \pi/6 \text{ rad/sec}$$

Two iron balls drawn in from radius r_1 to the axis.

so $K_1 = \frac{1}{2}(200)(\pi/6)^2 = 27.4$ ft-pndl $= 0.86$ ft-lb

and
$$K_2 = 10K_1 = 274 \text{ ft-pndl}$$
$$K_2 - K_1 = 247 \text{ ft-pndl}$$

The increase in kinetic energy is equal to the work done by the man in drawing the weights in. This is the required result, but we will show explicitly that the change in kinetic energy is the work done. When the iron balls are moving in a circle of radius r, the man must exert an inward force on each

$$F_{\text{cent}} = mr\omega^2$$

to hold them at radius r, as well as an upward force to hold them up.

If the radius is constant, no work is done by him in exerting this centripetal force. However, if the balls are moved inward or outward, he does positive or negative work. The force **F** and the displacement from the center **r** are in opposite directions, so the work done is $W = \int \mathbf{F}_{\text{cent}} \cdot d\mathbf{r} = -\int F_{\text{cent}}\, dr$. The work done in moving the two balls from radius r_1 to radius r_2 is

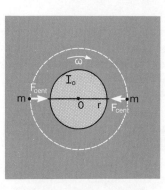

Horizontal force exerted on a ball to move it in.

$$W = 2\int \mathbf{F}_{\text{cent}} \cdot d\mathbf{r} = -2\int_{r_1}^{r_2} mr\omega^2\, dr$$

It is assumed that the process is quasi-static, that is the force is only infinitesimally greater than that required to hold the balls in circular orbit.

At every instant the angular mómentum is constant

$$(I_0 + 2mr^2)\,\omega = C$$

and using this the integral can be evaluated by substituting for ω^2

$$W = -C^2 \int_{r_1}^{r_2} \frac{2mr\,dr}{(I_0 + 2mr^2)^2}$$

$$= -C^2 \int \frac{dy/2}{y^2} \qquad\qquad y = I_0 + 2mr^2,\ dy = 4mr\,dr$$

$$= -\frac{C^2}{2}\left[-\frac{1}{y}\right] = \frac{C^2}{2}\left[\frac{1}{I_0 + 2mr^2}\right]_{r_1}^{r_2}$$

$$= \frac{C^2}{2}\left[\frac{1}{I_0 + 2mr_2^2} - \frac{1}{I_0 + 2mr_1^2}\right] = \frac{C^2}{2}\left[\frac{1}{I_2} - \frac{1}{I_1}\right]$$

The angular momentum is
$$\begin{aligned}C &= I_1\omega_1 = (I_0 + 2mr_1^2)\,\omega_1\\ &= I_2\omega_2 = (I_0 + 2mr_2^2)\,\omega_2\end{aligned}$$

And therefore
$$W = \tfrac{1}{2}I_2\omega_2^2 - \tfrac{1}{2}I_1\omega_1^2$$

Example: A thin rod of mass $2m$ rests on a smooth table. A pellet of mass m slides along the table at right angles to the rod, striking the rod at one end and sticking to it. What fraction of the initial kinetic energy is lost in the collision?

The only horizontal forces for the objects sliding on the smooth table are those the pellet and rod exert on one another, internal forces for the two-object system.

From conservation of linear momentum

$$mv = (m + 2m)V \qquad V = v/3$$

The speed V is the speed of the c-of-m of the system after collision. The position of the c-of-m is $l/3$ from the end where mass m sticks, or $l/6$ from the center of the rod (l = length of rod).

The moment of inertia of the system about the c-of-m is

$$I_c = m\left(\frac{l}{3}\right)^2 + 2m\left[\tfrac{1}{12}l^2 + \left(\frac{l}{6}\right)^2\right] = \tfrac{1}{3}ml^2$$

From conservation of angular momentum about the center of mass

$$mv\left(\frac{l}{3}\right) = I\omega = (\tfrac{1}{3}ml^2)\,\omega$$

$$\omega = v/l$$

where ω is the angular speed about the center of mass after collision.

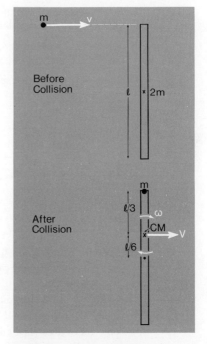

Before Collision

After Collision

Inelastic collision between a particle and a rod.

We cannot assume conservation of mechanical energy in the collision—it is an inelastic impact in which the objects stick together.

The initial kinetic energy is $K_1 = \frac{1}{2}mv^2$. The final kinetic energy is

$$K_2 = K_{\text{trans}} + K_{\text{rot}}$$
$$= \frac{1}{2}(3m)V^2 + \frac{1}{2}I_c\omega^2$$

$$= \frac{3}{2}m\left(\frac{v}{3}\right)^2 + \frac{1}{2}(\frac{1}{3}ml^2)\left(\frac{v}{l}\right)^2 = \frac{1}{3}mv^2$$

The fraction of kinetic energy lost is

$$\frac{K_1 - K_2}{K_1} = 1 - \frac{K_2}{K_1} = 1 - \frac{\frac{1}{3}mv^2}{\frac{1}{2}mv^2} = 1 - \frac{2}{3} = \frac{1}{3}$$

One-third of the initial kinetic energy is lost, that is, becomes thermal energy, in the collision.

Questions for discussion

1. Can you think of situations where energy is stored as kinetic energy of rotation?

2. Can you think of situations where kinetic energy of rotation is usefully changed to kinetic energy of translation, and vice versa?

3. Some of the energy expended in launching a projectile is sometimes used to give the projectile energy of rotation. Why?

4. Think of a real object spinning in space, free from any external forces. Its angular momentum will remain constant, but its rotational kinetic energy may gradually decrease. Why?

5. A rapidly spinning gyroscope is held with its axis horizontal. If support is removed from one side, the wheel precesses around a vertical axis at the other point of support. Does its axis remain horizontal? If it does, where does the extra energy of rotation come from? If it does not, why do we not observe the axis as tilted?

Problems

1. A 60-lb, 16-in.-diameter cylindrical grindstone is turning at 90 rpm when the blade of an axe is pressed against it, bringing it to rest in 10 sec. At what average rate is mechanical energy dissipated?

2. A solid cylinder of 2-kg mass is free to rotate around a fixed horizontal axle along its axis. A string is wound several times around it, a 0.5-kg block suspended from one end of the string, and a 0.3-kg block suspended from the other, on the opposite side of the cylinder. If the system is released from rest, calculate the speed of each block after the larger block has fallen 1 m.

3. A ship is stabilized with a massive wheel 3 m in diameter rotating at 1200 rpm.
(a) Assume that the wheel is a solid disc 20 cm wide made of metal of density 8 gm/cm³, and estimate the kinetic energy stored in it. **(b)** If it is set in motion by

applying power at an average rate of 1000 watts, how long does it take to get it up
to speed? **(c)** The fixed axis of the wheel is horizontal, at right angles to the ship's
length. What torque would be required to tilt it 10° in 10 sec? In what direction
would the torque have to be applied?

4. A "¼-hp" electric motor is using electric energy at a rate of 120 watts, turning a
3-in.-diameter pulley at 1200 rpm. The pulley is driving a belt looped around it;
the tension in the belt on one side of the pulley is 6 lb, on the other side 2 lb.
Determine the efficiency with which the motor is operating.

5. A 0.4-kg meterstick is free to swing about a fixed pivot at one end. If it is held in
the horizontal position, and released, find **(a)** the force exerted on it by the pivot
the instant after release, **(b)** its angular speed when it reaches the vertical position,
(c) the speed of its center of mass when it reaches the vertical position, **(d)** the force
exerted on it by the pivot when it is vertical. **(e)** Suppose the stick is initially
vertical, balanced on its pivot in unstable equilibrium. When it falls, determine
the force exerted on it by the pivot when it passes the horizontal and when it passes
the vertical positions.

6. A meterstick stands on end on a table, in unstable equilibrium. If it is disturbed,
with what speed does its center hit the table **(a)** if its lower end is in a frictionless
pivot, **(b)** if the table is smooth?

7. A symmetric rigid body of radius of gyration k about its axis of symmetry through
its center of mass rolls down an inclined plane without slipping. **(a)** What fraction
of its kinetic energy is translational kinetic energy at every instant? **(b)** If the
coefficient of static friction between the body and the plane is μ_s, what is the maximum plane angle θ_m such that the body will roll without slipping? **(c)** What are
the results for (a) and (b) for a solid cylinder on a plane with $\mu_s = 0.5$?

8. A box of sand is a cube 1 ft on a side weighing 100 lb. It sits on a floor, and is hit
by a 0.1-lb bullet moving at 1000 ft/sec parallel to the floor and parallel to a side
of the box, 6 in. above the floor and 3 in. from the center of the box. Assuming
the bullet becomes embedded in the box, determine linear and angular speeds of the
box just after impact, and compare the kinetic energies before and after impact.

9. A small marble rolls
without slipping on
the track shown,
starting 1 m above
the horizontal plane
and leaving the track
at a height of 0.25 m
and at an angle of 30°
above the horizontal.
Calculate its maxi-
mum height H and
horizontal range R.

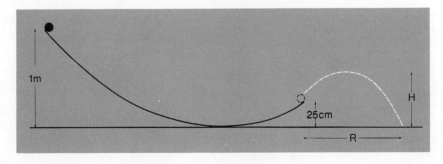

10. A circular puck of mass m is at rest flat on a smooth table. A pellet of the same
mass m is sliding on the table toward the puck, on a line that is tangential to the
edge of the puck. When the pellet touches the puck, it sticks. Determine the
fraction of the initial kinetic energy lost in the collision.

26

ENERGY OF A SYSTEM OF GAS MOLECULES

Our treatment of mechanics has been based on the concept of a particle, and all macroscopic or microscopic objects have been considered to be made up of particles. A particle has certain properties that determine its interaction with other particles—such properties as mass, charge, spin and magnetic moment—and it is assumed that these properties are constants for the particle, unchanged in an interaction. The particle has no internal structure (or at least no change-able internal structure) so it has no internal energy. The only kind of energy a free particle (one not acted upon by external forces) can have is kinetic energy.

In principle the detailed motion of any isolated system of particles can be completely described by the methods of classical dynamics. If we know the position and velocity of every particle in the system at some instant (the initial conditions), and know the forces between the particles, the laws of mechanics can be used to calculate the motion at any other time (past or future). In practice we cannot in general make these calculations at all. For a system with large numbers of particles we have no way of measuring the motion of every particle at a particular instant, so that we know the initial conditions. What is more, even if we know the initial conditions and know the force law for the interaction between the particles, the calculation of the motion for a many-particle system would be such a mammoth task that it is not practical even with modern computers.

For systems with a small number of interacting particles, such as the solar system (the sun and planets treated as particles) the motion of each particle can be computed to any desired degree of accuracy. This means that the position and velocity of each particle at any time can be calculated, but not that it is possible to determine an analytic expression for the position as a function of time, or to determine an equation for the path in space of each particle. Even the "three-body" problem cannot be solved explicitly.

The only many-particle system we have examined has been the idealization of a rigid body, where it is assumed that the particles are all at rest with respect to one another. For any rigid body the motion can be conveniently described as pure translation combined with pure rotation around the center of mass. (The only thing we have not worked out completely so far is the general rotation in three-dimension for bodies of arbitrary shape; we confined ourselves to rotation about an axis of symmetry, so that we could use a scalar moment of inertia.)

Much of our discussion has centered on a two-particle system, because it is the basic dynamical system (particles interact in pairs) and because we could work out the motion analytically in detail. We examined the orbits of the particles of an isolated two-particle system with the gravitational interaction between them (a planet and single satellite). We also discussed a two-particle system with a minimum in the potential energy of interaction (so that the particles are attracted if far apart, repelled if close together) such as a diatomic molecule, and we will have more to say about this system in this chapter.

In Part VI we are going to introduce a different approach to many-particle situations, the methods of statistical mechanics. We will conclude Part V on energy by examining what can be said about the energy of a system of gas molecules from the point of view of classical dynamics. Also, as a preview, we will state certain results from statistical mechanics and from quantum mechanics and apply these to the system of gas molecules.

THE IDEAL GAS

You probably have some sort of a mental picture of a quantity of gas in a container. Although individual molecules cannot be seen, you visualize them as tiny particles moving around rapidly, colliding with one another and the walls of the container.

If the interaction energy between the molecules is negligible with respect to the total energy of the system, the gas is called an **ideal gas.** Note that this does not mean that the molecules do not interact at all. They do "collide" with one another (and with the walls), which means that they do interact for brief periods of time, but the ideal gas assumption is that the energy associated with this interaction is negligible. The higher the density of the gas the more collisions there will be and the less valid this assumption will be.

What is your mental picture of a gas?

In general for any system of particles the total energy is the sum of the energies of the individual particles *and* the energy of interaction between the particles. The advantage of the ideal gas assumption is that the total energy of the system of molecules is simply the sum of the energies of the individual molecules. If there are N molecules, the total energy is $E = \sum_{i=1}^{N} E_i$. It is not necessary to include any interaction energy terms.

The concept of an ideal gas is a very useful one, used extensively in kinetic theory and in statistical mechanics. Like the idealization of the rigid body, it has the advantage that it represents the actual physical situation very well indeed under some conditions. Real gases behave like an ideal gas to a good degree of approximation unless they are close to liquefying. You are probably familiar with the ideal gas equation of state $pV = RT$, which we will discuss later.

The question at the moment is this: Can the molecules of an ideal gas be treated as particles? If so, the only kind of energy with which we are concerned is kinetic energy. For a system of N identical non-interacting particles, each of mass m,

$$E = \sum_{i=1}^{N} E_i = \sum K_i = \sum \tfrac{1}{2} m v_i^2$$

Whether or not this is an adequate model depends on the circumstances—that is, on the kind of experiments that are performed on the gas. This model is used in the kinetic theory of gases to deduce a number of results that are consistent with experiment. (In discussing impulse and momentum in Chapter 13 we deduced the expression $p = \tfrac{1}{3} n m \overline{v^2}$ for the pressure exerted by a gas.) On the other hand, there are some experimental measurements that are not consistent with this model. When a gas is heated its change in temperature depends on the kind of molecule; for monatomic gases it is satisfactory to treat the molecule as a particle, but for polyatomic gases this model is inadequate. We will in this chapter go into this question of heat absorbed by a gas (heat capacity) because it was in trying to explain the observed results that it was first recognized, about one hundred years ago, that there was something fundamentally wrong with classical physics as applied to atomic systems. Ultimately this led to quantum mechanics.

In order to examine some of the models that can be used to represent a molecule of gas, we will use as an example a diatomic molecule where we can work out explicit expressions for the energy.

ENERGY OF A DIATOMIC MOLECULE

As a first approximation the diatomic molecule can be treated as a single particle, as we have said. A somewhat better model is to treat it as a two-particle system (the two atoms treated as particles) with a fixed distance (the bond length) between the particles. The molecule is then a simple rigid body. This is the **rigid rotator** model, or dumbbell model.

A still better approximation is to treat the molecule as a two-particle system, but assume that the two particles can vibrate with respect to one another, a **non-rigid rotator** model. If it is assumed that the vibrations are simple harmonic, the two particles can be thought of as connected by an ideal spring, rather than a massless rigid rod as in the dumbbell model.

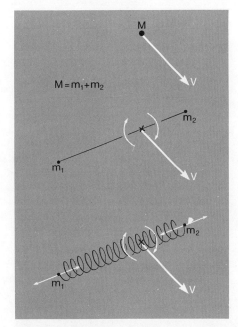

The next step would be to consider the constituents of the individual atoms as particles, treating each nucleus as a single particle and the orbital electrons as particles. This model would be very complex to work out in detail and in any case a waste of time because classical mechanics is not adequate for this.

We are in a position to give classical expressions for the energy of the rigid rotator model and for the non-rigid rotator model. We will do this because these models are used in quantum mechanics as well as in classical mechanics. In quantum mechanics the concept of a particle is different from what it is in classical mechanics—the motion of each particle moving in a well-defined orbit is given up—but it is still necessary to postulate some sort of model for the molecules.

Three models for a diatomic molecule.

For the rigid rotator the kinetic energy can be expressed as the total kinetic energy of the two particles, or as kinetic energy of translation plus kinetic energy of rotation

$$K = \tfrac{1}{2}m_1v_1^2 + \tfrac{1}{2}m_2v_2^2$$
$$= \tfrac{1}{2}(m_1 + m_2)V^2 + (\tfrac{1}{2}m_1v_{1c}^2 + \tfrac{1}{2}m_2v_{2c}^2)$$
$$= K_{\text{trans}} + K(\text{re c-of-m})$$

The angular momentum with respect to the c-of-m

is

$$L = m_1v_{1c}r_1 + m_2v_{2c}r_2$$
$$= m_1r_1^2\omega + m_2r_2^2\omega$$
$$= (m_1r_1^2 + m_2r_2^2)\,\omega = I\omega$$

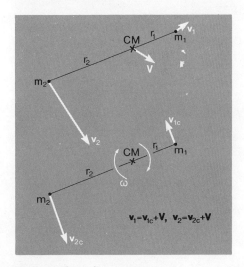

$$v_1 = v_{1c} + V, \quad v_2 = v_{2c} + V$$

Motion referred to an external frame, and to the c-of-m.

where I is the moment of inertia about the c-of-m, and ω is the angular speed.

$$K(\text{re c-of-m}) = \tfrac{1}{2}m_1v_{1c}^2 + \tfrac{1}{2}m_2v_{2c}^2 = \tfrac{1}{2}m_1r_1^2\omega^2 + \tfrac{1}{2}m_2r_2^2\omega^2 = \tfrac{1}{2}I\omega^2$$

The total kinetic energy is

$$K = K_{\text{trans}} + K_{\text{rot}} = \tfrac{1}{2}MV^2 + \tfrac{1}{2}I\omega^2 = \frac{P^2}{2M} + \frac{L^2}{2I}$$

The total mass $M = m_1 + m_2$ and the moment of inertia I are constants. The speed V is the speed of the c-of-m, *the* speed of the molecule.

The kinetic energy can be expressed in terms of the linear and angular speeds V and ω, or in terms of the linear and angular momenta $P = MV$ and $L = I\omega$. For an isolated molecule each energy term is constant. Note that V and ω are not related (as they are for a rolling object).

The total mechanical energy of the molecule is

$$E = K + U$$

where U is the potential energy of interaction of the particles. Since the particles are assumed to remain a fixed distance apart with this model, this energy U is constant. Only the kinetic energy changes if the molecule interacts with other systems. A collision (interaction) with another molecule will in general produce changes in both the kinetic energy of translation and of rotation.

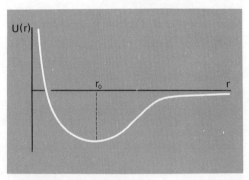

The non-rigid rotator model is more complex, because the two particles do not remain a fixed distance apart. Even if they did, the distance between them when the system was rotating would not be the same as when it was not. If the particles are a distance r_0 apart when at rest they will be a distance $R > r_0$ apart when rotating at a constant speed ω. The centripetal force on each particle is

Interaction potential for a diatomic molecule.

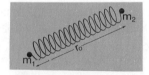

Non-rigid rotator model, assuming ideal elastic interaction.

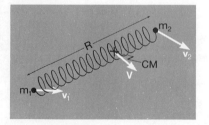

If the model rotates at a constant angular speed ω, the distance between the particles is $R > r_0$; in general there will be vibration as well.

provided by the restoring force, which depends on the extension $(R - r_0)$. If we assume a restoring force proportional to displacement, with force constant k

$$F_{\text{rest}} = k(R - r_0) = \mu\omega^2 R = \frac{L^2}{\mu R^3}$$

where μ is the reduced mass $\mu = m_1 m_2/(m_1 + m_2)$. The angular momentum is

$$L = I\omega = \mu R^2 \omega$$

When the particles are a constant distance R apart the system can be treated as a rigid rotator of energy $E = K + U$, where $K = K_{\text{trans}} + K_{\text{rot}}$, and U, the potential energy of interaction, is constant. Since there is an arbitrary zero in potential energy, and since we are always interested only in energy differences, we can choose this as the zero of potential energy. Then the potential energy of the system when the distance between the particles is r is

$$U = \tfrac{1}{2}k(r - R)^2$$

and the total mechanical energy is

$$E = K + U = \tfrac{1}{2}m_1 v_1^2 + \tfrac{1}{2}m_2 v_2^2 + \tfrac{1}{2}k(r - R)^2$$

Note that if the distance r between the particles is not constant, the rotational kinetic energy $\tfrac{1}{2}I\omega^2$ is not constant; as r changes, $I = \mu r^2$ changes, and ω changes in such a way that $L = I\omega$ is constant. Therefore the rotational kinetic energy changes.

We showed in Chapter 23 how the kinetic energy of a two-particle system could be expressed in terms of the relative position r and relative speed v_{rel} of the particles.

$$
\begin{aligned}
K &= \tfrac{1}{2}m_1 v_1^2 + \tfrac{1}{2}m_2 v_2^2 \\
&= \tfrac{1}{2}(m_1 + m_2)V^2 + (\tfrac{1}{2}m_1 v_{1c}^2 + \tfrac{1}{2}m_2 v_{2c}^2) \\
&= \tfrac{1}{2}MV^2 + \tfrac{1}{2}\mu v_{\text{rel}}^2 && \left(v_{\text{rel}}^2 = r^2 + r^2\left(\frac{d\theta}{dt}\right)^2\right) \\
&= \tfrac{1}{2}MV^2 + \tfrac{1}{2}\mu\left(\frac{dr}{dt}\right)^2 + \tfrac{1}{2}\mu r^2\left(\frac{d\theta}{dt}\right)^2 && \left(L = \mu r^2\left[\frac{d\theta}{dt}\right]\right) \\
&= K_{\text{trans}} + \tfrac{1}{2}\mu\left(\frac{dr}{dt}\right)^2 + \tfrac{1}{2}\frac{L^2}{\mu r^2} \\
&= K_{\text{trans}} + \tfrac{1}{2}\mu\left(\frac{dr}{dt}\right)^2 + \tfrac{1}{2}I\omega^2
\end{aligned}
$$

The total mechanical energy of the system is

$$
\begin{aligned}
E &= K + U \\
&= \tfrac{1}{2}MV^2 + \tfrac{1}{2}I\omega^2 + \tfrac{1}{2}\mu\left(\frac{dr}{dt}\right)^2 + \tfrac{1}{2}k(r - R)^2
\end{aligned}
$$

The first term is the translational kinetic energy, related to the motion of the c-of-m of the system. If there are no external forces, it will be constant. The other three terms represent internal energy of the system, and their **sum** is constant if there are no external forces. The final term is the potential energy of the system, and the other two terms represent the kinetic energy of internal motion of the system.

The three internal energy terms are interconnected and therefore not individually constant—the rotational and vibrational motions are coupled. However, it turns out that for real molecules the strength of the force constant k (which you recall is related to the shape of the potential energy curve near its minimum) is such that the deformation of the molecule is very small. That is, the bond length R when it is rotating is very nearly equal to the equilibrium length r_0, and when the molecule is vibrating as well the displacement $(r - R)$ is very small compared to R (or r_0). Later in this chapter we will do a numerical example to show this. For the present, we assume that it is a good approximation to treat $I = \mu r^2$ as constant. Then the rotational kinetic energy $\frac{1}{2}I\omega^2$ is constant (for a free molecule) and the total energy consists of three separate parts, associated with translation, rotation, and vibration.

$$E = E_{\text{trans}} + E_{\text{rot}} + E_{\text{vib}}$$

$$= \tfrac{1}{2}MV^2 + \tfrac{1}{2}I\omega^2 + \left[\tfrac{1}{2}\mu\left(\frac{dr}{dt}\right)^2 + \tfrac{1}{2}k(r - r_0)^2\right]$$

$$= \frac{P^2}{2M} + \frac{L^2}{2I} + E_{\text{vib}}$$

For an isolated molecule each term is constant. The energy of translation is that of a single particle of mass $M = m_1 + m_2$, moving at speed V. The energy of rotation is that of a rigid rotator of moment of inertia $I = \mu r_0^2$, rotating with angular speed ω. The energy associated with the vibrational motion is the same as that of a linear harmonic oscillator of mass μ. When $r = r_0$ this energy is totally kinetic, and when $(r - r_0)$ is a maximum it is totally potential; in general it is both. The frequency of vibration is $f_{\text{vib}} = (1/2\pi)\sqrt{k/\mu}$.

The frequency of vibration is a constant property of the molecule (like M, μ, I, k). The frequency of rotation $f_{\text{rot}} = \omega/2\pi$ depends on the initial conditions of motion.

If the energy of the molecule is changed, for example by making a collision with another molecule, the change may be in any one of the terms, or in all three, depending on the collision. Note, however, that it is only an approximation to think of the rotational and vibrational motions as independent of one another. (This means that in the spectra of diatomic gases there are lines representing transitions between rotational and vibrational energy states.)

From the point of view of classical dynamics, we have gone as far as we can go. For an ideal diatomic gas (N identical molecules) the total energy is simply the sum of the energies of the individual molecules. Using the non-rigid rotator model for the molecules

$$E = \sum_{i=1}^{N} E_i = \sum_{i=1}^{N} (E_{\text{trans}} + E_{\text{rot}} + E_{\text{vib}})_i$$

$$= \sum_{i=1}^{N} \left\{ \tfrac{1}{2}MV_i^2 + \tfrac{1}{2}I\omega_i^2 + \left[\tfrac{1}{2}\mu \left(\frac{dr_i}{dt} \right)^2 + \tfrac{1}{2}k(r_i - r_0)^2 \right] \right\}$$

For an isolated system this total energy will be constant but classical dynamics does not provide any information about the relative amounts of the different forms of energy, or about the way the energy is distributed among the molecules. Such information is provided by the methods of statistical mechanics. Later we will discuss this subject, but for the present we will state one result of classical statistical mechanics, the principle of equipartition of energy.

EQUIPARTITION OF ENERGY

The statement of equipartition of energy is essentially this. For a system of particles in thermal equilibrium, the average energy associated with each degree of freedom of the system is $\tfrac{1}{2}kT$, where T is the absolute temperature of the system, and k is Boltzmann's constant. (We are also using k for the force constant in the diatomic molecule, but it should be clear from the context which k is meant in any equation.)

$$k = 1.38 \times 10^{-23} \text{ joule/K}°$$

To understand this statement it is necessary to know what is meant by **thermal equilibrium,** and by **degree of freedom.** The concept of thermal equilibrium is not simple, but it is sufficient for our purposes to state that if a system is in thermal equilibrium it can be described by a relatively small number of macroscopic parameters such as pressure and temperature. These macroscopic properties of the system are related to the average behavior of the microscopic constituents of the system; the fact that chaotic microscopic behavior leads to steady macroscopic behavior (so we can speak of *the* pressure or *the* temperature) is a fundamental result of statistical mechanics.

One way of defining a degree of freedom is to say that the number of degrees of freedom of a system is equal to the number of **independent** terms in the expression for the total energy of the system.

Think for example of an ideal gas of N identical molecules, and treat each molecule as a particle. The energy of the system is

$$E = \sum_{i=1}^{N} E_i = \sum_{i=1}^{N} K_i = \sum_{i=1}^{N} \tfrac{1}{2}mv_i^2$$

It might appear that there are N terms in the energy, and therefore N degrees of freedom. However this is not so, because there are three degrees of freedom for each particle. The energy of each particle is

$$E_i = K_i = \tfrac{1}{2}mv_i^2 = \tfrac{1}{2}m\,(v_x^2 + v_y^2 + v_z^2)_i$$

where v_x, v_y and v_z are the components of velocity with respect to some coordinate system. The x-component of velocity can be changed independently of the y- and z-components. Therefore the total energy of the system of N molecules

$$E = \sum_{i=1}^{N} \tfrac{1}{2}m\,(v_x^2 + v_y^2 + v_z^2)_i$$

has $3N$ terms. If the system is in thermal equilibrium the equipartition principle states that the average energy associated with each degree of freedom is $\tfrac{1}{2}kT$, so that the total energy is

$$E = 3N(\tfrac{1}{2}kT) = \tfrac{3}{2}NkT$$

This can also be expressed by stating the average energy per molecule

$$\frac{E}{N} = \tfrac{1}{2}m\overline{v^2} = \tfrac{3}{2}kT$$

Of course, the energies of individual molecules may be greater or less than this value. The calculations of statistical mechanics give the average value, and also show how the energies are distributed about this average value.

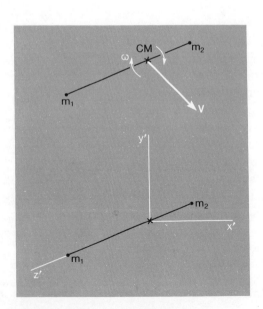

For the rigid rotator there are two rotational terms in the energy.

Now instead of treating the N identical molecules as particles, suppose we assume that the molecules are diatomic, and use the rigid rotator model. Each molecule is itself a two-particle system. How many terms are there in the energy? For each molecule

$$\begin{aligned} E &= K_{\text{trans}} + K_{\text{rot}} \\ &= \tfrac{1}{2}MV^2 + \tfrac{1}{2}I\omega^2 \\ &= \tfrac{1}{2}M(V_x^2 + V_y^2 + V_z^2) + \tfrac{1}{2}I(\omega_{x'}^2 + \omega_{y'}^2) \end{aligned}$$

There are three degrees of freedom associated with the center-of-mass motion, and **two** associated with rotation about the c-of-m. To see why, think of co-ordinate axes x', y', z' with the z'-axis lying along the line joining the particles. There are three independent rotations possible, with angular speeds $\omega_{x'}, \omega_{y'}, \omega_{z'}$ about the three axes. The corresponding energies will be $\tfrac{1}{2}I_{x'}\omega_{x'}^2$, $\tfrac{1}{2}I_{y'}\omega_{y'}^2$, $\tfrac{1}{2}I_{z'}\omega_{z'}^2$. The x'- and y'-axes are at right angles to the line joining the particles, and the moments of inertia about these axes are the same $I_{x'} = I_{y'} = \mu r^2$. The moment of inertia about the z'-axis is $I_{z'} = 0$, since the particles lie on this axis. There-fore, there are only two rotational degrees of freedom with this model. For a rigid body that is not one-dimensional (for example, representing a polyatomic molecule) there will be three rotational degrees of freedom.

For the N-molecule ideal gas system, using a rigid-rotator model, there are $5N$ degrees of freedom. If such a system is in thermal equilibrium, the total energy is $E = \frac{5}{2}NkT$.

The next step is to use a non-rigid rotator model for the individual molecules of the system. The energy of each molecule is then

$$E = E_{\text{trans}} + E_{\text{rot}} + E_{\text{vib}}$$

$$= \tfrac{1}{2}MV^2 + \tfrac{1}{2}I\omega^2 + \left[\tfrac{1}{2}\mu\left(\frac{dr}{dt}\right)^2 + \tfrac{1}{2}k(r - r_0)^2\right]$$

$$= \tfrac{1}{2}M(V_x^2 + V_y^2 + V_z^2) + \tfrac{1}{2}I(\omega_{x'}^2 + \omega_{y'}^2) + \left[\tfrac{1}{2}\mu\left(\frac{dr}{dt}\right)^2 + \tfrac{1}{2}k(r - r_0)^2\right]$$

In addition to the three translational and two rotational degrees of freedom, there are now two vibrational degrees of freedom, corresponding to the extra two terms in the energy. Note that these terms do not depend on the position or orientation of the molecule, only on the distance r between them, and its rate of change $\left(\frac{dr}{dt}\right)$. Any linear harmonic oscillator has two degrees of freedom.

With this model there are seven degrees of freedom per molecule, or $7N$ degrees of freedom for N independent molecules. If such a system is in thermal equilibrium the total energy is $E = \frac{7}{2}NkT$.

We now have three different expressions for the energy of a system of N ideal diatomic gas molecules in equilibrium, obtained by applying the equipartition principle to different models for the molecules.

$$E = \tfrac{3}{2}NkT \qquad \text{:particle model}$$
$$E = \tfrac{5}{2}NkT \qquad \text{:rigid rotator model}$$
$$E = \tfrac{7}{2}NkT \qquad \text{:non-rigid rotator model}$$

Which of these (if any) is in agreement with experiment? Before we discuss this question, some comments about the equipartition principle.

Application of the equipartition principle depends on three basic assumptions:

1. That classical statistics (the Maxwell–Boltzmann distribution) are valid. There are other forms of statistics (quantum statistics, leading to the Bose–Einstein and the Fermi–Dirac distributions) that apply to other systems, but classical statistics are applicable to a system of gas molecules.
2. That the energy is a continuous function of the co-ordinates. Our expres-sions for energy are derived from classical dynamics, and the energy can vary continuously. We will see that it is here that our classical model breaks down.

3. That each term in the energy depends on the square of a dynamic variable. This condition is fulfilled for the models we have used; the energy terms depend on V_x^2, on $\omega_{x'}^2$, on $(dr/dt)^2$, on $(r - r_0)^2$, etc. This condition means, however, that the equipartition principle does not apply to a system of gas molecules in the uniform field of the earth. Then there would be a term Mgz in the energy for each molecule. This term depends on the co-ordinate z (the height above some reference level) to the first power, not on z^2. For the molecules of gas in a container we can ignore this term in the energy, because it makes a negligible contribution. It is important in considering large volumes of gas—such as the atmosphere.

SPECIFIC HEAT CAPACITY

We developed above three different expressions for the energy of a system of ideal gas molecules, based on different models for the molecules. The result was

$$E = \frac{f}{2} NkT$$

where f is the number of degrees of freedom per molecule. For a particle model, $f = 3$; for a rigid rotator, $f = 5$; for a non-rigid rotator, $f = 7$.

In order to compare this theoretical result with experiment, all that is necessary is to add a measured amount of energy ΔE to the system and measure the corresponding temperature change ΔT. Since $\Delta E = \frac{f}{2} Nk \, \Delta T$, we can determine f. But hold on a minute. How do we know N? You can't count the gas molecules in a container. And how do you measure a quantity of energy?

We will not attempt to deal completely with these questions at this point, but will instead state certain results, to be justified later. We assume that the system consists of one **mole** of gas, meaning one gram-molecular-weight, or Avogadro's number N_0 molecules. One mole of any gas is described by the ideal gas equation of state $pV = RT$, if the pressure is low enough that the gas can be treated as an ideal gas. The universal gas constant R is related to Avogadro's number N_0 and Boltzmann's constant k by $R = N_0 k$. (Therefore, Boltzmann's constant $k = R/N_0$ is sometimes called the gas constant per molecule.) The ideal gas equation of state can be thought of as an experimental result, relating the observed pressure p, volume V and temperature T of the mole of gas, but it can be derived by the methods of statistical mechanics.

The energy of the system of gas molecules can be changed by doing work on the system (for example by compressing the gas with a piston in a cylinder) or by heat exchange (bringing the system into thermal contact with another system at a different temperature). The relation between these and the properties of the system are described by the laws of thermodynamics (which can be regarded as empirical laws, or can be derived by the methods of statistical mechanics).

You are probably familiar with the physical property called heat capacity. If a quantity of heat ΔQ is added to any system, and the temperature of the system changes by ΔT, the quantity $C = \Delta Q/\Delta T$ is called the **heat capacity** of the system. This property depends on (1) the quantity of matter in the system, (2) the temperature of the system, (3) the type of process in which the heat is added, (4) the kind of matter in the system. We comment on these factors in turn.

1. In order to have a property that depends on the kind of matter, but not on the quantity, we define the **specific heat capacity,** the heat capacity per unit quantity of matter. This may be per gm, per kg, per lb, etc., or per mole. The specific heat capacity per unit mass is $c = C/m$, where m is the mass of the system. The specific heat capacity per mole is usually called the **molar heat capacity,** and is $c = C/n$, where n is the number of moles in the system.

(A quantity called **specific heat** is also used. It is defined as the heat capacity of the system divided by the heat capacity of the same mass of water, and therefore has no dimensions. In certain units the specific heat capacity of water is approximately unity; e.g., 1 cal/gm-C°. For copper the specific heat capacity is 0.092 cal/gm-C°, and the specific heat is 0.092.)

2. Specific heat capacity is useful as a physical property because it is approximately independent of temperature (is a physical "constant" for the material). However, this approximation is valid for any substance only over a limited range of temperature. The specific heat capacity at any particular temperature is defined by the limit

$$c(T) = \lim_{\Delta T \to 0} \frac{1}{m}\frac{\Delta Q}{\Delta T} = \frac{1}{m}\frac{dQ}{dT}$$

where dQ is an infinitesimal amount of heat. (We do not write dQ because it is not an exact differential.)

If a system changes from temperature T_1 to T_2, the heat added is

$$\Delta Q = m \int_{T_1}^{T_2} c(T)\, dT$$

Only if c is independent of T in the range $T_1 \to T_2$ can we write

$$\Delta Q = mc(T_2 - T_1) = mc\,\Delta T$$

The original definition given $C = \Delta Q/\Delta T$ is actually the **average** heat capacity over the range ΔT.

3. The dependence of the heat capacity on the process can most easily be illustrated by thinking about an ideal gas. The state of the gas is described by the equation of state $pV = RT$, where V is the volume of one mole of gas at pressure p, temperature T. (For n moles of gas the equation is $pV = nRT$.) Think about the state of the gas as represented on a p–V diagram. At any

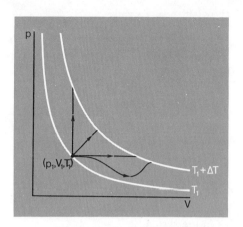

The temperature of a gas can be increased by different processes.

particular temperature T_1, the behavior of the gas is described by $pV = RT_1 = $ constant (Boyle's Law). The hyperbola $pV = RT_1$ on the p–V diagram is called an isotherm. At a higher temperature $T_1 + \Delta T$ there will be a different isotherm.

Now think of the gas in a particular state (p_1, V_1, T_1). The temperature of the gas can be changed to $T_1 + \Delta T$ by any number of different processes, and for each process the quantity of heat ΔQ added to the system will be different. The molar heat capacity is $c = \Delta Q / \Delta T$, and therefore there are an infinite number of different heat capacities, depending on the process. We are interested in two of these, the process at constant pressure (represented by the line parallel to the V-axis) and the process at constant volume (represented by the line parallel to the p-axis). The corresponding molar heat capacities are designated c_p and c_v. The molar heat capacity at constant pressure c_p is the one most easily measured experimentally, while the molar heat capacity at constant volume c_v is the one that is usually of interest theoretically.

If the heat capacity for one process is known, and the equation of state is known, then the laws of thermodynamics can be used to calculate the heat capacity for any other process. For the ideal gas for example the relation between c_p and c_v is

$$c_p - c_v = R$$

Thermodynamics does not lead to an absolute value for either c_p or c_v, only to a relation between them. As we will discuss shortly, the difference between c_p and c_v is comparable in magnitude to the molar heat capacities themselves, and therefore the process by which heat is added is important.

You can see physically why c_p is greater than c_v. When heat is added to the gas at constant volume, all of the added energy is used to increase the internal energy (and therefore the temperature) of the gas. When heat is added at con-

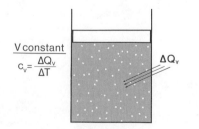

V constant
$c_v = \dfrac{\Delta Q_v}{\Delta T}$

ΔQ_v

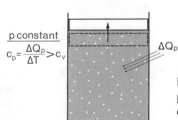

p constant
$c_p = \dfrac{\Delta Q_p}{\Delta T} > c_v$

ΔQ_p

Less heat needs to be added to produce the same temperature change for a process at constant volume than for a process at constant pressure.

stant pressure, the gas expands and therefore does work on its surroundings. Some of the added energy is used in doing this work, and therefore to produce the same temperature change of the gas more heat must be added.

Solids and liquids expand much less than gases when heated, so the difference between c_p and c_v is small, and $c_p \cong c_v$. It is usually c_p that is measured. One simple way of measuring specific heat capacity is the "method of mixtures." A quantity m_1 of a substance at temperature T_1 and known specific heat capacity c_1 (for example water) is brought in thermal contact ("mixed with") a quantity m_2 of a substance at temperature T_2 and unknown specific heat capacity c_2 (for example a block of metal) in an insulated container (a calorimeter). The combined system will come to a final equilibrium temperature T_f. If it is assumed that no heat is lost from the combined system, the heat lost by one substance is equal to the heat gained by the other. Assuming $T_1 > T_2$, constant specific heat capacities, and neglecting the heat capacity of the calorimeter,

$$m_1 c_1 (T_1 - T_f) = m_2 c_2 (T_f - T_2)$$

All quantities except c_2 can be measured, and c_2 calculated. Corrections can be made for heat losses from the system, and the heat capacity of the calorimeter.

The most convenient methods of measurement involve electric heating. If there is a resistor of resistance R in a gas, and a current i is passed through the resistor, the resistor converts electric energy to heat energy at a rate $i^2 R$. In a time t, a quantity of heat $\Delta Q = i^2 R t$ is added to the system, changing its temperature from T_1 to T_2. If the heat capacity of the resistor and container can be neglected, the average heat capacity of the gas is $C = \Delta Q / (T_2 - T_1)$. In general it is necessary to make corrections for the heat capacity of the resistor and container, and for heat losses from the system.

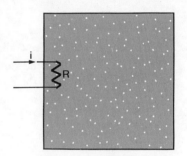

Heating coil immersed in a gas.

4. Specific heat capacity is a property that is useful in characterizing the thermal behavior of matter (although our primary interest at present is to relate it to the microscopic behavior of gases). Physical tables usually provide tables of c at room temperature for solids and liquids in units of cal/gm-C°. This is a convenient unit, which of course can be converted to joule/kg-C° (the mks unit) or any other (energy unit)/(mass unit)-(temp. unit). For most liquids c is in the range 0.4–1 cal/gm-C°, and for metals is smaller by about a factor of 10.

For gases, where the difference between c_p and c_v is significant, it is usual in tables to give $\gamma = c_p/c_v$, the **ratio of the specific heats.** For an ideal gas the molar specific heat capacities are related by $c_p - c_v = R$, and this is approximately true for real gases. Therefore, knowing γ, c_p and c_v are determined. There are methods by which the ratio γ can be measured directly; for example, the speed of sound in an ideal gas of molecular weight M is given by $v_{\text{sound}} = \sqrt{\gamma R T / M}$

The table shows the measured values of γ for a number of gases at room temperature ($\sim$15 °C).

Gas	γ	Gas	γ	Gas	γ	Gas	γ
He	1.66	H_2	1.41	HCl	1.41	NH_2	1.31
Ne	1.64	CO	1.40	Cl_2	1.36	CO_2	1.30
A	1.67	N_2	1.40	Br_2	1.32	H_2S	1.32
Kr	1.68	NO	1.40	I_2	1.30	N_2O	1.30
Xe	1.66	O_2	1.40			SO_2	1.26

CLASSICAL THEORY OF SPECIFIC HEAT CAPACITY OF GASES

We have digressed in order to establish some familiarity with the measurable physical property specific heat capacity. We now return to the expression we derived for the total energy of a system of N ideal gas molecules. Assuming the system is in thermal equilibrium, application of the equipartition principle gave

$$E = \frac{f}{2} NkT$$

where f, the number of degrees of freedom per molecule, depends on the model we choose for the individual molecules.

If the number of molecules is $N = N_0$, Avogadro's number, we are considering one mole of gas. Then $N_0 k = R$, the gas constant, and

$$E = \frac{f}{2} RT$$

When the total energy changes by an amount ΔE, the corresponding temperature change is ΔT, where $\Delta E = \frac{f}{2} R \Delta T$. The ratio $\Delta E/\Delta T = \frac{f}{2} R$ is the molar heat capacity at constant volume c_v. To see why, think about a quantity of heat ΔQ added to the system of gas molecules, with the volume kept constant. This will produce a temperature change ΔT, and by definition $c_v = \Delta Q/\Delta T$. For the ideal gas kept at constant volume, all of this added energy becomes energy of the individual molecules, because there is no work done by the system.

$$c_v = \frac{\Delta Q}{\Delta T} = \frac{\Delta E}{\Delta T} = \frac{f}{2} R$$

For the ideal gas

$$c_p - c_v = R \quad \text{so} \quad c_p = \frac{f}{2} R + R = \left(\frac{f+2}{2}\right) R$$

and
$$\gamma = \frac{c_p}{c_v} = \frac{(f+2)/2}{f/2} = \frac{f+2}{f}$$

For a particle model of the molecules, $f = 3$ and $\gamma = 5/3 = 1.67$. For a rigid rotator model $f = 5$ and $\gamma = 7/5 = 1.40$. For a non-rigid rotator model $f = 7$ and $\gamma = 9/7 = 1.29$.

We can compare these theoretical values with the experimental values of γ for various gases, in order to see which model is reasonable.

From the previous table you can see that for the five monatomic gases listed (the "noble" gases) $\gamma \cong 1.67$ and therefore it is a good approximation to treat the molecules as particles. The fact that there is some variation shows that this simple model does not completely represent the real physical situation.

For the first six of the nine diatomic gases listed, $\gamma \cong 1.40$, and it would appear that these molecules can be represented by the rigid rotator model. However, the last three, chlorine, bromine and iodine, do not fit this picture. Iodine is close to $\gamma = 1.29$, the value for a non-rigid rotator model.

These diatomic gases are listed in order of increasing molecular weight. These are H_2 (2), CO (28), N_2 (28), NO (30), O_2 (32), HCl (36), Cl_2 (76), Br_2 (160), I_2 (254). We shall see later the significance of the fact that for the heavier gases the vibrational motion becomes significant.

The classical theory predicts that c_v is a constant, independent of temperature. For limited ranges of temperature, this seems to be verified experimentally, but is not the case if the temperature range is too great. The range of temperature in which the ideal gas assumption is valid is limited. As the temperature of a gas is lowered the interaction between the molecules becomes significant (the gases liquefy at some temperature); as the temperature is increased the thermal energy becomes comparable with the dissociation energy, and some of the diatomic molecules dissociate. However, hydrogen behaves like an ideal diatomic gas over a wide enough range that the temperature variation can be

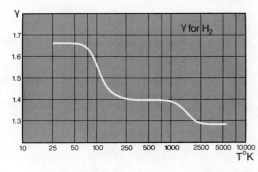 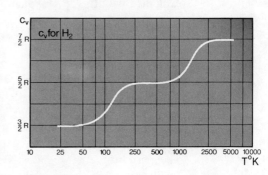

The ratio of heat capacities γ and the molar heat capacity at constant volume c_v as functions of temperature for hydrogen.

observed. Both γ and c_v are shown as a function of temperature (the temperature scale is logarithmic). Hydrogen remains a gas down to about 20°K (at atmospheric pressure). At low temperatures c_v is about $\frac{3}{2}R$, but rises to $\frac{5}{2}R$ in a range around room temperature and approaches $\frac{7}{2}R$ around 2500 °K.

At low temperatures the particle model is adequate, at intermediate temperatures the rigid rotator is the appropriate model, and at high temperatures the non-rigid rotator is required. The graph is sometimes described by saying that the degrees of freedom associated with vibration and rotation are successively "frozen out" as the temperature of the gas is lowered.

How can the fact that the specific heat of diatomic gases is different at different temperatures be explained? The essential point of this chapter is that from the point of view of classical physics **this result cannot be explained at all.**

The classical theory of specific heats of gases is based on the equipartition principle, which is in turn based on classical (Maxwell–Boltzmann) statistics. According to the equipartition principle, for a system in thermal equilibrium there is an average energy $\frac{1}{2}kT$ associated with each degree of freedom. If diatomic molecules can vibrate at all, there must be an average energy kT associated with this vibration, and it does not make sense physically to think of a perfectly rigid bond joining the two atoms. Similarly if the atom rotates at all, there must be an average energy $\frac{1}{2}kT$ associated with each rotational degree of freedom. Therefore as far as classical physics is concerned we must take into account rotational and vibrational degrees of freedom, as well as translational degrees of freedom.

As a matter of fact, from the viewpoint of classical physics we have no right to treat even a monatomic gas with a particle model. We may think of the nucleus of the atom as a particle, but what about the electrons and the various degrees of freedom associated with them?

The difficulties with the classical theory of specific heat were recognized by physicists during the latter part of the last century, and were only satisfactorily explained with the development of quantum mechanics.

QUANTUM THEORY OF
SPECIFIC HEAT CAPACITIES OF GASES

One essential difference between classical mechanics and quantum mechanics is that in classical mechanics energy is a continuously variable quantity, while in quantum mechanics a system can only take on certain specific values of energy. The permitted energy states depend on the particular system. A harmonic oscillator of frequency ν, for example, can only vibrate with a total mechanical energy $E = (n + \frac{1}{2})h\nu$, where n is an integer $(0,1,2, \cdots)$ and h is Planck's constant, $h = 6.6 \times 10^{-34}$ joule-sec. A rigid rotator of moment of inertia I can only have rotational energies given by

$$E = \frac{J(J+1)h^2}{8\pi^2 I}$$

where J is an integer ($J = 0,1,2,3, \cdots$). If we use a non-rigid rotator model for a diatomic molecule there are certain permitted vibrational energy levels (depending on the vibrational quantum number n) and certain permitted rotational energy levels (depending on the rotational quantum number J). Corresponding to the permitted rotational energy levels, there are also certain permitted values of the angular momentum $L = \sqrt{J(J+1)}\ \hbar = \sqrt{J(J+1)}\ h/2\pi$.

Later you may study the formulation of quantum mechanics, and see that such results are a natural consequence of this system of mechanics—that the quantum conditions are not arbitrarily imposed. For the present, we simply state these results, and comment that you are already familiar with "natural states" of some systems—the natural frequencies of vibration of a plucked string for example. The notion of energy as a non-continuous function may seem odd at first, simply because the quantized nature of energy is not usually apparent for macroscopic systems. For any macroscopic harmonic oscillator (a mass–spring system, for example) the frequency ν is such that spacing between energy levels, $h\nu = 6.6 \times 10^{-34}\nu$ joule, is much too small to be measured, so essentially the energy varies continuously. It is only in dealing with atomic systems that the gap between levels becomes comparable to the energy of the system.

One of the assumptions on which the equipartition principle is based is that the energy varies continuously. This is a valid assumption for the energy of translational motion of gas molecules, but not for vibrational or rotational motion, and this is why the classical theory is invalid.

The essential result of classical statistics is this: for a system of particles in thermal equilibrium at temperature T, the probability of finding a particle with a particular energy E_i is proportional to $\exp(-E_i/kT)$. (This exponential is called a Boltzmann factor.) This probability is a rapidly decreasing function of E_i, so states of low energy are more probable than states of high energy.

If the energy is a continuous function of the co-ordinates, as it is in classical dynamics (and if the energy is a quadratic function of the co-ordinates) classical statistics leads to the equipartition principle. If the energy is quantized, the equipartition principle does not apply.

Now think about a system of diatomic gas molecules in thermal equilibrium. The average energy of translation of a molecule is $\frac{3}{2}kT$, because equipartition applies. What can be said about rotation and vibration, where there are energy levels? According to classical statistics, the probability of a particular energy E is proportional to $\exp(-E/kT)$, and this means that on the average the numbers

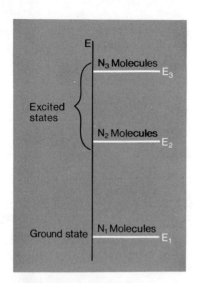

Distribution of molecules among quantized energy states.

of molecules N_1 and N_2 in two energy states E_1 and E_2 are related by

$$\frac{N_2}{N_1} = \frac{e^{-E_2/kT}}{e^{-E_1/kT}} = e^{-(E_2-E_1)/kT}$$

Suppose that E_1 is the state of lowest energy, or ground state. This is the most probable state. The number of molecules found with the higher energy E_2 (in the excited state) depends on the ratio $(E_2 - E_1)/kT$. If $(E_2 - E_1) \sim kT$, $N_2/N_1 = e^{-1} = 0.37$, and the numbers of molecules in the two states are comparable. However, if $(E_2 - E_1) \sim 10kT$, $N_2/N_1 = e^{-10} = 4.5 \times 10^{-5}$ and a negligible fraction of the molecules are in the excited state. If the thermal energy kT is small compared to the spacing between levels $(E_2 - E_1)$, almost all of the molecules will be in the ground state. Under these conditions, if a small quantity of heat ΔQ is added to the system, thermal equilibrium will be established at a higher temperature $T + \Delta T$. There will be a few more molecules in the excited energy state, but the number will still be negligible. This means that essentially all of the energy added becomes energy of translation. As far as the specific heat capacity $c_v = \Delta Q/\Delta T$ is concerned, the molecules are acting like particles, with kinetic energy of translation the only kind of energy they have.

Whether the rotational or vibrational motion contributes to the observed specific heat capacity depends on the magnitude of the spacing between energy levels compared to the thermal energy kT. To see the magnitudes involved, we will examine a particular molecule, carbon monoxide, using the following experimental information.

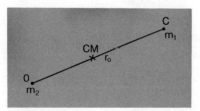

Model for CO molecule.

CO: Mass of carbon atom $m_1 = 12$ amu
Mass of oxygen atom $m_2 = 16$ amu
Bond length $r_0 = 1.12$ angstrom units
$= 1.12 \times 10^{-10}$ m
Vibrational frequency $\nu = 6.53 \times 10^{13}$ cps

Assuming a rigid rotator model, we can calculate the moment of inertia (about an axis through the c-of-m, at right angles to the line joining the particles).

$$\mu = \frac{m_1 m_2}{m_1 + m_2} = \frac{12 \times 16}{12 + 16} = 6.86 \text{ amu} = 1.14 \times 10^{-26} \text{ kg}$$

$$I = \mu r_0^2 = (1.14 \times 10^{-26})(1.12 \times 10^{-10})^2 = 1.43 \times 10^{-46} \text{ kg-m}^2$$

The rotational energy levels are given by

$$E_J = \frac{J(J+1)h^2}{8\pi^2 I} = BJ(J+1) \qquad (J = 0,1,2,\cdots)$$

where $\qquad B = \frac{h^2}{8\pi^2 I} = \frac{(6.63 \times 10^{-34})^2}{8\pi^2 (1.43 \times 10^{-46})} = 3.90 \times 10^{-23}$ joule

The energy levels corresponding to $J = 0, 1, 2, \cdots$ are $0, 2B, 6B, 12B, \cdots$. At room temperature

$$kT \sim 1.38 \times 10^{-23} \times 300$$
$$\sim 4 \times 10^{-21} \text{ joule} \sim 100B$$

Therefore at room temperature kT is not small compared to the spacing between rotational energy levels, and the rotational motion does contribute to the specific heat capacity. The spacing between the lowest energy levels (the most populated ones) is small compared to kT. The number of molecules in each state, which is proportional to $\exp(-E_J/kT)$, does not change very rapidly with energy, and the fact that the possible energies are discrete rather than continuous is relatively unimportant. This means that a classical description can be used, so it is a reasonable approximation to apply the equipartition principle.

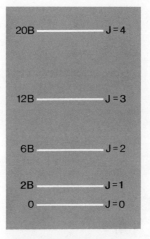

Rotational energy levels for diatomic molecules.

Since we are interested in the size of the energy gap between levels, compared to kT, it is convenient to introduce a quantity called the **characteristic temperature for rotation** θ_R, defined by

$$\theta_R = \frac{B}{k} = \frac{h^2}{8\pi^2 Ik}$$

For a gas at a temperature $T \ll \theta_R$, the thermal energy kT is small compared to the energy gap, and a negligible number of molecules are in excited rotational energy states. For $T \gg \theta_R$, the energy gap is small compared to kT, and the classical equipartition principle can be used. For $T \sim \theta_R$, there are appreciable numbers of molecules in excited rotational states, but the equipartition principle cannot be applied. For CO,

$$\theta_R = \frac{B}{k} = \frac{3.90 \times 10^{-23}}{1.38 \times 10^{-23}} = 2.8°\text{K}$$

Carbon monoxide only exists as a gas at temperatures much higher than this, so the equipartition principle applies. (Remember, however, that we are assuming ideal gas behavior, with negligible interaction between the molecules, so we cannot expect this model to apply if the gas is close to liquefying. A gas cannot be liquefied at temperatures above the critical temperature; for CO, this temperature is $-139°C$, and the ideal gas assumption is a good one at room temperature.)

The only molecular parameter appearing in the expression for the characteristic temperature is the moment of inertia I: $\theta_R \propto 1/I$. Only for the least massive diatomic gas, hydrogen, is I small enough that θ_R is high enough to be in the region where the substance behaves like an ideal gas. For hydrogen $\theta_R \sim 85°K$. As we have seen, for temperatures well below this $c_v = yR$, and for temperatures somewhat higher $c_v = \frac{5}{2}R$. As the temperature is increased through the transition region around θ_R, the rotational energy levels are gradually becoming populated, and a classical model is inadequate.

The fact that $\theta_R \propto 1/I$ also explains why a one-dimensional rigid rotator model (with the corresponding two degrees of freedom) can be used for the diatomic molecule. We pointed out before that there are three independent rotations possible, about three mutually perpendicular axes, with energies $\frac{1}{2}I_{x'}\omega_{x'}^2$, $\frac{1}{2}I_{y'}\omega_{y'}^2$, $\frac{1}{2}I_{z'}\omega_{z'}^2$. With the rigid rotator model the moment of inertia about the molecule axis $I_{z'} = 0$, and therefore there are only two terms in the energy, or two rotational degrees of freedom. However, for a real molecule $I_{z'}$, while it is very small, is not zero, and according to the equipartition principle there would have to be an average energy $\frac{1}{2}kT$ associated with the rotation around the z'-axis. This would give three rather than two rotational degrees of freedom, which is not observed. The quantum mechanical treatment explains why. Because $I_{z'}$ is very small, the energy of the corresponding first excited rotational energy state is very high, and all the molecules are always in the ground state as far as this rotation is concerned.

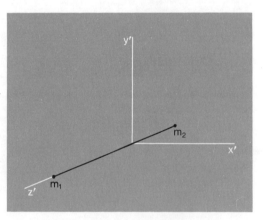

The z'-axis is along the axis of the one-dimensional molecule.

A similar argument explains why monatomic molecules can be treated as particles. The moment of inertia about any axis is so small that the atoms are always in the ground state as far as rotations are concerned.

So far we have considered only rotational energy levels, assuming a rigid rotator. Now look at the energy levels associated with vibrational motion. According to quantum mechanics the vibrational energy levels are given by

$$E_n = (n + \tfrac{1}{2})h\nu \qquad (n = 0,1,2, \cdots)$$

These levels are uniformly spaced an energy $h\nu$ apart. For CO the vibrational frequency is $\nu = 6.53 \times 10^{13}$ cps, so

$$hv = 6.63 \times 10^{-34} \times 6.53 \times 10^{13}$$
$$= 4.32 \times 10^{-20} \text{ joule}$$

At room temperature $kT \sim 4 \times 10^{-21}$ joule, so $kT \cong \frac{1}{10}(hv)$ and only a negligible fraction of the molecules are in excited vibrational energy states. The vibrational motion does not contribute to the specific heat capacity at room temperature.

As for rotation, it is useful to introduce a characteristic temperature. The **characteristic temperature for vibration** θ_v is defined by $k\theta_v = hv$. For a gas at a temperature $T \ll \theta_v$, the thermal energy kT is much less than the energy gap hv, and a negligible number of molecules are in excited vibrational states. For $T \gg \theta_v$, $hv \ll kT$, and the classical equipartition principle can be applied. Around $T \sim \theta_v$ there is a transition region.

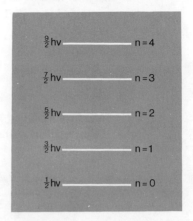

$\frac{9}{2}hv$	n = 4
$\frac{7}{2}hv$	n = 3
$\frac{5}{2}hv$	n = 2
$\frac{3}{2}hv$	n = 1
$\frac{1}{2}hv$	n = 0

Vibrational energy levels for diatomic molecules.

For CO
$$\theta_v = \frac{hv}{k} = \frac{4.32 \times 10^{-20}}{1.38 \times 10^{-23}} = 3130°K$$

If we assume that the vibrations are simple harmonic the frequency v is related to the molecular force constant k_0 (we use the subscript to distinguish this from Boltzmann's constant) by

$$v = \frac{1}{2\pi}\sqrt{\frac{k_0}{\mu}}$$

The frequency depends on k_0 (which is related to the shape of the interaction potential energy around its minimum) and on the reduced mass μ. Hydrogen has a smaller reduced mass than CO (for H_2, $\mu = 0.5$ amu) and a slightly smaller force constant, giving a higher characteristic temperature $\theta_v \sim 6000°K$.

For more massive molecules θ_v is lower: for Cl_2, $\theta_v \sim 800°K$; for Br_2, $\theta_v \sim 500°K$; for I_2, $\theta_v \sim 200°K$. This is the reason that γ approached 1.29 (corresponding to $c_v = \frac{7}{2}R$) at room temperature for gases of high molecular weight, as shown in the earlier table.

We can use this numerical example to examine an assumption we made earlier, that the bond length of the molecule is not changed appreciably as it rotates and vibrates. It was only by making this assumption that we could think of the rotational and vibrational energies separately.

For CO the force constant is

$$k_0 = 4\pi^2 \mu v^2 = 4\pi^2 (1.14 \times 10^{-26})(6.53 \times 10^{13})^2 = 1.92 \times 10^3 \text{ newton/m}$$

Think first of the molecule rotating without vibrating, at an angular speed ω, angular momentum $L = I\omega$. The distance between the particles is R, and the extension is $(R - r_0)$. The restoring force is the centripetal force.

$$k_0(R - r_0) = \mu\omega^2 R = \frac{L^2}{\mu R^3}$$

$$R - r_0 = \frac{L^2}{\mu k_0 R^3} \cong \frac{L^2}{\mu k_0 r_0^3}$$

We have here assumed the result we want to show, that $R \cong r_0$. We suppose that the molecule is in the first excited rotational state, $J = 1$ (for $J = 0, L = 0$). Then

$$L = \sqrt{J(J + 1)}\hbar = \sqrt{2}\hbar$$

$$= \sqrt{2}\frac{6.63 \times 10^{-34}}{2\pi} = 1.5 \times 10^{-34} \text{ joule-sec}$$

$$R - r_0 = \frac{(1.5 \times 10^{-34})^2}{(1.14 \times 10^{-26})(1.92 \times 10^3)(1.12 \times 10^{-10})^3} = 7.3 \times 10^{-16} \text{ m}$$

$$\frac{R - r_0}{r_0} \cong 6 \times 10^{-6}$$

For higher values of L the extension will be greater, but it is always very small compared to the unstretched bond length r_0.

If the molecule is vibrating as a harmonic oscillator the classical vibrational energy is

$$E_{\text{vib}} = \tfrac{1}{2}\mu \left(\frac{dr}{dt}\right)^2 + \tfrac{1}{2}k_0(r - r_0)^2$$

When the displacement of the particles is a maximum, the energy will be totally potential energy

$$E_{\text{vib}} = \tfrac{1}{2}k_0(r_{\text{max}} - r_0)^2$$

We suppose that the molecule is in the ground vibrational state, $E_{\text{vib}} = \tfrac{1}{2}h\nu$, and equate the classical and quantum energy expressions

$$\tfrac{1}{2}k_0(r_{\text{max}} - r_0)^2 = \tfrac{1}{2}h\nu$$

$$(r_{\text{max}} - r_0)^2 = \frac{h\nu}{k_0} = \frac{4.32 \times 10^{-20}}{1.92 \times 10^3} = 22.5 \times 10^{-24} \text{ m}^2$$

$$r_{\text{max}} - r_0 = 4.75 \times 10^{-12} \text{ m} \qquad \frac{r_{\text{max}} - r_0}{r_0} \cong 4 \times 10^{-2}$$

The maximum extension in the vibration is about 4% of the normal bond length r_0.

This was a rather peculiar calculation. We mixed quantum mechanical energy values with a classical expression for the energy. The correct energies could only be obtained from quantum mechanics, and we needed these in order to examine the assumption made in developing the classical expression for the energy of the non-rigid rotator model. The result indicates that the deformation of the molecule is small, and therefore that it is a reasonable approximation to treat rotational and vibrational energies as independent. However, this is an approximation; there is a coupling between the two motions, as shown by the fact that in the spectra of diatomic gases there are spectral lines corresponding to rotational–vibrational transitions.

In both quantum mechanics and classical mechanics calculations are based on particular models. The same models may be used, but the method of calculation is different in the two systems.

In this chapter we have concentrated on diatomic ideal gases, because the diatomic molecule is complex enough to illustrate the features we wished to examine, but simple enough to be represented by relatively simple models. It has the advantage that it only exhibits a single kind of vibration. A polyatomic molecule will in general have a number of different possible modes of vibration.

THE LIMITATIONS OF CLASSICAL MECHANICS

The purpose of this chapter has been to introduce the transition from classical (Newtonian) mechanics, the subject of the book so far, to two other areas of physics, quantum mechanics and statistical mechanics. Classical mechanics has a vast scope—almost all of the motions we observe on a macroscopic scale are adequately described by the laws of classical mechanics—but it has its limitations. The motions of the microscopic constituents of matter cannot in general be handled by classical mechanics, although sometimes a classical description is sufficient. The methods of quantum mechanics are usually necessary in dealing with motion at the microscopic level.

The essential difference between the classical and quantum mechanical description of a particle has to do with the **localizability** of the particle. Classically a particle has a well-defined trajectory, while in quantum mechanics it does not. Consequently whether or not a classical description is adequate can be decided by examining a quantity called the **de Broglie wavelength** of the particle, $\lambda = h/p = h/(mv)$, and comparing it with some minimum distance S that is necessary in order to describe the motion. If λ is small compared to S, a classical description will be valid.

Think of an ideal gas at room temperature and atmospheric pressure. The average kinetic energy of translation is

$$\overline{E}_t = \tfrac{3}{2}kT \sim 6 \times 10^{-21} \text{ joule}$$

The energy is related to the linear momentum p by $E_t = p^2/2m$. Suppose that the gas is hydrogen; then $m = 2/(6 \times 10^{23}) \sim 3 \times 10^{-24}$ gm $\sim 3 \times 10^{-27}$ kg, and the average momentum is

$$\bar{p} = \sqrt{2m\bar{E}_t} \cong \sqrt{2 \times 3 \times 10^{-27} \times 6 \times 10^{-21}} \sim 6 \times 10^{-24} \text{ kg-m/sec}$$

The de Broglie wavelength is

$$\lambda = \frac{h}{p} = \frac{6.6 \times 10^{-34}}{6 \times 10^{-24}} \sim 10^{-10} \text{ m} \sim 1 \text{ angstrom unit}$$

For any other gas m is larger, and λ is less. All ordinary gas molecules are about 1 or 2 angstrom units in size, so the de Broglie wavelength is somewhat less than the diameter of a molecule.

What length S should this wavelength λ be compared to? As far as translation (the overall motion of the molecule) is concerned, one important dimension is the average distance between molecules. If the molecules are far apart we can think of the individual molecules moving on well-defined trajectories without

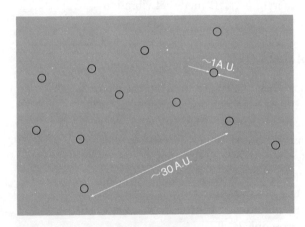

The average distance between gas molecules.

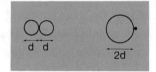

It is convenient to think of all molecules except one as particles at rest, and consider motion of a single molecule of diameter 2d.

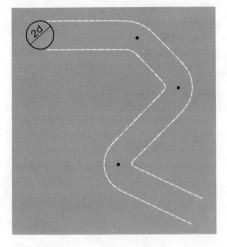

Volume swept out by the moving molecule.

interference with other molecules. Under the conditions we are assuming the number density is $n \sim 3 \times 10^{19}$ molecules/cm³. This means that the volume per molecule is $1/n \sim 3 \times 10^{-20}$ cm³, and the average distance between molecules is $\sim 1/\sqrt[3]{n} \sim 3 \times 10^{-7}$ cm ~ 30 angstrom units. Another length of interest is the average distance a molecule travels without colliding with another molecule, the **mean free path** l. We can roughly estimate this as follows. Think of each molecule as a hard sphere of diameter d ($d \sim 1$ angstrom unit). The molecules are all in motion, but suppose that they are all at rest except one, moving with a constant speed $\bar{v}$ (some sort of average speed of the molecules). Think of this molecule as having a diameter $2d$, and all the other molecules as points. Then the center-to-center distance in a collision is d, the same as if both molecules have a diameter d. As the "big" molecule moves, it sweeps out a volume of cross-sectional area πd^2 in space, colliding with all the "point" molecules in this volume. In time t it moves a distance $\bar{v}t$, sweeping out a volume $\pi d^2 \bar{v}t$, and making $n\pi d^2 \bar{v}t$ collisions (n is the number of molecules per unit volume). The average distance it moves between collisions is the mean free path l.

$$l = \frac{\text{distance moved in time } t}{\text{number of collisions in time } t} = \frac{\bar{v}t}{n\pi d^2 \bar{v}t} = \frac{1}{n\pi d^2}$$

A more accurate kinetic theory calculation, taking into account the relative motion of the molecules and the distribution of molecular speeds, shows that this result is a factor $\sqrt{2}$ too large, but the order of magnitude is right.

Taking $n \sim 3 \times 10^{19}$ molecules/cm^3, $d \sim 1$ angstrom unit $= 10^{-8}$ cm,

$$l \sim \frac{1}{3 \times 10^{19} \times \pi \times (10^{-8})^2} \sim 10^{-4} \text{ cm} \sim 10^4 \text{ angstrom units}$$

We have underestimated the effective diameter of molecules a little, and have neglected the factor $\sqrt{2}$. Actual mean free paths under standard conditions are of the order of 1000 angstrom units.

Both the average distance between molecules (~ 30 angstrom units) and the average distance between collisions (~ 1000 angstrom units) are large compared to the de Broglie wavelength (~ 1 angstrom unit). This suggests that a classical description can be applied to the translational motion of gas molecules, and this turns out to be the case.

The situation is different as far as the internal motions of the molecules are concerned. Rotation and vibration involve motion of the parts of the molecule with respect to one another, and the length S that is relevant is of the order of molecular dimensions. Since this is comparable to the de Broglie wavelength, a classical description may be inadequate. As we have seen in discussing specific heat capacity, at high temperatures (high energy and corresponding low λ) a classical description based on equipartition of energy applies, but at low temperatures (and correspondingly longer de Broglie wavelength) a quantum mechanical description is necessary.

You will be going into the formulation of quantum mechanics, but that will come later. Part VI deals with the formulation of statistical mechanics.

While in principle classical mechanics provides a complete description of the motion of a many-particle system, as we have pointed out it is not possible in practice to work out the motion unless the number of particles is quite small. Observable macroscopic systems involve of the order of 10^{20} particles, and a detailed analysis of motion is completely impractical. The approach of statistical mechanics is to make certain assumptions about microscopic behavior, and to use statistical methods to predict what average overall behavior this microscopic behavior is likely to produce.

As you will see, we will distinguish between classical statistics and quantum statistics. It might appear that classical statistics would be applicable to systems composed of classical particles (that is, particles whose motions can be described by the methods of classical mechanics) and quantum statistics would be applicable to particles that require a quantum mechanical description. However, it turns out that sometimes classical statistics can be applied to quantum particles, because the difference between the two kinds of statistics is that in classical statistics particles are assumed to be distinguishable (because they are localizable and you can think of tracing individual particles) and in quantum statistics they are not. Sometimes quantum particles can be assumed to be distinguishable, and therefore classical statistics applied.

We will attempt to develop some of the fundamental ideas of classical statistics, and to point out why quantum statistics are different.

Questions for discussion

1. What is meant by **the three-body problem?**

2. Should **heat capacity** have been called **thermal capacity?**

3. In kinetic-theory calculations molecules are often treated as particles with a "diameter." Would you expect molecules to have different effective diameters under different conditions?

4. A box full of gas weighs more than the box evacuated, by the amount of the weight of the gas. The gas molecules are not resting on the floor of the box, but are moving in space in the box. How do you explain why the box weighs more?

5. Think about a large box full of gas in thermal equilibrium, and in the earth's gravitational field. Is the upward pressure on the top of the box due to molecular bombardment the same as the downward pressure on the bottom of the box? Is the number density of molecules the same near the top as it is near the bottom of the box? Is it reasonable to assume that the gas density is the same throughout the box?

6. Using the rigid rotator model for a diatomic gas molecule, a quantum mechanical description leads to a lowest rotational energy state of zero angular momentum. Is it reasonable to visualize the molecules as little sticks moving around in pure translation, not rotating?

7. Is there a difference between what is meant by an inelastic collision of macroscopic bodies, and what is meant by an inelastic collision of molecules?

Problems

Many of these problems are kinetic theory calculations, based on the expressions for pressure due to molecular bombardment $p = \frac{1}{3}nm\overline{v^2}$ and molecular flux $N = \frac{1}{4}n\bar{v}$ discussed in Chapter 13, and on equipartition of energy and the expression for mean free path discussed in this chapter. These calculations are intended to give you some feeling for the order of magnitude of the numbers involved, as an introduction to Part VI. Reference is made in the problems to the "average speed" of gas molecules. You know that there are different kinds of averages, and the relation between these averages depends on the shape of the distribution of what is being averaged. From the average translational kinetic energy of a molecule in a system of gas molecules in thermal equilibrium, $\frac{1}{2}m\overline{v^2} = \frac{3}{2}kT$, the average speed called the root-mean-square speed $v_{\mathrm{rms}} = (\overline{v^2})^{1/2}$ can be determined, and this is not the same as the average speed $\bar{v}$. We will show in Part VI that for the distribution of molecular speeds $v_{\mathrm{rms}} = 1.09\bar{v}$, but for the calculations in this chapter ignore this difference, and assume that there is *an* average speed.

1. Calculate the temperatures at which the average speeds of molecules are equal to the escape speeds for the earth and for the moon, for hydrogen and for oxygen molecules.

2. The ionization energy of a typical atom is a few electron volts. To roughly what temperature must a gas be heated to produce a plasma? The plasma state of matter is one in which the atoms have been stripped of their electrons, so it is a gas of positive and negative particles. This is the normal state in a star, so most of the matter in the universe is in this state.

3. At what temperature is the mean translational kinetic energy of a molecule equal to that of a singly charged ion of the same mass which has been accelerated through a potential difference of **(a)** 1 volt, **(b)** 1000 volts? **(c)** What is the average translational kinetic energy of any gas molecule at room temperature ($\sim$300°K) in electron volts?

4. For a system of carbon monoxide molecules in thermal equilibrium at room temperature **(a)** compare the number of molecules N_0 in the rotational ground state ($J = 0$) with the number N_1 in the first excited rotational state ($J = 1$). **(b)** Compare the number of molecules N_0 in the vibrational ground state with the number N_1 in the first excited vibrational state. **(c)** Compare the numbers in the lowest two vibrational states at a temperature of 2000°K, and at a temperature of 4000°K.

5. Taking the characteristic temperature for rotation θ_R for hydrogen to be 85°K, at what temperature would the number of hydrogen molecules in the first excited rotational state be **(a)** 10%, **(b)** 90% of the number in the rotational ground state?

6. **(a)** In the Bohr model of a hydrogen atom, an electron in the first orbit has an energy (potential plus kinetic) of -13.6 ev. What is its kinetic energy? (Recall the relation between kinetic and potential energy for circular orbits under gravity.) What is its de Broglie wavelength? You can see that the classical Bohr model, with the electron a particle in orbit, is not valid. **(b)** What is the de Broglie wavelength of a "2500-volt" electron, for example an electron accelerated through this potential difference in a TV tube?

7. Think of a stream of particles, each of mass m, all moving vertically, bouncing up and down between the top and bottom of a box, making elastic collisions with the box. A particular particle has a speed v_1 just after hitting the top, and a speed v_2 just before hitting the bottom, a time t later. For this particle **(a)** what is the difference between the magnitude of the impulse it exerts on the box in a collision at the bottom and a collision at the top, **(b)** what is the number of collisions with the bottom in unit time, **(c)** what is the difference in the average force it exerts on the box at the bottom and at the top over a period of time? **(d)** For the stream of particles, is the pressure due to bombardment the same on the top and on the bottom, and is the number density n the same near the top as near the bottom of the box? **(e)** Can you explain why a box full of gas weighs more than the box evacuated? **(f)** Can you explain why in kinetic theory it is reasonable to assume that the number density n and the pressure p is the same throughout a volume of gas?

8. Estimate the size of molecules by thinking of them as hard spheres touching one another in a solid or liquid, and assuming some sort of structure, such as a cubic structure. For example, use water where you know its density and molecular weight. How many molecules in a cubic centimeter? About how far apart are they? Try a heavy metal like lead, atomic weight 207 and density 11.3 gm/cm³.

9. Suppose that all the molecules of gas at STP (convention for "standard temperature and pressure," 0°C = 273°K, and 1 atmosphere = 10^5 n/m²) in a cubic box 1 m³ in size were suddenly to all head in the same direction, straight toward one face of the box, at their average speed, and then bounced back elastically. What would be the force on the face produced by these collisions during the time the collisions were going on? (See Chapter 13.)

10. Use the principle of equipartition of energy and the expression for pressure produced by molecular collisions $p = n m \overline{v^2}/3$ (discussed in Chapter 13) to deduce **Avogadro's Law:** Equal volumes of any gas at the same pressure and temperature contain the same number of molecules. Can you deduce the ideal gas "equation of state" $pv = RT$ from this? Use kinetic theory arguments to justify **Dalton's Law of Partial Pressure:** For a mixture of non-interacting gases in a container, the pressure exerted by each gas is the same as if it were alone in the container, and the total pressure is the sum of these partial pressures.

11. Think about 1 m³ of neon gas at STP. (The atomic weight of neon is 20 gm/mole, and one mole of any gas at STP has a volume of 2.24×10^{-2} m³.) **(a)** Determine the total kinetic energy and the total linear momentum of the gas molecules. **(b)** Suppose that the neon molecules were all moving in the same direction at the same speed, the average speed if in thermal equilibrium. What would the total kinetic energy and total linear momentum be?

12. A container 1 m high contains neon gas at STP. Compare the average kinetic energy of molecules in the container with the difference in gravitational potential energy for a molecule at the top and a molecule at the bottom of the container.

13. **(a)** From the average energy of a neon molecule at STP estimate its average speed $\bar{v}$. Assume that the diameter of a neon molecule is 2 angstrom units, and estimate the mean free path, and the collision frequency, the number of collisions per second made by a molecule.

(b) Assume that a neon molecule striking the wall of a container reverses its velocity in a distance 1/100 of the molecular diameter and estimate the time of impact for the collision.

(c) In a problem in Chapter 13 it was shown that the flux density of gas molecules, the number hitting unit area in unit time, is $N = n\bar{v}/4$, where n is the number density. Estimate the number of collisions per second made by neon molecules with a spherical colloidal particle of diameter 2000 angstrom units suspended in neon gas. Would you expect the particle to fluctuate in position due to these collisions?

(d) If a 10-gm mass is shot upward with an initial kinetic energy equal to the total kinetic energy of 10 gm of neon at STP, how high will it rise?

(e) At what temperature would the average speed of neon molecules be equal to the escape speed from the earth?

14. Think about a fixed volume of gas as its temperature is changed. How does the collision frequency of the molecules depend on temperature? How does the mean free path of the molecules depend on temperature? Are these results reasonable physically?

15. **(a)** Air is a mixture of about 80% N_2 and 20% O_2 (by volume). What is the effective molecular weight of air? **(b)** What is the average speed of "air molecules" at room temperature? **(c)** The pressure in a vacuum system is 10^{-3} mm of Hg. There is a pinhole of area 10^{-10} cm² in the wall of the system. Assuming that every molecule hitting the hole passes through it, estimate the number of molecules leaking into the system in 1 hr. **(d)** If the vacuum system has a volume of 2000 cm³, estimate the increase in pressure in 1 hr due to the leak. (Note that $p \propto n$.)

16. Liquid water is in equilibrium with water vapor in a closed system at 100°C and 1 atm. At this temperature the heat of vaporization of water (the energy necessary to change unit mass of liquid to vapor state) is 540 cal/gm. **(a)** What is the volume of 1 gm of water vapor? **(b)** What is the number density of molecules in the water vapor? **(c)** Estimate the number of molecules from the vapor striking unit area of the liquid surface in unit time. **(d)** If each molecule striking the surface condenses, how many evaporate from unit area in unit time? **(e)** Compare the average kinetic energy of a vapor molecule with the energy required to transfer one molecule from the liquid to the vapor state.

17. A cylinder closed by a frictionless piston of area 100 cm² contains two moles of an ideal gas in thermal equilibrium at 0°C, 1 atm pressure. **(a)** What is the volume of the gas, and what is the external force necessary to hold the piston in place? **(b)** The piston is slowly moved in by increasing the force F on it, until the pressure is 2 atm. The process is slow enough that the temperature of the gas remains constant (an isothermal process). What is the volume after the compression? Recall Boyle's Law. **(c)** Show that if the external force F moves the piston through a small displacement Δx, the work done by the force $F \Delta x$ is equal to $p \Delta V$, the pressure times the change in volume of the gas, and determine the total work done by the force F as the pressure is changed from 1 to 2 atm. **(d)** What is the change in kinetic energy of the gas in the compression? **(e)** What happens to the energy expended by the agency exerting the force F?

Statistical mechanics VI

It is somewhat presumptuous to call this Statistical Mechanics because it provides only a limited introduction to the subject, and much of it is not about statistical mechanics directly. As will be discussed in Chapter 27, **statistical mechanics** is the name given to the "microscopic theory of heat," as opposed to **thermodynamics,** the name applied to the "macroscopic theory of heat." One of our aims is to indicate the relationships that exist between these two theories, and therefore much of Part VI is devoted to thermodynamics. In spite of this, the title Statistical Mechanics has been used to emphasize that the physical phenomena usually described under the heading of heat can be described, from a microscopic point of view, in terms of the concepts of mechanics that we have already introduced. In statistical mechanics it is not necessary to introduce any new fundamental quantity beyond those used in mechanics (mass, length, and time). This is not the case in the macroscopic theory, thermodynamics, where a new fundamental quantity (temperature) is introduced and given an operational definition.

Emphasizing that the fundamental quantities in classical dynamics and in statistical mechanics are the same is *not* to say that these two theories are the same. In statistical mechanics the concepts of mechanics and the laws of mathematical statistics are used to make predictions about the behavior of systems made up of very large numbers of particles. Such systems are too complex to be analyzed by the methods of classical dynamics we have developed. As will be indicated in Chapter 27, the fact that our knowledge about a complex physical system is necessarily incomplete is what leads to the recognition and definition of certain important physical quantities, temperature and entropy, that do not exist in classical mechanics theory.

Although we are unable to develop statistical mechanics in detail, we attempt in Part VI to lay the groundwork that will assist you in future study of the subject.

27

THEORIES OF HEAT

THERMODYNAMICS AND STATISTICAL MECHANICS

The next few chapters deal with what is broadly described as theory of "heat." Until well into the nineteenth century, that is for some two hundred years after the time of Newton and the basic formulation of classical mechanics, it was generally believed that heat was a sort of fluid that could be added to or liberated from other substances. It was only about one hundred odd years ago that it was recognized that heat could be classified as a form of energy, not a substance, and it was thirty or forty years more before it was realized that heat was not a new form of energy, but was mechanical energy of the constituent particles of matter—the energy associated with motion and interaction at the microscopic level.

Once this was accepted the term "heat" could be used to apply to a particular form of energy transfer between systems. Once the energy is in the system it becomes internal energy of the system. Rain falling on a lake provides an analogy; once the rain is in the lake it is no longer identifiable as rain, but is simply water.

The notions of heat as a form of energy transfer and of heat as the energy of disordered microscopic motion are intimately connected; the energy transfer we call heat flow between two systems takes place *because* each system has energy in the form of disorganized microscopic motion. However, the internal energy of a system can be changed not only by heat flow but also by doing mechanical work on the system—just as the amount of water in a lake can be changed not only by precipitation and evaporation but also by other methods (streams flowing in and out of the lake).

Classical theory of heat developed on two separate lines. One was "phenomenological thermodynamics," usually just called thermodynamics. This theory makes no assumptions about the microscopic structure of matter; it is a macroscopic theory based on certain generalizations, the laws of thermodynamics. It is useful in providing information about relationships between observable physical properties, but cannot be used to make predictions about the absolute magnitude of any physical property. For example it can be used to derive a relation between the specific heat capacities of a substance, but cannot be used to calculate the size of any specific heat capacity. It can be used to relate the various physical properties of an ideal gas, given the equation of state $pV = RT$, but it cannot be used to derive this equation.

Thermodynamics requires the introduction of another fundamental physical quantity (besides those used in mechanics). Usually the quantity called temperature is chosen, and therefore given an operational definition. This is done in terms of the properties of gases (the ideal gas temperature scale) or the properties of heat engines (the absolute thermodynamic temperature scale). These scales turn out to be identical.

The other development of the classical theory of heat was "statistical thermodynamics," usually called statistical mechanics. Here microscopic models for the constitutents of matter are assumed, and the laws of mathematical statistics are applied to groups of constituents to make predictions about the overall behavior of matter. These predictions can be compared with observations on real macroscopic systems. Statistical mechanics can be used to derive the laws of phenomenological thermodynamics, or to derive the equation of state for an ideal gas, or to derive a value for the specific heat capacity of a particular system. In statistical mechanics it is not necessary to introduce any new fundamental quantity; temperature is a defined quantity.

Of the classical theories of physics, the theory of heat is considered to be the most difficult to understand, and this means that we are limited in what we can do. We are trying in this book to provide you with certain basic skills, so that if you go on in physics—or in any other field—you can use these acquired skills, and we are also trying to give you some general understanding of what physics is all about, without worrying about working everything out. The second approach can be frustrating; phrases like "it turns out that..." or "it can be shown that..." are not particularly annoying if they deal with details, but can be very discouraging if they refer to the fundamentals of the subject. There is not much satisfaction for you in building up a structure of understanding if the foundation on which the structure rests is not understood. On the other hand, an approach where everything is worked out completely from the beginning is not only impossibly time-consuming, but likely to be dull.

So far we have been able to give a reasonably systematic development of the basic ideas of classical mechanics. We do not think it possible to give a comprehensive enough development of statistical mechanics to be very satisfactory, but we do not wish to omit this very important area entirely, so here in Part VI we attempt to deal with some features of thermodynamics and statistical mechanics. The topics covered are not really essential for your understanding of relativistic mechanics, quantum mechanics, and electromagnetic theory (the subjects covered in the second volume of this two-volume series), so it is possible for you to go on to the study of these subjects without going through these final chapters in detail.

In the present chapter we will comment on certain fundamental differences between the approach of classical mechanics and the approach of statistical mechanics. Without giving you any "working knowledge" of statistical mechanics, it may at least give you some idea of what the subject is about.

The next two chapters give a minimal treatment of basic thermodynamics. Some experience in handling the macroscopic concepts discussed here is useful in understanding statistical mechanics. The following chapter, on Random Events, deals primarily with the development of mathematical statistics. This is a chapter on basic skills—skills that have application in many fields, not only in statistical mechanics, although the chapter is placed here because statistical mechanics is based on the theory of probability. This chapter serves to introduce and work out the idea of a probability distribution, or statistical distribution. The basic problem is to calculate the overall result produced by a number of independent random events. The result will not be completely predictable; there will be different results with different probabilities—a distribution of results. The key point of the chapter, so far as statistical mechanics is concerned, is that if the number of independent random events producing an observable result is very large, the most probable result is overwhelmingly probable, and therefore is the only result observed in a real situation. Students who have studied mathematical statistics will not need to devote much time to this chapter. Like the earlier chapter on basic calculus, it is included for those who have not had this mathematical background.

Following this general chapter on statistics, the distribution of molecular speeds of a system of gas molecules is worked out, as a relatively simple example of the approach of statistical mechanics. This is a prelude to a discussion, in the chapter Classical Statistical Mechanics, of the central result of classical statistical mechanics, the Maxwell–Boltzmann distribution. Part VI (and this volume) is concluded with a chapter on The Distribution of Electromagnetic Radiation. It is here that some of the ideas of statistical mechanics are combined with those of quantum mechanics and electromagnetic theory, subjects developed in the second volume of this series.

STATISTICAL ENSEMBLES

Statistical mechanics provides a method of making predictions about systems that are too complex to be analyzed in detail. For a system of gas molecules we cannot know in practice the position and velocity of every particle in the system at some instant, and therefore we cannot calculate the subsequent motion of the particles using the methods of classical mechanics. However, there are fundamental similarities between the dynamical theory (classical mechanics) and the statistical theory. The basic concepts of dynamics such as velocity, force, energy are used in the statistical theory, and the laws of mechanics are assumed valid. What is different?

One difference is that statistical laws deal with average behavior of particles and give no information about individual particles. Statistical laws do not deal with precise numbers of particles, only average numbers—the average number with a given velocity, for example. The statistical theory predicts the average number, and also gives information about fluctuations from this average value.

The notion of average value is also used in dynamics—averages over time or space: the average velocity of a particle over a certain time, or over a certain distance, the average number of particles per unit volume in a gas (averaged over time, or over the volume of gas). Kinetic theory is a dynamic theory, and we made earlier kinetic theory calculations for the average pressure produced by gas molecules, and the average distance a molecule goes between collisions. In a dynamic theory average value is used as a convenience; we cannot count the actual number of gas molecules in one cubic centimeter at a given instant, but we believe that there is a definite number there.

Average value in statistical mechanics does not mean an average over time or space, but over an **ensemble.** An ensemble is not a physical entity, but a mental concept; it is a collection of systems that are similar to a real physical system, but not identical to it. We will think of an ensemble as made up of systems that are identical to the real system in that the number of particles are the same and the interactions are the same, but different from the real system in that the initial conditions are different. Probability theory is applied to the ensemble to calculate the distribution of results that would be found for some particular overall property of the systems (for example the number density), and from this distribution an average value for the property is calculated. The calculations give a perfectly definite result for the average value, and for the distribution about the average value, but this is an ensemble average, not an average for the real system. The predictions about the ensemble are precise, the predictions about the real system are not.

(Note that a precise prediction does not mean a precise result. A precise prediction is that if you toss 100 coins and count the number of heads, there is a 68% chance that the result will be between 45 and 55. This does not tell you what a particular result will be.)

Suppose that you measure the property for the real system. If you make a series of measurements over a long time, you might expect the distribution of results obtained to have an average value (a time average) that is very close to the ensemble average. If the real system is a complex (macroscopic) system, the distribution is so highly peaked that a single measurement can be expected to be very close to the time average. Will this be close to the predicted ensemble average?

It turns out that you cannot replace the ensemble average by the time average if the real system is *isolated*, but you *can* if it is loosely coupled to a temperature bath. This means that the system must have the possibility of exchanging energy with another system at the same temperature. The net exchange of energy will be zero, but it is the coupling with the temperature bath that enables us to think of the system as subject to random influences, and therefore to apply probability theory.

As the name implies, statistical mechanics is a mechanical theory, based on the concepts of mechanics, such as potential and kinetic energy. The fundamental quantities in statistical mechanics are those of mechanics: mass, length and time. However, there are certain quantities that arise in statistical mechanics **because knowledge about the real physical system is incomplete;** two such quantities are temperature and entropy. Temperature is a property that is introduced in statistical mechanics for an ensemble, not for an individual system. It is a property that determines whether or not a system will exchange energy with other systems **on the average.** For a completely isolated system there is the possibility of knowing the energy exactly and for such a system the concept of temperature has no meaning.

REVERSIBLE AND IRREVERSIBLE PROCESSES

The difference between the dynamic theory and the statistical theory can be emphasized by distinguishing between reversible and irreversible processes. The term process implies change, and a reversible process is one in which the change can take place in either direction.

The important point about the dynamic theory is this: **A conservative dynamical system undergoes reversible processes only.** We have stated that in classical dynamics we consider that all the fundamental forces are conservative; and this means that all systems are conservative if examined in fine enough detail, and therefore mechanical energy is conserved. What does it mean to say that such a system undergoes reversible processes only?

Think about a collision between two particles, with a conservative force between them, and no other forces acting—the basic dynamic system. Since the interaction is conservative, the collision is elastic; kinetic energy is conserved in the collision, as well as momentum.

The key question is this: Supposing you watched a movie showing the collision, would you know whether the film was being run forward or backward? Perhaps you can convince yourself that you would not—both movies would depict perfectly possible collisions. If you think of the motion in the center of mass frame of reference you can see that it is symmetric. If the collision is not elastic (for example if the particles stick together) you would be able to tell from the movie which way it was being run.

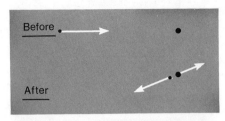

An elastic collision
is reversible.

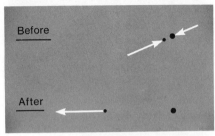

What is the effect of running the film backward? It is the **reversal of time.** The equations of motion describing the "forward" motion can be changed into the equations of motion describing the "backward" motion simply by changing the sign of the single parameter t wherever it occurs. Both motions are possible, and this is what is meant by a reversible process.

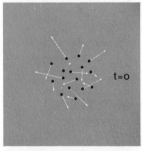

A system of molecules at some instant, and at some later instant.

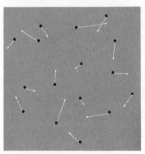

Now instead of just two particles colliding, think of a group of particles—again with conservative forces between the particles, and no external force on the system. Suppose at some instant ($t = 0$) the particles are in a small region of space (the particles are gas molecules in a box, and at $t = 0$ the walls of the box vanish). Think about watching a movie of the subsequent motion. Would you know whether the film was being run forward or backward? This time you would know. Looking at individual collisions between particles would not tell you, but the **overall** motion would. The particles would spread out, occupying more and more space (on the average) as time went on. If the film was run backward, you would see the particles coming together—and you wouldn't believe it.

What does classical dynamics tell us about this? **Nothing at all.** As far as dynamics is concerned, the process is completely reversible. If at some instant the velocity of every particle is reversed (replace t by $-t$ in the equations of motion) each particle would move back along precisely the same path it had followed the forward motion, until at $t = 0$ the system would be in its original configuration.

Something fundamental is missing from classical dynamics. In it there is no way of describing the fact that real processes have a direction, and are not reversible. For either the forward or backward motion energy is conserved, so the concept of energy conservation is not enough.

The question of direction is not a simple one, because it is not clear cut. If you watched the movie for only a short time, you might see the overall volume occupied by the particles decreasing, but this would not be enough to convince you that the film was running backward. On the average you expect that the volume will increase, but you know that there will be fluctuations, brief periods in which the volume will decrease.

We have of course applied classical dynamics to systems where mechanical energy was not conserved—systems where we introduced "frictional forces." However, we have always assumed there was an ideal limit, where the force of friction became negligible. A block sliding on a horizontal surface always comes to rest, but we can imagine the frictional force becoming less and less, and the block sliding farther and farther (this notion leads to Newton's first law, the law of inertia). The oscillations of a pendulum always die away, but we can imagine a system where the frictional forces are negligible, and the oscillations go on forever (simple harmonic motion). Classical dynamics is based on the concept of reversible processes, even though it can be applied to situations where there is some frictional dissipation of mechanical energy. We can always visualize a situation where this dissipation has a negligible effect over the time interval we are considering—the ideal limit.

The flow of heat is fundamentally an irreversible process; when a "hot" system and a "cold" system interact, there is a net transfer of energy from the hot to the cold system, and there is no single parameter in the detailed equations of motion of the particles making up the system such that a change in sign of the parameter (e.g., changing t to $-t$) will reverse the process. Such a process cannot be described by the methods of classical dynamics.

The statistical approach is suitable for the description of irreversible processes, because it has direction built in. In statistical mechanics the distribution of possible values of a particular property is calculated; those distributions that are observed for the physical system are those of highest probability. If changes occur in the system, they will take place in the direction of increasing probability. This is a one-way process, or an irreversible process, or a process with direction. However, since the direction is based on probability considerations, all that can be said is that one direction is more probable than the other—there is always the possibility of going backward. For macroscopic physical systems the probability distributions are highly peaked, and the probability of going backward becomes vanishingly small.

The direction of processes is described by a quantity called entropy. In statistical mechanics this quantity, like temperature, is introduced in terms of the properties of an ensemble. Since it is entropy that describes the direction of natural processes, it is sometimes picturesquely called "the arrow of time."

Questions for discussion

1. What is the significance of the adjective **phenomenological** modifying thermodynamics?

2. Can you give an operational definition for **temperature?**

3. What is the difference between kinetic theory and statistical mechanics?

4. Can you visualize how to do each of the following in a way that approximates a reversible process? **(a)** Heat a block of metal. **(b)** Heat a quantity of gas at constant volume. **(c)** Heat a quantity of gas at constant pressure. **(d)** Compress a quantity of gas at constant temperature. **(e)** Compress a quantity of gas with no heat transferred to or from the gas.

5. What does it mean to say that a conservative dynamical system undergoes reversible processes only?

6. Sometimes in watching a movie it is not possible to be sure whether the film is being run forward or backward. What kind of events convince you that the film is running backward?

28

THERMODYNAMICS:
FIRST LAW

Thermodynamics is sometimes described as dealing with the relation between heat and work. This is a short and rather loose way of saying that it deals with the relation between energy at the microscopic level (the energy of motion and interaction of atoms and molecules) and the energy of macroscopic motion (moving pistons or spinning flywheels or compressed springs or . . .).

Thermodynamics is a macroscopic theory in which no assumptions are made about the microscopic structure of matter. It is based on two empirical laws sometimes called the "principles of impotence": that no cyclic machine can create energy, and that no cyclic machine can convert heat energy totally into macroscopic forms of energy. The first law is an assumption of conservation of energy, the second law has to do with the direction of natural processes. We will discuss these two laws in this chapter and the next.

THERMODYNAMIC VARIABLES AND
THERMAL EQUILIBRIUM

As always in mechanics our attention is fixed on a certain quantity of matter— a system. A thermodynamic system is macroscopic, and therefore highly complex because it is made up of enormous numbers of particles. For illustrative purposes we will usually use an ideal gas, but the laws of thermodynamics apply to any macroscopic system. The essential requirement is that the system contain large numbers of particles, so that (in statistical mechanics terms) the most probable behavior is overwhelmingly probable, and therefore the behavior actually observed. Fluctuations from the most probable behavior are not dealt with by thermodynamics, and therefore are implicitly assumed to be negligible.

It is an experimental fact that the state of a macroscopic system can be described by a small number of observable quantities, called state variables or system variables or thermodynamic variables or thermodynamic co-ordinates.

Examples are the pressure exerted by a gas, the volume occupied by the gas, the temperature of the gas. Each of these quantities is assumed to have *a* value for a gas in a particular state. From a microscopic point of view these quantities fluctuate; pressure is an overall effect produced by molecular bombardment and is not constant, the volume occupied by any given number of molecules is not constant (density fluctuations), the temperature is related to the average kinetic energy of the molecules and is not constant. From a thermodynamic point of view the molecular origin is not of concern; the important thing is that these quantities have a measurable value.

State variables such as pressure and temperature that do not depend on the quantity of matter in the thermodynamic system are called **intensive** variables, while those such as volume that do depend on the quantity of matter are called **extensive** variables. An extensive variable for a specific unit of matter is called a specific variable; for example, if m gm or n moles of gas occupies a volume of V cm³, the specific volume is $v = V/m$ cm³/gm, or $v = V/n$ cm³/mole. The latter is also called the molar volume. In general capital letters are used to designate extensive variables, and the corresponding small letter used to designate the specific variable.

The assumption that state variables exist for the system is related to the concept of **thermal equilibrium.** If we measure the pressure of a gas, it will be constant only if the system is in thermal equilibrium. In spite of the chaotic microscopic activity in the system, the macroscopic properties do not change with time. Think of an empty cylinder closed by a piston. A box of gas is in the cylinder— the gas is the system. The box suddenly bursts, allowing the gas to fill the cylinder. The pressure of the gas (as measured by the force required to hold the piston in place) does not instantly reach a steady value, but will do so after some period of time. This time is described by a quantity called the relaxation time. Thermodynamics provides **no information** about the gas during this time—it

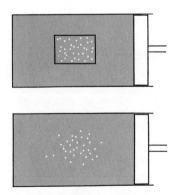

A volume of gas released
in an evacuated cylinder.

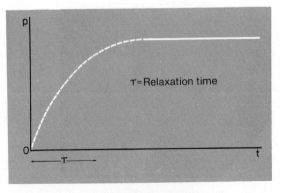

The pressure in the cylinder becomes
constant after some interval of time.

only deals with the final steady state, the state of thermal equilibrium.

It is called thermal equilibrium and not simply equilibrium because the final state depends not only on the external mechanical constraints on the system, but also on the surroundings in a way that is described by the property called temperature. The final pressure will depend on the temperature of the cylinder; if the cylinder is immersed in ice the final pressure will be different from the pressure there would be if it is immersed in hot water. The gas will not be in thermal equilibrium until the temperature of the gas is the same as the temperature of the cylinder.

You can see that the concept of thermal equilibrium of *a* system is related to the concept of thermal equilibrium *between* systems, which is in turn related to the property called temperature.

TEMPERATURE AND THE ZEROTH LAW

Think about two systems brought into thermal contact. This means that they can exchange energy by the process that is called heat flow. This is a process that takes place at the microscopic level, through the interaction between the particles of the systems. We cannot observe what is happening, but we can tell that something is happening because there are observable changes in the macroscopic properties of the systems. If a tank of gas and a hot stove are brought into thermal contact, the pressure of the gas is observed to rise.

Whether or not anything happens on the macroscopic level can always be described by the single property **temperature.** If two systems at the same temperature are in thermal contact, nothing happens. The two systems are in thermal equilibrium with each other. If two systems are brought into thermal contact, and something does happen, then we can say that they were not at the same temperature. Thus temperature is a property that determines whether or not a system is in thermal equilibrium with other systems.

Suppose there are three systems, *A, B* and *C*. The **zeroth law** of thermodynamics is this: If system *A* is in thermal equilibrium with system *B*, and system *B* is in thermal equilibrium with system *C*, then system *A* is in thermal equilibrium with system *C*. This may at first appear to be a trivial statement, but if you think about it you can see that it is not. It is not an obvious result that applies to any situation; two men *A* and *C* may both know lady *B*, but not necessarily know one another.

It is really quite an amazing thing, that the complex interaction called heat flow can be described by a single macroscopic property temperature, quite independent of any other property of the systems.

It is the zeroth law that makes the property temperature a useful quantity, and makes it possible to measure it. Later we will use this to introduce a temperature scale.

Thermal contact does not mean contact in a macroscopic physical sense necessarily; heat flow takes place because of a number of different mechanisms.

INTERNAL ENERGY AND THE FIRST LAW

In thermodynamics we are not in general interested in the macroscopic forms of energy of a system, such as its overall kinetic energy (due to motion of the center of mass of the system) or its overall potential energy (due to its position in a gravitational or electric field). We call the energy of the system that cannot be represented in some macroscopic way the **internal energy** of the system. This includes the kinetic energy of individual particles of the system (relative to the c-of-m) and the potential energy of interaction between particles (which may include electromagnetic energy). However, in thermodynamics we do not assume any particular microscopic model for the system, and therefore do not specify precisely what form the internal energy will take. We **assume** that a quantity called internal energy U exists for the system in a given state, which means we assume that U is a state function. Just as a system has macroscopic co-ordinates $p, V, T, \cdots$ it has an internal energy U.

If internal energy is a state function, the only way it can be changed is by an exchange of energy with the surroundings of the system, and we distinguish between two ways such an exchange can occur. One is by **work done** on the system by the surroundings (or vice versa). This is a macroscopically observable transfer of energy, describable in terms of the measurable external forces on the system and measurable changes in the macroscopic co-ordinates of the system. The other form of energy transfer takes place at the microscopic level (due to interactions between atoms) and is describable in terms of the single co-ordinate temperature. This is called **heat flow.**

The first law of thermodynamics is a statement of conservation of energy, based on the assumption that U is a state function and recognizing both the

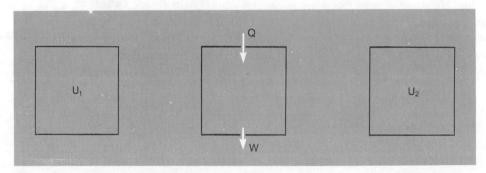

The internal energy of a system may change both because heat flows into the system from the surroundings and because the system does work on its surroundings.

macroscopic and microscopic forms of energy transfer to the system. If a system has initially internal energy U_1, has heat energy Q transferred to it, from the surroundings, and does work W on the surroundings, it will have a final internal energy U_2 such that

$$U_2 - U_1 = Q - W \qquad \text{:first law of thermodynamics}$$

We have chosen a sign convention such that heat transferred *from* the system *to* the surroundings is negative, and work done *by* the surroundings *on* the system is negative.

In terms of an infinitesimal quantity of heat dQ added, and an infinitesimal amount of work dW done, the first law is a statement that the change in internal energy of the system is

$$dU = dQ - dW$$

The notation dQ and dW is to indicate that Q and W are *not* state functions for the system. The heat added and work done depend on the kind of process, that is on the path by which the system is taken from the state of internal energy U_1 to the state of internal energy U_2. Both dQ and dW are inexact differentials, meaning that the integrated result over a finite change depends on the path. On the other hand, dU is an exact differential; the change in internal energy in a finite change depends only on the end states. The system has an internal energy U, but it is meaningless to speak of the heat Q or the work W of the system. This is the basic assumption of the first law.

Changes in the internal energy of a system are not directly observable. We can calculate the work done W and the heat transferred Q from measured changes in the thermodynamic co-ordinates. The difference is the change in internal energy.

The first law as stated applies to the thermodynamic system as a whole, giving the total change in internal energy, which is an extensive property of the system. It is often useful to use the specific internal energy u, and write the first law in the form

$$du = dq - dw$$

where dq and dw are the heat added to and the work done by unit mass (or 1 mole) of the system.

EQUATION OF STATE

The thermodynamic co-ordinates of a system are not all independent of one another. You cannot increase the temperature of a gas without a change occurring in some other co-ordinate; the pressure will increase, or the volume will increase, or both.

The co-ordinates are related to one another, and the relation between them is called the **equation of state** for the system. This relation may not be known, but it always exists. For an ideal gas the equation of state is $pv = RT$ (where v is the molar volume). Real gases are more accurately represented by an equation of state called Van der Waals' equation

$$\left(p + \frac{a}{v^2}\right)(v - b) = RT$$

where a and b are constants depending on the particular gas. This relation is valid over a wider range of conditions than the ideal gas equation, but at high temperature the a and b terms are small, and the ideal gas equation is reasonably accurate.

We will assume that any **two** of the thermodynamic co-ordinates can be changed independently, that is the state of the system is completely specified if any two of the co-ordinates are fixed. We will confine our attention to homogeneous systems, where the co-ordinates have the same value throughout the system (if a vapor is in equilibrium with a liquid the system as a whole is not a homogeneous system); and we will assume that the appropriate variables are those used so far, pressure, volume and temperature. A system described by these variables is usually called a **chemical system.**

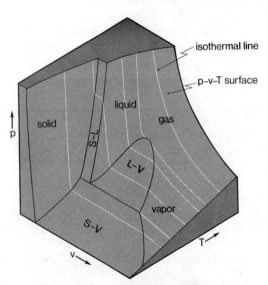

The pVT surface for a substance that contracts on freezing, showing the solid, liquid and vapour phases and the regions where different phases co-exist.

These assumptions restrict us to some extent, but nevertheless cover a great many physical situations. The limitation that we have made means that the only external forces on the system we are considering are macroscopic mechanical forces, exerted by springs or gravity or muscles, and are not electrical or magnetic. We will consider an example of "magnetic work" shortly. The assumption that an equation of state exists for a chemical system means that a relation of the form $F(p,V,T) = 0$ exists (but its form may not be known). If the magnitudes of any two co-ordinates are fixed (e.g., V and T) then the magnitude of any other state variable or function is fixed: $p = p(V,T)$ and $u = u(V,T)$. The equation $F(p,V,T) = 0$ can be interpreted as the equation of a three-dimensional surface in pVT "space," using the thermodynamic co-ordinates in the same way as spatial co-ordinates x,y,z. The state of a system is represented by a point on the surface, and changes in state (processes) are represented by lines on the surface.

The pVT surface for a typical substance is shown. In the upper part of the diagram the substance behaves like an ideal gas.

PROCESSES

We have stated that thermodynamics deals only with a system in thermal equilibrium, that is in a particular state, described by a particular set of variables $p,V,T,U, \cdots$. A process is a **change** in the state of the system. This presents a problem, as you can see. Thermodynamics only describes systems that are *not* changing, so how can it be useful in dealing with processes?

This is resolved using the concept of a **reversible process.** A reversible process is one where the changes take place in such a way that the system is always in thermal equilibrium. Thus a reversible process is a succession (an infinite succession) of equilibrium states, and in principle would take an infinite time to perform.

A reversible process is sometimes called a quasi-static process. The name reversible arises because, since the system is always in thermal equilibrium, the process can proceed in either direction at every instant.

No real macroscopic process is really reversible, but we can come as close as we please to this condition. In practical terms, what is required is that the process take place over a time that is long compared to the relaxation time for the system. (The relaxation time is a measure of the time that it takes for a system to attain thermal equilibrium if it is disturbed.) Think of a gas in a cylinder, and two states of volume V and volume $2V$, obtained by moving the piston out. If the piston is moved out instantaneously, the pressure exerted by the gas on it just after the move is zero. The pressure in the gas and the volume of the gas are not known. The situation is not reversible. However, if the piston is moved out slowly enough, the gas will have time to achieve thermal equilibrium at every instant, and the expansion process is approximately reversible.

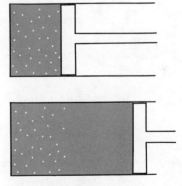

Piston moved out instantaneously.

We can visualize a reversible transfer of heat to a system as follows. A system A can only be in thermal equilibrium at temperature T if it is in thermal contact with another system B that is large enough (has a high enough heat capacity) compared

System A in thermal contact with reservoir B.

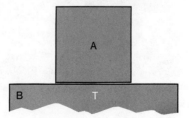

to A that its temperature T is constant, independent of whether or not heat flows between the two systems. The system B is called a heat reservoir, or a temperature bath.

In order to visualize a reversible transfer of heat to system A, think of it first in thermal contact with reservoir B (at temperature T) and then in thermal contact with another reservoir at an infinitesimally higher temperature $T + dT$. System A will then be in thermal equilibirium at temperature $T + dT$, and an amount of heat dQ will have been transferred to it. The amount of heat dQ will depend on the heat capacity C of the system: $dQ = C\,dT$.

To make a finite reversible change $T_1 \rightarrow T_2$ in the temperature of a system, we would have to visualize an infinite series of reservoirs differing infinitesimally

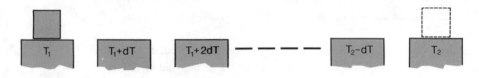

A finite reversible temperature change $T_1 \rightarrow T_2$.

in temperature. The system would be brought into thermal contact with each of the reservoirs in turn.

You can see why we expressed the first law of thermodynamics in terms of infinitesimal quantities.

$$dU = dQ - dW$$

In order that processes be reversible, only infinitesimal changes are possible. For finite changes, integrations $Q = \int dQ$ and $W = \int dW$ must be performed, and the results depend on the path of integration—that is, on the process. If the process were not considered to be reversible, then it would not be possible to specify the path, because the thermodynamic co-ordinates only exist for a system in thermal equilibrium.

A process in which no heat is transferred to the system is called an **adiabatic process.** For such a process $dQ = 0$ at every instant, $dU = -dW$, and $U_2 - U_1 = -W$. For an adiabatic process the change in internal energy is equal to the negative of the work done by the system.

It is sometimes useful to think of changes performed in such a way that one of the thermodynamic co-ordinates of the system is kept constant. Changes at constant temperature are called **isothermal** processes, changes at constant pressure are called **isobaric** processes, and changes at constant volume are called **isometric** processes.

WORK

We are restricting our attention to chemical systems, described by the co-ordinates p, V and T. The work done dW in an infinitesimal reversible process by any chemical system is $dW = p\,dV$. This can be shown to be so for a system of any shape, but we shall do so only for a gas in a cylinder. The cylinder is closed by a frictionless piston of area A. The gas in thermal equilibrium exerts a pressure p on the piston, and therefore to maintain equilibrium some external agency is exerting a force $F = pA$ on the piston. If the piston moves out a small distance dx the work done by the system on the surroundings is $dW = F\,dx$ (the work done by the surroundings on the system is $-F\,dx$, since the external force $\mathbf{F}$ and displacement dx are in opposite directions). The change in volume of the system is $dV = A\,dx$. Therefore

$$dW = F\,dx = pA\,dx = p\,dV$$

Work done in an infinitesimal volume change $dW = p\,dV$.

Note that we can only equate the internal force and the external (measured) force because we are considering a reversible process.

For an isometric change $dV = 0$, $dW = 0$, $dU = dQ$, and $U_2 - U_1 = Q$. For a process at constant volume the change in internal energy is equal to the heat transferred to the system.

For any other finite process the work done depends on *both* the process *and* the equation of state, because $W = \int p\,dV$ can only be integrated if the path of integration is known, and if p can be expressed as a function of V. The state of the system can be represented by a point on a p–V diagram (the projection of a pVT surface on the pV plane), and a process represented by a line on such a diagram. The work done in any process is the area under the curve representing the process.

$$W = \int_{V_1}^{V_2} p\,dV$$

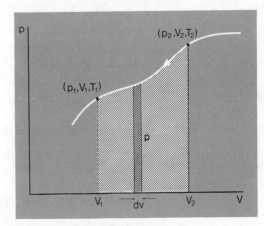

A process represented on a p–V diagram.

As an example, suppose that the system is an ideal gas, and the process is isothermal. The molar equation of state is $pv = RT$, and the molar work done is

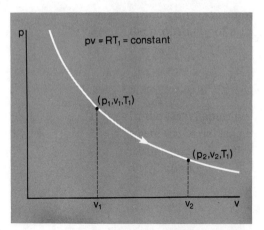

Isothermal process for an ideal gas.

$$w = \int_{v_1}^{v_2} p \, dv = \int_{v_1}^{v_2} \frac{RT}{v} \, dv$$

since the process is isothermal, T is constant ($T = T_1$, the initial value) during the process.

$$w = RT_1 \int_{v_1}^{v_2} \frac{dv}{v} = RT_1 \ln \frac{v_2}{v_1}$$

Since $p_1 v_1 = RT_1 = p_2 v_2$, this may be written in a number of ways

$$w = p_1 v_1 \ln \frac{v_2}{v_1} = RT_1 \ln \frac{p_1}{p_2}$$

If there are n moles of gas in the system, the work done is

$$W = nw = nRT_1 \ln \frac{V_2}{V_1}$$

If $v_2 > v_1$, $\ln v_2/v_1$ is positive and work is done on the surroundings by the system. If $v_2 < v_1$, $\ln v_2/v_1$ is the logarithm of a number less than unity, which is negative: then work is done by the surroundings on the system.

For a chemical system, "$p \, dV$" work is the only kind of work that can be done, but for other systems there are other possibilities. As one example, suppose that the system is an ideal gas, and all the gas molecules act like tiny magnets (they each have a magnetic dipole moment). If the system is not in an external magnetic field, the magnetic moments will be oriented in random directions, and there will be no overall macroscopic effect observable. However, if the system is in an external magnetic field B there will be a tendency for the magnetic moments to line up in the field direction, and this will lead to an overall property called the intensity of magnetization M of the system. For this system in addition to p, V and T the quantities B and M are thermodynamic co-ordinates. If the field B is changed slowly, "magnetic work" $W = \int B \, dM$ will be done on the system. "Mechanical work" $W = \int p \, dV$ may be done as well. For simplicity we will continue to consider only chemical systems.

TEMPERATURE AND THE IDEAL GAS

So far we have used the concept of temperature without specifying how to measure it, and have used the ideal gas equation of state $pv = RT$ without indicating where it came from. These two things are related, as you may know, but we will summarize some features of the relationship.

In thermodynamics temperature is given an operational definition—that is, we define how to measure it, we do not define it in terms of other physical quantities. The fact that it is possible to do this at all rests on the zeroth law, as we pointed out.

You recall that an operational definition of a quantity requires two things: the choice of a standard, and specification of how to make comparisons with the standard (this establishes a scale). To choose a standard of temperature means to choose some physical situation that is believed to always occur at the same temperature, for example the freezing of water. However, unlike mass, length and time, the **zero** of temperature is not apparent, so initially two fixed points were chosen, the **ice point** and the **steam point** (these refer to a mixture of ice and water, or a mixture of water and water vapor, at a pressure of 1 atmosphere). Arbitrary values are assigned these points; on the Celsius scale they are called 0°C and 100°C.

To compare temperatures any temperature-dependent property (thermoscopic or thermometric property) of matter may be used: for example, the length l of a mercury column enclosed in glass, the pressure p of a gas kept at constant volume, the volume V of a gas kept at constant pressure, the resistance R of a resistor, the potential difference ε developed at a junction between two metals. Suppose that x represents whatever thermoscopic property is used. A system with this property is our temperature-comparer, our thermometer.

When this system is in thermal contact with another system at the ice point, the value of x is x_i. When it is in thermal contact with another system at the steam point, the value of x is x_s. In thermal contact with any other system, the value of x can be observed. The temperature θ of the system is determined uniquely in terms of the measured values x, x_i and x_s. For example, the Celsius temperature can be defined as

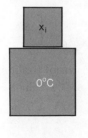

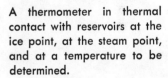

A thermometer in thermal contact with reservoirs at the ice point, at the steam point, and at a temperature to be determined.

$$\theta(\text{in } °C) = 100 \, \frac{x - x_i}{x_s - x_i}$$

This is all that is necessary in order to give an operational definition of temperature, but it has the difficulty that using different thermoscopic properties gives different temperature scales. A system at "50°C" for an observer using a resistance thermometer is at "50.1°C" for an observer using a mercury-in-glass thermometer. Furthermore, observers using different resistance thermometers will not agree with one another. This does not matter if everyone uses the same thermometer, but it is a nuisance and besides, we have an intuitive feeling

there should be a temperature scale that is independent of the particular temperature-dependent property we choose for measuring temperature.

The definition that we gave for Celsius temperature is simply an assumption that the property x is a linear function of temperature θ; that is, that

$$x = a\theta + b$$

At the ice point $$x_i = a(0) + b$$

At the steam point $$x_s = a(100) + b$$

Eliminating the constants a and b gives the previous expression for θ as a function of x. This assumption of linearity is all that we can do, so long as we have no basis for thinking that one particular thermoscopic property is more important than others.

The next step in the development of a temperature scale depends on the experimental observation that all gas thermometers give the **same** temperature scale, provided the gas pressure is low enough. This really involves the extrapolation of observations on real gases to zero pressure. It does not matter if the property chosen is pressure p (the constant-volume gas thermometer) or volume V (the constant-pressure gas thermometer). Experimentally it is more convenient to use the constant-volume thermometer.

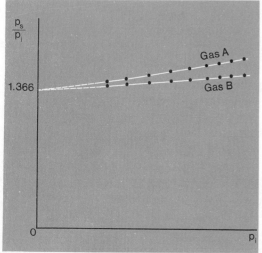

Think of such a thermometer in thermal contact with a system at the ice point (pressure p_i) and with a system at the steam point (pressure p_s). These pressures will depend on the kind of gas, the amount of gas and the constant volume used. Now suppose that some of the gas is removed from the system (or a larger constant volume is used for the same amount of gas) and p_i and p_s are measured again. They will both be less. This is repeated for the gas at lower and lower density, and the ratio p_s/p_i is plotted against p_i, in order to find (by extrapolation) the value of the ratio as $p_i \to 0$. The experimental fact is that although the curve obtained is slightly different for different gases, the limiting value of the ratio is **the same for all gases.** Its value is about 1.366.

Extrapolation to zero pressure gives the same result for all gases.

We can use this result to define a temperature scale that is independent of the properties of a particular material, by defining temperature in terms of this ratio.

$$\frac{T_s}{T_i} = \lim_{p_i \to 0} \frac{p_s}{p_i} = 1.366$$

For a system at any other temperature the experimental ratio (p/p_i) is determined and its temperature defined by

$$\frac{T}{T_i} = \lim_{p_i \to 0} \frac{p}{p_i}$$

These experiments would determine any temperature in terms of T_i, but would not fix the size of the temperature unit. This is done by choosing

$$T_s - T_i = 100 \text{ K}°$$

where K° means "Kelvin degrees." The zero of the Kelvin temperature scale is experimentally determined, but the size of the unit is arbitrary.

Combining $\dfrac{T_s}{T_i} = 1.366$ and $T_s - T_i = 100 \text{ K}°$ gives

$$T_i = 273.16°\text{K} \qquad T_s = 373.16°\text{K} \qquad T = 273.16 \lim_{p_i \to 0} \left(\frac{p}{p_i}\right)°\text{K}$$

The size of the Celsius degree and the Kelvin degree are the same, but the scales have a different zero.

$$\theta(\text{in °C}) = T(\text{in °K}) - 273.16$$

A temperature scale defined in terms of the experimental properties of gases as the pressure approaches zero is called an **ideal gas scale**. An ideal gas is defined **experimentally** by the behavior of real gases as the pressure approaches zero. We earlier defined it **theoretically** as one in which the potential energy of interaction between molecules is negligible in comparison with their kinetic energy.

The scale with the ice point at 0°C is normally the ideal gas Celsius scale, not a scale defined in terms of some arbitrary thermometric property. The scale with the ice point at 273.16°K is the **ideal gas absolute scale**.

The ideal gas scale provides a temperature scale that does not depend on the properties of a particular substance, but does depend on the general properties of gases, and therefore does not completely satisfy our feeling that temperature should exist as a property quite independent of whatever system is chosen for measuring it. The scale is completely satisfactory from an operational point of view, which is all that is necessary for its use in thermodynamics.

Later we will show that the laws of thermodynamics themselves make it possible to define a temperature scale (the **absolute thermodynamic scale**) that does not depend on the properties of gases. This will perhaps satisfy our feeling that temperature "exists" in some absolute sense, but is not of practical importance because the absolute thermodynamic scale is identical to the ideal gas absolute scale.

Recognition of the absolute scale of temperature showed that there is a zero of temperature that is experimental, not arbitrary; and therefore it is not really necessary to have two arbitrary fixed points in order to establish a standard of temperature. The single arbitrary fixed point used now is the triple point of water (where solid, liquid and gaseous water can coexist) whose temperature is **defined** to be $T = 273.16°K$ (the triple point is very close to the ice point in temperature, but the pressure is not atmospheric).

We have shown that for an ideal gas at constant volume the pressure is proportional to the absolute temperature $p \propto T$. Experiments with a constant-pressure gas thermometer, extrapolated to zero pressure, give an identical temperature scale, so that for an ideal gas at constant pressure, $V \propto T$. These two experimental facts taken together suggest that for an ideal gas, $pV = AT$, where A is a constant for a fixed quantity of gas. However, still another experimental fact makes the relation even simpler; if 1 mole is the quantity of gas, then the constant A is **the same for all gases,** a "universal constant." The only extensive variable in the equation is V. Using v for the molar volume, and the usual R for the gas constant, the equation of state is $pv = RT$. If there are n moles of gas in the system, the total volume is $V = nv$, and the equation of state describing the system as a whole is $pV = nRT$. The value of the constant R is of course experimentally determined.

Real gases are not ideal gases, but at ordinary temperatures and pressures the departure from ideal gas behavior is small, and requires quite precise measurements to detect. You probably remember that "one mole of any gas under standard conditions occupies a volume of 22.4 liters." This statement is not true; if you took exactly 1 mole (N_0 molecules) of different gases at exactly the same temperature and pressure they would not occupy exactly the same volume. The statement is only true to the extent that real gases act like the ideal gas. To determine the gas constant precisely it is necessary to do experiments on real gases and extrapolate to zero pressure. However, the value determined under "standard conditions" is reasonably close. Standard conditions (sometimes denoted SC, or STP, or NTP) means a temperature of $0°C \cong 273°K$ and a pressure of 1 atm. Therefore $R = pv/T = 1 \times 22.4/273$ atm-liter/mole-K°.

Atmospheric pressure is not constant, so a pressure of 1 atmosphere really means one **standard** atmosphere, defined as the pressure exerted by a mercury column 760.000 mm high at 0°C at a location where "standard gravity" acts. Standard gravity is 980.665 cm/sec². At 0°C the density of mercury is $\rho = 13.595$ gm/cm³. The pressure exerted by the mercury column is

$$p = \rho g h = 13.595 \times 980.665 \times 76.0000 \text{ dynes/cm}^2$$
$$= 1.0132 \times 10^6 \text{ dynes/cm}^2$$
$$= 1.0132 \times 10^5 \text{ newtons/m}^2$$
$$= 1 \text{ standard atmosphere}$$

Thus $$R = \frac{1.01 \times 10^6 \times 22.4 \times 10^3}{273} = 8.31 \times 10^7 \text{ ergs/mole-K}°$$

$$= 8.31 \text{ joules/mole-K}° = 1.98 \text{ cal/mole-K}°$$

The value $R \cong 2$ cal/mole-K° is reasonably accurate and easy to remember—another reason why the calorie as an energy unit survives! In mks units the gas constant should really be expressed in terms of the kilogram-molecular-weight (or kilomole) rather than the gram-molecular-weight (mole). Then $R = 8.31 \times 10^3$ joules/kilomole-K°.

You may be feeling that we have had to appeal to experiment very often in this section—and so we have. In thermodynamics temperature is an operationally defined quantity, and the ideal gas equation of state is an experimental result. (Of course it was originally an experimental result—remember Boyle's law and Charles' law?)

In statistical mechanics temperature is a derived quantity, and the equation of state of an ideal gas is a derived result. In some ways this seems much more satisfying, but do not lose sight of the fact that statistical mechanics is based on assumed microscopic models. Derived results must be compared with experimental results, and only if there is reasonable agreement can we have any faith in the validity of the models. The ultimate test of any theory is experiment.

SPECIFIC HEAT CAPACITIES OF THE IDEAL GAS

We have stated that thermodynamics is useful in deducing relationships between physical quantities. As an example we work out the relation between the specific heat capacities c_p and c_v for an ideal gas. These quantities were defined in Chapter 26 on the Energy of a System of Gas Molecules.

The first law, in terms of molar quantities, is

$$du = dq - dw$$
$$= dq - p\,dv \qquad \text{:for a chemical system}$$

Using subscript v's to refer to a process at constant volume

$$du_v = dq_v \qquad \text{:since } dv = 0$$

The specific heat at constant volume is defined by

$$c_v = \frac{dq_v}{dT_v} = \frac{du_v}{dT_v}$$

Any two of the thermodynamic co-ordinates can be varied independently; this means that u can be regarded as a function of p and T, $u(p,T)$, or as a function of v and T, $u(v,T)$, or as a function of p and v, $u(p,v)$. Changes in u can be expressed as

$$du = \left(\frac{\partial u}{\partial p}\right)_T dp + \left(\frac{\partial u}{\partial T}\right)_p dT$$

which is the rate of change of u with p, multiplied by the change in p, plus the rate of change of u with T, multiplied by the change in T. Similarly

$$du = \left(\frac{\partial u}{\partial v}\right)_T dv + \left(\frac{\partial u}{\partial T}\right)_v dT$$

or

$$du = \left(\frac{\partial u}{\partial v}\right)_p dv + \left(\frac{\partial u}{\partial p}\right)_v dp$$

Thus for a process at constant volume

$$du_v = \left(\frac{\partial u}{\partial T}\right)_v dT_v \quad \text{or} \quad \frac{du_v}{dT_v} = \left(\frac{\partial u}{\partial T}\right)_v$$

so

$$c_v = \left(\frac{\partial u}{\partial T}\right)_v$$

the partial derivative of u with respect to T, keeping v constant.

This is perfectly general, applying to any chemical system. For an ideal gas **the internal energy is a function of temperature only.** At present we can take this as an experimental fact, although later we will prove it using the laws of thermodynamics. From the point of view of the theoretical definition of an ideal gas it is a result that must be expected; an ideal gas is one for which the potential energy of interaction between molecules is negligible; therefore the distance between the molecules does not affect the energy of the system, and therefore the volume occupied by the gas does not affect the internal energy.

For an ideal gas then $u = u(T)$ only, and

$$c_v = \frac{du}{dT}$$

The first law becomes

$$dq = du + p\, dv$$
$$= c_v\, dT + p\, dv \qquad \text{:for an ideal gas only}$$

For a process at constant pressure

$$dq_p = c_v\, dT_p + p\, dv_p$$

and using the definition of the specific heat at constant pressure

$$c_p = \frac{dq_p}{dT_p} = c_v + p\frac{dv_p}{dT_p}$$

Just as the internal energy can be regarded as a function of any two co-ordinates, the volume can be regarded as a function of the co-ordinates p and T.

$$dv = \left(\frac{\partial v}{\partial p}\right)_T dp + \left(\frac{\partial v}{\partial T}\right)_p dT \quad \text{so} \quad dv_p = \left(\frac{\partial v}{\partial T}\right)_p dT_p$$

and

$$c_p = c_v + p\left(\frac{\partial v}{\partial T}\right)_p$$

The ideal gas equation of state is $pv = RT$, or $v = RT/p$. Differentiating with respect to T, keeping p constant

$$\left(\frac{\partial v}{\partial T}\right)_p = \frac{R}{p}$$

and therefore

$$c_p = c_v + R$$

We used this result in the discussion of the theory of specific heats in the chapter on energy of a system of gas molecules. Thermodynamics provides no information about the magnitudes of the specific heat capacities.

It is an experimental fact that for most gases under normal conditions the specific heat capacities are constant over some range of temperature. The ratio $\gamma = c_p/c_v$ is used to characterize the observed values. The table given in the earlier chapter shows that for monatomic gases $\gamma \cong 1.67$, corresponding to $c_v = \frac{3}{2}R$, $c_p = \frac{5}{2}R$. For diatomic gases (if the molecular weight is low), $\gamma \cong 1.40$, so that $c_v = \frac{5}{2}R$, $c_p = \frac{7}{2}R$.

ADIABATIC PROCESSES FOR THE IDEAL GAS

For the ideal gas the first law is

$$dq = c_v\, dT + p\, dv$$

This can be put in terms of changes in p and v using the ideal gas equation $pv = RT$. Forming the differential

$$p\, dv + v\, dp = R\, dT$$

so

$$dq = c_v\left(\frac{p\, dv + v\, dp}{R}\right) + p\, dv = \frac{c_v v\, dp + c_v p\, dv + Rp\, dv}{R}$$

An adiabatic process is one in which no heat is transferred to the system, $dq = 0$. For such a process

$$0 = c_v v\, dp + (c_v + R)p\, dv$$
$$= c_v v\, dp + c_p p\, dv$$

or dividing by pvc_v

$$\gamma\frac{dv}{v} + \frac{dp}{p} = 0$$

Over the range where γ can be considered constant, this relation can be integrated

$$\gamma\int\frac{dv}{v} + \int\frac{dp}{p} = 0$$

$$\gamma \ln v + \ln p = \text{constant}$$
$$\ln v^\gamma + \ln p = \text{constant}$$
$$\ln pv^\gamma = \text{constant}$$
$$pv^\gamma = K$$

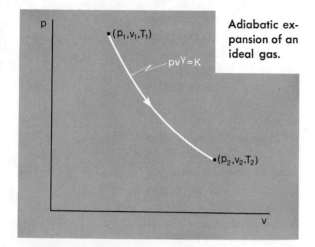

Adiabatic expansion of an ideal gas.

The magnitude of the quantity K is the same at every instant in the adiabatic process

$$p_1 v_1^\gamma = p_2 v_2^\gamma = p v^\gamma$$

In this process each of the three co-ordinates is changing. Using the equation of state, the process can be described in terms of v and T, or p and T.

$$p \left(\frac{RT}{p}\right)^\gamma = K \qquad p^{1-\gamma} T^\gamma = K_1$$

or

$$\left(\frac{RT}{v}\right) v^\gamma = K \qquad T v^{\gamma-1} = K_2$$

The curve representing an adiabatic process on a p–v diagram is always steeper at any point than the curve representing an isothermal process passing through the same point. For the adiabatic process, as we have seen,

$$\left(\frac{\partial p}{\partial v}\right)_{ad} = -\gamma \frac{p}{v}$$

From the ideal gas equation of state $p = RT/v$

$$\left(\frac{\partial p}{\partial v}\right)_T = RT \left(-\frac{1}{v^2}\right) = -\frac{p}{v}$$

for the isothermal process.

The slopes are related by the factor γ

$$\left(\frac{\partial p}{\partial v}\right)_{ad} = \gamma \left(\frac{\partial p}{\partial v}\right)_T$$

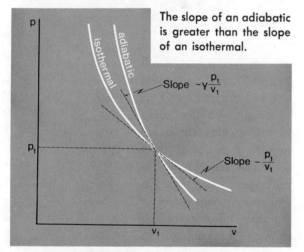

The slope of an adiabatic is greater than the slope of an isothermal.

Slope $-\gamma \dfrac{p_1}{v_1}$

Slope $-\dfrac{p_1}{v_1}$

Since the equation of the path is known, the work done in the adiabatic process (for the ideal gas) can be determined. Again it is assumed that γ is constant.

$$w_{ad} = \int p\, dv = K \int_{v_1}^{v_2} v^{-\gamma}\, dv$$

$$= K \left[\frac{v^{-\gamma+1}}{-\gamma+1}\right]_{v_1}^{v_2} = \frac{K}{1-\gamma} (v_2^{1-\gamma} - v_1^{1-\gamma})$$

$$= \frac{p_2 v_2 - p_1 v_1}{1-\gamma} \qquad K = p_1 v_1^\gamma$$
$$= p_2 v_2^\gamma$$

$$= \frac{R(T_2 - T_1)}{1-\gamma}$$

$$= \frac{(c_p - c_v)(T_2 - T_1)}{1 - c_p/c_v} = -c_v(T_2 - T_1)$$

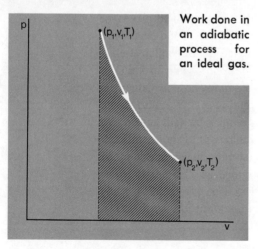

Work done in an adiabatic process for an ideal gas.

This can also be seen directly from the first law

$$dq = c_v\, dT + p\, dv = 0 \qquad \text{for adiabatic process}$$

$$\therefore \quad w_{ad} = \int p\, dv = -\int c_v\, dT \qquad \text{:assume that } c_v \text{ is constant}$$

$$= -c_v \int_{T_1}^{T_2} dT = -c_v(T_2 - T_1)$$

For an adiabatic expansion, w_{ad} is positive; work is done *by* the gas *on* the surroundings. Therefore $-c_v(T_2 - T_1)$ is positive, $(T_2 - T_1)$ is negative, and $T_2 < T_1$. The temperature of the gas is decreased. This is to be expected because no heat enters the system, work is done by the system, and therefore the internal energy of the system decreases. For an ideal gas (but *not* in general) T is proportional to the internal energy.

The fact that gases expanding and doing work become colder is the basis of operation of refrigerators.

Example: A cylinder contains 10 liters of oxygen under standard conditions. The gas is compressed to half its volume. Calculate the work done if the process is (a) isothermal, (b) adiabatic.

We assume (1) that oxygen can be treated as an ideal gas, (2) that since it is a diatomic gas $\gamma = 1.4$, and (3) that the processes are performed reversibly so that thermodynamics can be applied.

Then for the isothermal compression

$$W_T = p_1 V_1 \ln \frac{V_2}{V_1} = 1 \times 10 \times \ln \tfrac{1}{2} \text{ atm-liter}$$

$$= -10 \ln 2 \text{ atm-liters} = -6.93 \text{ atm-liters}$$

The atmosphere–liter is a satisfactory unit for energy, but the result can be expressed in other units. Using $p_1 = 1$ atm $= 1.01 \times 10^5$ n/m^2, and $V_1 = 10\ l = 10^4$ cm$^3 = 10^{-2}$ m^3

$$W_T = -1.01 \times 10^3 \ln 2 \text{ n-m} = -7.0 \times 10^2 \text{ joules}$$

In the isothermal process $pV = $ constant, so $p_2 = (V_1/V_2)\,p_1 = 2p_1 = 2$ atm.

In the adiabatic compression, $pV^\gamma = $ constant.

$$p_2 = \left(\frac{V_1}{V_2}\right)^\gamma p_1 = 2^{1.4} p_1 = 2.64 \text{ atm}$$

$$W_{ad} = \frac{p_2 V_2 - p_1 V_1}{1 - \gamma} = \frac{1.01 \times 10^5 \times 2.64 \times 0.5 \times 10^{-2} - 1.01 \times 10^5 \times 10^{-2}}{1 - 1.4}$$

$$= \frac{1.01 \times 10^3 (1.32 - 1)}{-0.4} = -8.1 \times 10^2 \text{ joules}$$

The work done on the gas in this process is greater than in the isothermal process.

The final temperature here is

$$T_2 = \frac{p_2 V_2}{p_1 V_1} T_1 = 2.64 \times \tfrac{1}{2} \times 273 = 360°\text{K} = 87°\text{C}$$

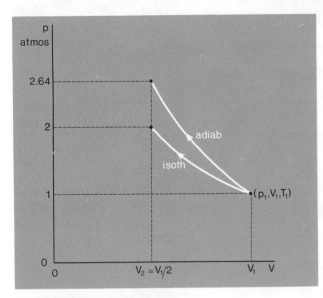

An isothermal and an adiabatic compression from V_1 to $V_1/2$.

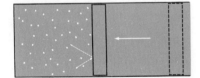

A moving piston will increase the energy of molecules hitting it.

We can check the calculations of W_{ad} as follows. The number of moles of gas is

$$n = \frac{pV}{RT} = \frac{1 \times 10}{(22.4/273) \times 273}$$

$$= \frac{10}{22.4} \text{ mole}$$

and the heat capacity (at constant volume) is

$$C_v = nc_v = n\left(\frac{5}{2} R\right)$$

$$= \frac{10}{22.4} \times \frac{5}{2} \times 8.31 \text{ joules/K}°$$

$$= 9.28 \text{ joules/K}°$$

$$W_{ad} = -C_v(T_2 - T_1)$$

$$= -9.28(360 - 273)$$

$$= -8.1 \times 10^2 \text{ joules}$$

In practical terms, how would these processes be performed? As the piston is moved in, gas molecules colliding with the piston will acquire extra energy—that is, the internal energy of the gas will tend to increase. If the piston is moved in very slowly, there is time for the gas to exchange energy with the walls of the cylinder, or in macroscopic terms heat flows out of the gas to the walls (surroundings) at the same rate that work is done on the gas, and the internal energy remains constant. This is the isothermal process. On the other hand, if the piston is moved in quickly there is not time for the gas to exchange heat energy with the walls, and the process is adiabatic. The internal energy (and the temperature) of the gas is increased by the work done. Thus the compression is isothermal if done slowly, adiabatic if done quickly. We assume, however, in applying thermodynamic considerations, that all processes are performed reversibly—that is, infinitely slowly. The only way to do the compression completely adiabatically would be to supply heat to the walls from some other source, keeping the walls at the same temperature as the gas as its temperature rises. Then no heat would be exchanged with the gas. Nevertheless it is a reasonable approximation to treat a sudden compression as a reversible adiabatic process, because the relaxation time for a gas is quite short.

COMPRESSIBILITY OF AN IDEAL GAS

One of the physical properties of matter is elasticity. If any substance is subjected to an external deforming force, there is an internal force opposing the deformation. For solids the deformation may be of different kinds—linear extension, bulk compression, twist or shear—and the physical constants called elastic moduli describe the properties of solids subjected to these various deformations. For small deformations, the deformation (strain) is proportional to the external force (stress) and the proportionality constants are the elastic moduli.

For fluids (gases and liquids) the elastic property of most interest is the compressibility—or, related to it, the bulk modulus.

If the pressure on a volume V of matter changes by an amount Δp, the volume changes by an amount ΔV. The ratio $\Delta V/V$ is the bulk strain produced by the change in stress Δp, and for small changes (as for a solid or liquid) $\Delta V/V \propto \Delta p$.

The **bulk modulus** β is defined as the ratio

$$\beta = -\frac{\Delta p}{\Delta V/V} = -V\frac{\Delta p}{\Delta V}$$

where the negative sign is introduced so that β is a positive quantity. If Δp is positive (a pressure increase) ΔV is negative (a volume decrease). Bulk modulus has the dimensions of pressure.

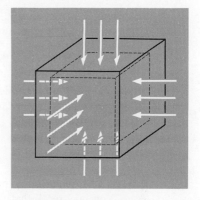

An increase in pressure Δp causes a decrease in volume ΔV.

For liquids or gases it is sometimes more convenient to use the **compressibility** K, defined as

$$K = \frac{1}{\beta} = -\frac{1}{V}\frac{\Delta V}{\Delta p}$$

This has the dimensions of (pressure)$^{-1}$. For water, for example, $K \sim 5 \times 10^{-5}$ (atm)$^{-1}$.

For gases the changes in volume may be so large that it is not reasonable to treat K as a constant. Also, as we have seen, in the last example, the rate of change of p with v depends on the process, therefore we distinguish between the isothermal compressibility K_T and the adiabatic compressibility K_{ad}.

$$K_T = -\frac{1}{V}\left(\frac{\partial V}{\partial p}\right)_T \qquad K_{ad} = -\frac{1}{V}\left(\frac{\partial V}{\partial p}\right)_{ad}$$

If the gas can be treated as an ideal gas, $v = RT/p$, and

$$K_T = -\frac{1}{v}\left(\frac{\partial v}{\partial p}\right)_T = -\frac{1}{v}\left(-\frac{RT}{p^2}\right) = \frac{1}{p}$$

and since

$$\left(\frac{\partial p}{\partial v}\right)_{ad} = \gamma\left(\frac{\partial p}{\partial v}\right)_T \qquad K_{ad} = \frac{K_T}{\gamma} = \frac{1}{\gamma p}$$

For an ideal gas the compressibility is inversely proportional to the pressure, the bulk modulus is directly proportional to the pressure.

Example: The propagation of sound waves in a substance involves periodic compression and expansion of the medium, and it can be shown that the speed of sound in a gas is given by

$$V_{\text{sound}} = \sqrt{\frac{\beta_{\text{ad}}}{\rho}} = \sqrt{\frac{1}{K_{\text{ad}}\rho}}$$

where ρ is the density. The adiabatic rather than the isothermal compressibility appears because at sound frequencies the successive compressions are so rapid that there is not time for heat transfer through the gas, and the process is adiabatic.

For an ideal gas, $K_{\text{ad}} = 1/\gamma p$, $V_{\text{sound}} = \sqrt{\gamma p/\rho}$. Both p and ρ depend on temperature, but if V_{sound} is expressed in terms of molecular weight rather than density the temperature dependence can be seen. The molecular weight M, density ρ, and molar volume v are related by $\rho = M/v$. Therefore the ideal gas equation of state may be written $p(M/\rho) = RT$, so

$$V_{\text{sound}} = \sqrt{\frac{\gamma RT}{M}}$$

For a particular gas γ and M are constants, and $V_{\text{sound}} \propto \sqrt{T}$.

You may recall that the speed of sound in air at room temperature ($\sim 300°\text{K}$) is about 1100 ft/sec $= 3.4 \times 10^4$ cm/sec. Air is a mixture of about 80% nitrogen ($M = 28$ gm/mole) and 20% oxygen ($M = 32$ gm/mole) giving an average molecular weight of about 29.

$$\gamma = \frac{V^2_{\text{sound}}M}{RT} = \frac{3.4^2 \times 10^8 \times 29}{8.3 \times 10^7 \times 300} \cong 1.4$$

as expected, since both gases are diatomic.

The speed of sound is comparable to the average speed of the gas molecules. Recalling the equipartition principle, the average kinetic energy of the molecules of an ideal gas is $\frac{3}{2}kT$.

$$\overline{\tfrac{1}{2}mv^2} = \tfrac{3}{2}kT$$

so the root-mean-square molecular speed is

$$v_{\text{rms}} = \sqrt{\frac{3kT}{m}} = \sqrt{\frac{3N_0kT}{N_0m}} = \sqrt{\frac{3RT}{M}}$$

Here N_0 is Avogadro's number, the number of molecules in 1 mole. Therefore $M = N_0m$, and $R = N_0k$.

Questions for discussion

1. What does it mean to say that thermodynamics is a macroscopic theory?

2. Are there theoretical postulates in thermodynamics, or is thermodynamics simply a statement of a number of experimental facts?

3. We stated that in thermodynamics no assumptions are made about the microscopic structure of matter, but many times made reference in this chapter to the molecular activity that gives rise to observable macroscopic effects. Are such references necessary in discussing thermodynamics?

4. Does the zeroth law of thermodynamics seem to you to be necessary, or does it appear to be a statement of the obvious?

5. Is internal energy of a system, as defined in thermodynamics, kinetic energy, potential energy, or both, or neither, or what?

6. It is usual to identify three different mechanisms of heat transfer, conduction, convection and radiation. What are the differences between these?

7. Can you think of examples of processes in which heat is added to a system but its temperature does not change? Can you think of examples in which heat is not added but the temperature changes?

8. You may have done an experiment to measure **the mechanical equivalent of heat** $J = 4.2$ joules/cal. Is this a physical quantity, like the acceleration due to gravity for example, or is it simply a unit conversion factor?

9. Equal volumes of two different fluids, one a liquid and the other a gas, are compressed at constant temperature. For which one would you expect the work done to be greater if the change in pressure is the same for each? if the change in volume is the same for each?

10. The adjectives **intensive, extensive** and **specific** are applied to **thermodynamic variables** of different kinds. Are these sensible choices for the meanings they are intended to convey?

11. On the sketch of a pvT surface for a typical substance in this chapter, can you identify the triple point (at which the solid, liquid and gas phases can co-exist) and the critical point? At temperatures higher than that at the critical point, it is impossible to liquefy a substance no matter how much the pressure is increased.

12. Why is a reversible process sometimes called a quasi-static process?

13. Can you see why it is necessary to specify both the temperature and the value of the acceleration due to gravity in defining the standard atmosphere in terms of the pressure exerted by a column of mercury?

14. If a substance is compressed, the work done in producing a particular change in volume is greater if the process is adiabatic than if it is isothermal. Can you see physically why this is so?

15. The corrective "a" and "b" terms in the Van der Waals equation of state help to take into account departures of real gases from ideal gas behavior. The term a/v^2 is related to the interaction between molecules (negligible for an ideal gas). Can you see why the corrective term on the pressure is proportional to $1/v^2$? The b term helps take into account the finite volume occupied by the gas molecules (negligible for an ideal gas). It is usually considered to be about four times the actual volume of the molecules. Can you see why it is not simply equal to the volume?

Problems

1. A man has a dietary intake of 3000 kcal per day. If this is totally converted into heat energy, what is the average rate of heat generation in watts? The man lifts 3-kg cartons a distance of 1 m onto a conveyor belt, at a rate of 10 cartons per minute. At what rate is he doing work?

2. A bubble of air is 2 mm in diameter when it is 30 ft below the surface of a lake. What is its diameter when it reaches the surface, assuming the temperature of the lake is constant? Is work done by or on the air in the bubble? What happens to the work done?

3. A 170-lb father helps his daughter move into the third floor of a university residence. One task is to blow up (by lung power) a plastic chair to a pressure 1 lb/in.^{2} above atmospheric pressure. The chair is initially completely deflated, and when blown up contains a volume of 2 ft^3 of gas. Compare the work done by the father in inflating the chair with the work he does each time he climbs the stairs 27 ft to the residence floor.

4. A copper block (specific heat 0.093) slides at a constant speed of 10 m/sec down a slope that makes an angle of 30° with the horizontal. Assuming that all the heat generated goes into the block, at what rate is its temperature changing?

5. If 1 gm of hydrogen, 1 gm of nitrogen, and 1 gm of carbon dioxide are in a 10-liter flask at 20°C, what are the density and pressure of the gas mixture?

6. Express the gas constant R in ft-lb/mole-K°.

7. The volume of an automobile tire is 1 ft^3 and the gauge pressure at 20°C is 25 psi. (Gauge pressure is the pressure above atmospheric pressure.) Take atmospheric pressure as 15 psi, assume that the volume of the tire is constant, and treat air as a diatomic ideal gas of molecular weight 29. **(a)** Determine the weight of air in the tire. **(b)** Assume that the tire is "inflated" by compressing the necessary volume of air from a pressure of one atmosphere to a gauge pressure of 25 psi in a reversible isothermal process at 20°C. Calculate the work done in the compression, in ft-lb. **(c)** Suppose that the same volume of air is compressed into the tire in a reversible adiabatic process, and determine the gauge pressure and the temperature just after the compression. Calculate the work done in the compression. Do you think that the actual process is closer to being isothermal or adiabatic? **(d)** Determine the gauge pressure when the tire is being used at high speed, operating at a temperature of 50°C.

8. A volume of 100 cm^3 of helium at 27° C and 1 atm is compressed to half its volume in a reversible process. Calculate the work done if the process is **(a)** isothermal, **(b)** adiabatic. **(c)** Determine the heat transferred in (a). **(d)** Determine the change in temperature in (b).

9. A cylinder contains 0.1 m^3 of a fluid at atmospheric pressure and room temperature. The cylinder is closed by a piston, and the pressure is increased to 10 atm in a reversible isothermal process. Calculate the percentage change in volume and the work done if the fluid is **(a)** an ideal gas, **(b)** water (compressibility 5×10^{-5} atm^{-1}).

10. The volume of 1 mole of a monatomic ideal gas, initially at STP, is halved. Calculate the work done in joules if the process is reversible and **(a)** isobaric, **(b)** isothermal, **(c)** adiabatic. **(d)** Determine the change in internal energy of the gas in each case. **(e)** What is the heat capacity appropriate to each of the three processes?

11. A mole of a monatomic ideal gas at (p_1, v_1, T_1) undergoes a process such that its pressure and volume are both doubled. The process is reversible and performed so that the pressure is proportional to the volume (a straight line on a p–v dia-

gram). Calculate work done, heat exchanged and change in internal energy of the gas, in terms of R and T_1. What is the molar heat capacity for the process?

12. An insulated cylinder contains 1 mole of a diatomic ideal gas at 20°C, 1 atm. Its axis is horizontal and one end is closed by a perfectly fitting frictionless piston of mass 1 kg, area 100 cm². If the cylinder is turned so that its axis is vertical, with the piston at the bottom, determine the new temperature of the gas.

13. The insulated cylinder shown is divided into two compartments A and B by a perfectly fitting, frictionless, insulated (non-conducting) piston. There is one mole of a diatomic ideal gas ($c_v = 5R/2$) in each compartment. Initially the gas on each side is in the same state (p_0, v_0, T_0). There is an electric heater in A, and heat is slowly added until the pressure is doubled. Determine the new temperature in each compartment (in terms of T_0), and the work done on the gas in B and the heat added to the gas in A (in terms of RT_0).

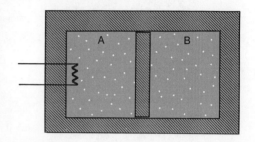

14. The speed of sound in a mixture of helium and neon at 27°C is 758 m/sec. Calculate the effective molecular weight and the composition of the mixture. (Take molecular weights of He and Ne as 4 and 20 gm/mole.)

15. An equation of state for real gases is sometimes expressed in the form $pv = A + Bp + Cp^2 + Dp^3 + \cdots$, where the coefficients $A, B, C, D, \cdots$ are functions of temperature T. This is called the virial expansion. (a) Express the Van der Waals equation of state $(p + a/v^2)(v - b) = RT$ in the form of the virial expansion to two terms, using the fact that the a and b terms are small (i.e., $pv \cong RT$). (b) At a particular temperature for any gas the coefficient B is equal to 0. This is called the Boyle temperature T_B for the gas. What is its physical significance? Determine T_B for a Van der Waals gas in terms of a, b and R. (c) The table gives values for a in n-m⁴/mole² and b in m³/mole for three gases. Determine T_B for these gases.

Gas	a	b
He	3.4×10^{-3}	2.3×10^{-5}
O_2	0.14	3.2×10^{-5}
CO_2	0.37	4.3×10^{-5}

16. A mole of oxygen occupies a volume of 1 liter at 0°C. Calculate the pressure exerted by the gas, assuming it is described by (a) the ideal gas equation of state, (b) the Van der Waals equation of state.

17. The a/v^2 term in the Van der Waals equation of state helps to take into account the interaction between molecules, and is sometimes called the internal pressure in the gas. Assuming the Van der Waals equation is valid, determine the ratio of this internal pressure to the total external pressure for one mole of oxygen at 0°C occupying a volume of (a) 22.4 liter, (b) 1 liter, (c) 0.1 liter.

18. The constant b in the Van der Waals equation of state is related to the finite volume occupied by the gas molecules. It turns out to be about four times the volume occupied. Use this to estimate the diameter of an oxygen molecule, assuming that the molecules are spherical.

19. Experiments show that the rate of heat flow through a slab of material is approximately proportional to the area A of conduction and to the temperature difference $T_2 - T_1$, and inversely proportional to the thickness d: $dQ/dt = K[A(T_2 - T_1)/d]$. The quantity K is called the coefficient of thermal conductivity of the material, and for a limited range of temperature can be considered constant. The ratio $(T_2 - T_1)/d$ is the temperature gradient in the material, and the coefficient K is defined more generally by $dQ/dt = -KA(dT/dx)$. The negative sign is introduced so that if dT/dx is negative (T decreasing as x increases) then dQ/dt will be positive, representing a heat flow in the positive x-direction.

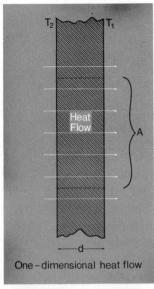

One–dimensional heat flow

For good conductors (metals such as copper, silver and gold) K is in the range 0.5–1 cal/sec-cm-C°, and for insulating materials is a factor 100 to 1000 times smaller.

(a) The cement wall of a basement is 20 cm thick. For cement, $K \sim 2 \times 10^{-3}$ cal/cm-sec-C°. Assume that the inside surface of the wall is at 20°C and the outside surface at 5°C, and estimate the rate of heat loss per square meter through the wall.

(b) Suppose the basement wall is coated on the inside with a 3-cm layer of insulation (such as asbestos) with a conductivity $K \sim 2 \times 10^{-4}$ cal/cm-sec-C°. Assuming the same temperatures at the outer and inner surfaces as in (a), calculate rate of heat loss per square meter and temperature at the interface between cement and insulator.

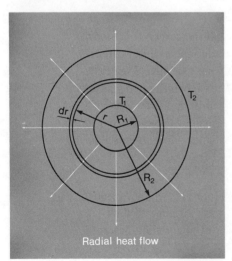

Radial heat flow

(c) There are many physical situations in which the heat flow is not one-dimensional. For cases of simply symmetry it is possible to use the definition of thermal conductivity to work out a general expression relating the rate of heat flow and geometric factors. As an example of cylindrical symmetry think of a long tube of material of conductivity K, of inner radius R_1, outer radius R_2. Suppose that the inner surface is maintained at a constant temperature T_1 (by an electric heater for example) and the outer surface at a lower constant temperature T_2. The heat flow will be radially outward. Work out the rate of heat flow per unit length of tube. Note that the equation $dQ/dt = -KA(dT/dr)$ can be applied to a thin-walled "tube" of radius r, thickness dr in the material, and note that in the steady state the rate of heat flow through all such tubes (as r goes from R_1 to R_2) is the same.

(d) The coefficient of thermal conductivity K of a plastic material is measured by molding a 16-cm-diameter sphere of the material around a copper sphere of 6-cm diameter. The spheres are concentric. The copper sphere contains a 5-watt heating coil and a thermocouple (so that its temperature can be determined). The outer surface of the system is maintained at 0°C in an ice bath, and the temperature of the copper sphere is measured to be 50°C when the system is in a steady state. Determine K.

29

THERMODYNAMICS:
SECOND LAW

The first law is a statement of conservation of energy, including the internal energy (microscopic energy) of a system, and identifying two forms of energy transfer, heat flow (microscopic transfer) and work done (macroscopic transfer). It provides no information about the direction of processes, only states that no process is possible that creates or loses energy.

Many processes are perfectly possible, from an energy point of view, and yet do not occur. The swings of a pendulum gradually die away, its macroscopic mechanical energy becoming microscopic mechanical energy; but the process never goes the other way with the pendulum swings increasing in amplitude and the microscopic mechanical energy turning into macroscopic mechanical energy. There are a variety of ways that the observed natural direction of macroscopic processes are described; we say that all macroscopic systems have "friction," and we say loosely that work tends to turn into heat. The aim of the second law of thermodynamics is to give a precise quantitative statement of the observed fact that macroscopic natural processes have a preferred direction.

HEAT ENGINES

Of course it is possible to convert heat energy into mechanical energy—that is, to convert the energy of microscopic motion and position into the energy of macroscopic motion. Any **heat engine** is a device for doing exactly this. Some understanding of the properties of heat engines is necessary in order to understand the second law, so we will say a little about these properties. Of course heat engines are of practical importance too.

In any heat engine a **working substance** is carried through a **cycle.** The working substance is the system to which we apply thermodynamic considerations. The fact that it is carried through a cycle means that at regular time intervals it is returned to its original state, and therefore, since internal energy is a state function, there is no **net** change in the internal energy. (We will assume that we always consider an integral number of cycles.) The working substance is a system on which work is done, and to which heat is transferred, but over many cycles it does not contribute to the energy of the engine.

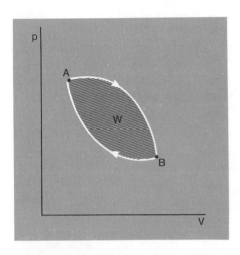

Work done in a cyclic process.

It is convenient to visualize the cyclic process for the working substance on a p–V diagram. During part of the cycle ($A \rightarrow B$) work W_{AB} is done *by* the working substance on the surroundings; this is represented by the area under the curve representing the process. During the rest of the cycle ($B \rightarrow A$) work W_{BA} is done *on* the working substance by the surroundings, represented by the area under the lower part of the curve. The **net** work done $W = W_{AB} - W_{BA}$ in the cycle is the difference, and is represented by the enclosed area describing the cycle.

When the working substance has been returned to the state represented by point A its net change in internal energy is zero: $\Delta U = 0 = Q - W$. Since the net work W has been done in the cycle, there must be a net heat $Q = W$ that is transferred *to* the working substance in the cycle. This does not mean that all the heat transferred to the working substance becomes mechanical work; there will be heat Q_{in} entering the system during part of the cycle, heat Q_{out} leaving the system during another part, and $Q = Q_{in} - Q_{out}$ for the whole cycle.

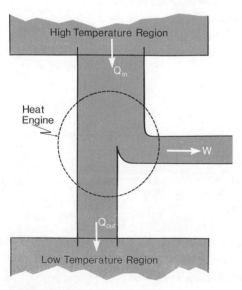

Energy flow in a heat engine.

The transfer of heat to the working substance depends on its thermal interaction with its surroundings; heat flows *in* when the surroundings are at a higher temperature than the system, heat flows *out* when the surroundings are at a lower temperature. It is useful to represent the energy transfers to the system on a diagram indicating the flow of heat from a high-temperature region to a low-temperature region. A heat engine is a device which converts some of this heat flow into work W, and therefore into macroscopic mechanical energy (e.g., moving a piston). The widths of the paths on the diagram are made proportional to the quanties of energy involved. The first law is the statement that $W = Q_{in} - Q_{out}$.

The aim of a heat engine is to convert as much heat energy into mechanical energy as possible; the heat input Q_{in} is what you pay for (fuel), the work output W is what you want, and the heat output Q_{out} is wasted. Therefore the **efficiency** η of a heat engine is defined as

$$\eta = \frac{\text{work output}}{\text{heat input}} = \frac{W}{Q_{in}} = \frac{Q_{in} - Q_{out}}{Q_{in}}$$

You are probably familiar with the operation of real heat engines. One distinction that is made is between internal and external combustion engines. The difference is in the way the heat energy is supplied to the working substance. A steam engine is an external combustion engine; water in a boiler is brought to a high temperature by heating the boiler externally, the water becomes superheated steam, and this steam is allowed to expand, moving a piston (doing work). Then the steam is condensed, returned to the boiler, and the cycle repeated. Heat is lost from the system in the condensing process.

In an internal combustion engine (such as a conventional automobile engine) the working substance is a mixture of air and gasoline vapor. Heat Q_{in} is sup-

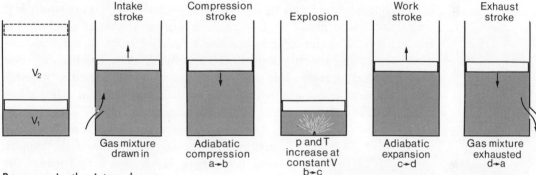

Processes in the internal combustion cycle (much simplified).

plied by an internal chemical reaction—the mixture is compressed and then ignited by an electric spark, and burns (explodes) reaching a high temperature. This hot gas mixture expands, moving a piston (doing work). In this engine the working substance is not recycled—after the expansion the gas mixture is exhausted, and it is here that heat energy Q_{out} is lost. Each cycle is started with a new mixture, but we can think of this working substance as going through a cyclic process.

The cycle is approximately represented by the cycle indicated, bounded by two adiabatics and two isometrics. With this idealized cycle, assuming that

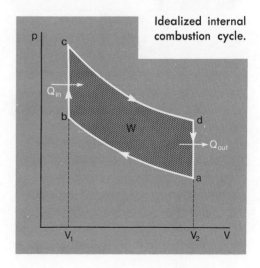

Idealized internal combustion cycle.

the processes are reversible and the gas mixture is an ideal gas, you should be able to show that the efficiency is

$$\eta = 1 - \frac{Q_{\text{out}}}{Q_{\text{in}}} = 1 - \frac{T_d - T_a}{T_c - T_b}$$

$$= 1 - \left(\frac{V_1}{V_2}\right)^{\gamma-1}$$

The appropriate ratio of maximum to minimum volume V_2/V_1 (the "compression ratio") depends on a number of factors, but is ~ 7. Using $\gamma \sim 1.4$(air), $\eta \cong 1 - (1/7)^{0.4} = 0.54$, or 54%. This is the theoretical efficiency for the idealized cycle, and actual efficiencies are of course lower.

CARNOT CYCLE

Heat engines operate by taking in heat from systems (sources) at relatively high temperatures, and giving up heat to other systems (sinks) at relatively low temperatures. For real engines there are a variety of sources and sinks, and their temperatures are not constant. It is a useful idealization to think of a heat engine exchanging energy only with systems at constant temperature. A system whose temperature is not affected if heat is exchanged with it is called a heat **reservoir.** It is a system with an infinite heat capacity.

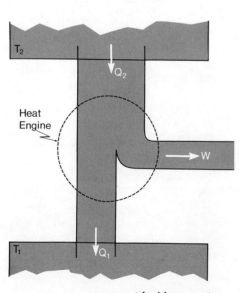

Ideal heat engine.

To operate a heat engine at all there must be at least one source and one sink, so the simplest ideal heat engine is one operating between two heat reservoirs, one at a low temperature T_1 and one at a high temperature T_2; it will take in heat $Q_{\text{in}} = Q_2$ from the high-temperature reservoir and give up heat $Q_{\text{out}} = Q_1$ to the low-temperature reservoir. We are going to apply thermodynamics to the working substance in this engine. We can do this only if we assume that the processes in the engine are **reversible.** This means that there is no choice about what the processes are. As long as the system is exchanging heat with either reservoir, it must be at the temperature of the reservoir (or infinitesimally different) so the processes are **isothermal.** If the system is not exchanging heat with the two reservoirs it is not exchanging heat with any system (there are *only* two reservoirs) so the processes are **adiabatic.**

The ideal reversible engine operating between two reservoirs is called a Carnot engine, and the corresponding cycle, bounded by two isothermals and two adiabatics, is the Carnot cycle.

It is not important to think about how such an engine could be "operated," since it is an idealization, but it may help to visualize the cycle to consider the working substance as a gas enclosed in a cylinder with a perfectly fitting frictionless piston. Piston and cylinder walls are made of perfect insulating material, but the base is a conductor of heat. This cylinder can be placed on one of three stands: reservoirs at T_2 and T_1, and an insulating stand. Initially the gas is at

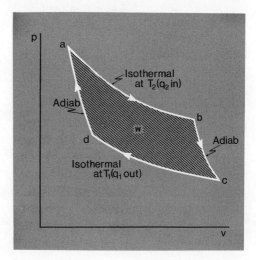

The Carnot cycle.

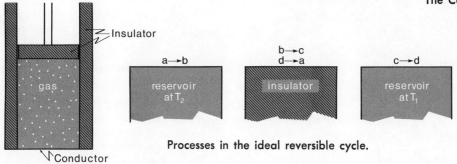

Processes in the ideal reversible cycle.

temperature T_2. The cylinder is placed on the T_2 reservoir, and the gas allowed to expand, process $a \rightarrow b$. Then the cylinder is placed on the insulating stand and allowed to expand still more, $b \rightarrow c$. Its temperature will drop (it is doing work on its surroundings—whatever is connected to the piston) and when it reaches T_1 the cylinder is moved to the reservoir at T_1. The gas is slowly compressed (work is done on it by the surroundings), giving up heat to the reservoir $c \rightarrow d$. This process must be stopped at the point d such that an adiabatic compression will bring the gas back to state a; process $d \rightarrow a$ is carried out on the insulating stand. It is fortunate that this cumbersome procedure is not of practical importance!

The importance of this ideal engine is that **its efficiency is the same no matter what working substance is used in it.** We have seen that work done and heat transferred in various processes depend on both the process *and* the properties of the matter involved (heat capacity and equation of state), and therefore we can only work out the efficiency of a heat engine by choosing a particular material as working substance.

The statement that the efficiency of the Carnot engine does not depend on the working substance can be justified on the basis of the second law of thermodynamics—as we will see. Knowing that it is so means that it is useful to calculate the efficiency using the simplest possible working substance—the ideal gas. Later we will be able to use this result.

We previously derived expressions for the work done in isothermal and adiabatic processes for an ideal gas. Referred to molar quantities

$$w_{ab} = RT_2 \ln (v_b/v_a) \qquad w_{bc} = -c_v (T_1 - T_2)$$
$$w_{cd} = RT_1 \ln (v_d/v_c) \qquad w_{da} = -c_v (T_2 - T_1)$$

Net work is
$$w = w_{ab} + w_{bc} + w_{cd} + w_{da} = RT_2 \ln \frac{v_b}{v_a} + RT_1 \ln \frac{v_d}{v_c}$$

Since for an adiabatic process of an ideal gas $Tv^{\gamma-1} = $ constant

$$\begin{aligned} T_1 v_d^{\gamma-1} &= T_2 v_a^{\gamma-1} \\ T_1 v_c^{\gamma-1} &= T_2 v_b^{\gamma-1} \end{aligned} \quad \text{or} \quad \frac{v_d}{v_c} = \frac{v_a}{v_b}$$

and
$$w = R(T_2 - T_1) \ln \frac{v_b}{v_a}$$

Along the isothermal $a \rightarrow b$, heat q_2 enters the system and work w_{ab} is done by the system. These are *not* equal in general, but *are* equal if the working substance is an ideal gas; for an ideal gas the internal energy is a function of temperature only, and therefore is constant along an isothermal.

$$q_2 = w_{ab} = RT_2 \ln (v_b/v_a)$$

The efficiency of the Carnot engine with an ideal gas as working substance is

$$\eta = \frac{q_2 - q_1}{q_2} = \frac{w}{q_2} = \frac{T_2 - T_1}{T_2}$$

Note that $q_2/q_1 = T_2/T_1$. We will use this fact after introducing the second law.

REFRIGERATORS AND HEAT PUMPS

A heat engine run backwards converts mechanical energy into heat energy. This may not seem a useful enterprise (it is the natural direction for processes to go) until you realize that it is also causing heat to flow "uphill," that is from a low-temperature region to a high-temperature region.

A device doing this is called a **refrigerator** if you are interested in the heat removed from the low temperature region, or a **heat pump** if you are interested in the heat delivered to the high temperature region.

Just as for a heat engine, we define the ratio (what you get out that you want)/(what you put in that you have to pay for), but this ratio is not called efficiency here, because it may be a number greater than unity. It is called a **coefficient of performance** *E*. For both refrigerators and heat pumps, what you have to pay for is the work input W. For a refrigerator, $E = Q_1/W$; for a heat pump, $E = Q_2/W$.

Corresponding to the ideal Carnot engine (the reversible engine operating between two reservoirs) there are ideal refrigerators and heat pumps, and for such systems using an ideal gas as working substance the result $Q_2/Q_1 = T_2/T_1$ applies.

For an ideal refrigerator

$$E = \frac{Q_1}{W} = \frac{Q_1}{Q_2 - Q_1} = \frac{T_1}{T_2 - T_1}$$

and for an ideal heat pump

$$E = \frac{Q_2}{W} = \frac{Q_2}{Q_2 - Q_1} = \frac{T_2}{T_2 - T_1}$$

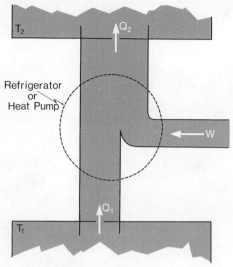

A refrigerator or a heat pump is a heat engine reversed.

ENTROPY AND THE SECOND LAW

The second law is an unusual (but not unique) form of physical law, because it is a statement about inequality rather than equality; we are going to define a quantity called entropy S, and a quantitative statement of the second law is that the net entropy change is positive in any macroscopic process: $\Delta S > 0$. We could equally well say that the net entropy change is not negative in any macroscopic process. The second law deals with the question of direction of natural processes, and it is sometimes more convenient in discussing direction to state what does *not* happen rather than what happens.

There are many possible statements related to the second law, in terms of things that do not happen. For example, a pendulum does not start swinging by abstracting heat energy from its surroundings; and in a system in thermal equilibrium spontaneous temperature differences do not arise. The task of thermodynamics is to show that all such statements are equivalent—and therefore to find some unifying feature.

Two famous statements are symbolized by the diagrams on the next page; loosely, "heat cannot flow uphill" and "heat energy cannot be converted completely into mechanical energy." More precisely, the Clausius statement is: "It is impossible to have a cyclic process whose sole result is the transfer of heat from a reservoir to another reservoir at a higher temperature." The Kelvin statement is: "It is impossible to have a cyclic process whose sole result is the removal of heat from a reservoir and the performance of an equal amount of work."

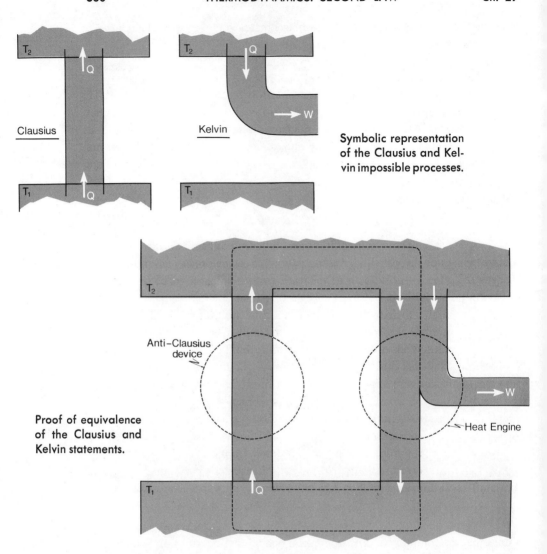

Symbolic representation of the Clausius and Kelvin impossible processes.

Proof of equivalence of the Clausius and Kelvin statements.

The equivalence of these statements is demonstrated by assuming that one is not true, and showing that then the other would not be true either. For example, suppose the Clausius statement is not true—some device does produce heat flow from T_1 to T_2. By coupling this device with any heat engine, energy changes in the T_1 reservoir could be eliminated, and the sole overall result would be a heat flow out of the T_2 reservoir, and the performance of an equal amount of work, thus violating the Kelvin statement.

Similar arguments can be concocted to relate any two statements about processes that do not happen, even though energetically possible. We can now prove a statement called **Carnot's theorem**: No heat engine operating between two

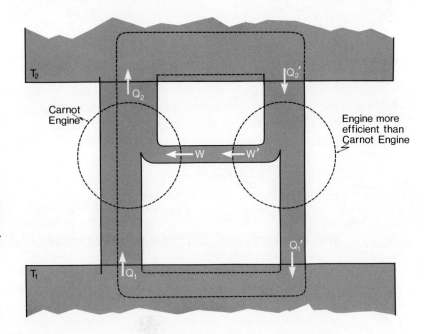

Proof of Carnot's theorem.

reservoirs can be more efficient than a Carnot (reversible) engine operating between the same reservoirs. Again the proof is made by assuming that the statement is not true, and showing that this violates one of the other statements.
Suppose that there is a real engine more efficient—then it will do the same
amount of work W for a smaller heat input Q_2' than the heat input Q_2 of the
reversible engine. By definition of the concept of reversibility, the Carnot engine
can be run backward, as a heat pump. This heat pump is coupled with the "more
efficient" real engine, with the work output of the engine providing the work
input for the heat pump. You can see from the diagram that the sole overall
result is a heat flow from the T_1 to the T_2 reservoir, contradicting the Clausius
statement.

As an introduction to the concept of entropy, we will look at the magnitudes
of certain quantities here. Neither the real (irreversible) engine nor the ideal
(reversible) engine undergoes any permanent change. The reservoir at T_2 absorbs a quantity of heat ($Q_2 - Q_2'$), and the reservoir at T_1 loses an equal quantity of heat ($Q_1 - Q_1'$).

If a quantity of heat Q flows into a system that is at a temperature T, the
entropy of the system is said to change by an amount $\Delta S = Q/T$. (We will
discuss this definition shortly.) The change in entropy of the T_2 reservoir is

$$\Delta S_2 = (Q_2 - Q_2')/T_2$$

and the change in entropy of the T_1 reservoir (which **loses** heat) is

$$\Delta S_1 = -(Q_1 - Q_1')/T_1$$

Since $Q_2 > Q_2'$, and $Q_1 > Q_1'$, ΔS_2 is positive (an entropy increase) and ΔS_1 is negative (an entropy decrease). Is the *net* entropy change ($\Delta S_1 + \Delta S_2$) positive or negative?

Since $Q_2 - Q_2' = Q_1 - Q_1'$, and $T_2 > T_1$, $|\Delta S_2| < |\Delta S_1|$; the increase in entropy of the T_2 reservoir is less than the decrease in entropy of the T_1 reservoir, and the overall result is an **entropy decrease.** Remember that this is a process that could not happen (according to the Clausius statement). If the flow of heat was the other way, from T_2 to T_1, there would be a net increase in entropy.

We return to say more about entropy shortly, but first digress to redefine temperature.

THE ABSOLUTE THERMODYNAMIC TEMPERATURE SCALE

A corollary of Carnot's theorem is this: All reversible engines operating between the same two reservoirs have the same efficiency. The proof is exactly the same as that given above for Carnot's theorem; assume the statement is not true, reverse the engine of lower efficiency and drive it with the one of higher efficiency, and the overall result violates the Clausius statement.

Thus the efficiency of a Carnot engine does not depend on the working substance—as we stated when we worked it out using an ideal gas. The result was

$$\eta = \frac{Q_2 - Q_1}{Q_2} = \frac{T_2 - T_1}{T_2}$$

and this is the efficiency of *every* ideal engine.

Now you can see how to define a temperature scale that does not depend on the properties of matter at all. Think of two reservoirs, and a reversible engine operating between them, taking in heat Q_2 from one and giving up heat Q_1 to the other. The ratio of the temperatures of the reservoirs can be **defined** as

$$\frac{T_2}{T_1} = \frac{Q_2}{Q_1}$$

The temperature ratio can be determined by measuring the quantities of energy Q_2 and Q_1. In addition to the temperature ratio, it would also be necessary to determine the size of the temperature unit—for example by setting $T_s - T_i = 100$ degrees, where T_s and T_i are the temperatures of the ice point and the steam point. The ratio T_s/T_i would be determined with the ideal heat engine thermometer. The temperature scale established by these procedures is called the Absolute Thermodynamic Temperature Scale.

The ideal heat engine used as a thermometer does not have to use an ideal gas as a working substance; the efficiency $\eta = 1 - (Q_2/Q_1)$ is the same for all ideal heat engines working between two reservoirs, so the ratio Q_2/Q_1 gives a unique determination of the temperature ratio.

The calculation made before for efficiency required the use of the ideal gas equation of state $pv = RT$. In this equation T is the temperature on the ideal gas absolute scale. However, the fact that $Q_2/Q_1 = T_2/T_1$ by definition for the absolute thermodynamic scale, and $Q_2/Q_1 = T_2/T_1$ by calculation using the ideal gas absolute scale, means that the two scales are identical. The important thing we have done is not to establish how to measure temperatures better (we would be hard put to it to find an ideal engine) but rather to establish that a temperature scale can be established without having to use the properties of a particular kind of matter (real gases at low pressures).

Note that temperature on the absolute thermodynamic scale is still given an operational definition—in terms of the properties of ideal heat engines, rather than the properties of matter. It is only in statistical mechanics that temperature can be given a non-operational definition.

THE CLAUSIUS INEQUALITY

Our discussion of the second law started with the Clausius and Kelvin statements because they are reasonable and acceptable in terms of your experience. We could have started with the second law in its more generally useful form, $\Delta S > 0$ for natural processes, but this would have given little insight into the concept of entropy.

We are going to develop the concept of entropy now, and demonstrate (1) that entropy is a state function, and (2) that entropy increases in natural processes. The proof is based on the Clausius inequality. (Note that this is *not* the same as the Clausius statement.)

Think of a working substance carried through a cyclic process, doing work and exchanging heat energy with a series of reservoirs. The Clausius inequality is

$$\sum \frac{Q_i}{T_i} \leq 0$$

where Q_i is the heat flowing into the system from a reservoir at temperature T_i. For real processes the number of heat reservoirs may become very large, and the amount of heat energy exchanged with each small. The inequality is then $\int dQ/T \leq 0$.

The Clausius inequality is based on the Kelvin statement of the second law. We show this for three reservoirs but the argument can be extended to any number. The working substance is carried through a cycle, so that the net work output is equal to the net heat input. The diagram indicates heat flow into the system from reservoirs at T_2 and T_3, and out to a reservoir at T_1, but we will

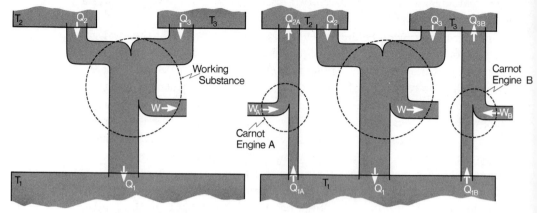

Diagram used to prove the Clausius inequality.

write the equations in a form where this does not matter. We use the same sign convention that we did in writing the first law; heat entering a system is positive, then heat entering a reservoir (leaving a system) is negative.

In order to apply the Kelvin statement, we want to eliminate the effect of all the reservoirs except one (we choose T_1) so we visualize Carnot engines operating between this one and each of the others. In our case there are two, both operated as refrigerators; engine A delivers heat Q_{2A} to reservoir T_2, and is operated so that $Q_{2A} + Q_2 = 0$, and engine B is operated so that $Q_{3B} + Q_3 = 0$.

For the Carnot engines, taking the sign convention into account,

$$-\frac{Q_{2A}}{Q_{1A}} = \frac{T_2}{T_1} \quad \text{and} \quad -\frac{Q_{3B}}{Q_{1B}} = \frac{T_3}{T_1}$$

and therefore

$$Q_{1A} = -\frac{T_1}{T_2} Q_{2A} = \frac{T_1}{T_2} Q_2$$

$$Q_{1B} = -\frac{T_1}{T_3} Q_{3B} = \frac{T_1}{T_3} Q_3$$

For the particular situation shown, Q_2, Q_3, Q_{1A}, Q_{1B} are positive, and Q_1, Q_{2A}, Q_{3B} are negative, but the equations apply for any directions of flow.

We have arranged the overall system so that there is a net transfer of heat only to reservoir T_1; the net amount transferred is $Q_1 + Q_{1A} + Q_{1B}$. According to the Kelvin statement of the second law, this **cannot be positive** because a positive amount would mean that the overall result was a net flow of heat out of the single reservoir, and the performance of an equal amount of work. Therefore

$$Q_1 + Q_{1A} + Q_{1B} \leq 0$$

or
$$Q_1 + \frac{T_1}{T_2} Q_2 + \frac{T_1}{T_3} Q_3 \leq 0$$

$$\frac{Q_1}{T_1} + \frac{Q_2}{T_2} + \frac{Q_3}{T_3} \leq 0$$

For a series of reservoirs $\sum Q_i/T_i \leq 0$, and for an infinite series of reservoirs, with an infinitesimal quantity of heat dQ exchanged with each

$$\int \frac{dQ}{T} \leq 0$$

Note particularly that the temperatures involved in this sum are the temperatures of the **reservoirs,** not the temperatures of the working substance in the system. We have *not* assumed that the cyclic process through which the system goes is reversible, so we *cannot* assume that when the system is exchanging heat with a reservoir it is at the same temperature as the reservoir. The Clausius inequality applies to real macroscopic processes, not just to ideal reversible processes.

ENTROPY A STATE FUNCTION

We now apply the Clausius inequality, which applies to any system carried through a cyclic process, to a system carried through a **reversible** cyclic process. Then at every instant the temperature of the system is the same as the temperature of the reservoir with which it is exchanging heat energy. The Clausius inequality becomes

$$\oint \frac{dQ}{T} \leq 0$$

where the temperatures are those **of the system** at every instant. Now we can indicate the cyclic process by the $\oint$ sign; before, the summation applied to the reservoirs, which were not carried through a cyclic process.

Now suppose that the system is carried through the same cycle, but **in the opposite direction.** Since it is reversible this is possible, and at every instant the heat dQ entering the system on the "forward" cycle will be replaced by heat $-dQ$ leaving the system on the "backward" cycle. The Clausius inequality for the backward cycle is

$$\oint \frac{(-dQ)}{T} \leq 0$$

Since $\oint \frac{dQ}{T} \leq 0$, and $- \oint \frac{dQ}{T} \leq 0$, the equality must apply.

$$\oint \frac{dQ}{T} = 0 \qquad \textbf{:for a reversible cycle}$$

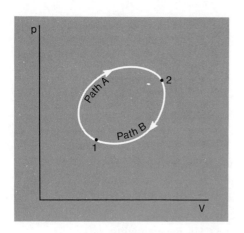

An arbitrary reversible cycle.

Now think of a working substance carried through any arbitrary reversible cycle (as represented by a closed curve on a p–V, or any other state diagram) and any two states of the system, represented by the points 1 and 2 on the diagram.

The sum (integral) for the whole path can be considered as the sum of two terms, one for path A (from 1 to 2), the other for path B (from 2 to 1).

$$\oint \frac{dQ}{T} = \int_{1}^{2}{}_{A} \frac{dQ}{T} + \int_{2}^{1}{}_{B} \frac{dQ}{T} = 0$$

Since the cycle is reversible

$$\int_{2}^{1}{}_{B} \frac{dQ}{T} = - \int_{1}^{2}{}_{B} \frac{dQ}{T}$$

so that

$$\int_{1}^{2}{}_{A} \frac{dQ}{T} = \int_{1}^{2}{}_{B} \frac{dQ}{T}$$

The original cycle was an arbitrary one, and therefore this result shows that the integral is **the same for any reversible process that takes the system from state 1 to state 2.** This means that there is a change in some state function of the system; if we set $dQ/T = dS$, then

$$\int_{1}^{2} \frac{dQ}{T} = \int_{1}^{2} dS = S_2 - S_1$$

The change in the quantity S in going from state 1 to state 2 does not depend on the path—it is a function only of the end points.

The state function S is called **entropy**, and the defining equation

$$\frac{dQ}{T} = dS$$

is the mathematical statement of the second law of thermodynamics. The first law introduces a state function U. It has an exact differential dU, the difference between the inexact differentials dQ and dW; $dU = dQ - dW$. The second law introduces a state function S. It has an exact differential dS, obtained by dividing the inexact differential dQ by the state variable T.

Note that the equation $dQ/T = dS$ is valid for **reversible processes only.** However, it is possible to calculate the entropy changes for real processes, because entropy is a state function. All that is necessary is to visualize a reversible process with the same end states as the real process, and calculate the entropy change for the imagined process. The entropy change for the real process is the same. Note also that only **changes** in entropy can be calculated. As far as the second law is concerned, there is no meaning to the concept of "absolute" entropy. (There is a third law of thermodynamics which does give meaning to entropy in absolute terms, but we will not go into this.) We will return to the calculation of entropy changes shortly.

THE PRINCIPLE OF THE INCREASE IN ENTROPY

Entropy changes are defined only for reversible processes, and **for any reversible process the net entropy change is zero.** To exchange heat in a reversible process, a system at temperature T must be in thermal contact with a reservoir at temperature T. If heat dQ is transferred to the system from the reservoir, there is an entropy change dS = dQ/T **of the system,** and an entropy change $dS =$ $- dQ/T$ **of the reservoir,** since it loses heat dQ (i.e., the amount of heat entering the reservoir is $-dQ$).

Entropy changes of system and reservoir are equal in magnitude, opposite in sign.

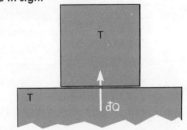

As far as macroscopic systems are concerned, there is no such thing as a reversible process—all real processes are irreversible. Then the Clausius inequality is the statement that $\int dQ/T < 0$; the equality sign only applies to reversible processes.

Think about a real process A in which an **isolated** system goes from a state 1 to a state 2. This process *cannot* be represented on a state diagram (such as a $p\text{-}V$ diagram) because during the irreversible process the system is not in equilibrium, and cannot be described by a set of state variables. Only the equilibrium end states 1 and 2 can be shown. Path A for the process is dotted to indicate that it should not really be shown on the diagram at all.

The fact that the process is irreversible does not mean, of course, that the system cannot be returned to its original state; an irreversible process is one that cannot be reversed from instant to instant, but the overall result can be reversed. We visualize a reversible process B that returns the system to its original state. The Clausius inequality, applied to the cycle as a whole, can be broken into two parts

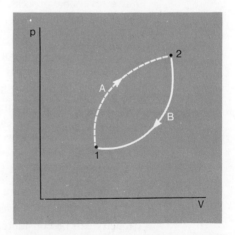

An irreversible process A for an isolated system, followed by a reversible process B to return the system to its initial state.

$$\int_{\substack{1 \\ A}}^{2} \frac{dQ}{T} + \int_{\substack{2 \\ B}}^{1} \frac{dQ}{T} < 0$$

The system was isolated during the real process A, and therefore no heat could be transferred to it in this part of the cycle; $dQ = 0$ at every point and the first integral is zero. The second integral is by definition $S_1 - S_2$. (The first integral is *not* $S_2 - S_1$, since $dS = dQ/T$ only for reversible processes.)

Therefore $\qquad\qquad S_1 - S_2 < 0 \qquad$ or $\qquad S_2 > S_1$

In the initial real process, the *only* system involved was the isolated system; its entropy increased from S_1 to S_2, and therefore the entropy of the universe as a whole increased from S_1 to S_2. When the system is returned to its original state, its entropy is changed back to S_1 from S_2, an entropy decrease. Its entropy increase has been wiped out, but the entropy increase of the universe has not, it has been passed on to some other system. The reversible process B could only be performed for the system by introducing other systems (e.g., a series of heat reservoirs, if temperature change is involved); the system could not be isolated for process B. In the reversible process there is *no* net change in entropy; the change in entropy $(S_1 - S_2)$ of the system is balanced by a change $-(S_1 - S_2)$ of other systems. Thus the entropy increase $(S_2 - S_1)$ is passed on.

In every natural process there is an entropy increase, and once this entropy appears, it can never be eliminated. This is another way of stating the second law of thermodynamics.

CALCULATION OF ENTROPY CHANGES

The entropy change is $dS = dQ/T$ when heat dQ enters a system at temperature T in a reversible process. It is expressed in a differential form because every real system has a finite heat capacity C, and therefore when heat enters the system its temperature changes; only by allowing an infinitesimal quantity dQ of heat to enter can we speak of *the* temperature T. (A reservoir is an idealized system with an infinite heat capacity.)

From the definition of heat capacity, $dQ = C\,dT$, so for reversible temperature changes $dS = C\,dT/T$, and if the heat capacity is **independent of temperature** the entropy change as the system goes from temperature T_i to temperature T_f is

$$\Delta S = S_f - S_i = C \ln (T_f/T_i)$$

As an example, think of bringing together a mass m of liquid of specific heat capacity c at temperature T_1 and an equal mass m of the same liquid at temperature T_2. For liquids over a reasonable range of temperature the specific heat capacity can be considered constant. By "bringing together" we mean that the two quantities of liquid are brought into thermal contact; this can be done by physically mixing them, or by simply placing them close together. We assume that the total system is isolated, that is, that the process takes place in a rigid adiabatic enclosure—"rigid" so that no work can be done on the surroundings, "adiabatic" so that no heat can be exchanged with the surroundings.

The two masses will exchange heat energy, and ultimately the system will be a mass $2m$ at a final temperature T_f. Assuming that $T_2 > T_1$, the final temperature is determined by the fact that the heat $+dQ$ gained by one system is equal to the heat $-dQ$ lost by the other:

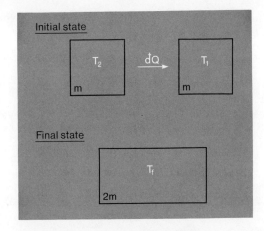

Initial state

Final state

$$-\int_{T_2}^{T_f} mc \, dT = +\int_{T_1}^{T_f} mc \, dT$$

or since the specific heat capacity c is assumed constant

$$-mc(T_f - T_2) = mc(T_f - T_1)$$

$$T_f = \frac{T_1 + T_2}{2}$$

Two equal masses, initially at different temperatures, in thermal contact.

If 100 gm of water at 100°C and 100 gm of water of 0°C are mixed in a calorimeter of negligible heat capacity, the result is 200 gm of water at 50°C. Here $m = 100$ gm, $T_2 = 373°$K, $T_1 = 273°$K, $c = 1$ cal/gm-K°. In calculating the final temperature it does not matter whether temperatures are expressed in Kelvin degrees or Celsius degrees, but it does matter as far as the calculation of entropy change is concerned. In the equation $dS = dQ/T$, T is the **absolute temperature.**

The entropy change of the mass m going from temperature T_1 to T_f is

$$\Delta S_1 = \int \frac{dQ}{T} = \int_{T_1}^{T_f} \frac{mc \, dT}{T} = mc \ln \frac{T_f}{T_1}$$

and the entropy change of the mass m going from T_2 to T_f is

$$\Delta S_2 = \int \frac{dQ}{T} = \int_{T_2}^{T_f} \frac{mc \, dT}{T} = mc \ln \frac{T_f}{T_2}$$

Since $T_1 < T_f < T_2$, ΔS_1 is positive and ΔS_2 is negative. The net entropy change for the overall process is

$$\Delta S = \Delta S_1 + \Delta S_2 = mc \ln \frac{T_f}{T_1} + mc \ln \frac{T_f}{T_2}$$

$$= mc \ln \frac{T_f^2}{T_1 T_2}$$

In terms of the initial temperature difference $\Delta T = T_2 - T_1$

$$\Delta S = mc \ln \frac{T_f^2}{[T_f - (\Delta T/2)][T_f + (\Delta T/2)]} = mc \ln \frac{T_f^2}{T_f^2 - (\Delta T/2)^2}$$

showing that the net entropy change for the process is **positive.**

If the initial temperature difference is small, the entropy change can be written in a convenient approximate form.

$$\Delta S = mc \ln \frac{1}{1 - (\Delta T/2T_f)^2} = -mc \ln \left[1 - \left(\frac{\Delta T}{2T_f} \right)^2 \right]$$

$$\cong -mc \left[- \left(\frac{\Delta T}{2T_f} \right)^2 \right] \qquad : \ln (1 + x) \cong x, \text{ if } x \ll 1$$

$$= mc \left(\frac{T_2 - T_1}{T_2 + T_1} \right)^2$$

For the numerical example given, $(\Delta T/2T_f)^2 = (50/323)^2 = (0.155)^2 = 0.024$, and the approximation is a good one.

$$\Delta S = 100 \times 1 \times 0.024 \text{ cal/K}° = 2.4 \text{ cal/K}°$$

We have calculated the entropy change for a real process, the mixing of two quantities of water at different temperatures. This is an irreversible process, meaning that we do not find the 200 gm of water naturally dividing itself up into two 100-gm sections, one at 0°C and one at 100°C.

How were we able to calculate the entropy change for this irreversible process? Remember we could only do this by visualizing a reversible process with the same end states, because only then can we use $dS = dQ/T$. In calculating entropy change we usually go ahead and use this without really thinking about the reversible process, but this can lead to difficulties, as we will see.

The reversible process in this case could be performed using an infinite series of heat reservoirs at temperatures T_1, $T_1 + dT$, $T_1 + 2\,dT$, $\cdots$, $T_f - dT$, T_f to heat one system from T_1 to T_f, and another infinite series at T_2, $T_2 - dT$, $T_2 - 2\,dT$, $\cdots$, $T_f + dT$, T_f to cool the other system from T_2 to T_f. What we calculated was the entropy change of the system when the processes were performed in this way. The entropy change in the real process is the same, because entropy is a state function.

After the real process for the isolated system, the water could be returned to its original state by using the two series of reservoirs. Then the entropy change of the water would be eliminated, but it would be passed on to the reservoirs.

One reason for an interest in entropy change is that it unifies the expression of direction in natural processes. The mixing of two 100-gm pots of water at 0°C and 100°C produces an entropy change of 2.4 cal/K°. This process really happens. A 200-gm pot of water at 50°C separating spontaneously into two parts at 0°C and 100°C would involve an entropy change of -2.4 cal/K°, and this process does not happen. Another reason for an interest in entropy change is that it describes quantitatively the loss of something. What is lost is not energy, but the availability of energy to do work. The two lots of water originally could have been used as source and sink for a heat engine, producing some work. After mixing we have a system at a single temperature, and you cannot use a heat engine with a single heat reservoir. It can be shown that whenever the entropy of the universe increases by an amount ΔS, there is a corresponding amount of work $T_0 \Delta S$ that cannot be produced (T_0 is some lowest possible working temperature).

Another way of describing entropy change is to say that it represents the degradation of energy from "higher" (more useful) macroscopic forms to "lower" (less useful) microscopic forms. Still another way is to say that an increase in entropy represents an increase in disorder; we will say more about this shortly.

ADIABATIC FREE EXPANSION OF AN IDEAL GAS

We will calculate the entropy change for another irreversible process, the adiabatic free expansion of an ideal gas. This process is not a real process, because it deals with an ideal substance and an idealized situation, but the expansion of a real gas into an evacuated enclosure is reasonably close.

A **free** expansion of a gas means the gas does no external work as it expands. An **adiabatic** free expansion means that the gas does not exchange heat with its surroundings either, so for such a process both W and Q are zero.

Think of a gas in equilibrium in an insulated rigid enclosure occupying a volume V_1. The volume V_1 is part of a larger enclosure, volume V_2. The rest of the enclosure is empty. The wall confining the gas to the smaller volume vanishes (or ruptures, or something). After some time the gas will be in equilibrium occupying the larger volume V_2. Thermodynamics tells us nothing about what happens during the actual turbulent expansion, because the gas is not in equilibrium, but it does describe the overall process.

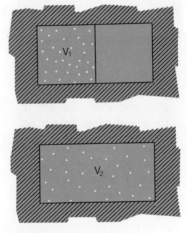

Adiabatic free expansion of a gas.

The assumption that the enclosure is evacuated and is rigid means that the gas can do no work on any other sytem as it expands: $W = 0$. The assumption that the walls of the enclosure are made of a perfect insulating material means that no heat is transferred to the gas: $Q = 0$. Therefore the first law says that $\Delta U = Q - W = 0$; there is no change in the internal energy in the overall process.

For an **ideal gas,** constant internal energy means that the temperature of the gas is unchanged as well, $\Delta T = 0$. For an ideal gas the internal energy does not depend on the volume; it is a function of temperature only, $U = U(T)$, so that if U is unchanged so is T. This is not so for real gases; in the expansion the molecules become farther apart, and this means that the potential energy of interaction (negligible for an ideal gas) is greater. The total internal energy is constant, so an increase in potential energy means a decrease in kinetic energy, and this means that the temperature decreases in an adiabatic free expansion of a real gas. This temperature change can be measured, although it is rather difficult because of the effect of the container. There is no such thing as a perfect insulator, and the heat capacity of the container is usually large compared to that of the gas, so the temperature change of the gas is masked by the fact that the container changes in temperature as well.

What about the entropy change for an ideal gas? $W = 0$, $Q = 0$, $\Delta U = 0$, $\Delta T = 0$, $\Delta S = ?$ Here it is important to recognize that $Q = 0$ does *not* mean $\Delta S = 0$; $dS = dQ/T$ only for reversible processes. To determine the change in entropy here, we must visualize a reversible process with the same end states. For the overall process, $\Delta T = 0$, so we must visualize a reversible isothermal process for the ideal gas. The gas can be changed isothermally and reversibly from V_1 to V_2 by enclosing it in a cylinder closed with a perfect piston. The gas is allowed to expand slowly from volume V_1 to volume V_2; as the gas does work dW on whatever system is connected to the piston, an equal amount of heat dQ flows into the gas from the walls of the cylinder, so that $dU = dQ - dW = 0$, and $dQ = dW = p\,dV$. The infinitesimal entropy change is

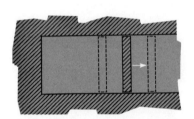

A reversible process with the same end states as the adiabatic free expansion of an ideal gas.

$$dS = \frac{dQ}{T} = \frac{p\,dV}{T} = nR\frac{dV}{V} \qquad \text{:using equation of state } pV = nRT$$

and over the whole reversible process is

$$\Delta S = S_2 - S_1 = nR \int_{V_1}^{V_2} \frac{dV}{V} = nR \ln \frac{V_2}{V_1}$$

The entropy change in the adiabatic free expansion from V_1 to V_2 is the same. This change is positive since $V_2 > V_1$.

ENTROPY AND PROBABILITY

It will be of interest to rewrite the result just obtained in a rather peculiar way, replacing the gas constant R by Boltzmann's constant k and Avogadro's number N_0 ($R = N_0 k$).

$$S_2 - S_1 = nN_0 k \ln \frac{V_2}{V_1} = k \ln \left(\frac{V_2}{V_1}\right)^{nN_0}$$

Writing the change $S_1 - S_2$ instead of $S_2 - S_1$

$$S_1 - S_2 = k \ln \left(\frac{V_1}{V_2}\right)^{nN_0}$$

This relation between the entropies in the two states can be given an interpretation in terms of simple probability considerations. Suppose that in the overall volume V_2 there is only one gas molecule. It seems reasonable to assume that it may be found anywhere in the whole volume with equal probability, so the probability of it being in the smaller volume V_1 rather than outside this volume is V_1/V_2. If there are two gas molecules in V_2, and if the presence of one does not influence the presence of the other (the ideal gas assumption) then the probability of **both** of them being simultaneously in V_1 rather than outside it is $(V_1/V_2)^2$. Similarly if there are three independent molecules, the probability of all three being found in V_1 at the same time is $(V_1/V_2)^3$, and so on.

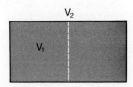

Volume V_1 is part of the larger volume V_2.

There are n moles of gas present, and a total of nN_0 molecules. Therefore $(V_1/V_2)^{nN_0}$ can be interpreted as the **probability** W that all of the molecules will simultaneously be found in the volume V_1, rather than in the larger volume V_2 available to them. (Do not be confused by the use of the symbol W both for probability and for work done.) The number nN_0 is very large for any observable quantity of gas, and therefore the number $(V_1/V_2)^{nN_0}$ is very small. The probability of finding the system of molecules in a volume less than the total volume available to them is extremely small. As far as thermodynamics is concerned, the probability is **zero**, because a process that goes from a state of higher to lower entropy cannot occur. Thinking of the system as a large number of independent particles (a microscopic picture) such a possibility is simply highly improbable, not totally impossible.

This is an example of the relationship that exists between the macroscopic theory of heat, thermodynamics, and the microscopic theory of heat, statistical mechanics.

Think of the state of volume V_2 as a reference state, and assign it an arbitrary entropy $S_2 = 0$. Then *the* entropy S in any other state of volume V_1 is given by

$$S = k \ln \left(\frac{V_1}{V_2}\right)^{nN_0} = k \ln W$$

The relation $S = k \ln W$, developed for this particular situation, is actually the general connection between thermodynamics and statistical mechanics. The task of statistical mechanics is to **calculate** probabilities W on the basis of some microscopic picture of matter. The states of matter that will be observed will be those of high probability; for systems with large numbers of particles, the most probable state is the only state actually observed.

The principle of the increase in entropy is a positive statement of thermodynamics: the entropy of an isolated system cannot decrease. The equivalent statistical mechanics statement—a system will tend to proceed from less probable to more probable states—is not so positive. There is always the possibility of going backward; it is just unlikely. Thermodynamics does not include such a possibility.

ENTROPY AND DISORDER

We used the particular example of adiabatic free expansion of an ideal gas to introduce the general relation between entropy and probability $S = k \ln W$.

Another general statement about entropy that is often made is "entropy is a measure of the disorder." The principle of the increase of entropy is then a statement that **disorder** increases in natural processes. From the statistical mechanics point of view this means that disorder is more probable than order. A shuffled deck of cards is more likely to be found in a disordered state than an ordered state.

The term **order** has a nice ring to it, but it is difficult to define in any general way, because it depends on a particular situation; this is why it is useful to be able to say that entropy is a measure of it—whatever it is. One characteristic of order is that an ordered state is more readily specified than a disordered state. A deck of cards is completely ordered if the cards are all in sequence, Spades AKQ..., Hearts AKQ..., etc., but what if the deck is shuffled once? It is then no longer completely ordered, but it is not in a random order either—some sequences will remain. If you turn up the eight of hearts, the probability that the next card is the seven of hearts is higher than if the cards were thoroughly shuffled.

What does **order** mean for gas molecules in an enclosure? The smaller the volume in which the molecules are found, the more completely the overall situation is specified—the more ordered the situation. The most disordered state is the one where the molecules occupy the whole volume, and this is the state observed.

More ordered
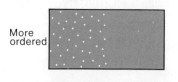

Less ordered

Why is the first state
more ordered?

THE FUNDAMENTAL EQUATION OF THERMODYNAMICS

The mathematical statement of the first law of thermodynamics is $dU = dQ - dW$, and that of the second law is $dS = dQ/T$ for reversible processes. These together give

$$T\,dS = dU + dW$$

This is often called the fundamental equation of thermodynamics. Just as all of classical mechanics is based on the fundamental equation $\mathbf{F} = m\mathbf{a}$, so all of thermodynamics is based on this equation. Like Newton's law, it is a concise expression summarizing a great deal of physical experience, and therefore some discussion is necessary in order to understand what it represents. That is what we have been doing so far in thermodynamics, setting up this basic relationship —and that is about all we are going to try to do. Unlike classical mechanics, where we applied the basic law to a wide variety of situations, we are not going to go much beyond this point in thermodynamics. The reason for introducing the subject was primarily to gain some familiarity with the macroscopic concepts of internal energy and entropy, in order to give an introduction to statistical mechanics; and we have done this.

However, we will go a little further in thermodynamics, in order to give some indication of its use. We continue to confine ourselves to systems where the only kind of work done is "$p\,dV$" work, and the fundamental equation becomes

$$T\,dS = dU + p\,dV$$

In this expression all quantities are state variables or state functions; so far we have introduced p, V, T, U and S, any two of which may be considered independent variables.

There are other state variables that have application in different physical situations (just as quantities like $p = mv$, and $K = \frac{1}{2}mv^2$, are useful in classical mechanics). Examples are enthalpy, $H = U + pV$; the Helmholtz function (or Helmholtz free energy), $F = U - TS$; and the Gibbs function (or Gibbs free energy), $G = F + pV$. Combining these with the fundamental equation gives a number of thermodynamic relations. We will look at one or two.

For an infinitesimal change

$$dF = dU - T\,dS - S\,dT$$

$$= -p\,dV - S\,dT \qquad \text{:using } T\,dS = dU + p\,dV$$

If V and T are considered independent variables, $F = F(V,T)$ and

$$dF = \left(\frac{\partial F}{\partial V}\right)_T dV + \left(\frac{\partial F}{\partial T}\right)_V dT$$

and comparing these relations

$$p = -\left(\frac{\partial F}{\partial V}\right)_T \qquad S = -\left(\frac{\partial F}{\partial T}\right)_V$$

Differentiating with respect to the variable indicated

$$\left(\frac{\partial p}{\partial T}\right)_V = -\left[\frac{\partial}{\partial T}\left(\frac{\partial F}{\partial V}\right)_T\right]_V \qquad \left(\frac{\partial S}{\partial V}\right)_T = -\left[\frac{\partial}{\partial V}\left(\frac{\partial F}{\partial T}\right)_V\right]_T$$

The order in which the function F is differentiated does not matter, so the right sides of these two equations are equal. Therefore

$$\left(\frac{\partial p}{\partial T}\right)_V = \left(\frac{\partial S}{\partial V}\right)_T$$

and this can be used as follows:

$$p = -\left(\frac{\partial F}{\partial V}\right)_T = -\left(\frac{\partial U}{\partial V}\right)_T + T\left(\frac{\partial S}{\partial V}\right)_T \qquad F = U - TS$$

$$= -\left(\frac{\partial U}{\partial V}\right)_T + T\left(\frac{\partial p}{\partial T}\right)_V$$

The equation

$$p + \left(\frac{\partial U}{\partial V}\right)_T = T\left(\frac{\partial p}{\partial T}\right)_V$$

is called the **energy equation,** because it gives information about the internal energy of a substance if the equation of state is known. For example, for an ideal gas, $pV = nRT$.

$$\left(\frac{\partial U}{\partial V}\right)_T = -p + T\left(\frac{\partial p}{\partial T}\right)_V = -p + T\left(\frac{nR}{V}\right) = -p + p = 0$$

Thus $U = U(T)$ only for an ideal gas. This is a fact that we have been assuming as reasonable, but we have not been able to show before that it follows from applying the first and second laws to the equation of state.

For a gas obeying the Van der Waals equation of state $[p + (a/v^2)](v - b) = RT$

$$p = \frac{RT}{v - b} - \frac{a}{v^2} \qquad \left(\frac{\partial p}{\partial T}\right)_v = \frac{R}{v - b}$$

$$\left(\frac{\partial U}{\partial V}\right)_T = \left(\frac{\partial u}{\partial v}\right)_T = -p + T\left(\frac{R}{v - b}\right) = \frac{a}{v^2}$$

For a "Van der Waals" gas the internal energy does depend on the volume. The Van der Waals constant a is related to the interaction between the molecules.

The energy equation enables us to write the first law as follows (using small letters, representing molar quantities):

$$dq = du + p\, dv$$

$$= \left(\frac{\partial u}{\partial T}\right)_v dT + \left(\frac{\partial u}{\partial v}\right)_T dv + p\, dv \qquad :u = u(v,T)$$

$$= c_v\, dT + \left[p + \left(\frac{\partial u}{\partial v}\right)_T\right] dv \qquad :c_v = \frac{dq_v}{dT_v} = \left(\frac{\partial u}{\partial T}\right)_v$$

$$= c_v\, dT + T\left(\frac{\partial p}{\partial T}\right)_v dv \qquad :\text{energy equation}$$

The molar heat at constant pressure is

$$c_p = \frac{dq_p}{dT_p} = c_v + T\left(\frac{\partial p}{\partial T}\right)_v \frac{dv_p}{dT_p}$$

$$c_p - c_v = T\left(\frac{\partial p}{\partial T}\right)_v \left(\frac{\partial v}{\partial T}\right)_p$$

The physical properties usually defined to relate volume changes and pressure or temperature changes are the (isothermal) compressibility K_T and the volume expansion coefficient β

$$K_T = -\frac{1}{v}\left(\frac{\partial v}{\partial p}\right)_T \qquad \beta = \frac{1}{v}\left(\frac{\partial v}{\partial T}\right)_p$$

$$\left(\frac{\partial p}{\partial T}\right)_v = -\left(\frac{\partial p}{\partial v}\right)_T \left(\frac{\partial v}{\partial T}\right)_p = \frac{(1/v)(\partial v/\partial T)_p}{-(1/v)(\partial v/\partial p)_T} = \frac{\beta}{K_T}$$

Therefore
$$c_p - c_v = T\left(\frac{\partial p}{\partial T}\right)_v \left(\frac{\partial v}{\partial T}\right)_p = \frac{\beta^2 vT}{K_T}$$

For an ideal gas, this difference reduces to R. Substitution of the numerical values of the physical properties for solids or liquids shows that the difference is much less than R.

Questions for discussion

1. Is it possible to have a process in which the entropy of a system decreases?

2. If the net entropy change for any reversible process is zero, and if thermodynamics only deals with reversible processes, how is it that we can calculate entropy changes?

3. If a heat pump is used to heat a house, is some of the energy entering the house energy that the homeowner does not pay for? If so, why does not everyone use such a heating system?

4. An **adiabatic process** is one in which zero heat is transferred to a system; but the entropy change is not necessarily zero in an adiabatic process. Since $dS = dQ/T$, how is this possible?

5. Does a refrigerator make a kitchen warmer or colder?

6. In a free expansion of a gas into an evacuated enclosure, once some gas has entered the enclosure, work must be done as more gas enters. How then can the process be described as one in which $W = 0$?

Problems

1. **(a)** Calculate the entropy change of 50 gm of water heated from 20°C to 100°C. **(b)** If the water is allowed to cool from 100°C to 20°C, what is its entropy change? **(c)** If the water is assumed to be heated reversibly from 20°C to 100°C by using a series of reservoirs differing infinitesimally in temperature, what is the entropy change of the water and of the reservoirs?

2. Twenty grams of ice at 0°C and 200 gm of water at 70°C are placed in an insulated 100-gm copper calorimeter at 20°C. Calculate the entropy change that occurs as the system comes to equilibrium. (The latent heat of fusion of water is 80 cal/gm; the specific heat of Cu is 0.093.)

3. The variation in specific heat capacity with temperature for certain metals is described, at temperatures close to absolute zero, by the Debye T^3 law. For copper, for example, $c_v = 2.0 \times 10^{-5}T^3$ cal/mole-K°. Determine the entropy change of a 10-gm block of copper heated from 10°K to 15°K. (Molecular weight of copper, 64 gm/mole.)

4. The volume of an ideal gas is doubled in a reversible isobaric process. Calculate the entropy change per mole **(a)** directly, **(b)** by visualizing reaching the same point by an isothermal expansion followed by an adiabatic compression.

5. A quantity of a monatomic ideal gas is initially at STP (point A on a p–v diagram). It is compressed isobarically to half its initial volume (point B), and then heated isometrically to a point C such that an adiabatic expansion returns it to its initial state. The processes are carried out reversibly. Suppose that the gas is the working substance in a heat engine, carried through the cycle A-B-C-A. **(a)** Determine the efficiency of the heat engine, and compare it with the efficiency of an ideal engine operating between reservoirs at the maximum and the minimum temperatures of the cycle A-B-C-A. **(b)** Determine the entropy change per mole of the gas in each part of the cycle A-B-C-A, and for the whole cycle.

6. Show that the efficiency of the idealized cycle bounded by two adiabatics and two isometrics (at V_1 and V_2) for the internal combustion engine, with an ideal gas as a working substance, is $\eta = 1 - (V_1/V_2)^{\gamma-1}$.

7. A monatomic ideal gas is carried through a cycle of reversible processes as follows: (1) its volume is doubled isobarically, (2) its pressure is halved isometrically, and (3) the gas is returned to its initial state by an isothermal compression. Calculate the efficiency of the cycle, and compare it with that of an ideal engine operating between reservoirs at the maximum and minimum temperatures of the cycle.

8. The area under a curve representing a reversible process on a p–v diagram is equal to the work done in the process. What is the area under a curve representing a reversible process on a T–S diagram? Represent the ideal reversible (Carnot) cycle on such a diagram, and use it to deduce the efficiency $(T_2 - T_1)/T_2$.

9. The annual heating cost for a house is $150 when oil is used as the fuel. The oil costs 17¢ per gallon, has a specific gravity of 0.85, and a calorific value of 15,000 Btu per pound (1 Btu, or British thermal unit, is the energy required to heat one pound of water through one Fahrenheit degree). It is estimated that 25% of the heat generated is lost up the chimney.

(a) Estimate the annual heating cost with electric energy, at 1.5¢ per kwh.

(b) Consider the cost of heating the house with a heat pump operated by an electric motor. Assume that the motor is 100% efficient, that the heat energy is obtained from a source (the earth outside) at 32°F and transmitted to the house at 120°F, and that the coefficient of performance of the heat pump is one-half that of an ideal heat pump operating between the same two temperatures. Calculate the annual cost of electricity.

(c) Calculate the annual cost if the same heat pump were operated by an ideal heat engine, for which the reservoir temperatures are assumed to be 700°F and 200°F. Assume that the only heat loss is the heat rejected by this engine (lost up the chimney) and that the same oil is used as fuel as was used to heat the house directly.

(d) The energy received at the earth's surface when the sun is directly overhead is about 2 cal/cm²-min (this is called the solar constant). Suppose that there were a special material available that would absorb and store all the radiation falling on it. Assuming an average 4 hr/day of "solar constant" sunshine, what area of this ideal material would be necessary to provide heat for the house?

10. An ideal gas is changed from a state (p_1,v_1,T_1) to a state (p_2,v_2,T_2). Write the specific entropy change $s_2 - s_1$ in terms of c_p, c_v and R, and (a) volume and temperature changes, (b) pressure and temperature changes, (c) pressure and volume changes.

11. The rating of a refrigeration machine may be given either in terms of the horse-power of the compressor motor or in terms of the number of tons of ice that the machine will make in a day. For a large machine the two figures are roughly the same. Calculate the coefficient of performance of a machine assuming they are the same, and assuming the ice is made from water initially at 0°C. (The latent heat of fusion for water is 80 cal/gm.)

12. Consult a handbook of physical constants to find the volume thermal expansion coefficient β, the isothermal compressibility K_T (or the isothermal bulk modulus $1/K_T$) and the specific volume v for a typical metal (e.g., copper) and use these to determine the difference in the molar specific heat capacities $c_p - c_v$ for the metal at room temperature. Compare the result to the gas constant R. From the specific heat capacity of the metal given in the handbook determine the molar heat capacity, and express the difference $c_p - c_v$ as a fraction of this. Determine γ for the metal.

13. (a) Show that if the volume of a solid is changed adiabatically through a small volume change Δv, the change in temperature is $\Delta T = -(\beta T/K_T c_v)\,\Delta v$.

(b) Estimate the temperature change of a block of metal (e.g., copper) at room temperature whose volume is decreased 0.1% adiabatically.

(c) What pressure in atmospheres is required to produce this change in volume?

(d) What temperature change would produce the same change in volume?

14. Show that the following expressions for specific heat capacity are correct.

$$c_v = (\partial u/\partial T)_v \qquad c_v = T(\partial s/\partial T)_v \qquad c_p = (\partial h/\partial T)_p \qquad c_p = T(\partial s/\partial T)_p$$

The enthalpy h (sometimes called the heat content) plays the same role for isobaric processes that the internal energy u does for isometric processes.

15. (a) Use the energy equation to derive an expression for the change in molar internal energy $u_2 - u_1$ of a Van der Waals gas as it is changed from a state (v_1, T_1) to a state (v_2, T_2). Assume that c_v for the gas can be considered constant. (b) A quantity of oxygen, initially at a pressure of 5 atm and a temperature of 20°C, undergoes an adiabatic free expansion that doubles its volume. Calculate the change in temperature of the gas, assuming the Van der Waals equation of state is valid. (The Van der Waals constant a for oxygen is 0.14 n-m^4/mole^2.)

16. In a process called a throttling process, or a Joule–Kelvin process, a continuous stream of gas is forced through a porous plug in a tube. The gas on both sides of the plug can be considered to be in a steady state of thermal equilibrium, even though the expansion through the plug is not a reversible process. On one side of the plug the pressure and temperature of the gas are p_1 and T_1, and on the other side p_2 and T_2.

(a) Consider 1 mole of gas as it moves through the plug (it may help to imagine pistons moving in the tube) and show that the net work done in forcing the gas through is $w = p_2 v_2 - p_1 v_1$.

(b) Assume that there is no heat transferred to the gas in the process, and show that the enthalpy h of the gas is constant in the throttling process. (Compare the adiabatic free expansion process, in which the internal energy is constant.)

(c) What is measured in the porous plug experiment is the temperature difference ΔT corresponding to a pressure difference Δp across the plug. The ratio $\Delta T/\Delta p$ in the constant enthalpy process is called the Joule–Kelvin coefficient μ. Prove that $\mu = (\partial T/\partial p)_h = (1/c_p)[T(\partial v/\partial T)_p - v]$.

(d) Show that for an ideal gas, $\mu = 0$; that is, the temperature is the same on both sides of the plug, independent of the pressure difference.

(e) For real gases the temperature may increase or decrease in passing through the plug, depending on the sign of μ. Show that for a Van der Waals gas the inversion takes place approximately at a temperature $2a/bR$.

(f) Show that μ may be written $\mu = -(1/c_p)\{(\partial u/\partial p)_T + [\partial(pv)/\partial p]_T\}$.
The first term represents departures from what is called **Joule's law** (for an ideal gas the internal energy is a function of temperature only) and the second term represents departures from **Boyle's law** (for an ideal gas the product of pressure and volume is a constant at a constant temperature). The first term always gives a cooling in the throttling process (can you see why?) but the second term may be positive or negative.

The departures of real gases from ideal gas behavior are observed much more easily in a porous plug experiment than in a free expansion experiment, because in the porous plug the gas is in a steady state and the walls of the tube are at the same temperature as the gas on either side of the plug. In the free expansion experiment the drop in temperature of the gas is masked because of the heat capacity of the container.

30

RANDOM EVENTS

This chapter deals with such topics as chance, probability and randomness, which might seem to have more to do with gambling than with an exact science like physics. As we emphasized at the beginning, the term exact science cannot be interpreted to mean that physicists know anything exactly; however, it can be interpreted to mean that they attempt to describe things in an exact or precise way. We are going to try to give precise meaning to some of the concepts of mathematical statistics and their application in physical situations.

We showed in Chapter 3 in discussing experimental measurement that the branch of mathematics called statistics has some applications in the handling and presentation of physical data, but the use of statistical considerations in physics goes much deeper than this. In statistical mechanics and in kinetic theory the methods of statistics are used to **predict** the macroscopic behavior of matter on the basis of the behavior of its microscopic constituents. Any physical system on which we can make direct observations is made up of 10^{20} or so atoms, and these enormous numbers mean, as you will see, that we can make statistical predictions about behavior with a high degree of confidence. However, there is a still more fundamental reason for introducing the methods of statistics. In classical statistical physics we think of an atom or a molecule as a particle that moves around, subject to the forces acting on it, in a completely predictable way—just like a baseball, only smaller. In principle if we knew all about a particular system at any instant (i.e., if we knew the position and velocity of every atom in the system) and if we knew what the forces were, we could use the laws of mechanics to calculate what it would be doing at any future time— just as we could for a baseball. Because there is such a large number of particles such calculations are impossible in practice, and statistical calculations are used; they make computation and prediction possible, but they are not necessary **in principle.** This is not the case in quantum mechanics because in this system of mechanics the behavior of atomic systems can be described **only** statistically, in terms of what are called probability functions. In classical physics the atom was pictured as a tiny massive nucleus (about 10^{-12} cm across) with electrons as particles moving in orbits (of diameter about 10^{-8} cm) around it, rather like

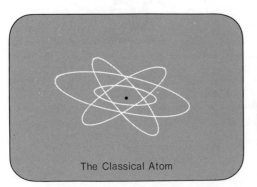

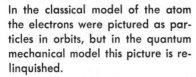

The Classical Atom

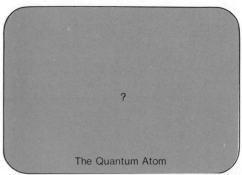

The Quantum Atom

In the classical model of the atom the electrons were pictured as particles in orbits, but in the quantum mechanical model this picture is relinquished.

the planets around the sun. This model of the atom was used to explain certain observed phenomena (some major features of spectra, for example) but turned out to be totally inadequate in many ways. In the quantum mechanical model of the atom the electron is still referred to as a particle, but it is not a particle in the classical sense of having a well-defined path or trajectory—that is, it cannot be considered as being in a definite place at a definite time. Instead, it is described by probability functions which may vary with position and time. A simple mechanistic particle picture is no longer possible.

Our discussion of probability and statistics is based on simple physical situations which are easy to visualize. We will work out the results for these situations in detail, because the results will have much more general usefulness. To a large extent this is a mathematical discussion, but by making reference to physical situations, and your intuition about them, we will be able to justify approximations. We have included whatever we thought we needed to make our story complete and comprehensible, but some mathematical sections which are not essential to the basic development have been set in smaller type.

HEADS I WIN

To begin with, think about the simplest possible example of a random situation, where only two results are possible—the tossing of a coin. Suppose that you tossed 100 coins (or tossed one coin 100 times) and recorded the results. How many heads would you expect? On the average you would expect 50 heads, but in a particular case you would not be surprised if it was not exactly 50. You would expect some deviation from the average or expected value. How much variation would you expect? Would you expect, if you performed the experiment many times, that most of your results would be between 45 and 55 heads—

that is, within 10% of the average value of 50? How many of the results of a large number of experiments would you expect to find in this range (from 45 to 55)—70% of them? 90% of them? How many in the range 40–60? In other words, how are the results distributed about the average value?

Suppose that instead of 100 coins you used 10,000. How would this change your results? Now you would expect that the average number of heads would be 5000, but because of the larger number you might expect the deviation from the average value to be greater. How much greater? Would you expect that in a large number of experiments, or trials, most of the results would be between 4950 and 5050, or within 1% of the average?

Clearly it would be useful if something precise like this could be said: If the 100 coin experiment is performed a large number of times, you can expect that in 68% of these the result will be within 10% of the expected value of 50 heads. This would mean that in a single experiment there is a 68% probability that the result will be between 45 and 55 heads. Statements like this can be made on the basis of experiment (recall the example at the beginning of this book) by actually performing the experiment a large number of times. If 100 coins are tossed 1000 times, and in 680 of these the result is between 45 and 55 heads, the statement above can be made; if the 100 coins are tossed 100 times, and in 68 of these there are between 45 and 55 heads the statement could be made, but with less confidence. The larger the number of trials, the more confidence we can have in experimentally determined probability statements, but there is always the possibility that still more trials would give a different result.

The task of a statistical theory is to make it possible to make statements about probabilities without performing a large number of experiments—that is, to **calculate** probabilities.

PROBABILITY

A statistical theory makes it possible to calculate what to expect as an overall result produced by a number of individual events, but the calculations always depend on some assumptions about the individual events. By *assuming* that for the toss of a single coin the probability of a head is $1/2$, we can calculate probabilities for what will happen if a number of coins are tossed. By *assuming* that the probability of throwing a particular number with a six-sided die is $1/6$, we can calculate probabilities for the behavior if a number of dice are tossed. By *assuming* that the probability for a single molecule of gas in a container of volume V_0 to be in a particular volume V is V/V_0 (which only means that we assume the molecule is just as likely to be in one part of the container as in another) we can calculate probabilities for the results of observations on numbers of molecules. This last is the basic kind of problem considered in statistical mechanics.

The probabilities assigned to the individual events in a statistical theory are called **a priori probabilities.** They may be based on experience, or experiment, or may just be statements of ignorance. We can see no reason why a coin should fall with a particular side up, so we say that a head or a tail is equally probable, and therefore the probability for each is 1/2. Similarly we know no reason why a die should land with a particular face up (assuming we are not using loaded dice) so we say that each of the six faces is equally probable, and the probability for any particular face to be up is 1/6.

Our assumption then is that what happens in an individual event is a matter of pure **chance.** Note that this means that other individual events cannot have any effect; if 100 coins are tossed, each coin behaves independently, uninfluenced by the other 99 coins. We call this chapter Random Events; one characteristic of random events is that individual events are independent of one another. A statistical theory makes it possible to calculate the overall effect produced by a number of random events with assumed a priori probabilities.

The assumption of independent or random events seems perfectly reasonable for a number of coins or a number of dice, but is not so obvious for a group of gas molecules in a container. You know that molecules interact with one another (otherwise gases would not condense to form liquids or solids) and therefore do *not* behave independently. When statistical considerations are applied to a gas it is assumed that the interaction between molecules is negligible; this model is called an ideal gas. The lower the pressure on a real gas, the more it behaves like this model, but even under normal atmospheric pressure the ideal gas approximation is reasonable for most gases.

So far this discussion has been rather general. We have stated the basic aim of a statistical theory, and have used a number of terms that are familiar to you —such terms as average, expected, probable, deviation, distribution. We must give some of these words precise meaning. In order to be specific we continue to base the discussion on a particular physical system, the tossing of a group of coins, but the results have broad applicability.

Instead of thinking about tossing 1 or 100 or 10,000 coins, think about tossing N coins, and counting the number n of them which are heads. We wish to calculate the probability of a particular value of n being observed. We call this probability P and will usually write it as $P(n)$ because it is a function of n; the probability of finding no heads ($n = 0$) or all heads ($n = N$) is certainly less than finding about equal numbers of heads and tails. $P(n)$ is a function with a maximum around $n = N/2$. Since n is not a continuous variable, but can take on only integral values from 0 to N, $P(n)$ is not a continuous function. It can be plotted as a histogram, or as a bar graph. We will usually use a bar graph, because it emphasizes that $P(n)$ is only defined for integral values of n. Although P depends on N as well as n, it is not usual to write $P(N,n)$ because we are

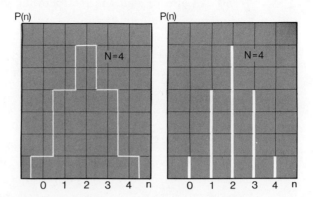

Probability distribution for tossing four coins, both as a histogram and as a bar graph.

thinking of situations where N is a fixed number.

What does it mean to say that the probability of finding n heads is P? It means this. If the N coins are tossed a large number of times, say $\mathfrak{N}$ times, and it is observed that there are $\mathfrak{N}_n$ of these where there are n heads, we define $P(n) = \mathfrak{N}_n/\mathfrak{N}$. The probability of this particular outcome, sometimes called the probability of this particular **event,** is simply the fraction of times it is observed in a large number of repeated trials of the same experiment. (The term event is used in statistics both for a particular overall result and for the individual effects which produce the result. By referring always to **individual** events in the second usage, confusion should be avoided.)

What does the rather loose expression "a large number of repeated trials" mean? To give precise definition to $P(n)$ it is necessary to consider that the number of trials becomes infinitely large.

$$P(n) = \mathfrak{N}_n/\mathfrak{N} \qquad (\mathfrak{N} \to \infty)$$

Statistical Ensembles: Rather than thinking about performing the same experiment on the real physical system an infinite number of times, it is more usual in statistical theories to visualize an assembly or an **ensemble** of $\mathfrak{N}$ systems, each identical to the real physical system and each subjected to the same experiment as the real system. If a particular result n occurs in $\mathfrak{N}_n$ of the systems, the fraction $\mathfrak{N}_n/\mathfrak{N} = P$ is defined to be the probability of occurrence of the result n. As $\mathfrak{N}$ is made larger and larger, there would be increasing reproducibility of the ratio $\mathfrak{N}_n/\mathfrak{N}$ and therefore this gives a precise or unambiguous definition of probability as $\mathfrak{N} \to \infty$.

The rules for combining probabilities are really a matter of common sense, but we shall state them here in general terms.

1. Probability of finding one or the other of two mutually exclusive events: If P_a is the probability of a particular result a, and P_b is the probability of a particular result b, then the probability of a or b is

$$P(a \text{ or } b) = P_a + P_b$$

This can also be stated in the following way. If a particular result can be reached in two mutually exclusive ways, with individual probabilities P_a and P_b, the probability of the result is $P_a + P_b$.

As an example, think of a six-sided die. The probability of throwing any particular number is $1/6$. The probability of throwing a *2* or a *5* is $1/6 + 1/6 = 1/3$. This corresponds to the first statement above. Suppose that the *2* and the *5* faces are painted black. The probability of throwing a black face is $1/6 + 1/6 = 1/3$. This corresponds to the second statement.

2. Probability of finding both of two mutually exclusive events: If two events A and B have probabilities P_A and P_B, and if the events are statistically independent (i.e., the occurrence of one does not affect the occurrence of the other), then the probability of finding both A and B is

$$P_{AB} = P_A P_B$$

As an example, think of tossing two dice, labeled A and B. The probability of finding a *2* on die A and a *5* on die B is $1/6 \times 1/6 = 1/36$. Note that this is *not* the probability of tossing *seven; seven* can be made up in other ways (*4* and *3, 6* and *1*). It is not even the probability of tossing a *5* and a *2*, because the *2* could be on die B and the *5* on die A. The probability of tossing a *5* and a *2* is $1/36 + 1/36 = 1/18$, using the previous rule.

Both of these rules can be extended to include larger number of events

$$P(a \text{ or } b \text{ or } c \cdots) = P_a + P_b + P_c + \cdots$$
$$P_{ABC} \cdots = P_A P_B P_C \cdots$$

If the events $a, b, c \cdots$ include all possible results, the first rule becomes (since one of the results will certainly occur)

$$1 = P_a + P_b + P_c + \cdots$$

which is called the **normalization condition** for probabilities. The sum of all possible probabilities is unity.

Derivation of Probability Rules: The two rules stated above follow directly from the definition $P(n) = \mathfrak{N}_n / \mathfrak{N}$ as $\mathfrak{N} \to \infty$. We shall use P_n instead of $P(n)$ to show this.

We use a subscript n to label any of the N mutually exclusive outcomes of experiments on a certain physical system. In an ensemble of similar systems, $\mathfrak{N}_1$ will exhibit outcome (or event) 1, $\mathfrak{N}_2$ of them event 2, and so on. Since the N events are mutually exclusive and cover all possible results

$$\mathfrak{N}_1 + \mathfrak{N}_2 + \cdots + \mathfrak{N}_N = \mathfrak{N}$$

or dividing by $\mathfrak{N}$ and using the definition of probability

$$P_1 + P_2 + \cdots + P_N = 1 \qquad \text{or} \qquad \sum_{n=1}^{N} P_n = 1$$

the normalization condition.

There are $\mathfrak{N}_a$ systems exhibiting an event a, and $\mathfrak{N}_b$ systems exhibiting an event b, and therefore $(\mathfrak{N}_a + \mathfrak{N}_b)$ systems exhibiting either event a or event b.

$$P(a \text{ or } b) = \frac{\mathfrak{N}_a + \mathfrak{N}_b}{\mathfrak{N}} = P_a + P_b$$

Now suppose that we distinguish between two different types of events. A system can exhibit N possible events of type labeled by A (where A takes on the values 1, 2, 3, $\cdots$, N) and *also* M possible events of type labeled by B (where B takes on the values 1, 2, 3, $\cdots$, M). In an ensemble $\mathfrak{N}$ of similar systems $\mathfrak{N}_A$ will exhibit a particular result A of the first type of event (whether or not they also exhibit the second type), $\mathfrak{N}_B$ will exhibit a particular result B of the second type (whether or not they also exhibit the first), and we shall label $\mathfrak{N}_{AB}$ the number that exhibit a joint occurrence of both the result A and the result B. Then $P_A = \mathfrak{N}_A/\mathfrak{N}$, $P_B = \mathfrak{N}_B/\mathfrak{N}$, and $P_{AB} = \mathfrak{N}_{AB}/\mathfrak{N}$.

In general it is not possible to relate these probabilities, because the presence of a type A event may influence whether or not there is a type B event. If this is not so, that is, if the occurrence of one type of event is unaffected by the occurrence of the other, the two types of events are called **statistically independent**. In this case, of the $\mathfrak{N}_A$ systems in the ensemble which exhibit a particular event A, a fraction P_B will also exhibit the particular event B. Therefore $\mathfrak{N}_{AB} = P_B \mathfrak{N}_A$

or

$$P_{AB} = \frac{\mathfrak{N}_{AB}}{\mathfrak{N}} = \frac{P_B \mathfrak{N}_A}{\mathfrak{N}} = P_A P_B$$

THE BINOMIAL DISTRIBUTION

We are going to calculate $P(n)$ for a toss of N coins, but first we shall look at the results of a few experiments. We tossed one coin 50 times and kept track of whether it came up heads H or tails T by putting points on a graph as shown. At each toss we moved one division to the right and up one if H, down one if T. This gives a graph with abscissa the number of tosses and ordinate the number

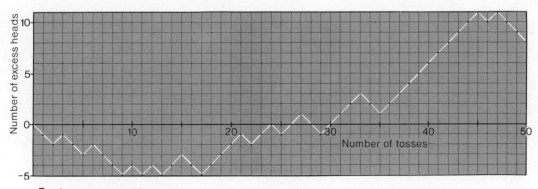

Tossing one coin 50 times.

of excess heads (a negative number is the number of excess tails). As you can see after 9 tosses we had 5 more T's than H's, after 24 tosses we had equal numbers, and after the total run of 50 we had an excess of 8 H's. At one point we tossed 10 H's in a row. If we tried to do this, the probability of doing it in one attempt is $1/2^{10} = 1/1024$, or less than one in a thousand. But it happened. Note that the sequence of 10 H's in a row is no more unlikely than the sequence T-T-H-T-T-H-T-T-T-H with which the graph began, because in both cases we have specified what we will get at each toss.

We repeated the 50-coin experiment three more times and the results for all four runs are shown on the same graph. The numbers of excess heads were 8,

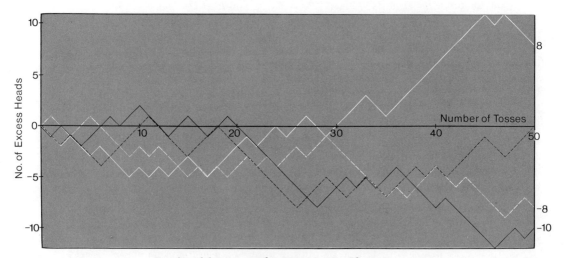

Results of four runs of tossing a coin 50 times.

0, -8 and -10, so that the actual numbers of heads were 29, 25, 21 and 20. These depart from the average or expected number of 25 by 16%, 0%, 16% and 20%.

If we add the results of any two of the 50-coin runs together, we get the result for a 100-coin run. For the six possible results, the deviation from the expected value of 50 is 0%, 2%, 8%, 8%, 10% and 18%. We are still not in a position to say anything about what sort of deviation we should expect. We have quoted the results to give you some feeling for what happens (perhaps you should toss a few coins yourself) and also to familiarize you with the graph used because it will be useful in our calculation of what to expect.

When N coins are tossed each coin may show H or T, so that there are 2^N possible results, all of which are equally likely since we have assumed random events and equal probability for H or T. The possible results for a few small values of N are as in the table.

		No. of H's			No. of H's
$N = 1$	H	1	$N = 4$	H-H-H-H	4
	T	0		H-H-H-T⌉	
				H-H-T-H⎪	
$N = 2$	H-H	2		H-T-H-H⎬	3
	H-T⌉			T-H-H-H⌋	
	T-H⌋	1		H-H-T-T⌉	
	T-T	0		H-T-T-H⎪	
				T-T-H-H⎪	
$N = 3$	H-H-H	3		H-T-H-T⎬	2
	H-H-T⌉			T-H-T-H⎪	
	H-T-H⎬	2		T-H-H-T⌋	
	T-H-H⌋			H-T-T-T⌉	
	H-T-T⌉			T-H-T-T⎪	
	T-H-T⎬	1		T-T-H-T⎬	1
	T-T-H⌋			T-T-T-H⌋	
	T-T-T	0		T-T-T-T	0

We are interested in the number n of coins that show H—we do not care **which** coins show H, just how many. This means for $N = 2$, for example, that the bracketed pair, each showing 1 H, are the same event for our purposes.

The probability of a particular event $P(n) = \mathfrak{N}_n/\mathfrak{N}$ as $\mathfrak{N} \to \infty$. If we toss N coins a very large number of times (or consider a statistical ensemble of a large number $\mathfrak{N}$ sets of N coins) our basic assumption is that each of the 2^N results will be found equally often. For $N = 2$, for example, where there are 4 possible results (H-H, H-T, T-H, T-T) each result will be found in $1/4$ of the observations. Therefore $\mathfrak{N}_{H-H} = (1/4)\mathfrak{N}$ as $\mathfrak{N} \to \infty$, and $P(2) = 1/4$. Similarly $P(0) = 1/4$, but since H-T and T-H are the same event, $P(1) = (\mathfrak{N}_{H-T} + \mathfrak{N}_{T-H})/\mathfrak{N} = 2/4$.

From the table you can see that for $N = 3$: $P(3) = 1/8$, $P(2) = 3/8$, $P(1) = 3/8$, $P(0) = 1/8$. For $N = 4$: $P(4) = 1/16$, $P(3) = 4/16$, $P(2) = 6/16$, $P(1) = 4/16$, $P(0) = 1/16$. (These results were used to draw the histogram for $N = 4$ shown before.) Note that P depends on both n and N.

Enumerating all the possible results is cumbersome even for these small values of N. The next step we take is to draw a diagram like the one we used before to represent the results of tossing 50 coins, plotting the number of excess heads against the number of tosses of a single coin. The abscissa can also be thought of as corresponding to the values of N. This time we have filled in all possible paths, or ways of reaching any point. Each vertical column corresponds to a particular value of N, shown along the top of the figure along with the value of 2^N, the number of possible results for this N. Now look at the places where the diagonal paths intersect. In any column, the top intersection corresponds to all H's ($n = N$), the next one down to $(N - 1)$ H's, the next to $(N - 2)$ H's and so on down to the bottom intersection corresponding to no H ($n = 0$). The numbers placed at the intersections show the number of ways that this particular point can be reached, starting at the left of the figure and moving from left to right on the diagonal paths. The intersections under $N = 2$ correspond to the three possible events 2-H's, 1-H and 0-H, but 1-H can be achieved by 2 paths, T-H or H-T. For each column the sum of the number of paths (or number of ways) is equal to 2^N.

The probability for a particular event can be written down from the table. For $N = 4$: $P(4) = 1/16$, $P(3) = 4/16$, etc. The numbers which appear in the diagram are called **binomial coefficients** because the numbers in any column, corresponding to a particular N, are the coefficients in the binomial expansion $(p + q)^N$, as you shall see.

While you may be able to see how to fill in other numbers in the diagram, we still have not given an expression which will give any entry.

Each entry gives the number of ways of choosing n events out of a total of N trials. In probability theory this is usually referred to as the number of combinations of N objects taken n at a time. It is sometimes denoted $_NC_n$, sometimes $\binom{N}{n}$, but we will use $C_N(n)$ because it is similar to our $P(n)$ notation.

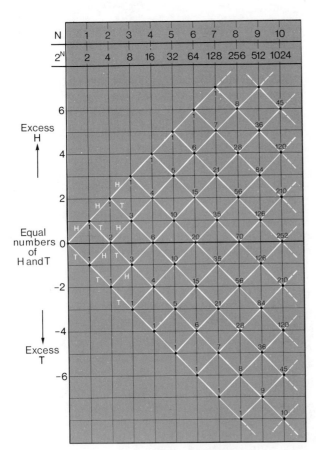

Possible results of tossing N coins (Pascal's triangle).

In general

$$C_N(n) = \frac{N!}{n!(N - n)!}$$

The derivation of this result is a straightforward mathematical problem, familiar if you have studied probability theory, but we will give it here so that you will not feel we have skipped part of the story.

Look at the table showing all the possible results (H-H-H-H, H-H-H-T, etc.) for $N = 4$, and think about such a table for the general cases of N tosses. The number $C_N(n)$ is the number of lines in the table in which H appears n times. For convenience we will label the n values of H as H_1, H_2, H_3, $\cdots$, H_n. Each line of the table has N entries, so we could put H_1 in any of the N positions; then H_2 could go in any of the remaining $(N - 1)$ positions; then H_3 in any of the remaining $(N - 2)$ positions, and so on down to the last one H_n, which could go in any one of $(N - n + 1)$ positions.

The total number of distinct lines in the table which could be produced in this way is obtained by multiplying together the number of possible locations of the H_1, H_2, H_3, $\cdots$, H_n. This would give

$$\text{Number of lines} = N(N - 1)(N - 2) \cdots (N - n + 1)$$

This is written more succinctly by using the factorial notation. By definition $N! \equiv N(N - 1)(N - 2) \cdots (2)(1)$; also $0! = 1$.

$$\text{Number of lines} = \frac{N(N - 1)(N - 2) \cdots (N - n + 1)(N - n)(N - n - 1) \cdots (2)(1)}{(N - n)(N - n - 1) \cdots (2)(1)}$$

$$= \frac{N!}{(N - n)!}$$

However, we have overcounted the number of lines because we have regarded two lines such as $H_1 H_2 \cdots$ and $H_2 H_1 \cdots$ (everything except first two entries the same) as two different events, and they are not; the subscripts on the H's were a convenience, but the H's are not distinguishable. We do not care which coins show heads, only how many. Any line which we have counted will contain the H_1, H_2, $\cdots$, H_n in certain positions and in some particular order, but the order does not matter, only the position. There will be a factor $n!$ too many lines, because the n subscripts in any line can be permuted in $n!$ ways. (The first subscript can have any one of n values, the next any of the remaining $(n - 1)$ values, and so on down to the last subscript which has the one remaining value. Therefore the subscripts can be arranged in $n(n - 1) \cdots (2)(1) = n!$ ways.)

Therefore the actual number of lines in the table with n H's will be

$$C_N(n) = \frac{N!}{n!(N - n)!}$$

We can now write down a general expression for the probability $P(n)$ of a particular value of n. Of the 2^N lines in the table, $C_N(n)$ have n H's in them.

$$P(n) = \frac{C_N(n)}{2^N} = \frac{1}{2^N} \frac{N!}{n!(N - n)!}$$

In order to show the form of $P(n)$ for different values of N, we have plotted bar graphs for $N = 1, 2, 3, 4, 10,$ and 50. These, showing how the $P(n)$ are distributed for the possible values of n, are the **probability distributions** for these cases, and $P(n)$ is called a **probability distribution**. (See at the top of page 712.)

For small values of N the calculation of $P(n)$ can be done directly, but for large N the factorial factors become formidable, and it is convenient to use logarithms. Mathematical tables give values for $\log x!$.

Each distribution is symmetric, with a maximum at $n = N/2$ when N is even, or straddling this value when N is odd. The $N = 10$ distribution has been replotted on the $N = 50$ distribution, which has a different scale. As N increases, the maximum in the distribution becomes lower and the distribution is broadened; the probability of finding exactly equal numbers of heads and

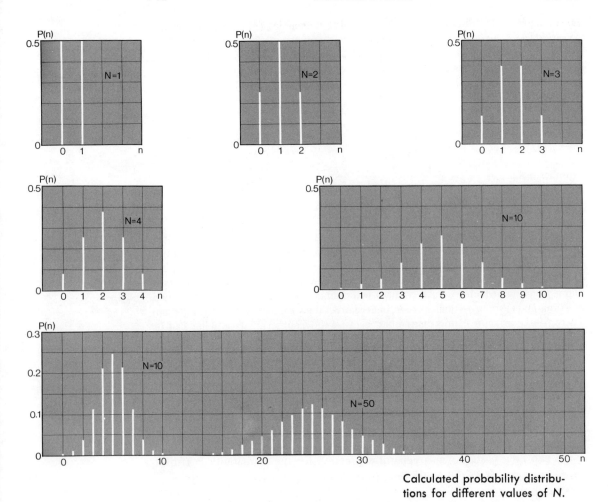

Calculated probability distributions for different values of N.

tails decreases as N increases. However, even though the distributions become more spread out as N increases, the probability of finding n **near** its maximum increases. For $N = 10$, with a maximum at $n = 5$, the probability of finding $n = 4$ or $n = 6$ (differing by 20% from the maximum) is nearly as large as finding $n = 5$; to be precise, $0.205/0.246 = 0.83$, or 83% as large. For $N = 50$, with a maximum at $n = 25$, the probability of finding $n = 20$ or $n = 30$ (differing by 20% from the maximum) is much less; $0.042/0.112 = 0.37$, or only 37% as great. We shall return to this point later, after we have investigated the form of $P(n)$ for large N, but first another digression.

The Binomial Distribution: The distribution $P(n)$ which we have developed is a special case of a more general distribution called the binomial distribution. It is special because we have allowed for only two possibilities for the independent random events

(H or T) and we have assumed these to be equally probable. We assigned an a priori probability $p = 1/2$ to the desired result H, and a probability $1/2$ that a result would not be H.

In general there will be a number of possible results for each independent event. To the desired result we assign a probability p. Two examples with p other than $1/2$ were given earlier: $p = 1/6$ for the probability of a particular face of a six-sided die facing upward, and $p = V/V_0$ for the probability of a gas molecule being in a volume V if free to move in a larger volume V_0. The probability that the result of an independent event is *not* the desired result we will call q. For the die, the probability of tossing a 5 is $p = 1/6$; the probability of tossing a number other than 5 is $q = 5/6$. For a gas molecule, the probability of not being in volume V is $q = (V_0 - V)/V_0$ (i.e., the probability of being in volume $[V_0 - V]$). It will always be so that $q = 1 - p$, because $(p + q)$ is the probability that some result is obtained, and this is unity.

Now think about the overall result of N random events. Think of making up a table like the one before listing all the possible results, but this time with H representing the desired result (of probability p) and T representing any other result (probability q). Each line in the table has N entries and represents a particular configuration (e.g., H-T-H-H-T . . .). The probability of an H in any particular position is p, the probability of a T in any particular position is q. We are interested in finding $P(n)$; this means that we are interested in those configurations (or lines) where n of the entries are H's, and therefore $(N - n)$ of the entries are T's. The probability of occurrence of such a configuration is

$$ \underbrace{p \times p \times p \times \cdots \times p}_{n \text{ factors}} \times \underbrace{q \times q \times q \times \cdots \times q}_{(N - n) \text{ factors}} = p^n q^{N-n} $$

because this is a combination of independent events and therefore the probability is the product of the individual probabilities. In the special case where $p = q = 1/2$, *all* configurations are equally probable, with a probability of $(1/2)^N$, but this is not so here. However, all configurations with n H's are equally probable.

This is the probability for a particular configuration with the H's in certain positions, but we are not interested in where the H's occur. We want to know how many configurations there are with n H's. This is the same calculation we made before, the number of ways of choosing n events out of a total of N trials, $C_N(n)$.

There are $C_N(n)$ configurations with n H's, and the probability for each is $p^n q^{N-n}$, so the probability for *any* configuration with n H's is

$$ P(n) = C_N(n) p^n q^{N-n} = \frac{N!}{n!(N - n)!} p^n q^{N-n} $$

$$ = \frac{N!}{n!(N - n)!} p^n (1 - p)^{N-n} $$

This is the binomial distribution. The origin of the name can be seen from the binomial expansion

$$ (q + p)^N = q^N + N q^{N-1} p + \frac{N(N - 1)}{2!} q^{N-2} p^2 + \frac{N(N - 1)(N - 2)}{3!} q^{N-3} p^3 + \cdots + p^N $$

$$ = \sum_{n=0}^{N} \frac{N!}{n!(N - n)!} p^n q^{N-n} $$

Each term in this expansion is the probability $P(n)$. It can be seen that since $p + q = 1$

$$\sum_{n=0}^{N} P(n) = 1$$

as it should be.

We will continue to base our discussion on the special case of the binomial distribution for which $p = q = 1/2$, because most of the features of the general distribution in which we are interested are exhibited by this special one.

We are next going to investigate the behavior of $P(n)$ for very large values of N. We could do this using the coin-tossing example, but we will use another one because it will provide some variety and also because the results may be easier to visualize.

THE RANDOM WALK

A particle is confined to movement along a straight line. It starts at some point (the origin O) and moves in discrete steps of constant length l. The direction of

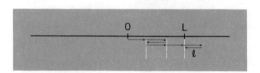

each step is determined randomly. The motion of the particle is called the random walk; the situation is sometimes described as the motion of a man who, starting at a particular point on a sidewalk (a bar exit?), manages to stay on the sidewalk but decides the direction of each step he takes, forward or back, by tossing a coin.

One-dimensional random walk of N steps of length l.

We are interested in finding the displacement L of the particle from its starting point O after N steps, each of length l. The result is not predictable except in a probabilistic sense; the best we can do is determine $P(L)$, the probability of a particular displacement L. To do this we will have to think about a large number of trials, or an ensemble of identical situations.

In general terms, we will expect that the average value $\bar{L}$ is zero; no matter how many steps are taken, since there is no preferred direction there will be no net progress **on the average.** On the other hand, the larger the number of steps the more likely it is that **in a particular case** the particle will be found some distance from the origin. We should like some way of defining this kind of progress. Over many trials L is as likely to be $(+)$ as $(-)$, so $\bar{L} = 0$, but we could use the absolute value $|\bar{L}|$ as a measure of progress. It turns out to be more convenient to use $\overline{L^2}$, the mean-square distance, or equivalently its square root $L_{\text{rms}} = [\overline{L^2}]^{1/2}$, the root-mean-square distance. We suggested that this kind of a measure of progress might be expected to increase as the number of steps N is increased. It happens that we can see that this is so, even without calculating the probability $P(L)$ in general, from the following argument.

We will compare the mean-square distance after N steps $\overline{L_N^2}$ with the mean-square distance after $(N + 1)$ steps $\overline{L_{N+1}^2}$, remembering that these represent averages over a large number of repeated trials. In any particular trial $L_{N+1} = L_N + l$ or $L_{N+1} = L_N - l$ since the next step will be in the same direction as L_N, or in the opposite direction. Squaring, $L_{N+1}^2 = L_N^2 + 2L_N l + l^2$ or $L_{N+1}^2 = L_N^2 - 2L_N l + l^2$. If the average is taken over many trials, we expect each result equally often, and therefore $\overline{L_{N+1}^2} = \overline{L_N^2} + l^2$. We know that after one step $L_1 = \pm l$ and therefore $\overline{L_1^2} = l^2$. Using the general relation, $\overline{L_2^2} = \overline{L_1^2} + l^2 = l^2 + l^2 = 2l^2$ and by induction

$$\overline{L_N^2} = Nl^2 \quad \text{or} \quad L_{\text{rms}} = \sqrt{N}\, l$$

The root-mean-square distance from the origin increases in proportion to the square root of the number of steps. After 25 steps, $L_{\text{rms}} = 5l$; after 100 steps, $L_{\text{rms}} = 10l$. It should be kept in mind, however, that in both cases the most probable value of L is **zero.** The quantity L_{rms} is a measure of the spread of the probability distribution $P(L)$.

In order to determine the distribution $P(L)$ it is only necessary to point out that we have already done it. We are dealing with a random situation in which there are only two possibilities, each of the same probability, for the individual random events. This is exactly the same mathematically as the coin-tossing problem for which we derived the distribution

$$P(n) = \frac{1}{2^N} \frac{N!}{n!(N - n)!}$$

for the probability of tossing n heads with N coins. In the random walk, suppose that the direction of each step is determined by a coin toss: if H, step in the $(+)$-direction, if T, step in the $(-)$-direction. The N steps correspond to N coin tosses; of these n are H, $(+)$-steps; $(N - n)$ are T $(-)$-steps. The displacement from the origin is

$$L = [n - (N - n)]l = (2n - N)l$$

Corresponding to each value of n, the number of H's, there is a unique value of L, the displacement. The L can be positive for an excess of heads ($n > N/2$) or negative for an excess of tails ($n < N/2$).

In order to help visualize a random walk, look back at the graphs we plotted earlier for experiments of tossing 50 coins, showing the number of excess heads plotted against the number of tosses. These can be interpreted as random walk graphs, with the ordinate the displacement L. (If the coin is tossed and the steps taken at regular time intervals, these can be considered displacement–time graphs.) For these four trials $L = 8l$, 0, $-8l$ and $-10l$. For $N = 50$, $L_{\text{rms}} =$

$\sqrt{50}l \cong 7l$. Remember that average values give no information about the result for a single run.

If we express $P(n)$ in terms of L by setting

$$n = \frac{1}{2}\left(N + \frac{L}{l}\right) = \frac{N}{2}\left(1 + \frac{L}{Nl}\right)$$

and

$$N - n = \frac{N}{2}\left(1 - \frac{L}{Nl}\right)$$

the expression becomes the probability distribution for L.

$$P(L) = \frac{1}{2^N}\frac{N!}{\{(N/2)\,[1 + (L/Nl)]\}!\,\{(N/2)\,[1 - (L/Nl)]\}!}$$

The shape of this distribution, for a few values of N, can be seen by looking back at the $P(n)$ distributions shown previously. The difference is only that instead of plotting n as abscissa we should plot

$$L = 2\left(n - \frac{N}{2}\right)l$$

Note that for a particular value of N there are N possible values of L, ranging from $-Nl$ to $+Nl$, spaced $2l$ apart. If N is even, L can take on only even integral multiples of l, and if N is odd L can take on only odd multiples of l.

The change in the abscissa has the effect of shifting all the distributions to be symmetric about the origin $L = 0$. The distributions for $N = 10$ and $N = 50$ are repeated here, as before on the same scale. Note that for $N = 10$ the maximum displacement $L_{\max} = 10l$, while for $N = 50$ the maximum displacement is $L_{\max} = 50l$. The graph is not shown for the whole range $-50l \rightarrow 50l$ because on the $P(L)$ scale used the probabilities for $L > 20l$ cannot be shown.

The $N = 50$ distribution is shown also plotted on a scale such that the maximum is the same as for the $N = 10$ distribution, and such that the limits for L are the same as for the $N = 10$ distribution.

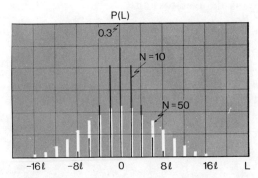

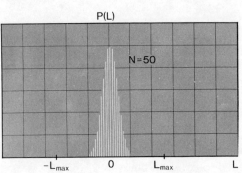

Probability distributions for a 10-step and a 50-step random walk.

Comparison of the two distributions in this way emphasizes that while the distribution does spread out as N increases (and therefore the **absolute** displacement possible increases) the **relative** displacement decreases.

Even though on the scale used for the last graph the individual values of L are so close together that the distribution looks continuous, this is misleading because the calculations are only made for discrete values of L. However, instead of thinking about calculated values for $P(L)$, suppose we think about what could be **observed** in a physical situation of this kind. Think, for example, about a coin-tossing gnat, trapped in a narrow slot one gnat wide and too deep to escape from. Not knowing which way to proceed to escape, in desperation he tries a random walk. We observe his progress through a microscope. If we make the field of view small, only a few gnat-steps wide, then we can observe his individual steps but he is likely to move out of the field of view if he takes more than a few steps. In order to watch his progress for a large number of steps, the field of view will have to be large. The larger the field the less likely we are to be able to observe that he is moving in discrete steps; the step size will get smaller and smaller compared to what we can resolve in the microscope. If we measure his position, using a scale in the microscope field, we will find that within our accuracy of measurement any position is possible—that is, his position varies continuously.

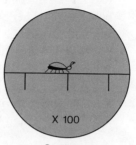

Gnat steps

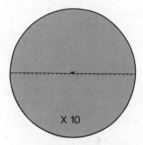

No Gnat steps

Observing gnat steps in the field of a microscope.

This rather artificial example helps make the point that an observed result produced by a large number of discrete random events can, within the limits of measurement possible, appear to take on continuous values. We shall later discuss some more realistic physical examples.

THE GAUSSIAN DISTRIBUTION

Now we are going to look at the form of the distribution $P(L)$ when the number of random events N becomes very large—so large that within the limits of observation possible L appears to be a continuous variable, and therefore $P(L)$ a continuous function.

Rather than work out the result using the displacement L it will be convenient to use a quantity ϵ, which is the fraction L is of the maximum displacement possible L_{max}. If all N steps were in the same direction $L_{max} = Nl$.

We define $\epsilon = L/L_{\max} = L/(Nl)$ and the probability distribution becomes

$$P(\epsilon) = \frac{1}{2^N} \frac{N!}{[(N/2)(1+\epsilon)]![(N/2)(1-\epsilon)]!}$$

We make the basic assumption that N is a large number: $N \gg 1$. Since the probability of having most of the steps in the same direction is small, we assume that L is small compared to $L_{\max}$: $\epsilon \ll 1$. This means that we are assuming that both n the number of $(+)$-steps, and $(N - n)$, the number of $(-)$-steps, are both large numbers. We are thus restricting ourselves to investigating the behavior of the probability distribution in the region of interest around the maximum value.

With these assumptions the three factorial terms in $P(\epsilon)$ are all factorials of large numbers. In order to change the form of the distribution, it is convenient to form the natural logarithm.

$$\ln P(\epsilon) = -N \ln 2 + \ln N! - \ln\left[\left(\frac{N}{2}\right)(1+\epsilon)\right]! - \ln\left[\left(\frac{N}{2}\right)(1-\epsilon)\right]!$$

We eliminate the factorial terms by using the Stirling approximation

$$M! \cong \sqrt{2\pi M}\left(\frac{M}{e}\right)^M \quad \text{or} \quad \ln M! \cong M \ln M - M + \tfrac{1}{2}\ln(2\pi M)$$

This formula may be found in mathematical tables. It is very accurate for large values of M. Even for M as low as 10, the error in $\ln M!$ is less than 0.1%.

Using this for the three factorial terms

$$\ln P(\epsilon) = -N \ln 2 + N \ln N - N + \tfrac{1}{2}\ln(2\pi N)$$

$$- \left(\frac{N}{2}\right)(1+\epsilon)\ln\left[\left(\frac{N}{2}\right)(1+\epsilon)\right] + \left(\frac{N}{2}\right)(1+\epsilon) - \tfrac{1}{2}\ln[\pi N(1+\epsilon)]$$

$$- \left(\frac{N}{2}\right)(1-\epsilon)\ln\left[\left(\frac{N}{2}\right)(1-\epsilon)\right] + \left(\frac{N}{2}\right)(1-\epsilon) - \tfrac{1}{2}\ln[\pi N(1-\epsilon)]$$

$$= -(N/2)[(1+\epsilon)\ln(1+\epsilon) + (1-\epsilon)\ln(1-\epsilon)]$$

$$- \tfrac{1}{2}[\ln(1+\epsilon) + \ln(1-\epsilon)] + \tfrac{1}{2}\ln(2\pi N) - \ln(\pi N)$$

Now we use the series expansion for $\ln(1 + x)$

$$\ln(1 + x) = x - \tfrac{1}{2}x^2 + \tfrac{1}{3}x^3 - \tfrac{1}{4}x^4 + \cdots \qquad (|x| < 1)$$

We are dealing with $\epsilon \ll 1$, so we take only as many terms in the expansion as is necessary to get a non-zero result.

$$(1+\epsilon)\ln(1+\epsilon) \cong (1+\epsilon)(\epsilon - \tfrac{1}{2}\epsilon^2) \cong \epsilon - \tfrac{1}{2}\epsilon^2 + \epsilon^2 = \epsilon + \tfrac{1}{2}\epsilon^2$$

$$(1-\epsilon)\ln(1-\epsilon) \cong (1-\epsilon)(-\epsilon - \tfrac{1}{2}\epsilon^2) \cong -\epsilon - \tfrac{1}{2}\epsilon^2 + \epsilon^2 = -\epsilon + \tfrac{1}{2}\epsilon^2$$

$$\ln(1+\epsilon) + \ln(1-\epsilon) \cong \epsilon - \tfrac{1}{2}\epsilon^2 - \epsilon - \tfrac{1}{2}\epsilon^2 = -\epsilon^2$$

The first term in $\ln P(\epsilon)$ becomes $-\frac{1}{2}N\epsilon^2$, and the second term $\frac{1}{2}\epsilon^2$. Since $N \gg 1$ the second term is negligible. The third and fourth terms can be combined to give $-\frac{1}{2}\ln\left(\frac{1}{2}\pi N\right) = -\ln\left(\frac{1}{2}\pi N\right)^{1/2}$.

$$\ln P(\epsilon) = -\frac{N}{2}\,\epsilon^2 - \ln\left(\tfrac{1}{2}\pi N\right)^{1/2}$$

or

$$P(\epsilon) = \sqrt{2/\pi N}\,e^{-N\epsilon^2/2}$$

In terms of the displacement L, since $\epsilon = L/(Nl)$

$$P(L) = \sqrt{2/\pi N}\,e^{-L^2/2Nl^2}$$

This is the probability for a particular value of L, on the assumptions that the total number of steps N is large, and that L is not near its maximum possible value $L_{\max} = Nl$.

We are interested in treating L as a continuous variable, rather than one varying in discrete steps, and therefore we must change from a probability function $P(L)$ to a probability density function $p(L)$, such that $p(L)\,dL$ is the probability that L will lie in the range L to $L + dL$. To do this we first recall that for a particular value of N the possible values of L are spaced a distance $2l$ apart. If we interpret $P(L)$ as the probability that L is in the range $2l$, then the probability that it is in the range dL is $P(L)(dL/2l)$, and this is $p(L)\,dL$.

$$p(L)\,dL = \sqrt{2/\pi N}\,e^{-L^2/2Nl^2}\left(\frac{dL}{2l}\right)$$

$$= \frac{1}{l\sqrt{2\pi N}}\,e^{-L^2/2Nl^2}\,dL$$

The probability density $p(L)$ is shown. The probability that L will lie between any two values L_1 and L_2 is

$$P(L_1 \to L_2) = \int_{L_1}^{L_2} p(L)\,dL$$

since it is the sum of the terms $p(L)\,\Delta L$ in this range, which becomes the integral as $\Delta L \to 0$. It is the area under the curve in this range.

We can verify that the function is properly normalized by calculating

The probability density distribution is Gaussian.

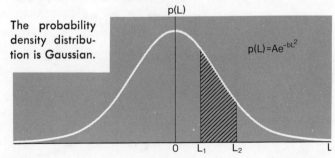

$p(L) = Ae^{-bL^2}$

$$P(-L_{\max} \to L_{\max}) = \int_{-L_{\max}}^{L_{\max}} p(L)\,dL$$

The value should be unity, since L certainly lies somewhere in this range. Note that we have already assumed that the value of $p(L)$ near $\pm L_{\max}$ is vanishingly small, and therefore that there is a negligible contribution to the integral for values of L approaching these limits. This means that we can change the limits of integration to $\pm\infty$ without affecting the result appreciably.

From tables of definite integrals $\int_{-\infty}^{\infty} e^{-ax^2}\,dx = \sqrt{\pi/a}$, so that

$$P(-L_{\max} \to L_{\max}) = \frac{1}{l\sqrt{2\pi N}} \int_{-\infty}^{\infty} e^{-L^2/2Nl^2}\,dL = \frac{1}{l\sqrt{2\pi N}}\sqrt{2\pi Nl^2} = 1$$

We have derived this distribution function for probability density for the special case of a one-dimensional random walk, but distributions of this form are very common. It is called the **Gaussian** distribution or **normal** distribution, and the graph of $p(L)$ vs. L is an example of the **bell curve**. We shall use the term Gaussian rather than normal because normal might suggest that behavior described by the distribution is what ought to happen. This is so in many physical situations, but there are other possible distributions as well. **The distribution is Gaussian whenever the observed result is the overall effect of a large number of random events.**

We can now calculate the average values $\bar{L}$ and $\bar{L^2}$. Averages such as this, based on calculation rather than on observation, are sometimes called **expected values** because they are the expected result if a large number of trials are made.

From the definition of average value

$$\bar{L} = \frac{\int\limits_{\text{all } L} Lp(L)\,dL}{\int\limits_{\text{all } L} p(L)\,dL} = \int_{-L_{\max}}^{L_{\max}} Lp(L)\,dL$$

$$= A \int_{-\infty}^{\infty} L\,e^{-L^2/2Nl^2}\,dL = 0$$

We have used the normalization condition, and have changed the limits $-L_{\max} \to L_{\max}$ to $-\infty \to \infty$ on the same basis as before. The result of the integration is zero, as may be seen from a table of integrals or by observing that for every value of L there is a value of $-L$ making the opposite contribution to the sum.

$$\bar{L^2} = A \int_{-\infty}^{\infty} L^2\,e^{-L^2/2Nl^2}\,dL \qquad A = \frac{1}{l\sqrt{2\pi N}}$$

From integral tables $\qquad \int_{-\infty}^{\infty} x^2\,e^{-ax^2}\,dx = \frac{1}{2a}\sqrt{\pi/a}$

$$\bar{L^2} = \frac{1}{l\sqrt{2\pi N}}\left(\frac{2Nl^2}{2}\sqrt{2\pi Nl^2}\right) = Nl^2$$

$$L_{\text{rms}} = [\bar{L^2}]^{1/2} = \sqrt{N}\,l$$

This result for the root-mean-square displacement was deduced at the beginning of the discussion of the random walk problem. It is a measure of the expected deviation from the average or expected value $\overline{L} = 0$. In more general circumstances it is called the **standard deviation** and denoted σ. Since it will be used in future expressions we will use this instead of the rather cumbersome L_{rms}.

$$\sigma \equiv L_{\text{rms}} = \sqrt{N}\, l$$

It is convenient to write $p(L)$ in terms of the standard deviation σ

$$p(L) = \frac{1}{\sqrt{2\pi}\,\sigma}\, e^{-L^2/2\sigma^2}$$

Note that some information about the shape of $p(L)$ is obtained by differentiating with respect to L.

$$p = A\, e^{-L^2/2\sigma^2}$$

$$\frac{dp}{dL} = A\, e^{-L^2/2\sigma^2}\left(-\frac{L}{\sigma^2}\right) \qquad \frac{d^2p}{dL^2} = A\, e^{-L^2/2\sigma^2}\left(-\frac{L}{\sigma^2}\right)^2 + A\, e^{-L^2/2\sigma^2}\left(-\frac{1}{\sigma^2}\right)$$

Setting the first derivative equal to zero shows where the curve has a maximum—as we know, at $L = 0$. Setting the second derivative equal to zero shows where the curve has a point of inflection. Canceling terms leaves

$$\left(\frac{L}{\sigma^2}\right)^2 - \frac{1}{\sigma^2} = 0 \qquad \text{or} \qquad L = \pm\sigma$$

There are points of inflection at $L = \pm\sigma$. Since $p(\sigma)/p(0) = e^{-1/2} = 0.6065$, the probability density is down to 0.6 of its maximum value at these points.

The probability density is shown plotted against L/l for the three values of N of 10,000, 40,000 and 160,000. The numbers have been chosen so that N increases by a factor 4. The values of $\sigma/l = \sqrt{N}$ are 100, 200, and 400. The abscissa can be regarded as number of steps from the origin, or as displacement L measured in units of the step length l.

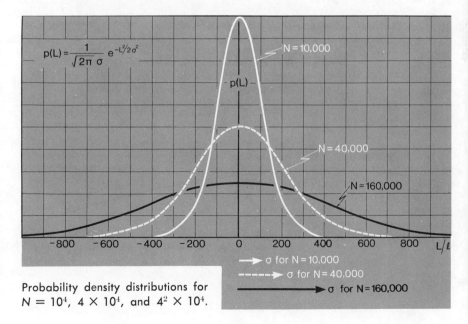

Probability density distributions for $N = 10^4$, 4×10^4, and $4^2 \times 10^4$.

The heights of the maxima $p(0) \propto 1/\sigma \propto 1/\sqrt{N}$ decrease as N is increased, and the widths of the curves as measured by $\sigma \propto \sqrt{N}$ increase as N is increased. The areas under the curves are the same.

GAUSSIAN DISTRIBUTION IN STANDARD FORM

For purposes of calculation it is useful to express the Gaussian distribution in a form in which the variable L is expressed in units of the root-mean-square length (or standard deviation) σ.

Setting $x = L/\sigma$, $dx = dL/\sigma$

$$p(L)\,dL = \frac{1}{\sqrt{2\pi}\,\sigma}\, e^{-L^2/2\sigma^2}\,dL = \frac{1}{\sqrt{2\pi}}\, e^{-x^2/2}\,dx = p(x)\,dx$$

The Gaussian distribution in **standard form** is $p(x) = \dfrac{1}{\sqrt{2\pi}}\, e^{-x^2/2}$

In this notation the single curve shown represents *all* Gaussian distributions. The distribution is said to be expressed in normal coordinates. In the table a

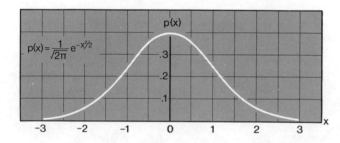

Gaussian distribution
in standard form.

few values are given for x, $p(x)$ and $P(0 \to x)$. This is the area under the curve in the range $0 \to x$ and is the probability that x will be in this range.

$$P(0 \to x) = \int_0^x p(x)\,dx$$

x	$p(x)$	$P(0 \to x)$	x	$p(x)$	$P(0 \to x)$
0	0.3989	0	1.0	0.2420	0.3413
0.2	0.3910	0.0793	2.0	0.0540	0.4773
0.4	0.3683	0.1554	3.0	0.0044	0.4987
0.6	0.3332	0.2258	4.0	0.0001	0.5000
0.8	0.2897	0.2881	5.0	0.0000	0.5000

To say $P(0 \to 1) = 0.3413$ means that there is a 34% chance that a single value of a measured quantity will be found within one standard deviation of the mean value of the quantity, on the high side. It is more useful to use $P(-1 \to 1) = 0.6826$, which says there is a 68% chance that an observed value of a measured quantity will lie within one standard deviation on either side of the mean, and a 32% chance it will be found outside these limits.

In the 10,000-step random walk distribution shown before, there is a 68% chance that an observed result will be within 100 steps of the starting position. There is a 95% chance it will be within 200 steps of the origin, and a 99.74% chance it will be within 300 steps. A random walk may clear the head, but it is no way to get anywhere.

GAUSSIAN DISTRIBUTION WITH
NON-ZERO AVERAGE VALUE

The random walk of N steps and the tossing of N coins are very similar situations; in both the result is determined by the binomial distribution (in the special case for $p = 1/2$)

$$P(n) = \frac{1}{2^N} \frac{N!}{n!(N-n)!}$$

This distribution applies to discrete (non-continuous) values of the variable n, but for large values of N leads to the Gaussian distribution, which applies to a continuous variable. We developed the Gaussian distribution for the random walk because it is somewhat simpler to deal with a distribution about an average value of zero than it is to deal with ones about a non-zero average value. For coin tossing the average number of heads $\bar{n} = N/2$, so that the average value is different for different N.

We can translate the random walk distribution

$$p(L)\,dL = \frac{1}{\sqrt{2\pi}\,\sigma}\,e^{-L^2/2\sigma^2}\,dL = \frac{1}{\sqrt{2\pi N}\,l}\,e^{-L^2/2Nl^2}\,dL$$

into the coin tossing distribution by using the relation between the number of heads n and displacement L.

$$n = \frac{1}{2}\left(N + \frac{L}{l}\right) \quad \text{or} \quad \frac{L}{l} = 2\left(n - \frac{N}{2}\right), \quad \frac{1}{l}\,dL = 2dn$$

$$\therefore \quad p(L)\,dL = \frac{2}{\sqrt{2\pi N}}\,e^{-\left(n-\frac{N}{2}\right)^2/\left(\frac{N}{2}\right)}\,dn = p(n)\,dn$$

or $$\qquad p(n) = \frac{1}{\sqrt{2\pi}(\sqrt{N}/2)}\,e^{-\left(n-\frac{N}{2}\right)^2/2\left(\frac{N}{4}\right)}$$

which we have written in this form so that if we set $\sigma = \sqrt{N}/2$ we have

$$p(n) = \frac{1}{\sqrt{2\pi}\,\sigma}\,e^{-\left(n-\frac{N}{2}\right)^2/2\sigma^2}$$

This is the probability density distribution for the number of heads n, which is now considered to be a continuous variable. The $p(n)$ has its maximum value at

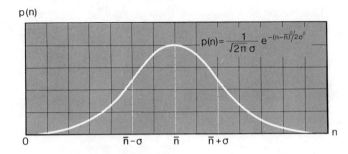

$$p(n) = \frac{1}{\sqrt{2\pi}\,\sigma}\,e^{-(n-\bar{n})^2/2\sigma^2}$$

The probability density distribution for coin tossing is Gaussian with a non-zero average value.

$n = N/2$, and is a Gaussian distribution symmetric about this value of n. The expected or average value $\bar{n} = N/2$, and the standard deviation $\sigma = \sqrt{N}/2$.

In this case note that σ is *not* n_{rms}. It is the root-mean-square **deviation** from the mean, as it was in the random walk, but this time the mean value is not zero.

$$\sigma = [\overline{(n-\bar{n})^2}]^{1/2}$$

The quantity σ^2 is also a measure of the spread of the distribution. It is the **variance** or the **dispersion.** Since

$$\sigma^2 = \overline{(n-\bar{n})^2} = \overline{(n^2 - 2\bar{n}n + \bar{n}^2)}$$
$$= \overline{n^2} - 2\bar{n}\bar{n} + \bar{n}^2 = \overline{n^2} - \bar{n}^2$$

the dispersion σ^2 (and therefore the average deviation σ) can be determined by calculating $\overline{n^2}$.

You can verify by direct integration that $\bar{n} = N/2$, that $\sigma = \sqrt{N}/2$ and that $p(n)$ is properly normalized. For example

$$\int_0^N \frac{1}{\sqrt{2\pi}\,\sigma}\,e^{-\left(n-\frac{N}{2}\right)^2/2\sigma^2}\,dn = \frac{1}{\sqrt{2\pi}\,\sigma}\int_{-N/2}^{N/2} e^{-x^2/2\sigma^2}\,dx \qquad \text{where } x = n - \frac{N}{2}$$

$$\cong \frac{1}{\sqrt{2\pi}\,\sigma}\int_{-\infty}^{\infty} e^{-x^2/2\sigma^2}\,dx$$

$$= \frac{1}{\sqrt{2\pi}\,\sigma}\,\sqrt{2\pi}\,\sigma = 1$$

The effect of increasing N is to lower the height of the maximum $p(\bar{n}) \propto 1/\sqrt{N}$ and to increase the spread of the distribution $\sigma \propto \sqrt{N}$, as for the random walk, and *also* to increase the average value $\bar{n} = N/2$. If we attempt to plot $p(n)$ for the three values of N of 10,000, 40,000 and 160,000 on the same scale as we did for the random walk, the graph does not show the shape of the distributions at all. The average values $\bar{n} = N/2$ are 5000, 20,000 and 80,000; and the standard deviations $\sigma = \sqrt{N}/2$ are 50, 100 and 200, too small to see on the same scale. Shifting the distributions to the origin, by subtracting the average value $\bar{n}$ in each case, we can compare the shapes of the three distributions as we did for the random walk. The graphs shown for the random walk can be used here by revising the labeling and the scale for the abscissa. Instead of $p(L)$ the vertical axis is $p(n - N/2)$. Recalling that

Probability density distributions for $N = 10^4$, 4×10^4, and $4^2 \times 10^4$.

$$\frac{L}{l} = 2\left(n - \frac{N}{2}\right) \quad \text{or} \quad n - \frac{N}{2} = \frac{1}{2}\left(\frac{L}{l}\right)$$

the numbers on the horizontal axis $(n - N/2)$ will all be half as great. In this case the values of σ are 50, 100 and 200 instead of 100, 200 and 400.

An N-event random walk and an N-event coin toss are mathematically similar but are not identical. The difference arises because the desired overall result is different; for the coins, it is the total number of heads n, for the random walk it is the displacement L, which depends on the total number of heads **less** the total number of tails. If there is one more head, there is one less tail, and L changes by two steps. This is the reason for the factor 2 between the two distributions.

ABSOLUTE AND RELATIVE FLUCTUATIONS

We began this chapter by asking some general questions about what you might expect if you tossed 100 coins or 10,000 coins. We asked if you would expect most of the results to fall between 45 and 55 heads if you tossed 100 coins many times. Now we can answer such questions precisely—at least to the extent that 100 can be considered a large number, and the Gaussian distribution applied.

For 100 coins the average number of heads $\bar{n} = N/2 = 50$ and the standard deviation $\sigma = \sqrt{N}/2 = 5$. Therefore there is a 68% chance that a particular result will be in the range 45 to 55, or within 10% of the average. There is a 95% chance of finding between 40 and 60 heads, a 20% variation.

For 10,000 coins $\bar{n} = 5000$ and $\sigma = 50$. There is a 68% chance of finding a result between 4950 and 5050, within 1% of the average, and a 95% chance of finding a variation within 2%.

This example emphasizes an extremely important general fact about random events. In any random situation the result is never certain; there will always be fluctuations from an average or expected result $\bar{n}$, and σ is a precise measure of these fluctuations. As the number of random events N increases, the magnitude of the **absolute** fluctuations $\sigma \propto \sqrt{N}$ increases, but the magnitude of the **relative** fluctuations $\sigma/\bar{n} \propto 1/\sqrt{N}$ **decreases**. Even though the absolute probability of observing the most probable result $\bar{n}$ decreases as N increases, the relative spread around this result decreases. This means that **the most probable result of a number of independent random events becomes overwhelmingly probable (and therefore the only result observed) as the number of events becomes very large.**

MEASURING HEADS

The calculations have shown what to expect for numbers of heads in coin-tossing experiments with N coins. What kind of experiments could be performed to see if the results agreed with the calculations? If N is large—even if only 100—the counting of heads will be laborious. It will be instructive to think about some method by which the overall effect of the number of heads could be measured without actually counting. The device discussed here we developed to use in the Physical Science Study Committee film *Random Events*, but you will be able to think of other ways of doing the same thing.

Instead of tossing coins we toss square cards which are white on one side (heads) and black on the other (tails). After they are tossed they are laid out to form a large square. This is illuminated, and the amount of light reflected from it is measured with a light meter. The meter can be calibrated so that it reads zero if all the cards are black (minimum reflection) and a maximum if all the cards are white (maximum reflection). It can be adjusted so that it has a linear response—that is, so that if 25% of the cards are white it will read one-quarter of its maximum deflection. The reading of the meter is then a direct measurement of the number of white cards (heads). In the PSSC film the cards were mounted so that they rotated freely (and **independently**) on vertical wires. They were all set spinning (a fan helps), and then a board was pressed against them to make a flat surface.

Think first about the situation where there are only 16 cards, each being 1 ft square. The light meter is calibrated to read from 0 (all black) to 16 (all white). If the experiment is performed a number of times, the observed result will fluctuate. The meter will read mostly numbers from 6 to 10 but occasionally 5 or 11, and once in a while 4 or 12. By taking a large number of readings we

N=16

n=9

A 16-card array.

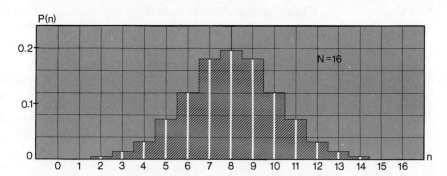

Calculated probability distribution for N = 16.

could acquire enough data to prepare an **experimental** probability distribution graph which would be similar to the calculated graph shown. This was calculated from the binomial distribution

$$P(n) = \frac{1}{2^N} \frac{N!}{n!(N-n)!} \qquad \text{with } N = 16$$

because the Gaussian distribution is not a good approximation for this value of N. The distribution is shown both as a bar graph and as a histogram. The area under the histogram is unity.

If our experimental distribution seemed to differ markedly from the calculated one, this would indicate that the apparatus did not fulfill the conditions under which the binomial distribution applies—for example, the cards might not be spinning independently. The experimental distribution is of course the one which is valid for the apparatus, not the calculated one.

Now think about the situation where there are many more cards made to fit the same overall area. Instead of a 4×4 array, we use a 16×16 array in a 4-ft square, so that there are 256 cards, each 3 in. square. If we perform the experiment a number of times, using the same scale as before for the light meter, we observe that the meter always reads about 8, no matter what pattern of cards is produced. As before, we can use the binomial distribution to make an exact calculation of what to expect, and we find that the probability of having exactly equal numbers of black and white square is **less** this time.

For $N = 16$ $\qquad P(8) = \dfrac{1}{2^{16}} \dfrac{16!}{8!\ 8!} = 0.196$

For $N = 256$ $\qquad P(128) = \dfrac{1}{2^{256}} \dfrac{256!}{128!\ 128!} = 0.050$

A 256-card array.

However, this time the light meter does not read in 16 discrete steps but in 256 steps, and therefore seems to read continuously. The range 7.5 to 8.5 on the meter corresponds to a range 128 ± 8 for n, so there are about 16 values for n near 128 which would contribute to a meter reading of 8. A rough calculation, using the peak value of $P(n) = 0.05$ for all n in this range gives $P(120 \rightarrow 136) \cong 16 \times 0.05 = 0.8$. This will be high because the peak value is used.

A calculation of $P(n)$ for all n is possible but cumbersome, and the Gaussian distribution gives a very good basis for calculation even though $N = 256$ is not very large. The probability density is

$$p(n) = \frac{1}{\sqrt{2\pi}\,\sigma} e^{-(n-\bar{n})/2\sigma^2}$$

where $\bar{n} = N/2 = 128$ and $\sigma = \sqrt{N}/2 = 8$. The peak value $p(\bar{n}) = 1/\sqrt{2\pi}\,\sigma = 1/\sqrt{2\pi}\,8 = 0.050$ as calculated from the binomial distribution.

Using the results previously calculated for the Gaussian distribution, we know there is a 68% probability that n will be within one standard deviation of

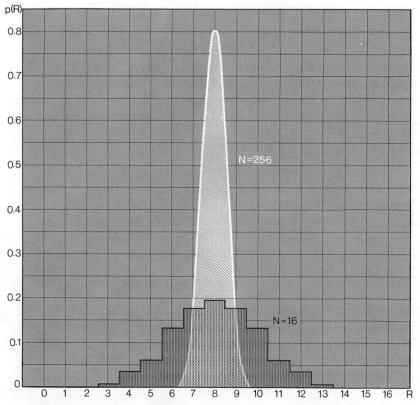

Calculated probability density distribution for $N = 256$, plotted against meter reading R for comparison with the $N = 16$ distribution.

the mean, that is, in the range $128 \pm 8 = 128 \pm 6.25\%$. In terms of readings on the light meter scale, there is a 68% chance that the reading will be $8 \pm 6.25\% = 8 \pm 0.5$, or between 7.5 and 8.5. Thus the reading will be closer to 8 than any other integral value for more than half of the observations.

This probability density, instead of being shown plotted against n, is shown plotted against meter reading R, so that it can be compared with the distribution for $N = 16$, for which n and R are the same number.

$$p(R) = \frac{1}{\sqrt{2\pi}\,\sigma}\, e^{-(R-\bar{R})/2\sigma^2}$$

where $\bar{R} = 8$ div (scale divisions), and $\sigma = 0.5$ div. The peak value $p(\bar{R}) = 1/\sqrt{2\pi}\,0.5 = 0.8$ (div)$^{-1}$. Note the product of $p(R)$ and R gives the probability P a dimensionless quantity. The probability of a reading within $R_1 \rightarrow R_2$ is

$$P(R_1 \rightarrow R_2) = \int_{R_1}^{R_2} p(R)\, dR$$

For the histogram for $N = 16$ only integral values of R occur. The area under both graphs is the same, unity.

The "sharpening" of the distribution as N increases is apparent. The number $N = 256$ is relatively small when compared to the numbers of atoms in physical systems, so that again we emphasize that the most probable result is what is almost always observed, and fluctuations from average behavior are almost never observed.

Whether or not fluctuations are observed depends on the sensitivity of the measuring instrument. In our experiment it was easy to calibrate the light meter so that it "counted" the number of white cards when there was a total of only 16 cards, but it would have been very difficult to calibrate it to do this precisely for 256 cards. Such a meter, reading from 0 to 16, might be read with confidence to the nearest fifth of a division, so that it could be used to count the white cards to within about 3 cards.

Most physical experiments involve the measurement of quantities that do not vary continuously, but normally appear to do so. An electric current for example is a flow of discrete electrons, but under most conditions this is not apparent. Using tiny currents and sensitive meters it is possible to observe fluctuations, and to see that the effect is a random one. Every electronic system has a basic noise level which arises because electron flow is a series of random events.

THE RANDOM WALK EXTENDED

The two situations which we have used to develop our story, coin tossing and the one-dimensional random walk, are real but are artificial rather than naturally occurring. They are the kind of simplified situations it is useful to use as models in order to try to understand similar but more complex natural situations.

In order to discuss the limitation of observability possible in the random walk experiment, we introduced a hypothetical coin-tossing gnat whose position was observed through a microscope. Perhaps you recognized that watching the gnat was rather like using a microscope to observe a particle in Brownian motion.

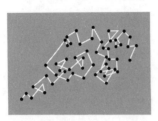

Positions of a suspended colloid particle at equal time intervals.

You are familiar with the fact that tiny particles suspended in a fluid (liquid or gas) move around in an apparently random way. The phenomenon, first observed by a botanist, Robert Brown, in 1827, is considered to be the first direct evidence for the particular or molecular structure of matter, because the motions of the particles is believed to be caused by the bombardment of molecules. On a macroscopic scale this bombardment appears to produce a constant, unfluctuating pressure, because the number of molecules colliding with even a small area is so large that fluctuations are not observable. If particles so small that they can just be detected in a microscope (of the order of the wavelength of light in size, $\sim 10^{-4}$ cm) are suspended in a solution, their area is so small that pressure fluctuations are observable. At any instant the pressure on one side of a particle may be different than on the opposite side so there is a resultant force and the particle moves. Each instant this force changes, so the particle jiggles about in a random way. If the position of the particle in the field of a microscope is recorded at convenient equal intervals of time (every 30 seconds or every minute), and these positions are joined by straight lines, a configuration like the one shown results. The lines are *not* the path of the particle—in the time interval it will have suffered billions of changes in direction —but it gives a picture of the kind of path the particle has. The path is a three-dimensional random walk, but it is observed in the microscope as a two-dimensional motion.

In the kinetic theory of gases a useful model is achieved by thinking of molecules as tiny particles which move in straight lines until they collide with one another or the walls of the container, and then go off in new directions. Again this is a three-dimensional random walk.

There are two basic differences between these kinds of random walk situations and the one-dimensional example we have worked out. One is that, since the motion can be in any direction, there is not the simple "heads-or-tails" choice of direction at each step, and therefore there is not the simplification that $p = 1/2$ for individual events. The second difference is that the "steps" are not of equal length l; they are randomly distributed around some average step length (for molecules this is called the mean free path). In the one-dimensional example with fixed step length l, only displacements L in discrete multiples of l were possible—although we assumed continuity in developing the Gaussian distribution. With steps of varying lengths, any value of L is possible, and it is a continuous variable.

It turns out that neither of these differences changes the result in any fundamental way. For a large number of steps N the probability distribution is Gaussian, and the root-mean-square distance from the starting point (or standard deviation) σ is proportional to $\sqrt{N}$.

If an alien gas, such as sulphur dioxide, is released at some point in a room, then the most probable position for any molecule to be in after some time is its starting point ($\overline{L} = 0$). However, as time goes on there are more and more collisions with other molecules (N increases) and the probability of its being observed further away increases. The statistical theory we have developed has applications in the study of **diffusion.**

Observations on the Brownian motion of suspended colloid particles, and application of statistical theory, led about 70 years ago to the first determination of the constant k (Boltzmann's constant) which is fundamental in atomic physics, and thereby to a determination of N_0, Avogadro's number.

A slightly different example of a random walk situation arises in polymer physics. A polymer molecule consists of a long chain of identical chemical units (monomers). Under some conditions such a chain can be very flexible, with essentially a free rotation possible about the bonds holding the units together, although the angle between bonds (the valence angle) remains fixed. The molecule can be thought of as a random walk with steps of equal length taken in three dimensions, but with a fixed angle between steps. This model and the statistical theory are used in the kinetic theory of rubberlike elasticity to provide an explanation of some of the properties of rubber and other high polymers.

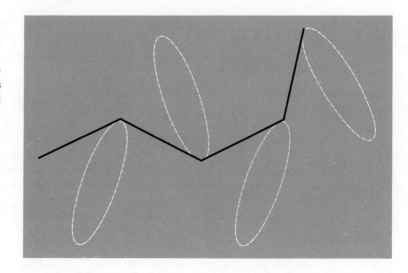

A long chain molecule described as a three-dimensional random walk.

OTHER DISTRIBUTIONS

A probability distribution appropriate for a particular physical system can be determined experimentally by making repeated measurements on the system. In this chapter we have been dealing with certain **theoretically** determined distributions which are applicable to a variety of physical situations, the essential similarity being that of an underlying randomness. If in an experimental situation we observe a fluctuating result, we cannot be sure if this is due to a random effect or not. However, if we take a reasonable number of measurements and find that they are grouped like a Gaussian distribution, then we assume that whatever is producing the fluctuations is a random effect. Thus the distribution is a test for randomness.

There are other theoretical probability distributions of importance in physics because they approximate different physical situations. We will discuss one called the Poisson distribution. It is another special case derivable from the binomial distribution, and therefore the result depends on random events. However, in this case the probability for individual random events is very small: $p \ll 1$.

Before looking at the Poisson distribution, we shall summarize what we have shown so far, and write down the Gaussian distribution in general.

The Gaussian Distribution in General: We have developed the binomial distribution for the special case where the probability for individual random events $p = 1/2$

$$P(n) = \frac{1}{2^N} \frac{N!}{n!(N-n)!}$$

and also the general binomial distribution

$$P(n) = \frac{N!}{n!(N-n)!} p^n q^{N-n} \qquad q = 1 - p$$

We have shown that for large values of N the special case leads to the Gaussian probability density distribution

$$p(n) = \frac{1}{\sqrt{2\pi(N/4)}} e^{-\left(n-\frac{N}{2}\right)^2 / 2\left(\frac{N}{4}\right)} = \frac{1}{\sqrt{2\pi}\,\sigma} e^{-(n-\bar{n})^2/2\sigma^2}$$

The general binomial distribution (p not necessarily $1/2$) also leads to a Gaussian distribution **provided** that p is neither very small ($p \ll 1$) nor very large ($q \ll 1$, $p \cong 1$). This is because in the derivation it is assumed that all values of n of interest, those near where $P(n)$ is a maximum at $\bar{n}$, are large numbers, and this would not necessarily be so if either p or q were very small.

The general Gaussian distribution is

$$p(n) = \frac{1}{\sqrt{2\pi Npq}} e^{-(n-Np)^2/2Npq}$$

The average values are

$$\bar{n} = Np \qquad \qquad \text{: the average value}$$
$$\sigma^2 = \overline{(n - \bar{n})^2} = Npq \qquad \text{: the dispersion or variance}$$
$$\sigma = \sqrt{Npq} \qquad \qquad \text{: the average deviation}$$

Note that the expected result of N random events, each of probability p, is Np as it must be. Again the average deviation from the expected result, σ, is proportional to $\sqrt{N}$.
  Writing $p(n)$ in terms of $\bar{n}$ and σ gives

$$p(n) = \frac{1}{\sqrt{2\pi}\,\sigma}\, e^{-(n-\bar{n})^2/2\sigma^2}$$

which is identical to the result in the special case.

THE POISSON DISTRIBUTION

In order to give you an idea of the kind of situation in which the Poisson distribution is useful we shall invent another possible, but not very probable, example. Suppose that after reading this book for some time you decide that you are really more interested in English than in physics, so to amuse yourself you count the number of grammatical errors you find on each page. As you go through the book the number varies—sometimes 2, sometimes 3, occasionally 5 or 6, or even 0. When you have finished you add up all the errors and divide by the number of pages and find that the average number of errors per page $\bar{n} = 2.5$. Since we are inventing the result we could invent an integral number but of course it does not have to be. We hope there are fewer errors than this, but we do not know how pedantic you may be.
  The probability question is this: If you open to a page at random, what is the probability that it will have 0, 1, 2 or any other particular number of errors? (Even though the average number of errors per page is 2.5, you will not find this number on any page!) What is the probability $P(n)$ that there are n errors on a particular page, if there is an average $\bar{n} = 2.5$ errors/page? This is the kind of question that is answered by the Poisson distribution **provided** the errors are distributed at random through the book. If we plot a graph showing n vs. number of pages with n errors, and it approximates a Poisson distribution, then we can take this as evidence that the errors are random.
  In this case we could use the binomial distribution to calculate the result precisely.

$$P(n) = \frac{N!}{n!(N-n)!}\, p^n q^{N-n} \qquad q = 1 - p$$

We know N, the total number of random events—it is the total number of errors in the book. We know p, the probability for an individual random event to occur. It is $p = \bar{n}/N$. Our assumption of randomness is the assumption that there is the **same** probability p for the number of errors on any page. Knowing N and p and $q = 1 - p$ we can calculate $P(n)$ for any n.

The value of the Poisson distribution is that it can be used even if N and p are not known separately, but the product $pN = \bar{n}$ is known.

You did not have to go through the whole book to determine a value for $\bar{n}$; you could have chosen a sample of m pages, counted the number of errors M in these pages, and calculated $\bar{n} = M/m$ errors per page. The larger the sample you used, the more confidence you would have in the result $\bar{n}$. In many experimental situations you have no way of knowing the number N, but you can determine an experimental value for $\bar{n}$.

The assumptions made in deriving the Poisson distribution from the binomial distribution are that the situation is one for which $p \ll 1$ and $n \ll N$. This also means that $N \gg 1$.

The binomial distribution is

$$P(n) = \frac{N!}{n!(N - n)!} \, p^n (1 - p)^{N-n}$$

The term $\dfrac{N!}{(N - n)!} = N(N - 1)(N - 2) \cdots (N - n + 1) \cong N^n$ $\qquad (n \ll N)$

The term $\qquad\qquad (1 - p)^{N-n} \cong e^{-Np}$

since $\qquad \ln (1 - p)^{N-n} = (N - n) \ln (1 - p)$

$$\cong N \ln (1 - p) \qquad\qquad (n \ll N)$$

$$\cong -Np \qquad\qquad (\ln [1 + x] \cong x \text{ if } x \ll 1)$$

$$\therefore \quad P(n) \cong \frac{N^n}{n!} \, p^n \, e^{-Np}$$

or since $\bar{n} = Np$ $\qquad\qquad P(n) = e^{-\bar{n}} \dfrac{\bar{n}^n}{n!}$

This is the Poisson distribution. It cannot be considered a continuous function because it is only valid for small values of n. The average value $\bar{n}$, and therefore the term $e^{-\bar{n}}$, are constants in a particular situation. The factor $n!$ in the denominator causes $P(n)$ to decrease rapidly as n increases. If $\bar{n} < 1$, the factor $\bar{n}^n$ also decreases as n increases, so that $P(n)$ is always decreasing as n increases. However, if $\bar{n} > 1$, the factor $\bar{n}^n$ causes $P(n)$ to increase at first as n increases from zero, reaching a maximum near $n = \bar{n}$, and then decreasing as $n!$ takes over.

You can verify the normalization condition

$$\sum_{n=0}^{N} P(n) = \sum_{n=0}^{\infty} P(n) = 1$$

where the limit can be changed because there is negligible contribution to $P(n)$

for large n. You can also verify that $\sum_{n=0}^{\infty} nP(n) = \bar{n}$, as it should.

Calculation of numerical values of $P(n)$ are simplified because $P(n) = (\bar{n}/n)P(n-1)$.

In the errors/page example $\bar{n} = 2.5$ and $e^{-2.5} = 0.0821$ so that $P(0) = 0.0821$, $P(1) = (2.5/1)0.0821 = 0.205$, $P(2) = (2.5/2)0.205 = 0.256$, etc. The result is shown in the figure. There is about an 8% chance of finding no errors on a page, a 20% chance of finding 1, a 26% chance of finding 2, up to a 1% chance of finding 7. Does this mean, since the book has more than 100 pages, there must be at least one page with 7 errors?

The distributions for $\bar{n} = 1/2, 1, 2, 3, 4$ and 5 are shown, with lines joining the appropriate points so that they can be identified and the trend observed. The larger the value of $\bar{n}$, the more symmetric such graphs are with respect to the maximum, and for large values of $\bar{n}$ the Poisson distribution becomes the Gaussian distribution.

As stated before, the Poisson distribution is useful because it applies to situations where we do not know the probability p that an individual event will happen, or the probability $(1-p)$ that it will not happen. We know how many times the event happened under certain conditions, and not how often it did not happen. Even so we can make repeated measurements for a number of trials and determine the average number $\bar{n}$.

You may have seen a Geiger counter used to detect the presence of a radioactive material. Each time the counter "clicks" it means that an atom has emitted a particle (α-particle or β-particle) and changed into a different kind of atom. The emitted particle passing through the Geiger counter produces the click (or the count, if the results are being recorded). Not all the particles emitted by the radioactive sample pass through the counter so that not all the atomic disintegrations are observed; the farther away from the source the counter is, the fewer counts there are. If you have heard such a counter you know that the noise does not appear to be regular—it is "click—click——click-click——click——click-click-click. . . ." Do the clicks come at random time intervals, or is there some sort of regularity? If they are random we can assume

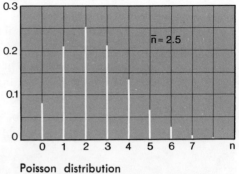

Poisson distribution for $\bar{n} = 2.5$.

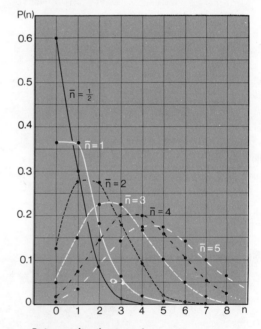

Poisson distributions for a series of values of $\bar{n}$.

that the disintegration of atoms is a random process, and this is important information in any attempt to develop a theory for disintegration.

This is the sort of situation in which the Poisson distribution is useful. We do not know the total number of atoms N which might disintegrate (and in any case are not observing all of the disintegrations) and we do not know the probability p that a particular atom will disintegrate (in any given time interval). However, it is reasonable to assume that p is small, for any reasonable time interval, because there are enormous numbers of atoms and if anything but a very tiny fraction of them disintegrated there would be so many clicks that individual ones would not be distinguishable.

n (counts/ interval)	$N(n)$ (experi- mental)	$P(n)$	$N(n)$ (calculated)
0	57	0.021	54
1	203	0.081	210
2	383	0.156	407
3	525	0.201	525
4	532	0.195	508
5	408	0.151	394
6	273	0.097	254
7	139	0.054	140
8	45	0.026	68
9	27	0.011	29
10	10	0.004	11
11	4	0.001	4
12	0	0.0005	1
13	1	0	0
14	1	0	0

The table and figure show the result of an experiment of this type of historical interest, performed by Rutherford and Geiger in 1910, and reported in the *Philosophical Magazine* of that year in an article "The Probability Variations in the Distribution of α Particles." The aim was "to settle whether the distribution of α-particles on an average is that to be anticipated if the α-particles are expelled at random [in regard to both] space and time." Disintegrations of atoms in a sample of polonium were detected by observing scintillations on a phosphorescent screen (Geiger had not yet developed the Geiger counter). A microscope was used to observe about 1 square millimeter of the screen, and scintillations were observed by eye and recorded by closing a switch that put a mark on a chronograph tape; about 2000 counts per day were

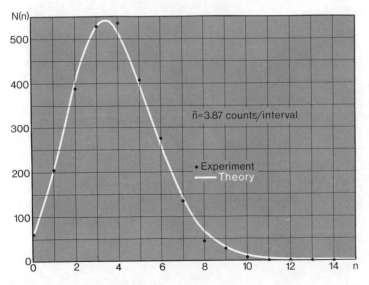

$\bar{n}=3.87$ counts/interval

• Experiment
—— Theory

Comparison of experimental results for α-particle emission with the Poisson distribution.

made in this way, and a total of 10,097 counts were recorded. The number of counts in each $\frac{1}{8}$-minute interval were recorded from the tape, for a total of 2608 such intervals. Thus $\bar{n}$, the average number of counts per $\frac{1}{8}$-minute interval, was $\bar{n} = 10,097/2608 = 3.87$ counts/interval. The actual number of counts per interval n varied from 0 to 14, with the frequency shown in the table; $N(n)$ (expt) is the number of intervals in which the number n counts were observed. The table also shows $P(n)$ calculated using the Poisson distribution for $\bar{n} = 3.87$, and $N(n)$ (calc) which is obtained by multiplying $P(n)$ by the total number of intervals. The values of $N(n)$ (calc) are shown on the graph by the continuous curve, in order to differentiate the calculated values from the experimental values, shown as points. The experiment was undertaken to see if the disintegration of atoms were random events; this was not thought to be necessarily the case because the disintegration of one atom might cause the disintegration of neighboring atoms. The paper concludes "the distribution of α-particles in time is in agreement with the laws of probability and the α-particles are emitted at random."

Questions for discussion

1. Suppose that you measure the value of a physical quantity x a number n times, and calculate the average value $\bar{x}$. Assuming that the variations in the measured values are random, would you expect the probability that $\bar{x}$ represents the "correct" value of the quantity to increase with n, with $\sqrt{n}$, with $1/n$, or with $1/\sqrt{n}$?

2. Under what conditions does the binomial distribution lead to the Gaussian distribution? Under what circumstances does it lead to the Poisson distribution?

3. We used the Poisson distribution to describe the emission of α-particles from a radioactive source. Could the experimental results be described using the Gaussian distribution?

Problems

1. Construct a histogram showing the probabilities of tossing each of the eleven numbers 2, 3, $\cdots$, 12, with a pair of six-sided dice, assuming that for each die the probability of a particular face being up is $p = 1/6$ and assuming that the two dice are statistically independent.

    What is the probability of throwing a number of 5 or less with the two dice? What is the probability of throwing either a 7 or an 11?

2. If three coins are tossed ("odd man out") what is the probability that all three coins will have the same side up? What is the probability that there will be an odd man?

3. What is the probability of being dealt a bridge hand (from a well-shuffled deck of cards) that contains all 13 cards in the same suit? What is the probability of being dealt the following hand: Spades, A 9 4; Hearts, J 9 6 4; Diamonds, Q 10 7; Clubs, K 8 5?

4. **(a)** What is the probability that two people will have the same birthday? **(b)** What is the probability that in a group of three people, two will have the same birthday? **(c)** For a group of N people, what is the average number of pairs with a common birthday? How large a group is necessary in order that this average number is greater than one? Is this number the probability that two of the group will have the same birthday? How large a group is necessary in order to be certain that two will have the same birthday?

5. The spread of the Gaussian distribution can be expressed in terms of the standard deviation σ, or in terms of the width of the distribution at points that are at one-half the peak value. **(a)** What is the value of $p(x)$, in terms of the peak value $p(0)$, for $x = \pm\sigma$? **(b)** What is the total width, in terms of σ, at points that are at one-half the peak value?

6. The deviation from the average value $\bar{x}$ can be represented by the average deviation, a.d. $= (\sum |\bar{x} - x_i|)/N$, or by the standard deviation, $\sigma = \{[\sum (\bar{x} - x_i)^2]/N\}^{1/2}$. For a Gaussian distribution these are related by a.d. $= \sqrt{2/\pi}\,\sigma$. Show that this is true for the special case of $\bar{x} = 0$, by calculating $\overline{|x|}$ for the Gaussian distribution.

7. **(a)** Calculate 10! exactly. **(b)** Determine ln 10! using 6-place tables. **(c)** Determine the value of ln 10! to 6 figures using the Stirling approximation $\ln M! = M \ln M - M + \frac{1}{2}\ln M + \frac{1}{2}\ln 2\pi$. **(d)** Determine the difference Δ between the results of (b) and (c), and the percentage error introduced in ln 10! by the Stirling approximation. **(e)** Show that the error introduced in the value of 10! is approximately $-\Delta \times 10!$, and calculate the value of 10! as given by the Stirling approximation. **(f)** What is the percentage error in 10! as determined by the Stirling approximation?

8. For very large values of M, the term $\frac{1}{2}\ln(2\pi M)$ in the Stirling approximation becomes negligible, and the approximation $\ln M! = M \ln M - M$ can be used. Determine the percentage error in using this approximation (rather than the more accurate one) for $M = 10$, $M = 100$, and $M = 1000$.

9. A coin is tossed 100 times. Determine the probability **(a)** that there is an equal number of heads (H) and tails (T) (consult a 6-place table giving logarithms of factorial numbers), **(b)** that there are exactly 20 more H's than T's, **(c)** that there are at least 20 more H's than T's.

10. A blindfolded monkey is placed at the center of a long stretched high wire. He takes 6-in. steps along the wire, the direction of each being random. **(a)** After 100 steps, he is less than 10 ft from his starting point. What is the probability that he should be at least 10 ft away? **(b)** After 400 steps, he is still within 10 ft of his initial position. What is the probability that he should be at least 10 ft away now? **(c)** About how many steps are necessary in order that he has a 50% chance of being at least 10 ft away?

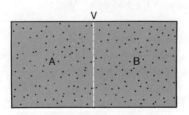

11. A volume V contains N ideal gas molecules. Think of the volume as having two halves A and B. The probability for a particular molecule to be in half A is $p = 1/2$. On the average there will be $N/2$ molecules in each half, but at any instant there will be fluctuations from this average state, with $N/2 + n$ molecules in one half and $N/2 - n$ molecules in the other.

(a) Use the binomial distribution determined for the coin-tossing situation to write down the probability $P(n)$ for a particular distribution. (Note that in the coin-tossing distribution n was the number of heads, whereas here n corresponds to the number of "excess heads.")

(b) Assume that $N \gg 1$, and $n \ll N$, and express the distribution $P(n)$ in Gaussian form.

(c) Assume that n can be treated as a continuous variable, and write down the probability density distribution $p(n)$. What is the average or expected value $\bar{n}$? What is the standard deviation σ?

(d) Determine the probability that at some instant all of the N molecules are in the A half of the volume, for $N = 2$, $N = 10$ and $N = 100$. For $N = 2$, what is the probability that both molecules will be in one half of the other?

(e) Determine the probability of finding the distribution in its average state $(n = 0)$ for $N = 2$, $N = 10$ and $N = 100$.

(f) Determine the probability that there is one extra molecule in half A, for $N = 2$ $N = 10$ and $N = 100$. (For $N = 100$, use the fact that $e^x \cong 1 + x$ for $x \ll 1$.)

(g) For $N = 10$, n in the range -1 to 1 corresponds to a fluctuation in the number in A of $\pm 20\%$. What is the probability of finding the distribution in this range? For $N = 100$, n in the range -10 to 10 corresponds to a fluctuation of the number in A of $\pm 20\%$. What is the probability of finding the distribution in this range?

(h) At STP the average number density in a gas is 2.7×10^{19} molecules/cm³. What volume of gas corresponds to $N = 100$?

(i) Show that if the number of molecules N is one million, the volume involved (at STP) is of the order of the wavelength of light in size. What is the probability of finding this system with fluctuations in the range $\pm 0.2\%$?

(j) For a volume of gas of about 4 cm³ at STP, $N = 10^{20}$ molecules. For this system, what is the probability of finding a fluctuation of one part in a million (i.e., of finding 10^{14} more molecules in one half than in the other)? What is the probability of finding the same number of molecules in both halves, to within two parts in 10^{10}?

12. A system consists of N gas molecules, each with a magnetic dipole moment m. This magnetic moment is related to the intrinsic angular momentum, or "spin," of the molecules, so we will call it the spin for short. Assume that the system is ideal, that is that the interaction between the spins is negligible and therefore the spins behave independently. Assume that if the system is in an external magnetic field the spins are either in the field direction (parallel) or in the opposite direction (anti-parallel). For a particular field the probability of a spin being parallel is p, the probability of being anti-parallel is $q = 1 - p$. For zero field $p = q = 1/2$. On the average there will be pN parallel spins and qN anti-parallel spins, giving an average magnetic dipole moment for the system as a whole $\overline{M} = N(p - q)m$, or an average magnetic moment per molecule $\overline{m} = (p - q)m$.

(a) Assume a general Gaussian distribution of spins, and show that the dispersion in the magnetic moment per molecule is $\sigma^2 = \overline{(m - \overline{m})^2} = 4pqm^2$, so that the standard deviation is $\sigma = 2\sqrt{pq}\, m$ and the standard deviation in the overall magnetic moment M is $\sigma = 2\sqrt{Npq}\, m$.

(b) Suppose that for a particular magnetic field $p = 0.51$ and $q = 0.49$. Determine the average magnetic moment $\overline{M}$, its standard deviation σ and the relative standard deviation $\sigma/\overline{M}$ for $N = 100$ and for $N = 10^{20}$. Note that for $N = 100$ the standard deviation is greater than the average magnetic moment, so that fluctuations would be large, but for the more realistic $N = 10^{20}$ the relative fluctuations would be very small and a single measurement could be expected to give "the" value of the magnetic moment M of the system.

13. The current flowing through a simple two-element vacuum tube (a diode) appears to be steady on a macroscopic scale, but is actually subject to fluctuations because the emission of electrons from the hot cathode is a random process. If the current is very small, and if all the electrons emitted are attracted to the anode (the current is not "space charge limited") these fluctuations can be detected. This is called the shot effect.

If we assume that the emissions of electrons are independent random events (that is, the emission of an electron is not influenced by the emission of other electrons) we can describe the process as follows.

Think of a very short time interval Δt, short enough so we can say there is a small probability p that an electron will be emitted in the interval, but a negligible probability that more than one electron will be emitted in the interval. In a time interval τ that is much larger than Δt, there will be a large number $N = \tau/\Delta t$ of the small intervals, and in each of these N intervals there is a probability p that an electron will be emitted, and a probability $q = 1 - p \cong 1$ that one will not be emitted.

(a) What is the total average charge $\overline{Q}$ emitted in time τ? **(b)** What is the average current $\overline{i}$ over the time interval? **(c)** What is the dispersion σ^2 in the charge emitted in time τ? **(d)** What is the dispersion σ^2 in the current in the interval? Express the result in terms of e, τ and $\overline{i}$. **(e)** Determine the standard deviation σ in the current and the relative standard deviation $\sigma/\overline{i}$ for a time interval of 1 sec and currents of 10^{-4} amp and 10^{-8} amp.

14. (a) Verify that for a Poisson distribution $P(n) = (\overline{n}/n)P(n - 1)$.

(b) Calculate the probabilities $P(n)$ for $\overline{n} = 0.5$ and for $\overline{n} = 2$, assuming a Poisson distribution, and show each distribution as a bar graph.

15. Colloidal particles are suspended in a solution. The number of particles that are found in the field of a microscope is counted, at equally spaced intervals of time. The number observed varies from 0 to 13, with an average of 4.40, over a series of 1000 observations. Assume that the Poisson distribution is applicable. **(a)** How should the average number observed and the "error" be expressed? (See Problem 16c.) **(b)** What is the most probable number observed? **(c)** What is the probability of observing zero particles? **(d)** What is the probability of observing 10 particles? **(e)** What is the relative probability of observing 4 rather than 5 particles? **(f)** What is the probability that in the 1000 observations one will give 13 particles?

16. (a) Show that for the Poisson distribution $\sum_{n=0}^{\infty} P(n) = 1$. (Note that $\overline{n}$ is a constant, and use the series expansion $e^x = 1 + x + x^2/2! + x^3/3! + \cdots = \sum_{n=0}^{\infty} x^n/n!$.)

(b) Show that for the Poisson distribution $\sum_{n=0}^{\infty} nP(n) = \overline{n}$. (Note that the first term in the series is zero, make a change of variable $l = n - 1$, and identify the series expansion for $e^{\bar{n}}$.)

(c) Show that for the Poisson distribution $\overline{n^2} = \sum_{n=0}^{\infty} n^2 P(n) = \bar{n}^2 + \bar{n}$, and therefore the dispersion is $\sigma^2 = \overline{n^2} - \bar{n}^2 = \bar{n}$, and the standard deviation is $\sigma = \sqrt{\bar{n}}$.

17. **Radioactive decay:** The radioactive disintegration of atomic nuclei is a random process. Decay is a matter of chance, and it is impossible to predict the time when a particular nucleus will decay. Nevertheless statistical predictions can be made. For a system of a large number of nuclei it is reasonable to assume that the probability a nucleus will decay in a short time interval dt is proportional to the size of the interval. If the number of nuclei is N, and the number decaying in the interval is dN, the probability of a nucleus decaying in the interval is dN/N, and this is proportional to dt.

$$dN/N \propto dt \qquad \text{or} \qquad dN/N = -\lambda \, dt$$

where the negative sign is introduced because dN is a decrease in the number N. The positive proportionality constant λ is called the decay constant or disintegration constant. It depends on the particular kind of radioactive material, and on the type of radioactive process (some atoms undergo both α-decay and β-decay, and the decay constant is different for the two processes).

The differential equation for decay can also be expressed as $dN/dt = -\lambda N$; the rate of decay (the number of atoms disintegrating per unit time) is proportional to the number present. On integration the relation becomes (see Problem 8 in Chapter 2) $N(t) = N_0 \, e^{-\lambda t}$, where N_0 is the number of atoms at time $t = 0$, $N(t)$ is the number at time t. This relation cannot be interpreted directly as a distribution function, because the total number of particles in the system is decreasing with time. However, a probability distribution function can be introduced by thinking about the fraction of atoms that have lifetimes in the range t to $t + dt$. This fraction is $f(t) \, dt$, where $f(t) = A \, e^{-\lambda t}$ is called the distribution function of radioactive lifetimes. It is a probability density distribution.

(a) Determine the normalization constant A in terms of the decay constant λ, using the fact that the fraction of nuclei with lifetimes in the range 0 to ∞ is unity.

(b) Determine the average lifetime $\bar{t}$ in terms of λ, and express $f(t)$ in terms of λ.

(c) Sometimes an exponential decay is described in terms of the half-life $t_{1/2}$, the time required for the number to decrease to one-half the initial value. Determine the relation between $t_{1/2}$ and $\bar{t}$.

(d) For a system of radioactive nuclei, determine the fraction that have lifetimes longer than some lifetime t_0. (e) What fraction have lifetimes longer than the average lifetime $\bar{t}$? (f) What fraction have lifetimes longer than the half-life $t_{1/2}$?

(g) Uranium-238 has a half-life of 4.5×10^9 years for the emission of α-particles. What fraction of the uranium nuclei have lifetimes longer than 10^{10} years? (h) What fraction have lifetimes in the range 10^9 to 10^{10} years?

(i) Radium-226 has a half-life of 1622 years for the emission of α-particles. In a system of 10^{20} radium nuclei, how many could be expected to have lifetimes of less than one year? (Recall that $e^{-x} \cong 1 - x$ for $x \ll 1$.) (j) How many could be expected to have lifetimes of less than 1 sec?

(k) Boron-12 decays into carbon-12 by β-decay (the emission of electrons) with a half-life of 2.7×10^{-2} sec. Estimate the probability for a boron nucleus to survive for 1 sec. (l) If there is 1 mole of boron at some instant, about how many boron nuclei are left after 1 sec?

18. **The distribution of free paths:** A physical situation mathematically similar to radio-active decay (discussed in the previous problem) is that of the distribution of free paths in a gas. In this case there is an exponential decay with distance, rather than with time.

Think of a large number N_0 of gas molecules at some instant. Ultimately each molecule will make a collision with another molecule, a random process. We are interested in the number N that have **not** made a collision after the group has moved a distance x, where x is the distance measured along the free path of each molecule. In moving a further distance dx, a number dN of the molecules will make a collision and be removed from the group. We assume that $dN = -pN\,dx$, that is that the number removed is proportional to the number present N and to the distance dx. The negative sign is introduced because dN is a decrease in the number N. The positive proportionality constant p is called the collision probability; it is assumed to be a constant for a particular gas under particular conditions of temperature and pressure.

The integrated form of the differential equation is $N = N_0\,e^{-px}$, an exponential decay of the number with distance. This is called the survival equation. The number of particles with free paths in the range x to $x + dx$ is $dN = -pN\,dx = -pN_0\,e^{-px}\,dx$. Therefore we can say that the fraction of the molecules with free paths in the range x to $x + dx$ is $f(x)\,dx$ where $f(x) = A\,e^{-px}$ is the distribution function for free paths.

(a) Express the normalization constant A in terms of the collision probability p.

(b) Determine the mean free path $l = \bar{x}$ in terms of p, and express the distribution function in terms of l.

(c) Sketch $f(x)$, using x/l as abscissa. What is the most probable free path?

(d) Determine the fraction of a system of gas molecules that have free paths greater than some distance x_0.

(e) Suppose that the mean free path in a gas is 0.1 mm. Roughly what is the pressure of the gas? Determine the fraction of the molecules that have free paths (f) greater than 0.1 mm, (g) greater than 0.2 mm, (h) greater than 1 mm, (i) between 0.01 mm and 0.1 mm, (j) in the range 0.1 ± 0.01 mm. (k) What is the probability that a molecule will have a free path within 10% of the mean free path?

31

THE DISTRIBUTION OF
MOLECULAR VELOCITIES

Before attempting to deal with classical statistical mechanics in general, and to discuss the classical distribution function called the Maxwell–Boltzmann distribution, we are going to examine a more specialized distribution, the distribution of velocities of a system of gas molecules, called the Maxwell distribution. This is a special case of the general distribution, and therefore can be derived from it, but we are going to derive it first as an example of the approach used in statistical mechanics. Such statistical mechanical concepts as "the density of points in phase space" will be more easily understood if we can make reference to "the density of points in velocity space" introduced here.

We described the distribution of molecular speeds in the chapter on measurement, as an example of a distribution function that could be observed experimentally or derived theoretically. It is this theoretical derivation that we undertake now.

VELOCITY SPACE

We fix our attention on a system of gas molecules in a container, and treat this as a system of identical particles. At a particular instant each particle will have a certain velocity, which can be represented by a vector. Think of all these velocity vectors as transferred to a common origin, and introduce a rectangular co-ordinate system in the space defined by these vectors. Every vector $\mathbf{v}$ will have components v_x, v_y, v_z in the directions of these axes. The space is called **velocity space** (see at the top of the next page).

Each velocity vector is completely specified in velocity space by the position of its end point (co-ordinates v_x, v_y, v_z) and therefore we speak of the **distribution of points in velocity space.** If we know the number of points in the "volume element" $dv_x\, dv_y\, dv_z$ at (v_x, v_y, v_z), then we know the number of molecules with an x-component of velocity in the range $v_x \rightarrow v_x + dv_x$, a y-component in the range

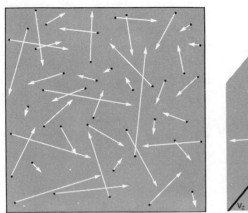

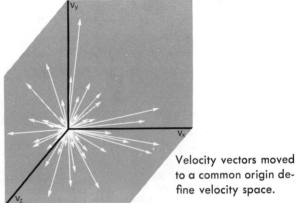

Velocity vectors moved to a common origin define velocity space.

$v_y \to v_y + dv_y$, and a z-component in the range $v_z \to v_z + dv_z$. The basic problem is to find an expression for this number.

The total number of points in velocity space is the same as the number N of gas molecules in real space. As the gas molecules move around in real space, colliding with one another, the individual points move around in velocity space, but we **assume** that the distribution of points is steady—does not change with time. One molecule makes a collision, and the point representing it moves to

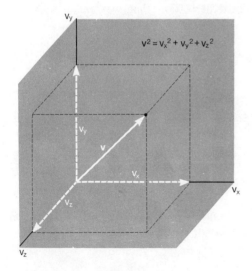

$$v^2 = v_x{}^2 + v_y{}^2 + v_z{}^2$$

Components in velocity space.

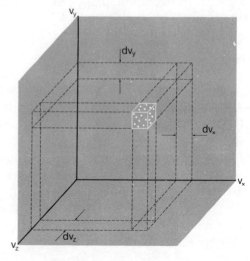

Volume element in velocity space.

another region of velocity space, but another one takes its place. The assumption is based on the fact that the number of molecules (and the number of points) is extremely large. Just as we assume that there is a large number of molecules in any volume element $dx\,dy\,dz$ in real space, we assume that there is a large number of points in any volume element $dv_x\,dv_y\,dv_z$ in velocity space. We speak of the gas density as being constant—meaning that we can think of the gas as a continuous fluid; of course, if we consider a volume a few angstrom units in size this is not valid. Similarly we are going to assume a continuous distribution of velocities—or a continuous distribution of points in velocity space, and determine an expression for the density in velocity space.

Note that the assumption of a steady distribution means that the total kinetic energy $K = \sum K_i = \sum \frac{1}{2}mv_i^2$ remains constant. The number of molecules with speeds in any particular range does not change, and therefore the total kinetic energy does not change. Thus our assumption satisfies conservation of energy—although energy could be conserved even if the distribution was not steady.

Note also that although we are using the concept of velocity space, we could equally well use **momentum space.** Corresponding to the velocity components v_x,v_y,v_z there are momentum components $p_x = mv_x$, $p_y = mv_y$, $p_z = mv_z$. The mass m of the particles is a constant, and therefore it does not matter whether we think of velocity space or momentum space. Later in discussing quantum statistics you will see that momentum space is more appropriate.

THE FORM OF THE
MAXWELL VELOCITY DISTRIBUTION

Let dN_{v_x} = number of molecules with x-component of velocity in the range $v_x \to v_x + dv_x$ = number of points in a slice of thickness dv_x, parallel to the v_y-v_z plane and a distance v_x from it. This number will be proportional to the total number of points N, to the thickness of the slice dv_x, and will depend on the location of the slice:

$$dN_{v_x} = Nf(v_x)\,dv_x$$

where $f(v_x)$ is a function to be determined.

We are assuming that there is no overall motion of the gas, and therefore all directions in velocity space are equivalent.

Therefore
$$dN_{v_y} = Nf(v_y)\,dv_y$$
$$dN_{v_z} = Nf(v_z)\,dv_z$$

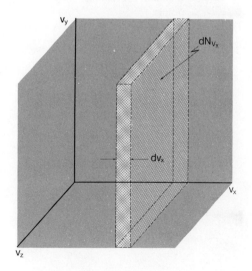

Volume element containing dN_{v_x} points.

The next assumption is the key one in deriving the Maxwell velocity distribution, and the one that is most difficult to justify. It is this: that of the dN_{v_x} molecules (those in the range $v_x \rightarrow v_x + dv_x$) the fraction that have a y-component of velocity in the range $v_y \rightarrow v_y + dv_y$ is the *same* as the fraction of all the molecules that have a y-component of velocity in this range. In other words, the possession of a particular y-component of velocity is not affected by the fact that the molecule already has a particular x-component of velocity. This assumption is based on the fact that dN_{v_x}, even though it is the number of points in the volume element of "infinitesimal" thickness dv_x, is nevertheless an extremely large number, and the fraction of this group that is cut off by a slice of thickness dv_y is itself a very large number. Let $d^2N_{v_x v_y}$ = number of molecules with x-component of velocity in range $v_x \rightarrow v_x + dv_x$, *and* y-component of velocity in range $v_y \rightarrow v_y + dv_y$ = number of points in the volume element formed by the intersection of the two slices. It is denoted d^2N, the superscript indicating that it is a differential of second order, requiring two integrations to give the total number.

The assumption is that

$$\frac{d^2N_{v_x v_y}}{dN_{v_x}} = \frac{dN_{v_y}}{N}$$

which gives

$$d^2N_{v_x v_y} = Nf(v_x)f(v_y)dv_x\, dv_y$$

Next we make the same assumption again, as far as the fraction of molecules with z-component of velocity in the range $v_z \rightarrow v_z + dv_z$ is concerned.

$$\frac{d^3N_{v_x v_y v_z}}{d^2N_{v_x v_y}} = \frac{dN_{v_z}}{N}$$

where $d^3N_{v_x v_y v_z}$ = number of points in the volume element $dv_x\, dv_y\, dv_z$.

Therefore

$$d^3N_{v_x v_y v_z} = Nf(v_x)f(v_y)f(v_z)dv_x\, dv_y\, dv_z$$

and the **density of points in velocity space** ρ is

$$\rho = \frac{d^3N_{v_x v_y v_z}}{dv_x\, dv_y\, dv_z} = Nf(v_x)f(v_y)f(v_z)$$

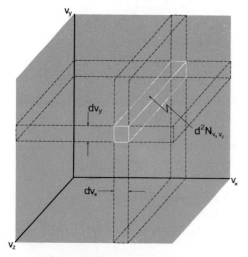

Volume element containing $d^2N_{v_x v_y}$ points.

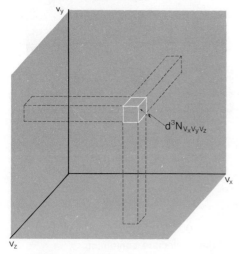

Volume element containing $d^3N_{v_x v_y v_z}$ points.

Now consider the difference in density $d\rho$ between two nearby points in velocity space.

$$d\rho = \frac{\partial \rho}{\partial v_x}\, dv_x + \frac{\partial \rho}{\partial v_y}\, dv_y + \frac{\partial \rho}{\partial v_z}\, dv_z$$

$$= Nf'(v_x)f(v_y)f(v_z)\, dv_x$$

$$+ Nf(v_x)f'(v_y)f(v_z)\, dv_y$$

$$+ Nf(v_x)f(v_y)f'(v_z)\, dv_z$$

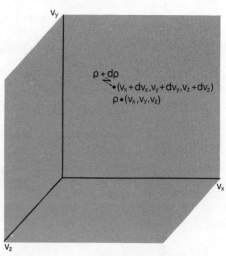

Difference in density at two nearby points in velocity space.

where $f'(v_x)$ is notation for $(d/dv_x)f(v_x)$.

As we have already pointed out, there is no preferred direction in velocity space, and this means that the density ρ must be the same at all points the same distance v from the origin. Choosing any two points the same distance from the origin, $d\rho = 0$, and with this condition the equation can be written, after dividing by $f(v_x)f(v_y)f(v_z)$, as

$$\frac{f'(v_x)}{f(v_x)}\, dv_x + \frac{f'(v_y)}{f(v_y)}\, dv_y$$

$$+ \frac{f'(v_z)}{f(v_z)}\, dv_z = 0$$

This is the equation that must be solved to find the form of the function f. If the three co-ordinates were all independent, then the solution would be obtained by setting each coefficient equal to zero; that is, we could choose $dv_y = dv_z = 0$, $dv_x \neq 0$, and this would require that $f'(v_x)/f(v_x) = 0$. Similarly the other two coefficients would have to be zero. However, the co-ordinates *cannot* be varied independently, because we have imposed the condition that the two points are on a sphere the same distance v from the origin. Therefore since

$$v^2 = v_x^2 + v_y^2 + v_z^2 = \text{constant}$$

$$0 = v_x\, dv_x + v_y\, dv_y + v_z\, dv_z$$

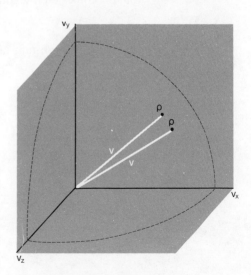

Points chosen to be equidistant from the origin.

This is called a condition equation because it imposes a condition on the relation between the differentials—they cannot be varied independently.

The solution of the earlier f-equation is obtained by combining it with the condition equation in a technique called the Lagrange method of undetermined multipliers. The condition equation is multiplied by an undetermined constant λ and added to the f-equation.

$$\left(\frac{f'(v_x)}{f(v_x)} + \lambda v_x\right) dv_x + \left(\frac{f'(v_y)}{f(v_y)} + \lambda v_y\right) dv_y + \left(\frac{f'(v_z)}{f(v_z)} + \lambda v_z\right) dv_z = 0$$

Suppose that λ is chosen so that the first coefficient is zero.

$$\frac{f'(v_x)}{f(v_x)} + \lambda v_x = 0$$

Then since any two of the variables can be varied independently (e.g., choosing $dv_y = 0$, $dv_z \neq 0$) the other two coefficients must be zero as well, in order that the equation be valid in general.

$$\frac{f'(v_y)}{f(v_y)} + \lambda v_y = 0 \qquad \frac{f'(v_z)}{f(v_z)} + \lambda v_z = 0$$

The form of f can be determined from any one of these equations,

$$\frac{1}{f(v_x)} \frac{d}{dv_x} f(v_x) + \lambda v_x = 0$$

$$\frac{df(v_x)}{f(v_x)} = -\lambda v_x \, dv_x$$

which becomes on integration

$$\ln f(v_x) = -\tfrac{1}{2}\lambda v_x^2 + \ln \alpha$$

where $\ln \alpha$ is a constant of integration. In exponential form

$$f(v_x) = \alpha e^{-\frac{1}{2}\lambda v_x^2}$$
$$= \alpha e^{-\beta^2 v_x^2}$$

where the constant $\lambda/2$ has been replaced by β^2.

The **form** of the function f has now been determined, although as yet we can attach no physical meaning to the constants α and β. We have

$$dN_{v_x} = Nf(v_x)\,dv_x = N\alpha e^{-\beta^2 v_x^2}\,dv_x$$

$$d^3 N_{v_x v_y v_z} = Nf(v_x)f(v_y)f(v_z)\,dv_x\,dv_y\,dv_z$$
$$= N\alpha^3 e^{-\beta^2(v_x^2 + v_y^2 + v_z^2)}\,dv_x\,dv_y\,dv_z$$
$$= N\alpha^3 e^{-\beta^2 v^2}\,dv_x\,dv_y\,dv_z$$

$$\rho = \frac{d^3 N_{v_x v_y v_z}}{dv_x dv_y dv_z} = N\alpha^3 e^{-\beta^2 v^2}$$

This is the Maxwell velocity distribution function. The density of points in velocity space is a maximum at the origin ($v = 0$), and the distribution is Gaussian.

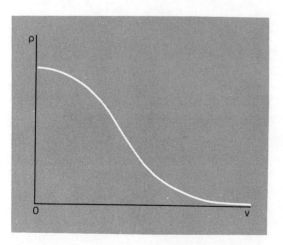

The Maxwell velocity distribution function.

Note that although the density distribution has a maximum at the origin, this does *not* mean that the most probable speed is zero. We will have to work out the relation between the density distribution and the speed distribution.

THE SPEED DISTRIBUTION FUNCTION

Let dN_v = number of molecules with **speeds** between v and $v + dv$ = number of points in a spherical shell of radius v and thickness dv in velocity space = volume of shell $\times$ density of points.

$$dN_v = (4\pi v^2\, dv)(N\alpha^3 e^{-\beta^2 v^2})$$

$$N(v) = \frac{dN_v}{dv} = 4\pi N\alpha^3 v^2 e^{-\beta^2 v^2}$$

The function $N(v)$, the number of molecules per unit speed interval, is the Maxwell distribution of molecular speeds. It is useful to compare it to the distribution of a particular component of molecular velocity.

$$N(v_x) = \frac{dN_{v_x}}{dv_x} = N\alpha e^{-\beta^2 v_x^2}$$

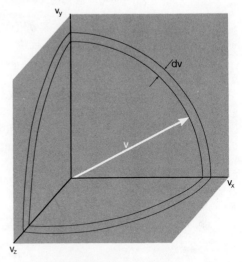

A spherical shell in velocity space.

The component of velocity v_x takes on positive and negative values from $-\infty$ to ∞. The distribution is symmetric with respect to the origin—as many molecules are moving to the right as to the left.

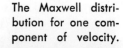

The Maxwell distribution for one component of velocity.

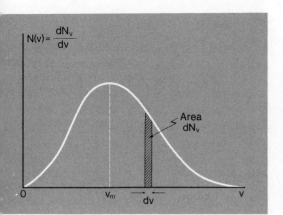

The Maxwell speed distribution function.

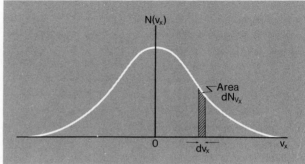

The speed v is the magnitude of the velocity, a positive scalar quantity. The maximum in the curve corresponds to the most probable molecular speed v_m. More molecules have "this" speed (i.e., speeds in this range) than any other speed. At this maximum

$$\frac{dN(v)}{dv} = 0 \qquad \text{so} \qquad \frac{d}{dv}[4\pi N\alpha^3 v^2 e^{-\beta^2 v^2}] = 0$$

$$2v\, e^{-\beta^2 v^2} + v^2(-2v\beta^2)e^{-\beta^2 v^2} = 0 \qquad v = v_m = 1/\beta$$

Thus the constant β can be replaced by the reciprocal of the most probable speed $\beta = 1/v_m$.

The constants α and β can be related by the fact that the total number of molecules N is constant.

$$N = \int_0^\infty dN_v = 4\pi N\alpha^3 \int_0^\infty v^2 e^{-\beta^2 v^2}\, dv = 4\pi N\alpha^3 \left(\frac{1}{4}\frac{\sqrt{\pi}}{\beta^3}\right)$$

giving

$$\alpha^3 = \beta^3/\pi\sqrt{\pi} \qquad \alpha = \beta/\sqrt{\pi}$$

$$N(v) = \frac{4N}{\sqrt{\pi}}\beta^3 v^2 e^{-\beta^2 v^2} = \frac{4N}{\sqrt{\pi}\, v_m^3}v^2 e^{-v^2/v_m^2}$$

Thus the speed distribution function is written in terms of the constant v_m, determined by the position of the peak in the curve. This is as far as we can go on the basis of the model we have used. In order to introduce the macroscopic variable **temperature,** we must make reference to experiment, or to some other theory. This can be done in a variety of ways. One is to compare the expression for the pressure exerted by the gas as calculated in the kinetic theory of gases, $p = \frac{1}{3}nm\overline{v^2}$, with the experimentally determined equation of state for an ideal gas, $p = nkT$. This gives

$$\tfrac{1}{2}m\overline{v^2} = \tfrac{3}{2}kT$$

an example of equipartition of energy; the average kinetic energy of the ideal gas "particle" is $3 \times \frac{1}{2}kT$.

In order to compare this relation with the speed distribution function we have derived, we need $\overline{v^2}$. From the definition of average value

$$\bar{v} = \frac{\int v\, dN_v}{N} = \frac{4\beta^3}{\sqrt{\pi}}\int_0^\infty v^3 e^{-\beta^2 v^2}\, dv = \frac{4\beta^3}{\sqrt{\pi}}\left(\frac{1}{2\beta^4}\right) = \frac{2}{\sqrt{\pi}\beta}$$

$$\overline{v^2} = \frac{\int v^2\, dN_v}{N} = \frac{4\beta^3}{\sqrt{\pi}}\int_0^\infty v^4 e^{-\beta^2 v^2}\, dv = \frac{4\beta^3}{\sqrt{\pi}}\left(\frac{3}{8}\frac{\sqrt{\pi}}{\beta^5}\right) = \frac{3}{2}\frac{1}{\beta^2}$$

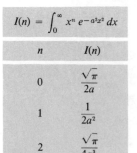

$$I(n) = \int_0^\infty x^n e^{-a^2 x^2}\, dx$$

n	$I(n)$
0	$\dfrac{\sqrt{\pi}}{2a}$
1	$\dfrac{1}{2a^2}$
2	$\dfrac{\sqrt{\pi}}{4a^3}$
3	$\dfrac{1}{2a^4}$
4	$\dfrac{3\sqrt{\pi}}{8a^5}$

Comparing this with the equipartition expression gives

$$\tfrac{1}{2}m\overline{v^2} = \tfrac{3}{2}kT = \tfrac{1}{2}m\left(\tfrac{3}{2}\frac{1}{\beta^2}\right) \qquad \beta^2 = \frac{m}{2kT} \qquad \beta = \sqrt{\frac{m}{2kT}}$$

and in terms of temperature the speed distribution function becomes

$$N(v) = \frac{4N}{\sqrt{\pi}}\left(\frac{m}{2kT}\right)^{3/2} v^2\, e^{-mv^2/2kT}$$

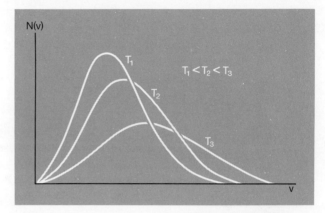

The distribution function is shown at three different temperatures; the higher the temperature, the broader the distribution. The area under each curve $\int N(v)\,dv = \int dN_v = N$ is the same.

For each curve the most probable speed v_m, the average speed $\bar{v}$, and the root-mean-square speed $v_{\mathrm{rms}} = \sqrt{\overline{v^2}}$ are related by

The speed distribution function at three temperatures.

$$v_m : \bar{v} : v_{\mathrm{rms}} = 1/\beta : 2/(\sqrt{\pi}\beta) : \sqrt{3}/(\sqrt{2}\beta)$$
$$= 1 : 2/\sqrt{\pi} : \sqrt{3/2} = 1 : 1.128 : 1.224$$

CALCULATIONS USING THE DISTRIBUTION FUNCTIONS

The distribution function for a single component of velocity is Gaussian, and therefore we can use some of the results of the last chapter.

$$N(v_x) = N\alpha e^{-\beta^2 v_x^2} = \frac{N\beta}{\sqrt{\pi}}\, e^{-\beta^2 v_x^2}$$

$$= \frac{N}{v_m\sqrt{\pi}}\, e^{-v_x^2/v_m^2}$$

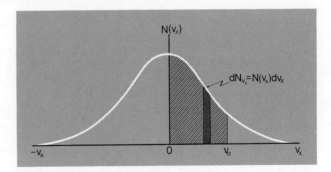

The number of molecules with an x-component of velocity in the range from 0 to some arbitrary value v_0 is

$$N_x(0 \rightarrow v_0) = \int_0^{v_0} dN_{v_x} = \int_0^{v_0} N(v_x)\,dv_x$$

$$= \frac{N}{v_m\sqrt{\pi}}\int_0^{v_0} e^{-v_x^2/v_m^2}\,dv_x$$

How many molecules with x-component of velocity in the range $0 \rightarrow v_0$?

Throughout this chapter we have dealt with numbers of molecules, but the whole discussion could equally well be carried out in terms of probabilities, by dividing any expression for numbers of molecules by the total number N. Thus the probability of a molecule having an x-component of velocity in the range $0 \to v_0$ is

$$P_x(0 \to v_0) = \frac{N(0 \to v_0)}{N} = \frac{1}{v_m \sqrt{\pi}} \int_0^{v_0} e^{-v_x^2/v_m^2}\, dv_x$$

In the last chapter we introduced the Gaussian distribution in standard form, where the variable is expressed in terms of the standard deviation σ, the root-mean-square deviation from the mean. For the x-component of velocity distribution,

$$\overline{v_x^2} = \frac{\int v_x^2\, dN_{v_x}}{N} = \frac{1}{v_m \sqrt{\pi}} \int_{-\infty}^{\infty} v_x^2 e^{-v_x^2/v_m^2}\, dv_x$$

$$= \frac{1}{v_m \sqrt{\pi}} \left(2 \times \frac{\sqrt{\pi}\, v_m^3}{4}\right) = \frac{v_m^2}{2}$$

(Note that the previous table of definite integrals gave $I(n) = \int_0^\infty x^n e^{-a^2 x^2}\, dx$; for $\int_{-\infty}^\infty$, the value of the integral is twice as great if n is even, and zero if n is odd. See p. 750.)

$$\sigma = (v_x)_{\text{rms}} = \frac{v_m}{\sqrt{2}}$$

Instead of using v_x as a variable, then, we use

$$x = \frac{v_x}{\sigma} = \frac{v_x}{v_m/\sqrt{2}} = \frac{\sqrt{2}\, v_x}{v_m} \qquad dx = \frac{\sqrt{2}}{v_m}\, dv_x$$

and the probability of an x-component of velocity in the range $0 \to v_0$ becomes

$$P_x(0 \to x_0) = \frac{1}{\sqrt{2\pi}} \int_0^{x_0} e^{-x^2/2}\, dx \qquad x_0 = \frac{\sqrt{2}\, v_0}{v_m}$$

$$= \int_0^{x_0} p(x)\, dx$$

where $p(x) = (1/\sqrt{2\pi})e^{-x^2/2}$ is the Gaussian distribution in standard form. In the last chapter we gave a table (p. 722) showing the values of $p(x)$ and $P(0 \to x)$ for a limited range of values. For example, $P(0 \to 1) = 0.34$. This means that a molecule has a 34% chance of having an x-component of velocity in the range $0 \to v_0 = v_m/\sqrt{2}$, or that 34% of all the molecules have x-components in this range. Since the distribution is symmetric, 68% of the molecules have x-components of velocity in the range $-v_m/\sqrt{2} \to v_m/\sqrt{2}$.

The speed distribution is not symmetric, and it is not Gaussian, but it can be expressed in terms of the Gaussian function. The number of molecules with speeds in the range between 0 and v_0 is

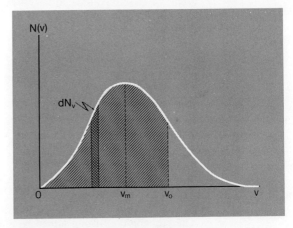

$$N(0 \to v_0) = \int_0^{v_0} dN_v$$

$$= \frac{4N}{\sqrt{\pi}\, v_m^3} \int_0^{v_0} v^2 e^{-v^2/v_m^2}\, dv$$

Changing the variable to $x = \sqrt{2}v/v_m$, $dx = \sqrt{2}\, dv/v_m$, this becomes

$$N(0 \to x_0) = \frac{2N}{\sqrt{2\pi}} \int_0^{x_0} x^2 e^{-x^2/2}\, dx$$

$$x_0 = \frac{\sqrt{2}\, v_0}{v_m}$$

How many molecules with speeds in the range $0 \to v_0$?

The form of this can be changed using integration by parts, $\int p\, dq = pq - \int q\, dp$. Setting $p = x$, $dq = xe^{-x^2/2}\, dx$, then $dp = dx$ and $q = -e^{-x^2/2}$.

$$N(0 \to x_0) = \frac{2N}{\sqrt{2\pi}} \left[-x_0 e^{-x_0^2/2} + \int_0^{x_0} e^{-x^2/2}\, dx \right]$$

$$= N \left[\frac{2}{\sqrt{2\pi}} \int_0^{x_0} e^{-x^2/2}\, dx - \frac{2}{\sqrt{2\pi}} x_0 e^{-x_0^2/2} \right]$$

$$= N \left[2 \int_0^{x_0} p(x)\, dx - \frac{2}{\sqrt{2\pi}} x_0 e^{-x_0^2/2} \right]$$

where $p(x)$ is as before the Gaussian distribution in standard form.

As an example, we will calculate the number of molecules with speeds less than the most probable speed v_m. Then $v_0 = v_m$, and $x_0 = \sqrt{2}$. From the table in the last chapter $\int_0^{\sqrt{2}} p(x)\, dx$ can be seen to be about 0.4; a more complete table of the probability integral shows that the result is actually 0.4213.

$$N(0 \to v_m) = N \left(2 \times 0.4213 - \frac{2}{\sqrt{2\pi}} \sqrt{2}\, e^{-1} \right)$$

$$= N(0.8426 - 0.416) = 0.427N$$

Thus 43% of the molecules have speeds less than v_m, and 57% speeds greater than v_m. In terms of probability, there is a 43% chance that a molecule will be moving at a speed less than v_m at any instant.

Note Re Use of Tables: We have used the Gaussian distribution in standard form

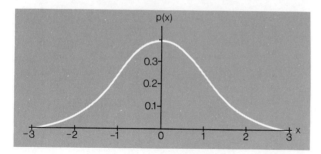

Gaussian distribution
in standard form.

$$p(x) = \frac{1}{\sqrt{2\pi}} e^{-x^2/2}$$

and the corresponding probability expression

$$P(0 \to x) = \int_0^x p(x)\, dx$$

$$= \frac{1}{\sqrt{2\pi}} \int_0^x e^{-x^2/2}\, dx$$

so that

$$P(0 \to \infty) = (1/\sqrt{2\pi})\, [(\sqrt{\pi}/2)\sqrt{2}] = \tfrac{1}{2}$$

The probability of being somewhere in the range $-\infty$ to ∞ is **unity,** as it should be. The distribution function has been normalized.

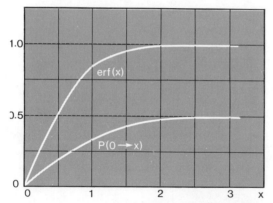

The relation between
$P(0 \to x)$ and erf(x).

Statistical or integral tables usually give values of what is called the probability integral, or the error function

$$\text{erf}\,(x) = \frac{2}{\sqrt{\pi}} \int_0^x e^{-x^2}\, dx$$

This function has a limiting value of 1, rather than $\tfrac{1}{2}$, and this means that in situations where the variable x can range from $-\infty$ to ∞ the function erf (x) cannot be interpreted as a probability.

While $P(0 \to x) = \tfrac{1}{2}\,\text{erf}\,(x)$ for $x \to \infty$, there is not in general a factor 2 relating the two functions. The general relation may be established as follows. Note that the exponential exponent in erf (x) is $-x^2$, and in $P(0 \to x)$ is $-x^2/2$, so a change in variable is required.

$$P(0 \to x) = \frac{1}{\sqrt{2\pi}} \int_0^x e^{-x^2/2}\, dx \quad :\text{set } y^2 = x^2/2$$

$$= \frac{1}{\sqrt{\pi}} \int_0^{x/\sqrt{2}} e^{-y^2}\, dy \quad x = \sqrt{2}\, y,\ dx = \sqrt{2}\, dy$$

$$= \tfrac{1}{2}\,\text{erf}\,(x/\sqrt{2})$$

For example, for $x = 1$, tables of the probability integral give erf $(1/\sqrt{2}) =$ erf $(0.7071) = 0.6826$, so $P(0 \to 1) = \tfrac{1}{2} \times 0.6826 = 0.3413$ as given in the table for $P(0 \to x)$ in Chapter 30 (p. 722).

If the error function is used in the expression for the number of molecules with speeds in the range $0 \to v_0$, it is more appropriate to use as a variable $x_0 = v_0/v_m$ rather than $\sqrt{2}$ times this. Then

$$N(0 \rightarrow v_0) = N\left[\operatorname{erf}(x_0) - \frac{2}{\sqrt{\pi}} x_0 e^{-x_0^2}\right] \qquad x_0 = v_0/v_m$$

Similarly the number of molecules with x-component of velocity in the range $0 \rightarrow v_0$ is

$$N_x(0 \rightarrow v_0) = (N/2)\operatorname{erf}(x_0) \qquad x_0 = v_0/v_m$$

and the number with x-component of velocity in the range $-v_0 \rightarrow v_0$ is

$$N_x(-v_0 \rightarrow v_0) = N\operatorname{erf}(x_0) \qquad x_0 = v_0/v_m$$

THE DISTRIBUTION IN ENERGY

You will have recognized that the exponential terms in all the distribution functions can be written in terms of the kinetic energy of the molecules.

$$dN_v = N(v)\,dv = \frac{4N}{\sqrt{\pi}}\left(\frac{m}{2kT}\right)^{3/2} v^2 e^{-mv^2/2kT}\,dv$$

The kinetic energy of any particle of mass m moving with speed v is $K = \frac{1}{2}mv^2$, and therefore the exponential is $\exp(-K/kT)$.

In order to find the distribution in **energy** $N(K)$ we must determine the number of molecules dN_K with energies in the range K to $K + dK$.

$$K = \tfrac{1}{2}mv^2 \qquad dK = mv\,dv \qquad \text{so} \qquad dv = \frac{dK}{mv} = \frac{dK}{\sqrt{2mK}}$$

$$dN_K = \frac{4N}{\sqrt{\pi}}\left(\frac{m}{2kT}\right)^{3/2}\left(\frac{2K}{m}\right)e^{-K/kT}\frac{dK}{\sqrt{2mK}}$$

$$= \frac{2N}{\sqrt{\pi}(kT)^{3/2}}\sqrt{K}\,e^{-K/kT}\,dK = N(K)\,dK$$

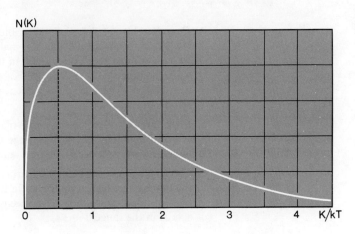

The kinetic energy distribution function.

The distribution function has a different shape from the distribution in speed. You can verify that the peak occurs at $K = \frac{1}{2}kT$.

We have translated the distribution into energy terms in order to illustrate the form that results; but in the approach that we have used to develop the distribution of speeds, the concept of energy is not central. We are going to go on now to discuss the general distribution function of statistical mechanics, and in this development the concept of energy is central; the assumption of conservation of energy (not just of kinetic energy) provides a basic condition equation in the derivation.

Problems

1. The speed distribution function $N(v) = dN_v/dv$ for a system of N particles is

$$N(v) = K \quad \text{for} \quad 0 \leq v \leq V$$
$$N(v) = 0 \quad \text{for} \quad v > V$$

where K and V are constants. (a) Draw the distribution function, and determine the average speed $\bar{v}$ and the root-mean-square speed v_{rms} in terms of V. (b) Determine the standard deviation in terms of V.

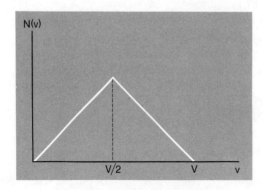

2. The speed distribution function for a system of N particles has the form indicated. (a) What is the average speed $\bar{v}$ and the most probable speed v_m? (b) Determine v_{rms} and the average deviation $\sigma = (\overline{v^2} - \bar{v}^2)^{1/2}$. (See Problem 16 in Chapter 3.)

3. Consult tables of the probability integral, or the error function, and determine, for a system of molecules in thermal equilibrium, the fraction of the molecules with x-components of velocity (a) in the range $0 \rightarrow v_m$, (b) in the range $-v_m \rightarrow v_m$, (c) in the range $-2v_m \rightarrow 2v_m$. (d) For a system of 10^{20} molecules, how many could be expected to have an x-component of velocity whose magnitude is greater than $2v_m$, at any instant?

4. Is the number of molecules whose magnitude of x-component of velocity lies in a certain range (e.g., $|v_x|$ in the range $0 \rightarrow v_m$) greater or less than the number of molecules whose speeds lie in the same range?

5. Use tables of the probability integral (or the error function) to determine (a) what fraction of a system of molecules in thermal equilibrium have speeds in the range $0 \rightarrow v_m$, (b) what fraction have speeds in the range $0 \rightarrow \bar{v}$, (c) what fraction have speeds in the range $0 \rightarrow v_{\text{rms}}$.

6. The **median** divides the area of a distribution function in half. For the distribution of molecular speeds, for example, this is the value of v such that equal numbers of molecules have higher speeds and have lower speeds. Verify that for the speed distribution function the median speed is $1.09 \, v_m$.

7. Estimate the probability that the speed of a molecule is **(a)** at least twice, **(b)** at least three times its most probable speed.

8. **(a)** For the distribution function for a single component of velocity determine the position of the points of inflection, in terms of the most probable speed v_m. **(b)** For the speed distribution function determine the position of the points of inflection, in terms of v_m.

9. **(a)** For a system of oxygen molecules at room temperature (20 °C) determine v_m, $\bar{v}$, and v_{rms}. **(b)** Determine the fraction of molecules with x-components of velocity in the range -500 to 500 m/sec. **(c)** Determine the fraction of molecules with speeds in the range 0 to 500 m/sec. **(d)** Determine the probability of a molecule having an x-component of velocity of magnitude greater than 500 m/sec. **(e)** Determine the probability of a molecule having a speed greater than 500 m/sec.

10. **(a)** Determine the most probable speed for a system of helium molecules at temperatures of 100 °K, 400 °K, 1600 °K, 6400 °K.

(b) Determine the percentage of molecules with speeds greater than 1000 m/sec for a system of helium molecules at each of the temperatures in (a).

(c) For a system of helium molecules at a temperature of 6400 °K, what percentage of the molecules have a speed higher than the escape speed from the earth's surface?

11. From the distribution function for kinetic energy $N(K)$, **(a)** determine the most probable energy K_m, in terms of kT, and compare the result with $\frac{1}{2}mv_m^2$, **(b)** determine the average energy $\overline{K}$, in terms of kT, and compare the result with $\frac{1}{2}m\bar{v}^2$ and $\frac{1}{2}m\overline{v^2}$. From tables of definite integrals

$$\int_0^\infty x^{3/2} \, e^{-ax} \, dx = 3\sqrt{\pi}/(4a^{5/2})$$

(c) What percentage of molecules have kinetic energies greater than the average kinetic energy?

12. Plot the kinetic energy distribution function $N(K)$ by calculating $N(K)$ in terms of the peak value $N(K_m) = N(\frac{1}{2}kT)$ for $K/kT = 0.1, 0.25, 0.5, 0.7, 1.0, 1.5, 2.0, 2.5, 3.0, 4.0$.

13. **(a)** For a system of ideal gas molecules in thermal equilibrium at 300 °K, determine the most probable kinetic energy K_m and the average kinetic energy $\overline{K}$, in electron-volts. **(b)** Compare the number of molecules with energy 10^{-2} ev to the number with energy 10^{-3} ev. **(c)** Compare the number with energy 10^{-2} ev to the number with energy 10^{-1} ev.

32

CLASSICAL
STATISTICAL MECHANICS

We have already indicated that a rigorous development of statistical mechanics is beyond our scope, but we emphasize this fact again because it might appear that in this chapter we really come to grips with this subject. It should be kept in mind that we are presenting a simplified approach, one which does not raise some subtle but important aspects of the subject. Just as your first study of motion was limited perhaps to motion in a straight line, so that the vector character of the quantities involved was not apparent, so there are aspects of statistical mechanics that are not apparent in this limited introductory treatment.

SYSTEMS CONSIDERED IN STATISTICAL MECHANICS

Statistical mechanics attempts to predict the behavior of systems consisting of very large numbers of identical particles that are weakly interacting. The aim is to calculate the most probable distribution of energy for the system. The reason that the particles must be weakly interacting is this: if the particles are not interacting at all, they can never exchange energy, and the energy distribution is fixed by the initial conditions of the system. On the other hand, if the particles are strongly interacting, then there is a potential energy of interaction that is a mutual property of a pair (or more) of particles, and cannot be assigned to an individual particle; then an energy distribution in terms of energy of individual particles could not be determined. Therefore **weakly interacting** means that the particles interact sufficiently to exchange energy, but not enough that the potential energy of interaction makes a significant contribution to the total energy. An ideal gas is one example of a system of weakly interacting particles, and although there are others we will focus our attention on this system, in order to be as specific as possible.

At the outset it may be useful to indicate one basic difference between statistics as applied to "classical particles" and as applied to "quantum particles."

A quantum particle means one that must be described by the methods of quantum mechanics. Any such particle in a system can only take on certain permitted values of energy; we say that there are certain **energy levels** or **energy states** in which the particle may be found. Its state may be completely specified by a set of quantum numbers. For a particular physical situation the possible states (called the **accessible states**) depend on certain macroscopic parameters, for example the volume occupied by the system.

On the other hand, a classical particle, meaning one whose motion can be adequately described by the methods of classical mechanics, can take on any value of energy, subject to whatever macroscopic constraints there are on the system. There is a continuum of accessible states. Energy is a continuous variable, and the state of the particle cannot be specified by a set of quantum numbers.

Our assumption that the system consists of **identical** particles means that the states accessible to a particle (whether a classical or a quantum particle) are exactly the same for all particles.

One source of difficulty that arises in statistical mechanics is this. We are going to determine a distribution function $f(E_i)$ that gives the average number of particles in a state of energy E_i, but this is *not* the same as the number of particles with energy E_i. This is because of what is called **degeneracy**, meaning different states that have the same energy. For quantum particles this means that there are states that have different sets of quantum numbers, but the same energy. For classical particles this means particles that have different positions and momenta, but the same energy. The situation is analogous to one discussed in the last chapter; we determined $d^3N_{v_x v_y v_z}$, the number of particles with components of speed in the ranges v_x to $v_x + dv_x$, v_y to $v_y + dv_y$, v_z to $v_z + dv_z$, and this was *not* the same as dN_v, the number of particles with speeds in the range $v \rightarrow v + dv$. To find this number we had to consider a spherical shell in velocity space.

The number of states with the same energy E_i is called the **statistical weight** $g(E_i)$. The number of particles with energy E_i is then the product of the distribution function $f(E_i)$, and the statistical weight $g(E_i)$

$$N(E_i) = f(E_i)g(E_i)$$

In dealing with a continuous energy distribution, we cannot speak of the number of particles with an energy E_i, but only of the number dN_E with energy in the range E to $E + dE$.

Then
$$dN_E = N(E)dE$$
$$= f(E)g(E)dE$$

where $N(E)$ is the number per unit energy interval, and $g(E)$ is the number of states per unit energy interval, called the **density of states.** We will return to this point.

PHASE SPACE

Think about a monatomic ideal gas, considered to be a system of weakly inter-acting identical particles. We showed in Chapter 26, on the Energy of a System of Gas Molecules, that a simple particle model is inadequate in dealing with polyatomic gases, because the individual molecules could have "internal energy" of vibration and rotation.

From a microscopic point of view the state of the monatomic ideal gas system is completely specified if the position and velocity of each particle is known; we would have to know x,y,z,v_x,v_y,v_z for each of the N particles, or a total of $6N$ quantities. The specification of each of these $6N$ quantities, to within certain limits, is called a **microstate** of the system.

Just as it was useful to introduce the concept of velocity space in discussing the distribution of molecular velocities, it is useful to introduce the concept of **phase space** here. This is a 6-dimensional space with co-ordinate axes $x,y,z,v_x,v_y,$ v_z. Corresponding to every particle at every instant there is a "point" in phase space, with co-ordinates (x,y,z,v_x,v_y,v_z). As the particles move around in real space, changing position and velocity, the points in phase space move around. Our problem is to determine the distribution of points in phase space. This means of course we are assuming that there is "a" distribution, one that does not change as time goes on.

(Phase space is usually defined as position–momentum space rather than position–velocity space as we have done. In Chapter 31 in developing the distribution of molecular speeds we stated that instead of velocity space (v_x,v_y,v_z) we could use momentum space with co-ordinates (p_x,p_y,p_z). Similarly phase space can be defined with co-ordinates (x,y,z,p_x,p_y,p_z). Classically it makes no difference, but in quantum statistics it does make a difference because a micro-state is defined in a different way than it is in classical statistics.)

Think of phase space as being divided up into equal 6-dimensional volume elements, each of volume $dx\ dy\ dz\ dv_x\ dv_y\ dv_z$. We will call these volume ele-ments **cells.** We are going to develop a continuous distribution function, and this means that we assume that the dimensions of a cell are small compared to the dimensions of the container occupied by the gas, and the range of velocities of the gas molecules, but large enough to contain large numbers of points. We think of the cells as being numbered $1, 2, 3, \cdots, i, \cdots$ and the numbers of phase points in the cells is then $N_1, N_2, N_z, \cdots, N_i, \cdots$.

The density of points in phase space is

$$\rho = \frac{N_i}{dx\,dy\,dz\,dv_x\,dv_y\,dv_z}$$

and we are assuming that ρ is a continuous function of the co-ordinates.

Note: We are going to apply statistical considerations to determine the most probable distribution of points in phase space. You will recall that in the chapter on Random Events we stated that precise probabilistic calculations should be done on the basis of a statistical **ensemble,** a collection of systems similar to the real system. Rather than thinking about the real system as time goes on, we think about the ensemble. Each system in the ensemble contains N particles, and its state is completely specified by giving $6N$ co-ordinates, so we visualize a phase space of $6N$ dimensions. Then a point in phase space represents the state of a system in the ensemble, and the statistical problem becomes that of determining the most probable distribution of points in this space. This approach gives a deeper significance to concepts such as thermal equilibrium, and temperature, than we are going to be able to provide, but it is somewhat too abstruse for us to tackle here.

MICROSTATES AND MACROSTATES

A microstate of the system is the specification of which cell every phase point of the system is in. Then the position and velocity of each particle are specified to within narrow limits.

The macroscopic observable properties of the gas do not depend on this specification; they depend on **how many** points are in each cell, not on **which** points are in the cells. The gas density depends on the **number** of particles per unit volume, the gas pressure depends on the **number** of particles with velocities in a certain range, and so on. The specification of the number of points in each cell, the N_i, is sufficient to determine the macroscopic properties of the system, and this specification is called a **macrostate** of the system.

The fundamental hypothesis of statistical mechanics is that **all accessible microstates are equally probable.** By accessible microstates we mean those that are permitted by the external constraints on the system. If the gas is confined to a volume V, this places a constraint on the possible positions of the particles; if the total energy of the system is E, this places a constraint on the energies accessible to individual particles.

The assumption that all accessible microstates are equally probable is based on there being nothing in the laws of mechanics, as applied to the individual particles, to make one microstate preferable to another. A point moves around in phase space, being as likely to be found in one "place" as another, just as a gas molecule moving in a volume in real space is as likely to be found in one part of the volume as another. Because the cells in phase space have been made of equal volume, a point is as likely to be in one cell as another.

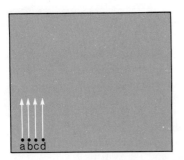 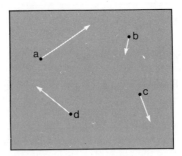

These two microstates are equally probable.

Think carefully about what this assumption means, looking at four molecules moving in a container. It says that the two microstates indicated are equally probable; in one, the molecules are all in one corner of the container, moving in the same direction at the same speed; in the other, the molecules are distributed throughout the volume, moving in different directions with different speeds. Note, however, that in each case the position and velocity of each molecule are precisely specified. The second possibility may appear to be more likely than the first, but only because there are a lot of situations that "look like" this. But situations that look the same are similar macrostates, not microstates.

By analogy, compare two bridge hands, one an unusual one, the other an average hand. The probability of being dealt either of these hands is very small,

These two bridge hands are equally probable.

and is **exactly the same for each.** In each case every card in the hand is specified, and these two microstates are equally probable. There are, however, many hands that look like the second one—this is what is meant by "an average hand."

THERMODYNAMIC PROBABILITY

Observable physical properties depend on the macrostates of the system. Corresponding to any particular macrostate $N_1, N_2, N_3, \cdots$ there will be a number of different microstates. This number is called the **thermodynamic probability** W of the macrostate. It is called thermodynamic probability, and not simply probability, because normally probabilities are numbers less than unity. Here W is greater than unity, and for large numbers of particles is a very large number.

The assumption of equal probabilities for the microstates makes it possible to determine W. The N particles $a, b, c, d, \cdots$ can be arranged in sequence in $N!$ different ways, since the first position can be filled in N ways, the second in $(N - 1)$ ways, and so on. These sequences do not each represent a different microstate, however, because the sequence of the particles in a particular cell does not matter; if molecules a, c and f are in cell i, then $N_i = 3$ whether the sequence is $acf, afc, fac, fca, caf, cfa$. Therefore we must divide the total number of ways the sequences can be formed $N!$ by the number of permutations $N_i!$ in each cell in order to get the number corresponding to a particular set of N's (a particular macrostate).

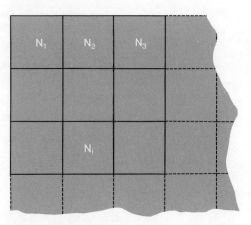

Distribution of particles (points) amongst cells in phase space.

$$W = \frac{N!}{N_1! \, N_2! \, N_3! \, \cdots \, N_i! \, \cdots} = \frac{N!}{\pi N_i!}$$

where π is notation for the product of terms.

It is more convenient to deal with the logarithm of W than with W itself.

$$\ln W = \ln N! - \sum \ln N_i!$$

We now use the approximation $\ln M! \cong M \ln M - M$, valid for large M.

If N and all the N_i are very large numbers (remember the assumption that the cells contain large numbers of phase points)

$$\ln W = (N \ln N - N) - \sum (N_i \ln N_i - N_i)$$
$$= N \ln N - N - \sum N_i \ln N_i + \sum N_i$$
$$= N \ln N - \sum N_i \ln N_i$$

since $\sum N_i = N$.

THE MAXWELL–BOLTZMANN DISTRIBUTION

We have an expression for the thermodynamic probability, the number of microstates corresponding to a particular macrostate (a particular set of N_i's). As the points move around in phase space, the numbers N_i will vary, and the number W will vary. We assume that the system is in a state of equilibrium, which means we assume that we observe a particular macrostate, the state of maximum thermodynamic probability W_{max}.

As a result of molecular motions and collisions there will be some variation in the numbers N_i, even though the system is in its state of maximum thermodynamic probability. We denote this variation by δN_i. (We will treat the variations δN_i as though they were differentials dN_i, but will not use this notation because we are actually dealing with partial derivatives. This discussion should be plausible, but can be made more mathematically rigorous.) If the probability W (and its logarithm) are at the maximum, the variation produced by the δN_i will be zero.

$$\delta(\ln W_{max}) = \delta(N \ln N) - \delta(\sum N_i \ln N_i)$$
$$= -\sum \ln N_i \, \delta N_i - \sum N_i \delta(\ln N_i)$$
$$= 0$$

However, $\sum N_i \delta(\ln N_i) = \sum N_i \dfrac{\delta N_i}{N_i} = \sum (\delta N_i) = 0$, since $N = \sum N_i$ is constant.

This leaves for the equilibrium distribution

$$\sum \ln N_i \, \delta N_i = 0$$

If the N_i's could be varied independently, the coefficient of each term in this equation would have to be zero. However, there are two conditions that must be considered. One is that the total number of particles is constant, so that

$$\sum (\delta N_i) = 0$$

The other is that the total energy of the system is constant. Our division of phase space into cells makes it possible for us to refer to an energy E_i associated with each cell; a particle with its phase point in cell i has energy E_i. The value of E_i will depend on the position of the cell in phase space—that is, on the co-ordinates (x,y,z,v_x,v_y,v_z) of the cell. The energy of the N_i particles whose phase points are in the cell i is $N_i E_i$, and the total energy of the system is $U = \sum N_i E_i$. We have used the symbol U because this is the total internal energy of the system, the same as that defined by the first law in thermodynamics. If we assume that the system is isolated, this energy is constant and therefore

$$\delta U = \sum E_i \, \delta N_i = 0$$

We combine the two condition equations with the equation describing the equilibrium distribution, using the method of Lagrange undetermined multipliers described in the last chapter. Using the undetermined multipliers $-\ln \alpha$ and β gives

$$\sum \ln N_i \, \delta N_i - \ln \alpha \sum (\delta N_i) + \beta \sum E_i \, \delta N_i = 0$$

$$\sum (\ln N_i - \ln \alpha + \beta E_i) \, \delta N_i = 0$$

In this equation the δN_i may be regarded as effectively independent, and the coefficient of each term must be zero.

$$\ln N_i - \ln \alpha + \beta E_i = 0$$

$$N_i = \alpha \, e^{-\beta E_i}$$

This gives the form of the Maxwell–Boltzmann distribution: the number of particles in the state of energy E_i is a rapidly decreasing function of energy. As usual the distribution can equally well be interpreted as a probability distribution. The probability of a particle being in a state of energy E_i is

$$\frac{N_i}{N} = \frac{\alpha}{N} e^{-\beta E_i}$$

The constant α can be eliminated by using $\sum N_i = N$

$$N = \sum \alpha \, e^{-\beta E_i} = \alpha \sum e^{-\beta E_i} = \alpha Z$$

The quantity $Z = \sum e^{-\beta E_i}$ is called the **partition function** for the system. Its value depends on the particular system.

In terms of the partition function

$$N_i = \frac{N}{Z} e^{-\beta E_i}$$

While we have referred to this as the number of particles in the state E_i, it must always be kept in mind that this number is based on a statistical prediction. It is the **average** number, or the **expected** number. The average over what? It is not an average over space (what would be observed at a given instant of time) nor an average over time (what would be observed at a fixed point in space as time went on) but an average over both space and time. More precisely, it is an **ensemble average,** the result that would be expected for an ensemble of $\mathfrak{N}$ systems similar to the real system, as $\mathfrak{N} \to \infty$.

THERMODYNAMIC PROPERTIES

A rigorous development of statistical mechanics would show that such concepts as thermal equilibrium, entropy, and temperature, arise as a consequence of the properties of a statistical ensemble of systems similar to the real system.

The two methods by which systems can exchange energy, heat and work, would turn out to have significance in microscopic terms; a thermal interaction (heat exchange) is one which does not change the accessible states of the systems, while in a non-thermal (adiabatic) interaction there are changes in the macroscopic variables of the system, and this gives rise to changes in the accessible states. This second kind of energy exchange is called work.

In our less sophisticated treatment all that we can do is define entropy and temperature in a way that is consistent with the macroscopic laws of thermodynamics. From a thermodynamic point of view an isolated system in equilibrium will be in a state of maximum entropy, since if the system is not in equilibrium processes will occur to bring it into this state, and in any natural process the entropy increases. From the point of view of statistical mechanics, an isolated system in equilibrium is in a state of maximum thermodynamic probability. If it is not in the state, it will tend toward this state. This implies that entropy S and thermodynamic probability W are related, although it does not tell us how. To get results that are consistent with the laws of thermodynamics, it is necessary to assume that

$$S = k \ln W$$

where k is Boltzmann's constant. We gave one example of this relationship in the chapter on the Second Law.

Using this definition of entropy we can relate the internal energy U and the entropy S of our system.

$$\ln W = N \ln N - \sum N_i \ln N_i \qquad\qquad N_i = \frac{N}{Z} e^{-\beta E_i}$$
$$= N \ln N - \sum N_i (\ln N - \ln Z - \beta E_i)$$
$$= N \ln N - \ln N \sum N_i + \ln Z \sum N_i + \beta \sum N_i E_i$$
$$= N \ln Z + \beta U$$

$$S = k \ln W = Nk \ln Z + k\beta U$$

The thermodynamic relation between S and U is given by the combined first and second law

$$dU = T\,dS - p\,dV$$

If we consider that S and V are the independent variables of a thermodynamic system, then $U = U(S,V)$ and

$$dU = \left(\frac{\partial U}{\partial S}\right)_V dS + \left(\frac{\partial U}{\partial V}\right)_S dV$$

Comparing coefficients, we see that $T = \left(\frac{\partial U}{\partial S}\right)_V$. This gives an expression for temperature as used in thermodynamics. To be consistent, we take this as the definition of temperature in statistical mechanics

$$S = Nk \ln Z + k\beta U$$

$$\left(\frac{\partial S}{\partial U}\right)_V = k\beta \qquad\qquad :N, k, Z, \beta \text{ are constants}$$

$$= \frac{1}{T}$$

This identifies the constant β as $1/kT$.

The Maxwell–Boltzmann distribution function is then

$$N_i = \frac{N}{Z} e^{-E_i/kT} \qquad Z = \sum e^{-E_i/kT}$$

All macroscopic thermodynamic quantities can be expressed in terms of the partition function Z (this function is sometimes called the **sum over states,** a more descriptive name).

$$S = Nk \ln Z + U/T$$

Since
$$\frac{dZ}{dT} = \sum \left(\frac{E_i}{kT^2}\right) e^{-E_i/kT} = \frac{1}{kT^2} \sum E_i\, e^{-E_i/kT}$$

$$U = \sum N_i E_i = \frac{N}{Z} \sum E_i\, e^{-E_i/kT} = \frac{N}{Z} kT^2 \frac{dZ}{dT}$$

$$= NkT^2 \frac{d(\ln Z)}{dT}$$

The Helmholtz free energy is

$$F = U - TS = -NkT \ln Z$$

Recalling the thermodynamic relation $p = -(\partial F/\partial V)_T$

$$p = NkT \left[\frac{\partial}{\partial V}(\ln Z)\right]_T$$

This is the equation of state of the system. Thus if the partition function Z can be determined, all of the thermodynamic properties of the system can be worked out.

Although we started out with reference to a monatomic ideal gas in developing these results, this was just so that we could give a specific example of the dimensions of phase space. The co-ordinates of phase space do not appear in the result, and the expressions obtained can be applied to any system of weakly interacting particles. If co-ordinates other than those giving position and velocity are necessary to describe the state of an individual particle, it is necessary to add other dimensions to phase space, corresponding to these co-ordinates. The number of dimensions of phase space is equal to the number of degrees of freedom of an individual particle.

For example, think about a diatomic ideal gas, using as a model for individual molecules a rigid rotator of moment of inertia I. The expression for the energy of a molecule will contain rotational energy terms $\frac{1}{2}I\omega_x^2 + \frac{1}{2}I\omega_y^2$. We can treat the gas as a system of weakly interacting "particles" by extending the dimensions of phase space to include the co-ordinates ω_x and ω_y (the components of angular velocity). If a non-rigid rotator model is used, two more co-ordinates are necessary to handle the kinetic and potential energy of vibration.

THE MAXWELL–BOLTZMANN DISTRIBUTION FUNCTION

The central result we have obtained is that for a system of weakly interacting particles in thermal equilibrium at a temperature T, the average number of particles in state E_i is proportional to $e^{-E_i/kT}$, called the **Boltzmann factor.** Equivalently it can be said that the probability of a particle being in state E_i is proportional to the Boltzmann factor. The proportionality constant is determined by a normalization condition; the sum of the particles is N, or the sum of the probabilities is unity.

The Maxwell–Boltzmann distribution **function** then is written in general as

$$f(\dot{E_i}) = A\,e^{-E_i/kT}$$

where A is a constant determined by a normalization condition.

This result is applicable (if Maxwell–Boltzmann statistics are applicable) whether E_i can take on only certain discrete values (as for a quantum particle) or can be considered to be a continuous variable. Remember, however, that if energy varies continuously it becomes meaningless to speak of the number of particles with an energy E; instead we must consider the number of particles with energy in the range E to $E + dE$

$$dN_E = N(E)\,dE$$

where $N(E)$ is the number of particles per unit energy interval. The number dN_E will be the product of the number of particles in the state E, given by the Maxwell–Boltzmann function, and the number of energy states in the range E to $E + dE$.

$$N(E)\,dE = f(E)g(E)\,dE$$

where $g(E)$ is the density of states, the number of states per unit energy interval.

Suppose for example we think about the kinetic energy of the particles, a continuous function of the speed v. The number of states with speeds in the range v to $v + dv$ can be found by counting the number of points in velocity space in this range; this number is proportional to the volume of the spherical

shell, $4\pi v^2\,dv$. This can be translated into energy
terms using

$$E = \tfrac{1}{2}mv^2$$

$$dE = mv\,dv = \sqrt{2mE}\,dv$$

$$4\pi v^2\,dv = 4\pi \left(\frac{2E}{m}\right)\frac{dE}{\sqrt{2mE}} = B\sqrt{E}\,dE$$

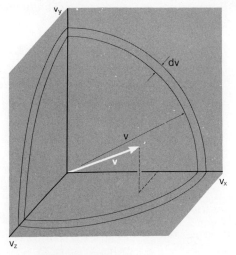

Spherical shell in
velocity space.

where B is a constant. Therefore the number of
states in the range E to $E + dE$ is

$$g(E)\,dE = C\sqrt{E}\,dE$$

where C is a constant.

The energy distribution is then given by

$$N(E)\,dE = f(E)g(E)\,dE$$

$$= A\,e^{-E/kT}\,C\sqrt{E}\,dE$$

$$= D\sqrt{E}\,e^{-E/kT}\,dE$$

where D is a constant, determined by the normalization conditions.

The function $N(E) = D\sqrt{E}\,e^{-E/kT}$ is the distribution function for kinetic
energy, the same function $N(K)$ described in the previous chapter.

EQUIPARTITION OF ENERGY

In the chapter on the Energy of a System of Gas Molecules we used the principle
of equipartition of energy, and stated that it was a result of classical statistics.
Now we can show this.

The principle of equipartition of energy states that there is an average energy
$\tfrac{1}{2}kT$ associated with each degree of freedom of a system; the number of degrees
of freedom is equal to the number of independent terms in the expression for
the energy of the system. The conditions under which the principle applies are
(1) Maxwell–Boltzmann statistics are applicable, (2) the energy associated with
the degree of freedom is a continuous function of a co-ordinate, (3) the energy
is a quadratic function of the co-ordinate. Note that by a co-ordinate we mean
not just the co-ordinates (x,y,z) of ordinary space, but any of the co-ordinates
that are necessary to define phase space for the particular system. These will
include the components of velocity (v_x,v_y,v_z) or alternatively the components of
momentum (p_x,p_y,p_z).

The assumptions (3) and (2) mean that associated with some co-ordinate u
there is a term in the total energy of a particle of the form $E_u = bu^2$, where b is
a constant. Assumption (1) means that there is a probability $P(E_u) = B\,e^{-E_u/kT}$
(where B is a constant) of finding a particle in a state with this energy.

From the definition of average value

$$\bar{E}_u = \frac{\int E_u\, P(E_u)\, du}{\int P(E_u)\, du} = \frac{Bb \int u^2\, e^{-bu^2/kT}\, du}{B \int e^{-bu^2/kT}\, du}$$

where the integration is carried out over all values of the co-ordinate u. Suppose that u can vary from 0 to ∞. Then the integrations give (using the table in the last chapter)

$$\bar{E}_u = \frac{b[(\sqrt{\pi}/4)\,(kT/b)^{3/2}]}{[(\sqrt{\pi}/2)\,(kT/b)^{1/2}]} = \tfrac{1}{2}kT$$

If the integration limits are $-\infty$ to ∞, both integrals are twice as great, and the result is the same. This is equipartition of energy. It is called equipartition because the energy is equally partitioned between the various degrees of freedom of the particle, or system.

The assumption that the co-ordinate can become infinitely large may not be justified. For any system not all states are accessible, because of constraints on the system. Think for example of a component $\tfrac{1}{2}mv_x^2$ of kinetic energy. Since the total energy of the system is constant, it is clear that v_x cannot be allowed to become infinite. However, in calculating the integrals it is reasonable to replace $\int_0^{u_{max}}$ by $\int_0^{\infty}$ because of the exponential factor $\exp(-bu^2/kT)$. This is a rapidly decreasing function of u, and therefore the contribution to the sum for large values of u becomes negligible.

There are two mathematical features of the Maxwell–Boltzmann distribution function that make calculations with this function relatively simple. One is that just mentioned, the fact that it is a rapidly decreasing function so that it is possible to replace integrals over finite limits by ones over infinite limits. The other (and more important one) is the fact that it is possible to separate the integrals over different co-ordinates because of the properties of the exponential function. This will be illustrated in the next section.

THE MONATOMIC IDEAL GAS

Although we used the system of a monatomic ideal gas to help visualize phase space, we have not really used the properties of this system yet.

We now think of our system as N particles, each of mass m, confined to an enclosure of volume V. The state of each particle is characterized by the six co-ordinates x,y,z,v_x,v_y,v_z, so phase space has six dimensions. For convenience we will assume that N is Avogadro's number, so that we are dealing with one mole of gas.

We assume for the present that external gravitational forces on the particles are negligible. Then the potential energy of the particles is constant, **provided** the position is anywhere in the volume V. Since potential energy always includes an arbitrary constant, we call the potential energy **zero** in all cells in phase space such that the co-ordinates x,y,z are in the volume V, and **infinity** for all cells outside this volume. Then the probability of a molecule being in these cells is proportional to $e^{-\infty} = 0$.

The partition function $Z = \sum e^{-E_i/kT}$ is a sum over all the states of the system; for states with position co-ordinates in V all the energy of the particles is translational kinetic energy and $E_i = \frac{1}{2}mv_i^2$, and for states with position co-ordinates outside V the energy $E_i = \infty$ and there is no contribution to the sum. Therefore we can take

$$Z = \sum e^{-mv_i^2/2kT}$$

where the summation is now not over all states, but only over those with position co-ordinates in V. These are the accessible states.

Phase space was divided into cells of volume $dx\,dy\,dz\,dv_x\,dv_y\,dv_z$. These cells had to be of equal volume; otherwise the assumption that all microstates are equally probable would not have been reasonable (phase points would be more likely to be in cells of larger volume). Therefore we can introduce a constant $H = dx\,dy\,dz\,dv_x\,dv_y\,dv_z$. Then Z can be evaluated by multiplying it by $H/H = dx\,dy\,dz\,dv_x\,dv_y\,dv_z/H$ and, since in this example the energy is a continuous function of the co-ordinates, integrating over the volume of phase space corresponding to position co-ordinates in V.

$$Z = \frac{1}{H} \iiint\!\!\iiint e^{-mv^2/2kT}\,dx\,dy\,dz\,dv_x\,dv_y\,dv_z$$

or since

$$v^2 = v_x^2 + v_y^2 + v_z^2$$

$$Z = \frac{1}{H} \iiint_{\text{vol}} dx\,dy\,dz \int_{-\infty}^{\infty} e^{-mv_x^2/2kT}\,dv_x \int_{-\infty}^{\infty} e^{-mv_y^2/2kT}\,dv_y \int_{-\infty}^{\infty} e^{-mv_z^2/2kT}\,dv_z$$

$$= \frac{V}{H} \left(\frac{2\pi kT}{m}\right)^{3/2}$$

Note that the integration over phase space can be divided into separate integrals over the various co-ordinates, because of the properties of the exponential function; $e^{A+B} = e^A e^B$. Integration of the position co-ordinates over the appropriate volume of phase space gives the actual volume V. It is assumed, on the basis of the argument given in the last section, that the speed component co-ordinates v_x, v_y, v_z can be considered to vary from $-\infty$ to ∞.

As we stated earlier, once the partition function of a system has been determined all the other properties of the system can be worked out.

The number of phase points in a cell is

$$N_i = \frac{N}{Z} e^{-E_i/kT} = \frac{NH}{V} \left(\frac{m}{2\pi kT}\right)^{3/2} e^{-mv_i^2/2kT}$$

which for the continuous distribution it is more appropriate to write as

$$d^6 N = \frac{N}{V} \left(\frac{m}{2\pi kT}\right)^{3/2} e^{-mv^2/2kT} \, dx \, dy \, dz \, dv_x \, dv_y \, dv_z$$

since integration over six co-ordinates is necessary to produce the total number N.

The distribution in space is obtained by integrating over all values of v_x, v_y, v_z. This gives

$$d^3 N_{xyz} = \frac{N}{V} dx \, dy \, dz \qquad \text{or} \qquad \frac{d^3 N_{xyz}}{dx \, dy \, dz} = \frac{N}{V}$$

This is the number density in ordinary space, and is constant. We are assuming a continuous distribution, and since the energy of the particles does not depend on position there is a uniform distribution in the volume V. This of course is not true if the volume element is too small.

The distribution in velocity space is obtained by integrating over x,y,z and this simply gives V so that

$$d^3 N_{v_x v_y v_z} = N \left(\frac{m}{2\pi kT}\right)^{3/2} e^{-mv^2/2kT} \, dv_x \, dv_y \, dv_z$$

which you can verify is the Maxwell distribution obtained directly in the last chapter, and discussed there.

The equation of state is $\quad p = NkT \left[\frac{\partial}{\partial V} (\ln Z)\right]_T$

which since $Z = KVT^{3/2}$ (where K is a constant) gives

$$p = \frac{NkT}{V} = \frac{RT}{V}$$

We took N to be Avogadro's number, so $Nk = R$, and V is the molar volume. This is the equation of state that·was developed empirically in thermodynamics.

The internal energy of the system is

$$U = NkT^2 \frac{d(\ln Z)}{dT}$$

$$= NkT^2 \frac{d}{dT} (\ln K + \ln V + \tfrac{3}{2} \ln T) = \tfrac{3}{2} NkT = \tfrac{3}{2} RT$$

This is the internal energy per mole, and is consistent with the equipartition principle. The molar specific heat at constant volume is $c_v = (\partial U/\partial T)_V = \tfrac{3}{2} R$.

The molar entropy is

$$S = Nk \ln Z + U/T$$
$$= R \ln V + \tfrac{3}{2}R \ln T + \text{a constant}$$
$$= R \ln V + c_v \ln T + \text{a constant}$$

again consistent with the results of thermodynamics.

All of these results apply to a monatomic ideal gas. Suppose that instead we think about a diatomic or polyatomic ideal gas—are any of the results still applicable? There will be additional terms in the expression for the energy of individual molecules, depending on the model assumed, and corresponding additional dimensions of phase space. The partition function will be different, and so will the extensive properties internal energy and entropy. However, perhaps you can see that the expressions giving the distribution in real space d^3N_{xyz} and the distribution in velocity space $d^3N_{v_xv_yv_z}$ will be the same as before; these will now refer to the position and velocity of the center of mass of each molecule. The partition function will again be proportional to the volume V, and therefore the equation of state will be the same $pV = RT$.

The essential assumption is that the molecules of the gas are weakly inter-acting, so that the potential energy of interaction is negligible, and the total energy is the sum of the energies of the individual molecules. We have said that statistical mechanics is applicable to systems of weakly interacting particles. Do we refer then to the polyatomic gas molecules as particles? This question "When is a particle a particle?" is one we have discussed before; nothing is a particle if examined closely enough, but on a gross enough scale every system can be treated as a particle. As far as the translational motion of the polyatomic gas is concerned, the molecules can be treated as particles; there is a uniform distribution in space, the velocities are described by the Maxwell distribution, and the macroscopic behavior is described by the ideal gas equations of state. However, the molecules also have internal energy (of rotation and vibration) and this has an effect on such macroscopic properties as specific heat capacity. Therefore while we may refer to the molecules as particles, we must keep in mind the limitations of this model.

The picture is complicated by the fact that the internal motions of the mole-cules can only be adequately described by the methods of quantum mechanics. There are only certain permitted states of energy; at low temperatures all molecules are in the lowest energy state (rotational and vibrational degrees of freedom are "frozen out") and the molecules behave as simple classical particles. As the temperature increases some molecules are found in higher states of internal energy. At high enough temperatures the spacing between energy levels becomes small compared to the thermal energy kT, and again the mole-cules can be treated classically (equipartition of energy can be used) but the "particles" now have rotational and vibrational degrees of freedom.

It is more precise to say that statistical mechanics deals with systems of weakly interacting identical **systems** than to say that it deals with systems of weakly interacting identical particles.

DISTRIBUTION IN
A UNIFORM GRAVITATIONAL FIELD

In the last section we dealt with an ideal gas, assuming that there was no external gravitational force on the molecules. We continue to think about an ideal gas, but now suppose that the system is in a uniform gravitational field of intensity **g**.

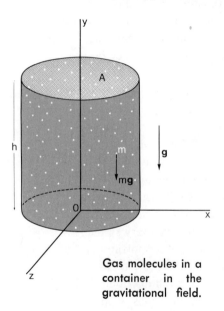

Gas molecules in a container in the gravitational field.

Think of the gas as confined to a container as indicated, of cross section A perpendicular to the **g**-direction, and height h. Choosing a co-ordinate system with origin at the bottom of the container, and y-axis upward (opposite to the **g**-direction), each molecule will have a gravitational potential energy mgy in addition to whatever other energy it has.

$$E = mgy + \text{other terms}$$

Integration of the Maxwell–Boltzmann distribution function over all co-ordinates in phase space except the spatial co-ordinates x, y, z will give the distribution in real space of the form

$$d^3N_{xyz} = B\, e^{-mgy/kT}\, dx\, dy\, dz$$

where B is the result of summation over the other co-ordinates. It can be evaluated from the normalization condition

$$N = B \iint dx\, dz \int_0^h e^{-mgy/kT}\, dy$$

The integration over $dx\, dz$ gives the cross sectional area of the container A. In order to integrate over y, we first assume that h is large enough that, because of the exponential term, the contribution to the integral at the upper limit becomes negligible. Then $\int_0^h$ can be replaced by $\int_0^\infty$ and the result is

$$N = BA \left(\frac{kT}{mg}\right) \qquad B = \frac{Nmg}{AkT}$$

Then
$$\frac{d^3N_{xyz}}{dx\, dy\, dz} = \frac{Nmg}{AkT}\, e^{-mgy/kT}$$

The left side is the number of molecules per unit volume in real space, the number density n. This number is a constant if there is no external field on the gas, but here it decreases exponentially with y

$$n = n_0\, e^{-mgy/kT}$$

where n_0 is the number density at $y = 0$, the bottom of the container. The assumption that y can vary from 0 to ∞ means that the container must be high enough that the density becomes effectively zero at some height in the container, and therefore the container does not really need a top.

To some extent this model represents the distribution of air molecules in the atmosphere, but there are two significant differences; we have assumed that the gravitational field $\mathbf{g}$ is uniform, and that the temperature T is constant. The earth's field decreases with height, and so does the actual temperature of the atmosphere. We have worked out the distribution in an isothermal atmosphere.

The result can be expressed in terms of pressure, using the ideal gas equation of state in the form $p = nkT$.

Then
$$p = \frac{Nmg}{A}\, e^{-mgy/kT} = p_0\, e^{-mgy/kT} = p_0\, e^{-Mgy/RT}$$

where p_0 is the pressure at $y = 0$. Note that $p_0 = Nmg/A$, the total weight of the molecules divided by the area. In this form the relation is sometimes called the law of atmospheres. The form of the exponential coefficient can be expressed in terms of macroscopic quantities:

$$\frac{m}{k} = \frac{N_0 m}{N_0 k} = \frac{M}{R}$$

where N_0 is Avogadro's number and M is the molecular weight of the gas.

The distribution can also be applied to a container of finite height, although then the normalization condition will give a different value of B. The ratio of densities at two heights will be

$$\frac{n_2}{n_1} = e^{-mg(y_2 - y_1)/kT}$$

In order to see that the difference is negligible for ordinary containers, it is necessary to put in some numbers. Taking air as the gas, $M \sim 30\ \text{gm/mole}$, and considering a container 1 m high, the ratio of densities between top and bottom of the container depends on the exponent

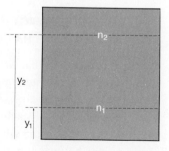

The number density decreases with height.

$$\frac{mg(y_2 - y_1)}{kT} = \frac{Mg(y_2 - y_1)}{RT} \sim \frac{30 \times 10^3 \times 10^2}{8 \times 10^7 \times 300} \sim 10^{-4}$$

(the numbers have been expressed in cgs units). Using $e^x \cong 1 + x$ for $x \lll 1$

$$\frac{n_2}{n_1} = e^{-10^{-4}} \cong 1 - 10^{-4} = 0.9999$$

The densities at the top and bottom of the container are not appreciably different. You can see why it is not necessary to consider the gravitational potential energy of gas molecules in working out the molecular distributions. As another way of looking at it, you can compare the gravitational potential energy mgh of a molecule at the top of the container, with the average translational kinetic energy $\frac{3}{2}kT$.

$$\frac{mgh}{3kT/2} \sim 10^{-4}$$

Again this shows that the potential energy difference is negligible.

Although the gas molecules cannot be observed directly, an equivalent system can be formed by suspending tiny particles in a solution—a colloidal suspension. The distribution of such particles is described by Maxwell–Boltzmann statistics. The distribution with height is exponential, as described by the previous equations, except that the effective value of g is different because of the buoyant effect of the fluid. For such a distribution the number of particles in a small volume can actually be counted, and therefore the average value of n as a function of y observed experimentally. One of the first measurements of k (and therefore of N_0) was made by Perrin in 1909 in an experiment of this kind.

In this section we have applied Maxwell–Boltzmann statistics to a situation where the energy mgy is a continuous function of a co-ordinate, but equipartition of energy does not apply because the energy is not a quadratic function of the co-ordinate. In the next section we apply these statistics to a situation where equipartition does not apply because the energy is not a continuous function.

AVERAGE ENERGY OF A SYSTEM OF HARMONIC OSCILLATORS

We have said that Maxwell–Boltzmann statistics can be applied to any system of weakly interacting particles in thermal equilibrium. We now apply this to a system of N linear harmonic oscillators in thermal equilibrium. The oscillators are all identical, each with a frequency of vibration $\nu = (1/2\pi)\sqrt{k_0/m}$ where m is the mass of the vibrating particle and k_0 is the force constant. Later we will think about what real physical system this system of oscillators might represent.

The energy of each of the oscillators as given by classical mechanics is

$$E_i = \tfrac{1}{2}mv_x^2 + \tfrac{1}{2}k_0x^2$$

where x is a co-ordinate axis along the line of motion of the particle, with its origin at the midpoint of oscillation. There are two quadratic terms in the energy, and therefore the equipartition principle states that there is an average energy $2(\frac{1}{2}kT)$ for each oscillator, and an average energy NkT for the whole system.

Suppose, however, that the oscillators cannot be described by classical mechanics, but that quantum mechanics must be used. The essential result of quantum mechanics is that the oscillators can only be in certain permitted states of energy $E_n = (n + \frac{1}{2})h\nu$, where h is Planck's constant and n is an integer $n = 0, 1, 2, \cdots$. The energy is not a continuous function, and the equipartition principle cannot be applied. We continue to assume, however, that Maxwell–Boltzmann statistics are applicable; that is, that the average number of molecules in state E_n is proportional to $e^{-E_n/kT}$.

To work out the distribution we could determine the partition function Z, this time as a sum rather than an integral, and use it to determine the properties of the system. However, it may be more informative to work directly with the distribution.

If N_n is the average number of particles in the state E_n, then

$$N_n = A\,e^{-E_n/kT} = A\,e^{-(n+1/2)h\nu/kT}$$

$$= A\,e^{-(n+1/2)x}$$

where A is constant and $x = h\nu/kT$ is a constant. The number of particles in the ground state is

$$N_0 = A\,e^{-1/2x}$$

and in higher states is

$$N_1 = A\,e^{-(3/2)x} = N_0\,e^{-x}$$

$$N_2 = A\,e^{-(5/2)x} = N_0\,e^{-2x}$$

$$N_n = A\,e^{-(n+1/2)x} = N_0\,e^{-nx}$$

Distribution of particles amongst the energy levels for the system of harmonic oscillators.

The total number of particles in all states is

$$N = \sum_{n=0}^{\infty} N_n = N_0 \sum_{n=0}^{\infty} e^{-nx}$$

$$= N_0(1 + e^{-x} + e^{-2x} + \cdots)$$

This is an infinite geometric series, with first term $a = 1$ and common ratio $r = e^{-x}$. The sum of such a series is $a/(1 - r)$, as you can verify by forming the binomial expansion of $(1 - r)^{-1}$.

$$N = \frac{N_0}{1 - e^{-x}}$$

The total energy of the particles in each state is

$$N_n E_n = N_0\, e^{-nx}(n + \tfrac{1}{2})h\nu$$
$$= \tfrac{1}{2}N_0 h\nu\, e^{-nx} + N_0 h\nu n\, e^{-nx}$$

and the total energy overall is

$$E = \sum_{n=0}^{\infty} N_n E_n = \tfrac{1}{2}N_0 h\nu \sum_{n=0}^{\infty} e^{-nx} + N_0 h\nu \sum_{n=0}^{\infty} n\, e^{-nx}$$

$$= \tfrac{1}{2}N_0 h\nu \frac{1}{(1 - e^{-x})} + N_0 h\nu\, e^{-x}(1 + 2e^{-x} + 3e^{-2x} + \cdots)$$

The second sum can be evaluated by noting the binomial expansion

$$\frac{1}{(1-y)^2} = (1 - y)^{-2} = 1 + 2y + 3y^2 + \cdots$$

Using this, and setting $N_0 = N(1 - e^{-x})$, gives

$$E = \tfrac{1}{2}Nh\nu + N\frac{h\nu}{e^{h\nu/kT} - 1}$$

and an average energy per quantum oscillator

$$\bar{E}_{\text{osc}} = \frac{E}{N} = \tfrac{1}{2}h\nu + \frac{h\nu}{e^{h\nu/kT} - 1}$$

The first term is not temperature dependent, and is called the **zero point energy** because all the particles in the system would have this energy as the temperature approached zero. For $x = h\nu/kT \ll 1$, e^x becomes very large and the second term approaches zero. As $T \to 0$, $\bar{E}_{\text{osc}} \to \tfrac{1}{2}h\nu$. At low temperatures all of the particles are in the ground state.

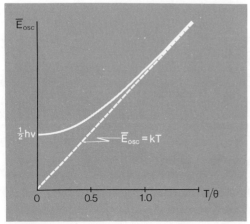

Average energy of a harmonic oscillator.

For $x \ll 1$, $e^x \cong 1 + x$ and the second term becomes

$$\frac{h\nu}{1 + h\nu/kT - 1} = kT$$

the same as given by equipartition of energy. When the spacing between levels $h\nu$ is small compared to the thermal energy kT, a classical description of the individual oscillators becomes satisfactory. The zero point energy is negligible if $h\nu \ll kT$, so at high temperatures $\bar{E}_{\text{osc}} = kT$. Introducing a constant called the characteristic temperature for vibration, θ, defined by $\theta = h\nu/k$, the limiting cases are described by $T \ll \theta$ and $T \gg \theta$.

Macroscopic measurements of the energy of a system are made by observing the changes in temperature that occur when thermal energy is added to the system—that is, by measuring the heat capacity of the system. We will suppose that the number of oscillators N is Avogadro's number, so that we have one mole of oscillators, and are dealing with the molar heat capacity c. The molar heat capacity associated with the vibrational motion of the system of oscillators is predicted to be

$$c_{\text{vib}} = \frac{dE}{dT} = -\frac{Nh\nu}{(e^{h\nu/kT} - 1)^2} e^{h\nu/kT} \left(-\frac{h\nu}{kT^2}\right)$$

$$= R\left(\frac{\theta}{T}\right)^2 \frac{e^{\theta/T}}{(e^{\theta/T} - 1)^2} = RF\left(\frac{\theta}{T}\right)$$

$$R = Nk$$

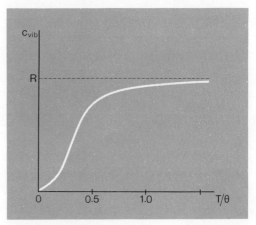

This function has the form indicated: for $T \gg \theta$, $c_{\text{vib}} = R$. At $T = \theta$

$$c_{\text{vib}} = R\frac{e}{(e - 1)^2} = 0.92R$$

At $T = 2\theta$

$$c_{\text{vib}} = R(0.5)^2 \frac{e^{0.5}}{(e^{0.5} - 1)^2} = 0.98R$$

Molar heat capacity of a system of oscillators.

Our model has been a system of weakly interacting linear harmonic oscillators in thermal equilibrium at a temperature T. Does this represent any real physical system? We can give two examples where it provides useful information about real situations.

For an ideal gas of diatomic molecules, one form of energy that each molecule can have is vibrational energy; in Chapter 26 on the Energy of a System of Gas Molecules we showed how the energy could be expressed, assuming a non-rigid (harmonic) rotator as a model. As long as the energy can be expressed as a sum of essentially independent terms $E_i = E_{\text{trans}} + E_{\text{rot}} + E_{\text{vib}}$ (we gave a numerical example to show the extent to which this approximation is valid) then the distribution function $e^{-E_i/kT}$ can be divided into the product of functions depending on the different co-ordinates, and these functions dealt with separately, as we have seen in the examples. This means that the model just described gives the contribution to the total internal energy due to the vibrational motion of the diatomic molecules, and the contribution to the molar heat capacity due to vibration. The heat capacity involved is c_v, the molar heat capacity at constant volume. (Any other heat capacity involves external work done on or by the system, and then the heat capacity is not the rate of change of internal energy with temperature.) The contribution to c_v due to vibration ranges from 0 (for $T \ll \theta$) to R (for $T > \theta$), as discussed in the earlier chapter, but now we have the specific expression c_{vib} for the contribution as a function of temperature. For a diatomic molecule

$$c_v = c_{\text{trans}} + c_{\text{rot}} + c_{\text{vib}}$$

where $c_{\text{vib}} = RF(\theta/T)$ as sketched earlier.

The other situation in which the model provides insight is in the theory of the heat capacity of solids. As a model of a solid we can think of an array of particles vibrating about certain equilibrium positions (lattice sites). The particles represent molecules held in the lattice by the electromagnetic interaction with their neighbors (indicated symbolically by springs in the diagram).

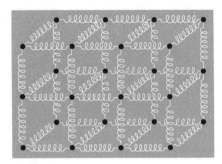

Model of a crystalline solid.

It certainly does not seem reasonable to treat this as a system of weakly interacting particles, where Maxwell–Boltzmann statistics can be applied. Nevertheless, the expression for the molar heat capacity obtained by making this assumption is in fair agreement with experiment.

We assume, then, that the particles are all identical, each with a fixed characteristic frequency of vibration ν. This is the same as in our system of linear harmonic oscillators, but now there is one important difference; these oscillators are free to oscillate in three dimensions. The classical expression for the energy of a particle would be

$$E_i = \tfrac{1}{2}mv^2 + \tfrac{1}{2}k_0r^2$$
$$= \tfrac{1}{2}m\,(v_x^2 + v_y^2 + v_z^2) + \tfrac{1}{2}k_0(x^2 + y^2 + z^2)$$

Instead of 2 degrees of freedom for each of the N particles, there are now 6 degrees of freedom per particle. The results determined for the system of linear harmonic oscillators must be multiplied by 3.

If the number of particles N is Avogadro's number, the molar heat capacity is then

$$c_{\text{vib}} = 3RF\left(\frac{\theta}{T}\right)$$

The curve has the same shape as that sketched earlier, but now the limiting value at high temperatures is $3R$ rather than R.

These particles do not have energy of translation or rotation, like the diatomic molecules, and therefore this gives the total heat capacity of the system. The agreement with experiment is good at high temperatures, but not as satisfactory at low temperatures.

The fact that $c_v \cong 3R$ for solids at high temperatures is an experimental result that is known as the Law of Dulong and Petit. You can verify this by consulting tables of physical constants. For aluminum, for example, c is 0.216 cal/gm-C°; its atomic weight is 27, so $c = 0.216 \times 27 = 5.8$ cal/mole-K°. In these units $R \cong 2$ cal/mole-K°. For aluminum the characteristic temperature θ is about 300 °K.

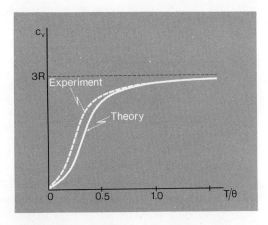

Molar heat capacity of solids.

The theory using this model, first proposed by Einstein, is called the Einstein theory of the specific heat of solids. As we pointed out, the fit with experiment becomes unsatisfactory at low temperatures. Near $T = 0$, the theory predicts an exponential dependence of c_v on T, while experimentally $c_v \propto T^3$. This is called the Debye T^3 law, because it agrees with a more refined theory of specific heats proposed by Debye. This theory, instead of assuming that the particles each have a fixed frequency of oscillation ν, assumes that there is a range of values $0 \rightarrow \nu_{max}$ for this quantity. In this way compensation is made for the fact that this is not really a system of weakly interacting particles.

In a metallic solid it is generally useful to assume that there are a number of free electrons, meaning electrons that are not fixed to particular atoms in lattice sites, but instead move through the lattice. This assumption is necessary in order to explain the high electrical and thermal conductivity of such materials, but it raises a question with respect to the heat capacity. There is roughly one free electron for each atom, or about N free electrons in the metal, and in some respects these can be thought of as constituting a "free electron gas"—that is, a system of particles moving around inside the metal like gas molecules in a container. According to the concepts of classical statistics, these particles must participate in equipartition of energy (at least at high temperatures) and therefore should make a contribution of the order of $\frac{3}{2}R$ to the molar heat capacity of the metal. No such contribution is observed (although the free electrons do contribute significantly to the heat capacity at very low temperatures).

The reason that the free electron gas can be neglected in the theory of specific heats is not that an electron is a quantum particle (after all, the lattice particles must be treated as quantum particles at low temperatures) but is that the system of free electrons cannot be handled by the methods of classical statistics.

QUANTUM STATISTICS

We have stated several times that Maxwell–Boltzmann statistics can be applied to any system of weakly interacting particles—whether classical or quantum particles. We have not said that this always gives valid results (results verified by experiment), because it does not always do so. Just as the motion of a particle under certain conditions must be described by quantum mechanics rather than classical mechanics, so the distribution of a system of particles under certain conditions must be described by quantum statistics rather than classical statistics. We will not develop quantum statistics, but will give the form of the resulting distribution functions.

The definition of a macrostate (which determines the observable properties of a system) is the same in quantum as in classical statistics. The fundamental difference lies in the definition of a microstate. In classical statistics a microstate means the specification of which cell in phase space every point (corresponding to every particle) is in. Interchanging two points a and b between two cells changes the microstate, but not the macrostate, of the system. The number of microstates corresponding to a particular macrostate was obtained by permuting the letters a, b, c, $\cdots$ representing the phase points. This means that we are thinking of the identical particles as distinguishable from one another, at least in principle. From the point of view of quantum mechanics this is impossible, and the classical definition of a microstate is meaningless. Instead in quantum statistics a microstate is defined in terms of the limit of localizability of a particle.

One of the fundamental principles of quantum mechanics is the Heisenberg uncertainty principle. In one form this states that if a particle is located to within a certain range of position Δx, and its corresponding momentum is known to within a certain range Δp_x, then the product of these uncertainties cannot be less than the fundamental constant h. This means, taking y- and z-co-ordinates into account, that in a 6-dimensional phase space with co-ordinates x,y,z,p_x,p_y,p_z a phase point can only be specified as somewhere in a volume h^3, and not more precisely. This volume is so small that it is reasonable to assume that a cell in phase space (the "infinitesimal" volume of phase space $dx\, dy\, dz\, dp_x\, dp_y\, dp_z$) is much larger, and therefore to assume that there is a large number of these h^3 volumes per cell.

A microstate in quantum statistics is defined on the basis of how the phase points (now representing indistinguishable particles) can be distributed among these tiny h^3 volumes within the cells in phase space. The resulting most probable distribution depends on whether or not it is assumed an unlimited number of phase points can occupy the same volume h^3. If this number is unlimited, the resulting distribution is the Bose–Einstein distribution function, of form

$$f_{\mathrm{BE}}(E_i) = \frac{1}{A\, e^{E_i/kT} - 1}$$

In some circumstances the number of phase points that can occupy the same volume h^3 cannot be greater than 2. This limitation is related to a quantum mechanical principle called the Pauli exclusion principle. The resulting distribution is the Fermi–Dirac distribution function, of form

$$f_{\text{FD}}(E_i) = \frac{1}{A\, e^{E_i/kT} + 1}$$

Recalling the Maxwell–Boltzmann distribution function

$$f_{\text{MB}}(E_i) = A\, e^{-E_i/kT}$$

you can see that the distributions of quantum statistics reduce to the classical distribution under conditions where the term $+1$ (or -1) in the denominator is negligible. It turns out that this is the situation when the density of points in phase space is relatively low.

Remember that in classical statistics the particles, even though identical, are considered to be distinguishable in principle. In a gas at low density the molecules are relatively far apart (~ 30 times the molecular diameter under standard conditions) and for this reason can be thought of as distinguishable on the basis of location. In a solid the atoms, even though close together, are fixed at the lattice sites and therefore again can be thought of as distinguishable on the basis of location. As we have seen, classical statistics can be applied to both these systems with some success.

Such an argument cannot be made for the free electrons in a metal; according to quantum mechanics, an electron can only be considered as localized to a region of the order of atomic dimensions, and since there is about one free electron per lattice atom this means that the distance between the electrons is comparable to their "size." It is necessary to use the Pauli exclusion principle in describing electrons, and this means that the appropriate statistics are Fermi–Dirac statistics. It can be shown using these statistics that the free electron gas makes a negligible contribution to the heat capacity of metals at ordinary temperatures.

Bose–Einstein statistics have application in describing the low temperature properties of liquid helium (a "quantum liquid") and in describing the properties of a photon gas. The application to a photon gas (electromagnetic radiation) leads to the Planck distribution of electromagnetic energy. It is with a few comments concerning this distribution that we conclude this volume, because it is here that some of the ideas of statistical mechanics, electromagnetic theory, and quantum mechanics all come together. Planck's original development in 1900 of the distribution of electromagnetic radiation is often considered to mark the beginning of quantum ideas in physics.

Problems

1. Think of a system of 10 particles, and suppose that there are 10 cells in phase space. (a) Determine the thermodynamic probability W of the macrostate with all the particles in one particular cell. (b) Determine W for the macrostate with

one particle in each cell. **(c)** Determine W for the macrostate with one particle per cell in eight of the cells, and 2 particles in one of the cells.

2. Think of a system of a large number of particles N, and a phase space of two cells. 1 and 2. Assume that the energy E of a particle is the same for both cells. $E_1 = E_2 = E_0$, a constant. **(a)** Determine the partition function Z for the system. **(b)** Determine the number of particles N_1 and N_2 in each cell. **(c)** Determine the internal energy U of the system, and the entropy S of the system.

3. Think of a system of a large number of particles N, and a phase space of two cells, 1 and 2. Assume that the energy of a particle with phase point in cell 1 is zero, $E_1 = 0$, and the energy of a particle with phase point in cell 2 is $E_2 = E_0 \neq 0$. **(a)** Determine the partition function Z for the system. Express the result in terms of $\theta = E_0/k$, where θ is called the characteristic temperature for the system. **(b)** Determine the number of particles N_1 and N_2 in each cell, and note the values of these numbers for $T \ll \theta$ and for $T \gg \theta$. Determine N_1 and N_2 at $T = \theta$. Sketch N_1 and N_2 as a function of T/θ, on the same graph. **(c)** Determine the internal energy U of the system, and sketch U as a function of T/θ. **(d)** Determine the heat capacity of the system.

4. Think of a system of N particles and a phase space of m cells, assume that the energy corresponding to each cell is the same, E_0, and assume $N \gg m$. **(a)** Determine the number N_i of phase points in each cell, the internal energy U and the entropy S. **(b)** Determine the thermodynamic probability W of the least probable macrostate and of the most probable macrostate.

5. As seen in the previous problem, and as you would expect, the most probable distribution for a system of particles among phase cells of equal energy is a uniform one. Think about N molecules of an ideal gas occupying a fixed volume. Visualize the volume as divided into two equal parts, and consider the phase space for the system as having two cells A and B corresponding to the two volumes.

(a) Use the relation $\ln W = N \ln N - \sum N_i \ln N_i$ to determine W/W_{max}, where W_{max} is the thermodynamic probability of the most probable macrostate and W is the thermodynamic probability of a macrostate with an excess of n phase points in cell A and a deficiency of n phase points in cell B. (Assume that $n \ll N$.)

Compare the result with Problem 11 of Chapter 30. What is the difference between the ratio W/W_{max} and the probability distribution $P(n)$ of the earlier problem?

(b) Suppose that $N = 10^{20}$ molecules (corresponding to a volume of about 4 cm³ at STP). Determine the probability W (relative to the maximum probability W_{max}) that half A of the volume will contain an excess of 10^{10} molecules at some instant (a fluctuation of 2 parts in 10^{10}). Determine the difference in entropy between the two states. Which is the state of higher entropy?

6. For a system of N identical weakly interacting harmonic oscillations, each of frequency ν, the possible energy states for each oscillator are $E_n = (n + \tfrac{1}{2})h\nu$ where $n = 0, 1, 2, \cdots$. Determine the partition function Z for the system and use it to find the internal energy U. Verify that the result is the same as found in this chapter.

7. For a system of diatomic ideal gas molecules in equilibrium at a temperature equal to the characteristic temperature for vibration, determine the fraction of the molecules in the two lowest vibrational energy states. What is the probability that a molecule will be in the lowest state?

8. Show that the Einstein theory for heat capacity of a solid predicts that the molar heat capacity increases exponentially with temperature at very low temperatures.

9. The molar heat capacity of a solid using as a model a system of three-dimensional harmonic oscillators all with the same frequency ν (the Einstein theory) involves a single parameter characteristic of the particular material. The heat capacity may be written as $c_v = 3RF(\theta/T)$, using the "characteristic temperature" θ as the parameter, or as $c_v = 3RF(h\nu/kT)$ using the "characteristic frequency" ν as the parameter.

(a) Assume that for aluminum $\theta = 300\,°K$. What is the characteristic frequency ν for aluminum? What is the value of the function $F(\theta/T)$ at room temperature (about $300\,°K$) for aluminum? What is the value of $F(\theta/T)$ at $T = \theta/2$?

(b) A crude estimate of ν can be made from the melting point T_m of a solid, by thinking of the atoms as particles in SHM at frequency ν at the lattice sites, with an amplitude that increases as the temperature is increased, and assuming that melting occurs when the amplitude is of the order of the interatomic distance (or lattice spacing) d. The total energy of each three-dimensional oscillator is then $3kT_m$. Assume a simple cubic lattice, and estimate the lattice spacing d for aluminum. (Use $\rho = 2.7\,gm/cm^3$, $M = 27\,gm/mole$.) Estimate ν from the melting point for aluminum, $660\,°C$.

10. A system of ideal gas molecules is in an isothermal uniform gravitational field.
(a) Determine the probability $p(y)$ of a molecule being at a height y above some reference level. (b) Determine the average gravitational potential energy $\bar{u} = mg\bar{y}$ of a molecule. Would you expect the result to be $\frac{1}{2}kT$, as given by equipartition of energy?

11. Assuming that the earth's atmosphere is an ideal gas at a constant temperature of $20\,°C$, and neglecting the variation in g, at what height is the pressure $\frac{1}{2}$ of an atmosphere? At what height is it $\frac{1}{100}$ of an atmosphere? What is the actual fractional change in g at these heights?

12. A two-dimensional monatomic ideal gas is one in which the molecules are free to move in a plane of area A. There are N molecules, each of mass m, in equilibrium at temperature T. (a) Determine the partition function Z for the gas. (b) Determine the equation of state (note that "pressure" for the two-dimensional gas is force per unit length on the periphery of area A). (c) Determine c_A, the molar heat capacity at constant area.

13. Suppose that a system of uniform spherical colloidal particles each 10^{-4} cm in diameter are suspended in water at $27\,°C$. The density of the material in the particles is 0.1% higher than the density of water. (a) Determine the effective value of "g" for the particles (i.e., such that the resultant downward force due to gravity on a particle is $mg_{\text{effective}}$). (b) Compare the number density of the particles at two points differing in height by 1 mm, assuming that the distribution of the particles can be described by Maxwell–Boltzmann statistics.

14. A system of ideal gas molecules is rotating in a centrifuge. In the frame of reference of the centrifuge, there is an outward force on each molecule $F_{cf} = m\omega^2 r$, where r is the distance from the axis of rotation. (a) Determine the centrifugal potential energy of a molecule, choosing the zero of potential energy at the axis. (b) Determine the density ρ of the gas as a function of r.

33

THE DISTRIBUTION OF ELECTROMAGNETIC RADIATION

The Planck distribution of the energy of electromagnetic radiation was used as an example of a distribution function at the end of Chapter 3 on Measurement. It describes the energy emitted from a black body as a function of frequency (or wavelength).

We cannot give all the details of the development of the distribution, but we will summarize the essential features of two different developments of it, one similar to Planck's original derivation and one based on quantum statistics.

BLACK BODY RADIATION AND CAVITY RADIATION

You know that all substances at a temperature T above absolute zero emit electromagnetic radiation. Systems of atoms and molecules that are far apart (gases) emit radiation at certain discrete frequencies (characteristic of the kind of atom) but when all jammed together in a solid there is radiation produced at all frequencies—a continuous spectrum.

Rate of energy emission per unit area from a solid.

In general the total energy E emitted from unit area of surface of a solid in unit time is a function of both the temperature T of the solid *and* the material of the surface. For an ideal radiator, or black body radiator, the energy emitted is a function of temperature only: $E = \sigma T^4$, where σ is a constant (Stefan's constant $\sigma = 5.67 \times 10^{-8}$ watt/m²-(K°)⁴).

The term **black body** arises because an ideal radiator is defined in terms of its absorptive properties. Radiation falling on a surface is in general partially absorbed and partially reflected; a black body is one that absorbs all the radiation falling on it—there is no reflection, so the body "looks" black. In order for a body to be able to reach thermal equilibrium, it must radiate as much energy as it absorbs, and therefore the best absorber is also the best emitter of radiation.

We are interested in the energy $E(\nu)\,d\nu$ emitted by a black body in the frequency range ν to $\nu + d\nu$. The function $E(\nu)$ is the spectral distribution function to be determined. It is related to the total energy emitted (per unit area, in unit time) by $\int_0^\infty E(\nu)\,d\nu = E$. Rather than deal with the energy emitted by a black body, it is convenient to deal with the energy in an enclosure, or cavity. This means the radiation bouncing around in a cavity, with solid walls at temperature T. It can be shown using thermodynamic arguments that the spectral distribution in the cavity is the same as the spectral distribution of radiation emitted by a black body. You can see that a small hole in the walls of the cavity acts like a black body, in that radiation entering the cavity through the hole is not likely to be reflected back out.

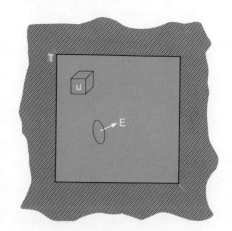

Energy flux and energy density in a cavity.

The **energy flux** E in the cavity (energy crossing unit area in unit time) is related to the **energy density** u in the cavity (energy per unit volume) in exactly the same way that the number flux N in a gas (the number of molecules crossing unit area in unit time) is related to the number density n. This relation is $N = \frac{1}{4}n\bar{v}$, where $\bar{v}$ is the average speed of the molecules. The radiation in the cavity has a speed c, the speed of light, and the relation is $E = \frac{1}{4}uc$. Considering the radiation in the frequency range $d\nu$, the relation is $E(\nu) = \frac{1}{4}u(\nu)c$, where $u(\nu)\,d\nu$ is the energy per unit volume of radiation in the frequency range ν to $\nu + d\nu$. The distribution function $u(\nu)$ has the same form as the function $E(\nu)$, and it is this function we will determine.

MODES OF VIBRATION AND DEGREES OF FREEDOM

Think about a string stretched between two fixed supports, and waves being reflected back and forth along the string. This system has certain natural frequencies of vibration, corresponding to conditions where there is a standing

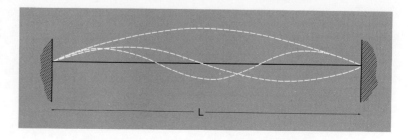

Standing waves on a string.

L

wave on the string. The boundary condition that the ends of the string are fixed means that the system can only vibrate in such a way that there are an integral number of half wavelengths on the string: $L = n(\lambda/2)$, where n is an integer.

The number of modes of vibration of the system corresponding to wavelength λ is then $n = 2L/\lambda$ and the number of modes of vibration corresponding to wavelength $\lambda + d\lambda$ is

$$n + dn = \frac{2L}{\lambda + d\lambda} = \frac{2L}{\lambda}\left(1 + \frac{d\lambda}{\lambda}\right)^{-1} \cong \frac{2L}{\lambda}\left(1 - \frac{d\lambda}{\lambda}\right)$$

Therefore the number of modes of vibration in the wavelength range λ to $\lambda + d\lambda$ is

$$dn = \frac{2L}{\lambda^2}\,d\lambda$$

and the number of modes of vibration per unit length in the range λ to $\lambda + d\lambda$ is

$$\frac{2}{\lambda^2}\,d\lambda$$

We have used this one-dimensional situation to introduce the concept of the number of modes of vibration. A similar argument can be used to show that the number of modes of vibration of a solid, per unit volume, in the range λ to $\lambda + d\lambda$ is

$$\frac{4\pi\,d\lambda}{\lambda^4}\qquad\text{or}\qquad\frac{8\pi\,d\lambda}{\lambda^4}$$

The factor 2 depends on whether or not the waves being reflected around in the solid are longitudinal waves or transverse waves; for transverse waves there are two independent directions of polarization, and the factor 2 is necessary.

We have used the notion of waves moving on strings or in solids because you should be familiar with this idea, but what we are really interested in is the number of modes of vibration of a cavity. The electromagnetic radiation in a cavity bounces around in the cavity in the same way that elastic waves bounce around in a solid. Electromagnetic waves are transverse waves, and the number of modes of vibration per unit volume in a cavity in the range λ to $\lambda + d\lambda$ is

$$n(\lambda)\,d\lambda = \frac{8\pi}{\lambda^4}\,d\lambda$$

The relation between wavelength and frequency is $c = \lambda\nu$, where c is the velocity of the wave—in this case, the velocity of electromagnetic radiation.

$$\lambda = \frac{c}{\nu}\qquad d\lambda = -\frac{c}{\nu^2}\,d\nu$$

The number of modes of vibration per unit volume in the frequency range ν to $\nu + d\nu$ is therefore

$$n(\nu)\,d\nu = \frac{8\pi\nu^2}{c^3}\,d\nu$$

This result can be interpreted in different ways, as you will see. One way is to think of it as giving the number of degrees of freedom per unit volume in the range ν to $\nu + d\nu$. The number of degrees of freedom of what? We have said that the number of degrees of freedom of a system of particles is equal to the number of independent terms in the expression for the energy of the particles. What particles are involved here? Now we must differentiate between the original approach of Planck, and the approach using quantum statistics.

THE PLANCK LAW

Planck related the radiation in a cavity to the source of the radiation, the atoms in the walls of the cavity.

Think of the walls of the cavity as containing an enormous number of harmonic oscillators, of various frequencies ν. The walls are continuously absorbing radiation, and emitting radiation. Corresponding to radiation in the frequency range ν to $\nu + d\nu$, there must be a system of oscillators of this frequency in the walls. In thermal equilibrium the average energy of the radiation will be the same as the average energy of the system of oscillators, and corresponding to the number of degrees of freedom $n(\nu) \, d\nu$ we can think of an equal number of independent harmonic oscillators in the walls.

Then the energy density of radiation in the range ν to $\nu + d\nu$ is the product of the number of modes of vibration (or number of degrees of freedom, or number of oscillators) per unit volume in this range, multiplied by the average energy of an oscillator.

$$u(\nu) \, d\nu = n(\nu) \, d\nu \times \bar{E}_{osc}$$

First consider the result if the system of oscillators is considered to behave classically. Then equipartition of energy applies, and the average energy is

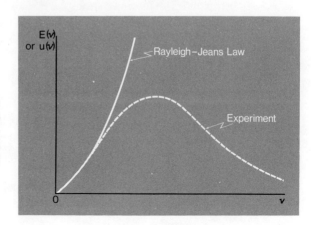

The spectral distribution of radiation as predicted by the classical Rayleigh–Jeans law and as observed experimentally.

$\bar{E}_{osc} = kT$.

$$u(\nu)\, d\nu = \frac{8\pi\nu^2}{c^3}\, d\nu \times kT = \frac{8\pi kT}{c^3}\nu^2\, d\nu$$

$$E(\nu) = \frac{c}{4}\, u(\nu) = \frac{2\pi kT}{c^2}\nu^2$$

This result fits the experimental facts at low frequencies (long wavelengths) and is called the classical or Rayleigh–Jeans radiation law. However, at high frequencies the energy density approaches infinity, which does not make sense. This is called the ultraviolet catastrophe.

It was this breakdown in classical theory that led Planck to the original quantum hypothesis. He found that agreement with experiment could be obtained if, instead of assuming that an oscillator could take on any value of energy, he assumed that the only energies permitted were in integral multiples of a constant times the frequency: $E_{osc} = nh\nu$. (The constant later became known as Planck's constant h.)

Note that the expression we have used before $E_{osc} = (n + \frac{1}{2})h\nu$ is a **result** of quantum mechanics as applied to a harmonic oscillator, but this came later. We have shown using classical statistics that the average energy of a quantum oscillator is

$$\bar{E}_{osc} = \tfrac{1}{2}h\nu + \frac{h\nu}{e^{h\nu/kT} - 1}$$

The first term, the zero point energy, arises because the energy is quantized in half-integral rather than integral multiples of $h\nu$. This did not appear in Planck's theory.

Using the average energy of Planck's quantized oscillator, the energy distribution becomes

$$u(\nu)\, d\nu = \frac{8\pi\nu^2}{c^3}\, d\nu \times \frac{h\nu}{e^{h\nu/kT} - 1}$$

The Planck distribution function

$$u(\nu) = \frac{8\pi h\nu^3}{c^3}\frac{1}{e^{h\nu/kT} - 1}$$

is in very good agreement with experiment. It reduces to the Rayleigh–Jeans law if $h\nu \ll kT$, that is at low frequencies or high temperatures. If $h\nu \gg kT$ the -1 in the denominator becomes negligible. The result is called the Wien radiation law, and is usually sufficiently accurate in the visible region of the spectrum.

We emphasize that this description of the Planck theory is intended to give only the essence of the theory, and is certainly not exhaustive.

THE PHOTON GAS

The Planck distribution function can be obtained by taking a different approach. Instead of considering the interaction between the radiation in an enclosure and the sources of radiation in the walls, attention is focussed on the radiation itself, treated as a system of particles to which the methods of statistics can be applied. Since Planck's quantum oscillators could only take on discrete values of energy $nh\nu$, they could only absorb or emit energy in discrete amounts $h\nu$. These packages of energy came to be called photons. A photon of electromagnetic energy has some of the properties of a material particle, and the electromagnetic waves being reflected around in an enclosure can be thought of as a photon gas.

In thinking about gas molecules bouncing around in a container, we know that individually they make collisions with the walls in which they gain or lose energy. However, for a system in thermal equilibrium we assume that on the average there is no net gain or loss, and the total energy of the gas is constant. Therefore we can think of the collisions with the walls as being perfectly elastic (or think of the walls as being perfectly reflecting), and speak of the gas as **isolated,** exchanging no energy with its surroundings. It is, however, because the system is not really isolated that the concept of thermal equilibrium exists.

Similarly, although the electromagnetic radiation in a cavity is continuously being absorbed and emitted by the walls, we can think of the walls as being perfect reflectors, and the radiation as being isolated. In terms of a photon model for the radiation, the photons bounce around in the cavity like gas molecules in a container, and we do not have to consider that they are continuously disappearing into the walls, and reappearing again. The atomic oscillators in the walls are necessary to maintain thermal equilibrium, but we ignore them.

With this model, the number of modes of vibration $n(\nu)\, d\nu$ can be interpreted as the density of states in the frequency range ν to $\nu + d\nu$. The energy of a photon is $h\nu$, and therefore the density of **energy** states in the frequency range ν to $\nu + d\nu$ is

$$g(\nu)\, d\nu = h\nu\, n(\nu)\, d\nu = \frac{8\pi h\nu^3}{c^3}\, d\nu$$

The total energy density of the system of photons in the frequency range ν to $\nu + d\nu$ is the product of the appropriate distribution function $f(E)$ and the density of energy states $g(\nu)\, d\nu$. We stated in the last chapter that the appropriate statistics for describing a photon gas are Bose–Einstein quantum statistics,

$$f_{\mathrm{BE}}(E_i) = \frac{1}{Ae^{E_i/kT} - 1}$$

although we could not show this. We must also state without proof that in using the distribution function for photons the constant $A = 1$. (This relates to there being no constant total number of particles N for a photon gas.)

The energy density in the range ν to $\nu + d\nu$ is then

$$u(\nu)\, d\nu = g(\nu)\, d\nu\, f_{BE}(h\nu) = \frac{8\pi h\nu^3}{c^3} \frac{1}{e^{h\nu/kT} - 1}\, d\nu$$

This is the same result as obtained in the last section by considering the oscillators in the walls. We have approached this distribution from these two different theoretical viewpoints in order to emphasize once again that the theories of physics are based on models. The same result can be obtained using two different models. *Which model is correct?*

Problems

These problems are intended primarily to develop some familiarity with the laws of thermal radiation, rather than to illustrate the rather abbreviated theoretical development of this chapter.

1. A black body, which radiates energy at a rate given by $E = \sigma T^4$, is an idealization. The emissive properties of matter are described by the property called emissivity ϵ, defined by $E = \epsilon E_0$, where E_0 is the emissive power of a black body at the same temperature. The emissivity depends on the material, on the surface condition of the material, and on the temperature. For polished tungsten at 1000 °K, for example, $\epsilon = 0.11$.

   Suppose that a piece of tungsten is in equilibrium in a cavity at 1000 °K. Determine the rate (in watts/cm²) at which radiant energy is absorbed, reflected and emitted by the tungsten **(a)** if it is coated with soot and assumed to act as a black body, **(b)** if it is polished.

2. A furnace is operating at a temperature of 1000 °F. There is a circular hole 1 cm in diameter in the furnace wall. Determine the rate (in watts) at which energy is lost due to radiation from the hole, assuming black body radiation.

3. A spherical body of radius r, density ρ and specific heat capacity c is in space, radiating as a black body and receiving negligible radiation. Deduce an expression for the time required for it to cool from T °K to $(T/2)$ °K.

4. In general the net rate of energy transfer due to radiation between two bodies at different temperatures T_1 and T_2 depends on geometric factors as well as on the temperatures and emissive properties of the bodies. However, if one body surrounds the other, that is the body at temperature T_2 is in a cavity in the body at

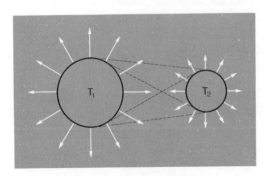
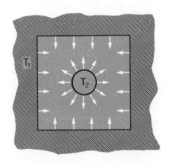

temperature T_1, then geometric factors do not affect the net rate of energy transfer.

(a) Suppose that $T_2 > T_1$, and the body at T_2 is a black body. At what rate E_1 is energy falling on its surface, per unit area? At what rate E_2 is it emitting energy, per unit area? What is the net rate at which it is losing energy, per unit area?

(b) A relation called Newton's Law of Cooling was discussed in Problem 8 of Chapter 2. This law states that the rate of heat loss from a body is proportional to the temperature excess of the body (i.e., to the temperature excess of the body above its surroundings). Is this law valid for heat loss due to radiation? Show that it is a reasonable approximation if the temperature excess is small.

5. A solid copper sphere 1 cm in diameter is coated with soot, heated to 100 °C, and suspended in an evacuated enclosure, the walls of which are maintained at 20 °C. Assume that the sphere acts as a black body, and use $\rho = 9.0\,\text{gm/cm}^3$ and $c = 0.092$ for copper. (a) Calculate the initial rate of temperature change of the sphere. (b) Calculate the rate of temperature change of the sphere when it is at 50 °C, assuming Newton's law of cooling and using the initial cooling rate found in (a). Determine the percentage error introduced by making this assumption. (c) If the time required for the sphere to cool from 100 °C to 50 °C were calculated assuming Newton's law of cooling (an exponential decay) would this time be too large or too small?

6. The radiation in a cavity exerts a pressure on the walls of the cavity (the radiation pressure) given by $p = u/3$, where u is the energy density of the radiation. The energy density is a function of temperature T only, and the total energy in a cavity of volume V is $U = uV$. Treat the radiation in a cavity as a thermodynamic system, and apply the energy equation $p + (\partial U/\partial V)_T = T(\partial p/\partial T)_V$ to deduce the relation between energy density and temperature.

7. Think of the radiation in an insulated evacuated cylinder of volume V at temperature T. The radiation exerts a pressure $p = u/3$, where u is the energy density, and $u = aT^4$ (see previous problem). Apply the first law of thermodynamics to determine the relationship between V and T for adiabatic changes in the volume of the cylinder. Suppose the cylinder is initially at 0 °C, and find the temperature that results from an adiabatic compression to half the initial volume.

8. From the Planck distribution for energy density $u(v,T)$ determine the Planck distribution for the rate of radiation from a black body $E(v,T)$ and use this to determine the total rate of radiation from a black body $E(T) = \int_0^\infty E(v,T)\,dv$. You will need the integral $\int_0^\infty x^3(e^x - 1)^{-1}\,dx = \pi^4/15$. Thus determine Stefan's constant σ in terms of k, c and h. Verify that $\sigma = 5.67 \times 10^{-8}\,\text{watt/m}^2\text{-(K}°)^4$.

9. (a) For some purposes it is useful to think of a beam of monochromatic radiation of frequency v as a stream of photons, each photon having an energy $\epsilon = hv$. Suppose there are n photons per unit volume in the beam, and determine photon flux N (number of photons crossing unit area in unit time) in terms of n and c, and energy flux E. Express the energy flux in terms of the energy density u in the beam.

(b) In order to determine the radiation pressure exerted by the beam, assume that each photon has a mass m determined by $\epsilon = mc^2$. (This relation between mass and energy is a result of the special theory of relativity.) What is the momentum of a photon? Assume that the beam of radiation hits a wall and is totally absorbed, and determine the pressure p on the wall.

(c) Estimate the momentum of a photon of radiation in the middle of the visible region of the spectrum. Estimate the number density of these photons in a monochromatic light beam that produces a radiation pressure of 1 microdyne/cm² when falling normally on a surface and being completely absorbed. Estimate the intensity of this beam in microwatts/cm². Is it an intense beam?

(d) In a cavity the energy flux is $E = uc/4$ and the radiation pressure is $p = u/3$. What is the origin of the numerical factors $1/4$ and $1/3$ in these expressions?

10. (a) The Planck distribution may be expressed in terms of frequency ν or wavelength λ. The rate at which energy is emitted per unit area from a black body, in the wavelength range λ to $\lambda + d\lambda$, is $E(\lambda)\, d\lambda$. Determine $E(\lambda)$.

(b) The **Wien radiation law** $E(\lambda) = (c_1/\lambda^5) \exp(-c_2/\lambda T)$ is an approximation of the Planck law, in which the term (-1) in the factor $[\exp(c_2/\lambda T) - 1]$ is neglected. Determine c_2 and show that in the visible region of the spectrum the Wien radiation law is a good approximation for temperatures up to at least 1000 °K. What is the error involved in using it, instead of the Planck law, (c) for $\lambda = 6000$ angstrom units and $T = 5000$ °K? (d) for $\lambda = 6000$ angstrom units and $T = 10,000$ °K?

11. An optical pyrometer is an instrument for measuring the temperatures of objects at high temperatures by comparing the radiation from the object with that from an electrically heated filament. Looking through the pyrometer at a hot furnace, for example, the filament is seen with an image of the furnace as a background. The current through the filament is adjusted until it "disappears" against this background, and the current is a measure of the furnace temperature. (The temperature measured is sometimes called **brightness temperature** because it is not the true temperature unless the hot object is acting as a black body.)

One way of calibrating a pyrometer is to "chop" the radiation received from the hot object by placing a rotating disc with an open segment in it in front of the pyrometer. If the disc has an opening of angle θ radians, the intensity of the radiation received will be decreased by a factor $\theta/2\pi$. If the disc is rotated rapidly, the image appears to be of constant intensity.

Suppose that a pyrometer has been calibrated up to 1000 °C by using thermocouples. The radiation from a furnace falls on it through a rotating disc of open angle 60°, and the temperature of the furnace appears to be 1000 °C. Calculate the actual temperature of the furnace, assuming that the pyrometer has filters so that it operates with radiation in a narrow wavelength region around 6000 angstrom units (red light).

12. (a) The Planck distribution function $E(\lambda)$ has a maximum at a wavelength λ_m determined by forming $dE/d\lambda$ and setting it equal to zero. Show that this procedure leads to the relation $(1 - x/5)\, e^x = 1$, where $x = hc/kT\lambda_m$, and verify that the solution is $x = 4.965$. Determine the numerical value of the constant K in the relation $\lambda_m T = K$. This relation is called the **Wien displacement law.**

(b) For what range of temperatures is the peak in the spectral distribution in the visible region of the spectrum?

13. The maximum in the sun's spectral distribution curve occurs at a wavelength of about 4900 angstrom units. The energy received at the earth's surface when the sun is directly overhead is about 2 cal/min-cm². (This is called the **solar constant.**) Estimate the temperature of the sun's surface from each of these facts.

Appendix A

CONVERSION TABLES

These tables are useful for converting fundamental or derived quantities in the various systems of units used in mechanics. Tables are provided for the fundamental quantities mass, length, and time and for the derived quantities force and energy. Other derived quantities can be worked out from these. The numerical conversion factors are stated to four figures, one more than can usually be read on a slide rule.

The terms kilogram, gram and pound are used for both mass and force. Conversions involving these may depend on the value of g (e.g., a force of 1 kilogram = g newtons $\cong$ 9.8 n; a mass of 1 pound = $1/g$ slug $\cong 1/32$ slug $\cong 3.1 \times 10^{-2}$ slug). The numerical factors in the tables are based on the standard value of g: $g = 9.80665$ m/sec^2 = 32.1740 ft/sec^2.

Time	sec	min	hr	day	year
1 sec =	1	1.667×10^{-2}	2.778×10^{-4}	1.157×10^{-5}	3.169×10^{-8}
1 min =	60	1	1.667×10^{-2}	6.944×10^{-4}	1.901×10^{-6}
1 hr =	3600	60	1	4.167×10^{-2}	1.141×10^{-4}
1 day =	8.640×10^4	1440	24	1	2.738×10^{-3}
1 year =	3.156×10^7	5.259×10^5	8.766×10^3	365.2	1

Length	cm	m	in.	ft	mile
1 cm =	1	10^{-2}	0.3937	3.281×10^{-2}	6.214×10^{-6}
1 m =	100	1	39.37	3.281	6.214×10^{-4}
1 in. =	2.540	2.540×10^{-2}	1	8.333×10^{-2}	1.578×10^{-5}
1 ft =	30.48	0.3048	12	1	1.894×10^{-4}
1 mile =	1.609×10^5	1609	6.336×10^4	5280	1

Note: 1 angstrom unit = 10^{-10} m   1 light-year = 9.46×10^{15} m
1 X-unit = 10^{-13} m   1 parsec = 3.084×10^{16} m
1 micron (μ) = 10^{-6} m   1 yard = 3 ft
1 millimicron (mμ) = 10^{-9} m   1 fathom = 6 ft
1 mil = 10^{-3} in.   1 rod = 16.5 ft
1 nautical mile = 1.1508 (statute) mile = 6076 ft

Area units   1 acre = 4840 yd^2 1 barn = 10^{-28} m^2

Speed units   30 miles/hr = 44 ft/sec   1 knot = 1 nautical mile/hr

Mass	kg	gm	lb	amu	slug
1 kg =	1	1000	2.205	6.024×10^{26}	6.852×10^{-2}
1 gm =	10^{-3}	1	2.205×10^{-3}	6.024×10^{23}	6.852×10^{-5}
1 lb =	0.4536	453.6	1	2.732×10^{26}	3.108×10^{-2}
1 amu =	1.660×10^{-27}	1.660×10^{-24}	3.660×10^{-27}	1	1.137×10^{-28}
1 slug =	14.59	1.459×10^{4}	32.17	8.789×10^{27}	1

Note: 1 ton = 2000 lb   1 long ton = 2240 lb
        1 lb = 16 oz   1 metric ton = 1000 kg

Force	n	dyne	pndl	kg	gm	lb
1 newton =	1	10^{5}	7.233	0.1020	102.0	0.2248
1 dyne =	10^{-5}	1	7.233×10^{-5}	1.020×10^{-6}	1.020×10^{-3}	2.248×10^{-6}
1 poundal =	0.1383	1.383×10^{4}	1	1.410×10^{-2}	14.10	3.108×10^{-2}
1 kg =	9.807	9.807×10^{5}	70.93	1	10^{3}	2.205
1 gm =	9.807×10^{-3}	980.7	7.093×10^{-2}	10^{-3}	1	2.205×10^{-3}
1 lb =	4.448	4.448×10^{5}	32.17	0.4536	453.6	1

Note—Units of pressure (force/area):

     1 atmosphere = 1.013×10^{5} n/m^2 = 1.013×10^{6} dynes/cm^2 = 14.70 lb/in.^{2} = 76 cm of Hg

     1 bar = 10^{6} dynes/cm^2 1 millibar = 10^{3} dynes/cm^2

Energy	j	erg	ft-pndl	ft-lb	cal	ev
1 joule =	1	10^{7}	23.73	0.7376	0.2389	6.242×10^{18}
1 erg =	10^{-7}	1	2.373×10^{-6}	7.376×10^{-8}	2.389×10^{-8}	6.242×10^{11}
1 ft-pndl =	4.214×10^{-2}	4.214×10^{5}	1	3.108×10^{-2}	1.007×10^{-2}	2.630×10^{17}
1 ft-lb =	1.356	1.356×10^{7}	32.17	1	0.3239	8.464×10^{18}
1 calorie =	4.186	4.186×10^{7}	99.31	3.087	1	2.613×10^{19}
1 electron-volt =	1.602×10^{-19}	1.602×10^{-12}	3.801×10^{-18}	1.182×10^{-19}	3.827×10^{-20}	1

Note—Power units:

     1 watt = 1 joule/sec, 1 kw = 10^{3} watts, 1 hp = 550 ft-lb/sec = 0.7457 kw
     1 watt-sec = 1 j = 1 n − m   1 hp-hr = 1.980×10^{6} ft-lb
     1 kwh = 3.6×10^{6} j   1 British thermal unit (BTU) = 252.0 cal
     1 Mev = 10^{6} ev   = 777.9 ft-lb

Mass–energy equivalence: 1 amu = 931.0 Mev

For electromagnetism a fourth fundamental quantity is required in addition to mass, length, and time. We use the mksa system of units exclusively for our presentation of electromagnetism. In this system the fourth fundamental quantity is electric current and the unit used for it is the ampere. The mks system of units is used for the other three. Another system in common use is the Gaussian system; in it the fourth fundamental quantity is taken as electric charge, with basic unit the statcoulomb, and the cgs system is used for mass, length, and time. The table below shows the units used for various derived quantities in the mksa system and their equivalent in the Gaussian system.

Electromagnetism	mksa unit	gaussian equivalent
charge	coulomb	3×10^9 statcoulombs
current	ampere	3×10^9 statamperes
	(coulombs/sec)	(statcoulombs/sec)
potential difference	volt	$\frac{1}{300}$ statvolt
	(joules/coulomb)	(erg/statcoulomb)
electric field	volts/m	$\frac{1}{3} \times 10^{-4}$ statvolt/cm
magnetic induction	webers/m² (tesla)	10^4 gauss
electric displacement	coul/m²	$3 \times 4\pi \times 10^5$ statvolts/cm
magnetic intensity	amp-turns/m	$4\pi \times 10^{-3}$ oersted
magnetic flux	weber	10^8 maxwells

The factors 3 in the above should be replaced by $C \times 10^{-8}$ where C is the measured speed of electromagnetic interaction in m/sec. The value to 4 figures is 2.998.

Mathematical constants and relations

Constants: $\pi = 3.14159$ $\log \pi = 0.4971$ $e = 2.71828$

Angles: 1 revolution $= 360° = 2\pi$ radians $1° = 60'$ $1' = 60''$
    1 rad $= 57°17'45'' = 57.3°$ $1° = 0.0175$ rad

Logarithms: $\log N = 0.4343 \ln N$ $\ln N = 2.3026 \log N$ $\ln 2 = 0.6931$

Trigonometric identities: $\sin^2 \theta + \cos^2 \theta = 1$
    $\sin (A \pm B) = \sin A \cos B \pm \cos A \sin B$
    $\cos (A \pm B) = \cos A \cos B \mp \sin A \sin B$

Factorial: $n! = n(n-1)(n-2) \cdots 3 \cdot 2 \cdot 1$, $0! = 1$

Series: $(1 + x)^n = 1 + nx + \dfrac{n(n-1)}{2!} x^2 + \dfrac{n(n-1)(n-2)}{3!} x^3 + \cdots + x^n$ $|x| \le 1$

$\left. \begin{array}{l} \sin \theta = \theta - \theta^3/3! + \theta^5/5! - \cdots \\ \cos \theta = 1 - \theta^2/2! + \theta^4/4! - \cdots \end{array} \right\} \theta$ in radians
$\ln (1 + x) = x - x^2/2 + x^3/3 - x^4/4 + \cdots$ $|x| \le 1$

Appendix B

TRIGONOMETRIC FUNCTIONS

Angle		Sine	Cosine	Tangent	Angle		Sine	Cosine	Tangent
Degrees	Radians				Degrees	Radians			
0°	0.000	0.000	1.000	0.000					
1°	0.018	0.018	1.000	0.018	46°	0.803	0.719	0.695	1.036
2°	0.035	0.035	0.999	0.035	47°	0.820	0.731	0.682	1.072
3°	0.052	0.052	0.999	0.052	48°	0.838	0.743	0.669	1.111
4°	0.070	0.070	0.998	0.070	49°	0.855	0.755	0.656	1.150
5°	0.087	0.087	0.996	0.087	50°	0.873	0.766	0.643	1.192
6°	0.105	0.105	0.995	0.105	51°	0.890	0.777	0.629	1.235
7°	0.122	0.122	0.993	0.123	52°	0.908	0.788	0.616	1.280
8°	0.140	0.139	0.990	0.141	53°	0.925	0.799	0.602	1.327
9°	0.157	0.156	0.988	0.158	54°	0.942	0.809	0.588	1.376
10°	0.175	0.174	0.985	0.176	55°	0.960	0.819	0.574	1.428
11°	0.192	0.191	0.982	0.194	56°	0.977	0.829	0.559	1.483
12°	0.209	0.208	0.978	0.213	57°	0.995	0.839	0.545	1.540
13°	0.227	0.225	0.974	0.231	58°	1.012	0.848	0.530	1.600
14°	0.244	0.242	0.970	0.249	59°	1.030	0.857	0.515	1.664
15°	0.262	0.259	0.966	0.268	60°	1.047	0.866	0.500	1.732
16°	0.279	0.276	0.961	0.287	61°	1.065	0.875	0.485	1.804
17°	0.297	0.292	0.956	0.306	62°	1.082	0.883	0.470	1.881
18°	0.314	0.309	0.951	0.325	63°	1.100	0.891	0.454	1.963
19°	0.332	0.326	0.946	0.344	64°	1.117	0.899	0.438	2.050
20°	0.349	0.342	0.940	0.364	65°	1.134	0.906	0.423	2.145
21°	0.367	0.358	0.934	0.384	66°	1.152	0.914	0.407	2.246
22°	0.384	0.375	0.927	0.404	67°	1.169	0.921	0.391	2.356
23°	0.401	0.391	0.921	0.425	68°	1.187	0.927	0.375	2.475
24°	0.419	0.407	0.914	0.445	69°	1.204	0.934	0.358	2.605
25°	0.436	0.423	0.906	0.466	70°	1.222	0.940	0.342	2.747
26°	0.454	0.438	0.899	0.488	71°	1.239	0.946	0.326	2.904
27°	0.471	0.454	0.891	0.510	72°	1.257	0.951	0.309	3.078
28°	0.489	0.470	0.883	0.532	73°	1.274	0.956	0.292	3.271
29°	0.506	0.485	0.875	0.554	74°	1.292	0.961	0.276	3.487
30°	0.524	0.500	0.866	0.577	75°	1.309	0.966	0.259	3.732
31°	0.541	0.515	0.857	0.601	76°	1.327	0.970	0.242	4.011
32°	0.559	0.530	0.848	0.625	77°	1.344	0.974	0.225	4.331
33°	0.576	0.545	0.839	0.649	78°	1.361	0.978	0.208	4.705
34°	0.593	0.559	0.829	0.675	79°	1.379	0.982	0.191	5.145
35°	0.611	0.574	0.819	0.700	80°	1.396	0.985	0.174	5.671
36°	0.628	0.588	0.809	0.727	81°	1.414	0.988	0.156	6.314
37°	0.646	0.602	0.799	0.754	82°	1.431	0.990	0.139	7.115
38°	0.663	0.616	0.788	0.781	83°	1.449	0.993	0.122	8.144
39°	0.681	0.629	0.777	0.810	84°	1.466	0.995	0.105	9.514
40°	0.698	0.643	0.766	0.839	85°	1.484	0.996	0.087	11.43
41°	0.716	0.656	0.755	0.869	86°	1.501	0.998	0.070	14.30
42°	0.733	0.669	0.743	0.900	87°	1.518	0.999	0.052	19.08
43°	0.751	0.682	0.731	0.933	88°	1.536	0.999	0.035	28.64
44°	0.768	0.695	0.719	0.966	89°	1.553	1.000	0.018	57.29
45°	0.785	0.707	0.707	1.000	90°	1.571	1.000	0.000	∞

ANSWERS TO
ODD-NUMBERED PROBLEMS

Chapter 2

3. 150 ft

5. (a) 160 ft (b) 4.80 ft/sec² (c) $v = 0.064t^3$

7. (a) 0.195 cal (b) 0.219 cal (c) 0.203 cal

9. (a) $\theta_i = 150$ C° (b) $K = 0.060$ sec⁻¹ (c) Slopes -4.9, -2.8, -1.4 C°/sec (d) $\lambda = 16.7$ sec (e) $t_{1/2} = \lambda \ln 2 = 11.5$ sec (f) 83 sec

Chapter 3

1. $71 \pm 3\%$, $3.68 \pm 0.1\%$, $0.1178 \pm 1\%$, $53.67 \pm 0.06\%$

3. 3, 5, 1, 2, 4, undetermined, 3, 4

5. (a) 3.00019 (b) 14.967 (c) 512.34 (d) 16.04 (e) 6.0440 (f) 5.0182 (g) 39.068 (h) 22.34

7. $\log p = 8.00 - 3.20 \times 10^3/T$; at $t = 190$ °C, $p = 12.3$ mm of Hg; at $t = 100$ °C, $dp/dT = 0.015$ mm of Hg/K°; at $t = 200$ °C, $dp/dT = 0.57$ mm of Hg/K°

9. (b) $c_p = 0.444T^3 + 0.712T$ mj/mole-K°, 34.1 mj/mole

11. (a) Too large, by 3.9 cm (c) $6.9 \times 10^{-4}\%$ change/sec (d) larger (e) 79.38 cm³

13. (a) $ML^{-1}T^{-1}$, dyne-sec/cm² $\equiv$ gm/cm-sec (b) $ML^{-1}T^{-1}$ (c) $F = cvr\eta$, where c is dimensionless (d) about 0.5 ft/sec, about 10 hours

15. Mean 64.9(5), median 64.6, rms 65.7, $\delta_{\rm rms} = 9.8$

17. (a) $A = 2/x_0$ (b) $\bar{x} = 0$, $x_{\rm rms} = \delta_{\rm rms} = x_0(1/12 - 1/2\pi^2)^{1/2} = 0.18x_0$

Chapter 4

1. 122 min

3. 90°

5. Area $= \frac{1}{2}|\mathbf{A} \times \mathbf{B}|$

7. (a) 42° (b) 70° (c) 132° (d) 138° (e) 110°; no

9. 90°, 53°, 90°, 124°

13. (a) $|\mathbf{A}| = \sqrt{29}$ m, $|\mathbf{B}| = \sqrt{30}$ m, $\mathbf{A} \cdot \mathbf{B} = -16$ m², $\mathbf{A} \times \mathbf{B} = 7\mathbf{i} - 23\mathbf{j} + 6\mathbf{k}$ m², $\mathbf{A} + \mathbf{B} = -\mathbf{i} + \mathbf{j} + 5\mathbf{k}$ m, $\mathbf{A} - \mathbf{B} = 9\mathbf{i} + 3\mathbf{j} + \mathbf{k}$ m; 123°; $\mathbf{B} - \mathbf{A} = -9\mathbf{i} - 3\mathbf{j} - \mathbf{k}$ m, $|\mathbf{B} - \mathbf{A}| = \sqrt{91} = 9.5$ m; $\mathbf{A} \times \mathbf{B}/|\mathbf{A} \times \mathbf{B}| = 0.282\mathbf{i} - 0.928\mathbf{j} + 0.242\mathbf{k}$
(b) $\mathbf{A} = 4.4\mathbf{i}' - 0.8\mathbf{j}' + 3\mathbf{k}'$ m, $\mathbf{B} = -4.6\mathbf{i}' + 2.2\mathbf{j}' + 2\mathbf{k}'$ m; $|\mathbf{A}| = \sqrt{29}$ m, $|\mathbf{B}| = \sqrt{30}$ m, $\mathbf{A} \cdot \mathbf{B} = -16$ m², $\mathbf{A} \times \mathbf{B} = -8.2\mathbf{i}' - 22.6\mathbf{j}' + 6\mathbf{k}'$ m², $\mathbf{A} + \mathbf{B} = -0.2\mathbf{i}' + 1.4\mathbf{j}' + 5\mathbf{k}'$ m, $\mathbf{A} - \mathbf{B} = 9\mathbf{i}' - 3\mathbf{j}' + \mathbf{k}'$ m, 123°, $\mathbf{B} - \mathbf{A} = -9\mathbf{i}' + 3\mathbf{j}' - \mathbf{k}'$ m, $|\mathbf{B} - \mathbf{A}| = \sqrt{91} = 9.5$ m, $\mathbf{A} \times \mathbf{B}/|\mathbf{A} \times \mathbf{B}| = -0.331\mathbf{i}' - 0.913\mathbf{j}' + 0.242\mathbf{k}'$

Chapter 5

1. 20 ft/sec

3. Nearly a year; about 30,000 times the distance to the sun

5. (a) 15 m/sec, no (b) 5 sec

7. Pass at 2.6 sec and 8.4 sec

9. $\mathbf{r} = 27\mathbf{i} + 6\mathbf{j} + 6\mathbf{k}$, $\mathbf{v} = 15\mathbf{i} + 5\mathbf{j} + 2\mathbf{k}$, $r = 28.3$ m, $v - v_0 = 12.2$ m/sec

11. (a) $\mathbf{r} = 3t^2\mathbf{i} + (5t - 4t^2)\mathbf{j}$ m, $\mathbf{v} = 6t\mathbf{i} + (5 - 8t)\mathbf{j}$ m/sec (b) $r = 13.4$ m, $v = 16.3$ m/sec (c) $16x^2 + 9y^2 - 75x + 24xy = 0$ (d) $\mathbf{v_0} = 3\mathbf{i}' + 4\mathbf{j}'$, $\mathbf{a} = -10\mathbf{j}'$ (e) $\mathbf{r} = 3t\mathbf{i}' + (4t - 5t^2)\mathbf{j}'$ m, $\mathbf{v} = 3\mathbf{i}' + (4 - 10t)\mathbf{j}'$ m/sec (f) $r = 13.4$ m, $v = 16.3$ m/sec (g) $9y' = 12x' - 5(x')^2$

13. (a) g, 0, 0.6g, 0.8g (b) g, 0, g, 0 (c) 6.8 km, 1.5 km (d) 3.9 km, 1.3 km

15. 1.9 ft, 0.8%; either, depending on the spin of the ball

17. 76° or 40°

19. $h = L^2/2R = 0.66$ ft, $v_0 = \sqrt{Rg} = 2.6 \times 10^4$ ft/sec $\cong 5$ miles/sec, same as satellite in circular orbit at the earth's surface; no, particles in accelerators approach c in speed, factor 10^4 higher in speed.

21. 0.61 cm, 1.94×10^7 m/sec at 22° below horizontal

23. $\theta = 0.084$ rad $= 4.8°$

25. (a) π ft/sec, 0.031g (b) 35π m/sec, $2.5 \times 10^5 g$ (c) 100π/3 ft/sec, $1.03 \times 10^3 g$ (d) 60 mph, 0.18g (e) 20 mph, 1.3g (f) 60 mph, 194g (g) 2300 mph, $2.8 \times 10^{-4}g$ (h) 67,000 mph, $6.1 \times 10^{-4}g$ (i) 3×10^8 m/sec, $9.2 \times 10^{15}g$

27. (a) π ft/sec, 1.8g (b) 50π/3 ft/sec, 510g (c) $\pi/4$ ft/sec, 0.15g (d) 8π/5 ft/sec, 0.2g (e) 55 cm/sec, 0.44g (f) 2π mm/sec, 4000g (g) 6π cm/sec, 0.36g (h) 2π cm/sec, 40g (i) $2\pi \times 10^{-6}$ cm/sec, $4 \times 10^{-5}g$ (j) 2.6×10^4 ft/sec, 1g (k) 200π m/sec, $4 \times 10^{15}g$

29. (a) 20 cm, 5π rad/sec, 2.5 cps, 0.4 sec (b) 0.4π rad, 72°, 0.08 sec, 0.2T (c) $x = 6.18$ cm, $v = -2.98$ m/sec, $a = -15.2$ m/sec²

31. 0.635 sec

33. (a) 120° (b) 151°

35. 5.6 sec

37. (a) 150 rev, 100 rev (b) 48 sec, 60 rpm (c) 54.5 sec, 2.85 ft/sec

Chapter 6

1. (a) 700 mph west (b) 100 mph east (c) 500 mph 37° west of north (d) 650 mph 64° west of north

3. (a) 12 min (b) 13.8 min (c) 5.66 mph (d) 9.2 mph

5. 0.11 mi, 7.7 min

7. (a) $t_0/(1 + u/V)$ (b) $t_0/(1 - u/V)$ (c) $t_0/(1 - u^2/V^2)^{1/2}$ (d) $t_0/(1 - u^2/V^2)$ (e) $t_0/(1 - u^2/V^2)^{1/2}$

9. (a) 42° (b) $(5\mathbf{i} + 10\mathbf{j})/3$ m/sec (c) $2\mathbf{i} - 2\mathbf{j}$ m/sec (d) $(4\mathbf{i} - 4\mathbf{j})/3$ m/sec (e) $(5\mathbf{i} + 10\mathbf{j})/3$ m/sec (f) 11%

11. (a) 14.4 ft below top of shaft (b) 6.6 ft above top of shaft (c) 21.8 ft below top of shaft

13. 3.3 ft/sec², 1.2 times as far as truck

15. 12.5 cm, 6.5×10^{-8} sec, 45 cm

Chapter 7

1. 7.6 sec after A applies brakes and moves 94 m; 28.2 m/sec
3. 2 ft in each case
5. (a) 2.35 rad/sec² (b) 12 rev (c) 9.1 ft/sec² at 49° downward from horizontal, 1550 ft/sec² downward vertically
7. (a) 3.4 cm/sec² down (b) 0.14 cm/sec² west
9. (a) 27 ft (b) No (c) 3.17 ft/sec, 1.02 ft/sec²

Chapter 9

1. (a) 0.102 (b) 102 (c) 0.225 (d) 10^5 (e) 7.2 (f) 0.031 (g) 0.0142 (h) 1.39×10^4 (i) 454 (j) 4.45×10^5
3. 1.4 kg
5. (a) 2 kg (b) g, 0 (c) 151°
7. (a) 5 m/sec² (b) 2.5 m/sec² (c) 1.1 m/sec², zero
9. 3360 lb at 63° above the horizontal, 0.504; 240 ft
11. 1.25 sec
13. 0.625 sec, 1.88 ft; 1.08 sec, 3.46 ft/sec
15. $\mu_s = 0.40$, $\mu_k = 0.35$; 19.3°
17. 2.5 kg perpendicular to the wall, 2.7 kg upward at 68° from wall
19. (a) $H = 225$ ft, $R = 1200$ ft (b) $H = 263$ ft, $R = 1238$ ft (c) $H = 258$ ft, $R = 1210$ ft
21. With origin at right angle corner, c-of-m at $(a/3, b/3)$
23. $2R/\pi$ from center of circle
25. $x = -(n - 3)d/(n - 1)2$, for $n > 3$
27. (a) 0.85 poise; streamline, since $R \sim 0.3$ (b) 6.7×10^{-3} sec; yes

Chapter 10

1. (a) 100 kg (b) 120.4 kg (c) 79.6 kg (d) 120.4 kg (e) 0.639 sec, 0.582 sec, 0.716 sec (f) 1.20 m up, 1.25 m up, 1.07 m up
3. Yes; no (slips at 66 rpm)
5. (a) 2.0×10^{20} n (b) 8×10^{-8} n, grav. force $\sim 10^{-45}$ n
7. (a) 0° (b) 5° 20′ (c) 23′ (d) 17°
9. $2.1g$; 620 lb up, 220 lb down; 4200 ft
11. (a) 0.403 (b) 22° (c) 46.4 mph, zero
13. 3.44 sec, 18.6 ft/sec in the direction the truck is moving, 27.3 ft
15. 21.9 lb, 11.8 lb; 12.4°, 6.7°
17. $v = v_0/(1 + \mu v_0 t/R)$, $S = (R/\mu) \ln (v_0/v) = (R/\mu) \ln (1 + \mu v_0 t/R)$

Chapter 11

1. 463 m/sec = 1040 mph, 7.45×10^3 m/sec = 16,700 mph, 4.22×10^7 m = 26,300 miles from the center of the earth, in the equatorial plane
3. 7.2°; 17.6 n = 1.79 kg; 1.79 kg if found by suspension from a spring balance, but depends on how define apparent weight
5. (a) 0.34 n up, 0 (b) 0.34 n up, 0.15 n E (c) 0.34 n up, 0 (d) 0, 0 (e) 0, 0.15 n perpendicular to velocity and axis (f) 0.29 n perp. to axis outward, 0.13 n E (g) 0.29 n perp. to axis outward, 0.075 n E (h) 0.29 n perp. to axis outward, 0.15 n perp. to axis outward

ANSWERS TO ODD-NUMBERED PROBLEMS

Chapter 12

1. **(a)** 10 cm, 4π rad/sec, 2 cps, 0.5 sec **(b)** 0.2π rad, $36°$; 0.05 sec, $0.1T$ **(c)** 8.09 cm, -73.8 cm/sec, -12.8 m/sec² **(d)** 3.16×10^4 dyne/cm = 31.6 n/m, the same **(e)** $y = 6.21$ cm
3. 0.1 ft, 2.01 cps; 0.3 ft, 2.01 cps
5. 0.72 sec; any integral multiple of 5.7 mph
7. **(a)** 0.585 kg **(b)** 3.7 cm
9. Length $= d$
11. 0.767 sec; no; 0.768 ft
13. 2.5 lb; 4.74 ft
15. **(a)** $T_1 = 2.01$ sec, $T_2 = 2.11$ sec, $T_2 - T_1 = 0.0980$ sec, $\omega_1 - \omega_2 = 0.146$ rad/sec **(b)** 0.146 rad $= 8.35°$ **(c)** 10.8 sec, 21.6 sec
17. **(a)** 0.2 sec, 2 sec **(b)** 0.2 sec, 1.82 sec
19. 26.7 cm; yes; no, because as speed approaches 2 rev/sec, extension approaches infinity
21. $f = 0.75$ cps, $y = 0.02 \sin(1.5\pi t)$ ft
23. $F = -2k[(y^2 + l^2)^{1/2} - l](y^2 + l^2)^{-1/2}y$, $F = -ky^3/l^2$
25. **(a)** $T = 2\pi[m/(k_1 + k_2)]^{1/2}$, $k = k_1 + k_2$
    (b) $T = 2\pi[m(k_1 + k_2)/k_1k_2]^{1/2}$, $1/k = 1/k_1 + 1/k_2$
    (c) As in (a)
    In (a), no. In (c), no.

Chapter 13

1. **(a)** 85 lb up **(b)** 5 lb-sec down **(c)** (1) 5 lb-sec up, (2) 5 lb-sec up, (3) 10 lb-sec up **(d)** 7.5 lb-sec down **(e)** 7500 lb down **(f)** 0
3. 37 pndl-sec at $19°$ above horizontal
5. $\mathbf{J} = \mathbf{i} - 5\mathbf{j}$ n-sec, $90°$
7. 10 n $\cong$ 1 kg, 3.2 sec, neglecting increase in mass of block and change in relative velocity of bullets
9. **(a)** (1) 0.5 lb-sec, 5 lb, (2) 0.25 lb-sec, 2.5 lb, (3) 0.333 lb-sec, 10/3 lb, (4) $\pi/8 = 0.392$ lb-sec, 3.92 lb **(b)** 4 ft, 0, 0.44 ft, 1.3 ft
11. 460 m/sec, 32 cm
13. **(a)** and **(b)** $\mathbf{v}_1 = 2\mathbf{i} + \mathbf{j}$ m/sec **(c)** m_1 through $40°$, m_2 through $56°$ **(d)** no
15. 3.75 ft/sec; no
17. **(a)** $0.5v_0$ **(b)** $0.5v_0$ **(c)** $0.5v_0$ **(d)** $0.6v_0$ **(e)** $(37/60)v_0 = 0.617v_0$ **(f)** $(-23/60)v_0 = -0.383v_0$
19. **(a)** $dm/dt = mg/v_0$ **(b)** $dm/dt = 2mg/v_0$ **(c)** 0.64 ton/sec, 40 tons, 40 ton-sec, 32 ft/sec

Chapter 14

1. $[\tau] = ML^2T^{-2}$, $[l] = ML^2T^{-1}$, $[Jr] = ML^2T^{-1}$, $[I] = ML^2$; mks: n-m, kg-m²/sec, n-m-sec, kg-m²; cgs: dyne-cm, gm-cm²/sec, dyne-cm-sec, gm-cm²; fps: pndl-ft, lb-ft²/sec, pndl-ft-sec, lb-ft²
3. $l_x = yp_z - zp_y$, $l_y = zp_x - xp_z$, $l_z = xp_y - yp_x$
5. 17,800 mph, 13,600 mph; period greater in elliptic orbit
7. **(a)** 1200 lb-ft **(b)** 60,000 lb-ft **(c)** 13.3 lb-ft, no **(d)** 5 lb-ft **(e)** 188.5 n-m, both

9. **(a)** $F = 2$ kg up, pivot 1 kg down   **(b)** $F = 2.5$ kg, pivot 1 kg down   **(c)** $F = 2.5$ kg, pivot 2.1 kg inward at 45° below horizontal   **(d)** $F = 2$ kg, pivot 1 kg down **(e)** $F = 1.6$ kg, pivot 1.0 kg inward at 16° below horizontal

11. **(a)** 60 gm-cm/sec, 1800 gm-cm²/sec   **(b)** 60 dyne-sec, 1800 dyne-cm-sec   **(c)** 120 dyne-sec   **(d)** 240 dyne-sec   **(e)** 3 rad/min   **(f)** 4.8 rad/min   **(g)** 4 rad/min

Chapter 15

1. 40 rpm, tension decreased by factor 8/27
3. **(a)** 21 kg, 1.3 kg   **(b)** 41.1 j, 6.6 j; inelastic collision
5. **(a)** 7.4 pndl/ft, amplitudes 1.5 and 0.5 in.   **(b)** Both blocks vibrate in SHM with amplitude 1 in., periods 2.83 sec and 1.63 sec
7. 0.1245 ft/sec², 0.498 rad/sec², 4.98 lb, 24.98 lb; yes; 8 sec
9. **(a)** $a = 5$ ft/sec², $\alpha = 0$ **(b)** $a = 5$ ft/sec², $\alpha = 5$ rad/sec²   **(c)** $a = 5$ ft/sec², $\alpha = 1.25$ rad/sec²
11. **(a)** Center of mass moves 50 cm at right angles to original rod position, and rod rotates 23°   **(b)** Center of mass moves 40 cm at right angles to original rod position, and rod rotates 18°
13. **(a)** 0.5 m from the 0.3-kg particle, 3.27 m/sec²   **(b)** $a_{0.3\text{ kg}} = 1.96$ m/sec², $a_{0.1\text{ kg}} = 5.88$ m/sec², $a_{0.2\text{ kg}} = 3.92$ m/sec²

Chapter 16

1. **(a)** $\frac{1}{2}mR^2$ **(b)** $(3/2)mR^2$
3. **(a)** $mD^2/12$ **(b)** $mD^2/6$
5. **(a)** 20 lb-ft²   **(b)** 0, 10.3 rad/sec²
7. $(k^2 + h^2)^{1/2}$
9. $I = 0.595mR^2$
11. **(a)** $V = 2\pi^2a^2b$ **(b)** $40\pi^2$ gm   **(c)** $160\pi^2$ gm-cm², too low   **(d)** $I = m(b^2 + a^2/4) = 170\pi^2$ gm-cm²
13. **(a)** $5l/9$ **(b)** $7ml^2/18$ **(c)** $13ml^2/162$
15. 2 oz-ft²
17. **(a)** 50 rad/sec   **(b)** 87 rad/sec
19. 5000 rpm
21. **(a)** 32 rpm   **(b)** 11.4 rpm   **(c)** 13.3 rpm
23. **(a)** 10 m/sec²   **(b)** 10 m/sec   **(c)**(1) 10 m/sec, (2) 5 m/sec
25. $I = 10$ lb-ft², $\tau = 32$ pndl-ft

Chapter 17

1. **(a)** 1.92 sec   **(b)** 1.67 sec
3. 1.0 sec
5. At $R/\sqrt{2}$ from center, $L = \sqrt{2}\,R$
7. **(a)** $I_0 = MR^2$ **(b)** $I_C = MR^2(1 - 4/\pi^2)$ **(c)** $I_D = 2MR^2(1 - 2/\pi)$ **(d)** $T = 2\pi\sqrt{2R/g}$ for both
9. **(a)** $J = 1.25$ n-sec at 67 cm below pivot   **(b)** $J = 1.47$ n-sec, $J' = -0.22$ n-sec **(c)** $J = 1.09$ n-sec, $J' = 0.16$ n-sec
11. **(a)** 25 in.   **(b)** 6.5 lb-ft²   **(c)** 7.7 rad/sec, 12.8 ft/sec, 6 pndl-sec in opposite direction to the blow
13. π^2 rad/sec, $4\pi^3$ rad/sec²; $\pi^2/2$ cm/sec, $2\pi^3$ cm/sec²; at the ends
15. **(a)**(1) 0.047 rad $\sim 2.7°$, (2) 0.75 rad $\sim 43°$ **(b)** 176 sec

Chapter 18

1. (a) 98 ft/sec = 67 mph; skids because $\mu = 1.5$ **(b)** 27%, 0.68
3. (a) 8.9 ft **(b)** 7 ft **(c)** 5.9 ft; yes
5. 18.9 sec, 0.63 ft/sec, 15.2 rad/sec = 145 rpm
7. (a) 150 lb **(b)** 3π ft, no
9. (a) $a = (5/7)g \sin \theta$ **(b)** $a = 5gx/7(R - r)$ **(c)** $T = 2\pi[7(R - r)/5g]^{1/2}$ **(d)** Period of sphere is $\sqrt{7/5} = 1.18$ times greater
11. (a) hoop arrives back at boy, rolling without slipping at 8 ft/sec **(b)** hoop moves 8 ft and stops, falls over **(c)** hoop ends up rolling forward without slipping at 4 ft/sec
13. $\sqrt{4/7}v_0 = 0.76v_0$

Chapter 19

1. (a) 168 lb-ft²/sec **(b), (c)** and **(d)** 3040 pndl-ft = 95 lb-ft
3. About 65 lb-ft²/sec, 5 lb-ft
5. 0.42 ft/sec; factor 22 greater
7. (a) $K = gd/k^2$, where k is radius of gyration **(b)** $K = 2.5g/R$ **(c)** $K = 2g/R$ **(d)** $K = 2.5gr/R$ **(e)** 0.41 rev/sec, 0.33 rev/sec, 0.41 rev/sec, 2.1 rev/sec

Chapter 20

1. (a) (1) 600 ft-lb, (2) 520 ft-lb, (3) 520 ft-lb **(b)** 600 ft-lb, 520 ft-lb, 520 ft-lb **(c)** 300 ft-lb, 130 ft-lb, 310 ft-lb
3. 12.5 mile-lb = 6.6×10^4 ft-lb, zero, 550 ft-lb/sec = 1 hp, 1 hp
5. (a) (1) $W = 10$ kg-m, $F = 6.63$ kg, (2) $W = 10$ kg-m, $F = 11.2$ kg **(b)** (1) $W = 0.84$ kg-m, $F = 1.69$ kg, (2) $W = 1.72$ kg-m, $F = 3.54$ kg
7. (a) (1) $W = 14.4$ ft-lb, $J = 12$ lb-sec, (2) $W = 38.4$ ft-lb, $J = 12$ lb-sec **(b)** (1) $W = 24$ ft-lb, $J = 15.5$ lb-sec, (2) $W = 24$ ft-lb, $J = 8.4$ lb-sec
9. 7350 erg, 5750 erg, 244 dyne = 0.25 gm
11. (a) 575 ft **(b)** $\bar{f} = 5w/\pi = 1.6w$; yes; $F = 18w$
13. (a) 0.2 kg-cm = 1.96×10^{-2} j **(b)** 1.6 kg-cm = 0.157 j, 0.4 kg **(c)** 3 cm
15. (a) $J = 10$ n-sec **(b)** $v_0 = 20$ m/sec **(c)** $K_0 = 100$ j **(d)** $W = 100$ j **(e)** $v = 4t - 0.2t^2$, $x = 2t^2 - 0.2t^3/3$, $x_0 = 133$ m **(g)** $\bar{F}_{time} = J/t_0 = 1$ n, $\bar{F}_{disp} = W/x_0 = 0.75$ n
17. (a) $\omega_2 = 4\omega_1$, $v_2 = 2v_1$, $F_2 = 8F_1$, $K_2 = 4K_1$, $W = 3K_1$ **(b)** no **(c)** $K_2 = K_1$, $v_2 = v_1$, $\omega_2 = 2\omega_1$, $T_2 = 2T_1$; no

Chapter 21

1. 2.65×10^7 m/sec, 6.2×10^5 m/sec, 1.45×10^4 m/sec
3. $J = 1.76 \times 10^5$ pndl-sec, $W = 0$, $U = 1.94 \times 10^5$ ft-pndl, $k = 1.55 \times 10^6$ pndl/ft
5. 8 ft/sec, 7.59 ft/sec
7. (a) 6.4 cm **(b)** 225 j, 0.375 j **(c)** 1.5 n-sec, and 4×10^{-3} n-sec
9. 675 ft/sec; 99.9%; probably not
11. $R/3$
13. (a) 2.5R **(b)** 1.67R, 1.85R

15. 0.9, 19%, 12%, 22

17. (a) $v = \pm\omega(x_0^2 - x^2)^{1/2}$ (b) $U = E/4$, $K = 3E/4$ (c) $x = \pm x_0/\sqrt{2}$

19. (a) $v^2 = 8.62x - 100x^2$ (b) $x = 4.31$ cm   (c) 8.62 cm   (d) 6.27 cm

21. (a) $k = 1.65 \times 10^4$ n/m   (b) 1.2 mm   (c) 0.012 j   (d) 3.6 mm   (e) no

23. (a) $E_0 = -K_0 = U_0/2 = -L_0^2/(2mr_0^2)$ (b) $r_{max} = (2 + \sqrt{2})r_0 = 3.4r_0$,
   $r_{min} = (2 - \sqrt{2})r_0 = 0.59r_0$, $-K/U = (2 + \sqrt{2})/4 = 0.85$; one

Chapter 22

1. $T = 2\pi/(4\pi\rho G/3)^{1/2} = 89$ min

3. (a) $0.56R$ (b) $\sqrt{2}R$

5. (a) 3.0×10^{-14} m   (b) 6.7×10^{-14} m

7. (a) $U(x,y) = k\{[(l + x)^2 + y^2]^{1/2} - l\}^2/2 + k\{[(l - x)^2 + y^2]^{1/2} - l\}^2/2$
   (b) $F_x = -2kx$; yes
   (c) $F_y = -2k[(l^2 + y^2)^{1/2} - l](l^2 + y^2)^{-1/2}y$; no; yes; $F_y = -ky^3/l^2$

Chapter 23

1. (a) Gm^2/d (b) Gm^2/d

3. (a) $-3Gm^2/D$ (b) $-(4 + \sqrt{2})Gm^2/D$

5. (a) $v = \sqrt{2Gm/D}$ (b) $\sqrt{(2 + 1/\sqrt{2})Gm/D}$ (c) ∞

7. $\mathbf{v}_3 = (11\mathbf{i} + 2\mathbf{j} - 4\mathbf{k})/3$ cm/sec, 26 erg; no—an energy difference

9. 0.125 Mev, 6.825 Mev

11. 9.8 ft/sec; time to fall is $[\ln (2 + \sqrt{3})]/\sqrt{8} = 0.466$ sec

Chapter 24

1. (a) 89 lb   (b) 100 lb

3. $E/m = 3g_0R/4$

5. (a) 5×10^9 j   (b) 1.25×10^9 j   (c) 8.7×10^6 j; yes

7. (a) 2.1×10^4 ft/sec $= 4$ miles/sec   (b) 23% high   (c) 4% high   (d) Using average
   g gives 15.9 minutes, integration 19.0 min

9. (a) 26,300 miles from the center of the earth, in the equatorial plane   (b) 23.8 n
   outward; no

11. (a) $v_1 = v_0/\sqrt{3}$, $T = 3\sqrt{3}T_0$ (b) $r_p = 3R/2$, $r_a = 9R/2$, $e = 1/2$, period same as
   circular orbit $3\sqrt{3}T_0$

13. (a) R (b) $R/2$, $v_0/\sqrt{3}$, $2\pi R/3 = 8400$ miles

Chapter 25

1. 59 ft-pndl/sec

3. (a) 10^8 j   (b) 28 hr   (c) 2.8×10^4 n-m

5. (a) 0.1 kg up   (b) 5.4 rad/sec   (c) 2.7 m/sec   (d) 1.0 kg up   (e) 0.6 kg horizontal,
   and 0.1 kg up, 1.6 kg up

7. (a) fraction $(1 + k^2/r^2)^{-1}$ (b) $\tan \theta_m = \mu_s(1 + r^2/k^2)$ (c) 2/3, $\theta_m = 56°$

9. $H = 38.4$ cm, $R = 125$ cm

Chapter 26

1. Earth: 10^4 °K for H_2, 1.6×10^5 °K for O_2; Moon: 450 °K for H_2, 7200 °K for O_2
3. (a) 7700 °K (b) 7.7×10^6 °K (c) 0.039 ev
5. (a) 37 °K (b) 800 °K
7. (a) $2m(v_2 - v_1)$ (b) $1/2t$ (c) mg (d) No, no (e) Pressure on bottom greater than pressure on top (f) Variation from top to bottom negligible for box of reasonable size
9. 6×10^5 n
11. (a) 1.52×10^5 j, zero (b) 1.52×10^5 j, 5.2×10^2 kg-m/sec
13. (a) 6×10^4 cm/sec, 3×10^{-5} cm, 2×10^9 collisions/sec (b) 1.4×10^{-14} sec (c) 5×10^{14} collisions/sec (d) 17 km (e) 10^5 °K
15. (a) 28.8 gm/mole (b) 500 m/sec (c) 1.1×10^{17} mols/hr (d) 1.7×10^{-3} mm of Hg
17. (a) 4.48×10^{-2} m³, 10^3 n (b) 2.24×10^{-2} m³ (c) $4.5 \times 10^3 \ln 2$ j $= 1940$ j (d) Zero (e) Transferred out as heat flow through walls of cylinder

Chapter 28

1. 146 watts, 4.9 watts
3. About the same, 5000 ft-lb
5. 0.3 gm/liter, 1.34 atm
7. (a) 90 gm $\sim$ 0.2 lb (b) -5650 ft-lb (c) 45 psi, 160 °C, -6950 ft-lb (d) 29 psi
9. (a) 90%, -2.3×10^4 j (b) 0.045%, -25 j
11. $3RT_1/2$, $6RT_1$, $9RT_1/2$, $2R$
13. $T_B = 1.22T_0$, $T_A = 2.78T_0$, $W_B = -0.55RT_1$, $Q_A = 5RT_1$
15. (a) $pv = RT + (b - a/RT)p$ (b) $T_B = a/bR$ (c) 18 °K, 530 °K, 1000 °K
17. (a) 2.8×10^{-3} (b) 0.064 (c) 0.72
19. (a) 15 cal/sec-m² (b) 6 cal/sec-m², 11 °C
    (c) $dQ/dt = 2\pi K(T_1 - T_2)/(\ln R_2/R_1)$ per unit length
    (d) $K = 4.0 \times 10^{-4}$ cal/cm-sec-C°

Chapter 29

1. (a) 12 cal/K° (b) -12 cal/K° (c) 12, -12 cal/K°
3. 2.5×10^{-3} cal/K°
5. (a) 23.7%, 69% (b) -3.44 cal/K°, 3.44 cal/K°, 0, 0
7. 12.3%, 50%
9. (a) $370 (b) $113 (c) $79 (d) 130 ft²
11. $E = 4.7$
13. For copper (b) heated 0.58 C° (c) 1350 atm (d) cool 20 C°
15. (a) $u_2 - u_1 = c_v(T_2 - T_1) + a(1/v_1 - 1/v_2)$ (b) $T_2 - T_1 = -0.70$ C°

Chapter 30

1. Prob. 1/36, 2/36, 3/36, $\cdots$, 6/36, 5/36, $\cdots$, 1/36; 5/18, 2/9
3. 6.28×10^{-12}, 1.57×10^{-12}
5. (a) $p(\sigma) = 0.6065p(0)$ (b) Width $= 2\sigma(2 \ln 2)^{1/2} = 2.36\sigma$
7. (a) $10! = 3,628,800$ (b) $\ln 10! = 15.1045$ (c) $\ln 10! \cong 15.0961$
    (d) $\Delta = 0.0084$, error 0.056% (e) $10! \cong 3.598 \times 10^6$ (f) 0.84%

9. (a) 7.96% **(b)** 1.08% **(c)** 2.27%

11. (a) $P(n) = (1/2)^N N!/[(N/2 + n)!(N/2 - n)!]$

(b) $P(n) = (2/\pi N)^{1/2} \exp(-2n^2/N)$

(c) $p(n) = (2/\pi N)^{1/2} \exp(-2n^2/N)$, $\bar{n} = 0$, $\sigma = n_{\text{rms}} = N^{1/2}/2$

(d) $P(1) = 1/2^2 = 1/4$, $P(5) = 1/2^{10} = 1/1024$, $P(50) = 1/2^{100} = 8 \times 10^{-31}$, probability in one half or the other (for $N = 2$) is $1/2$

(e) $P(0) = 1/2 = 0.5$, $P(0) = 252/2^{10} = 0.246$, $P(0) = 1/(50\pi)^{1/2} = 0.080$

(f) $P(1) = 1/4 = 0.25$, $P(1) = 210/2^{10} = 0.205$,
$P(1) = \exp(-2 \times 10^{-2})/(50\pi)^{1/2} = 0.078$

(g) $P(-1,0,1) = 0.656$, $P(-10$ to 10, or -2σ to $2\sigma) = 0.955$

(h) 3.7×10^{-20} cm^3

(i) $P(-2\sigma$ to $2\sigma) = 0.955$

(j) $P(10^{14}) \cong 10^{-10^8}$, $P(-2\sigma$ to $2\sigma) = 0.955$

13. (a) $\bar{Q} = Npe = \tau pe/\Delta t$ **(b)** $\bar{i} = \bar{Q}/\tau = pe/\Delta t$ **(c)** $\sigma^2 = Npqe^2 \cong Npe^2 = \tau pe^2/\Delta t$
(d) $\sigma^2 \cong Npe^2/\tau^2 = e\bar{i}/\tau$ **(e)** $\sigma = 4 \times 10^{-12}$ amp, $\sigma/\bar{i} = 4 \times 10^{-8}$; $\sigma = 4 \times 10^{-14}$ amp, $\sigma/\bar{i} = 4 \times 10^{-6}$

15. (a) $\bar{n} \pm \sqrt{\bar{n}} = 4.4 \pm 2.1$ **(b)** $n = 4$ **(c)** $P(0) = 0.0123$ **(d)** $P(10) = 0.0092$ **(e)** $P(4)/P(5) = 1.14$ **(f)** $P(13) = 0.00046$, so in 1000 trials probability 0.46 that one is 13

17. (a) $A = \lambda$ **(b)** $\bar{t} = 1/\lambda$, $f(t) = (1/\bar{t}) \exp(-t/\bar{t})$ **(c)** $t_{1/2} = \bar{t} \ln 2 = 0.693\bar{t}$ **(d)** $\exp(-t_0/\bar{t})$ **(e)** 0.368 **(f)** 0.5 **(g)** 0.214 **(h)** 0.643 **(i)** 4.27×10^{16} **(j)** 2.0×10^{10} **(k)** $\sim 10^{-11}$ **(l)** $\sim 10^{13}$ nuclei

Chapter 31

1. (a) $\bar{v} = 0.5V$, $v_{\text{rms}} = V/\sqrt{3} = 0.58V$ **(b)** $\sigma = V/\sqrt{12} = 0.29V$

3. (a) 0.4213 **(b)** 0.8426 **(c)** 0.9953 **(d)** 4.7×10^{17} molecules

5. (a) 0.428 **(b)** 0.531 **(c)** 0.608

7. (a) 4.6% **(b)** 0.04%

9. (a) $v_m = 390$ m/sec, $\bar{v} = 440$ m/sec, $v_{\text{rms}} = 480$ m/sec **(b)** 0.93 **(c)** 0.65 **(d)** 0.07 **(e)** 0.35

11. (a) $K_m = kT/2$, $\frac{1}{2}mv_m^2 = kT$ **(b)** $\bar{K} = 3kT/2$, $\frac{1}{2}m\bar{v}^2 = 4kT/\pi$, $\frac{1}{2}m\overline{v^2} = 3kT/2$ **(c)** 39.2%

13. (a) $K_m = 1.3 \times 10^{-2}$ ev, $\bar{K} = 3.9 \times 10^{-2}$ ev **(b)** $N(10^{-2}$ ev$)/N(10^{-3}$ ev$) = 2.22$ **(c)** $N(10^{-2}$ ev$)/N(10^{-1}$ ev$) = 10.2$

Chapter 32

1. (a) $W = 1$ **(b)** $W = 10! = 3.6 \times 10^6$ **(c)** $W = 1.8 \times 10^6$

3. (a) $Z = 1 + \exp(-\theta/T)$ **(b)** $N_1 = N[1 + \exp(-\theta/T)]^{-1}$;
$N_2 = N[1 + \exp(\theta/T)]^{-1}$; for $T \ll \theta$, $N_1 \cong N$, $N_2 \cong 0$; for $T \gg \theta$,
$N_1 \cong N_2 \cong N/2$; for $T = \theta$, $N_1 = 0.73N$, $N_2 = 0.27N$

(c) $U = NE_0[1 + \exp(\theta/T)]^{-1}$ **(d)** $C = (NE_0\theta/T^2) \exp(\theta/T)[1 + \exp(\theta/T)]^{-2}$

5. (a) $W/W_{\text{max}} = \exp(-4n^2/N)$; W/W_{max} is the relative probability of the two states, and $P(n)$ is a normalized probability distribution

(b) $W/W_{\text{max}} = e^{-16} = 1.2 \times 10^{-7}$, $\triangle S = 2.2 \times 10^{-22}$ j/K°, the uniform distribution

7. 0.632, 0.232; 0.632

9. (a) 6.3×10^{12} sec^{-1}, 0.92, 0.73 **(b)** $d \sim 2.5 \times 10^{-8}$ cm, $\nu = 10^{12}$ sec^{-1}

11. 6 km, 40 km; 0.2%, 1.2%

13. (a) $g_{\text{effec}} = 10^{-3}g$ **(b)** $n_2/n_1 = e^{-0.30} = 0.74$

Chapter 33

1. **(a)** 5.67, 0, 5.67 watt/cm² **(b)** 0.62, 5.05, 0.62 watt/cm²
3. $7\rho cr/(9\sigma T^3)$
5. **(a)** $dT/dt = 3\sigma(T_2^4 - T_1^4)/(r\rho c) = 0.117$ C°/sec **(b)** 0.044 C°/sec, 30% **(c)** Too small
7. $VT^3 = $ constant, 71°
9. **(a)** $N = nc$, $E = N\epsilon = nch\nu = uc$ **(b)** $h\nu/c = h/\lambda$, $p = u$ **(c)** $\sim 10^{-22}$ gm-cm/sec, $\sim 3 \times 10^5$ photons/cm³, ~ 3000 μwatt/cm², fairly intense **(d)** Radiation traveling in all directions in the cavity
11. 1140 °C
13. 5900 °K, 5800 °K

INDEX